Andhra/ Telangana

EAMCET

CHAPTERWISE SOLUTIONS 2019 - 1991

PHYSICS

All Online Question Papers of **2019 & 2018** are Covered

Compiled & Edited by
Arihant 'Expert Team'

arihant
ARIHANT PRAKASHAN (Series), Meerut

arihant

ARIHANT PRAKASHAN (Series), MEERUT

Administrative & Production Offices

Regd. Office

'Ramchhaya' 4577/15, Agarwal Road, Darya Ganj, New Delhi -110002
Tele: 011- 47630600, 43518550

Head Office

Kalindi, TP Nagar, Meerut (UP) - 250002
Tel: 0121-7156203, 7156204

Sales & Support Offices

Agra, Ahmedabad, Bengaluru, Bareilly, Chennai, Delhi, Guwahati, Hyderabad, Jaipur, Jhansi, Kolkata, Lucknow, Nagpur & Pune.

ISBN 978-93-24192-46-2

PRICE ₹315.00

Published by Arihant Publications (India) Ltd.

For further information about the books published by Arihant, log on to www.arihantbooks.com or e-mail at info@arihantbooks.com

Follow us on

PREFACE

Whenever a student decides to prepare for any examination his/her first and foremost curiosity is to know about the type of questions that are expected in the exam. This becomes more important in the context of competitive entrance examinations where there is neck-to-neck competition.

To serve this need we are presenting before you this book containing Error Free **Chapterwise Solutions of EAMCET Physics Questions** from the **year 1991 to 2019.**

It has been our efforts to provide correct solutions to the best of our knowledge and opinion. Detailed explanatory discussions follow the answers. Discussions are not just sketchy–rather, have been drafted in a manner that the students will surely be able to answer some other related questions too ! Going through this book, the students would be able to have the complete idea of the questions being asked in the test.

We hope these chapterwise solved papers would be highly beneficial to the students. We would be grateful if any discrepancies or mistakes in the questions or answers are brought to our notice so that these could be rectified in subsequent editions.

Publisher

CONTENTS

SOLVED PAPERS

CHAPTERS

SYLLABUS

PHYSICS

Physical World What is Physics?, Scope and excitement of Physics, Physics, technology and society, Fundamental forces in nature, Gravitational Force, Electromagnetic Force, Strong Nuclear Force, Weak Nuclear Force, Towards Unification of Forces, Nature of physical laws.

Units and Measurements Introduction, The international system of units, Measurement of Length, Measurement of Large Distances, Estimation of Very Small Distances: Size of a Molecule, Range of Lengths, Measurement of Mass, Range of Masses, Measurement of time , Accuracy, precision of instruments and errors in measurement, Systematic errors, random errors, least count error, Absolute Error, Relative Error and Percentage Error, Combination of Errors, Significant figures, Rules for Arithmetic Operations with Significant Figures, Rounding off the Uncertain Digits, Rules for Determining the Uncertainty in the Results of Arithmetic Calculations, Dimensions of Physical Quantities, Dimensional Formulae and dimensional equations, Dimensional Analysis and its Applications, Checking the Dimensional Consistency of Equations, Deducing Relation among the Physical Quantities.

Motion in a Straight Line Introduction, Position, path length and displacement, Average velocity and average speed, Instantaneous velocity and speed, Acceleration, Kinematic equations for uniformly accelerated motion, Relative velocity.

Motion in a Plane Introduction, Scalars and vectors, Position and Displacement Vectors, Equality of Vectors, Multiplication of vectors by real numbers, Addition and subtraction of vectors - graphical method, Resolution of vectors, Vector addition - analytical method, Motion in a plane, Position Vector and Displacement, Velocity, Acceleration, Motion in a plane with constant acceleration, Relative velocity in two dimensions, Projectile motion, Equation of path of a projectile, Time of Maximum height, Maximum height of a projectile, Horizontal range of projectile, Uniform circular motion.

Laws of Motion Introduction, Aristotle's fallacy, The law of inertia, Newton's first law of motion, Newton's second law of motion, Newton's third law of motion, Impulse, Conservation of momentum, Equilibrium of a particle, Common forces in mechanics, friction, Circular motion, Motion of a car on a level road, Motion of a car on a Banked road, Solving problems in mechanics.

Work, Energy and Power Introduction, The Scalar Product, Notions of work and kinetic energy : The work-energy theorem, Work, Kinetic energy, Work done by a variable force, The work-energy theorem for a variable force, The concept of Potential Energy, The conservation of Mechanical Energy, The Potential Energy of a spring, Various forms of energy: the law of conservation of energy, Heat, Chemical Energy, Electrical Energy, The Equivalence of Mass and Energy, Nuclear Energy, The Principle of Conservation of Energy, Power, Collisions, Elastic and Inelastic Collisions, Collisions in one dimension, Coefficent of Restitution and its determination, Collisions in Two Dimensions.

Systems of Particles and Rotational Motion Introduction, What kind of motion can a rigid body have?, Centre of mass, Centre of Gravity, Motion of centre of mass, Linear momentum of a system of particles, Vector product of two vectors, Angular velocity and its relation with linear velocity, Angular acceleration, Kinematics of rotational motion about a fixed axis, Torque and angular momentum, Moment of force (Torque), Angular momentum of particle, Torque and angular momentum for a system of a particles, conservation of angular momentum, Equilibrium of a rigid body, Principle of moments, Moment of inertia, Theorems of perpendicular and parallel axes, Theorem of perpendicular axes, Theorem of parallel axes, Dynamics of rotational motion about a fixed axis, Angular momentum in case of rotations about a fixed axis, Conservation of Angular Momentum, Rolling motion, Kinetic Energy of Rolling Motion.

Oscillations Introduction, Periodic and oscillatory motions, Period and frequency, Displacement, Simple harmonic motion (S.H.M.), Simple harmonic motion and uniform circular motion, Velocity and acceleration in simple harmonic motion, Force law for Simple harmonic Motion, Energy in simple harmonic motion, Some systems executing Simple Harmonic Motion, Oscillations due to a spring, The Simple Pendulum, Damped simple harmonic motion, Forced oscillations and resonance.

Gravitation Introduction, Kepler's laws, Universal law of gravitation, The gravitational constant, Acceleration due to gravity of the Earth, Acceleration due to gravity below and above the surface of Earth, Gravitational potential energy, Escape speed, Earth satellite, Energy of an orbiting satellite, Geostationary and polar satellites, Weightlessness.

Mechanical Properties of Solids Introduction, Elastic behaviour of solids, Stress and strain, Hooke's law, Stress-strain curve, Elastic moduli, Young's Modulus, Determination of Young's Modulus of the Material of a Wire, Shear Modulus, Bulk Modulus, Poisson's Ratio, Applications of elastic behaviour of materials.

Mechanical Properties of Fluids Introduction, Pressure, Pascal's Law, Variation of Pressure with Depth, Atmosphere Pressure and Gauge Pressure, Hydraulic Machines, Streamline flow, Bernoulli's principle, Speed of Efflux: Torricelli's Law, Venturi-meter, Blood Flow and Heart Attack, Dynamic Lift, Viscosity, Variation of Viscocity of fluids with temperature, Stokes' Law, Reynolds number, Surface tension, Surface Energy, Surface Energy and Surface Tension, Angle of Contact, Drops and Bubbles, Capillary Rise, Detergents and Surface Tension.

Thermal Properties of Matter Introduction, Temperature and heat, Measurement of temperature, Ideal-gas equation and absolute temperature, Thermal expansion, Specific heat capacity, Calorimetry, Change of state, Regelation, Latent Heat, Heat transfer, Conduction, thermal conductivity, Convection, Radiation, Black body Radiation, Greenhouse Effect, Newton's law of cooling,

Thermodynamics Introduction, Thermal equilibrium, Zeroth law of thermodynamics, Heat, Internal Energy and work, First law of thermodynamics, Specific heat capacity, Thermodynamic state variables and equation of State, Thermodynamic process, Quasi-static Isothermal Process, Adiabatic Process, Isochoric Process, Cyclic process, Heat engines, Refrigerators and heat pumps, Second law of thermodynamics, Reversible and irreversible processes, Carnot engine, Carnot's theorem.

Kinetic Theory Introduction, Molecular nature of matter, Behaviour of gases, Boyle's Law, Charles' Law, Kinetic theory of an ideal gas, Pressure of an Ideal Gas, Law of equipartition of energy, Specific heat capacity, Monatomic Gases, Diatomic Gases, Polyatomic Gases, Specific Heat Capacity of Solids, Specific Heat Capacity of Water, Mean free path.

Waves Introduction, Transverse and longitudinal waves, Displacement relation in a progressive wave, The speed of a travelling wave, The principle of superposition of waves, Reflection of waves, Beats, Doppler effect.

Ray Optics and Optical Instruments Introduction, Reflection of Light by Spherical Mirrors, Refraction, Total Internal Reflection, Refraction at Spherical Surfaces and by Lenses, Refraction through a Prism, Dispersion by a Prism, Some Natural Phenomena due to Sunlight , Optical Instruments.

Wave Optics Introduction, Huygens Principle, Refraction and reflection of plane waves using Huygens Principle, Coherent and Incoherent Addition of Waves, Interference of Light Waves and Young's Experiment, Diffraction, Polarisation.

Electric Charges and Fields Introduction, Electric Charges, Conductors and Insulators, Charging by Induction, Basic Properties of Electric Charge, Coulomb's Law, Forces between Multiple Charges, Electric Field, Electric Field Lines, Electric Flux, Electric Dipole, Dipole in a Uniform External Field, Continuous Charge Distribution, Gauss's Law, Application of Gauss's Law.

Electrostatic Potential and Capacitance Introduction, Electrostatic Potential, Potential due to a Point Charge, Potential due to an Electric Dipole, Potential due to a System of Charges, Equipotential Surfaces, Potential Energy of a System of Charges, Potential Energy in an External Field, Electrostatics of Conductors, Dielectrics and Polarisation, Capacitors and Capacitance, The Parallel Plate Capacitor, Effect of Dielectric on Capacitance, Combination of Capacitors, Energy Stored in a Capacitor, Van de Graaff Generator.

Current Electricity Introduction, Electric Current, Electric Currents in Conductors, Ohm's law, Drift of Electrons and the Origin of Resistivity, Limitations of Ohm's Law, Resistivity of various Materials, Temperature Dependence of Resistivity, Electrical Energy, Power, Combination of Resistors — Series and Parallel, Cells, emf, Internal Resistance, Cells in Series and in Parallel, Kirchhoff's Laws, Wheatstone Bridge, Meter Bridge, Potentiometer.

Moving Charges and Magnetism Introduction, Magnetic Force, Motion in a Magnetic Field, Motion in Combined Electric and Magnetic Fields, Magnetic Field due to a Current Element, Biot-Savart Law, Magnetic Field on the Axis of a Circular Current Loop, Ampere's Circuital Law, The Solenoid and the Toroid, Force between Two Parallel Currents, the Ampere, Torque on Current Loop, Magnetic Dipole, The Moving Coil Galvanometer.

Magnetism and Matter Introduction, The Bar Magnet, Magnetism and Gauss's Law, The Earth's Magnetism, Magnetisation and Magnetic Intensity, Magnetic Properties of Materials, Permanent Magnets and Electromagnets.

Electromagnetic Induction Introduction, The Experiments of Faraday and Henry, Magnetic Flux, Faraday's Law of Induction, Lenz's Law and Conservation of Energy, Motional Electromotive Force, Energy Consideration: A Quantitative Study, Eddy Currents, Inductance, AC Generator.

Alternating Current Introduction, AC Voltage Applied to a Resistor, Representation of AC Current and Voltage by Rotating Vectors — Phasors, AC Voltage Applied to an Inductor, AC Voltage Applied to a Capacitor, AC Voltage Applied to a Series LCR Circuit, Power in AC Circuit: The Power Factor, LC Oscillations, Transformers.

Electromagnetic Waves Introduction, Displacement Current, Electromagnetic Waves, Electromagnetic Spectrum.

Dual Nature of Radiation and Matter Introduction, Electron Emission, Photoelectric Effect, Experimental Study of Photoelectric Effect, Photoelectric Effect and Wave Theory of Light, Einstein's Photoelectric Equation: Energy Quantum of Radiation, Particle Nature of Light: The Photon, Wave Nature of Matter, Davisson and Germer Experiment.

Atoms Introduction, Alpha-particle Scattering and Rutherford's Nuclear Model of Atom, Atomic Spectra, Bohr Model of the Hydrogen Atom, The Line Spectra of the Hydrogen Atom, de-Broglie's Explanation of Bohr's Second Postulate of Quantisation.

Nuclei Introduction, Atomic Masses and Composition of Nucleus, Size of the Nucleus, Mass-Energy and Nuclear Binding Energy, Nuclear Force, Radioactivity, Nuclear Energy.

Semiconductor Electronics Materials, Devices And Simple Circuits Introduction, Classification of Metals, Conductors and Semiconductors, Intrinsic Semiconductor, Extrinsic Semiconductor, *p-n* Junction, Semiconductor diode, Application of Junction Diode as a Rectifier, Special Purpose *p-n* Junction Diodes, Junction Transistor, Digital Electronics and Logic Gates, Integrated Circuits.

Communication Systems Introduction, Elements of a Communication System, Basic Terminology Used in Electronic Communication Systems, Bandwidth of Signals, Bandwidth of Transmission Medium, Propagation of Electromagnetic Waves, Modulation and its Necessity, Amplitude Modulation, Production of Amplitude Modulated Wave, Detection of Amplitude Modulated Wave.

AP EAMCET

Engineering Entrance Exam

Online Question Paper 2019 *(Solved)*

20 April Shift I
Session 1 (10:00 AM to 1:00 PM)

1. If the charge of electron e, mass of electron m, speed of light in vacuum c and Planck's constant h are taken as fundamental quantities, then the permeability of vacuum μ_0 can be expressed as

(a) $\frac{h}{mc^2}$ (b) $\frac{hc}{me^2}$ (c) $\frac{h}{ce^2}$ (d) $\frac{mc^2}{he^2}$

2. The velocity of an object moving in a straight line path is given as a function of time by $v = 6t - 3t^2$, where v is in ms^{-1}, t is in s. The average velocity of the object between, $t = 0$ and $t = 2$ s is

(a) 0 (b) 3 ms^{-1} (c) 2 ms^{-1} (d) 4 ms^{-1}

3. A gun and a target are at the same horizontal level separated by a distance of 600 m. The bullet is fired from the gun with a velocity of 500 ms^{-1}. In order to hit the target, the gun should be aimed to a height h above the target. The value of h is
(Acceleration due to gravity, $g = 10\ ms^{-2}$)

(a) 2.4 m (b) 3.6 m (c) 7.2 m (d) 10.8 m

4. A projectile is thrown in the upward direction making an angle of 60° with the horizontal with a velocity of 140 ms^{-1}. Then the time after which its velocity makes an angle 45° with the horizontal is
(Acceleration due to gravity, $g = 10\ ms^{-2}$)

(a) 0.5124 s (b) 51.24 s
(c) 5.124 s (d) 512.4 s

5. The maximun value of the applied force F such that the block as shown in the arrangement does not move is
(Acceleration due to gravity, $g = 10\ ms^{-2}$)

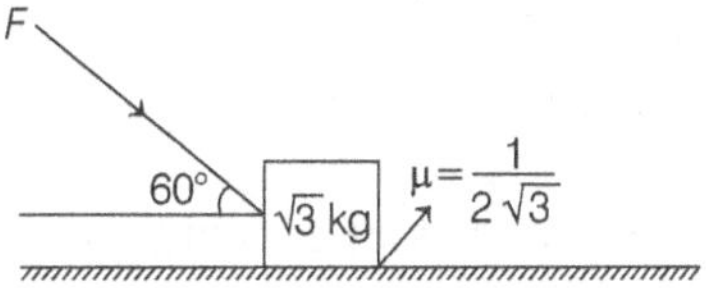

(a) 20 N (b) 15 N (c) 25 N (d) 10 N

6. A rough inclined plane BCE of height $\left(\frac{25}{6}\right)$ m is kept on a rectangular wooden block $ABCD$ of height 10 m, as shown in the figure. A small block is allowed to slide down from the top E of the inclined plane. The coefficient of kinetic friction between the block and the inclined plane is $\frac{1}{8}$ and the angle of inclination of the inclined plane is $\sin^{-1}(0.6)$. If the small block finally reaches the ground at a point F, then DF will be (Acceleration due to gravity, $g = 10\ ms^{-2}$)

(a) $\frac{5}{3}$ m (b) $\frac{10}{3}$ m (c) $\frac{13}{3}$ m (d) $\frac{20}{3}$ m

7. Two particles P and Q each of mass 3m lie at rest on the X-axis at points $(-a, 0)$ and $(+a, 0)$, respectively. A third particle R of mass 2 m initially at the origin moves towards the particle Q. If all the collisions of the system of 3 particles are elastic and head on, the total number of collisions in the system is

(a) 2 (b) 3 (c) 4 (d) 5

8. A motor engine pumps 1800 L of water per minute from a well of depth 30 m and allows to pass through a pipe of cross-sectional area

$30\ cm^2$. Then the power of the engine is (Acceleration due to gravity, $g = 10\ ms^{-2}$)

(a) 20.5 kW (b) 15.5 kW (c) 10.5 kW (d) 9.5 kW

9. A solid sphere of 100 kg and radius 10 m moving in a space becomes a circular disc of radius 20 m in one hour. Then the rate of change of moment of inertia in the process is

(a) $\frac{40}{9}$ kg m^2 s^{-1} (b) $\frac{10}{9}$ kg m^2 s^{-1}

(c) $\frac{50}{9}$ kg m^2 s^{-1} (d) $\frac{25}{9}$ kg m^2 s^{-1}

10. A semicircular plate of mass m has radius r and centre c. The centre of mass of the plate is at a distance x from its centre c. Its moment of inertia about an axis passing through its centre of mass and perpendicular to its plane is

(a) $\frac{mr^2}{2}$ (b) $\frac{mr^2}{4}$ (c) $\frac{mr^2}{2} + mx^2$ (d) $\frac{mr^2}{2} - mx^2$

11. Two bodies of masses m_1 and m_2 initially at rest at infinite distance apart move towards each other under gravitational force of attraction. Their relative velocity of approach when they are separated by a distance r is (G = universal gravitational constant.)

(a) $\left[\frac{2G(m_1 - m_2)}{r}\right]^{1/2}$ (b) $\left[\frac{2G(m_1 + m_2)}{r}\right]^{1/2}$

(c) $\left[\frac{r}{2G(m_1 m_2)}\right]^{1/2}$ (d) $\left[\frac{r}{2G}m_1m_2\right]^{1/2}$

12. A planet is revolving around the Sun as shown in the figure. The radius vectors joining the Sun and the planet at points A and B are 90×10^6 km and 60×10^6 km, respectively. The ratio of velocities of the planet at the points A and B when its velocities make angle 30° and 60° with major-axis of the orbit is

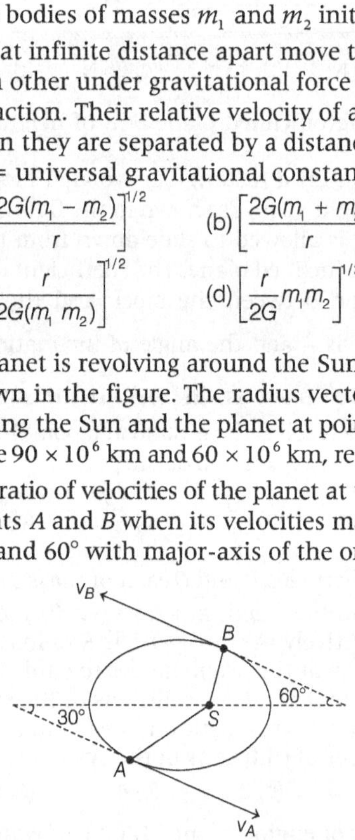

(a) $\frac{3}{2\sqrt{3}}$ (b) $\frac{2}{\sqrt{3}}$ (c) $\frac{1}{\sqrt{3}}$ (d) $\frac{\sqrt{3}}{2}$

13. A solid copper cube of 7 cm edge is subjected to a hydraulic pressure of 8000 kPa. The volume contraction of the copper cube is (Bulk modulus of copper = 140 GPa)

(a) 196×10^{-3} cm^3 (b) 19.6×10^{-6} cm^3

(c) 19.6×10^{-3} cm^3 (d) 196×10^3 cm^3

14. A long cylindrical glass vessel has a pinhole of diameter 0.2 mm at its bottom. The depth to which the vessel can be lowered vertically in a deep water bath without the water entering into the vessel is (surface tension of water, $T = 0.07$ Nm^{-1}, acceleration due to gravity, $g = 10$ ms^{-2})

(a) 14 cm (b) 7 cm (c) 21 cm (d) 28 cm

15. The focal length of a spherical mirror made of steel is 150 cm. If the temperature of the mirror increases by 200 K, its focal length become (coefficient of linear expansion of steel $\alpha = 12 \times 10^{-6}$°C^{-1}.)

(a) 186.3 cm (b) 153.6 cm

(c) 150.036 cm (d) 150.36 cm

16. A metal rod of length 10 cm and area of cross-section 2.8×10^{-4} m^2 is covered with a non-conducting substance. One end of it is maintained at 80°C, while the other end is put in ice at 0°C. It is found that 20 gm of ice melts in 5 min. The thermal conductivity of the metal in Js^{-1} m^{-1} K^{-1} is (Latent heat of ice is 80 cal g^{-1}.)

(a) 70 (b) 80 (c) 90 (d) 100

17. A gas expands with temperature according to the relation, $V = kT^{2/3}$, where k is a constant. Work done when the temperature changes by 60 K is (R = universal gas constant.)

(a) 10 R (b) 20 R (c) 50 R (d) 40 R

18. An ideal gas is taken through the cycle $A \to B \to C \to A$ as shown in the figure. If the net heat supplied to the gas in the cycle is 5 J. The magnitude of work done during the process $C \to A$ is

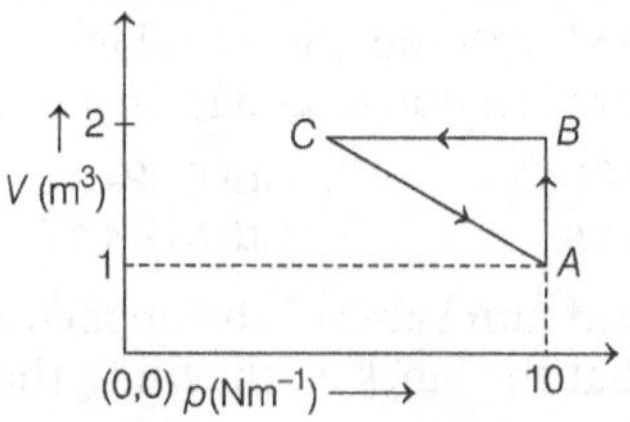

(a) 5 J (b) 10 J (c) 15 J (d) 20 J

19. The average translational kinetic energy of a molecule in a gas becomes equal to 0.69 eV at temperature about,
[Boltzmann's constant $= 1.38 \times 10^{-23}$ J K^{-1}]

(a) 3370°C (b) 3388°C
(c) 5333°C (d) 5060°C

20. An earthquake generates both transverse *S* and longitudinal *P* waves in the earth with speeds 4.5 km s^{-1} and 8.0 km s^{-1}, respectively. A seismograph records that the first *P*-wave arrives 3.5 minutes earlier than the first S-wave. From the seismograph, the epicentre of the earthquake is located at a distance.

(a) 1080 km (b) 2468 km
(c) 2160 km (d) 4320 km

21. An observer moves towards a stationary source of sound with a speed $\frac{1}{5}^{\text{th}}$ of the speed of sound. The wavelength and frequency of the waves emitted by the source are λ and f respectively. The apparent frequency and wavelength heard by the observer are respectively,

(a) 1.2 f, λ (b) f, 1.2 λ
(c) 0.8 f, 0.8 λ (d) 1.2f, 1.2 λ

22. An object is placed 0.1 m infront of a convex lens of focal length 20 cm made of a material of refractive index 1.5. The surface of the lens away from the object is silvered. If the radius of curvature of the silvered surface is 22 cm, then the distance of the final image from the silvered surface is

(a) 10 cm (b) 11 cm (c) 12 cm (d) 13 cm

23. In a Young's double slit experiment, if the slit separation is twice the wavelength of light used, then the maximum number of interference maxima is

(a) 0 (b) 3 (c) 5 (d) 7

24. Three charges of each magnitude 100 μC are placed at the corners *A*, *B* and *C* of an equilateral triangle of side 4 m. If the charges at points *A* and *C* are positive and the charge at point *B* is negative, then the magnitude of total force acting on the charge at *C* and angle made by it with *AC* are

(a) 5.625 N, 60° (b) 0.5625 N, 60°
(c) 5.625 N, 30° (d) 0.5625 N, 30°

25. An inclined plane making an angle 30° with the horizontal is placed in a uniform horizontal electric field of 100 Vm^{-1} as shown in the figure. A small block of mass 1 kg and charge, 0.01C is allowed to slide down from rest from a height, $h = 1$ m. If the coefficient of friction is 0.2, then the acceleration of the block is nearly,
(Acceleration due to gravity, $g = 10$ ms^{-2})

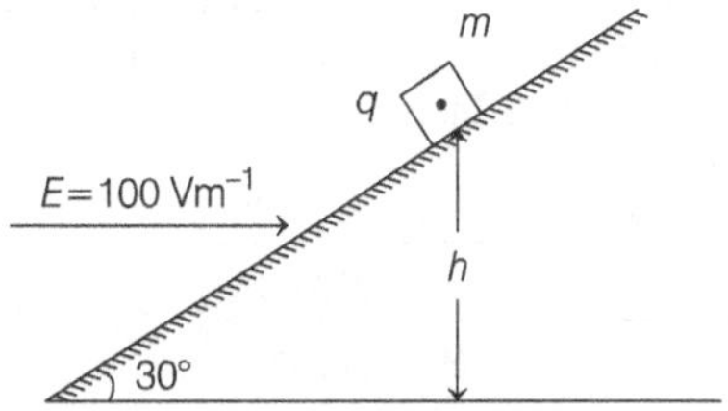

(a) 1.3 ms^{-2} (b) 2.3 ms^{-2} (c) 3.3 ms^{-2} (d) 4.3 ms^{-2}

26. A capacitor is made of a flat plate of area *A* and a second plate of stair-like structure as shown in the figure. The area of each stair is $\frac{A}{3}$ and the height is *d*. The capacitance of the arrangement is

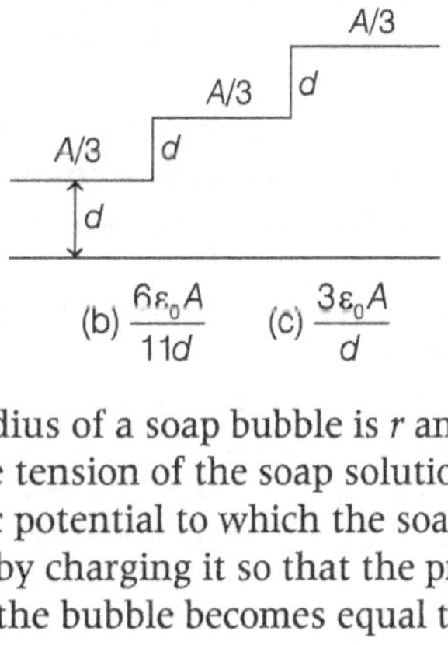

(a) $\frac{\varepsilon_0 A}{3d}$ (b) $\frac{6\varepsilon_0 A}{11d}$ (c) $\frac{3\varepsilon_0 A}{d}$ (d) $\frac{11\varepsilon_0 A}{18d}$

27. The radius of a soap bubble is *r* and the surface tension of the soap solution is *S*. The electric potential to which the soap bubble be raised by charging it so that the pressure inside the bubble becomes equal to the pressure outside the bubble is
(ε_0= permittivity of the free space)

(a) $\sqrt{\frac{Sr}{8\varepsilon_0}}$ (b) $\sqrt{\frac{Sr}{4\varepsilon_0}}$ (c) $\sqrt{\frac{4Sr}{\varepsilon_0}}$ (d) $\sqrt{\frac{8Sr}{\varepsilon_0}}$

28. The ratio of heats generated through shunt and galvanometer is 7 : 5 when they are connected to make an ammeter. If the resistance of the galvanometer is 112 Ω then the resistance of the shunt is

(a) 80 Ω (b) 8 Ω (c) 15.6 Ω (d) 1.56 Ω

29. When an inductor of inductance $\frac{6}{\pi}$ H, a capacitor of capacitance $\frac{50}{\pi}$ μF and resistor of resistance R are connected in series with an AC supply of rms voltage 220 V and frequency 50 Hz, the rms current through the circuit is 440 mA. Match the inductive reactance, X_L the capacitive reactance, X_C the resistance R and the impedance Z of the circuit given in List-I with the corresponding values given in List-II.

List- I	List- II
(A) X_L	(i) 200 Ω
(B) X_C	(ii) 300 Ω
(C) R	(iii) 500 Ω
(D) Z	(iv) 600 Ω

	A	B	C	D
(a)	(iv)	(ii)	(i)	(iii)
(b)	(iv)	(iii)	(i)	(ii)
(c)	(iv)	(i)	(ii)	(iii)
(d)	(i)	(iv)	(iii)	(ii)

30. Assertion (A) When proton and a neutron enter into a transverse magnetic field with equal speeds, then they trace a circular paths of equal radii.

Reason (R) In a transverse magnetic field the period of revolution of a charged particle in a circular path is directly proportional to the mass of the particle.

(a) Both (A) and (R) are correct and (R) is the correct explanation of (A).
(b) Both (A) and (R) are correct but (R) is not the correct explanation of (A).
(c) (A) is correct but (R) is not correct.
(d) (A) is not correct but (R) is correct.

31. If only $\frac{1}{51}^{\text{th}}$ of the main current is to be passed through a galvanometer then the shunt required is R_1 and if only $\frac{1}{11}^{\text{th}}$ of the main voltage is to be developed across the galvanometer, then the resistance required R_2. Then $\frac{R_2}{R_1}$

(a) $\frac{1}{500}$ (b) $\frac{50}{9}$ (c) $\frac{500}{3}$ (d) 500

32. The magnetic field at the centre C of the arrangement shown in figure is

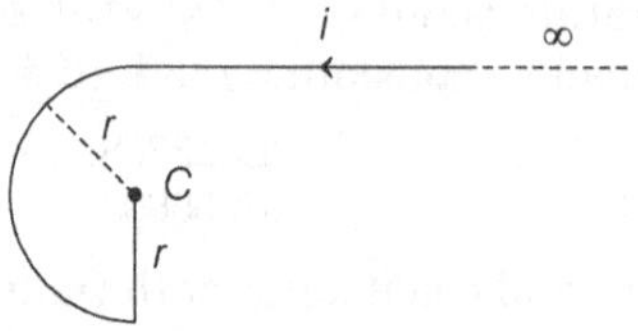

(a) $\frac{\mu_0 i}{2\pi r}(1+\pi)$ (b) $\frac{\mu_0 i}{4\pi r}(1+\pi)$
(c) $\frac{\mu_0 i}{\pi r}(1+\pi)$ (d) $\frac{\mu_0 i}{r}(1+\pi)$

33. To measured a magnetic field between the magnetic poles of a loud speaker, a small coil having 30 turns and 2.5 cm^2 area is placed perpendicular to the field and removed immediately. If the total charge flown through the coil is 7.5×10^{-3}C and the total resistance of wire and galvanometer is 0.3 Ω, then the magnitude of the magnetic field is

(a) 0.03 T (b) 0.3 T (c) 3 T (d) 3×10^2T

34. In an oscillating LC circuit, the maximum charge on the capacitor is Q. The charge on the capacitor when the energy is stored equally between the electric and magnetic fields is

(a) $\frac{Q}{2}$ (b) $\frac{Q}{\sqrt{3}}$ (c) Q (d) $\frac{Q}{\sqrt{2}}$

35. An electromagnetic wave of frequency 1×10^{14} Hz is propagating along z-axis. The amplitude of electric field is 4 Vm^{-1}, then energy density of the electric field will be (Permittivity of free space $= 8.8 \times 10^{-12}$ C^2 N^{-1} m^{-2})

(a) 35.2×10^{-13} Jm^{-3} (b) 70.4×10^{-13} Jm^{-3}
(c) 70.4×10^{-12} Jm^{-3} (d) 35.2×10^{-12} Jm^{-3}

36. In a photoelectric experiment, a monochromatic light is incident on the emitter plate E, as shown in the figure. When switch S_1 is closed and switch S_2 is open, the photoelectrons strike the collector plate C with a maximum kinetic energy of 1 eV. If switch S_1 is open and switch S_2 is closed and the frequency of the incident light is doubled the photoelectrons strike the collector plate with a maximum kinetic energy of 20 eV. The threshold wavelength of the emitter plate is

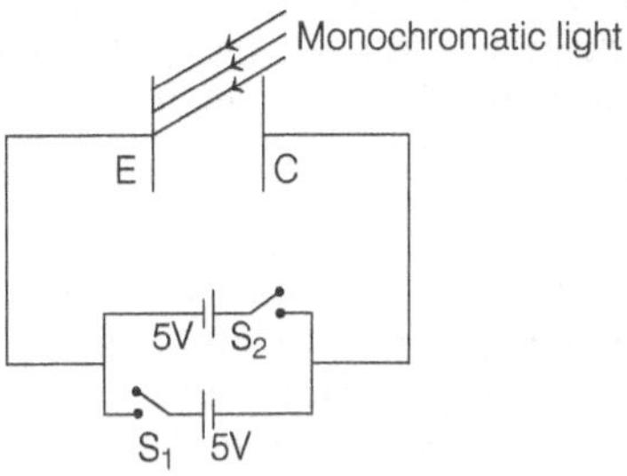

(a) 5233.3 Å (b) 4133.3 Å (c) 4166.7 Å (d) 5336.7 Å

37. In a system, a particle *A* of mass *m* and charge $-2q$ is moving in the nearest orbit around a very heavy particle *B* having charge $+q$. Assuming Bohr's model of the atom to be applicable to this system, the orbital angular velocity of the particle *A* is

(a) $\dfrac{2\pi m^2 q^2}{\varepsilon_0 h^4}$ (b) $\dfrac{3\pi m^3 q^2}{\varepsilon_0^3 h^2}$

(c) $\dfrac{2\pi m q^4}{\varepsilon_0^2 h^3}$ (d) $\dfrac{5\pi m^2 q^3}{\varepsilon_0^3 h^2}$

38. In a nuclear reactor the activity of a radioactive substance is 2000/s. If the mean life of the products is 50 minutes, then in the steady power generation, the number of radio nuclides is

(a) 12×10^5 (b) 60×10^5 (c) 90×10^5 (d) 15×10^5

39. In a *p*-type semiconductor the donor level is at 50 meV above the valence band. To produce one electron, the maximum wavelength of light photon required is (Planck's constant, $h = 6.6 \times 10^{-34}$ Js and speed of light in vacuum, $c = 3 \times 10^8 \text{ ms}^{-1}$)

(a) 0.0248 μm (b) 0.248 μm
(c) 2.48 μm (d) 24.8 μm

40. A signal of frequency 10 kHz and peak voltage 10V is used to amplitude modulate a carrier of frequency 1 MHz and peak voltage 20 V. The side-band frequencies in kHz are

(a) 1010, 990 (b) 910, 1090
(c) 10, 11 (d) 1.01, 0.99

Answers

1.	(c)	2.	(c)	3.	(c)	4.	(c)	5.	(a)	6.	(d)	7.	(a)	8.	(c)	9.	(a)	10.	(d)
11.	(b)	12.	(b)	13.	(c)	14.	(a)	15.	(d)	16.	(d)	17.	(d)	18.	(a)	19.	(d)	20.	(c)
21.	(a)	22.	(b)	23.	(c)	24.	(a)	25.	(b)	26.	(d)	27.	(d)	28.	(a)	29.	(c)	30.	(d)
31.	(d)	14.	(b)	33.	(b)	34.	(d)	35.	(c)	36.	(b)	37.	(c)	38.	(b)	39.	(a)	40.	(a)

Scan this QR code from your mobile phone to get the explanations of this paper.
Or
Visit : *http://tinyurl.com/y3kjxqv2*

20 April Shift II
Session 2 (3:00 PM to 6:00 PM)

1. A physical quantity obtained from the ratio of the coefficient of thermal conductivity to the universal gravitational constant has a dimensional formula $[M^{2a} L^{4b} T^{2c} K^d]$, then the value of $\dfrac{a+b}{c+b} - d$ is

(a) $+\dfrac{3}{2}$ (b) $-\dfrac{1}{2}$ (c) $-\dfrac{3}{2}$ (d) $+\dfrac{1}{2}$

2. A body starting from rest at $t = 0$ moves along a straight line with a constant acceleration. At $t = 2$ s, the body reverses its direction keeping the acceleration same. The body returns to the initial position at $t = t_0$, then t_0 is

(a) 4 s (b) $(4 + 2\sqrt{2})$ s
(c) $(2 + 2\sqrt{2})$ s (d) $(4 + 4\sqrt{2})$ s

3. A thin uniform rod of length L is resting against a wall and the floor as shown in the figure. Its lower end A is pulled towards left with a constant velocity v. Then the downward velocity v' of the other end B when the rod makes an angle θ with the floor is

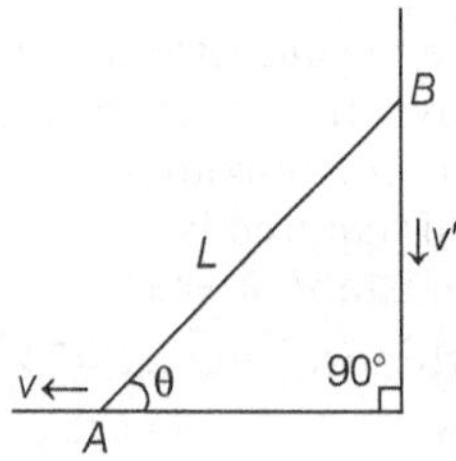

(a) v (b) $v \cos\theta$
(c) $v \sin\theta$ (d) $v \cot\theta$

4. Two boys conducted experiments on the projectile motion with stopwatch and noted some readings. As one boy throws a stone in air at the same angle with the horizontal, the other boy observes that after 4 s, the stone is moving at an angle 30° to the horizontal and after another 2 s it is travelling horizontally. The magnitude of the initial velocity of the stone is (Acceleration due to gravity, $g = 10\ \text{ms}^{-2}$.)

(a) $40\sqrt{3}\ \text{ms}^{-1}$ (b) $20\sqrt{3}\ \text{ms}^{-1}$
(c) $10\sqrt{3}\ \text{ms}^{-1}$ (d) $50\sqrt{3}\ \text{ms}^{-1}$

5. A force of $(2.6\hat{\mathbf{i}} + 1.6\hat{\mathbf{j}})$ N acts on a body of mass 2 kg. If the velocity of the body at time, $t = 0$ is $(3.6\hat{\mathbf{i}} - 4.8\ \hat{\mathbf{j}})\ \text{ms}^{-1}$, the time at which the body will just have a velocity along x-axis only is

(a) 1 s (b) 2 s (c) 3 s (d) 6 s

6. The force required to move a body up a rough inclined plane is double the force required to prevent the body from sliding down the plane. If the angle of inclination of the plane is 60°, then the coefficient of friction is

(a) $\frac{1}{3}$ (b) $\frac{1}{\sqrt{2}}$ (c) $\frac{1}{\sqrt{3}}$ (d) $\frac{1}{2}$

7. A particle moves in the x-y plane under the action of a force,

$$\mathbf{F} = K\left[\frac{x}{(x^2 + y^2)^{\frac{3}{2}}}\hat{\mathbf{i}} + \frac{y}{(x^2 + y^2)^{\frac{3}{2}}}\hat{\mathbf{j}}\right]$$ where, K is a constant. Work done by the force when the particle moves from $(0, a)$ to $(a, 0)$ along a circular path of radius a about the origin is

(a) $\frac{2K\pi}{a}$ (b) $\frac{K\pi}{a}$ (c) $\frac{K\pi}{2a}$ (d) 0

8. A disc of mass 100 g slides down from rest on an inclined plane of 30° and come to rest after travelling a distance of 1m along the horizontal plane. If the coefficient of friction is 0.2 for both inclined and horizontal planes, then the work done by the frictional force over the whole journey, approximately, is (Acceleration due to gravity, $g = 10\ \text{ms}^{-1}$)

(a) 0.106 J (b) 0.05 J (c) 0.306 J (d) 0.2 J

9. Two identical discs are moving with the same kinetic energy. One rolls and the other slides. The ratio of their speeds is

(a) 1 : 2 (b) 1 : 1 (c) 2 : 3 (d) $\sqrt{2} : \sqrt{3}$

10. A tangential force F acts at the top of a thin spherical shell of mass m and radius R. The acceleration of the shell if it rolls without slipping is (f = rolling friction)

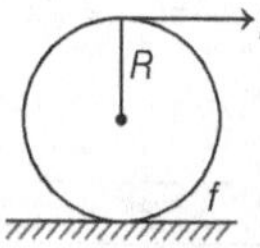

(a) $\frac{5F}{6m}$ (b) $\frac{6F}{5m}$ (c) $\frac{3F}{2m}$ (d) $\frac{F}{6m}$

11. A simple pendulum is placed inside a lift, which is moving with a uniform acceleration. If the time periods of the pendulum while the lift is moving upwards and downwards are in the ratio 1:2, then the acceleration of the lift is (Acceleration due to gravity, $g = 10\ \text{ms}^{-2}$)

(a) $6\ \text{ms}^{-2}$ (b) $0\ \text{ms}^{-2}$ (c) $3\ \text{ms}^{-2}$ (d) $2\ \text{ms}^{-2}$

12. Two bodies each of mass m are hung from a balance whose scale pans differ in a vertical height by h. If the mean density of the earth is ρ, the error in weighing is

(a) $\frac{4\pi\rho\ Gmh}{3}$ (b) $\frac{3\pi\rho\ Gmh}{4}$ (c) $\frac{8\pi\rho\ Gmh}{3}$ (d) $\frac{3\pi\rho\ Gmh}{8}$

13. A one metre steel wire of negligible mass and area of cross-section $0.01\ \text{cm}^2$ is kept on a smooth horizontal table with one end fixed. A ball of mass 1 kg is attached to the other end. The ball and the wire are rotating with an angular velocity of ω.

If the elongation of the wire is 2 mm, then ω is (Young's modulus of steel $= 2 \times 10^{11}$ Nm^{-2})

(a) 5 rad s^{-1} (b) 10 rad s^{-1}
(c) 15 rad s^{-1} (d) 20 rad s^{-1}

14. A cylindrical tank has a hole of area 2 cm^2 at its bottom, If water is poured into the tank from a tube above it at the rate of 100 cm^3 s^{-1}, then the maximum height upto which water can rise in the tank is (Acceleration due to gravity, $g = 10$ ms^{-2})

(a) 2.5 cm (b) 1.25 cm (c) 5.5. cm (d) 3.5 cm

15. The densities of wood and benzene at 0°C are 880 kg m^{-3} and 900 kg m^{-3}, respectively. The coefficient of volume expansion is $1.2 \times 10^{-3} C^{-1°}$ for wood and $1.5 \times 10^{-3°} C^{-1}$ for benzene. Then the temperature at which a piece of wood just sinks in benzene is

(a) 88°C (b) 90°C (c) 83.3°C (d) 90.3°C

16. A window used to thermally insulate a room from outside consists of two parallel glass sheets each of area 2.6 m^2 and thickness 1 cm separated by 5 cm thick stagnant air. In the steady state, the room glass interface is at 18°C and the glass-outdoor interface is at −2 °C. If the thermal conductivities of glass and air are respectively 0.8 $Wm^{-1}K^{-1}$ and 0.08 Wm^{-1} K^{-1}, the rate of flow of heat through the window is

(a) 15 W (b) 40 W (c) 60 W (d) 80 W

17. Five moles of Hydrogen gas initially at STP is compressed adiabatically so that its temperature becomes 673 K. The increase in internal energy of the gas is ($R = 8.3$ J mol^{-1} K^{-1}, $\gamma = 1.4$ for diatomic gas)

(a) 80.5 kJ (b) 21.55 kJ (c) 41.50 kJ (d) 65.55 kJ

18. One mole of a monatomic ideal gas undergoes the process $A \rightarrow B$ in the given p-V diagram. Specific heat capacity in the process is

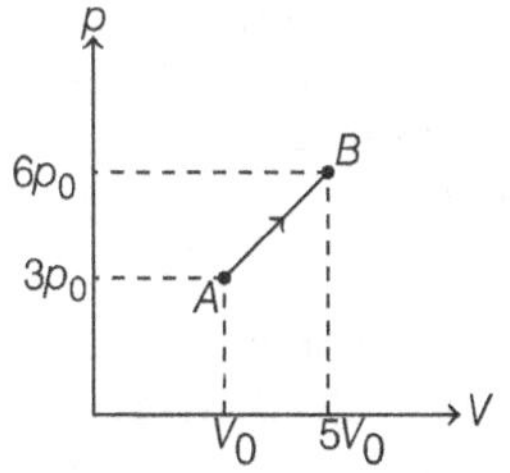

(a) $\frac{13R}{3}$ (b) $\frac{13R}{6}$ (c) $\frac{7R}{3}$ (d) $\frac{2R}{3}$

19. If the speed of sound in a mixture of 2 moles of Helium and 2 moles of Hydrogen at temperature $\frac{972}{5}$ K is $n \times 100$ ms^{-1}, then the value of n is (Take, $R = \frac{25}{3}$ J mol^{-1} K^{-1})

(a) 9 (b) 10 (c) 100 (d) 90

20. A siren placed at a railway platform is emitting a sound of frequency 5 kHz. A passenger sitting in a moving train A records the frequency of the siren as 5.5 kHz. During his return journey by train B he records the frequency of the siren as 6 kHz. The ratio of the speed of train B to that of train A is

(a) $\frac{242}{252}$ (b) 2 (c) $\frac{5}{6}$ (d) $\frac{11}{6}$

21. The speed of a transverse wave travelling in a wire of length 50 cm, cross-sectional area 1 mm^2 and mass 5 g is 80 ms^{-1}. The Young's modulus of the material of the wire is 4×10^{11} Nm^{-2}. The extension in the length of the wire is

(a) 8×10^{-5} m (b) 8×10^{-4} m
(c) 16×10^{-5} m (d) 16×10^{-4} m

22. An object is fixed at the bottom of a vessel and water is filled in the vessel upto a height of 10 cm. A plane mirror is placed at a height of 7 cm from the surface of water in such a way that its reflecting surface faces the water. The distance of the image from the mirror is (Refractive index of water, $n = 1.33$)

(a) 7.5 cm (b) 7 cm (c) 14.5 cm (d) 21.8 cm

23. The angular deviation of 5th order dark fringe is 12° in a single slit experiment. If the width of the slit is 9 μm then the wavelength of the incident light is

(a) 4862 Å (b) 5892 Å (c) 6022 Å (d) 3768 Å

24. Three infinitely long charged sheets are placed as shown in the figure. The electric force acting on a charge $-q$ placed at the point P is (σ = surface charge density, ε_0 = permittivity of the free space)

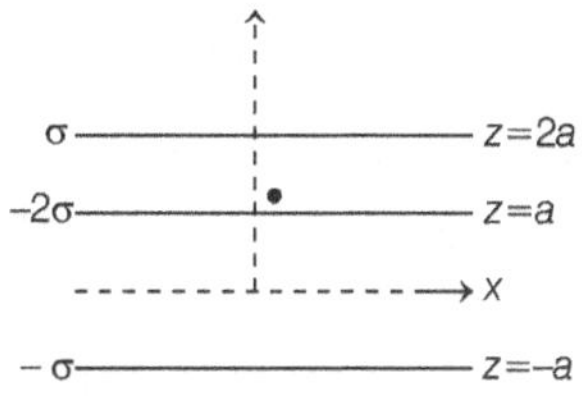

(a) $+\frac{2\sigma}{\varepsilon_0}\hat{\mathbf{k}}$ (b) $-\frac{2\sigma}{\varepsilon_0}\hat{\mathbf{k}}$ (c) $+\frac{4\sigma}{\varepsilon_0}\hat{\mathbf{k}}$ (d) $-\frac{4\sigma}{\varepsilon_0}\hat{\mathbf{k}}$

25. **Assertion** (A) Half of the charge of an electron does not exist.
Reason (R) Electric charge is quantized.
(a) Both (A) and (R) are correct and (R) is the correct explanation of (A).
(b) Both (A) and (B) are correct but (R) is not the correct explanation of (A).
(c) (A) is correct but (R) is not correct.
(d) (A) is not correct but (R) is correct.

26. The potential difference between two points $A(2,1,0)$ m and $B(0,2,4)$ m in an electric field $(x\hat{\mathbf{i}} - 2y\hat{\mathbf{j}} + z\hat{\mathbf{k}})\ \text{Vm}^{-1}$ is
(a) 2 V (b) 3 V (c) 1 V (d) 6 V

27. Three point charges of 3 μC, 4 μC, and 5 μC are arranged at the three corners of a right angled triangle *ABC* as shown in the figure. The work done in moving the charges at *A* and *C*, so that the three charges are located at the three corners of an equilateral triangle of side 3 cm is

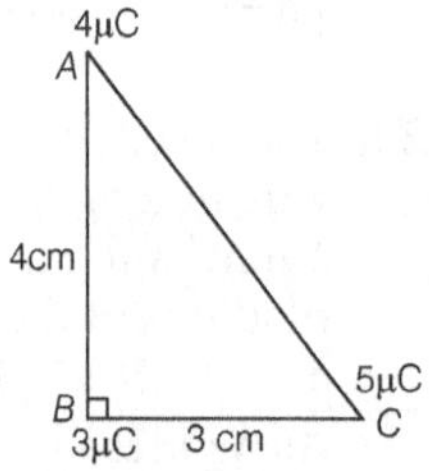

(a) 0.3 J (b) 1.1 J (c) 2.2 J (d) 3.3 J

28. Four resistors *A*, *B*, *C* and *D* form a Wheatstone bridge as shown in the figure. The bridge is balanced when $C = 100\ \Omega$. If *A* and *B* are interchanged, the bridge balances for $C = 121\ \Omega$. The value of *D* is

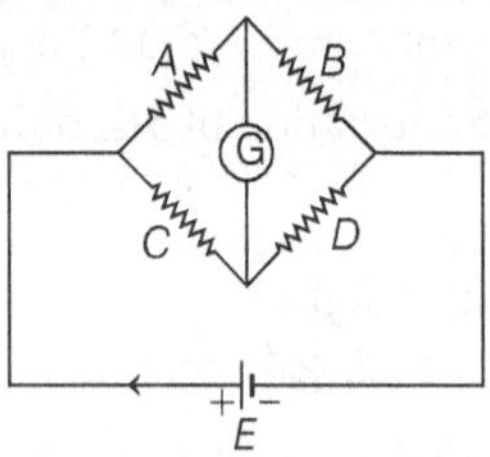

(a) 10 Ω (b) 100 Ω (c) 110 Ω (d) 120 Ω

29. In the circuit shown, if the current through the resistor *R* is $\frac{1}{5}$ A, the value of *R* is

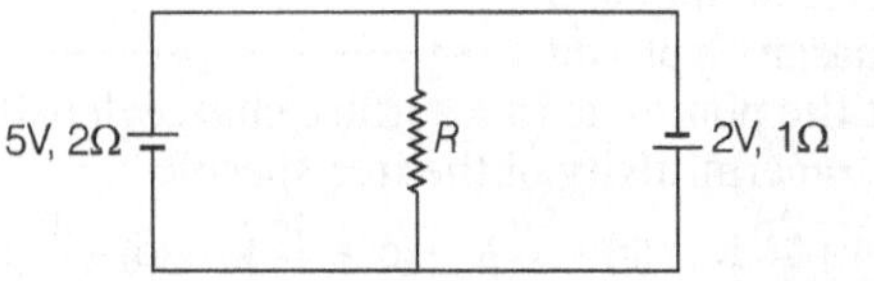

(a) 2Ω (b) 3Ω (c) 5Ω (d) 1Ω

30. An electron accelerated through a potential difference *V*, passes through a uniform transverse magnetic field and experiences a force *F*. If the accelerating potential is increased to 2V, the electron in the same magnetic field will experience a force.
(a) F (b) $\frac{F}{2}$ (c) $\sqrt{2}\,F$ (d) $2F$

31. A coil in the shape of an equilateral triangle of side 2 cm is suspended from a vertex such that it hangs in a vertical plane between the poles of a permanent magnet producing a horizontal magnetic field of 100×10^{-3} T. The magnetic field is parallel to the plane of the coil. For the moment of couple acting on the coil to be $2\sqrt{3} \times 10^{-5}$Nm, the current to be passed through the coil is
(a) 0.5 A (b) 1 A (c) 2 A (d) 4 A

32. A metal rod is subjected to cycles of magnetisation at the rate of 42 Hz. Density of the metal is 6×10^3 kg m^{-3} and its specific heat capacity is 0.1×10^{-3} cal kg^{-1}°C^{-1}. If the area of its *B*-*H* loop corresponds to energy density of 10^{-2} Jm^{-3}, then the rise in its temperature in one minute is
(a) 5°C (b) 10°C (c) 15°C (d) 20°C

33. A coil is placed in a time varying magnetic field. The power dissipated due to current induced in the coil is P_1. If the number of turns is doubled and radius of the wire is halved, the power dissipated is P_2. Then $P_1 : P_2$ is
(a) 1 : 4 (b) 3 : 2 (c) 2 : 1 (d) 4 : 1

34. If the emf of an AC source is given by $6\sin\omega t + 4\sin 2\omega t$ V, then the rms value of the emf is
(a) $\sqrt{10}$ V (b) $\sqrt{26}$ V (c) $\sqrt{32}$ V (d) $\sqrt{20}$ V

35. A lamp delivers a luminous flux of 100 W to an absorber of area 1 cm^2. The force due to radiation pressure is
(a) 3.3×10^{-4} N (b) 16.5×10^{-7} N
(c) 3.3×10^{-6} N (d) 3.3×10^{-7} N

36. An electron of charge *e* and mass *m* moving with an initial velocity $v_0\hat{\mathbf{i}}$ is subjected to all electric field $E_0\hat{\mathbf{j}}$. The de-Broglie wavelength of the electron at a time *t* is

(Initial de-Broglie wavelength of the electron = λ_0)

(a) λ_0 (b) $\lambda_0\sqrt{1+\frac{e^2E_0^2t^2}{m^2v_0^2}}$

(c) $\frac{\lambda_0}{\sqrt{1+\frac{e^2E_0^2t^2}{m^2v_0^2}}}$ (d) $\frac{\lambda_0}{\left(1+\frac{e^2E_0^2t^2}{mv_0^2}\right)}$

37. Match the following List-I with List-II in connection with Bohr's atomic model.

List I		List II	
(A)	Speed of revolution of electron	(i)	$\frac{1}{4\pi\epsilon_0}\frac{2\pi Ze^2}{nh}$
(B)	Kinetic energy	(ii)	$-\left(\frac{1}{4\pi\epsilon_0}\right)^2\frac{2\pi^2me^4Z^2}{n^2h^2}$
(C)	Total energy	(iii)	$\left(\frac{1}{4\pi\epsilon_0}\right)^2\frac{2\pi^2me^4Z^2}{n^2h^2}$
(D)	Frequency	(iv)	$\left(\frac{1}{4\pi\epsilon_0}\right)^2\frac{4\pi^2Z^2e^4m}{n^3h^3}$

The correct answer is

	A	B	C	D
(a)	i	iii	ii	iv
(b)	ii	iv	iii	i
(c)	iii	i	iv	ii
(d)	iii	i	ii	iv

38. Half-life of a radioactive substance is 18 minutes. The time interval between its 20% decay and 80% decay in minutes is

(a) 6 (b) 9 (c) 18 (d) 36

39. In a transistor, the value of α varies between $\frac{20}{21}$ and $\frac{100}{101}$. Then the value of β varies between

(a) 1 and 10 (b) 0.95 and 0.99
(c) 20 and 100 (d) 200 and 300

40. A TV tower has a height of 5 m in a region of population density $\frac{1000}{\pi}$ per square kilometre. Number of people that can receive the transmission is nearly, (in thousands)

(a) 128 (b) 64
(c) 256 (d) 32

Answers

1.	(d)	2.	(b)	3.	(d)	4.	(a)	5.	(d)	6.	(c)	7.	(d)	8.	(c)	9.	(d)	10.	(b)
11.	(a)	12.	(c)	13.	(d)	14.	(b)	15.	(c)	16.	(d)	17.	(c)	18.	(b)	19.	(a)	20.	(b)
21.	(a)	22.	(c)	23.	(d)	24.	(b)	25.	(a)	26.	(b)	27.	(d)	28.	(c)	29.	(d)	30.	(c)
31.	(b)	32.	(b)	33.	(a)	34.	(b)	35.	(d)	36.	(c)	37.	(a)	38.	(d)	39.	(c)	40.	(b)

Scan this QR code from your mobile phone to get the explanations of this paper.
Or
Visit : *http://tinyurl.com/y6qtp9t9*

21 April Shift I
Session 1 (10:00 AM to 1:00 PM)

1. Two intervals of time are measured as $\Delta t_1 = (2.00 \pm 0.02)$s and $\Delta t_2 = (4.00 \pm 0.02)$s. The value of $\sqrt{(\Delta t_1)(\Delta t_2)}$ with correct significant figures and error is

(a) (2.828 ± 0.01)s (b) (2.83 ± 0.01)s
(c) (2.828 ± 0.0075)s (d) (2.83 ± 0.0075)s

2. The speed of a particle changes from $\sqrt{5}\,\text{ms}^{-1}$ to $2\sqrt{5}\ \text{ms}^{-1}$ in a time t. If the magnitude of change in its velocity is 5 ms^{-1}, the angle between the initial and final velocities of the particle is

(a) 30° (b) 45° (c) 60° (d) 90°

3. If the maximum height and range of a projectile are 3 m and 4 m respectively, then the velocity of the projectile is (Take, $g = 10\ ms^{-2}$)

(a) $20\sqrt{\frac{6}{5}}\ ms^{-1}$ (b) $10\sqrt{\frac{3}{2}}\ ms^{-1}$
(c) $10\sqrt{\frac{2}{3}}\ ms^{-1}$ (d) $20\sqrt{\frac{5}{6}}\ ms^{-1}$

4. A body is projected at an angle other than 90° with the horizontal with same velocity. If the time of ascent of the body is ls, then the maximum height it can reach is (Take, $g = 10\ ms^{-2}$)

(a) 5 m (b) 10 m (c) 2.5 m (d) 75 m

5. The position-time (x-t) graph of a moving body of mass 2 kg is shown in the figure. The impulse on the body at $t = 4$ s is

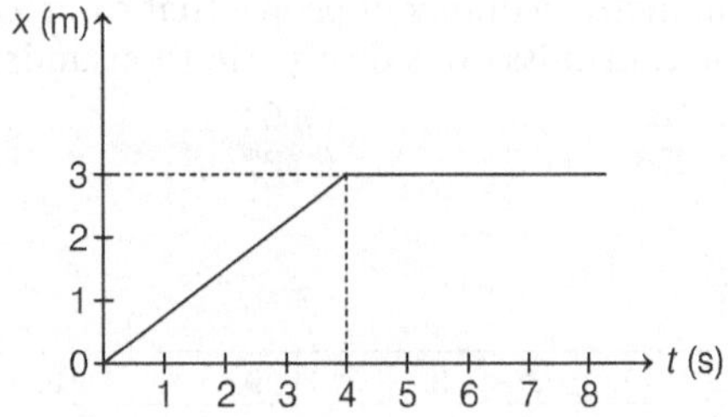

(a) 1.5 kg-ms^{-1} (b) – 1.5 kg-ms^{-1}
(c) 1 kg-ms^{-1} (d) 2 kg-ms^{-1}

6. A block of mass m is lying on a rough inclined plane having an inclination $\alpha = \tan^{-1}\left(\frac{1}{5}\right)$. The inclined plane is moving horizontally with a constant acceleration of $a = 2\ ms^{-2}$ as shown in the figure. The minimum value of coefficient of friction, so that the block remains stationary with respect to the inclined plane is (Take, $g = 10\ ms^{-2}$)

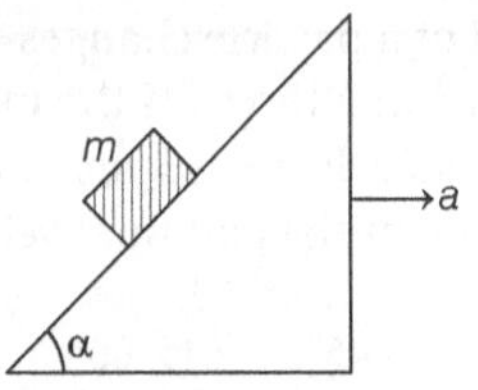

(a) $\frac{2}{9}$ (b) $\frac{5}{12}$ (c) $\frac{1}{5}$ (d) $\frac{2}{5}$

7. Potential energy of a body of mass 1 kg free to move along X-axis is given by $U(x) = \left(\frac{x^2}{2} - x\right)$ J. If the total mechanical energy of the body is 2 J, then the maximum speed of the body is (Assume only conservative force acts on the body)

(a) $\sqrt{5}\ ms^{-1}$ (b) 5 ms^{-1} (c) 3.5 ms^{-1} (d) $\sqrt{8}\ ms^{-1}$

8. A cylindrical well of radius 2.5 m has water upto a height of 14 m from the bottom. If the water level is at a depth of 6 m from the top of the well, then the time taken (in minutes) to empty the well using a motor of 10 HP is approximately, (Take, $g = 10\ ms^{-2}$)

(a) 30 (b) 80 (c) 98 (d) 90

9. A flywheel of mass 1 kg and radius vector $(2\hat{\mathbf{i}} + \hat{\mathbf{j}} + 2\hat{\mathbf{k}})$ m is at rest. When a force $(3\hat{\mathbf{i}} + 2\hat{\mathbf{j}} - 4\hat{\mathbf{k}})$ N acts on it tangentially, it can rotate freely. Then, its angular velocity after 4.5 s is

(a) $\frac{2}{9}\sqrt{261}$ rad s^{-1} (b) $\frac{3}{2}\sqrt{261}$ rad s^{-1}
(c) $\sqrt{261}$ rad s^{-1} (d) $\frac{5}{9}\sqrt{261}$ rad s^{-1}

10. Three identical spheres each of diameter $2\sqrt{3}$ m are kept on a horizontal surface such that each sphere touches the other two spheres. If one of the sphere is removed, then the shift in the position of the centre of mass of the system is

(a) 12 m (b) 1 m (c) 2 m (d) $\frac{3}{2}$ m

11. For a particle executing simple harmonic motion, the displacement-time (x-t) graph is as shown in the figure. The acceleration of the particle at $t = \frac{4}{3}$ s is

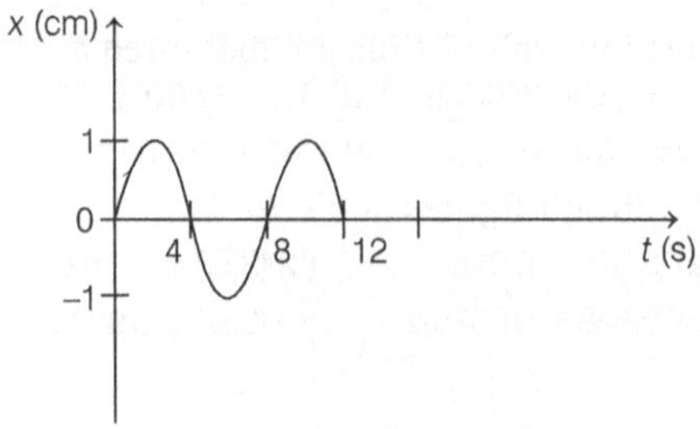

(a) $-\frac{\sqrt{3}}{32}\pi^2$ cm s^{-2} (b) $\frac{32}{\sqrt{3}}\pi^2$ cm s^{-2}
(c) $+\frac{\sqrt{3}}{32}\pi$ cm s^{-2} (d) $+\frac{32}{\sqrt{3}}\pi$ cm s^{-2}

12. Two masses 90 kg and 160 kg are separated by a distance of 5 m. The magnitude of intensity of the gravitational field at a point which is at a distance 3 m from the 90 kg mass and 4 m from the 160 kg mass is (Universal gravitational constant, $G = 6.67 \times 10^{-11}$ N-m^2 kg^{-2}).

(a) 94.3×10^{-10} N kg^{-1} (b) 9.43×10^{-10} N kg^{-1}
(c) 9.43×10^{-12} N kg^{-1} (d) 94.3×10^{-12} N kg^{-1}

13. The following four wires are made of the same material. If same tension is applied to each, the wire having largest extension is

(a) length 0.5 m, diameter 0.5 mm.
(b) length 1 m, diameter 1 mm.
(c) length 2 m, diameter 2 mm.
(d) length 3 m, diameter 3 mm.

14. A liquid drop of density ρ is floating half immersed in a liquid of surface tension S and density $\frac{\rho}{2}$. If the surface tension S of the liquid is numerically equal to 10 times of acceleration due to gravity, then the diameter of the drop is :

(a) $\sqrt{\frac{20}{\rho}}$ (b) $\sqrt{\frac{80}{\rho}}$ (c) $\sqrt{\frac{60}{\rho}}$ (d) $\sqrt{\frac{40}{\rho}}$

15. A block of metal is heated to a temperature much higher than the room temperature and placed in an evacuated cavity. The curve which correctly represents the rate of cooling (T is temperature of the block and t is the time.)

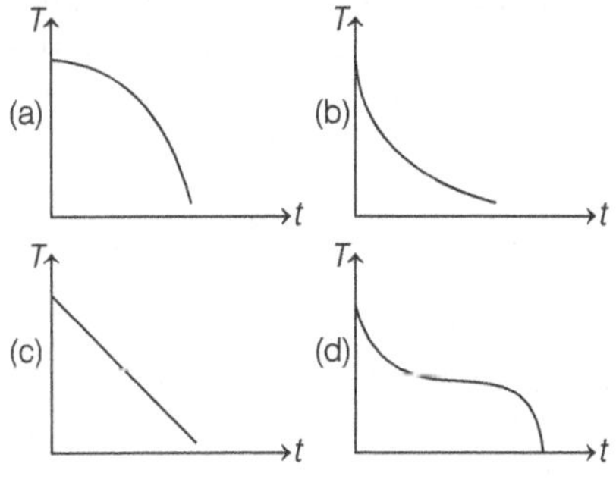

16. A solid copper sphere of density ρ, specific heat capacity C and radius r is initially at 200K. It is suspended inside a chamber whose walls are at 0 K. The time required (in μs) for the temperature of the sphere to drop to 100 K is

(σ is Stefan's constant and all the quantities are in SI units.)

(a) $48\frac{r\rho C}{\sigma}$ (b) $\frac{1}{48}\frac{r\rho C}{\sigma}$ (c) $\frac{27}{7}\frac{r\rho C}{\sigma}$ (d) $\frac{7}{27}\frac{r\rho C}{\sigma}$

17. Match the temperatures of the source and sink (T_1 and T_2 respectively) of a Carnot heat engine given in List-I with the corresponding efficiencies given in List-II.

List-I		List-II
A. $T_1 = 500$ K, $T_2 = 300$ K	(i)	0.2
B. $T_1 = 500$ K, $T_2 = 350$ K	(ii)	0.3
C. $T_1 = 800$ K, $T_2 = 400$ K	(iii)	0.4
D. $T_1 = 450$ K, $T_2 = 360$ K	(iv)	0.5

The correct match is

Codes

	A	B	C	D		A	B	C	D
(a)	(iii)	(iv	(ii)	(i)	(b)	(iv)	(iii)	(ii)	(i)
(c)	(iii)	(i)	(iv)	(ii)	(d)	(iii)	(ii)	(iv)	(i)

18. A hammer of mass 200 kg strikes a steel block of mass 200 g with a velocity 8 ms^{-1}. If 23% of the energy is utilized to heat the steel block, the rise in temperature of the block is (specific heat capacity of steel, = 460 J kg^{-1} K^{-1})

(a) 8 K (b) 16 K
(c) 12 K (d) 24 K

19. At a temperature of 314 K and a pressure of 100 kPa, the speed of sound in a gas is 1380 ms^{-1}. The radius of each gas molecule is 0.5Å. The frequency of sound at which the wavelength of sound wave in the gas becomes equal to the mean free path of the gas molecules is (Boltzmann constant = 1.38×10^{-23} JK^{-1}.)

(a) 1000 MHz (b) $1000\sqrt{2}$ MHz
(c) $\frac{1000}{\sqrt{2}}$ MHz (d) 500 MHz

20. At a temperature of 27°C, two identical organ pipes produce notes of frequency 140 Hz. If the temperature of one pipe is raised to 57.75°C, then the number of beats produced per second is

(a) 7 (b) 5 (c) 3 (d) 9

21. A source of sound S in the form of a block kept on a smooth horizontal surface is connected to a spring, as shown in the figure. If the spring oscillates with an amplitude of 50 cm along horizontal between the wall and the observer O, the maximum frequency heard by the observer is 12.5% more than the minimum frequency heard by him. If the mass of the source of sound is 100 g, the force constant of the spring is (Speed of sound in air is 340 ms^{-1})

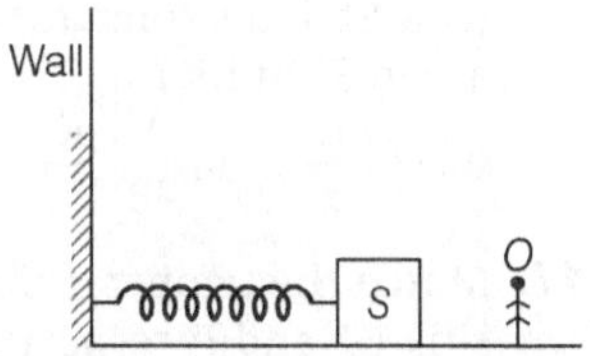

(a) 40 Nm^{-1} (b) 80 Nm^{-1} (c) 160 Nm^{-1} (d) 320 Nm^{-1}

22. A girl of height 150 cm with her eye level at 140 cm stands in front of plane mirror of height 75 cm fixed to a wall. The lower edge of the mirror is at a height of 85 cm above her feet level. The height of her image the girl can see in the mirror is

(a) 130 cm (b) 140 cm (c) 120 cm (d) 150 cm

23. Unpolarised light from air incidents on the surface of a transparent medium of refractive index 1.414 such that the reflected light is completely polarised. Match the angles given in List-I with the corresponding values given in List-II.

List-I		List-II
A. Angle of reflection	(i)	$2\sin^{-1}\left(\sqrt{\frac{2}{3}}\right)$
B. Angle of refraction	(ii)	$\sin^{-1}\left(\sqrt{\frac{2}{3}}\right) - \sin^{-1}\left(\frac{1}{\sqrt{3}}\right)$
C. Angle between incident and completely polarised light	(iii)	$\sin^{-1}\left(\frac{1}{\sqrt{3}}\right)$
D. Angle of deviation of the incident ray	(iv)	$\cos^{-1}\left(\frac{1}{\sqrt{3}}\right)$

The correct match is

Codes

	A	B	C	D		A	B	C	D
(a)	(ii)	(iii)	(i)	(iv)	(b)	(ii)	(iii)	(iv)	(i)
(c)	(iv)	(i)	(iii)	(ii)	(d)	(iv)	(iii)	(i)	(ii)

24. The electric field intensity at a point on the axis of an electric dipole in air is 4 NC^{-1}. Then the electric field intensity at a point on the equatorial line which is at a distance equal to twice the distance on the axial line and if the dipole is in a medium of dielectric constant 4 is

(a) 1 NC^{-1} (b) $\frac{1}{8}$ NC^{-1} (c) 16 NC^{-1} (d) $\frac{1}{16}$ NC^{-1}

25. Two small spheres of each charge q, mass m and material density d are suspended from a fixed point with the help of inextensible light thread. When the spheres are in air, the angle between the threads is 90°. When the spheres are suspended in a liquid of density $\frac{2}{3}d$, the angle between the threads is 60°. The value of dielectric constant of the liquid is

(a) $6\sqrt{3}$ (b) $2\sqrt{5}$ (c) $5\sqrt{3}$ (d) $7\sqrt{2}$

26. The potential difference $(V_A - V_B)$ in the arrangement shown in the figure is ($q = 1\,\mu C$, $x = 2$ cm, $y = 3$ cm)

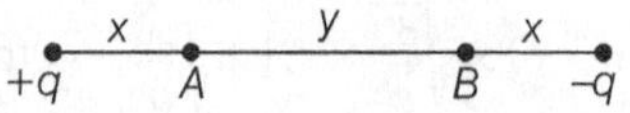

(a) 5.4×10^5 V (b) 2.7×10^5 V
(c) 5.4×10^2 V (d) 2.7×10^2 V

27. In a parallel plate capacitor the separation between plates is $3x$. This separation is filled by two layers of dielectrics, in which one layer has thickness x and dielectric constant $3k$, the other layer is of thickness $2x$ and dielectric constant $5k$. If the plates of the capacitor are connected to a battery, then the ratio of potential difference across the dielectric layers is

(a) $\frac{1}{2}$ (b) $\frac{4}{3}$ (c) $\frac{3}{5}$ (d) $\frac{5}{6}$

28. **Assertion** (A) When a wire of aluminium and another wire of silicon are heated from room temperature to 80°C, the conductivity of aluminium increases and that of silicon decreases.

Reason (R) Aluminium has positive temperature coefficient of resistivity and silicon has negative temperature coefficient of resistivity.

(a) Both (A) and (R) are correct and (R) is the correct explanation of (A).
(b) Both (A) and (R) are correct but (R) is not the correct explanation of (A).
(c) (A) is correct but (R) is not correct.
(d) (A) is not correct but (R) is correct.

29. The walls of a closed cubical box of edge 60 cm are made of material of thickness 1 mm and thermal conductivity, 4×10^{-4} cal s^{-1}cm^{-1}°C^{-1}. The interior of the box is maintained 1000°C above the outside temperature by a heater placed inside the box and connected across 400 V DC supply. The resistance of the heater is

(a) 4.41 Ω (b) 44.1 Ω (c) 0.441 Ω (d) 441 Ω

30. A galvanometer of resistance $G\ \Omega$, is shunted by a resistance $S\ \Omega$. To keep the main current in the circuit unchanged, the resistance to be connected in series with the galvanometer is

(a) $\frac{G^2}{S+G}$ (b) $\frac{S}{S+G}$ (c) $\frac{S^2}{S+G}$ (d) $\frac{SG}{S+G}$

31. A proton and an α-particle are simultaneously projected in opposite direction into a region of uniform magnetic field of 2 mT perpendicular to the direction of the field. After some time it is found that the velocity of proton has changed in direction by 90°. Then at this time, the angle between the velocity vectors of proton and α-particle is

(a) 60° (b) 90° (c) 45° (d) 180°

32. A bar magnet placed in a uniform magnetic field making an angle θ with the field experiences a torque. If the angle made by the magnet with the field is doubled, the torque experienced by the magnet increases by 41.4%. The initial angle made by the magnet with the magnetic field is

(a) 60° (b) 30° (c) 90° (d) 45°

33. A metal rod AB of length 50 cm is moving at a velocity 8 ms^{-1} in a magnetic field of 2T. If the field is at 60° with the plane of motion as shown in the figure, then the potentials V_A and V_B are related by

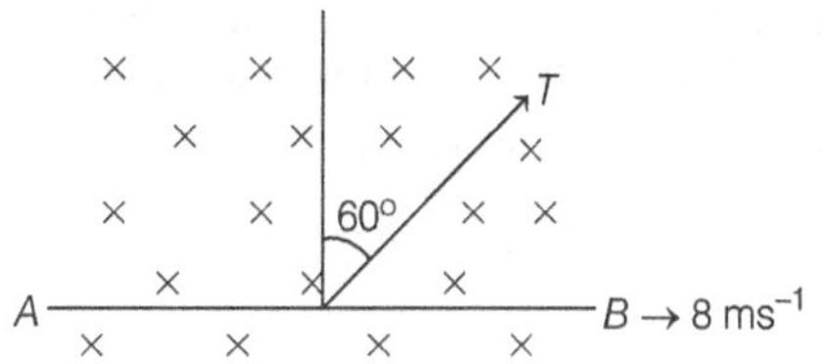

(a) $V_A - V_B = 8$ V (b) $V_A - V_B = 4$V
(c) $V_B - V_A = 8$V (d) $V_B - V_A = 4$V

34. In the given electrical circuit, if the switch S is closed then the maximum energy stored in the inductors is :

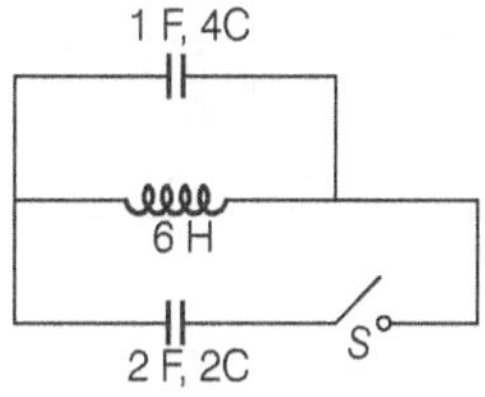

(a) 3 J (b) 9 J (c) 12 J (d) 6 J

35. Which of the following is/are the property/properties of a monochromatic electromagnetic wave propagating in the free space?

1. Electric and magnetic fields will have a phase difference $\frac{\pi}{2}$.
2. The energy of the wave is distributed equally between electric and magnetic fields.
3. The pressure exerted by the wave is the product of its speed and energy density.
4. The speed of the wave is equal to the ratio of the magnetic field to the electric field.

(a) 1 and 3 (b) Only 2 (c) 2 and 3 (d) Only 4

36. The maximum kinetic energy of a photoelectron liberated from the surface of lithium with work function 2.35 eV by electromagnetic radiation whose electric component varies with time as : $E = a[1 + \cos(2\pi f_1 t)]\cos 2\pi f_2 t$ (where a is a constant) is ($f_1 = 3.6 \times 10^{15}$ Hz, and $f_2 = 1.2 \times 10^{15}$ Hz and Planck's constant $h = 6.6 \times 10^{-34}$ Js)

(a) 2.64 eV (b) 7.55 eV (c) 12.52 eV (d) 17.45 eV

37. Magnetic moment due to the motion of the electron in nth energy state of hydrogen atom is proportional to ....

(a) n^{-2} (b) n (c) n^2 (d) n^3

38. The rate of disintegration of a radioactive sample is R and the number of atoms present at any time t is N. When $\frac{R}{N}$ is taken along Y-axis and t is taken along X-axis, the correct graphs is

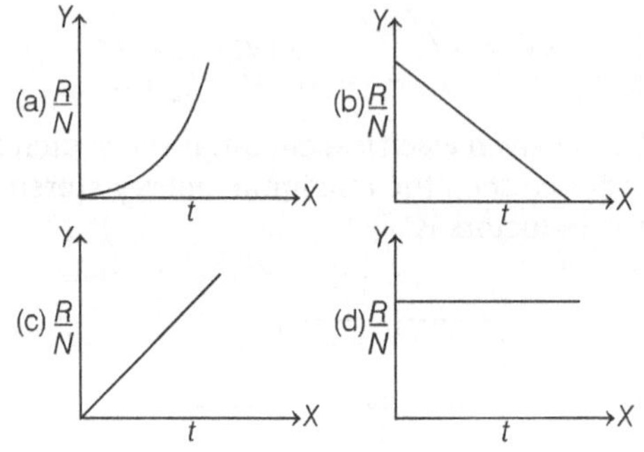

39. For an *LED* to emit light in visible region of the electromagnetic spectrum, it can have energy band gap in the range of,
(Plank's constant, $h = 6.6 \times 10^{-34}$ Js and speed of light, $e = 3 \times 10^{8}$ ms^{-1} in vacuum)

(a) 0.1 eV to 0.4 eV (b) 0.9 eV to 1.6 eV
(c) 1.7 eV to 3.1 eV (d) 0.5 eV to 0.8 eV

40. A transmitting antenna of height 20 m and the receiving antenna of height h are separated by a distance of 40 km for satisfactory communication in line of sight (Los) mode. Then the value of h is
(Give, radius of earth is 6400 km.)

(a) 40 m (b) 45 m
(c) 30 m (d) 25 m

Answers

1.	(b)	2.	(d)	3.	(c)	4.	(a)	5.	(b)	6.	(b)	7.	(a)	8.	(b)	9.	(c)	10.	(b)
11.	(a)	12.	(b)	13.	(a)	14.	(b)	15.	(b)	16.	(b)	17.	(d)	18.	(b)	19.	(b)	20.	(a)
21.	(c)	22.	(c)	23.	(d)	24.	(d)	25.	(a)	26.	(a)	27.	(d)	28.	(d)	29.	(c)	30.	(a)
31.	(c)	32.	(d)	33.	(b)	34.	(a)	35.	(b)	36.	(d)	37.	(b)	38.	(d)	39.	(c)	40.	(b)

Scan this QR code from your mobile phone to get the explanations of this paper.
Or
***Visit** : http://tinyurl.com/y27s5bhv*

21 April Shift II
Session2 (3:00 PM to 6:00 PM)

1. N divisions on the main scale of a vernier calipers coincide with $(N + 1)$ division of the vernier scale. If each division of main scale is a units, then the least count of the calipers is :

(a) $\frac{a}{N}$ (b) a (c) $\frac{a}{N+1}$ (d) $\frac{Na}{N+1}$

2. When a body is in SHM, then match the following.

List-I	List-II
A. Velocity is maximum	I. At extreme position
B. KE is $\left(\frac{3}{4}\right)^{th}$ of the total energy	II. At mean position
C. PE is $\left(\frac{3}{4}\right)^{th}$ of total energy	III. At half of the amplitude
D. Acceleration is maximum	IV. At $\frac{\sqrt{3}}{2}$ times of the amplitude

The correct answer is

	A	B	C	D
(a)	III	I	IV	II
(b)	I	III	IV	II
(c)	II	III	IV	I
(d)	II	I	IV	III

3. Ship A is moving Westwards with a speed of 20 km h^{-1} and another ship B which is at 200 km South of A is moving Northwards with a speed of 10 km h^{-1}. The time after which the distance between them is shortest and the shortest distance between them respectively,

(a) 4 h, $80\sqrt{5}$ km (b) $50\sqrt{2}$ h, $\sqrt{10}$ km
(c) $100\sqrt{2}$ h, $2\sqrt{10}$ km (d) $80\sqrt{5}$ h, 4 km

4. A body is projected at an angle of 60° with the horizontal such that the vertical component of its initial velocity is 40 ms^{-1}. The magnitude of velocity of the projectile at one quarter of its time of flight is nearly,

(Acceleration due to gravity, $g = 10$ ms^{-2})

(a) 3.54 ms^{-1} (b) 35.40 ms^{-1}
(c) 30.54 ms^{-1} (d) 34.5 ms^{-1}

5. A block of mass 48 kg kept on a smooth horizontal surface is pulled by a rope of length 4 m by a horizontal force of 25 N applied to the other end. If the linear density of the rope is 0.5 kg m^{-3}, the force acting on the block is

(a) 24 N (b) 25 N (c) 12 N (d) 13 N

6. Two blocks A and B of masses 1.5 kg and 0.5 kg, respectively are connected by a massless inextensible string passing over a frictionless pulley as shown in the figure. Block A is lifted until block B touches the ground and then block A is released. The initial height of block A is 80 cm when block B just touches the ground. The maximum height reached by block B from the ground after the block A falls on the ground is

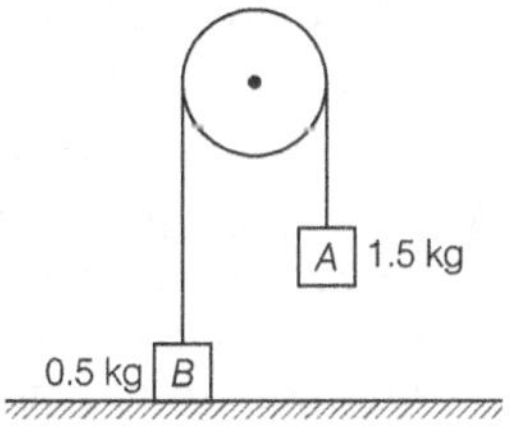

(a) 80 cm (b) 120 cm (c) 140 cm (d) 160 cm

7. A body is released from a height of 30 m vertically downwards. The speed of the body at which potential energy is twice that of kinetic energy is
(Acceleration due to gravity, $g = 10$ ms^{-2})

(a) $20\sqrt{2}$ ms^{-1} (b) $10\sqrt{2}$ ms^{-1}
(c) 10 ms^{-1} (d) 20 ms^{-1}

8. The work done by a force $\mathbf{F} = -5x^4\hat{\mathbf{i}}$ N in displacing a body from, $x = 2$ m to $x = -2$ m is

(a) 6 J (b) 8 J (c) 64 J (d) 0 J

9. A wheel having moment of inertia 2 kg-m^2 about its axis, rotates at 50 rpm about the same axis. The torque required to stop the wheel in one minute is

(a) $\frac{\pi}{10}$ Nm (b) $\frac{\pi}{18}$ Nm (c) $-\frac{\pi}{12}$ Nm (d) $\frac{3\pi}{8}$ Nm

10. The angular retardation of a rotating flywheel is proportional to the angle through which it rotates. If its kinetic energy gets reduced by ΔE while it rotates through at an angle θ, then

(a) $\Delta E \propto \theta^2$ (b) $\Delta E \propto \sqrt{\theta}$ (c) $\Delta E \propto \theta$ (d) $\Delta E \propto \theta^{\frac{3}{2}}$

11. One end of a spring of force constant k is fixed to a vertical wall and the other to a block of mass m resting on a smooth horizontal surface. There is another wall at a distance, x_0 from the block. The spring is then compressed by $2x_0$ and released. The time taken by the block to strike the other wall is

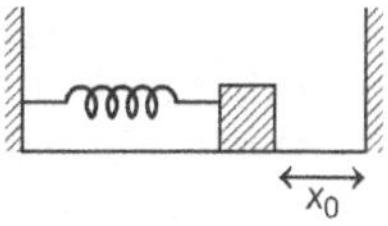

(a) $\frac{1}{6}\pi\sqrt{\frac{m}{k}}$ (b) $\sqrt{\frac{m}{k}}$ (c) $\frac{2\pi}{3}\sqrt{\frac{m}{k}}$ (d) $\frac{\pi}{4}\sqrt{\frac{m}{k}}$

12. The amplitude of a damped oscillator becomes half in one minute. The amplitude after 3 minutes will be $\frac{1}{x}$ times the original. Then, x is

(a) 4 (b) 8 (c) 6 (d) 12

13. A uniform rod of length l and density ρ is revolving about a vertical axis passing through its one end. If ω is the angular velocity of the rod then the centrifugal force per unit area of the rod is

(a) $\frac{\rho\omega^2 l^2}{4}$ (b) $\frac{\rho\omega^2 l^2}{12}$ (c) $\frac{\rho\omega^2 l^2}{2}$ (d) $\frac{\rho\omega^2 l^2}{8}$

14. Two capillary tubes of same length each of 50 cm but of different radii 4 mm and 2 mm are connected in series. When water flows, the pressure difference between the ends of the first tube is

(a) $\frac{p}{2}$ (b) $\frac{p}{17}$ (c) $\frac{p}{4}$ (d) $\frac{p}{8}$

15. Two metal plates P and Q of same material are arranged as shown in the figure. If both the plates are uniformly heated through the same range of temperature, then

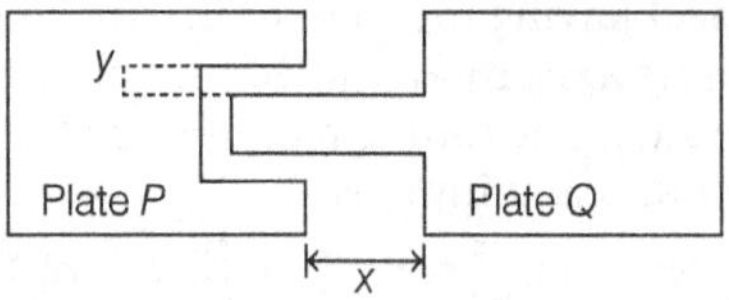

(a) both x and y increase
(b) both x and y decrease
(c) x decreases and y increase
(d) x increases and y decrease

16. A liquid of mass 250 g is kept warm in a vessel using an electric heater. The liquid is maintained at 57°C when the power supplied by the heater is 30 W and surrounding temperature is 27°C. As the heater is switched off, it took 10 s time for the temperature of the liquid to fall from 47°C to 46.9°C. The specific heat capacity of the liquid is

(a) 8000 $J kg^{-1}K^{-1}$ (b) 9000 $J kg^{-1}K^{-1}$
(c) 6000 $J kg^{-1}K^{-1}$ (d) 12000 $J kg^{-1}K^{-1}$

17. The amount of heat that must be supplied to 35 g of oxygen at room temperature to raise its temperature by 80°C at constant volume is (Molecular mass of oxygen is 32 and $R = 8.3 \text{ J mol}^{-1} \text{ K}^{-1}$)

(a) 2.84 kJ (b) 1.68 kJ (c) 1.81 kJ (d) 2.88 kJ

18. A Carnot engine of efficiency 40%, takes heat from a source maintained at a temperature of 500 K. It is desired to have an engine of efficiency 60%. Then, the source temperature for the same sink temperature must be

(a) 650 K (b) 750 K (c) 550 K (d) 850 K

19. For a gas the value of $\frac{R}{C_V} = 0.4$, so the gas is (R-universal gas constant)

(a) monoatomic (b) diatomic
(c) triatomic (d) polyatomic

20. A cylindrical tube open at both ends has a fundamental frequency f in air. The tube is dipped vertically in water so that 60% of the tube is in water. Then, the fundamental frequency of air column is

(a) $\frac{f}{2}$ (b) $\frac{5f}{4}$ (c) $\frac{3f}{4}$ (d) $2f$

21. A train approaching a railway crossing at a speed of 120 km/h sounds a whistle of frequency 576 Hz, when it is 288 m away from the crossing. The frequency heard by the observer standing on the road perpendicular to the track from the crossing at a distance of 384 m is (Speed of sound in air = 340 ms^{-1})

(a) 632 Hz (b) 612 Hz (c) 512 Hz (d) 472 Hz

22. A small object is enclosed in a transparent solid sphere of radius 8 cm. The object is situated at 2 cm from the centre of the sphere. If its image appears to be at 3.2 cm from the nearest side, then the refractive index of the material of the sphere is

(a) 1.62 (b) 1.45 (c) 1.55 (d) 1.50

23. A Young's double slit experimental setup is immersed in water of refractive index 1.33. It has slit separation 1 mm and the distance between slits and screen is 1.33 m. If the wavelength of incident light on slits is 6300 Å, then the fringe width on the screen is

(a) 6.3 mm (b) 0.63 mm (c) 0.63 m (d) 6.3 m

24. In a hydrogen atom, an electron of mass 9.1×10^{-31} kg revolves about a proton in circular orbit of radius 0.53 Å. The radial acceleration and angular velocity of electron are respectively,

(a) 9×10^{22} ms^{-2}, 4.1×10^{16} s^{-1}
(b) 4.1×10^{16} ms^{-2}, 9×10^{22} s^{-1}
(c) 9×10^{16} ms^{-2}, 4.1×10^{22} s^{-1}
(d) 4.1×10^{22} ms^{-2}, 9×10^{16} s^{-1}

25. Two long parallel plates A and B are separated by a distance of 4 cm with an electric field of 45.5 Vm^{-1} between the plates normally from plate A to plate B, as shown in the figure. An electron is projected from plate A with velocity v at an angle of 30° with the surface of plate A. The maximum value of v so that the electron does not hit plate B is (Assume gravity free space, charge of electron = 1.6×10^{-19} C and mass of electron = 9.1×10^{-31} kg)

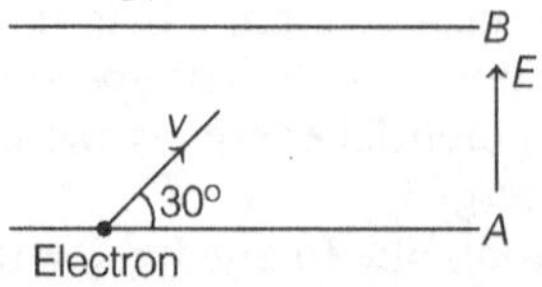

(a) 400 km s^{-1} (b) 3200 km s^{-1}
(c) 800 km s^{-1} (d) 1600 km s^{-1}

26. Three point charges of 2 mC each are kept at the vertices of an equilateral triangle of side 50 cm. If the system is supplied energy at the rate of 2 kW, the time taken to move one of the charges to the mid point of the line joining the other two charges is

(a) 18 s (b) 36 s (c) 72 s (d) 144 s

27. Two identical charged spheres separated by a distance repel each other with a force *F*. If 10% of electrons are transferred from one sphere of the other, then the force between them becomes

(a) F (b) $1.21\,F$ (c) $0.99\,F$ (d) $0.81\,F$

28. In the given circuit, the electric currents through 15Ω and 6Ω, respectively are :

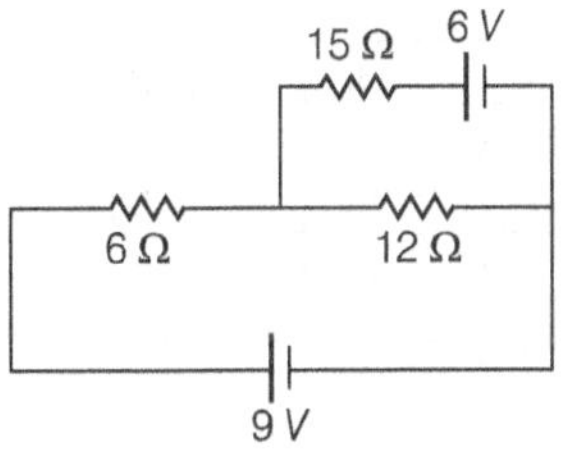

(a) 0 A, 0.5 A (b) 0 A, 1 A (c) 0.5 A, 1 A (d) 1 A, 0 A

29. In the given circuit, the current through 2Ω resistor is

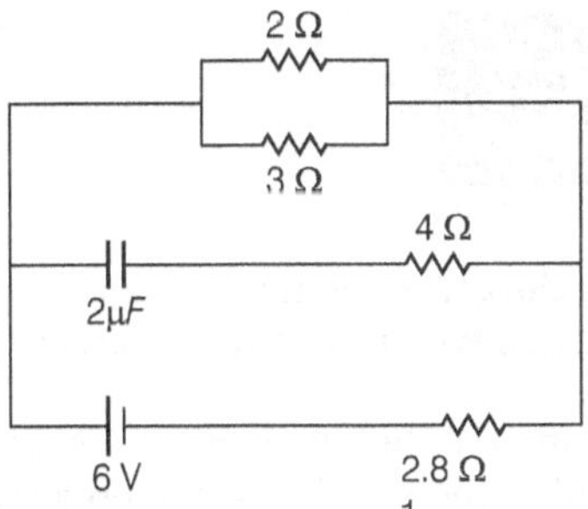

(a) 9 A (b) 0.9 A (c) $\frac{1}{9}$ A (d) $\frac{1}{0.9}$ A

30. A circular coil connected to a battery of emf *E* produced a certain magnetic induction field at its centre. The coil is unwound, stretched to double its length rewound into a coil of $\frac{1}{3}^{rd}$ of the original radius and connected to a battery of emf *E* to produce same field at the centre. Then, *E* is

(a) $\frac{2E}{9}$ (b) $\frac{3E}{7}$ (c) $\frac{9E}{4}$ (d) $\frac{E}{6}$

31. Assertion (A) The work done by the electrostatic force is zero when a point charge moves in a circular path around another charge.

Reason (R) The dot product of force and displacement vectors gives work done.

(a) Both (A) and (R) are correct and (R) is the correct explanation of (A).
(b) Both (A) and (R) are correct but (R) is not the correct explanation of (A).
(c) (A) is correct but (R) is not correct.
(d) (A) is not correct but (R) is correct.

32. The magnetic susceptibility of a paramagnetic substance at $-173°$ C is 1.5×10^{-2}. To have the susceptibility 0.5×10^{-2}, the change in temperature in °C is

(a) 100 (b) 180
(c) 200 (d) 220

33. A coil of mean area 500 cm^2 and having 1000 turns is held with its plane perpendicular to a uniform field of 0.4 G. If the coil is turned through 180° in $\frac{1}{10}$ second, then the average induced emf is (Take, $1\,G = 10^{-4}\,T$)

(a) 0.04 V (b) 0.4 V
(c) 4 V (d) 40 V

34. An emf of 15 V is applied to a circuit containing 5 H inductance and 10 Ω resistance. The ratio of the currents at time, $t = \infty$ and $t = 1$ s is

(a) $\frac{e}{e^2-1}$ (b) $\frac{e^2}{e-1}$
(c) $\frac{e}{1-e^2}$ (d) $\frac{e^2}{e^2-1}$

35. The amplitude of the electric field in a parallel beam of plane electromagnetic waves of intensity 53.1 W m^{-1} is (Permittivity of free space $= 8.85 \times 10^{-12}\,C^2N^{-1}m^{-2}$)

(a) 400 NC^{-1} (b) 50 NC^{-1}
(c) 100 NC^{-1} (d) 200 NC^{-1}

36. An α-particle moves in a circular path of radius 1 cm in a uniform magnetic field of 0.125 T. The de-Broglie wavelength associated with the α-particle is

(a) 1.65×10^{-12} m (b) 3.3×10^{-12} m
(c) 4.95×10^{-12} m (d) 6.6×10^{-12} m

37. When a hydrogen atom emits a photon during a transition from $n = 4$ to $n = 2$, its recoil speed is about,

(a) 4.28 ms^{-1} (b) 0.814 ms^{-1}
(c) 2.07 ms^{-1} (d) 0.407 ms^{-1}

38. If the binding energy of N^{14} is 7.5 MeV per nucleons and that of N^{15} is 7.7 MeV per nucleon, then the energy is required to remove a neutron from N^{15} is

(a) 5.25 MeV (b) 0.2 MeV
(c) 10.5 MeV (d) 0.4 MeV

39. In the following common-emitter circuit, $\beta = 100$ and $V_{CE} = 7$ V. If V_{BE} is negligible, then the base current is

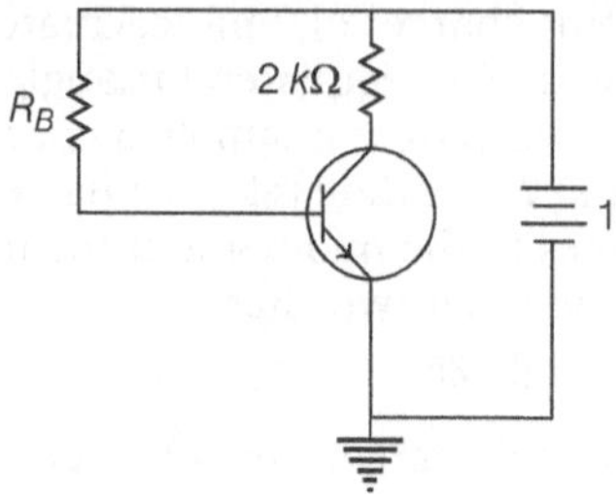

(a) 0.01 mA (b) 0.04 mA (c) 0.02 mA (d) 0.03 mA

40. The frequency suitable for beyond-the-horizon communication using sky waves is

(a) 10^{12} Hz (b) 10^9 Hz (c) 10^7 Hz (d) 10^4 Hz

Answers

1.	(c)	2.	(c)	3.	(a)	4.	(c)	5.	(a)	6.	(b)	7.	(b)	8.	(c)	9.	(b)	10.	(a)
11.	(c)	12.	(b)	13.	(c)	14.	(b)	15.	(b)	16.	(d)	17.	(c)	18.	(b)	19.	(b)	20.	(b)
21.	(b)	22.	(d)	23.	(b)	24.	(a)	25.	(d)	26.	(c)	27.	(c)	28.	(a)	29.	(b)	30.	(a)
31.	(a)	32.	(c)	33.	(a)	34.	(d)	35.	(d)	36.	(a)	37.	(b)	38.	(c)	39.	(b)	40.	(c)

Scan this QR code from your mobile phone to get the explanations of this paper.
Or
***Visit** : http://tinyurl.com/y2ghdpsx*

22 April Shift I
Session 1 (10:00 AM to 1:00 PM)

1. If 1% and 2% are the errors in the measurement of mass and density of a cube respectively, then the error in the measurement of length is

(a) 1% (b) 3% (c) 2% (d) 4%

2. A body travelling along a straight line path travels first half of the distance with a velocity 7ms^{-1}. During the travel time of the second half of the distance, first half time is travelled with a velocity 14ms^{-1} and the second half time is travelled with a velocity 21 ms^{-1} . Then the average velocity of the body during the journey is

(a) 14 ms^{-1} (b) 10 ms^{-1}
(c) 9 ms^{-1} (d) 12 ms^{-1}

3. Assertion (A) The range of a projectile is maximum when the angle of projection is 45°.

Reason (R) The range of a projectile depends only on the angle of projection.

(a) Both (A) and (R) are true and (R) is the correct explanation of (A).
(b) Both (A) and (R) are true but (R) is not the correct explanation of (A).
(c) (A) is true but (R) is false.
(d) (A) is false but (R) is true.

4. A car moving with a certain velocity, jumps from an inclined plane placed at one bank of a river and reaches the other bank by attained a maximum height of 80 m.

If the same car, moving with the same velocity jumps from another inclined plane having different angle of inclination and reaches the same point on the other bank by attaining maximum height of 45 m, then the width of the river is

(a) 80 m (b) 60 m
(c) 125 m (d) 240 m

5. A system containing masses and pulleys connected on an inclined plane is shown in the figure. If the system is in equilibrium then the value of m is

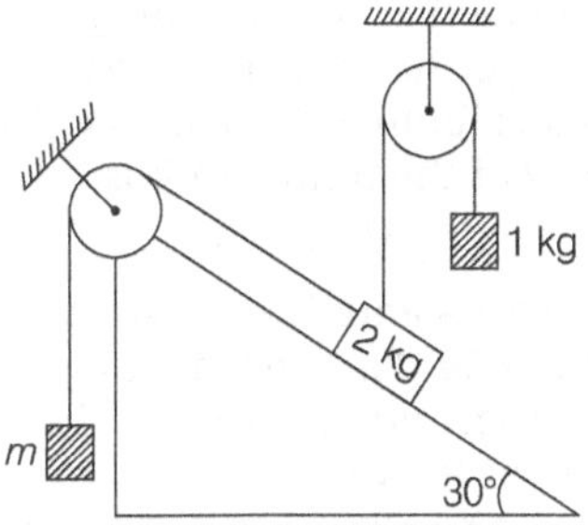

(a) 1 kg (b) 0.5 kg
(c) 0.75 kg (d) 0.25 kg

6. In the arrangement shown in the figure, the coefficient of friction between two blocks is 0.5. The force of friction between the two blocks is (Assume that the 4 kg block is placed on a smooth horizontal surface.) (Acceleration due to gravity = $10 ms^{-2}$.)

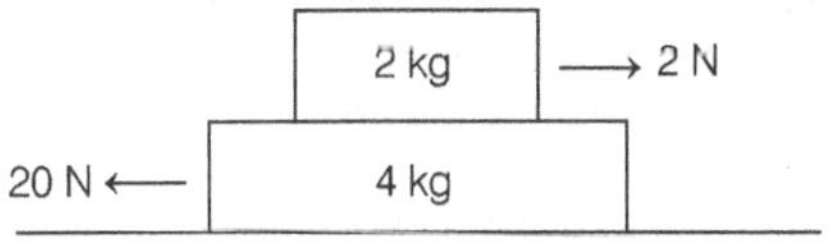

(a) 8 N (b) 10 N
(c) 6 N (d) 4 N

7. In the arrangement shown in the figure, work done by the string on the block of mass 0.36 kg during the first second after the blocks are released from state of rest is (Ignore friction and mass of the string.)

(Acceleration due to gravity, $g = 10 ms^{-2}$)

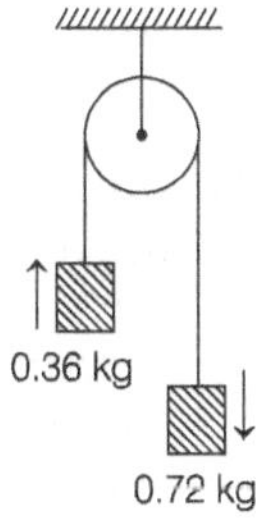

(a) 8 J (b) 4 J (c) 12 J (d) 2 J

8. A man who is running has half the kinetic energy of a boy of half his mass. The man speeds up by $1 ms^{-1}$ and then has the same kinetic energy as the boy. The initial speed of the boy is

(a) $\sqrt{2} + 1 ms^{-1}$ (b) $2(\sqrt{2} + 1) ms^{-1}$
(c) $\sqrt{2} ms^{-1}$ (d) $2 ms^{-1}$

9. A solid sphere rolls down without slipping on a smooth inclined plane of inclination $\sin^{-1}(0.42)$. If the acceleration due to gravity is $10 ms^{-2}$, the acceleration of the rolling sphere is

(a) $1 ms^{-2}$ (b) $2 ms^{-2}$ (c) $3 ms^{-2}$ (d) $4 ms^{-2}$

10. A thin wire of length l having a linear density ρ is bent into a circular loop with C as its centre as shown in the figure. The moment of inertia of the loop about the line AB is

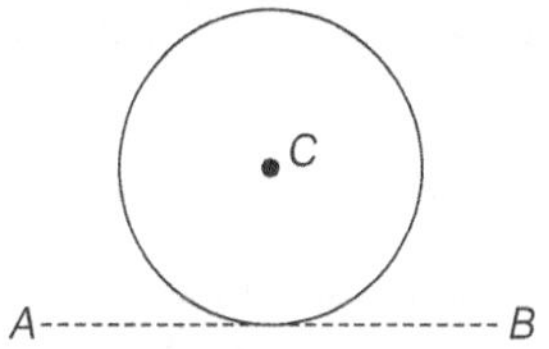

(a) $\frac{5}{16}\frac{\rho l^3}{\pi^3}$ (b) $\frac{1}{16}\frac{\rho l^3}{\pi^3}$ (c) $\frac{1}{8}\frac{\rho l^3}{\pi^3}$ (d) $\frac{3}{8}\frac{\rho l^3}{\pi^2}$

11. A particle executing SHM along a straight line has zero velocity at points A and B whose distance from O on the same line OAB are a and b, respectively. If the velocity at the mid point between A and B is v, then its time period is

(a) $\frac{\pi(b+a)}{v}$ (b) $\pi\left(\frac{b-a}{v}\right)$ (c) $\left(\frac{b+a}{2v}\right)$ (d) $\left(\frac{b-a}{2v}\right)$

12. A rocket is launched straight up from the surface of the earth. When its altitude is $\frac{1}{3}$ of the radius of the earth, its fuel runs out and therefore it coasts. If the rocket has to escape from the gravitational pull of the earth, the minimum velocity with which it should coast is (Escape velocity on the surface of the earth is $11.2 kms^{-1}$.)

(a) $11.2 km s^{-1}$ (b) $10.7 km s^{-1}$
(c) $9.7 km s^{-1}$ (d) $8.7 km s^{-1}$

13. Two wires of equal length and equal cross sectional areas are suspended as shown in the figure. Their Young's modulii are Y_1 and Y_2, respectively.

The equivalent Young's modulus is

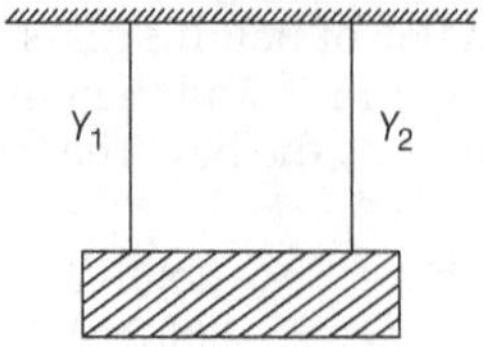

(a) $Y_1 + Y_2$ (b) $\frac{Y_1 + Y_2}{2}$ (c) $\frac{Y_1 Y_2}{Y_1 + Y_2}$ (d) $\sqrt{Y_1 Y_2}$

14. A rain drop of radius r is falling through air, starting from rest. The work done by all the forces on the drop, when it attains terminal velocity, is proportional to

(a) r^3 (b) r^7 (c) r^5 (d) r^4

15. Which of the following statement is correct regarding p-V graph?

1. Slope of p-V graph in an isothermal process is $-\frac{p}{V}$.
2. Slope of p-V graph in an adiabatic process is $-\frac{p}{V}$.
3. Slope of p-V graph in an isochoric process is $-\frac{\gamma p}{V}$.
4. Slope of p-V graph in an isobaric process is zero.

(a) 1, 3, 4 are correct (b) 2, 3 are correct
(c) 1, 4 are correct (d) 2, 3, 4 are correct

16. Two metallic spheres P and Q are made of same material have same smoothness but the weight of P is 8 times that of Q. If the two are heated to same temperature and left to cool, then the ratio of rate of cooling of Q to that of P is

(a) 4 (b) 8 (c) 2 (d) 1

17. Three moles of an ideal monotomic gas performs a cycle $ABCDA$ as shown in the figure. The temperatures of the gas at the states A, B, C and D are 400 K, 800 K, 2400 K and 1200 K, respectively. The work done by the gas during this cycle is (R is universal gas constant)

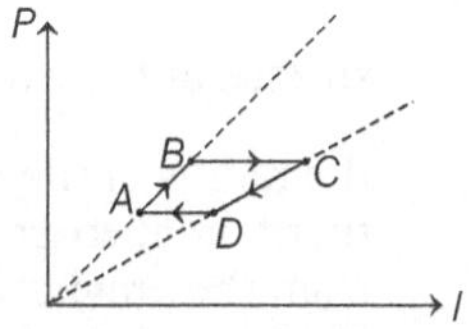

(a) 1200 R (b) 3600 R (c) 2400 R (d) 2000 R

18. An insulated system contains 4 moles of an ideal diatomic gas at temperature T. When a heat Q is supplied to the gas, 2 moles of the gas is dissociated into atoms and the temperature remained constant. Then the relation between Q and T is (R = universal gas constant.)

(a) $Q = RT$ (b) $Q = 2RT$ (c) $Q = 3RT$ (d) $Q = 4RT$

19. Under standard conditions, the density of a gas is $\frac{1400}{1089}$ kg - m^{-3} and the speed of sound propagation in it is 330 ms^{-1}, then the number of degrees of freedom of the gas molecules is

(a) 2 (b) 7 (c) 5 (d) 3

20. When the air column of a resonance tube is vibrated together with a tuning fork, 3 beats are heard per second, either the temperature of the air column is 51°C or 16°C. The frequency of the tuning fork is

(a) 128 Hz (b) 98 Hz (c) 105 Hz (d) 256 Hz

21. Two sources A and B are producing notes of frequency 680 Hz. A listener moves from A to B with a constant velocity v. if the speed of sound in air is 340 ms^{-1}, the value of y so that he hears 10 beats per second is

(a) 2.0 ms^{-1} (b) 2.5 ms^{-1} (c) 3.0 ms^{-1} (d) 3.5 ms^{-1}

22. A thin converging lens of focal length 25 cm forms a sharp image of an object on a screen placed at a distance of 75 cm from the lens. Later the screen is moved closer to the lens by a distance 25 cm. The distance through which the object is to be shifted so that its image on the screen is sharp again is

(a) 50 cm towards the lens
(b) 50 cm away from the lens
(c) 12.5 cm towards the lens
(d) 12.5 cm away from the lens

23. A ray of light is incident on the surface of a glass plate of refractive index $\sqrt{3}$ at the polarising angle. The angle of refraction of the ray is

(a) 30° (b) 45° (c) 60° (d) 37°

24. Six point charges each of the magnitude Q are placed at the vertices of a regular hexagon of side a as shown in the figure. Electric field intensity on the line passing through the centre O and perpendicular to the plane of the figure at a large distance $x (>> a)$ from O is $\left(\text{Let, } \frac{1}{4\pi \epsilon_0} = k\right)$

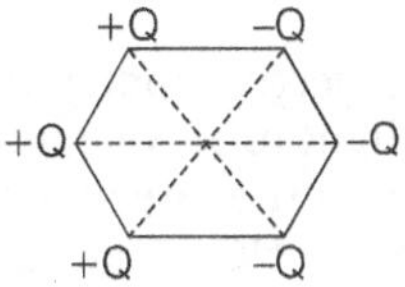

(a) $k \times \frac{4Qa}{x^3}$ (b) $k \times \frac{2Qa}{x^3}$ (c) $k \times \frac{8Qa}{x^3}$ (d) 0

25. A ball of mass 1 g having a charge of 20 μC is tied to one end of a string of length 0.9 m can rotate in a vertical plane in a uniform electric field 100 NC^{-1} directed upwards. The minimum horizontal velocity that must be given to the ball at the lowest position so that it completes the vertical circle is (Let, $g = 10 ms^{-2}$)

(a) 9 ms^{-1} (b) 18 ms^{-1} (c) 36 ms^{-1} (d) 6 ms^{-1}

26. A regular hexagon of side 5 cm has a charge 10 μC at each of its vertices. The potential at the centre of hexagon is

(a) 0 V (b) 18×10^5 V (c) 1.08×10^7 V (d) 1.08×10^5 V

27. The potential in an electric field varies as $V = (x^2 - y^2)$. The electric lines of the force in X-Y plane are

(a)
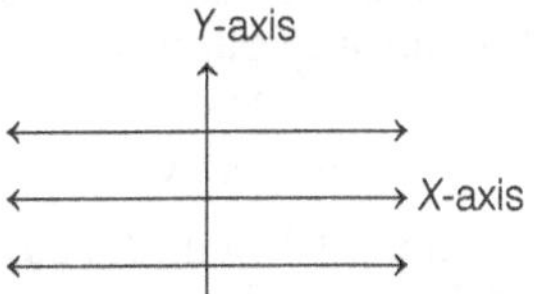

(b)
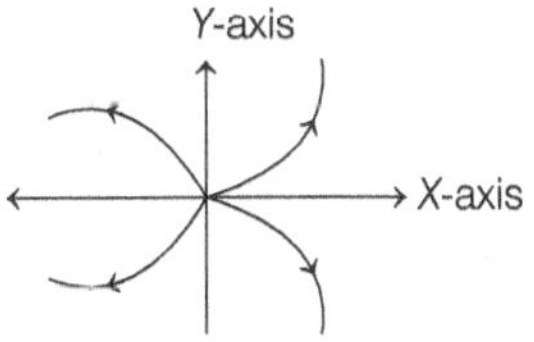

(c)
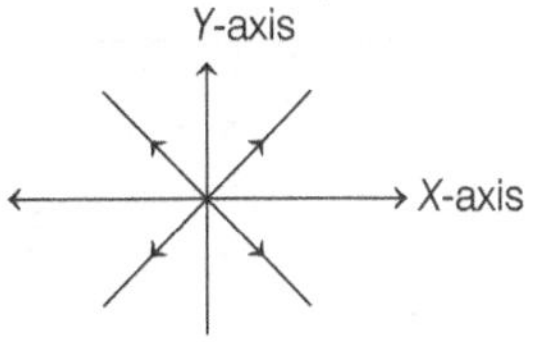

(d)
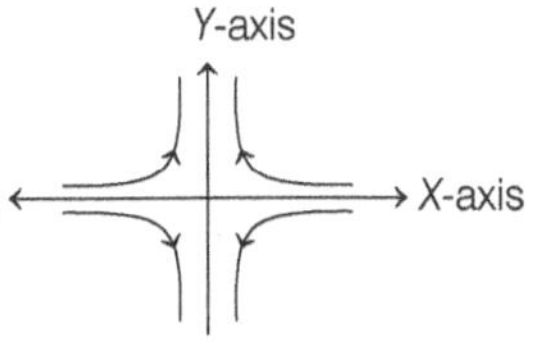

28. The length of a potentiometer wires is l. A cell of emf E is balanced at a length $\left(\frac{l}{3}\right)$ from positive end of the wire. If the length of the wire is increased by $\left(\frac{l}{2}\right)$, the distance at which the same cell gives the balancing point is

(Cell in the primary is ideal and no series resistance is present in the primary circuit.)

(a) $\frac{2l}{3}$ (b) $\frac{l}{2}$ (c) $\frac{l}{6}$ (d) $\frac{4l}{3}$

29. n identical resistance are taken in which $\frac{n}{2}$ resistors are joined in series in the left gap and the remaining $\frac{n}{2}$ resistances are joined in parallel in the right gap of a metre bridge. Balancing length in cm is

(a) $100 \cdot \frac{n^2}{n^2 + 4}$ (b) $100 \cdot \frac{n^2}{n^2 + 1}$

(c) $400 \cdot \frac{1}{n^2 + 4}$ (d) $400 \cdot \frac{1}{n^2 + 1}$

30. The magnetic field normal to the plane of a coil of N turns and radius r which carries a current i is measured on the axis of the coil at a distance h from the centre of the coil. This is smaller than the field at the centre by the fraction,

(a) $\frac{3}{2} \cdot \frac{h^2}{r^2}$ (b) $\frac{2}{3} \cdot \frac{h^2}{r^2}$ (c) $\frac{3}{2} \cdot \frac{r^2}{h^2}$ (d) $\frac{2}{3} \cdot \frac{r^2}{h^2}$

31. A small block of mass 20 g and charge 4 mC is released on a long smooth inclined plane of inclination angle of 45°, A uniform horizontal magnetic field of 1 T is acting parallel to the surface, as shown in the figure. The time from the start when the block loses contact with the surface of the plane is

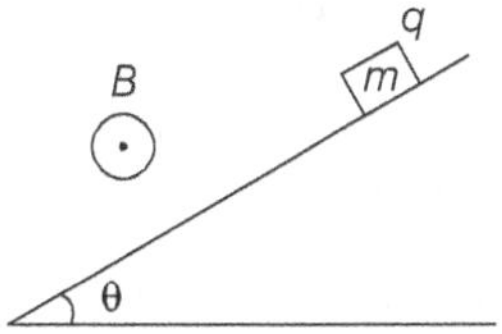

(a) 2 s (b) 3 s

(c) 5 s (d) 6 s

32. Match the following List-I with List-II.

	List-I		List-II
A.	$\oint EdA$	(i)	0
B.	$\oint BdA$	(ii)	$-\frac{d\phi_B}{dt}$
C.	$\oint Edl$	(iii)	$\frac{Q}{\epsilon_0}$
D.	$\oint Bdl$	(iv)	$\mu_0(i_c + i_d)$

Codes

	A	B	C	D		A	B	C	D
(a)	(iii)	(ii)	(i)	(iv)	(b)	(iv)	(i)	(iii)	(ii)
(c)	(iii)	(i)	(ii)	(iv)	(d)	(iii)	(i)	(iv)	(ii)

33. Two concentric coplanar circular conducting loops have radii R and r ($R >> r$). Their mutual inductance is proportional to

(a) $\frac{r}{R}$ (b) $\frac{R}{r}$ (c) $\frac{r^2}{R}$ (d) $\frac{R^2}{r}$

34. When an inductor L and a resistor R in series are connected across a 12 V, 50 Hz supply, a current of 0.5 A flows in the circuit. The current differs in the phase from applied voltage by $\frac{\pi}{3}$ radian. Then the value of R is

(a) 10 Ω (b) 3 Ω (c) 12 Ω (d) 15 Ω

35. A point source of electromagnetic radiation has an average power output of 960 W. The peak value of the electric field at a distance 400 cm from the source is

(a) 60 Vm^{-1} (b) 120 Vm^{-1} (c) 30 Vm^{-1} (d) 180 Vm^{-1}

36. All electrons ejected from a metallic surface by incident light of wavelength 400 nm travelled 1 m in the direction of uniform electric field of 2 NC^{-1} and came to rest. The work function of the surface is

(a) 1.1 eV (b) 2.2 eV
(c) 3.1 eV (d) 5.1 eV

37. Speed of electron in its 1st Bohr's orbit is given by $2.18 \times 10^6 \text{ms}^{-1}$. If the time period of electron in n th orbit is measured as 4.10 femto second, the value of n is

(a) 1 (b) 2
(c) 3 (d) 4

38. A radioactive substance of half life 138.6 days is placed in a box. After n days only 20% of the substance is present then the value of n is
[ln (5) = 1.61]

(a) 693 (b) 138.6
(c) 277.2 (d) 322

39. Three amplifiers with voltage gains 10, 20 and 30 are connected in series. If the input signal has a peak value of 1 mV then the peak value of the output voltage is

(a) 6 V (b) 60 V
(c) 0.6 V (d) 0.06 V

40. A TV tower has a height 160 m. Its coverage range is nearly (Earth's radius, R_e = 6400 km)

(a) 45255 m
(b) 55265 m
(c) 452.55 km
(d) 552.65 m

Answers

1.	(a)	2.	(b)	3.	(c)	4.	(d)	5.	(b)	6.	(a)	7.	(a)	8.	(b)	9.	(c)	10.	(d)
11.	(b)	12.	(c)	13.	(b)	14.	(b)	15.	(c)	16.	(c)	17.	(c)	18.	(a)	19.	(c)	20.	(c)
21.	(b)	22.	(d)	23.	(a)	24.	(a)	25.	(d)	26.	(c)	27.	(c)	28.	(b)	29.	(a)	30.	(a)
31.	(c)	32.	(c)	33.	(c)	34.	(c)	35.	(a)	36.	(a)	37.	(c)	38.	(d)	39.	(a)	40.	(a)

Scan this QR code from your mobile phone to get the explanations of this paper.
Or
Visit : http://tinyurl.com/y44hyqf2

22 April Shift II
Session 2 (3:00 PM to 6:00 PM)

1. If A represents density, B represents velocity, C represents specific heat capacity and D represents wavelength, then the quantity having the dimensions of product of A, B, C and D is

(a) Stefan's constant (b) Boltzmann's constant
(c) thermal conductivity (d) universal gas constant

2. A ball dropped from a building of height 12 m falls on a slab of 1 m height from the ground and makes a perfect elastic collision. Later the ball falls on a wooden table of height 0.5 m, makes inelastic collision and falls on the ground. If the coefficient of restitution between the ball and the table is 0.5, then the velocity of the ball while touching the ground is about (Acceleration due to gravity, $g = 10\ ms^{-2}$)

(a) $15.5\ ms^{-1}$ (b) $14.5\ ms^{-1}$
(c) $9.2\ ms^{-1}$ (d) $8.2\ ms^{-1}$

3. Two food packets are thrown with the same velocity in the same direction with different angles of projection simultaneously. The angle of projection of one packet is 15°. At the same moment one boy starts running from rest from the point of projection with an acceleration of $10\ ms^{-2}$ to catch them. If he caught one packet at a distance of 20 m and other packet in $\frac{1}{2}$ s later the first packet, then the angle of projection of the second packet is (Acceleration due to gravity, $g = 10\ ms^{-2}$)

(a) $\frac{1}{2}\sin^{-1}\left(\frac{25}{32}\right)$ (b) $\frac{1}{2}\sin^{-1}\left(\frac{8}{9}\right)$
(c) $\frac{1}{2}\sin^{-1}\left(\frac{7}{8}\right)$ (d) $\frac{1}{2}\sin^{-1}\left(\frac{5}{6}\right)$

4. A body is projected up a smooth inclined plane of length $20\sqrt{2}$ m from point A as shown in the figure. The top B of the inclined plane is connected to a well of diameter 40 m. If the body just manages to cross the well then the velocity of projection is (Acceleration due to gravity, $g = 10\ ms^{-2}$)

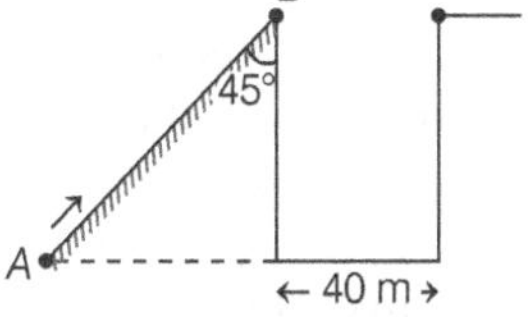

(a) $40\ ms^{-1}$ (b) $40\sqrt{2}\ ms^{-1}$
(c) $20\ ms^{-1}$ (d) $20\sqrt{2}\ ms^{-1}$

5. A body is acted on by a force given by $F = (15 + 3t^2)$ N. The impulse received by the body during the first 2 seconds is

(a) 28 Ns (b) 38 Ns (c) 30 Ns (d) 19 Ns

6. A body starts sliding down from the top of an inclined plane at an angle θ with the horizontal direction. The first one third of the incline is smooth, the next one third has coefficient of friction $\frac{\mu}{2}$ and the last one third has coefficient of friction μ.
If the body comes to rest at the bottom of the plane then the value of μ is

(a) $\frac{\tan\theta}{2}$ (b) $\frac{3\tan\theta}{2}$ (c) $\tan\theta$ (d) $2\tan\theta$

7. A motor pump a liquid of density ρ through a pipe of cross-sectional area A. If the liquid moves with a speed v in this pipe, then the rate of kinetic energy imparted to the liquid is proportional to

(a) v^2 (b) v^3 (c) v^4 (d) $\sqrt{v}$

8. Two particles 1 and 2 are allowed to descend on two frictionless chords OP and OQ as shown in the figure. The ratio of the speeds of the particles 1 and 2, respectively when they reach the circumference is

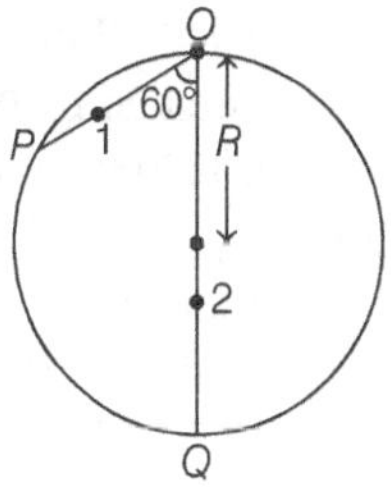

(a) $\frac{1}{2}$ (b) 2
(c) $\frac{3}{2}$ (d) $\frac{2}{3}$

9. A uniform rod of mass m and length l is pivoted smoothly at point O as shown in figure. If a horizontal force F acts at the bottom of the rod and ω is the angular velocity of the rod which is a function of angle of rotation θ, then the maximum angular displacement of the rod is (Acceleration due to gravity, g)

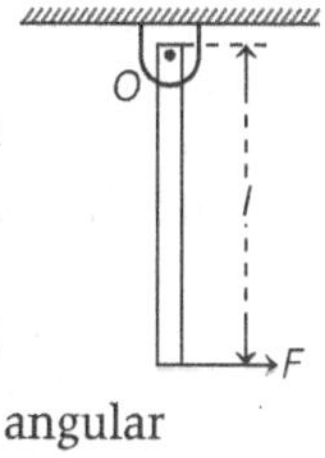

(a) $\theta = 2\sin^{-1}\left(\frac{2F}{mg}\right)$ (b) $\theta = 2\cos^{-1}\left(\frac{2F}{mg}\right)$

(c) $\theta = 2\tan^{-1}\left(\frac{2F}{mg}\right)$ (d) $\theta = 2\cot^{-1}\left(\frac{2F}{mg}\right)$

10. An electric motor of power 75 W rotates a flywheel of moment of inertia 0.36 kg - m^2 at a constant rate of 100 rad s^{-1}. If the power is switched off, the time taken for the wheel to come to rest is

(a) 12 s (b) 24 s (c) 36 s (d) 48 s

11. A particle is executing simple harmonic motion along a straight line *PQ*. At three points *A*, *B* and *C* on the line *PQ*, lying on one side of the mean position, the velocities of the particles are $8 \text{ ms}^{-1}, 7 \text{ ms}^{-1}$ and 4 ms^{-1}, respectively. If $AB = BC = 1$ m, the velocity of the particle at mean position is

(a) 9 ms^{-1} (b) $\sqrt{47} \text{ ms}^{-1}$ (c) $\sqrt{65} \text{ ms}^{-1}$ (d) 10 ms^{-1}

12. The gravitational potential difference between the surface of a planet and a point 20 m above it is 16 J kg^{-1}. The work done in moving a 4 kg body by 8 m on a slope of 60° from the horizontal is

(a) 22.17 J (b) 2.217 J (c) 221.7 J (d) 0.2217 J

13. The area of cross-section of steel wire is 0.1 cm^2 and Young's modulus of steel is $2 \times 10^{11} \text{ N m}^{-2}$. The force required to stretched by 0.1% of its length is

(a) 1000 N (b) 2000 N (c) 5000 N (d) 4000 N

14. A sphere of radius *R* has a concentric spherical cavity of radius *r*. The relative density of the material of the sphere is σ. It just floats when placed in tank full of water. The value of $\frac{R}{r}$ is

(a) $\left(\frac{\sigma}{\sigma - 1}\right)^{\frac{1}{3}}$ (b) $\left(\frac{\sigma - 1}{\sigma}\right)^{\frac{1}{3}}$ (c) $\left(\frac{\sigma}{\sigma - 1}\right)^{\frac{1}{2}}$ (d) $\left(\frac{\sigma - 1}{\sigma}\right)^{\frac{1}{2}}$

15. Figure shows a system of two concentric spheres of radii r_1 and r_2 at the temperatures T_1 and T_2, respectively. The radial rate of flow of heat in a substance filled between the two concentric spheres is proportional to

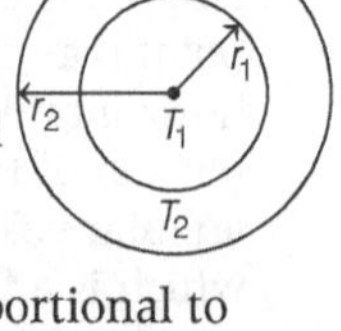

(a) $r_2 - r_1$ (b) $\ln\left(\frac{r_2}{r_1}\right)$ (c) $\frac{r_2 - r_1}{r_1 r_2}$ (d) $\frac{r_1 r_2}{r_2 - r_1}$

16. A composite bar of uniform cross-section is made of 25 cm of copper, 10 cm of nickel and 15 cm of aluminium with perfect thermal contacts. The free copper end of the rod is at 100°C and the free aluminium end is at 0°C. If $K_{Cu} = 2 K_{Al}$ and $K_{Al} = 3 K_{Ni}$, then the temperatures of Cu-Ni and Ni-Al junctions are respectively,

(Assume no loss of heat occurs from the sides of the rod, *K*-thermal conductivity).

(a) 82.3 °C, 31.3 °C (b) 78.3 °C, 26.1 °C
(c) 70 °C, 23.3 °C (d) 90.3 °C, 30.1 °C

17. The specific heat capacities of three liquids *A*, *B* and *C* are in the ratio, 1 : 2 : 3 and the masses of the liquids are in the ratio 1 : 1 : 1. The temperatures of the liquids *A*, *B* and *C* are 15 °C, 30 °C and 45 °C, respectively. Then matched the resultant temperature of the mixture given in list-II with the corresponding mixture given in list-I.

	List I		List II
A.	Mixture of liquids *A* and *B*	(i)	25 °C
B.	Mixture of liquids *B* and *C*	(ii)	35 °C
C.	Mixture of liquids *C* and *A*	(iii)	37.5 °C
D.	Mixture of liquids *A*, *B* and *C*	(iv)	39 °C

Codes

	A	B	C	D		A	B	C	D
(a)	(i)	(ii)	(iii)	(iv)	(b)	(ii)	(i)	(v)	(iii)
(c)	(i)	(iv)	(iii)	(ii)	(d)	(iv)	(i)	(iii)	(ii)

18. A gas ($\gamma = 1.5$) undergoes a cycle of adiabatic, isobaric and isochoric processes in an order. If the volume of the gas is doubled in the adiabatic process then the efficiency of the cycle is approximately,

(a) 18% (b) 46.4%
(c) 38.5% (d) 9.25%

19. The *y*-components of velocities of the molecules of a gas are $-7, -6, -5, -4, -3, -2, -1, 0, +1, +2, +3, +4, +5, +6, +7 \text{ ms}^{-1}$ then the rms velocity is

(a) $\sqrt{\frac{56}{3}} \text{ ms}^{-1}$ (b) $\sqrt{\frac{28}{3}} \text{ ms}^{-1}$

(c) $\sqrt{\frac{112}{3}} \text{ ms}^{-1}$ (d) $\sqrt{\frac{84}{3}} \text{ ms}^{-1}$

20. A metal wire of length 80 cm, area of cross-section 3 mm^2 and material density 3000 kg m^{-3} is joined to another metal wire of length 60 cm, area of cross-section 1 mm^2 and material density 9000 kg-m^{-3}.

The free ends of the two wires are stretched between two rigid supports and a tension of 40 N is produced in the wires. The minimum frequency of the tuning fork which can produce stationary waves with the joint of the wires as a node is

(a) $\frac{200}{3}$ Hz (b) $\frac{400}{3}$ Hz (c) $\frac{500}{3}$ Hz (d) $\frac{700}{3}$ Hz

21. A source producing sound of frequency 720 Hz is falling freely from the top of a tower of height 20 m. The frequency of sound heard by an observer on the top of the tower when the source just reaches the ground is (Acceleration due to gravity, $g = 10$ ms^{-2} and speed of sound in air = 340 ms^{-1})

(a) 660 Hz (b) 680 Hz (c) 740 Hz (d) 760 Hz

22. In a spherical glass marble of radius 6 cm, a small air bubble is formed at 1 cm from the centre of the marble. The apparent position of the air bubble from the nearest point on the surface of the marble is about, (refractive index of glass is 1.5.)

(a) 3.3 cm (b) 4.6 cm (c) 5.4 cm (d) 7.0 cm

23. In a Young's double slit experiment, the two slits are separated by 0.5 cm and the screen is at 0.5 m from the slits. If 20000 bright fringes are counted per meter on the screen, then the wavelength of light used is

(a) 5000 Å (b) 5890 Å (c) 6000 Å (d) 5460 Å

24. A dipole has two charges + 1 μC and − 1 μC and each of mass 1 kg. The separation between the charges is 1 m. An electric field 20×10^3 Vm^{-1} is applied on the dipole. If the dipole is deflected through 2° from the equilibrium position, then the time taken by it to come to equilibrium position again is

(a) 2.5 π s
(b) 5 π s
(c) 15 π s
(d) π s

25. In the following four cases, charged particles are at equal distances from the origin. Arranged them in the descending order of magnitude of the net electric field at the origin.

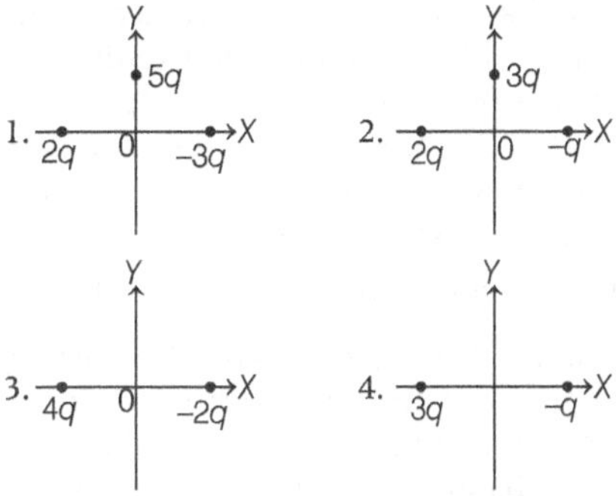

(a) 1, 2, 3, 4
(b) 2, 1, 3, 4
(c) 1, 3, 2, 4
(d) 4, 3, 2, 1

26. A capacitance of 2 μF is required in an electrical circuit across a potential of 1.0 kV. A large number of 1 μF capacitors are available which can withstand a potential difference not more than 300 V. The minimum number of capacitors required to achieve this is

(a) 24 (b) 32 (c) 8 (d) 16

27. A charge 5C is placed at the centre of shell of radius, $r = 3$ m and having charges 5 C. The potential at a point $\frac{r}{2}$ distance from the centre of the shell will be

(a) -9×10^0 V
(b) 30×10^9 V
(c) 45×10^9 V
(d) -15×10^9 V

28. Electrical energy costs 25 paisa per kilowatt hour. Assuming that no energy is wasted, the cost of heating 4.6 kg of water from 25 °C to the boiling point is

(a) 25 paisa (b) 50 paisa (c) 20 paisa (d) 10 paisa

29. A 500 W heater is designed to operate at 200 V potential difference. If it is connected across 160 V line, the heat it will produce in 20 minutes is

(a) 384 kJ (b) 483 kJ (c) 843 kJ (d) 348 kJ

30. A wire of length 44 cm carrying a current of 2 A is bent and the two ends are joined. This shape is placed in a uniform magnetic field of 50 mT. If the magnetic field is in North-South direction, then the maximum torque acting on the shape is

(a) 1.54×10^{-3} Nm
(b) 0.77×10^{-3} Nm
(c) 3.08×10^{-3} Nm
(d) Zero

31. A toroid has a non-ferromagnetic core of inner radius 20.5 cm and outer radius 21.5 cm, around which 4200 turns of a wire are wound. If the current in the wire is 10 A, the magnetic field inside the core of the toroid is $(\mu_0 = 4\pi \times 10^{-7}\ \text{Hm}^{-1})$

(a) 20 mT (b) 40 mT (c) 20 π mT (d) 40 π mT

32. Two short bar magnets *A* and *B* are arranged co-axially. The distance between their centres is 30 cm. A compass needle placed on their axis at a distance of 6 cm from *B* shows no deflection. The ratio of the magnetic moments of *A* and *B* is

(a) 16 : 1 (b) 1 : 16 (c) 64 : 1 (d) 1 : 64

33. A circular coil of area 0.1 m^2 having 200 turns is placed in a magnetic field of 40 T. The plane of the coil makes 30° with the field. If the field is removed for 0.1 s then the induced emf in the coil is

(a) 4000 V (b) $4000\sqrt{3}$ V (c) 2000 V (d) $2000\sqrt{3}$ V

34. A coil has an inductance 0.7 H and it is joined in series with a resistance of 220 Ω. When AC of 220 V, 50 Hz is applied to it, then wattless component in the circuit is

(a) 5 A (b) 0.5 A (c) 0.7 A (d) 7 A

35. A plane electromagnetic wave propagating in a non-magnetic dielectric medium is given by $E = E_0 [4 \times 10^{-7} x - 50t]$, where *x* is in metre and *t* is in second. If the relative permeability of the medium, $\mu_r = 1$ then the dielectric constant of the medium is

(a) 2.42 (b) 5.76 (c) 8.26 (d) 4.84

36. All electrons ejected from a metal surface by the incident light of wavelength 200 nm can be stopped before travelling 1 m in the direction of uniform electric field of 4 NC^{-1}. The work function of the metal surface is

(a) 2 eV (b) 2.2 eV (c) 4 eV (d) 6.2 eV

37. A hydrogen atom emits a photon of wavelength $\frac{36}{35R}$ when it is jumped from its *n*th excited state to the ground state. Then the quantum number *n* is

(*R* is Rydberg constant.)

(a) 8 (b) 7 (c) 5 (d) 6

38. **Assertion** (A) Fragments produced in the fission of ${}_{92}U^{235}$ are radioactive.

Reason (R) The fragments in the fission of ${}^{235}U$ have a proton to neutron ratio of 2.5.

(a) Both (A) and (R) are correct and (R) is the correct explanation of (A).
(b) Both (A) and (R) are correct but (R) is not the correct explanation of (A).
(c) (A) is correct but (R) is not correct.
(d) (A) is not correct but (R) is correct.

39. In the circuit given, the current through Zener diode is

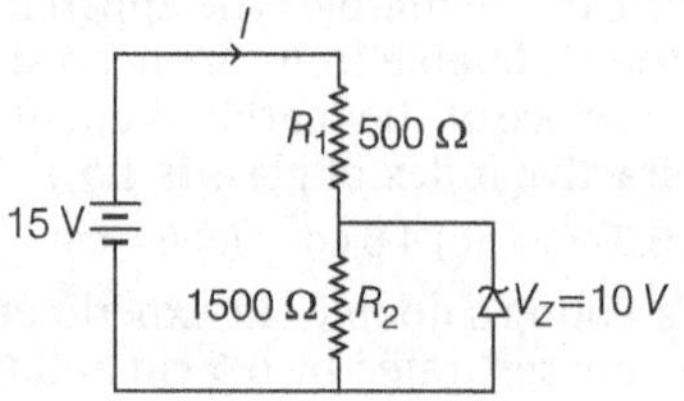

(a) 10 mA (b) 6.67 mA (c) 3.33 mA (d) 5 mA

40. Co-axial cable, a widely used wire medium for transmission of signals offers a bandwith of approximately.

(a) 600 kHz (b) 750 MHz (c) 850 GHz (d) 500 Hz

Answers

1.	(c)	2.	(d)	3.	(a)	4.	(d)	5.	(b)	6.	(d)	7.	(b)	8.	(a)	9.	(c)	10.	(d)
11.	(c)	12.	(a)	13.	(b)	14.	(a)	15.	(d)	16.	(b)	17.	(c)	18.	(a)	19.	(a)	20.	(c)
21.	(b)	22.	(a)	23.	(a)	24.	(a)	25.	(c)	26.	(b)	27.	(c)	28.	(d)	29.	(a)	30.	(a)
31.	(b)	32.	(c)	33.	(b)	34.	(b)	35.	(b)	36.	(b)	37.	(d)	38.	(c)	39.	(c)	40.	(*)

Scan this QR code from your mobile phone to get the explanations of this paper.
Or
Visit : http://tinyurl.com/y2fmtk76

23 April Shift I
Session 1 (10:00 AM to 1:00 PM)

1. **Assertion** (A) The number 0.00764 has three significant figures.
Reason (R) If the number is less than 1, the zeros on the right of the decimal point but to the left of the first non-zero digit are not significant.
(a) Both (A) and (R) are true and (R) is the correct explanation of (A).
(b) Both (A) and (R) are true but (R) is not the correct explanation of (A).
(c) (A) is true but (R) is false.
(d) (A) is false but (R) is true.

2. A car moving with a velocity 6.25 ms^{-1} is decelerated with $2.5\sqrt{v}$ ms^{-2} (v is instantaneous velocity). Time taken by the car to come to rest is
(a) 2 s (b) 3 s (c) 2.5 s (d) 4 s

3. A bullet fired from a gun falls at a distance half of its maximum range. The angle of projection of the bullet is
(a) 45° (b) 60° (c) 30° (d) 15°

4. A body is projected at an angle of 45° from a point on the ground at a distance of 30 m from the foot of a vertical pole of height 20 m. The body just crosses the top of the pole and strikes the ground at a distance s from the foot of the pole on the other side of the pole. Then, s
(a) 20 m (b) 30 m (c) 50 m (d) 60 m

5. An explosion blows a stationary rock into three parts. Two parts of masses 1 kg and 2 kg moves at right angles to one another with velocities 12 ms^{-1} and 8 ms^{-1}, respectively. If the velocity of third part is 4 ms^{-1}, the mass of the rock is
(a) 8 kg (b) 5 kg (c) 17 kg (d) 3 kg

6. Four blocks A, B, C and D of masses 6 kg,3kg, 6 kg and 1 kg respectively are connected by light strings passing over frictionless pulleys as shown in the figure. The strings P and Q are horizontal. The coefficient of friction between the horizontal surface and the block B is 0.2 and the blocks A and B move together. If the system is released from rest then the tension in the string Q is (Acceleration due to gravity, $g = 10$ ms^{-2})

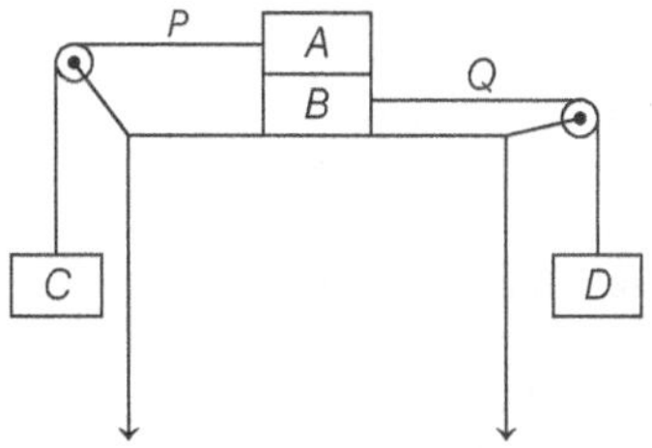

(a) 48 N (b) 24 N (c) 12 N (d) 6 N

7. A constant power of 7 W is supplied on a toy car of mass 15 kg. The distance travelled by the car when its velocity increases from 3 ms^{-1} to 5 ms^{-1} is
(a) 56 m (b) 7 m (c) 61 m (d) 70 m

8. A body A moving with momentum P collides one-dimensionally with another stationary body B of same mass. During impact, A gives impulse J to B. Then which of the following is/are correct?
(a) The total momentum of A and B is P before and after impact and $(P-J)$ during the impact.
(b) During the impact, B gives impulse of magnitude J to A.
(c) The coefficient of restitution is $\left[\frac{2J}{P}-1\right]$.
(d) The coefficient of restitution is $\left[\frac{2J}{P}+1\right]$.
(a) Only (a) is correct. (b) (a) and (c) are correct.
(c) (b) and (c) are correct. (d) Only (c) is correct.

9. In the figure shown, the blocks have equal masses. Friction, mass of the string and the mass of the pulley are negligible. The magnitude of the acceleration of the centre of mass of the two blocks is (Acceleration due to gravity = g).

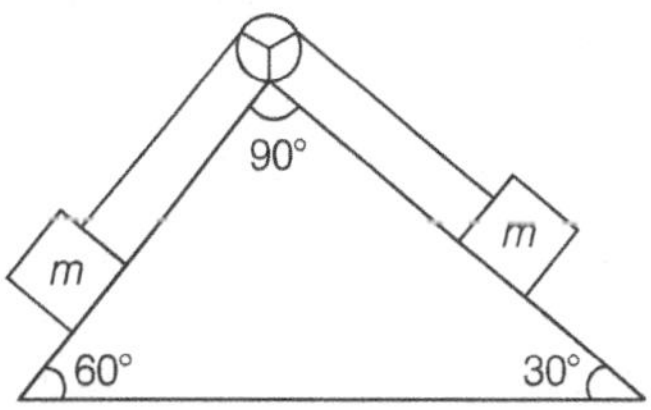

(a) $\left(\frac{\sqrt{3}-1}{\sqrt{2}}\right)g$ (b) $\frac{g}{2}$

(c) $(\sqrt{3}-1)g$ (d) $\left(\frac{\sqrt{3}-1}{4\sqrt{2}}\right)g$

10. A wheel of radius 8 cm is attached to a support so as to rotate about a horizontal axis through its centre. A string of negligible mass wrapped around its circumference carries a mass of 0.4 kg attached to its free end. When the mass is released, it descends through 1 m in 10 seconds, then its moment of inertia is (Acceleration due to gravity, $g = 10\ \text{ms}^{-2}$)

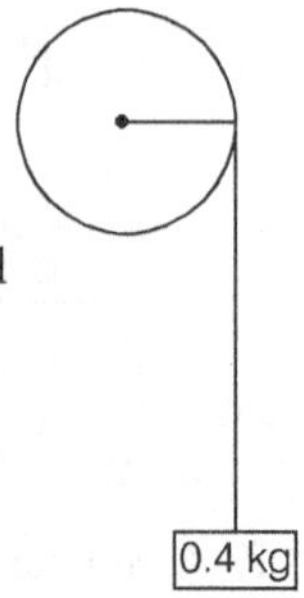

(a) 1.277 kg m² (b) 2.177 kg m²
(c) 21.77 kg m² (d) 12.77 kg m²

11. A body of mass 1 kg is suspended from a spring of negligible mass. Another body of mass 500 g moving vertically upwards hits the suspended body with a velocity of 3 ms^{-1} and gets embedded in it. If the frequency of oscillation of the system of the two bodies after collision is $\frac{10}{\pi}$ Hz, the amplitude of the motion and the spring constant are respectively,

(a) 5 cm, 300 Nm^{-1} (b) 10 cm, 300 Nm^{-1}
(c) 10 cm, 600 Nm^{-1} (d) 5 cm, 600 Nm^{-1}

12. The gravitational field in a region is given by $\mathbf{E} = (5\hat{\mathbf{i}} + 12\hat{\mathbf{j}})\ \text{Nkg}^{-1}$. If a particle of mass 2 kg is moved from the origin to the point (12 m, 15 m) in this region, the change in gravitational potential energy is

(a) – 450 J (b) – 480 J (c) – 240 J (d) – 500 J

13. A uniform wire of length 10 m and diameter 0.6 mm is stretched by 6 mm with certain force. If the Poisson's ratio of the material of the wire is 0.3, then the change in diameter of the wire is

(a) 108×10^{-8} m (b) 108×10^{-6} m
(c) 10.8×10^{-8} m (d) 1.08×10^{-8} m

14. Two tubes of same length and diameters 4 mm and 8 mm are joined together to form a U-shaped tube open at both the ends. If the U-tube contains water, then the difference between the levels of water in the two limbs of the tube is

(Surface tension of water at the temperature of experiment is $7.3 \times 10^{-2}\ \text{Nm}^{-1}$, angle of contact = 0°, density of water = $1.0 \times 10^{3}\ \text{kg m}^{-3}$ and acceleration due to gravity = 10 ms^{-2})

(a) 3.65 mm (b) 36.5 mm
(c) 0.365 mm (d) 365 mm

15. A uniform metal bar of length 10 m with a crack at its midpoint is clamped between two rigid supports. The bar buckles upward due to temperature rise of 40°C. If the coefficient of linear expansion of the metal is $2.5 \times 10^{-6}\ °\text{C}^{-1}$, the maximum displacement of the mid-point of the bar is

(a) 11.3 cm (b) 22.3 cm (c) 33.3 cm (d) 44.3 cm

16. Three rods each of length l and cross sectional area A joined in series between two heat reservoirs as shown in the figure. Their conductivities are 2 K, K and $\frac{K}{2}$, respectively. Assuming that the conductors are insulated from surroundings, the temperatures T_1 and T_2 of the junctions in steady state condition are respectively.

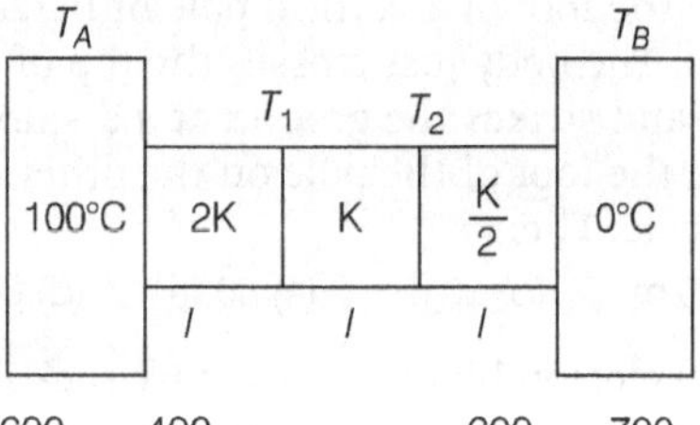

(a) $\frac{600}{7}$ °C, $\frac{400}{7}$ °C (b) $\frac{600}{7}$ °C, $\frac{700}{4}$ °C
(c) $\frac{500}{6}$ °C, $\frac{600}{5}$ °C (d) $\frac{600}{4}$ °C, $\frac{400}{7}$ °C

17. Two heat engines X and Y of same efficiency are connected in series in such a way that the sink of X works as source of Y. X receives heat at 900 K and rejects some heat to its sink at TK and in turn Y rejects heat to its sink at 400 K, then the temperature T is

(a) 550 K (b) 600 K (c) 650 K (d) 700 K

18. The specific heat capacities of an ideal gas at the constant pressure and at constant volume are 620 $\text{Jkg}^{-1}\text{K}^{-1}$ and 420 $\text{Jkg}^{-1}\text{K}^{-1}$ respectively.

The density of the gas at STP is approximately,

(a) 2.88 kgm^{-3} (b) 4.86 kgm^{-3}
(c) 3.88 kgm^{-3} (d) 1.86 kgm^{-3}

19. Three closed vessels A, B and C are at the same temperature T and contain gases. Vessel A contains only O_2, B contains only N_2 and C contains a mixture of equal quantities of O_2 and N_2. If the rms speed of O_2 molecules in vessel A is v_1 and that of N_2 molecules in vessel B is v_2 then the rms speed of O_2 molecules in vessel C is

(a) $\left(\frac{v_1 + v_2}{2}\right)$ (b) v_1 (c) $(v_1 v_2)$ (d) $\frac{v_1}{2}$

20. Match the following List I with List II.

List I		List II
(A) Transverse wave	(i)	Vibrations parallel to the direction of propagation
(B) Longitudinal wave	(ii)	Vibrations perpendicular to the direction of propagation
(C) Beats	(iii)	Superposition of waves travelling in the opposite directions
(D) Stationary waves	(iv)	Superposition of waves travelling in same direction

The correct answer is

	A	B	C	D		A	B	C	D
(a)	(ii)	(i)	(iii)	(iv)	(b)	(ii)	(i)	(iv)	(iii)
(c)	(iii)	(iv)	(i)	(ii)	(d)	(iv)	(i)	(ii)	(iii)

21. A police car moving at 22 ms^{-1} chases a motor cyclist. The police man sounds horn at 176 Hz, while both of them move towards a stationary siren of frequency 165 Hz. If the number of beats heard by the motor cyclist per second is zero, then the speed of motorcycle is (Speed of sound in air = 330 ms^{-1})

(a) 33 ms^{-1} (b) 22 ms^{-1} (c) 44 ms^{-1} (d) 11 ms^{-1}

22. When an object is moved along the principle axis of a concave mirror placed in air, the image coincides with the object if the object is 50 cm from the mirror. If the mirror is placed at a depth of 20 cm in a transparent medium, the image coincides with the object when the object is 40 cm from the mirror. The refractive index of the liquid is

(a) $\frac{5}{4}$ (b) $\frac{4}{3}$ (c) $\frac{3}{2}$ (d) $\frac{5}{3}$

23. In a Young's double slit experiment, light of wavelength 5900 Å is used. When the slits are 2 mm apart, the fringe width is 1.2 mm. If the slit separation is increased to one and half times the previous value, then the fringe width will be

(a) 0.9 mm (b) 0.8 mm (c) 1.8 mm (d) 1.6 mm

24. Two particles with charges + 3.72 μC and +1.86 μC are some distance apart. If 20% of the charge is transferred from first particle to second particle then the electrostatic force between them is

(a) decreases by 12% (b) increases by 12%
(c) increases by 4% (d) decreases by 4%

25. ABC is a right angled triangle in which $AB = 3$ cm, $BC = 4$ cm and right angle is at B. Three charges +15μC, +12μC and − 20 μC are placed respectively at A, B and C. The force acting on the charge at B is

(a) 1250 N (b) 3500 N (c) 1200 N (d) 2250 N

26. A spherical capacitor has outer sphere of radius 5 cm and inner sphere of radius 2 cm. When the inner sphere is earthed, its capacity is C_1 and when the outer sphere is earthed its capacity is C_2. Then $\frac{C_1}{C_2}$ is

(a) $\frac{5}{2}$ (b) $\frac{2}{5}$ (c) $\frac{7}{3}$ (d) $\frac{3}{7}$

27. The charge on 4 μF capacitor, in the given circuit is

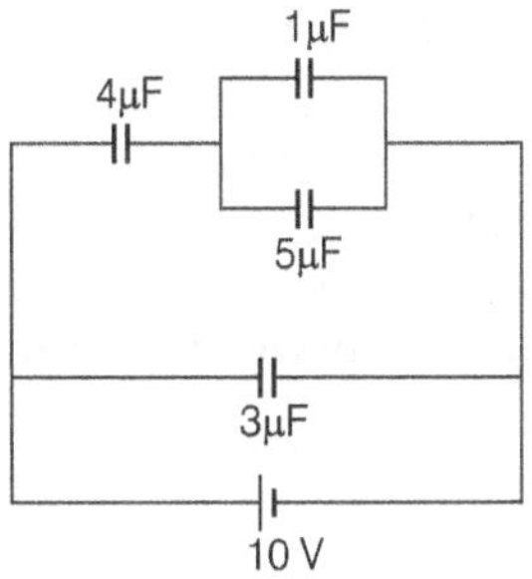

(a) 24 μC (b) 100 μC
(c) 2.4 μC (d) 30 μC

28. A cell of emf ε and internal resistance r is connected across a variable load resistance R. The graph drawn between its terminal voltage and resistance R is

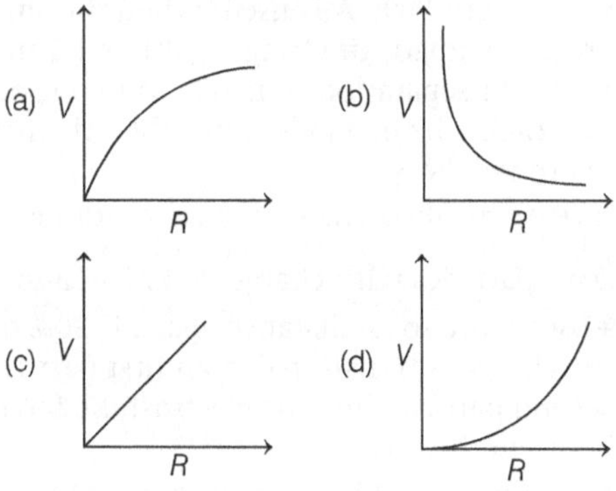

29. In a meter-bridge if the left and right gaps are connected with 2 Ω and 3 Ω resistances, respectively then the bridge is balanced. The resistance to be connected with 3Ω resistance to get the balancing point at midpoint of the bridge wire is

(a) 3 Ω in series (b) 3 Ω in parallel
(c) 6 Ω in series (d) 6 Ω in parallel

30. Magnetic field at the centre of a circular loop of area A is B. Then the magnetic moment of the loop is

(μ_0-permeability of the free space)

(a) $\frac{BA^2}{\mu_0 \pi}$ (b) $\frac{BA\sqrt{A}}{\mu_0}$
(c) $\frac{BA\sqrt{A}}{\mu_0 \pi}$ (d) $\frac{2BA\sqrt{A}}{\mu_0 \sqrt{\pi}}$

31. A circular coil of radius 10 cm with 100 turns carrying a current of 0.5 A lies in a magnetic field of 2 T such that the normal drawn to the plane of the coil makes an angles θ with the direction of the field. Work done in rotating the coil to change the angle θ from 0° to 180° is

(a) π J (b) 2π J
(c) 4π J (d) 8π J

32. The resultant magnetic moment of three magnetic dipoles, each of the magnetic moment M shown in the arrangement is

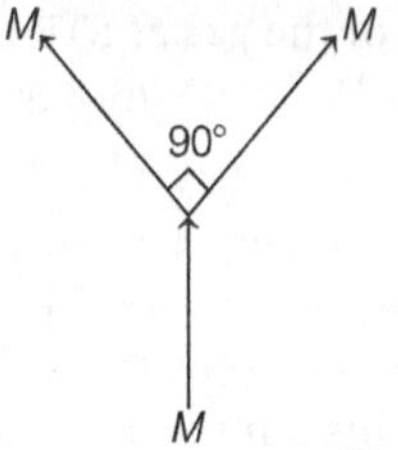

(a) $\sqrt{2}\,M$ (b) $(\sqrt{2}+1)M$
(c) $(\sqrt{2}-1)M$ (d) M

33. A long solenoid with 2000 turns per meter has a small loop of radius 3 cm placed inside the solenoid normal to its axis. If the current through the solenoid increases steadily from 1.5 A to 5.5 A in $\frac{\pi^2}{100}$ s, the induced emf in the loop is

(a) 0.144 mV (b) 0.288 mV
(c) 0.072 mV (d) 0.316 mV

34. In the given circuit, the angular frequency of the voltage source is 70×10^3 rad s^{-1}. The circuit effectively behaves like,

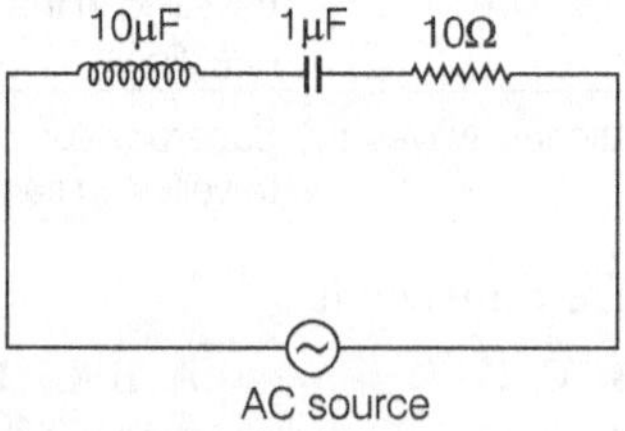

(a) purely resistive circuit
(b) series RL circuit
(c) series RC circuit
(d) series LC circuit with $R = 0$

35. A parallel plate capacitor consists of two circular plates each of radius 2 cm, separated by a distance of 0.1 mm. If the potential difference across the plates is varying at the rate of 5×10^6 Vs^{-1}, then the value of displacement current is

(a) 5.56 A (b) 5.56 mA (c) 0.556 mA (d) 2.28 mA

36. Light of wavelength 488 nm produced by an Agron laser is used in the photoelectric effect. When light from this spectral line is incident on the cathode, the stopping potential of the photoelectrons is 0.38 V. The work function of the cathode material is

(a) 2.16 eV (b) 216 eV
(c) 21.6 eV (d) 0.216 eV

37. If the first excitation potential of a hypothetical hydrogen like atom is 15 V, then the third excitation potential of the atom is

(a) 13.6 V (b) $\frac{4}{75}$ V
(c) $\frac{15}{16}$ V (d) $\frac{75}{4}$ V

38. The energy released when one nucleus of $_{92}U^{235}$ undergoes fission is 188 MeV. The energy released when 100 g of $_{92}U^{235}$ undergoes fission is

(a) 3.55×10^{12} J
(b) 7.71×10^{12} J
(c) 3.55×10^{13} J
(d) 7.71×10^{13} J

39. The value of Y_1 and Y_2, respectively in the following logic circuit if both A and B are 1.

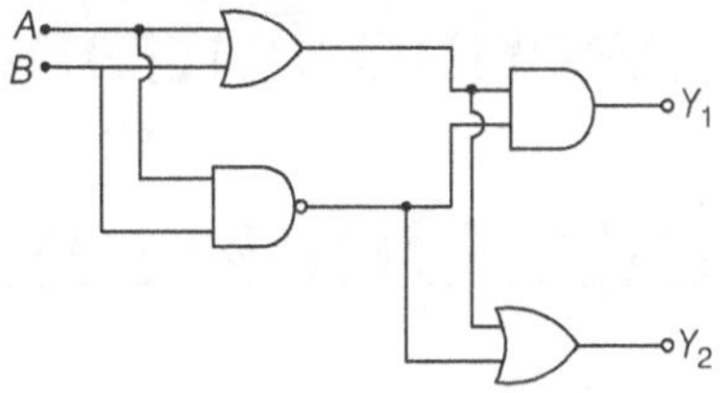

(a) 1, 1 (b) 1, 0 (c) 0, 1 (d) 0, 0

40. If E_c and E_m are peak values of carrier and modulating signals, respectively then for 100% modulation,

(a) $E_c = \frac{E_m}{2}$ (b) $\frac{E_c^2}{2} = E_m^2$ (c) $E_c = E_m$ (d) $E_c = 2E_m$

Answers

1.	(a)	2.	(a)	3.	(d)	4.	(d)	5.	(a)	6.	(c)	7.	(d)	8.	(c)	9.	(d)	10.	(a)
11.	(d)	12.	(b)	13.	(c)	14.	(a)	15.	(b)	16.	(a)	17.	(b)	18.	(d)	19.	(b)	20.	(b)
21.	(b)	22.	(c)	23.	(b)	24.	(b)	25.	(d)	26.	(a)	27.	(a)	28.	(a)	29.	(d)	30.	(d)
31.	(b)	32.	(b)	33.	(b)	34.	(c)	35.	(c)	36.	(a)	37.	(d)	38.	(b)	39.	(c)	40.	(c)

Scan this QR code from your mobile phone to get the explanations of this paper.
Or
Visit : http://tinyurl.com/y4efdrtv

TS EAMCET

Engineering Entrance Exam

Online Question Paper 2019 *(Solved)*

03 May Shift I

Session 1 (10:00 AM to 1:00 PM)

1. Match the following fundamental forces of nature with their relative strength.

List-I		List-II
(A) Strong nuclear force	(i)	10^{-2}
(B) Weak nuclear force	(ii)	1
(C) Electromagnetic force	(iii)	10^{-39}
(D) Gravitational force	(iv)	10^{-13}

The correct match is

	A	B	C	D		A	B	C	D
(a)	(ii)	(iv)	(i)	(iii)	(b)	(iii)	(ii)	(iv)	(i)
(c)	(ii)	(iii)	(iv)	(i)	(d)	(iv)	(ii)	(i)	(iii)

2. Identify the incorrect statement among the following.

(a) A true length of 5.678 km has been measured in two experiments as 5.5 km and 5.51 km, respectively. The second measurement has more precision.

(b) Length of 1 m and 0.5 m have been both measured with the same absolute error of 0.01 m. Both the measurement are equally accurate.

(c) The numbers of significant digits in 1.6 and 0.60 are both two.

(d) The number 2.445 can be rounded to two decimal place as 2.45.

3. Ball-1 is dropped from the top of a building from rest. At the same moment, ball-2 is thrown upward towards ball-1 with a speed 14 m/s from a point 21 m below the top of building. How far will the ball-1 have dropped when it passes ball-2. (Assume, acceleration due to gravity, $g = 10\ \text{m/s}^2$.)

(a) $\frac{45}{4}$ m (b) $\frac{52}{6}$ m (c) $\frac{37}{2}$ m (d) $\frac{25}{2}$ m

4. Rain is falling at an angle of 30° from the vertical due to the wind with a speed of 40 m/s. A car is travelling horizontally in the direction opposite to the wind, at a speed of 40 m/s. At what angle from the vertical will it experience the rain falling from?

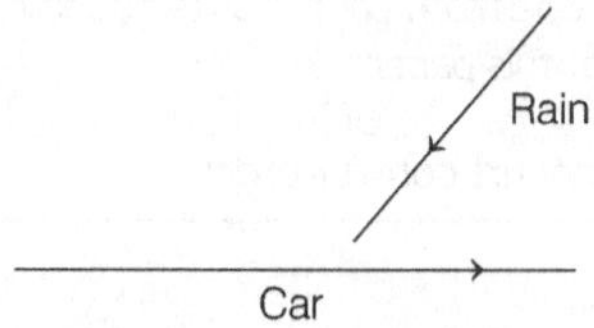

(a) 30° (b) 60°
(c) 90° (d) 120°

5. Two touching blocks 1 and 2 are placed on an inclined plane forming an angle 60° with the horizontal. The masses are m_1 and m_2 and the coefficient of friction between the inclined plane and the two blocks are 1.5 μ and 1.0 μ, respectively. The force of reaction between the blocks during the motion is (g = acceleration due to gravity)

(a) $(m_2 - m_1)\mu g$ (b) $(m_2 + m_1)\mu g$
(c) $\frac{1}{2}\frac{m_1 m_2}{m_1 + m_2}\mu g$ (d) $\frac{1}{4}\frac{m_1 m_2}{m_1 + m_2}\mu g$

6. Three blocks are connected by massless strings on a frictionless inclined plane of 30° as shown in the figure. A force of 104 N is applied upward along the incline to mass m_3 causing an upward motion of the blocks.

What is the acceleration of the blocks? (Assume, acceleration due to gravity, $g = 10 \text{ m/s}^2$)

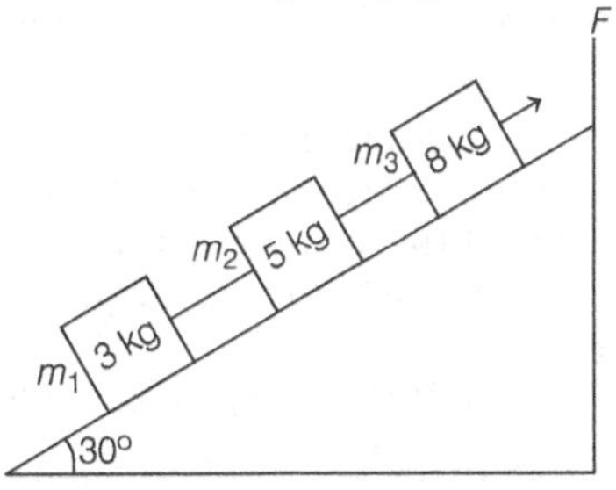

(a) 6.0 m/s^2 (b) 4.5 m/s^2
(c) 3.0 m/s^2 (d) 1.5 m/s^2

7. Consider a system of two masses and a pulley shown in the figure. The coefficient of friction between the two blocks and also between block and table is 0.1. Find the force F, that must be given to the 0.8 kg block such that it attains acceleration of 5 m/s^2. (Assume, acceleration due to gravity, $g = 10 \text{ m/s}^2$.)

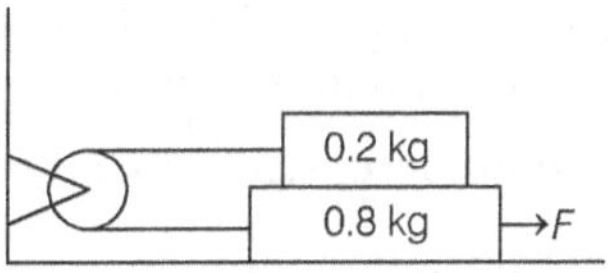

(a) 6.4 N (b) 7.1 N (c) 6.0 N (d) 7.8 N

8. A box of mass 3 kg moves on a horizontal frictionless table and collides with another box of mass 3 kg initially at rest on the edge of the table at height 1 m. The speed of the moving box just before the collision is 4 m/s. The two boxes stick together and fall from the table. The kinetic energy just before the boxes strike the floor is (Assume, acceleration due to gravity, $g = 10 \text{ m/s}^2$)

(a) 40 J (b) 80 J (c) 96 J (d) 72 J

9. A ball of mass 2 kg is thrown from a tall building with velocity,

$\mathbf{v} = (20 \text{ m/s})\,\hat{\mathbf{i}} + (24 \text{ m/s})\,\hat{\mathbf{j}}$ at time $t = 0$ s.

Change in the potential energy of the ball after, $t = 8$ s is (The ball is assumed to be in air during its motion between 0 s and 8 s, $\hat{\mathbf{i}}$ is along the horizontal and $\hat{\mathbf{j}}$ is along the vertical direction. (Take $g = 10 \text{ m/s}^2$)

(a) −2.56 kJ (b) 0.52 kJ (c) 1.76 kJ (d) −2.44 kJ

10. The balls A, B and C of masses 50 g, 100 g and 150 g, respectively are placed at the vertices of an equilateral triangle. The length of each side is 1 m. If A is placed at (0, 0) and B is placed at (1, 0) m, find the coordinates (x, y) for the centre of mass of this system of the balls

(a) $\left(\frac{7}{12}, \sqrt{\frac{3}{4}}\right)$ m (b) $\left(\frac{5}{18}, \sqrt{\frac{1}{4}}\right)$ m
(c) $\left(\frac{7}{12}, \sqrt{\frac{3}{2}}\right)$ m (d) $\left(\frac{5}{18}, \sqrt{\frac{3}{4}}\right)$ m

11. Three bodies, a ring, a solid disc and a solid sphere roll down the same inclined plane without slipping. The radii of the bodies are identical and they start from rest. If V_S, V_R and V_D are the speeds of the sphere, ring and disc, respectively when they reach the bottom, then the correct option is

(a) $V_S > V_R > V_D$ (b) $V_D > V_S > V_R$
(c) $V_R > V_D > V_S$ (d) $V_S > V_D > V_R$

12. A vertical spring mass system has the same time period as simple pendulum undergoing small oscillations. Now, both of them are put in an elevator going downwards with an acceleration 5 m/s^2. The ratio of time period of the spring mass system to the time period of the pendulum is (Assume, acceleration due to gravity, $g = 10 \text{ m/s}^2$)

(a) $\sqrt{\frac{3}{2}}$ (b) $\sqrt{\frac{2}{3}}$ (c) $\frac{1}{\sqrt{2}}$ (d) $\sqrt{2}$

13. Consider a spherical planet which is rotating about its axis such that the speed of a point on its equator is v and the effective acceleration due to gravity on the equator is $\frac{1}{3}$ of its value at the poles. What is the escape velocity for a particle at the pole of this planet.

(a) 3 v (b) 2 v (c) $\sqrt{3}$ v (d) $\sqrt{2}$ v

14. Consider a system of blocks X, A and B as shown in the figure. The blocks A and B have equal mass and are connected by a massless string through a massless pully. The coefficient of friction between block A and X or B and X is 0.5. If block X moves on the horizontal frictionless surface what should be its minimum acceleration such that blocks A and B remain stationary. (g = acceleration due to gravity.)

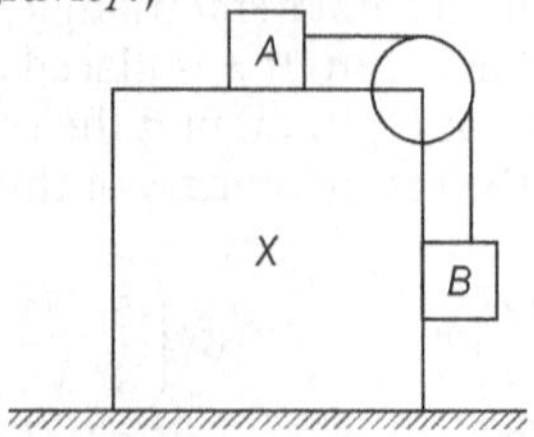

(a) $\frac{g}{3}$ (b) $3g$ (c) $\frac{g}{4}$ (d) $\frac{3g}{4}$

15. How much pressure (in atm) is needed to compress a sample of water by 0.4% ? (Assume, Bulk modulus of water $\approx 2.0 \times 10^9$ Pa)

(a) 60 atm (b) 70 atm (c) 80 atm (d) 90 atm

16. The tension in a massless cable connected to an iron ball of 100 kg when it is submerged in sea water is ($\rho_{iron} = 8 \times 10^3$ kg/m^3 and $\rho_{sea\ water} = 1000$ kg/m^3, $g = 10$ m/s^2)

(a) 950 N (b) 846 N (c) 875 N (d) 933 N

17. The area of a circular copper coin increases by 0.4% when its temperature is raised by 100°C. The coefficient of linear expansion of the coin is :

(a) 1×10^{-5}/°C (b) 2×10^{-5}/°C
(c) 3×10^{-5}/°C (d) 4×10^{-5}/°C

18. A 210 W heater is used to heat 100 g water. The time required to raise the temperature of this water from 25 °C to 100 °C is (specific heat capacity of water = 4200 J/Kg-°C)

(a) 100 s (b) 125 s (c) 150 s (d) 200 s

19. One mole of nitrogen gas being initially at a temperature of $T_0 = 300$ K is adiabatically compressed to increase its pressure 10 times. The final gas temperature after compression is (Assume, nitrogen gas molecules as rigid diatomic and $100^{1/7} = 1.9$)

(a) 120 K (b) 750 K (c) 650 K (d) 570 K

20. Two gases A and B are contained in two separate, but otherwise identical containers. Gas A consists of monatomic molecules, each with atomic mass of $4u$ whereas Gas B consists of rigid diatomic molecules, each with atomic mass of $20u$. If gas A is kept at 27°C, at what temperature should gas B be kept so that both have the same rms speed?

(a) 27°C (b) 54°C (c) 270°C (d) 62°C

21. Standing waves are produced in a string 16 m long. If there are 9 nodes between the two fixed ends of the string and the speed of the wave is 32 m/s, what is the frequency of the wave?

(a) 5 Hz (b) 10 Hz (c) 30 Hz (d) 20 Hz

22. A highway truck has two horns A and B. When sounded together, the driver records 50 beats in 10 seconds. With horn B blowing and the truck moving towards a wall at a speed of 10 m/s, the driver noticed a beat frequency of 5 Hz with the echo. When frequency of A is decreased the beat frequency with two horns sounded together increases. Calculate the frequency of horn A. (Speed of sound in air = 330 m/s)

(a) 75 Hz (b) 85 Hz (c) 90 Hz (d) 95 Hz

23. When light of an unknown polarisation is examined with a polaroid, it is found to exhibit maximum intensity I_0 along y-axis and minimum intensity $\frac{2I_0}{3}$ along x-axis. The intensity transmited through a polaroid with pass axis at 45° to y-axis (in x-y plane) is

(a) $\frac{5}{8}I_0$ (b) $\frac{I_0}{2}$ (c) $\frac{5}{6}I_0$ (d) $\frac{I_0}{4}$

24. In a Young's double slit experiment, mth order and nth order of bright fringes are formed at point P on a distant screen, if monochromatic source of wavelength 400 nm and 600 nm are used respectively. The minimum value of m and n are respectively,

(a) 4,6 (b) 3,2 (c) 2,3 (d) 4,2

25. Two small conducting balls of identical mass 20 g and identical charge 10^{-10} C hang from non-conducting threads of length, $L = 300$ cm. If the equilibrium separation of balls is x and $x << L$ then the magnitude of x is (Assume, $4\pi \epsilon_0 = \frac{1}{9 \times 10^9}$ F/m and $g = 10$ m/s^2)

(a) $\frac{2}{5^{1/3}}$ mm (b) $\frac{3}{10^{1/3}}$ mm

(c) $\frac{3^{1/3}}{10}$ mm (d) $\frac{3^{2/3}}{5}$ mm

26. The space between the two large parallel plates is filled with a material of uniform charge density ρ. Assume that one of the plate is kept at $x = 0$. The potential at any point x between these plates is given by (A and B are constants).

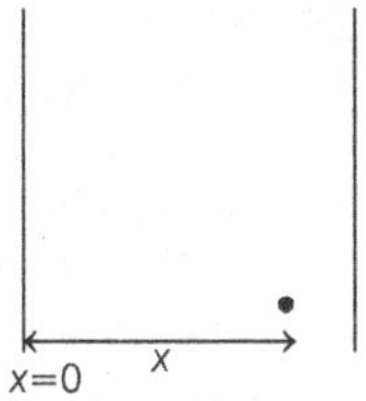

(a) $-\dfrac{\rho x^3}{2\epsilon_0}$ (b) $-\left(\dfrac{\rho x^2}{2\epsilon_0} + Ax\right)$

(c) $-\left(\dfrac{\rho x^2}{2\epsilon_0} + Ax + B\right)$ (d) $-\left(\dfrac{\rho x^3}{4\epsilon_0} + Ax^2 + Bx\right)$

27. Identify the correct statement among the following.

(a) Resistivity of metals decreases with temperature because more electrons are available for conduction.
(b) Resistivity of metals increases with temperature because number of electrons decreases.
(c) Resistivity of metals increases with temperature because number of collisions between electrons increases.
(d) Resistivity of metals decreases with temperature because superconductivity sets in.

28. For the circuits A and B as shown in the figure, identify the correct option.

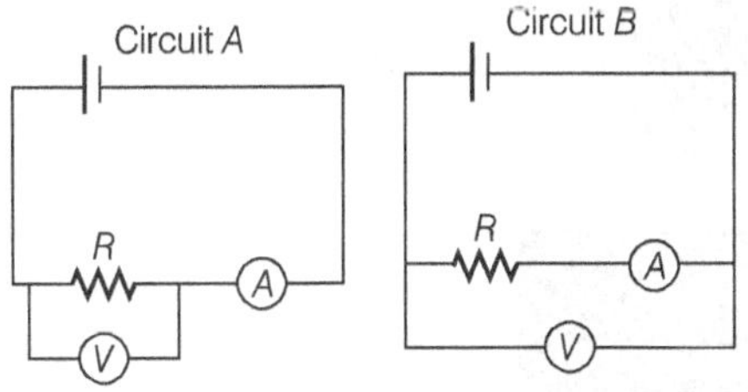

(a) Circuit A is for accurate measurement of high resistance and B is for low resistance.
(b) Circuit A is for accurate measurement of low resistance and B is for high resistance.
(c) Both circuits can accurately measured high resistance only.
(d) Both circuits can accurately measured low resistance only.

29. Two infinitely long straight wires A and B, each carrying current I are placed on x and y-axis, respectively. The current in wires A and B flow along $-\hat{\mathbf{i}}$ and $\hat{\mathbf{j}}$ directions respectively. The force on a charged particle having charge q, moving from position, $\mathbf{r} = d(\hat{\mathbf{i}} + \hat{\mathbf{j}})$ with velocity $\mathbf{v} = v\hat{\mathbf{i}}$ is

(a) $\dfrac{\mu_0 Iqv}{2\pi d}\hat{\mathbf{j}}$ (b) $\dfrac{\mu_0 Iqv}{\pi d}\hat{\mathbf{j}}$ (c) $\dfrac{\mu_0 Iqv}{\sqrt{2}\pi d}\hat{\mathbf{k}}$ (d) 0

30. A long straight wire carrying current 16 A is bent at 90° such that half of the wire lies along the positive x-axis and other half lies along the positive y-axis. What is the magnitude of the magnetic field at the point, $\mathbf{r} = (-2\hat{\mathbf{i}} + 0\,\hat{\mathbf{j}})$ mm? (Assume, $\dfrac{\mu_0}{4\pi} = 10^{-7}$ H m^{-1})

(a) 1.2 mT (b) 0.8 mT (c) 3.2 mT (d) 1.6 mT

31. The magnitude of the force vector acting on a unit length of a thin wire carrying a current $I = 8$ A at a point O, if the wire is bent as shown in the figure with a radius, $R = 10\pi$ cm is

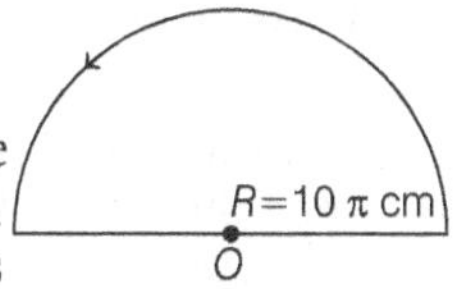

(a) 64 μN/m (b) 32 μN/m
(c) 20 μN/m (d) 100 μN/m

32. A 10 Ω coil of 180 turns and diameter 4 cm is placed in a uniform magnetic field so that the magnetic flux is maximum through the coil's cross-sectional area. When the field is suddenly removed a charge of 360 μC flows through a 618 Ω galvanometer connected to the coil, find the magnetic field.

(a) 12 T (b) 6 T (c) 1 T (d) 8 T

33. An inductor coil is connected to a capacitor and an AC source of rms voltage 8V in series. The rms current in the circuit is 16 A and is in phase with emf. If this inductor coil is connected to 6 V DC battery, the magnitude of steady current is

(a) 8 A (b) 10 A (c) 12 A (d) 16 A

34. An electromagnetic wave of frequency 3.0 MHz passes from vacuum into a non-magnetic medium with permittivity, $\epsilon = 16\,\epsilon_0$. Where, ϵ_0 is the free space permittivity. The change in wavelength is

(a) −75 m (b) +75 m (c) −50 m (d) +50 m

35. A particle of charge q, mass m and energy E has de-Broglie wavelength λ. For a particle of charge $2q$, mass $2m$ and energy $2E$, the de-Broglie wavelength is

(a) $\dfrac{\lambda}{4}$ (b) 2λ (c) 8λ (d) $\dfrac{\lambda}{2}$

36. The collision of an electron with kinetic energy 5.5 eV and a hydrogen atom in its ground state can be described as

(a) completely inelastic
(b) may be completely inelastic
(c) may be partially elastic
(d) elastic

37. An alloy is composed of two radioactive materials A and B having equal weight. The half life of A and B are 10 yrs and 20 yrs respectively. After time t, the alloy was found to consist of $\left(\frac{1}{e}\right)$ kg of A and 1 kg of B.

If the atomic weight of A and B are same, then the value of t is (Assume, $\ln 2 = 0.7$)

(a) $\left(\frac{200}{7}\right)$ yrs
(b) $\left(\frac{10}{7}\right)$ yrs
(c) 7 yrs
(d) 70 yrs

38. When a zener diode is used as a regulator with zener voltage of 10 V, nearly five times the load current passes through the zener diode. What should be the series resistance for the zener diode. If load resistance is 2kΩ and the unregulated voltage supplied is 16 V.

(a) 500 Ω
(b) 100 Ω
(c) 200 Ω
(d) 800 Ω

39. The logic circuit below has the truth table, same as that of

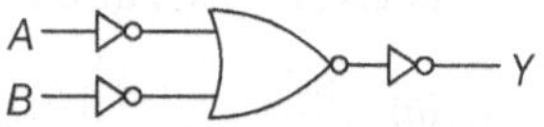

(a) NOR gate
(b) NAND gate
(c) AND gate
(d) OR gate

40. A message signal is used to modulate a carrier frequency. If the peak voltages of message signal and carrier signals are increased by 0.1% and 0.3% respectively, then the percentage change in modulation index is

(a) 0.4
(b) 0.0
(c) −0.4
(d) −02

Answers

1.	(a)	2.	(b, d)	3.	(a)	4.	(b)	5.	(d)	6.	(d)	7.	(a)	8.	(d)	9.	(a)	10.	(c)
11.	(d)	12.	(c)	13.	(c)	14.	(a)	15.	(c)	16.	(c)	17.	(b)	18.	(c)	19.	(d)	20.	(c)
21.	(b)	22.	(a)	23.	(c)	24.	(b)	25.	(b)	26.	(c)	27.	(c)	28.	(b)	29.	(b)	30.	(b)
31.	(a)	32.	(c)	33.	(c)	34.	(a)	35.	(d)	36.	(d)	37.	(a)	38.	(c)	39.	(b)	40.	(d)

Scan this QR code from your mobile phone to get the explanations of this paper.
Or
Visit : *http://tinyurl.com/y4hed5xg*

03 May Shift II
Session 2 (3:00 PM to 6:00 PM)

1. Which of the following represents fundamental forces of nature?

(a) Gravitational force; Coulomb's force; Strong surface tension force; weak van der Waal's force.
(b) Gravitational force; Electromagnetic force; Strong viscous force; Weak nuclear force.
(c) Gravitational force; Magnetostatic force; Strong nuclear force; Weak frictional force.
(d) Gravitational force; Electromagnetic force; Strong nuclear force; Weak nuclear force.

2. Match the physical quantities given in List-I with dimensions in List-II.

List I	List II
A. Gravitational potential	(i) $[M^0L^2T^{-2}K^{-1}]$
B. Stefan's constant	(ii) $[M^{-1}L^3T^{-2}]$
C. Permittivity	(iii) $[ML^0T^{-3}K^{-4}]$
D. Specific heat capacity	(iv) $[M^{-1}L^{-3}T^4I^2]$

(The dimension of mass, length, time, temperature and current are M, L, T, K and I, respectively). The correct match is

	A	B	C	D		A	B	C	D
(a)	IV	I	III	II	(b)	I	IV	II	III
(c)	III	II	I	IV	(d)	II	III	IV	I

3. Consider a car initially at rest, starts to move along a straight road first with acceleration $5\ m/s^2$, then with uniform velocity and finally, decelerating at $5\ m/s^2$, before coming to a stop. Total time taken from start to end is $t = 25$ s. If the average velocity during that time is 72 km/hr, the car moved with uniform velocity for a time of

(a) 15 s (b) 30 s (c) 155 s (d) 2 s

4. A boy runs on a horizontal road with a speed of 4 m/s while it is raining. He sees that the rain is making an angle θ with the vertical while running from West to East. However, when he runs from East to West, the angle is α. The rain is pouring down at an angle 45° with the vertical normal and at a speed of 8 m/s as shown in the figure. The ratio $\frac{\tan\theta}{\tan\alpha}$ is

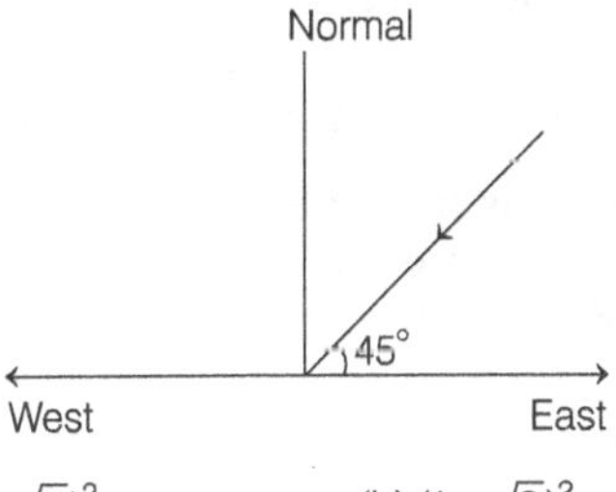

(a) $(1-\sqrt{2})^2$ (b) $(1+\sqrt{2})^2$
(c) $(1+\sqrt{2})$ (d) $(\sqrt{2}-1)$

5. A ball is projected vertically up from ground. Boy A standing at the window of first floor of a nearby building observes that the time interval between the ball crossing him while going up and the ball crossing him while going down is 2s. Another boy B standing on the second floor notices that time interval between the ball passing him twice, during up motion and down motion is 1s. Calculate the difference between the vertical positions of boy B and boy A (Assume, acceleration due to gravity, $g = 10\ m/s^2$)

(a) 8.45 m (b) 3.75 m (c) 4.25 m (d) 2.50 m

6. A bar of mass m resting on a smooth horizontal plane starts moving due to force $|\mathbf{F}| = \frac{mg}{9}$. The magnitude of the force remains constant with time. The force vector makes an angle θ with the horizontal which varies with the distance covered as $\theta = Cx$. If the constant, $C = 10\left(\frac{\text{degree}}{\text{meter}}\right)$, then the speed of the bar, when θ becomes equal to 30° for the first time, is (Take, $g = 10\ m/s^2$)

(a) 0.33 m/s (b) 0.50 m/s
(c) 1.0 m/s (d) 0.8 m/s

7. A particle of mass m is moving along a circle of radius R such that its tangential acceleration a_t varies with distance covered x as $a_t = ax^2$ where α is a constant. The kinetic energy, K of the particle varies with the distance as $K = \beta x^c$, where β and c are constants. The values of β and c are

(a) $\beta = \frac{m\alpha}{3}; c = 3$ (b) $\beta = \frac{m\alpha}{4}; c = 4$
(c) $\beta = \frac{m\alpha}{2}; c = 4$ (d) $\beta = \frac{m\alpha}{2}; c = 3$

8. A mass of 2 kg initially at a height of 1.2 m above an uncompressed spring with spring constant 2×10^4 N/m, is released from rest to fall on the spring. Taking the acceleration due to gravity as $10\ m/s^2$ and neglecting the air resistance, the compression of the spring in mm is

(a) 20 (b) 40
(c) 50 (d) 60

9. A bullet of mass 1 kg fired with a speed $2\ ms^{-1}$ from $x = 0$ passes through a block of wood whose centre is kept at a distance of 10 m from the origin as shown in the figure. The retarding force F_r on the bullet within the wooden block is $-0.5/x$. The minimum length of the block (upto one decimal digit) required to completely stop the bullet is (Assume, $e^4 = 55$)

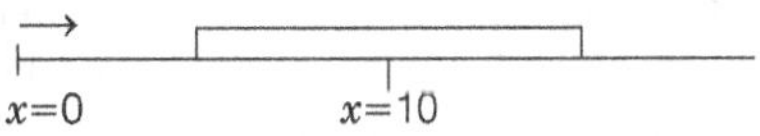

(a) 10.1 m (b) 9.2 m
(c) 9.7 m (d) 19.3 m

10. A solid spherical ball rolls on a horizontal surface at 10 m/s and continues to roll up on an inclined surface as shown in the figure. If the mass of the ball is 11 kg and frictional losses are negligible, the value of h where the ball stop and starts rolling down the inclination is (Assume, $g = 10\ \text{m/s}^2$)

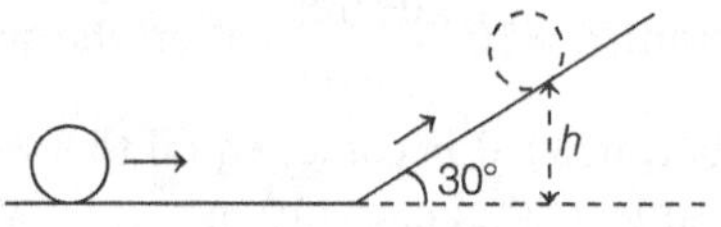

(a) 8 m (b) 6 m (c) 7 m (d) 10 m

11. A long cylinderical rod is welded to a thin circular disc of diameter 0.5 m at a point on its circumference. The rod is in the same plane as that of the disc and forms a tangent to the disc. The radius of gyration of the disc about the rod (in m) is

(a) $\frac{1}{4}$ (b) $\sqrt{\frac{5}{8}}$ (c) $\frac{1}{2}$ (d) $2\sqrt{2}$

12. A particle of mass 0.1 kg is executing simple harmonic motion of amplitude 0.1 m. When the particle passes through the mean position, its kinetic energy is 8×10^{-3}J. If the initial phase is 45°, the equation of its motion is (Assume, $x(t)$ as the position of the particle at time t.)

(a) $x(t) = 0.1\sin\left(4t + \frac{\pi}{4}\right)$ (b) $x(t) = 0.1\sin\left(16t + \frac{\pi}{4}\right)$

(c) $x(t) = 0.1\sin\left(2\left(t + \frac{\pi}{4}\right)\right)$ (d) $x(t) = 0.1\sin\left(2t + \frac{\pi}{4}\right)$

13. If a satellite has to orbit the earth in a circular path every 6 hrs, at what distance from the surface of the earth should be satellite placed (radius of earth, $R_e = 6400$ km) (Assume, $\frac{GM}{4\pi^2} = 8.0 \times 10^{12}\ \text{N/m}^2\text{/kg}$, where, G and M are gravitational constant and mass of earth and $10^{1/3} = 2.1$.

(a) 15100 km (b) 8720 km (c) 20600 km (d) 5560 km

14. A copper wire of cross-sectional area 0.01 cm^2 is under a tension of 22 N. Find the percentage change in the cross-sectional area. (Young's modulus of copper $= 1.1 \times 10^{11}\ \text{N/m}^2$ and Poisson's ratio = 0.32)

(a) 12.6×10^{-3} (b) 8.6×10^{-3}
(c) 6.4×10^{-3} (d) 2.8×10^{-3}

15. A cylindrical tank with a large diameter is filled with water. Water drains out through a hole at a bottom of the tank. If the cross-sectional area of the hole is 6 cm^2 then the drainge rate (in $\text{m}^3\text{/s}$) when the depth of the water is 0.2 m, is

(a) 1.0×10^{-3} (b) 8.2×10^{-2}
(c) 2.2×10^{-3} (d) 1.2×10^{-3}

16. The surface tension of the soap water solution is $\frac{1}{10\pi}$ N/m. The free energy of the surface layer of a soap bubble of diameter 5 mm will be

(a) 2.5×10^{-6} J (b) 1×10^{-7} J
(c) 8×10^{6} J (d) 5×10^{-6} J

17. Statement A Convection involves flow of matter within a fluid due to unequal temperatures of its parts.

Statement B A hot bar placed under a running tap water loses heat due to effect of convection with in water.

Statement C Heat transfer always involves temperature different between two systems. Identify the correct option.

(a) A, B, C are true (b) Only A and C are true
(c) Only A and B are true (d) Only B and C are true

18. A body cools from 70°C to 40°C in 5 min. Calculate the time it takes to cool from 60° C to 30° C. The temperature of the surroundings is 20° C.

(a) 1 min (b) 7 min (c) 6 min (d) 15 min

19. One mole of ideal gas goes through a process pV^3 = constant, where p and V are pressure and volume, respectively. Let W be the work done by the gas as its temperature is increased by ΔT. The value of $|W|$ is (R is the universal gas constant.)

(a) $R\Delta T$ (b) $\frac{1}{3}R\Delta T$ (c) $R^3\Delta T$ (d) $\frac{R}{2}\Delta T$

20. An ideal gas is placed in a tank at 27°C. The pressure is initially 600 kPa. One fourth of the gas is then released from the tank and thermal equilibrium is established. What will be the pressure if the temperature is 327° C?

(a) 900 kPa (b) 1000 kPa
(c) 1050 kPa (d) 1250 kPa

21. Which of the following equation represents a simple harmonic motion? (ω is the angular frequency, A is amplitude of oscillation and $i = \sqrt{-1}$

(a) $\frac{dx}{dt} = i\omega\sqrt{x^2 - A^2}$ (b) $\frac{d^2x^2}{dt^2} = \omega^2 x$

(c) $\frac{d^2x}{dt^2} = i\omega\sqrt{x^2 - A^2}$ (d) $\frac{d^2x}{dt^2} = \omega x^2$

22. A musician on a moving vehicle plays a tone at 880 Hz note. When the vehicle was approaching a listener, he receives it as 888 Hz tone. The speed of the vehicle is (Assume the velocity of sound is 333 m/s.)

(a) 6 m/s (b) 5 m/s (c) 3 m/s (d) 1 m/s

23. Three lenses of focal lengths +10 cm, −10 cm and +30 cm are placed at distance of 30 cm, 35 cm and 45 cm, respectively from an object. The distance between the object and the image formed is

(a) 100 cm (b) 75 cm (c) 30 cm (d) 45 cm

24. In a Young's double slit experiment, a thin sheet of refractive index 1.6 is used to cover one slit while a thin the sheet of refractive index 1.3 is used to cover the second slit. The thickness of both the sheets are same and the wavelength of light used is 600 nm. If the central point on the screen is now occupied by what had been the 10th bright fringe ($m = 10$), then the thickness of covering sheets is

(a) 50 μm (b) 8 μm (c) 20 μm (d) 40 μm

25. An infinite line of charge with uniform line charge density of 1 C/m is palced along the y-axis. A charge of 1C is placed on the x-axis at a distance of $d = 3$ m from the origin. At what distance r from the origin on the x-axis, the total electric field is zero. (Assume, $0 < r < d$)

(a) 1 m (b) 2 m (c) 2.5 m (d) 1.75 m

26. A capacitor of capacitance 4 μF is charged to a potential difference of 6 V with a battery. The battery is removed and in its place another capacitor of capacitance is 8 μF introduced and the circuit is closed. The potential difference attained by each of the capacitors in V is

(a) 2 (b) 4 (c) 6 (d) 8

27. Estimate the magnitude of current that passes through a wire, if 0.1 mol of electrons flow through it in 40 min. (Assume, Avagadro's number $= 6.0 \times 10^{23}$)

(a) 4 A (b) 9 A (c) 12 A (d) 14 A

28. Find the potential difference between a and b, as shown in the below circuit,

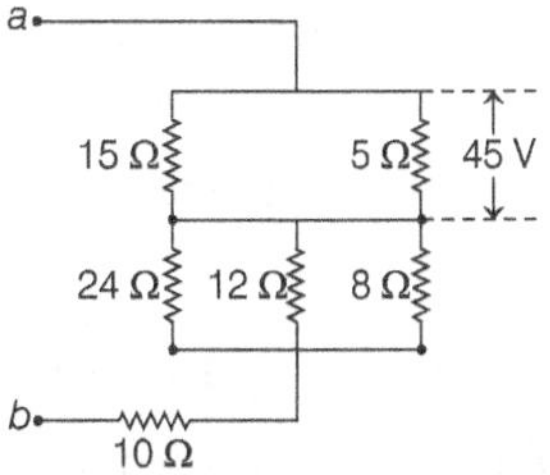

(a) 165 V (b) 198 V (c) 213 V (d) 224 V

29. A metal disc of radius, $a = 10$ cm rotates with a constant angular speed of $\omega = 200$ rad/s about its axis. The potential difference between the centre and the rim of the disc under a uniform magnetic field, $B = 5$ mT directed perpendicular to the disc, is

(a) 2 mV (b) 5 mV (c) 10 mV (d) 15 mV

30. A proton accelerated by a potential difference 500 kV flies through a uniform transverse magnetic field 0.1 T. The field is spread on a region of 1.0 cm thickness. The angle through which the proton gets deviated from its original direction is : (mass of proton $= 1.6 \times 10^{-27}$ kg and charge of proton $= 1.6 \times 10^{19}$ C)

(a) 0.01 rad (b) 0.1 rad (c) 0.05 rad (d) 0.08 rad

31. A toroid has an iron core with an internal magnetic field of 10 π mT, when the current in the winding of 1500 turns per meter is 10 A. Determine the field due to magnetisation ($\mu_0 = 4\pi \times 10^{-7} \text{Hm}^{-1}$)

(a) (4π) mT (b) (10π) mT (c) $\left(\frac{8}{\pi}\right)$ mT (d) $\left(\frac{\pi}{4}\right)$ mT

32. A conducting wire bent but in the shape of semicircle has length L and moves in its plane with constant velocity v. A uniform magnetic field B exists in the direction perpendicular to the plane of the wire.

The velocity makes an angles 45° to diameter joining free ends and the emf induced between the ends of the wire is $\Phi = \alpha(BvL)$. The value of constant α is

(a) $\sqrt{2}$ (b) $\frac{2}{\pi}$ (c) $\frac{1}{\sqrt{2}}$ (d) $\frac{\sqrt{2}}{\pi}$

33. A sinusoidal voltage with a frequency of 50 Hz is applied to a series LCR circuit with a resistance of 5Ω, inductance of 20 mH and a capacitance of 500 μF. The magnitude of impedance of the circuit is closed to

(a) 19.2 Ω (b) 14.4 Ω (c) 9.6 Ω (d) 5 Ω

34. The concept of displacement current solves an ambiguity in

(a) Gauss's law (b) Faraday's law
(c) Ampere's law (d) Coulomb's law

35. A photodiode sensor is used to measure the output of a 300 W lamp kept 10 m away. The sensor has an opening of 2 cm in diameter. How many photons enter the sensor if the wavelength of the light is 660 nm and the exposure time is 100 ms. (Assume that all the energy of the lamp is given off as light and $h = 6.6 \times 10^{-34}$ Js)

(a) 3.6×10^{13} (b) 2.8×10^{13}
(c) 2.5×10^{13} (d) 1.8×10^{13}

36. To excite the spectral line of wavelength 4960 Å of an atom, an excitation energy of 7.7 eV is required. The ground state energy of the atom is 10.5 eV. The energies of two levels involved in the emission of 4960 Å line are : (Assume $hc = 1240$ eV-nm, where h is planck's constant and c is speed of light.)

(a) 14.2 eV, 16.1 eV (b) 12.2 eV, 18.2 eV
(c) 15.7 eV, 20.5 eV (d) 15.7 eV, 18.2 eV

37. In one average life-time of a radioactive nuclei,

(a) more than half the active nuclei decay.
(b) half the active nuclei decay.
(c) less than half the active nuclei decay .
(d) all the nuclei decay.

38. The truth table for the given logic circuit is

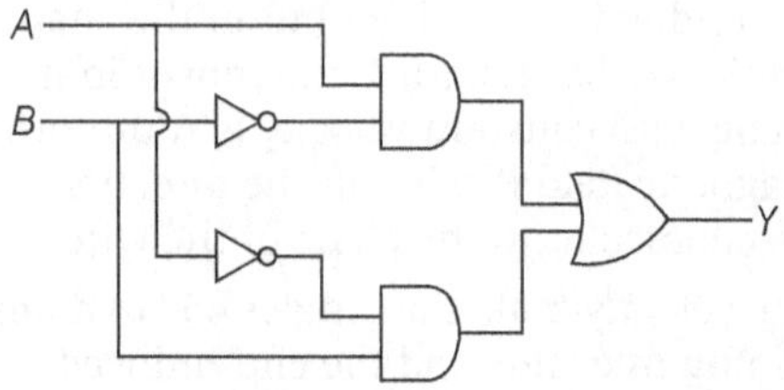

(a)

A	B	Y
0	0	0
0	1	1
1	0	1
1	1	0

(b)

A	B	Y
0	0	1
0	1	1
1	0	1
1	1	0

(c)

A	B	Y
0	0	0
0	1	0
1	0	0
1	1	1

(d)

A	B	Y
0	0	1
0	1	0
1	0	0
1	1	0

39. In a transistor circuit, the collector current is changed by 8.9 mA, if the emitter current is changed to 9.0 mA. The value of current amplification factor β is

(a) 89 (b) 92
(c) 84 (d) 96

40. The transmitting antenna placed at the top of a tower has a height of 45 m from the ground. The distance between receiving and transmitting antennas is 40 km and the radius of earth is 6400 km. The minimum height (in m) at which the receiving antenna is to be placed for satisfactory communication in LOS made, is

(a) 5 (b) 15
(c) 20 (d) 25

Answers

1.	(d)	2.	(d)	3.	(a)	4.	(b)	5.	(b)	6.	(a)	7.	(a)	8.	(c)	9.	(*)	10.	(c)
11.	(b)	12.	(a)	13.	(b)	14.	(a)	15.	(d)	16.	(d)	17.	(b)	18.	(b)	19.	(d)	20.	(a)
21.	(a)	22.	(c)	23.	(b)	24.	(c)	25.	(b)	26.	(a)	27.	(a)	28.	(c)	29.	(b)	30.	(a)
31.	(a)	32.	(d)	33.	(d)	34.	(c)	35.	(c)	36.	(d)	37.	(a)	38.	(a)	39.	(a)	40.	(c)

Scan this QR code from your mobile phone to get the explanations of this paper.
Or
Visit : http://tinyurl.com/y3xgymml

04 May Shift I
Session 1 (10:00 AM to 1:00 PM)

1. Albert Einstein was confermed with the Nobel prize in physics for his work on
(a) special theory of relativity
(b) Bose-Einstein Statistics
(c) photoelectric effect
(d) general relativity

2. A quantity z, to be estimated has a dependency on the variables a, b and c as $z = ab^2c^{-2}$. The percentage of error in the measurement of a, b and c are respectively, 2.1%, 1.3% and 2.2%. The percentage of error in the measurement of z would then be
(a) 5.6% (b) 1.6% (c) 1.0% (d) 9.1%

3. The nature of a graph drawn for a freely falling body with time on the x-axis and speed on the y-axis is (Assuming initial speed to be zero.)
(a) a straight line with positive y-axis intercept.
(b) a straight line passing through the origin.
(c) a parabola.
(d) a straight line parallel to y-axis with positive x-axis intercept.

4. A particle A moves along the line, $y = 30$ m with a constant velocity, $\mathbf{v}$ parallel to x-axis. At the moment particle A passes the y-axis, a particle B starts from the origin with zero initial speed and a constant acceleration, $\mathbf{a} = 0.40$ m/sec^2. The angle between $\mathbf{a}$ and y-axis is 60°. If the particles A and B collide after sometimes, then the value of $|\mathbf{v}|$ will be
(a) 2 m/s (b) 3 m/s
(c) 4 m/s (d) 5 m/s

5. A ball moves one-fourth $\left(\frac{1^{\text{th}}}{4}\right)$ of a circle of radius R in time T. Let v_1 and v_2 be the magnitudes of mean speed and mean velocity vector. The ratio $\frac{v_1}{v_2}$ will be
(a) $\frac{\pi}{2}$ (b) $\frac{3}{\pi}$ (c) $\frac{2}{\sqrt{3}\,\pi}$ (d) $\frac{\pi}{2\sqrt{2}}$

6. A 4 kg object has a velocity, $3.0\,\hat{\mathbf{i}}$ m/s at some instant. Eights seconds later, its velocity is $(8.0\,\hat{\mathbf{i}} + 10.0\,\hat{\mathbf{j}})$ m/s. Assuming that the object is subjected to a constant net force, the magnitude of the force is
(a) $\frac{5\sqrt{5}}{2}$ N (b) $\frac{5\sqrt{3}}{8}$ N (c) $\frac{8\sqrt{5}}{3}$ N (d) $\frac{10\sqrt{3}}{7}$ N

7. A block of mass 10 kg, initially at rest, makes a downward motion on 45° inclined plane. Then the distance travelled by the block after 2s is

(Assume the coefficient of kinetic friction to be 0.3 and $g = 10$ ms^{-2})
(a) $7\sqrt{2}$ m (b) $\frac{9}{\sqrt{2}}$ m (c) $10\sqrt{2}$ m (d) $5\sqrt{2}$ m

8. Conservative forces are defined as the force for which,
(a) work done depends only on the initial and final positions.
(b) work done depends on the initial and final positions and also on the path taken.
(c) work done depends only on the path taken.
(d) work done depends only on the initial position.

9. A rocket motor consumes 100 kg of fuel per second exhausting it with a speed of 5 km/s. The speed of the rocket when its mass is reduced to $\frac{1^{\text{th}}}{20}$ of its initial mass, is (Assume initial speed to be zero and ignored gravitational and viscous forces.)

(a) 20 km/s (b) 40 ln(2) km/s
(c) 5 ln (20) km/s (d) 10 ln(10) km/s

10. Ball A of mass 50 gm and speed 10 m/s collides with other ball B of mass 10 gm and speed 15 m/s travelling in opposite direction with each other. Determine the final speed of ball B, if the coefficient of restitution is $\frac{2}{5}$.

(a) $\frac{40}{3}$ m/s (b) $\frac{75}{3}$ m/s (c) $\frac{91}{8}$ m/s (d) $\frac{85}{6}$ m/s

11. A solid sphere of mass 5 kg rolls on a plane surfaces. Find its kinetic energy at an instant when its centre moves with speed 4 m/s.

(a) 56 J (b) 45 J (c) 75 J (d) 105 J

12. A body of mass 0.3 kg hangs by a spring with a force constant of 50 N/m. The amplitude of oscillations is damped and reaches $\frac{1}{e}$ of its original value in about 100 oscillations. If ω and ω' are the angular frequencies of undamped and damped oscillations respectively, then percentage of $\left(\frac{\omega - \omega'}{\omega}\right)$ is

(a) $\left(\frac{1}{800\pi}\right)$ (b) $\left(\frac{\pi^2}{600}\right)$ (c) $\left(\frac{1}{800\pi^2}\right)$ (d) $\left(\frac{\pi}{400}\right)$

13. If a planet of mass 6.4×10^{23} kg can be compressed into a sphere such that the escape velocity from its surface is 8×10^4 m/s, then what should be the radius of the sphere? (Gravitational constant, $G = 6.6 \times 10^{-11}$ $\text{Nm}^{-2}\text{kg}^{-2}$)

(a) 40.4 km (b) 13.2 km (c) 20.4 km (d) 6.8 km

14. A horizontal aluminium rod of diameter 4 cm projected 6 cm from a wall. An object of mass 400 π kg is suspended from the end of the rod. The shearing modulus of aluminium is 3.0×10^{10} N/m^2. The vertical deflection of the end of the rod is ($\because g = 10$ m/s^2)

(a) 0.01 mm (b) 0.02 mm (c) 0.03 mm (d) 0.04 mm

15. A water tank kept on the ground has an orifice of 2 mm diameter on the vertical side. What is the minimum height of the water above the orifice for which the output flow of water is found to be turbulent? (Assume, $g = 10$ m/s^2, $\rho_{\text{water}} = 10^3$ kg/m^3, viscosity = 1 centi-poise)

(a) 3 cm (b) 4 cm (c) 6 cm (d) 2 cm

16. A copper ball of radius 3.0 mm falls in an oil tank of viscosity 1 kg/ms. Then, the terminal velocity of the copper ball will be (Density of oil = 1.5×10^3 kg/m^3, Density of copper = 9×10^3 kg/m^3 and $g = 10$ m/s^2.)

(a) 18×10^{-2} m/s (b) 25×10^{-2} m/s
(c) 15×10^{-2} m/s (d) 20×10^{-2} m/s

17. The wavelength of the radiation emitted by a black body is 1 mm and Wien's constant is 3×10^{-3} mK. Then the temperature of the black body will be

(a) 3 K (b) 30 K (c) 300 K (d) 3000 K

18. A hot body placed in air cools down to a lower temperature. The rate of decrease of temperature is proportional to the temperature difference from the surrounding. The body loses 60% and 80% of maximum heat it can loose in time t_1 and t_2 respectively. The ratio t_2 / t_1 will be

(a) $\frac{\ln(10)}{\ln(2)}$ (b) $\frac{\ln(8)}{\ln(6)}$ (c) $\frac{\ln(1)}{\ln(3)}$ (d) $\frac{\ln(5)}{\ln\left(\frac{5}{2}\right)}$

19. A Carnot engine with efficiency η operates between two heat reservoirs with temperatures T_1 and T_2, where $T_1 > T_2$. If only T_1 is changed by 0.4%, the change in efficiency is $\Delta\eta_1$, whereas if only T_2 is changed by 0.2%, the efficiency is changed by $\Delta\eta_2$. The ratio $\frac{\Delta\eta_1}{\Delta\eta_2}$ is approximately,

(a) – 2 (b) – 4
(c) + 3 (d) + 4

20. An ideal gas in a closed container is heated so that the final rms speed of the gas particles increases by 2 times the initial rms speed. If the initial gas temperature is 27°C, then the final temperature of the ideal gas is :

(a) 1200°C (b) 927°C (c) 827°C (d) 1473°C

21. Consider two tuning forks with natural frequency 250 Hz. One is moving away and another is moving towards a stationary observer at same speed. If the observer hears beats of frequency 5 Hz, then the speed of the tuning fork is : (Given, speed of sound wave is 350 m/s.)

(a) 2.5 m/s (b) 3.5 m/s (c) 5.0 m/s (d) 2.0 m/s

22. A drone fitted with siren in flying directly away from the drone operator and towards a distant building at a speed of 15 m/s. The siren produces sound of frequency 780 Hz. What is the frequency that the operator hears in the echo reflected from the building. [Speed of sound is 340 m/s.]

(a) 766 Hz (b) 800 Hz (c) 816 Hz (d) 840 Hz

23. A point object O is placed on the axis of a cylindrical piece of glass of refractive index 1.6 as shown in the figure. One surface of the glass piece is convex with radius of curvature 3 mm. The point appeared to be at 5 mm on the axis when viewed along the axis and from right side of convex surface. The distance of the point object from the convex surface is :

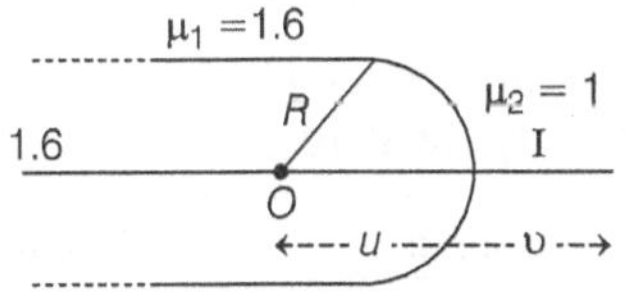

(a) 4 mm (b) 6 mm (c) 3 mm (d) 2.5 mm

24. The limit of resolution of a telescope is 2.5×10^{-7} rad. If the telescope is used to detect light of wavelength 500 nm coming from a star, the diameter of the objective lens used by telescope is

(a) 244 cm (b) 258 cm (c) 228 cm (d) 264 cm

25. A non-conducting solid sphere has radius R and uniform charge density. A spherical cavity of radius $\frac{R}{4}$ is hollowed out of the sphere. The distance between center of sphere and center of cavity is $\frac{R}{2}$. If the charge of the sphere is Q after the creation of the cavity and the magnitude of electric field at the center of the cavity is $E = K\left(\frac{Q}{4\pi \epsilon_0 R^2}\right)$, determined the approximate value of K.

(a) 0.32 (b) 0.78 (c) 0.51 (d) 0.45

26. A metal plate of thickness 2 mm and area $36\pi \text{cm}^2$- is slide into a parallel plate capacitor of plate spacing 6 mm and area $36\pi \text{ cm}^2$. The metal plate is at a distance 3 mm from one of the plates. What is the capacitance of this arrangement? $\left(\text{Let } \frac{1}{4\pi \epsilon_0} = 9 \times 10^9 \text{ Nm}^2\text{C}^{-2}\right)$

(a) 8 pF (b) 15 pF (c) 25 pF (d) 20 pF

27. For the circuit shown in the figure, calculate the resistance between the points A and B.

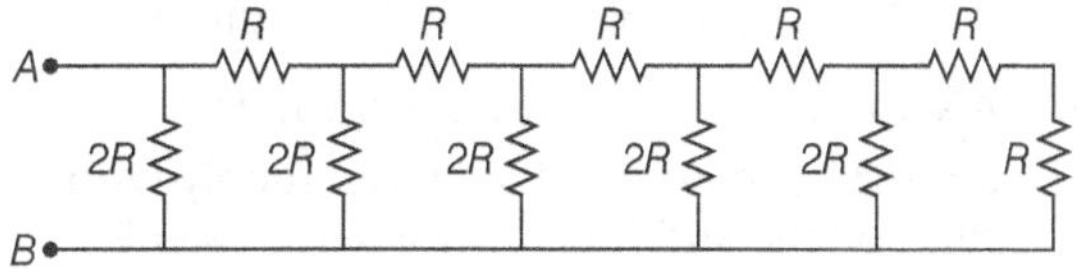

(a) 0.5 R (b) R (c) 15 R (d) $\frac{6}{5}$ R

28. If the resistances are chosen for the circuit shown in figure in such a way that no current flows through the battery with emf E_1, the voltage V_2 across R_2 and the current I_3 flowing through R_3 are respectively,

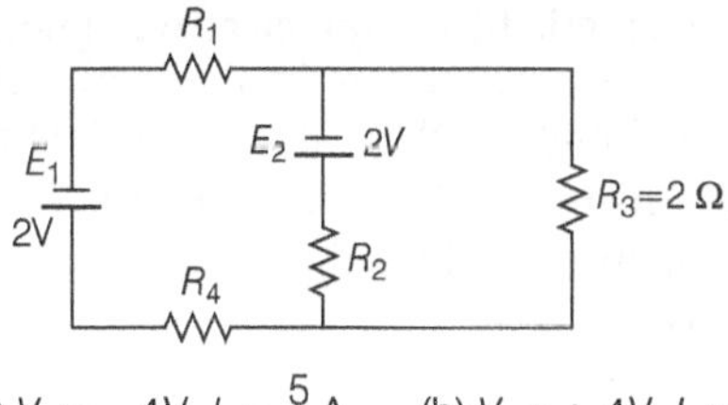

(a) $V_2 = -4\text{V}, I_3 = \frac{5}{2}\text{A}$ (b) $V_2 = +4\text{V}, I_3 = \frac{5}{2}\text{A}$

(c) $V_2 = -3\text{V}, I_3 = 1\text{A}$ (d) $V_2 = +3\text{V}, I_3 = 2\text{A}$

29. A semi-circular loop of radius 30 cm wire carries current 6 A. An uniform magnetic field 0.5 T is present perpendicular to the plane of the loop. What is the magnitude of force exerted on the wire?

(a) 0.9 N (b) 1.8 N (c) 0.8 N (d) 1.4 N

30. A dielectric circular disc of radius R carries a uniform surface charge density σ. If it rotates about its axis with angular velocity ω, the magnetic field at the cente of disc is :

(a) $\frac{\mu_0\sigma\omega R^2}{2\pi}$ (b) $\frac{\mu_0\sigma\omega R}{2}$
(c) $\frac{\mu_0\sigma\omega R^2}{4}$ (d) $\frac{\mu_0\sigma\omega R^2}{2\sqrt{2}}$

31. The earth's magnetic field at the geometric poles is $\sqrt{10} \times 10^{-5}$ T. The magnitude of the field at a point on the earth's surface where the radius makes an angle θ with the axis of earth's assumed magnetic dipole is 5×10^{-5} T. The magnitude of θ in degree is :
(a) 30° (b) 60° (c) 45° (d) 75°

32. Consider a current in a circuit falls from 6.0 A to 1.0 A in 0.2 s. If an average emf of 150 V is induced by the circuit, then the self inductance of the circuit is
(a) 2 H (b) 6 H (c) 4 H (d) 8 H

33. A series *LCR* circuit with $L = 0.5$ H and $R = 10\,\Omega$ is connected to an AC supply with rms voltage and frequency equal to 200 V and $\frac{150}{\pi}$ Hz, respectively. The magnitude of the capacitance is varied so that current amplitude in the circuit becomes maximum.The rms voltage difference across the inductor is
(a) 3000 V (b) 2500 V (c) 2000 V (d) 2600 V

34. The magnetic field of an electromagnetic-wave obeys the relation in a certain region is $B = 10^{-12} \sin(5 \times 10^6 t)$ T, where *t* is the time. Then, the induced emf, in a 300 turns in coil of area 20 cm^2 oriented perpendicular to the field is
(a) $-2 \times 10^{-5} \cos(5 \times 10^6 t)$ V
(b) $-3 \times 10^{-6} \cos(5 \times 10^6 t)$ V
(c) $-2.5 \times 10^{-6} \cos(5 \times 10^6 t)$ V
(d) $-3.3 \times 10^{-6} \cos(5 \times 10^6 t)$ V

35. The wavelength of a charged particle of mass 8.0×10^{-31} kg, charge 1.6×10^{-19} C and kinetic energy 3 keV will be (Planck constant, $h = 6.4 \times 10^{-34}$ Js)
(a) 0.4 Å (b) 2.1 Å (c) 1.0 Å (d) 1 Å

36. Let λ_P and λ_L be the longest wavelengths observed in the Paschen and Lyman series respectively. Choose the correct option
(a) $4 < \frac{\lambda_P}{\lambda_L} < 6$ (b) $7 < \frac{\lambda_P}{\lambda_L} < 8$
(c) $15 < \frac{\lambda_P}{\lambda_L} < 16$ (d) $30 < \frac{\lambda_P}{\lambda_L} < 32$

37. A radioactive nucleus can decay in two different processes with half life 0.7 hr and 0.3 hr.

The effective average life of the nucleus in minutes approximately is
(value of ln 2 = 0.7)
(a) 14 (b) 18
(c) 24 (d) 26

38. **Assertion (A)** Si and GaAs are the preferred materials for solar cells.

Reason (R) Both these materials have energy band gaps much below the energy level corresponding to the maximum solar irradiance In the solar spectrum.

The correct answer is
(a) (A) is correct but (R) is incorrect.
(b) Both (A) and (R) are correct and (R) is the correct explanation of (A).
(c) Both (A) and (R) are correct but (R) is not the correct explanation of (A).
(d) Both (A) and (R) are incorrect.

39. The truth table of a logic gate is given below. then identify the gate.

Input		Output
A	B	Y
0	0	1
0	1	1
1	0	1
1	1	0

(a) NOT gate (b) OR gate
(c) AND gate (d) NAND gate

40. A transmitting antenna has a height 20 m. What will be the height of receiving antenna, if the maximum distance between them for satisfactory communication in line-of-sight (LOS) mode is 40 km? (The earth radius is 6400 km.)
(a) 25 m (b) 30 m
(c) 60 m (d) 45 m

Answers

1.	(c)	2.	(d)	3.	(b)	4.	(b)	5.	(d)	6.	(a)	7.	(a)	8.	(a)	9.	(c)	10.	(d)
11.	(a)	12.	(c)	13.	(b)	14.	(b)	15.	(*)	16.	(c)	17.	(a)	18.	(d)	19.	(a)	20.	(b)
21.	(b)	22.	(c)	23.	(a)	24.	(a)	25.	(c)	26.	(c)	27.	(b)	28.	(c)	29.	(b)	30.	(b)
31.	(c)	32.	(b)	33.	(a)	34.	(b)	35.	(a)	36.	(c)	37.	(b)	38.	(a)	39.	(d)	40.	(d)

Scan this QR code from your mobile phone to get the explanations of this paper.
Or
Visit : *http://tinyurl.com/yygd232g*

04 May Shift II
Session 2 (3:00 PM to 6:00 PM)

1. Identify the correct option.

(a) The range of the gravitational force is large but not infinite.
(b) The range of electromagnetic force is large but lesser than the range of gravitational force.
(c) The range of weak nuclear force is smaller than the range of strong nuclear force, gravitation force and electromagnetic force.
(d) The range of the weak as well as strong nuclear force is of the the order of 10^{-10} m.

2. A current carrying conductor obeys Ohm's law ($V = RI$). If the current passing through the conductor is $I = (5 \pm 0.2)$ A and voltage developed is $V = (60 \pm 6)$ V, then find the percentage of error is resistance, R

(a) 18 (b) 6 (c) 14 (d) 2

3. A particle covers a distance from A to B over a period of time; the distance *versus* time plot is the shown below. Then which of the following is true for the motion of the particle?

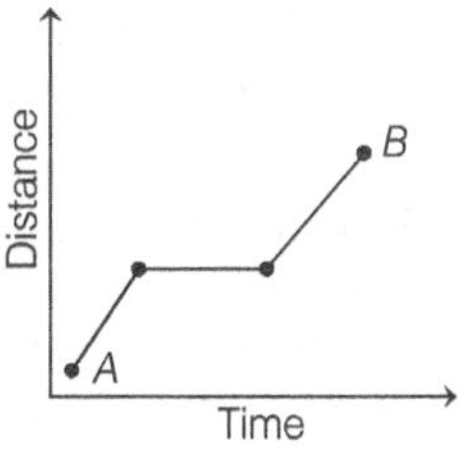

(a) Both average speed and instantaneous speed are always zero.
(b) Average speed is always non-zero but instantaneous speed can be zero.
(c) Instantaneous speed is always non-zero but average speed can be zero.
(d) Both average speed and instantaneous speed are always non-zero.

4. An iron rod of length 1.5 m lying on a horizontal table is pulled up form one end along a vertical line so as to move it with a constant velocity 3m/s, while the other end of the rod slides along the floor. After how much time the speed of the end sliding on the floor equals to the speed of the end being pulled up.

(a) $\frac{1}{2\sqrt{2}}$ s (b) $\frac{1}{\sqrt{2}}$ s
(c) $3\sqrt{2}$ s (d) $\frac{1}{4}$ s

5. A boy standing on a moving truck throws a projectile such that he is able to catch it back after the truck has moved 100 m. If the truck is moving horizontally along a straight line with a constant speed 30 m/s, at what speed (relative to the truck) must the projectile is thrown. (Assume, $g = 10$ m/s^2)

(a) $\frac{55}{3}$ m/s (b) $\frac{43}{2}$ m/s
(c) $\frac{50}{3}$ m/s (d) $\frac{23}{2}$ m/s

6. A body rotates about a stationary axis. If the angular deceleration is proportional to square root of angular speed, then the mean angular speed of the body, given ω_0 as the initial angular speed, is

(a) $\frac{\omega_0}{\sqrt{2}}$ (b) $\frac{\omega_0}{4}$
(c) $\frac{\omega_0}{2}$ (d) $\frac{\omega_0}{3}$

7. In the pulley system shown in the figure, the mass of A is half of that of rod B. The rod length is 500 cm. The mass of pulleys and the threads may be neglected. The mass A is set at the same level as the lower end of the rod and then released. After releasing the mass A, it would reach the top end of the rod B in time (Assume, $g = 10 \text{ m/s}^2$)

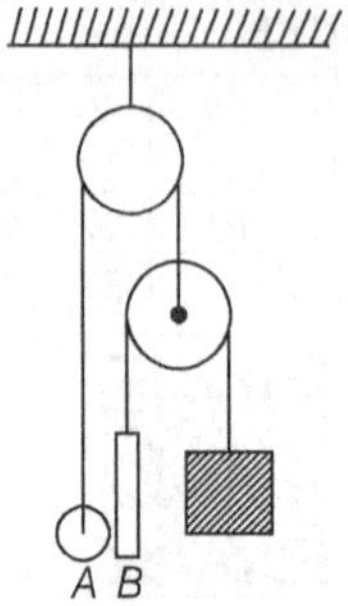

(a) 2.0 s (b) 1.0 s (c) 3.0 s (d) 4.0 s

8. A light rigid wire of length 1 m is attached to a ball A of mass 500 g to one end. The other end of the wire is fixed, so that the wire can rotate freely in the vertical plane about its fixed end. At the lowest point of the circular motion, the ball is given a horizontal velocity 6 m/s. Determined the radial component of the acceleration of the ball, when this rigid wire makes an angle 60° with the upward vertical. (Take, $g = 10 \text{ m/s}^2$)

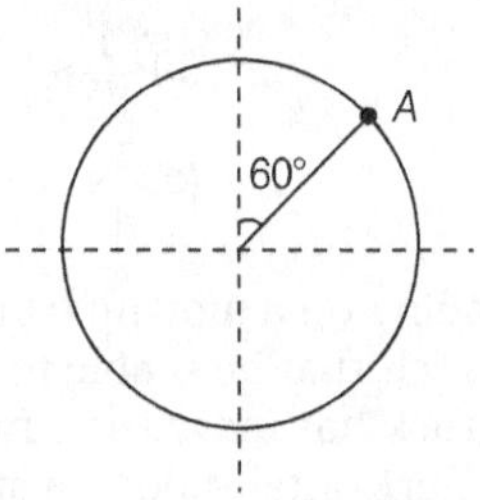

(a) 10 m/s^2 (b) 6 m/s^2
(c) 18 m/s^2 (d) 25 m/s^2

9. A block of mass 2 kg is connected to an ideal spring and is placed on a smooth horizontal surface. The spring is pulled to move the block and at an instant, the speed of end A of the spring and speed of the block were measured to be 6 m/s and 3 m/s, respectively. At this moment the potential energy stored in the spring in increasing at a rate 15 J/s. Find the acceleration of the block at this instant.

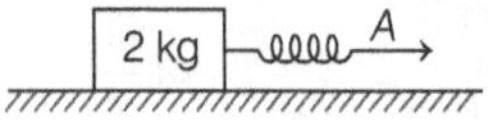

(a) 1.5 m/s^2 (b) 3.0 m/s^2
(c) 4.5 m/s^2 (d) 2.5 m/s^2

10. A uniform sphere of radius R and mass m is placed on an inclined plane which makes an angle 45° to the horizontal. For which of the following value of coefficient of friction, the sphere rolls without slipping,

(a) $\frac{3}{7}$ (b) $\frac{1}{2}$ (c) $\frac{5}{8}$ (d) $\frac{1}{7}$

11. A circular ring of mass 10 kg rolls along a horizontal floor. The center of mass of the ring has a speed 1.5 m/s. The work required to stop the ring is

(a) 10 J (b) − 6 J (c) 14.5 J (d) − 22.5 J

12. If the displacement of a body is given by $x = 3\cos\left[2\pi t + \frac{\pi}{4}\right]$ m, then the acceleration of the body at $t = 2$ s is

(a) 0 (b) $-6\sqrt{2}\,\pi^2 \text{ m/s}^2$
(c) $-10\,\pi^2 \text{ m/s}^2$ (d) $-12\sqrt{2}\,\pi^2 \text{ m/s}^2$

13. If the acceleration due to gravity g doubles and the radius of earth becomes half that of the present value, then the value of escape velocity is (Assume, $g = 10 \text{ m/s}^2$ and radius of earth, $R = 6400$ km)

(a) 12 km/s (b) $16\sqrt{2}$ km/s
(c) $8\sqrt{2}$ km/s (d) $4\sqrt{2}$ km/s

14. A uniform rod of length L is rotated in a horizontal plane about a vertical axis through one of its ends. The angular speed of rotation is ω. Find increase in length of the rod, if ρ and Y are the density and Young's modulus of the rod respectively,

(a) $\frac{\rho\omega^3 Y}{4L^2}$ (b) $\frac{4\rho\,\omega^2 L^3}{3Y}$ (c) $\frac{\rho\omega^3 L^3}{3Y}$ (d) $\frac{\rho\omega^3 L^3}{8Y}$

15. A cylindrical vessel of height 50 cm is filled with water and rests on a table. A small hole is made at the height h from the bottom of the vessel so that the water jet could hit the table surface at a maximum distance x_{max} from the vessel as shown in the figure. The value of x_{max} will be (Neglect the viscosity of water.)

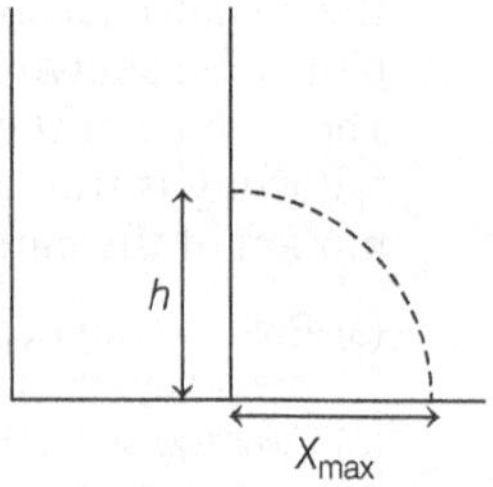

(a) 15 cm (b) 35 cm (c) 50 cm (d) 40 cm

16. A cubical block of wood, of length 10 cm, floats at the interface between oil of density 800 kg/m^3 and water. The lower surface of the block is 1.5 cm below the interface. If the depth of water is 10 cm below the interface and oil is upto 10 cm above the interface then the difference in pressure at the lower and the upper face of the wooden block is (Assume density of water, $\rho = 1000$ kg/m^3 and acceleration of gravity, $g = 10$ m/s^2)

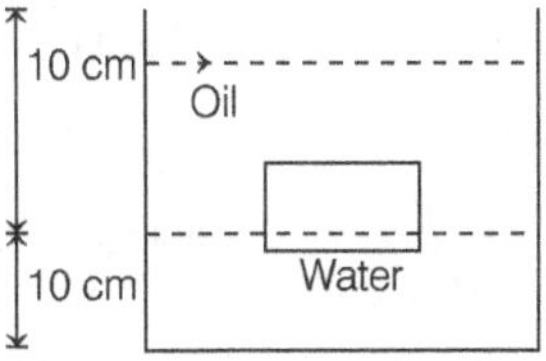

(a) 850 Pa (b) 780 Pa (c) 800 Pa (d) 830 Pa

17. A vessel of volume V contains ideal gas having mass density ρ at temperature T and pressure p. After a portion of the gas is let out, the pressure in the vessel is decreased by Δp. The mass of the released gas is

(a) $\rho V \Delta p / p$ (b) $\frac{\Delta p}{p}$

(c) $\frac{\rho}{p}$ (d) $(\rho V)^2 \Delta p / p$

18. A cup of coffee cools from 150°F to 144°F in 1 min in a room temperature at 72°F. How much time with the coffee take to cool from 110°F to 104°F in the same room?

(a) 1.55 min (b) 2.14 min (c) 2.89 min (d) 3.35 min

19. An ideal gas at initial temperature T_0 and initial volume V_0 is expanded adiabatically to a volume $2V_0$. The gas is then expanded isothermally to a volume $5V_0$ and there after compressed adiabatically so that the temperature of the gas becomes again T_0. If the final volume of the gas is αV_0, then the value of constant α is

(a) 2.5 (b) 1.5 (c) 2.0 (d) 3.0

20. A thermally insulated vessel containing monatomic gas is moving with a speed of 30 m/s. If the vessel suddenly stops, the increase in gas temperature is (Molar mass of gas = 83 g/mol and $R = 8.3$ J/K mol)

(a) 1 K (b) 3 K (c) 4 K (d) 6 K

21. A string of length 100 cm has three resonant frequencies, 120 Hz, 200 Hz and 280 Hz. If a node is formed at the end of the string, the speed of the transverse wave on this string is :

(a) 60 m/s (b) 80 m/s
(c) 100 m/s (d) 120 m/s

22. Two particles executing simple harmonic motion as described by $y_1 = 30 \sin\left(2\pi t + \frac{\pi}{3}\right)$ and $y_2 = 10\,(\sin 2\pi t + \sqrt{3}\cos 2\pi t)$ have amplitudes A_1 and A_2 respectively. The ratio $A_1 : A_2$ is

(a) 2 : 1 (b) 1 : 1 (c) 3 : 2 (d) 1 : $\sqrt{3}$

23. Two lenses A and B having focal lengths 2.0 cm and 5.0 cm, respectively are placed 14 cm apart. Lens A is placed to the left of lens B. An object is placed 3 cm to the left of lens A. The distance of the image from lens A will be

(a) $\frac{40}{3}$ cm (b) $\frac{82}{3}$ cm (c) $\frac{112}{5}$ cm (d) $\frac{92}{5}$ cm

24. The pass-axes of two polarisers were kept such that the incident unpolarised beam of intensity I_0, gets completely blocked. Another polariser was introduced in between these two polarisers with its pass-axis 60° with respect to the pass-axis of the first one. The output intensity would then become

(a) 0 (b) $\frac{3}{32}I_0$ (c) $\frac{3}{16}I_0$ (d) $\frac{3}{8}I_0$

25. A negative charge is placed at the centre of the non-conducting sphere. The direction of electric field on any point at the surface of the sphere is

(a) radially inward
(b) radially outward
(c) along the tangent to the surface
(d) no electric field produced

26. A spherical drop of liquid carrying charge, Q has potential V_0 at its surface. If two drops of same charge and radius combine to form a single spherical drop, then the potential at the surface of new drop is (Assume, $V = 0$ at infinity.)

(a) $2^{\frac{1}{3}}V_0$ (b) $4^{\frac{1}{3}}V_0$ (c) $6^{\frac{1}{3}}V_0$ (d) $2^{\frac{-1}{3}}V_0$

27. Calculate the voltage across AB terminals in the given circuit,

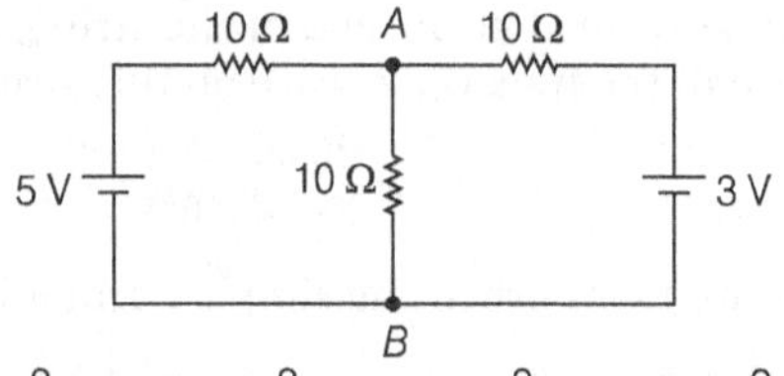

(a) $\frac{3}{8}$ V (b) $\frac{8}{3}$ V (c) $\frac{3}{2}$ V (d) $\frac{2}{3}$ V

28. When subjected to a voltage of 10 V, the current through a resistor at a temperature of 40°C is 0.1 A. The temperature coefficient of resistance of the material of the resistor is $2\times10^{-4}\,°C^{-1}$. The temperature of the resistor in °C when the current drops to 0.098 A is

(a) 142 (b) 167 (c) 181 (d) 206

29. A magnetic field of 5×10^{-5} T is produced at a perpendicular distance of 0.2 m from a long straight wire carrying electric current. If the permeability of free space is $4\pi\times10^{-7}$ T m/A. The current passing through the wire in A is

(a) 45 (b) 40 (c) 50 (d) 30

30. A long wire carries a current of 18 A kept along the axis of a long solenoid of radius 1 cm. The field due to the solenoid is 8.0×10^{-3}T. The magnitude of the resultant field at a point 0.6 mm from the solenoid axis is (Assume, $\mu_0 = 4\pi\times10^{-7}$ Tm/A)

(a) 6×10^{-3} T (b) 6×10^{-4} T
(c) $2\sqrt{7}\times10^{-3}$ T (d) 10×10^{-3} T

31. A small bar magnet experiences a torque of 0.016 Nm when placed with its axis at 30° with an external field of 0.04 T. If the bar magnet is replaced by a solenoid of cross-sectional area of 1 cm^2 and 1000 turns but having the same magnetic moment as that of bar magnet, then the current flowing through the solenoid is

(a) 2 A (b) 4 A (c) 6 A (d) 8 A

32. A rod of length 80 cm rotates about its mid point with a frequency of 10 rev/s. The potential difference (in volts) between two ends of the rod due to a magnetic field, $B = 0.5$ T directed perpendicular to the rod is

(a) π (b) $1.6\,\pi$ (c) $2\,\pi$ (d) $0.8\,\pi$

33. LCR circuit, the resonance frequency of circuit increases two times of the initial circuit by changing C and C' and R from 100 Ω to 400 Ω, while the inductance was kept the same. The ratio C/C', is

(a) 2 (b) 8
(c) 16 (d) 4

34. In a travelling plane electromagnetic wave, the maximum magnetic field is 1.26×10^{-4} T. The intensity of the wave is (Assume, $\mu_0 = 1.26\times10^{-6}$ H/m)

(a) $1.56\times10^6\ \frac{W}{m^2}$ (b) $1.89\times10^6\ \frac{W}{m^2}$
(c) $8.92\times10^5\ \frac{W}{m^2}$ (d) $4.62\times10^6\ \frac{W}{m^2}$

35. A cobalt (Co) plate is placed at a distance of 1 m from a point source of power 1 W. Assume a circular area of the plate of radius, $r = 1$ Å is exposed to the radiation and ejects photo electrons. The light energy is considered to be spread uniformly and the work function of cobalt is 5 eV. The minimum time the target should be exposed to the light source to eject a photoelectron (Assuming no reflection losses) is

(a) 320 s (b) 450 s
(c) 860 s (d) 100 s

36. A hydrogen sample is prepared in a particular excited state A of quantum number, $n_A = 3$. The ground state energy of hydrogen atom is $-|E|$. The photons of energy $\frac{|E|}{12}$ are absorbed in the sample which results in the excitation of some electrons to excited state B of quantum number n_B, whose value is

(a) 6 (b) 4
(c) 5 (d) 7

37. The half life of neutron is 693 seconds. What fraction of neutrons will decay when a beam of neutrons, having kinetic energy of 0.084 eV, travells a distance of 1 km?

(mass of neutron $= 1.68\times10^{-27}$ kg, and $\ln 2 = 0.693$)

(a) 60×10^{-5} (b) 15×10^{-5}
(c) 25×10^{-5} (d) 50×10^{-5}

38. For a given truth table A, B and C are inputs and Y is the output, then the functional form of the circuit is

A	B	C	Y
0	0	0	1
0	0	1	1
0	1	0	0
0	1	1	0
1	0	0	1
1	0	1	1
1	1	0	0
1	1	1	0

(a) $\overline{A}$ (b) $\overline{B}$
(c) $\overline{A} + BC$ (d) $A + B + C$

39. Two diodes are connected in the following fashion. Provision is made to connect either +5 V or ground (0 V) to the points A to B. The output Q will act as

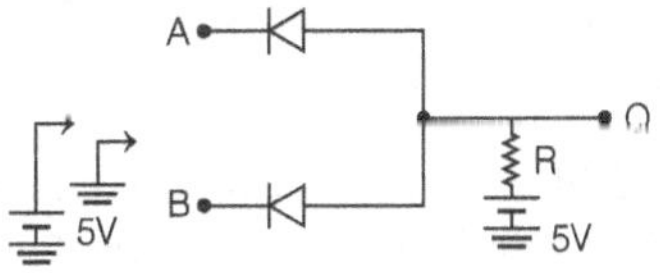

(a) OR gate (b) AND gate
(c) XOR gate (d) NAND gate

40. Carrier waves are used for communicating signals over long distance, because
(a) carrier waves can be generated very easily.
(b) low frequencies can not be easily modulated by the carrier waves.
(c) low frequencies can be transmitted over long distances.
(d) carrier waves generated at higher frequencies can be transmitted over long distances.

Answers

1.	(c)	2.	(c)	3.	(b)	4.	(*)	5.	(c)	6.	(d)	7.	(b)	8.	(b)	9.	(a)	10.	(a,b,c)
11.	(d)	12.	(b)	13.	(a)	14.	(c)	15.	(c)	16.	(d)	17.	(a)	18.	(b)	19.	(a)	20.	(b)
21.	(b)	22.	(c)	23.	(b)	24.	(b)	25.	(a)	26.	(b)	27.	(b)	28.	(a)	29.	(c)	30.	(d)
31.	(d)	32.	(d)	33.	(d)	34.	(b)	35.	(a)	36.	(a)	37.	(*)	38.	(b)	39.	(b)	40.	(d)

Scan this QR code from your mobile phone to get the explanations of this paper.
Or
Visit : *http://tinyurl.com/y3wpnmeu*

06 May Shift I
Session 1 (10:00 AM to 1:00 PM)

1. Match the following table.

	List-I		List-II
A.	Michelson-Morley experiment	I.	The existence of anti-matter
B.	Stern-Gerlach experiment	II.	The existence of de-Broglie matter waves
C.	Davisson-Germer experiment	III.	Electrons have spins
D.	Anderson discovery of positron	IV.	The non-existence of ether

	A	B	C	D
(a)	IV	II	I	II
(b)	II	III	IV	I
(c)	I	II	IV	III
(d)	IV	III	II	I

2. Consider a spongy block of mass m floating on a flowing river. The maximum mass of the block is related to the speed of the river flow v, acceleration due to gravity g and the density of the block ρ such that $m_{\max} = kv^x g^y \rho^z$ (k is constant). The values of x, y and z should then respectively be (Mass of the spongy block is assumed to vary due to absorption of water by it)
(a) 6, 3, 2 (b) 6, −3, 1 (c) 3, 6, 1 (d) 6, 1, 3

3. A ball is thrown vertically upward from the ground at time, $t = 0$ s. It passes the top of a tower at $t = 3$ s and 2 s later it reaches and its maximum height. The height of the tower is (Acceleration due to gravity, $g = 10\ m/s^2$)

(a) 105 m (b) 125 m (c) 85 m (d) 65 m

4. Rain is falling vertically with a speed of 30 m/s. A man rides a bicycle with a speed of 10 m/s from East to West direction. At what the angle with the vertical, he sees the rain falling?

(a) $\tan^{-1}\left(\frac{1}{3}\right)$ towards West (b) $\tan^{-1}(3)$ towards West

(c) $\tan^{-1}\left(\frac{1}{3}\right)$ towards East (d) $\tan^{-1}(3)$ towards East

5. An archer shoots an arrow from a height 4.2 m above the ground with a speed 40 m/s and at an angle 30° as shown in the figure. Determine the horizontal distance R covered by the arrow, when it hits the ground, (Take $g = 10\ m/s^2$)

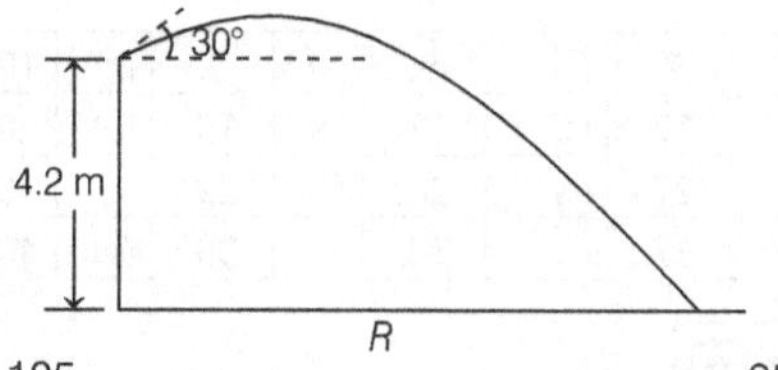

(a) $\frac{185}{\sqrt{3}}$ m (b) $84\sqrt{3}$ m (c) $68\sqrt{3}$ m (d) $\frac{95}{\sqrt{3}}$ m

6. A bullet enters a wooden block with velocity 120 m/s. The bullet travels 1.5 s in the block before its velocity reduces to zero due to resistance force which is proportional to the square root of the velocity. The distance travelled by the bullet in the wooden block is

(a) 10 m (b) 60 m (c) 25 m (d) 40 m

7. A bouncing ball of mass 200 g falls from the height of 5 m on a horizontal ground. After every impact with the ground, the velocity of the ball decreases by $\frac{1}{2}$ times.

The total momentum, the ball imparts on to the ground after 3 impacts is (Let $g = 10\ m/s^2$)

(a) $\frac{14}{4}$ kg m/s (b) $\frac{20}{6}$ kg m/s

(c) $\frac{26}{12}$ kg m/s (d) $\frac{21}{4}$ kg m/s

8. A block of mass 100 g is suspended vertically from a massless spring system of spring constant, $k = 1$ N/m each. The block is hit from above to impart an impulse of 2 Ns. Calculate the maximum displacement from the Equilibrium position of the block. (Take, $g = 10\ m/s^2$)

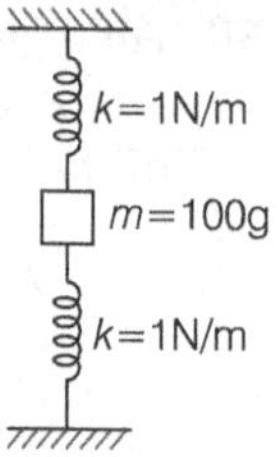

(a) 2 m (b) 4m (c) 5 m (d) 9 m

9. A metal chain of mass 2 kg and length 90 cm over hangs a table with 60 cm on the table. How much work needs to be done to put the hanging part of the chain back on the table? (Let $g = 10\ m/s^2$)

(a) 2 J (b) 10 J (c) 1 J (d) 3 J

10. A thin circular disc of mass 12 kg and radius 0.5 m rotates with an angular velocity of 100 rad/s. The rotational kinetic energy of the disc is

(a) 12.2 kJ (b) 5.5 kJ (c) 9.2 kJ (d) 7.5 kJ

11. The distance between Sun and Earth is 1.6×10^{11} m and the radius of Earth is 6.4×10^6 m. The ratio of the angular momentum of Earth around the Sun to the angular momentum around its own axis is approximately (Assume Earth as a solid sphere with uniform mass density and rotates around the Sun in a circular path.)

(a) 2.0×10^2 (b) 5.1×10^8 (c) 4.3×10^6 (d) 8.7×10^{12}

12. A uniform rod of length 1.8 m suspended by an end is made to undergo small oscillations. Find the length of the simple pendulum having the mass and time period equal to that of the rod.

(a) 3.6 m (b) 1.2 m (c) 2.4 m (d) 4.2 m

13. A planet of mass m moves around the Sun along an elliptical path with a period of revolution T. During the motion, the planet's maximum and minimum distance from Sun is R and $\frac{R}{3}$ respectively. If $T^2 = \alpha R^3$, then the magnitude of constant α will be

(a) $\frac{10}{9} \cdot \frac{\pi}{Gm}$ (b) $\frac{20}{27} \cdot \frac{\pi^2}{Gm}$ (c) $\frac{32}{27} \cdot \frac{\pi^2}{Gm}$ (d) $\frac{1}{18} \cdot \frac{\pi^2}{Gm}$

14. A copper wire and an aluminium wire have lengths in the ratio 5 : 2, diameters in the ratio 4 : 3 and forces applied in the ratio 4 : 5. Find the ratio of increase in length of the copper wire to that aluminium wire. (Let $Y_{Cu} = 1.1 \times 10^{11}\ \text{Nm}^{-2}$, $Y_{Al} = 0.7 \times 10^{11}\ \text{Nm}^{-2}$)

(a) $\frac{176}{63}$ (b) $\frac{63}{88}$ (c) $\frac{189}{11}$ (d) $\frac{33}{89}$

15. Consider a water droplet of diameter 0.2 mm where the outside pressure is 1.5 N/cm^2 at 25°C. The pressure inside the droplet, when the surface tension at 25 °C is 0.08 N/m is

(a) 0.32 N/cm^2 (b) 1.18 N/cm^2
(c) 1.82 N/cm^2 (d) 1.66 N/cm^2

16. A hydrophilic surface is characterised by the contact angle at the water solid interface. The value of contact angle should be

(a) > 90° (b) < 90° (c) = 90° (d) = 180°

17. The temperature of a body is increased from $T_1 = 127$ °C to $T_2 = 227$ °C. The ambient temperature is 27°C. The energies emitted per second by the body at T_1 and T_2 are E_1 and E_2 respectively. The ratio of $\frac{E_2}{E_1}$ is

(a) 1.8 (b) 2.7 (c) 3.1 (d) 4.3

18. Two thin metallic spherical shells of radii 20 cm and 30 cm, respectively are placed with their centres coinciding. A material of thermal conductivity α is filled in the space between the shells. The inner shell is maintained at 300 K and the outer shell at 310 K. If the rate at which heat flows radially through the material is 40 W, find the value of α (in units of J s^{-1} m^{-1} K^{-1}).

(a) $\frac{3}{\pi}$ (b) $\frac{4\pi}{3}$ (c) $\frac{5}{3\pi}$ (d) $\frac{\pi}{2}$

19. Pressure at the Earth's surface is $p_0 = 10^5$ Pa and the density of air at Earth's surface is $\rho_0 = 1.4$ kg/m^3. At height h from the surface of Earth the density of air is reduced to $\frac{\rho_0}{2}$, the value of h is (Assume that the temperature is constant through out the earth's atmosphere and let $\ln(2) = 0.7$)

(a) 10,500 m (b) 5,000 m
(c) 1,500 m (d) 2,800 m

20. Consider an ideal gas at pressure p, volume V and temperature T. The mean free path for molecules of the gas is L. If the radius of gas molecules, as well as pressure, volume and temperature of the gas are doubled, then the mean free path will be

(a) $\frac{5L}{2}$ (b) $\frac{L}{4}$ (c) $\frac{L}{8}$ (d) $2L$

21. Two identical sinusoidal waves are moving in the same direction along a stretched string, interfere with each other. The phase difference between them is 120°. The amplitudes of both the waves are same. If the amplitude of the resultant wave due to interference is 2 mm, the amplitude of each wave is

(a) 1 mm (b) 2 mm (c) $\sqrt{3}$ mm (d) $2\sqrt{3}$ mm

22. A whistle of frequency 660 Hz moves in a circle of radius 1 m at an angular speed of 10 rad/s. The highest frequency heard by a listener at a long distance and at rest with respect to the center of the circle is (Let speed of sound = 340 m/s.)

(a) 700 Hz (b) 640 Hz (c) 720 Hz (d) 680 Hz

23. An object O is placed at 7 cm to the left of a concave mirror of radius of curvature 12 cm as shown in the figure. The position of the image will be at a distance of

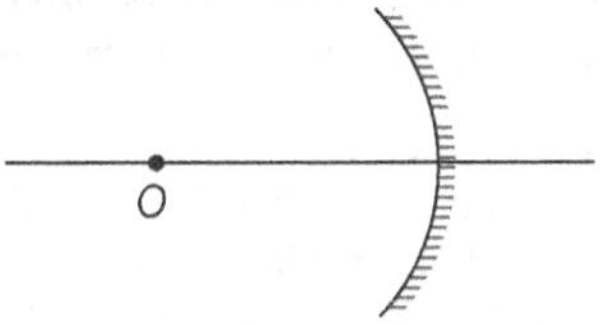

(a) 20 cm from the mirror to the left.
(b) 30 cm from the mirror to the right.
(c) 42 cm from the mirror to the left.
(d) 42 cm from the mirror to the right.

24. Light consisting of a plane waves of wavelength, $\lambda_1 = 8 \times 10^{-5}$ cm and $\lambda_2 = 6 \times 10^{-5}$ cm generates an interference pattern in Young's double slit experiment. If n_1 denotes the n_1th dark fringe due to light of wavelength λ_1 which coincides with n_2th bright fringe due to light of wavelength λ_2, then

(a) $n_1 = 3, n_2 = 1$ (b) $n_1 = 4, n_2 = 5$
(c) $n_1 = 1, n_2 = 2$ (d) $n_1 = 3, n_2 = 2$

25. A spherical volume contains a uniformly distributed charge of density 1.0×10^{-6} C/m^3. Find the electrical field (in N/C) at a point inside the volume at a distance 1 mm from the centre. $\left(\text{Let } \frac{1}{4\pi \epsilon_0} = 9 \times 10^9 \text{ Nm}^2\text{C}^{-2}\right)$

(a) $\frac{8}{\pi}$ (b) 6π (c) $\frac{\pi}{6}$ (d) 12π

26. Four identical metal plates are located in air at equal distance d from each other. The area of each plate is S. If the outer most plates are connected by a conducting wire as shown in the figure the capacitance between points A and B will be

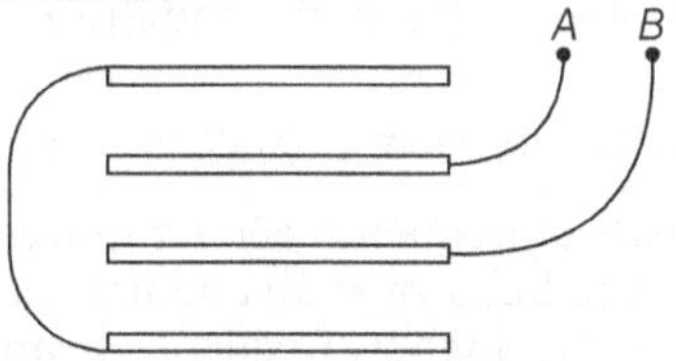

(a) $\frac{\varepsilon_0 S}{d}$ (b) $\frac{3}{2}\frac{\varepsilon_0 S}{d}$ (c) $\frac{1}{2}\frac{\varepsilon_0 S}{d}$ (d) $\frac{2}{3}\frac{\varepsilon_0 S}{d}$

27. The resistance of a device component decreases as the current through it increases and it is described by the relation, $R = \frac{0.2I}{I-4}$, where I is the current. Determined the minimum power deliver. (Assume, $I > 4$)

(a) 22.4 W (b) 18.6 W (c) 19.8 W (d) 21.6 W

28. A 100 W tungsten light bulb has a resistance of 250 Ω when it as turned ON and 25Ω when turned OFF. The ambient room temperature is 25°C. Find the temperature of the filament when the bulb is turned ON.
(Let $\alpha_{\text{tungsten}} = 4.5 \times 10^{-3}/°\text{C}$)

(a) 2600 °C (b) 2025 °C
(c) 2500 °C (d) 2625 °C

29. Two particles carrying equal charges move parallel to each other with the speed 150 km/s. If $\mathbf{F}_1$ and $\mathbf{F}_2$ are magnetic and electric forces between two charged particles then, $\frac{|\mathbf{F}_1|}{|\mathbf{F}_2|}$ is $\left(\text{Let } \mu_0\varepsilon_0 = \frac{1}{9 \times 10^{16}} \text{ s}^2/\text{m}^2\right)$

(a) 1.0×10^{-6} (b) 1.5×10^{-7}
(c) 3.0×10^{-6} (d) 2.5×10^{-7}

30. A very long wire carrying a current $4\sqrt{2}$ A is bent at a right angles. The magnitude of magnetic field ($|\mathbf{B}|$) at a point P lying on a line perpendicular to the bent wire at a distance, $d = 20$ cm from the point of the bending will be (Let $\mu_0 = 4\pi \times 10^{-7}$ H/m)

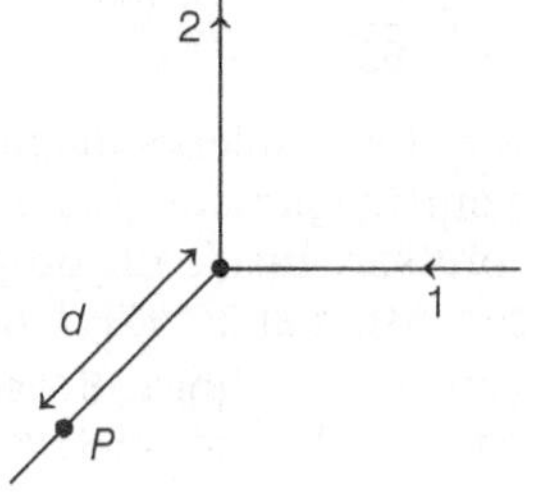

(a) 1 μT (b) 0.8 μT (c) 2 μT (d) 4 μT

31. Identify the incorrect statement from the following.

(a) The susceptibility of a diamagnetic material is a positive quantity.
(b) Paramagnetic materials obey Curie's law.
(c) Ferromagnetic materials have permanent magnetic domains.
(d) In soft ferromagnetic material, the magnetisation disappear on removal of the external field.

32. Consider a toroid with rectangular cross section, of inner radius a, outer radius b and height h, carrying n number of turns. Then the self-inductance of the toroidal coil when current I passing through the toroid is

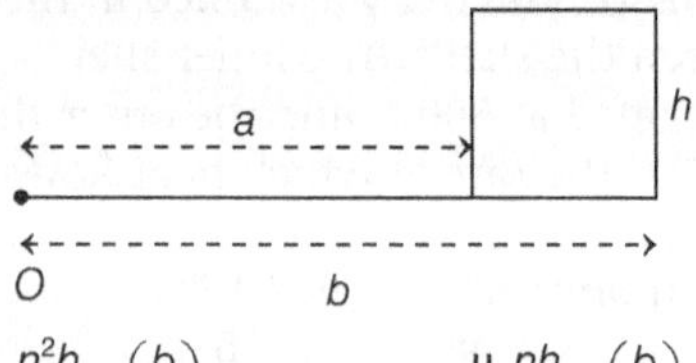

(a) $\frac{\mu_0 n^2 h}{2\pi} \ln\left(\frac{b}{a}\right)$ (b) $\frac{\mu_0 nh}{2\pi} \ln\left(\frac{b}{a}\right)$
(c) $\frac{\mu_0 n^2 h}{2\pi} \ln\left(\frac{a}{b}\right)$ (d) $\frac{\mu_0 nh}{2\pi} \ln\left(\frac{a}{b}\right)$

33. A coil is connected to an AC source with peak emf, 8 V and frequency $\frac{30}{\pi}$ Hz. The coil has resistance of 8 Ω. If the average power dissipated by the coil is 0.4 W, then the inductance of the coil is

(a) 0.8 H (b) 2.0 H
(c) 1.4 H (d) 0.4 H

34. A flashlight of intensity 9 W/cm^2 illuminates a perfectly reflective surface of area 300 cm^2. The average force exerted on the surface due to the incident light photons is

(a) 0 N (b) 14 μN (c) 18 μN (d) 12 μN

35. A parallel beam of monochromatic light of frequency ν is incident on a surface. The intensity of the beam is I and area of the surface is A. Find the force exerted by the light of beam on the surface is perfectly reflecting and the light beam is incident at an angle of incidence θ. (The speed of light is denoted as c.)

(a) $\frac{2IA\sin^2\theta}{\pi c}$ (b) $\frac{IA\cos^2\theta}{c}$

(c) $\frac{2IA\cos^2\theta}{c}$ (d) $\frac{IA\cos^2\theta}{\sqrt{2}c}$

36. Monochromatic radiation is incident on hydrogen (H) sample which is in ground state. If the hydrogen atoms emit radiation of ten different wavelengths after absorbing the incident radiation, then the wavelength of the incident radiation is (Let $hc = 1242$ eV-nm)

(a) 84.4 nm (b) 102.6 nm (c) 72.5 nm (d) 95.1 nm

37. Two radioactive materials R_1 and R_2 have decay constants 6λ and λ, respectively. The half life of R_2 is 1.4×10^{17} s. Initially they contain some number of nuclei.

The time at which the ratio of the remaining nuclei of R_2 to that of R_1 will be e is (Let $\ln 2 = 0.7$)

(a) 2×10^{16} s (b) 4×10^{16} s

(c) 3×10^{16} s (d) 5×10^{16} s

38. A person applies a sine wave and square wave to an AND gate as shown in the figure (i) and (ii). Assuming that both the voltages are applied in phase, the person observes the output at E and F on (i) and (ii), respectively. [Assume minimum voltage of 5 V is equivalent to logic (i)]

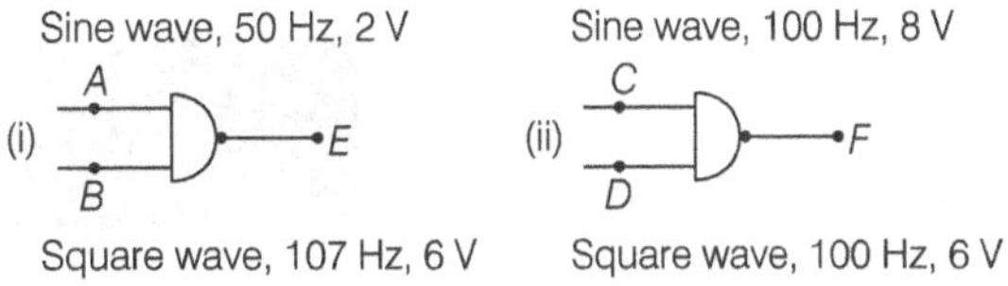

(a) Square wave at 50 Hz and square wave at 100 Hz.

(b) Sine wave at 50 Hz and square wave at 100 Hz.

(c) No output and sine wave at 100 Hz.

(d) No output and pulsed wave at 100 Hz.

39. Consider an amplifier circuit in which a transistor is used in common-emitter mode. The load resistance 3 kΩ. When a signal of 30 mV is added to base emitter voltage, the base current is changed by 30 μA and the collector current is changed by 3 mA. The power gain in this circuit will be

(a) 10000 (b) 20000

(c) 30000 (d) 40000

40. A message signal is used to modulated a carrier signal of frequency 5 MHz and peak voltage of 40 V. In the process, two side-bands are produced seperated by 40 kHz. If the modulation index is 0.75, then the peak voltage and frequency of the messages signal, respectively are

(a) 60 V ; 10 kHz (b) 60 V ; 20 kHz

(c) 30 V ; 10 kHz (d) 30 V ; 20 kHz

Answers

1.	(d)	2.	(b)	3.	(a)	4.	(a)	5.	(b)	6.	(*)	7.	(d)	8.	(b)	9.	(c)	10.	(d)
11.	(c)	12.	(b)	13.	(c)	14.	(b)	15.	(d)	16.	(b)	17.	(*)	18.	(c)	19.	(*)	20.	(b)
21.	(b)	22.	(d)	23.	(c)	24.	(c)	25.	(d)	26.	(b)	27.	(d)	28.	(b)	29.	(d)	30.	(d)
31.	(a)	32.	(a)	33.	(d)	34.	(c)	35.	(c)	36.	(d)	37.	(b)	38.	(d)	39.	(c)	40.	(d)

Scan this QR code from your mobile phone to get the explanations of this paper.

Or

Visit : *http://tinyurl.com/y2tsxop9*

AP EAMCET

Engineering Entrance Exam

Online Question Paper 2018 *(Solved)*

22 April Shift I
Session 1 (10:00 AM to 1:00 PM)

1. Two resistance 60.36 Ω and 30.09 Ω are connected in parallel. The equivalent resistance is

(a) 20 ± 0.08 Ω (b) 20 ± 0.06 Ω
(c) 20 ± 0.03 Ω (d) 20 ± 0.10 Ω

2. Assertion (A) The velocity of a projectile at a point on its trajectory is equal to the slope at that point.

Reason (R) The velocity vector at a point always along the tangent to the trajectory at that point.

(a) Both A and R are true and R is the correct explanation of A
(b) Both A and R are true but R is not the correct explanation of A
(c) A is true but R is false
(d) A is false but R is true

3. A body is projected from the ground at an angle of $\tan^{-1}\left(\frac{8}{7}\right)$ with the horizontal. The ratio of the maximum height attained by it to its range is

(a) 8 : 7 (b) 4 : 7 (c) 2 : 7 (d) 1 : 7

4. A body is projected with a speed u at an angle θ with the horizontal. The radius of curvature of the trajectory, when it makes an angle $\left(\frac{\theta}{2}\right)$ with the horizontal is (g-acceleration due to gravity)

(a) $\frac{u^2\cos^2\theta\sec^3\left(\frac{\theta}{2}\right)}{\sqrt{3}g}$ (b) $\frac{u^2\cos^2\theta\sec^3\left(\frac{\theta}{2}\right)}{2g}$

(c) $\frac{2u^2\cos^3\theta\sec^2\left(\frac{\theta}{2}\right)}{g}$ (d) $\frac{u^2\cos^2\theta\sec^3\left(\frac{\theta}{2}\right)}{g}$

5. Sand is to be piled up on a horizontal ground in the form of a regular cone of a fixed base of radius R. Coefficient of static friction between the sand layers is μ. Maximum volume of the sand can be piled up in the form of cone without slipping on the ground is

(a) $\frac{\mu R^3}{3\pi}$ (b) $\frac{\mu R^3}{3}$

(c) $\frac{\pi R^3}{3\mu}$ (d) $\frac{\mu\pi R^3}{3}$

6. A block of mass 2 kg is being pushed against a wall by a force $F = 90$ N as shown in the figure. If the coefficient of friction is 0.25, then the magnitude of acceleration of the block is

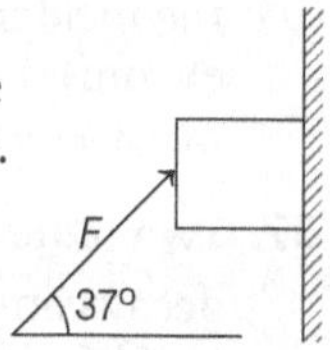

(Take, $g = 10\ \text{ms}^{-2}$) $\left(\sin 37° = \frac{3}{5}\right)$

(a) 16 ms^{-2} (b) 8 ms^{-2} (c) 38 ms^{-2} (d) 54 ms^{-2}

7. A body of mass 2 kg thrown vertically from the ground with a velocity of 8 ms^{-1} reaches a maximum height of 3 m. The work done by the air resistance is (acceleration due to gravity = 10 ms^{-2})

(a) 4J (b) 60J (c) 64J (d) 8J

8. The system of two masses 2 kg and 3 kg as shown in the figure is released from rest. The work done on 3 kg block by the force of gravity during first 2 seconds of its motion is ($g = 10\ \text{ms}^{-2}$)

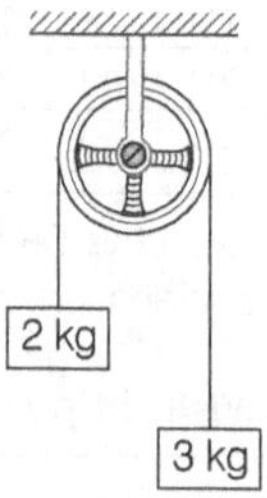

(a) 120 J (b) 80 J
(c) 40 J (d) 30 J

9. A rigid metallic sphere is spinning around its own axis in the absence of external torque. If the temperature is raised, its volume increases by 9%. The change in its angular speed is

(a) increases by 9% (b) decreases by 9%
(c) increases by 6% (d) decreases by 6%

10. Two spheres *P* and *Q*, each of mass 200 g are attached to a string of length one metre as shown in the figure. The string and the spheres are then whirled in a horizontal circle about *O* at a constant angular speed. The ratio of the tension in the string between *P* and *Q* to that of between *P* and *O* is (*P* is at mid-point of the line joining *O* and *Q*)

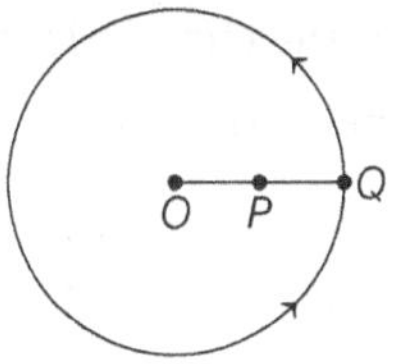

(a) $\frac{1}{2}$ (b) $\frac{2}{3}$ (c) $\frac{3}{2}$ (d) $\frac{2}{1}$

91. The potential energy of a simple harmonic oscillator of mass 2 kg at its mean position is 5 J. If its total energy is 9 J and amplitude is 1 cm, then its time period is

(a) $\frac{\pi}{100}$ s (b) $\frac{\pi}{50}$ s (c) $\frac{\pi}{20}$ s (d) $\frac{\pi}{10}$ s

12. Three masses *m*, 2*m* and 3*m* are arranged in two triangular configurations as shown in figure 1 and figure 2. Work done by an external agent in changing, the configuration from figure 1 to figure 2 is

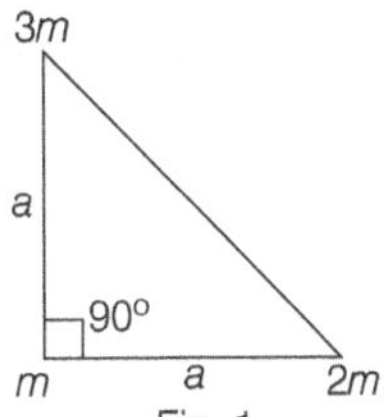

Fig. 1

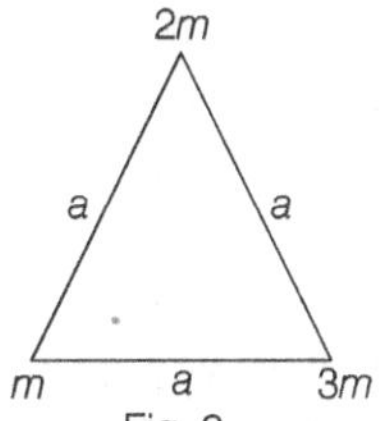

Fig. 2

(a) $\frac{6Gm^2}{a}\left[2-\frac{6}{\sqrt{2}}\right]$ (b) 0

(c) $\frac{Gm^2}{a}\left[6+\frac{6}{\sqrt{2}}\right]$ (d) $-\frac{Gm^2}{a}\left[6-\frac{6}{\sqrt{2}}\right]$

13. Two equal and opposite forces each *F* act on a rod of uniform cross-sectional area *a* as shown in the figure. Shearing stress on the section *AB* will be

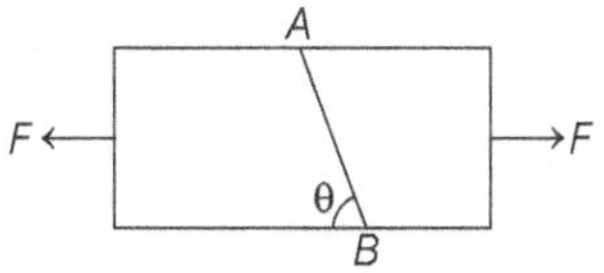

(a) $\frac{F\sin\theta\cos\theta}{a}$ (b) $\frac{F\sin\theta}{a}$ (c) $\frac{F\cos\theta}{a}$ (d) $\frac{F\sin^2\theta}{a}$

14. A body is suspended by a light string. The tensions in the string when the body is in air, when the body is totally immersed in water and when the body is totally immersed in a liquid are respectively 40.2N, 28.4N and 16.6N. The density of the liquid is

(a) 1200 kg - m^{-3} (b) 1600 kg - m^{-3}
(c) 2000 kg - m^{-3} (d) 2400 kg - m^{-3}

15. Steam at 100°C is passed into 1 kg of water contained in a calorimeter at 9°C till the temperature of water and calorimeter is increased to 90°C. The mass of the steam condensed is nearly

(water equivalent of calorimeter = 0.1 kg, specific heat of water = $1\,\text{cal}\,\text{g}^{-1}\,°\text{C}^{-1}$ and latent heat of vaporisation = $540\,\text{cal}\,\text{g}^{-1}$)

(a) 81g (b) 162 g (c) 243 g (d) 486 g

16. Three very large plates of same area are kept parallel and close to each other. They are considered as ideal black surfaces and have very high thermal conductivity. First and third plates are maintained at absolute temperatures 2*T* and 3*T* respectively. Temperature of the middle plate in steady state is

(a) $\left(\frac{65}{2}\right)^{\frac{1}{4}}T$ (b) $\left(\frac{97}{4}\right)^{\frac{1}{4}}T$ (c) $\left(\frac{97}{2}\right)^{\frac{1}{4}}T$ (d) $(97)^{\frac{1}{4}}T$

17. A thermally insulated vessel with nitrogen gas at 27°C is moving with a velocity of 100 ms^{-1}. If the vessel is stopped suddenly, then the percentage change in the pressure of the gas is nearly (assume entire loss in KE of the gas is given as heat to gas and *R* = 8.3 $\text{Jmol}^{-1}\text{K}^{-1}$)

(a) 1.1 (b) 0.93 (c) 0.5 (d) 2.25

18. Match the following lists.

List I	List II
A Zeroth law of thermodynamics	I Direction of flow of heat
B First law of thermodynamics	II Work done is zero
C Free expansion of a gas	III Thermal equilibrium
D Second law of Thermodynamics	IV Law of conservation of energy

The correct answer is

	A	B	C	D		A	B	C	D
(a)	II	IV	III	I	(b)	III	IV	II	I
(c)	III	I	II	IV	(d)	I	III	IV	II

19. For a molecule of an ideal gas, the number density is $2\sqrt{2}\times10^{8}\text{cm}^{-3}$ and the mean free path is $\frac{10^{-2}}{\pi}$ cm. The diameter of the gas molecule is

(a) 5×10^{-4} cm
(b) 0.5×10^{-4} cm
(c) 2.5×10^{-4} cm
(d) 4×10^{-4} cm

20. A solid ball is suspended from the ceiling of a motor car through a light string. A transverse pulse travels at the speed 60 cm^{-1} on the string, when the car is at rest. When the car accelerates on a horizontal road, then speed of the pulse is 66 cm^{-1}. The acceleration of the car is nearly ($g = 10\ \text{ms}^{-2}$)

(a) 4.3 ms^{-2} (b) 2.9 ms^{-2} (c) 6.8 ms^{-2} (d) 5.5 ms^{-2}

21. A reflector is moving with 20 ms^{-1} towards a stationary source of sound. If the source is producing sound waves of 160 Hz, then the wavelength of the reflected wave is (speed of sound in air is 340 ms^{-1})

(a) $\frac{17}{8}$m (b) $\frac{17}{11}$m (c) $\frac{17}{9}$m (d) $\frac{17}{16}$m

22. A light ray incidents normally on one surface of an equilateral prism. The angle of deviation of the light ray is (refractive index of the material of the prism = $\sqrt{2}$)

(a) 60° (b) 30° (c) 0° (d) 120°

23. Two polaroids are placed in the path of unpolarised light beam of intensity I_0 such that no light is emitted from the second polaroid. If a third polaroid whose polarisation axis makes an angle θ with that of the first polaroid is placed between the polaroids, then intensity of light emerging from the last polaroid is

(a) $\left(\frac{I_0}{8}\right)\sin^2 2\theta$
(b) $\left(\frac{I_0}{4}\right)\sin^2 2\theta$
(c) $\left(\frac{I_0}{2}\right)\cos^2 \theta$
(d) $I_0\cos^2 \theta$

24. Two points charges are kept in air with a separation between them. The force between them is F_1, if half of the space between the charges is filled with a dielectric constant 4 and the force between them is F_2. If $\frac{1}{3}$rd of the space between the charges is filled with dielectric of dielectric constant 9. Then $\frac{F_1}{F_2}$ is

(a) $\frac{27}{64}$ (b) $\frac{16}{81}$ (c) $\frac{81}{64}$ (d) $\frac{100}{81}$

25. A simple pendulum with a bob of mass 40g and charge +2μC makes 20 oscillation in 44 s. A vertical electric field magnitude $4.2\times10^{4}\text{NC}^{-1}$ pointing downward is applied. The time taken by the pendulum to make 15 oscillation in the electric field is (acceleration due to gravity = 10 ms^{-2})

(a) 30 s (b) 60 s (c) 90 s (d) 15 s

26. A parallel plate capacitor has a capacity 80×10^{-6} F, when air is present between its plates. The space between the plates is filled with a dielectric slab of dielectric constant 20. The capacitor is now connected to a battery of 30V by wires. The dielectric slab is then removed. Then, the charge passing through the wire is

(a) 12×10^{-3}C
(b) 25.3×10^{-3}C
(c) 120×10^{-3}C
(d) 45.6×10^{-3}C

27. Three uncharged capacitors of capacities C_1, C_2 and C_3 are connected as shown in the figure. *A*, *B* and *C* are at potentials V_1, V_2 and V_3, respectively, then the potential at *O* is

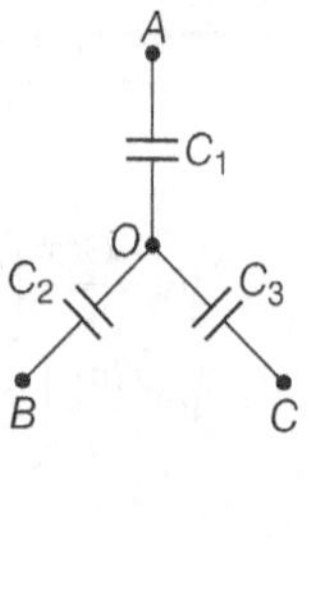

(a) $\frac{C_1V_1 + C_2V_2 + C_3V_3}{C_1 + C_2 + C_3}$

(b) $\dfrac{C_1V_1 + C_2V_2 - C_3V_3}{C_1 + C_2 + C_3}$

(c) $\dfrac{C_1V_1 - C_2V_2 - C_3V_3}{C_1 + C_2 + C_3}$

(d) zero

28. The equivalent resistance between A and B is 6 Ω. The value of R_1 is

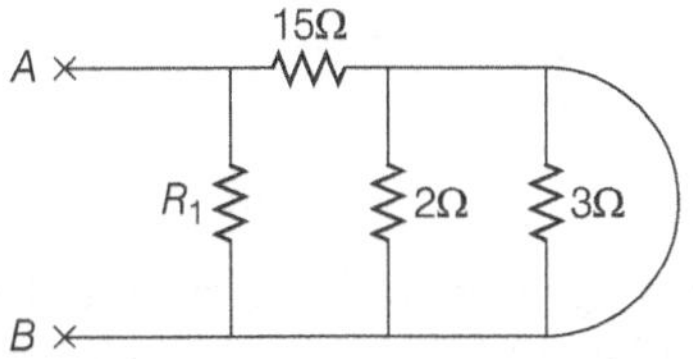

(a) 20 Ω (b) 10 Ω (c) 5 Ω (d) 25 Ω

29. A battery of emf 10 V is connected to a uniform wire AB of 1m length and having a resistance of 10 Ω in series with a 10Ω resistor as shown in the figure. Two cells of emf 2V and 3V having internal resistance 2 Ω and 3 Ω, respectively are connected as shown in the figure. If the galvanometer shows null deflection at point J on the wire, then the distance of point J from the point B is.

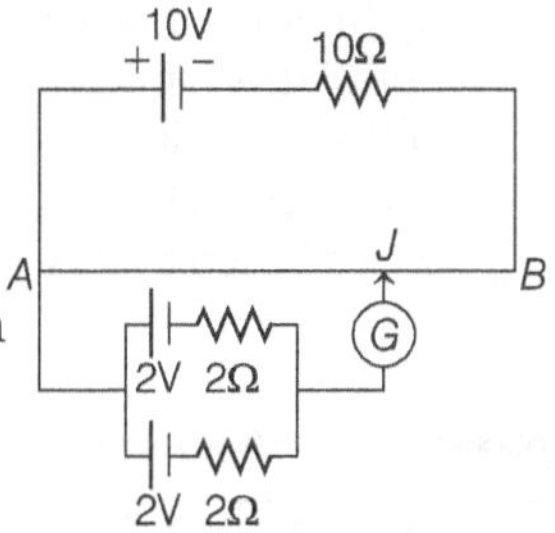

(a) 48 cm (b) 50 cm (c) 52 cm (d) 54 cm

30. Two infinitely long wires carry currents 4A and 3A placed along X-axis and Y-axis respectively. Magnetic field at a point $P(0, 0, d)$ m will be ...... T.

(a) $\dfrac{4\mu_0}{2\pi d}$ (b) $\dfrac{3\mu_0}{2\pi d}$ (c) $\dfrac{7\mu_0}{2\pi d}$ (d) $\dfrac{5\mu_0}{2\pi d}$

31. Two moving coil galvanometer, X and Y have coils with resistance 10 Ω and 14 Ω cross-sectional areas $4.8 \times 10^{-3} \text{m}^2$ and $2.4 \times 10^{-3} \text{m}^2$, number of turns 30 and 45 respectively. They are placed in magnetic field of 0.25 T and 0.50 T respectively. Then, the ratio of their current sensitivities and the ratio of their voltage sensitivities are respectively

(a) 2 : 3, 14 : 15 (b) 5 : 7, 2 : 1
(c) 2 :13, 1 : 2 (d) 14 : 15, 2 : 9

32. Two short bar magnets each of magnetic moment of 9 Am^2 are placed such that one is at $x = -3$ cm and the other at $y = -3$ cm. If their magnetic moments are directed along positive and negative X-directions respectively, then the resultant magnetic field at the origin is

(a) 100T (b) 10T (c) 0.1T (d) 0.001T

33. A conducting rod PQ of length 1 m is moving with a uniform speed 2 ms^{-1} in a uniform magnetic field of 4 T which is directed into the paper. A capacitor of capacity 10 μF is connected as shown in the figure. Then, the charge on the plates of the capacitor are

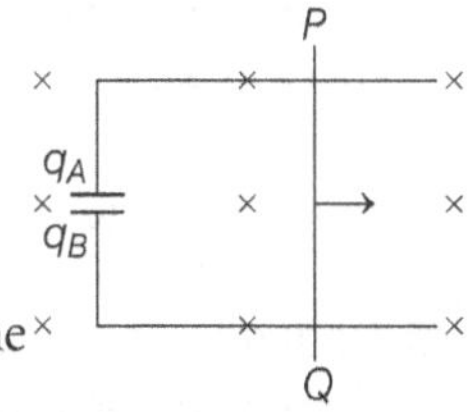

(a) $q_A = +80\,\mu\text{C}, q_B = -80\,\mu\text{C}$
(b) $q_A = -80\,\mu\text{C}, q_B = +80\,\mu\text{C}$
(c) $q_A = +1.25\,\mu\text{C}, q_B = 1.25\,\mu\text{C}$
(d) $q_A = -1.25\,\mu\text{C}, q_B = +1.25\,\mu\text{C}$

34. For the AC circuit shown below, phase difference between emf and current is $\dfrac{\pi}{4}$ radian as shown in the graph. If the impedance of the circuit is 1414 Ω,

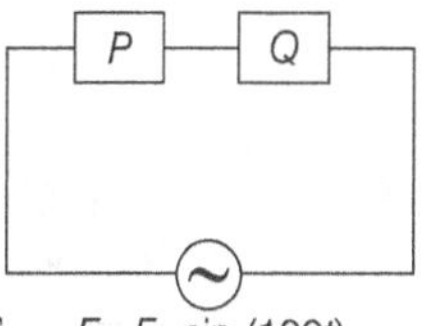

then the values of P and Q are

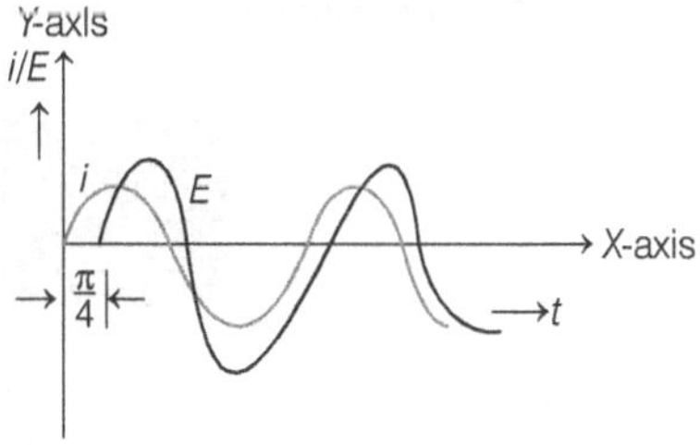

(a) 1 kΩ, 10 μF (b) 1 kΩ, 1 μF
(c) 1 kΩ, 10 mH (d) 1 kΩ, 1 mH

35. In a plane electromagnetic wave, the electric field oscillates with a frequency $2 \times 10^{10}\ \text{s}^{-1}$ and amplitude 40 Vm^{-1}, then the energy density due to electric field is
$(\varepsilon_0 = 8.85 \times 10^{-12}\ \text{Fm}^{-1})$

(a) $1.52 \times 10^{-9}\ \text{Jm}^{-3}$ (b) $2.54 \times 10^{-19}\ \text{Jm}^{-3}$
(c) $3.54 \times 10^{-9}\ \text{Jm}^{-3}$ (d) $4.56 \times 10^{-9}\ \text{Jm}^{-3}$

36. Photons of frequencies equal to the frequencies of H_β and H_∞ lines of hydrogen incident on a photosensitive plate, whose threshold frequency is equal to the frequency of H_α line of hydrogen. The ratio of the maximum kinetic energies of the emitted electrons is

(a) 7 : 16 (b) 3 : 4 (c) 8 : 27 (d) 5 : 36

37. Hydrogen atom is in its nth energy state. If de-Broglie wavelength of the electron is λ, then

(a) $\lambda \propto \frac{1}{n^2}$ (b) $\lambda \propto \frac{1}{n}$ (c) $\lambda \propto n^2$ (d) $\lambda \propto n$

38. If 200 MeV of energy is released in the fission of one nucleus of $^{235}_{92}U$, then the number of nuclei that must undergo fission to release an energy of 1000 J is

(a) 3.125×10^{13} (b) 6.25×10^{13}
(c) 12.5×10^{13} (d) 3.125×10^{14}

39. If the diodes are ideal in the circuit given below, then the current through the cell is

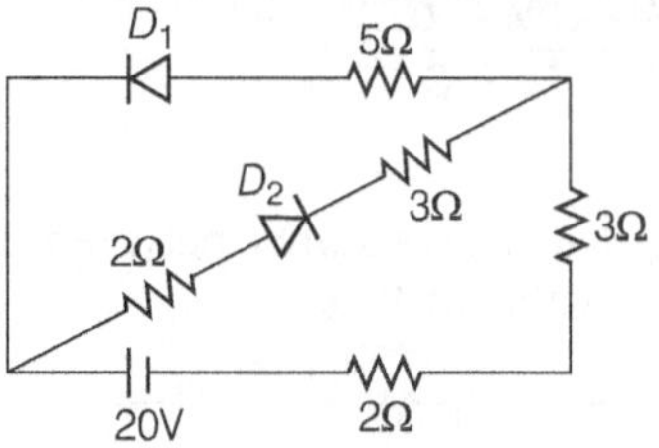

(a) 4 A (b) 1.5 A
(c) 2 A (d) 3 A

40. If a message signal of frequency 10 kHz and peak voltage 12 V is used to modulate a carrier wave of frequency 1 MHz, the modulation index is 0.6. To make the modulation index 0.75, the carrier peak voltage should be

(a) decreased by 25% (b) increased by 25%
(c) decreased by 20% (d) increased by 20%

Answers

1.	(a)	2.	(d)	3.	(c)	4.	(d)	5.	(d)	6.	(b)	7.	(a)	8.	(a)	9.	(d)	10.	(b)
11.	(a)	12.	(d)	13.	(a)	14.	(c)	15.	(b)	16.	(c)	17.	(d)	18.	(b)	19.	(a)	20.	(c)
21.	(c)	22.	(a)	23.	(a)	24.	(d)	25.	(a)	26.	(d)	27.	(a)	28.	(b)	29.	(c)	30.	(d)
31.	(a)	32.	(c)	33.	(a)	34.	(a)	35.	(c)	36.	(a)	37.	(d)	38.	(a)	39.	(c)	40.	(c)

Scan this QR code from your mobile phone to get the explanations of this paper.
Or
Visit : *http://tinyurl.com/y39t9kvx*

22 April Shift II
Session 2 (3:00 PM to 6:00 PM)

1. In a system, unit of mass is A kg, length is B m and time is C s, then the value of 10 N in this system is

(a) $10\ A^{-1}B^{-1}C^{-2}$ (b) $10\ A^{-1}B^{-1}C^{2}$
(c) $10\ ABC^{-2}$ (d) $5A^{-1}BC^{2}$

2. Assertion (A) The angle between acceleration and velocity of a body is one-dimensional motion is always zero.
Reason (R) One-dimensional motion is along a straight line.

(a) Both (A) and (R) are true and (R) is the correct explanation of (A).
(b) Both (A) and (R) are true but (R) is not the correct explanation of (A).
(c) (A) is true but (R) is false.
(d) (A) is false but (R) is true.

3. A projectile is given an initial velocity of $(\hat{i} + 2\hat{j})\ ms^{-1}$. The equation of its path is ($g = 10\ ms^{-2}$)

(a) $y = 2x - 5x^2$ (b) $y = x - 5x^2$
(c) $4y = 2x - 5x^2$ (d) $y = 2x - 25x^2$

4. A body projected with some velocity at an angle 45° with the horizontal from the origin in XY-plane passes through a point at (4, 3) m. Its horizontal range is

(a) 10 m (b) 14 m (c) 18 m (d) 16 m

5. A block of mass 10 kg is placed on a horizontal frictionless surface and is attached to a cord which passes over two light frictionless pulleys as shown in the figure. The hanging block tied to the other end of the cord is initially at rest 2 m above the horizontal floor. If the hanging block strikes the floor 2 s after the system is released, then weight of the hanging block is .... ($g = 10\ ms^{-2}$)

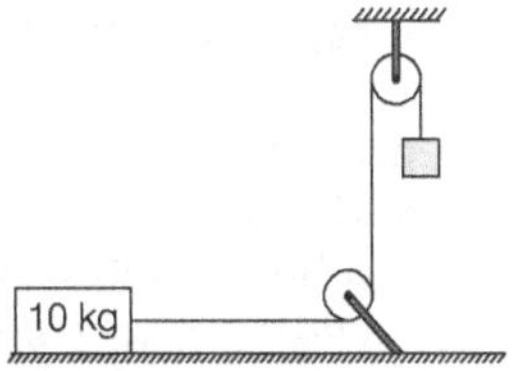

(a) 22.22 N (b) 11.11 N (c) 1.11 N (d) 2.22 N

6. A double inclined plane as shown in the figure has fixed horizontal base and smooth faces with the same angle of inclination of 30°. A block of mass 300 g is on one face and is connected by a cord passing over a frictionless pulley to a second block of mass 200 g kept on another face. The acceleration with which the system of the blocks moves is .... % of acceleration due to gravity.

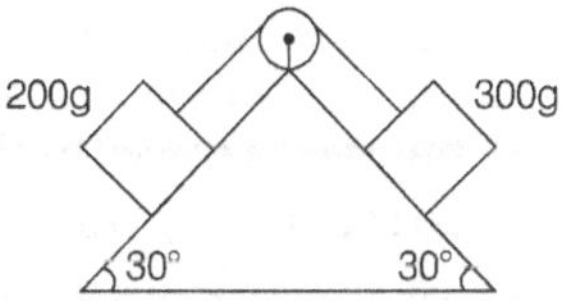

(a) 5 (b) 10 (c) 15 (d) 20

7. A canon shell fired breaks into two equal parts at its highest point. If one part retraces the path to the canon with kinetic energy E_1 and kinetic energy of the second part is E_2, then

(a) $E_2 = 15E_1$ (b) $E_2 = E_1$ (c) $E_2 = 4E_1$ (d) $E_2 = 9E_1$

8. A uniform chain of mass m and length l is on a smooth horizontal table with $\left(\frac{1}{n}\right)^{th}$ part of its length is hanging from one end of the table. The velocity of the chain, when it completely slips off the table is

(a) $\sqrt{gl\left(1-\frac{1}{n^2}\right)}$ (b) $\sqrt{2gl\left(1+\frac{1}{n^2}\right)}$

(c) $\sqrt{2gl\left(1-\frac{1}{n^2}\right)}$ (d) $\sqrt{2gl}$

9. Two particles of masses in the ratio 1 : 2 are placed along a vertical line. The lighter particle is raised through a height of 9 cm. To raise the centre of mass of the system by 2 cm, the heavier particle should be

(a) moved 1.5 cm downward
(b) moved 2 cm upward
(c) moved 1.5 cm upward
(d) moved 2 cm downward

10. A solid sphere and a ring of same radius roll down an inclined plane without slipping. Both start from rest from the top of the inclined plane. If the sphere and the ring reach the bottom of the inclined plane with velocities v_s and v_r respectively, then $\frac{v_r^2}{v_s^2}$ is

(a) 0.2 (b) 0.5 (c) 0.7 (d) 0.9

11. A particle is executing SHM. The time taken for $\left(\frac{3}{8}\right)^{th}$ of oscillation from extreme positions is x. Then, the time taken for the particle to complete $\left(\frac{5}{8}\right)^{th}$ of oscillation from mean position is

(a) $\frac{5x}{4}$ (b) $\frac{7x}{4}$ (c) $\frac{21x}{8}$ (d) $\frac{7x}{12}$

12. An object is thrown vertically upwards from the surface of the earth with a velocity x times the escape velocity on the earth ($x < 1$), then the maximum height to which its rises from the centre of the earth is (radius of earth is R)

(a) $R(1-x)^2$ (b) $\frac{R}{(1-x^2)}$ (c) $\frac{1-x^2}{R}$ (d) $\frac{x^2}{1-R}$

13. A sphere of mass 2 kg and diameter 4.5 cm is attached to the lower end of a steel wire of 2 m length and area of cross-section $0.24 \times 10^{-6}\ m^2$. The wire is suspended from 205 cm high ceiling of a room. When the system is made to oscillate as a simple pendulum, the sphere just grazes the floor at its lowest position. The velocity of the sphere at the lowest position is (Young's modulus of steel $= 2 \times 10^{11}\ Nm^{-2}$ and acceleration due to gravity $= 10\ ms^{-2}$)

(a) $10\ ms^{-1}$ (b) $12\ ms^{-1}$
(c) $15\ ms^{-1}$ (d) $18\ ms^{-1}$

14. A spherical body of density ρ is floating half immersed in a liquid of density d. If σ is the surface tension of the liquid, then the diameter of the body is

(a) $\sqrt{\frac{3\sigma}{g(2\rho - d)}}$ (b) $\sqrt{\frac{6\sigma}{g(2\rho - d)}}$

(c) $\sqrt{\frac{4\sigma}{g(2\rho - d)}}$ (d) $\sqrt{\frac{12\sigma}{g(2\rho - d)}}$

15. As shown in the figure, an equilateral triangle ABC is formed by joining three rods of equal lengths and D is the midpoint of AB. Coefficient of linear expansion of the material of AB is α_1 and that of AC and BC is α_2. If the length DC remains constant for small changes in temperature, then

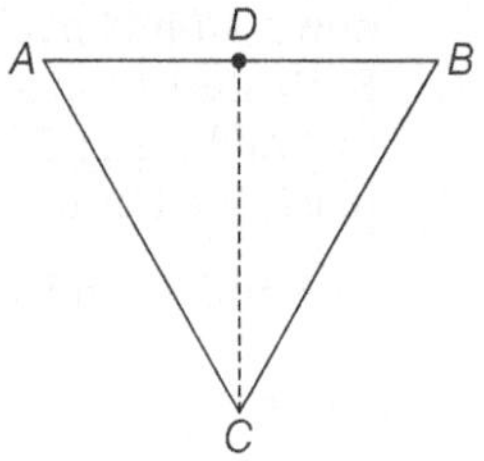

(a) $\alpha_1 = \alpha_2$ (b) $\alpha_1 = 4\alpha_2$ (c) $\alpha_2 = 4\alpha_1$ (d) $\alpha_1 = \frac{\alpha_2}{2}$

16. Match the following List I with List II.

List I	List II
A. When ice melts into water	I. Volume increases
B. When water changes into steam	II. Volume decreases
C. Melting point of ice	III. Increases with increase of pressure
D. Boiling point of water	IV. Decreases with increase in pressure

Codes

	A	B	C	D
(a)	I	II	III	IV
(b)	II	I	IV	III
(c)	III	II	IV	I
(d)	II	I	III	IV

17. A cylindrical vessel of uniform cross-section consisting of a gas of $\gamma = 1.5$ is divided into two parts A and B using a piston. Initially the piston is kept fixed such that part A has pressure p and volume $5V$ and the part B has pressure $8p$ and volume V. If the piston is let free and the gas is allowed to undergo adiabatic process, then the final volume of the gas in part A is

(a) 3 V (b) $\frac{8}{3}$ V (c) $\frac{10}{3}$ V (d) $\frac{13}{3}$ V

18. A diatomic ideal gas is used in Carnot's engine as working substance. During adiabatic expansion of the cycle, if the volume of the gas increases from V to $32V$, then the efficiency of the engine is

(a) 0.25 (b) 0.5 (c) 0.67 (d) 0.75

19. The absolute temperature at which the rms speed of a hydrogen molecule is equal to its escape speed from the moon's surface is (where, R is radius of moon is r, g is acceleration due to gravity on Moon's surface, m is mass of hydrogen molecules and k is Boltzmann constant)

(a) $\frac{mgR}{2k}$ (b) $\frac{2mgR}{k}$ (c) $\frac{3mgR}{2k}$ (d) $\frac{2mgR}{3k}$

20. An object of density 2000 kg - m^{-3} is hung from a thin light wire. The fundamental frequency of the transverse waves in the wire is 200 Hz. If the object is immersed in water such that half of its volume is submerged, then the fundamental frequency of the transverse waves in the wire is

(a) 200 Hz (b) 173.2 Hz (c) 100 Hz (d) 141.4 Hz

21. An observer and a source emitting sound of frequency 120 Hz are on the X-axis. The observer is stationary while the source of sound is in motion given by the equation $x = 3\sin\omega t$ (x is in metres and t is in seconds). If the difference between the maximum and minimum frequencies of the sound observed by the observers is 22 Hz, then the value of ω is (speed of sound in air = 330 ms^{-1})

(a) 33 rad s^{-1} (b) 36 rad s^{-1}
(c) 20 rad s^{-1} (d) 10 rad s^{-1}

22. As shown in the figure, a parallel beam of light incidents on the upper part of a prism of angle 1.8° and material of refractive index 1.5. The light emerging out from the prism falls on a concave mirror of radius of curvature 40 cm. This distance of the point from the principal axis of the mirror where the light rays are focussed after reflection from the mirror is

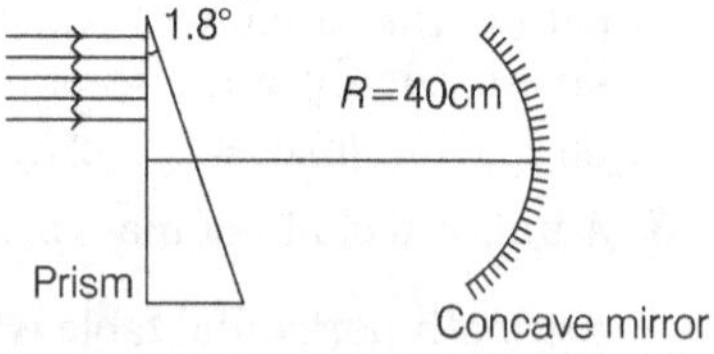

(a) 4.76 cm (b) 1.57 mm (c) 3.14 mm (d) 6.28 mm

23. A microscope has an objective of aperture 8 mm and focal length of 5 cm. The minimum separation between two objects to be just resolved by the microscope is (wavelength of light used = 5500 Å)

(a) 2.2 μm (b) 3.4 μm (c) 4.2 μm (d) 3.6 μm

24. The electric field due to a short electric dipole at a distance r on the axial line from its mid-point is x times the electric field at a distance $2r$ on the equatorial line from the mid-point of dipole. Then, the value of x is

(a) 16 (b) 9 (c) 25 (d) 36

25. A point charge q is placed at origin. Let $\mathbf{E}_A$, $\mathbf{E}_B$ and $\mathbf{E}_C$ be the electric fields at three points A (1, 2, 3), B (1, 1, – 1) and C (2, 2, 2) respectively due to the charge q. Then, the relation between them is

1. $\mathbf{E}_A \perp \mathbf{E}_B$
2. $\mathbf{E}_A \parallel \mathbf{E}_C$
3. $|\mathbf{E}_B| = 4\,|\mathbf{E}_C|$
4. $|\mathbf{E}_B| = 8\,|\mathbf{E}_C|$

(a) 1 , 4 are correct (b) 2, 4 are correct
(c) 1, 3 are correct (d) 2, 3 are correct

26. An electric dipole consists of two particle each of mass 1 kg separated by 1 m carrying charges 1 μC and – 1μC respectively. It is in equilibrium in a uniform electric field of 2×10^4 Vm^{-1}. If it is deflected by a small angle 2°, minimum time taken by it to come back again to the mean position is (in seconds)

(a) 2.5 π (b) 2 π (c) 5 π (d) 4 π

27. One plate of a parallel plate capacitor is connected to a spring as shown in the figure. The area of each plate of the capacitor is A and the distance between the plates is d, when the battery is not connected and the spring is unstretched. After connecting the battery, in the steady state the distance between the plates is 0.75 d, then the force constant of the spring is

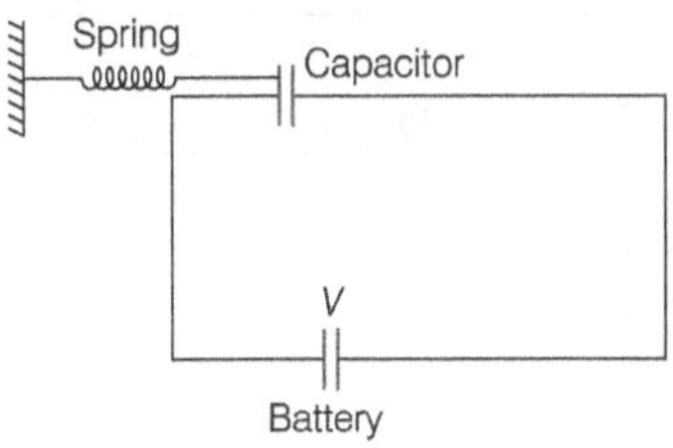

(a) $\frac{3}{8}\frac{\varepsilon_0 V^2 A}{d^3}$ (b) $\frac{8}{3}\frac{\varepsilon_0 V^2 A}{d^3}$

(c) $\frac{9}{32}\frac{\varepsilon_0 V^2 A}{d^3}$ (d) $\frac{32}{9}\frac{\varepsilon_0 V^2 A}{d^3}$

28. Two cells P and Q each of emf 2.16 V are connected in series with a resistor of 19.6 Ω. An ideal voltmeter reads 2V, when connected across the cell P and 1.92 V when connected across the cell Q. The ratio of the internal resistances of the cell P and Q is

(a) 1 : 2 (b) 2 : 3
(c) 3 : 4 (d) 1 : 3

29. A resistor has bands with colours orange, green, silver and gold. Then, the resistance of the resistor is

(a) (350± 5) m Ω (b) (350 ± 17.5) m Ω
(c) (35± 5%) m Ω (d) (250± 5%) m Ω

30. A beam of protons enters a uniform magnetic field of 0.314 T with a velocity 4×10^5 ms^{-1} in a direction making an angle 60° with the direction of the magnetic field.The path of the beam is (mass of proton = 1.6×10^{-27} kg)

(a) a circle of radius 0.2 m
(b) a straight line
(c) a helix with a pitch 4 cm
(d) a helix with a pitch 4 mm

31. The magnetic field due to a current carrying loop of radius 3 cm at a point on its axis at a distance of 4 cm from its centre of 54 μ T. Then, the value of the magnetic field at the centre of the loop is

(a) 250 μT (b) 150 μT
(c) 75 μT (d) 125 μT

32. A short bar magnet of magnetic moment 0.21 A-m^2 is placed with its axis perpendicular to the direction of the horizontal component of the earth's magnetic field. The distance of the point on the axis of the magnet from the centre of the magnet where the resultant magnetic field is inclined at 45° with the horizontal component of the earth's field direction is

(horizontal component of the earth's magnetic field = 4.2×10^{-5} T)

(a) 12 cm (b) 20 cm
(c) 5 cm (d) 10 cm

33. The length of a wire required to make a solenoid of length l and self-induction L is

(a) $\sqrt{\frac{4\pi L l}{\mu_0}}$ (b) $\sqrt{\frac{L l}{4\pi\mu_0}}$ (c) $\sqrt{\frac{2\pi L l}{\mu_0}}$ (d) $\sqrt{\frac{\mu_0 L l}{4\pi}}$

34. An inductor and a resistor are connected in series to an AC source. The current in circuit is 500 mA, if the applied AC voltage is $8\sqrt{2}$ V at a frequency of $\frac{175}{\pi}$ Hz and the current in the circuit is 400 mA, if the same AC voltage at a frequency of $\frac{225}{\pi}$ Hz is applied. The values of the inductance and the resistance are respectively

(a) 60 mH, 71 Ω (b) $\sqrt{60}$ mH, 71 Ω
(c) $\sqrt{60}$ mH, $\sqrt{71}$ Ω (d) 60 mH, $\sqrt{71}$ Ω

35. An electromagnetic wave of frequency 2 MHz propagates from vacuum to a non-magnetic medium of relative permittivity 9. Then its' wavelength

(a) increases by 100 m (b) increases by 50 m
(c) decreases by 50 mm (d) decreases by 100 m

36. The figures shows the variation of photo-current i with anode potential V for three differential radiations. Let I_a, I_b and I_c be the intensities and f_a, f_b and f_c be the frequencies for the curves a, b and c respectively. Then

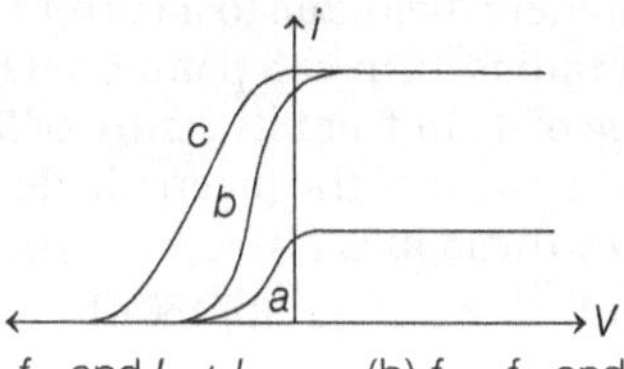

(a) $f_a = f_b$ and $I_a \neq I_b$ (b) $f_a = f_c$ and $I_a = I_c$
(c) $f_a = f_b$ and $I_a = I_b$ (d) $f_b = f_c$ and $I_b = I_c$

37. A stationary hydrogen atom undergoes a transition from $n = 5$ to $n = 4$. Recoil speed of the atom is (R = Rydberg constant, h = Planck's constant and m = mass of the proton).

(a) $\frac{Rh}{m}$ (b) $\frac{9m}{400Rh}$ (c) $\frac{9Rh}{400m}$ (d) $\frac{7Rh}{400}$

38. The half life of $^{238}_{92}U$ against α-decay is 13.86×10^{16}s. The activity of 1 g sample of $^{238}_{92}U$ is

(a) $1.26 \times 10^4\ s^{-1}$ (b) $1.26 \times 10^{-4}\ s^{-1}$
(c) $12.6 \times 10^4\ s^{-1}$ (d) $12.6 \times 10^{-4}\ s^{-1}$

39. An *n-p-n* transistor is connected in common-emitter configuration as shown in the figure. If the collector current is 5 mA, $V_{BE} = 0.6$ V, $V_{CE} = 3$ V and common-emitter current amplification factor is 50, then the values of R_1 and R_2 are respectively.

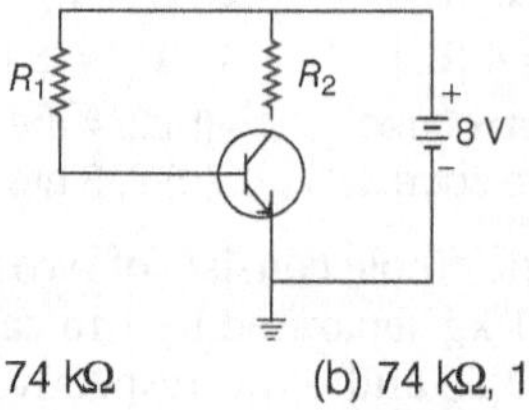

(a) 1 kΩ, 74 kΩ (b) 74 kΩ, 1 kΩ
(c) 37 kΩ, 2 kΩ (d) 2 kΩ, 37 kΩ

40. The maximum distance between the transmitting and receiving TV towers is 65 km. If the ratio of the heights of the TV transmitting tower to receiving tower is 36 : 49, the heights of the transmitting and receiving towers respectively are (radius of earth = 6400 km)

(a) 51.2 m, 80 m (b) 70.3 m, 95.7 m
(c) 30 m, 65 m (d) 25 m, 75 m

Answers

1.	(b)	2.	(d)	3.	(a)	4.	(d)	5.	(b)	6.	(b)	7.	(d)	8.	(a)	9.	(a)	10.	(c)
11.	(b)	12.	(*)	13.	(a)	14.	(a)	15.	(b)	16.	(b)	17.	(c)	18.	(d)	19.	(d)	20.	(b)
21.	(d)	22.	(b)	23.	(c)	24.	(a)	25.	(c)	26.	(a)	27.	(d)	28.	(b)	29.	(b)	30.	(c)
31.	(a)	32.	(d)	33.	(a)	34.	(d)	35.	(d)	36.	(a)	37.	(c)	38.	(a)	39.	(b)	40.	(b)

Scan this QR code from your mobile phone to get the explanations of this paper.
Or
Visit : http://tinyurl.com/yyer7j2v

23 April Shift I
Session 1 (10:00 AM to 1:00 PM)

1. **Assertion** (A) Energy per unit volume and angular momentum can be added dimensionally.
Reason (R) Physical quantities having same dimensions can be added or subtracted.
(a) Both (A) and (R) are true and (R) is the correct explanation of (A)
(b) Both (A) and (R) are true but (R) is not the correct explanation of (A)
(c) (A) is true but (R) is false
(d) (A) is false but (R) is true

2. A body is projected vertically upwards with a velocity u from the top of a tower. Time taken by it to reach the ground is n times, then the time taken by it to reach the highest point in its path. Height of the tower is
(a) $\frac{nu^2(n-1)}{2g}$ (b) $\frac{nu^2(n-2)}{g}$
(c) $\frac{nu^2(n-2)}{2g}$ (d) $\frac{u^2}{2g}(n+1)$

3. A body is projected horizontally from the top of a tower of height 180 m with a velocity of 20 ms^{-1}. If acceleration due to gravity is 10 ms^{-2}, then match the following.

List I	List II
(A) Velocity of the body after 1 second (in ms^{-1})	(I) 5
(B) Horizontal displacement of the body after 1 second (in metres)	(II) 20
(C) Vertical displacement of the body after 1 second (in metres)	(III) 10
(D) Vertical velocity of the body after 1 second (in ms^{-1})	(IV) 22.4

	A	B	C	D
(a)	IV	II	III	I
(b)	I	II	III	IV
(c)	IV	II	I	III
(d)	II	IV	I	III

4. Two towers A and B, each of height 20 m are situated a distance 200 m apart. A body thrown horizontally from the top of the tower A with a velocity 20 ms^{-1} towards the tower B hits the ground at point P and another body thrown horizontally from the top of tower B with a velocity 30 ms^{-1} towards the tower A hits the ground at point Q. If a car starting from rest from P reaches Q in 10 seconds, then the acceleration of the car is (acceleration due to gravity = 10 ms^{-2})
(a) 1 ms^{-2} (b) 2 ms^{-2} (c) 3 ms^{-2} (d) 4 ms^{-2}

5. A particle of mass $4M$ which is initially at rest explodes into three pieces of masses M, M and $2M$. The equal masses move along X and Y-axes with velocities 4 ms^{-1} and 6 ms^{-1}, respectively. The magnitude of the velocity of the heavier mass is
(a) $\sqrt{17}$ ms^{-1} (b) $2\sqrt{13}$ ms^{-1}
(c) $\sqrt{13}$ ms^{-1} (d) $\frac{\sqrt{13}}{2}$ ms^{-1}

6. As shown in the figure, two particle each of mass m tied at the ends of a light string of length $2a$ are kept on a frictionless horizontal surface. When the mid-point (P) of the string is pulled vertically upwards with a small but constant force F,the particles move towards each other on the surface. Magnitude of acceleration of each particle, when the separation between them becomes $2x$ is

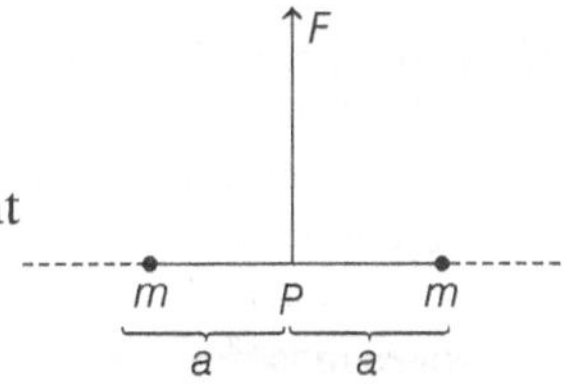

(a) $\frac{F}{2m}\frac{a}{\sqrt{a^2-x^2}}$ (b) $\frac{F}{2m}\frac{x}{\sqrt{a^2-x^2}}$
(c) $\frac{F}{2m}\frac{x}{a}$ (d) $\frac{F}{2m}\frac{\sqrt{a^2-x^2}}{x}$

7. A particle is released from a height H. At a certain height, its kinetic energy is half of its potential energy with reference to the surface of the earth. Height and speed of the particle at that instant are respectively
(a) $\frac{H}{3}, \sqrt{\frac{2gH}{3}}$ (b) $\frac{H}{3}, 2\sqrt{\frac{gH}{3}}$
(c) $\frac{2H}{3}, \sqrt{2gH}$ (d) $\frac{2H}{3}, \sqrt{\frac{2gH}{3}}$

8. A bullet of mass 10 g pierces through a plate A of mass 500 g and then gets embedded into a second plate B of mass 1.49 kg as shown in the figure. Initially, the two plates A and B are at rest and move with same velocity after collision.

The percentage loss in the initial kinetic energy of the bullet, when it is between the plates A and B is _____

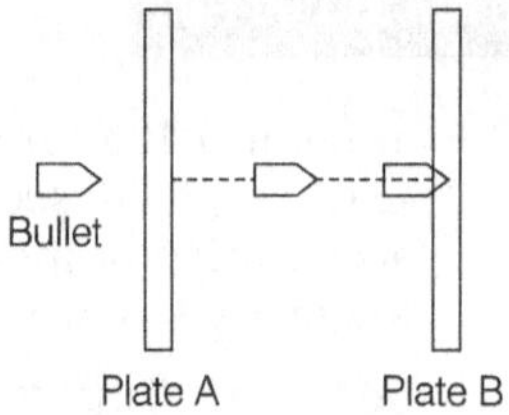

(Neglect any loss of material of the plates during the collision)

(a) 25 (b) 56.25 (c) 43.75 (d) 75

9. The moment of inertia of a body about a given axis is 12 kg-m^2. Initially, the body is at rest. In order to produce a rotational kinetic energy of 15000 J, an angular acceleration of 10 rads^{-2} must be applied about that axis for a duration of

(a) 2 s (b) 4 s (c) 10 s (d) 5 s

10. A light rope is wound around a hollow cylinder of mass 4 kg and radius 40 cm. If the rope is pulled with a force of 40 N, its angular acceleration is

(a) 0.40 rads^{-2} (b) 0.25 rads^{-2}
(c) 25 rads^{-2} (d) 40 rads^{-2}

11. In the case of a simple pendulum executing SHM at $t = 0$, the bob is not at the mean position. The graph drawn between the tension (T) in the string and time (t) is

(a)
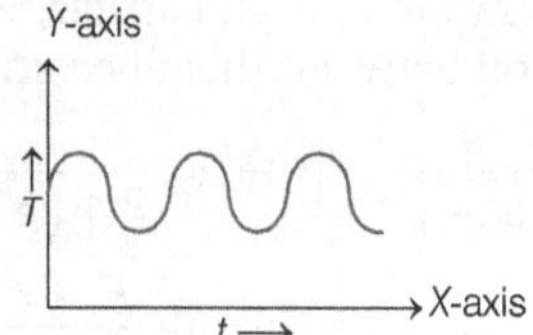

(b)
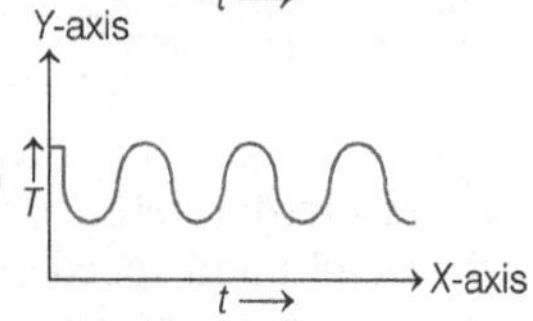

(c)
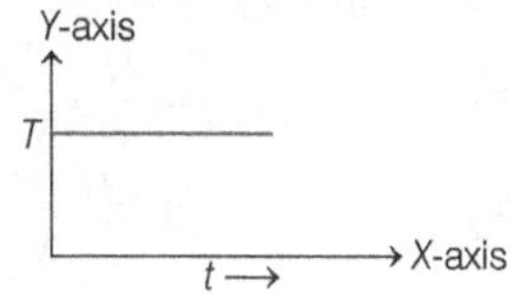

(d)
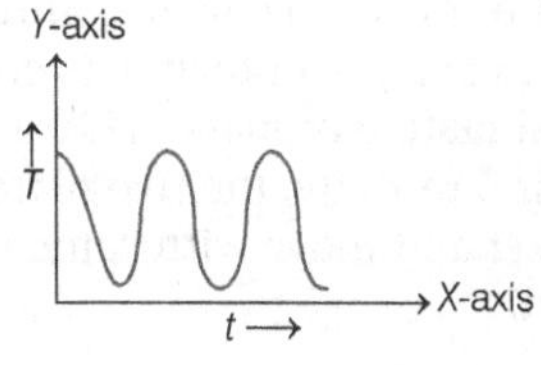

12. An artificial satellite of mass m is moving along an elliptical path around the earth. The areal velocity of the satellite is proportional to

(a) m (b) m^{-1} (c) m^0 (d) $m^{1/2}$

13. A rubber cube of side 5 cm has one face fixed, while a tangential force 1800 N is applied on its opposite face. If modulus of rigidity of rubber is 2.4×10^6 Nm^{-2}, then the lateral displacement of the strained face is _____

(a) 3 mm (b) 5 mm (c) 15 mm (d) 1.5 mm

14. Water stands upto height h behind the dam as shown in the figure. The front view of the dam gate is also shown in the adjoining figure. Density of water is ρ and acceleration due to gravity is g. If atmospheric pressure force is also considered, then the point of application of total force acting on the dam due to water above O is

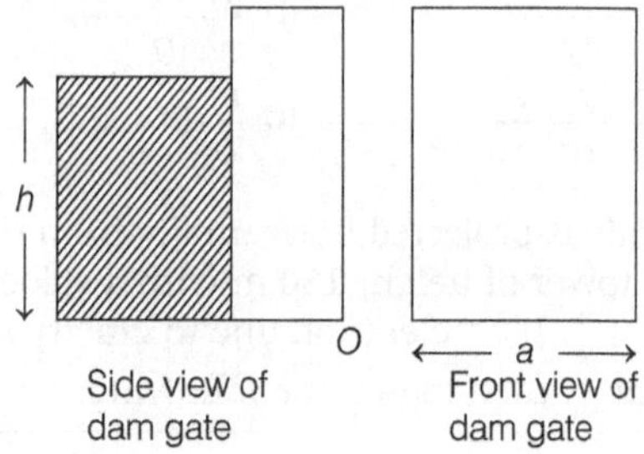

(a) $\frac{h}{4}$ (b) $\frac{h}{3}$ (c) h (d) $\frac{h}{2}$

15. The time taken for a calorimeter containing 75 g of water at 62°C to cool to 58°C is 9 minutes. When the calorimeter contains 105 g of water, it takes 12 minutes to cool from 62°C to 58°C. The water equivalent of the calorimeter is

(a) 10 g (b) 15 g (c) 20 g (d) 30 g

16. Three rods of same dimensions have thermal conductivities $3K$, $2K$ and K. They are arranged as shown in the figure below. Then in the steady state the temperature of the junction P is

(a) $\frac{200}{3}$°C (b) $\frac{100}{3}$°C (c) 75°C (d) $\frac{50}{3}$°C

17. Freezing compartment of a refrigerator is at 0°C and room temperature is 27.3°C. Work done by the refrigerator to freeze 1 g of water at 0°C is ($L_{ice} = 80$ cal g^{-1})

(a) 336 J (b) 33.6 J (c) 3.36 J (d) 40 J

18. Tyre of a bicycle has volume 2×10^{-3} m^3. Initially, the tube is filled 75% of its volume by air at atmospheric pressure 10^5 Nm^{-2}. When a rider is on the bicycle, the area of contact of tyre with road is 24×10^{-4} m^2. The mass of rider with bicycle is 120 kg. If a pump delivers a volume 500 cm^3 of air in each stroke, then the number of strokes required to inflate the tyre is ($g = 10$ ms^{-2})

(a) 10 (b) 11 (c) 21 (d) 20

19. A diatomic gas consisting of rigid molecules is at a temperature of 87°C. If the moment of inertia of the rotating diatomic rigid molecule is 2.76×10^{-39} gcm^2, then the rms angular speed of the molecule is (Boltzmann constant = 1.38×10^{-23} JK^{-1})

(a) 6×10^{12} rads^{-1} (b) 3×10^{12} rads^{-1}
(c) 6×10^{13} rads^{-1} (d) 3×10^{13} rads^{-1}

20. If the length of a stretched string is shortened by x% and the tension is increased by 44%. Then the ratio of the final and initial fundamental frequencies is 1 : 2, then the value of x is

(a) 20 (b) 30
(c) 40 (d) 60

21. A small source of sound vibrating at a frequency 500 Hz is rotated along a circle of radius $\frac{100}{\pi}$ cm at a constant angular speed of 5 revolutions per second. The minimum and maximum frequency of the sound observed by a listener situation in the plane of the circle is (speed of sound is 332 ms^{-1})

(a) 338.5 Hz, 612.5 Hz (b) 485.4 Hz, 535.6 Hz
(c) 435.3 Hz, 565.6 Hz (d) 485.4 Hz, 515.5 Hz

22. A lens forms real and virtual images of an object, when the object is at u_1 and u_2 distances respectively. If the size of the virtual image is double that of the real image, then the focal length of the lens is (take, the magnification of the real image as m)

(a) $\left(\frac{u_1 + u_2}{2}\right) m$ (b) $\left(\frac{u_1 - u_2}{3}\right) 2m$
(c) $\left(\frac{u_1 - u_2}{2}\right) 3m$ (d) $\left(\frac{u_1 + u_2}{3}\right) 2m$

23. Two point sources S_1 and S_2 separated by a distance 10 μm emit light waves of wavelength 4 μm in phase. A circular wire of radius 40 μm is placed around the sources as shown in figure, then
(O is the centre of the circle and $OS_1 = OS_2$)

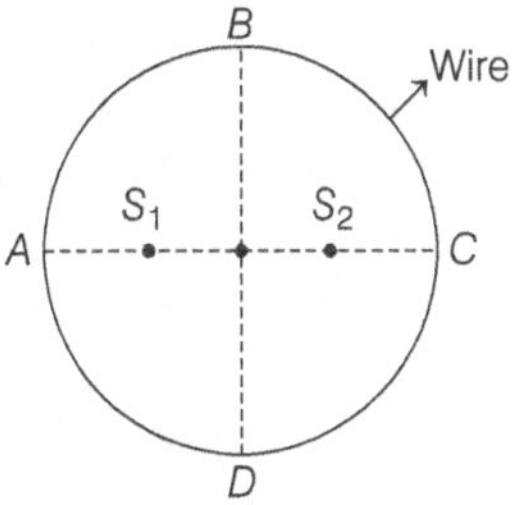

(a) points A and B are dark and points C and D are bright
(b) points A and B are bright and point C and D are dark
(c) points A and C are dark and points B and D are bright
(d) points A and C are bright and points B and D are dark

24. Two equally charged metal spheres A and B repel each other with a force of 4×10^{-5} N. Another identical uncharged sphere C is touched to A and then placed at the mid- point of the line joining the spheres A and B. The net electric force on the sphere C is

(a) 4×10^{-5} N from C to A
(b) 4×10^{-5} N from C to B
(c) 8×10^{-5} N from C to A
(d) 8×10^{-5} N from C to B

25. Four positive point charges $+q$ are kept at the four corners of a square of side l. The net electric field at the mid-point of any one side of the square is

$\left(\text{Take, } \frac{1}{4\pi\varepsilon_0} = k\right)$

(a) $\frac{4kq}{l^2}$ (b) $\frac{16kq}{5\sqrt{5}l^2}$
(c) $\frac{8kq}{\sqrt{5}l^2}$ (d) $\frac{kq}{l^2}$

26. Four capacitors marked with capacitances and breakdown voltages are connected as shown in the figure. The maximum emf of the source, so that no capacitor breaks down is

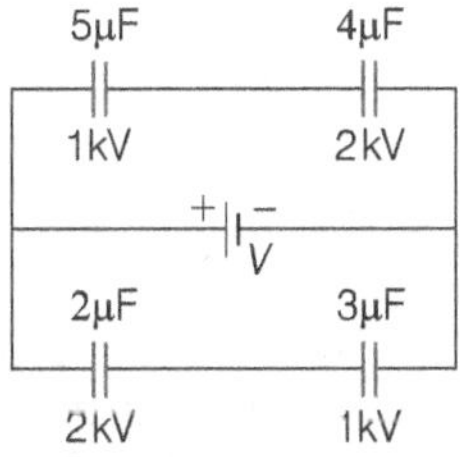

(a) 10.5 kV (b) 5.25 kV (c) 2.25 kV (d) 1.25 kV

27. A Van de Graaff generator has a spherical metal shell as an electrode which is at a potential 15×10^6 V. If the dielectric strength of the surrounding medium is 5×10^7 Vm^{-1}, then the diameter of the shell is

(a) 30 cm (b) 15 cm (c) 60 cm (d) 120 cm

28. A DC source with internal resistance R_0 is connected to three identical resistors each of resistance R as shown in the figure. If the thermal power generated in the circuit is highest, then

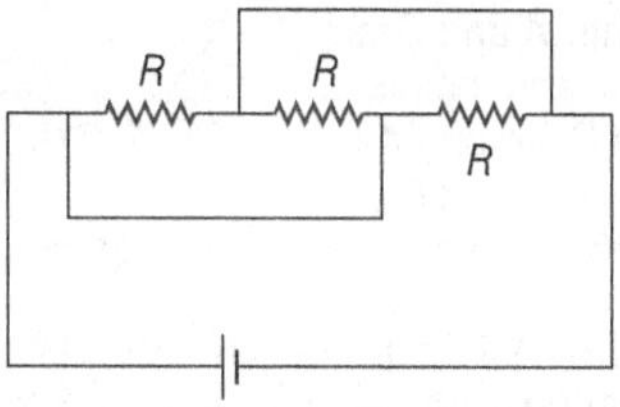

(a) $R = 2R_0$ (b) $R = 3R_0$

(c) $R = \frac{R_0}{3}$ (d) $R = R_0$

29. In a potentiometer, a wire of length 10 m having resistance 50 Ω is used. A battery of 5 V and a resistor of 450 Ω are connected in series to the wire. If an unknown battery of emf E balances the potentiometer at 450 cm, then the value of E is

(a) 0.225 V (b) 1.25 V (c) 2.25 V (d) 0.0225 V

30. A long straight wire carrying electric current i is bent at its mid-point to form an angle of 45° as shown in the figure. Magnetic field at a point P at a distance d from the point Q of bending is

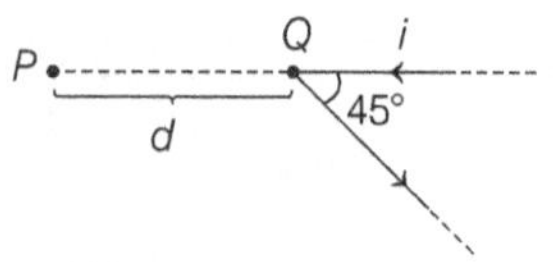

(a) $\frac{\mu_0 i}{4\pi d}[\sqrt{2} - 1]$ (b) $\frac{\mu_0 i}{2\pi d}[\sqrt{2} - 1]$

(c) $\frac{\mu_0 i}{4\pi d}$ (d) $\frac{\mu_0 i}{2\pi d}$

31. A current carrying square loop is placed near a straight infinitely long current carrying wire as shown in the figure. The torque acting on the loop is

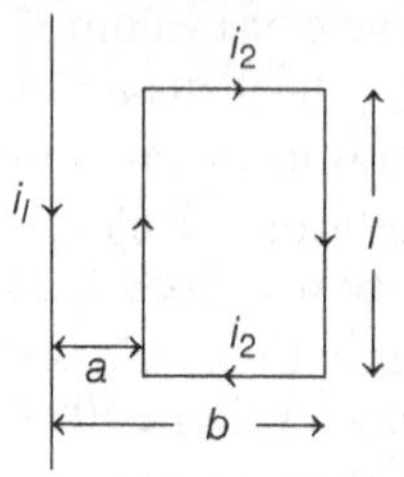

(a) $\frac{\mu_0}{2\pi}\frac{i_1 i_2 l}{ab}$ (b) $\frac{\mu_0}{2\pi}\frac{i_1 i_2 l}{a(a+b)}$

(c) $\frac{\mu_0}{2\pi}\frac{i_1 i_2 l(b-a)}{ab}$ (d) 0

32. At a certain place, the horizontal component of earth's magnetic field is $\frac{1}{\sqrt{3}}$ times the vertical component. The angle of dip at that place is

(a) 30° (b) 45° (c) 60° (d) 90°

33. The energies required to set up in a cube of side 10 cm

(i) a uniform electric field of 10^7 Vm^{-1} and

(ii) a uniform magnetic field of 0.25 Wbm^{-2}

are respectively about

($\mu_0 = 4\pi \times 10^{-7}$ Hm^{-1}, $\varepsilon_0 = 8.9 \times 10^{-12}$ Fm^{-1})

(a) 0.445 J, 25 J (b) 4.45 J, 2.5 J

(c) 44.5 J, 25 J (d) 0.44 J, 2.5 J

34. The rms value of emf is given by $E = (8 \sin \omega t + 6 \cos \omega t)$ volt is

(a) $5\sqrt{2}$ V (b) $7\sqrt{2}$ V

(c) 10 V (d) $10\sqrt{2}$ V

35. An electromagnetic radiation has an energy 14.4 keV. To which region of the electromagnetic spectrum it belongs?

(a) Infrared (b) Visible

(c) Ultraviolet (d) X-ray

36. An α-particle and a proton are accelerated from rest by the same potential, then the ratio of their de-Broglie wavelength is

(a) $2\sqrt{2} : 1$ (b) $1 : 2\sqrt{2}$

(c) 1 : 2 (d) 2 : 1

37. The difference between the radii of nth and $(n+1)^{th}$ orbits of hydrogen atom is equal to the radius of $(n-1)^{th}$ orbit of hydrogen.

The angular momentum of the electron in the nth orbit is ______ (h is Planck's constant).

(a) $\frac{h}{\pi}$ (b) $\frac{2h}{\pi}$ (c) $\frac{3h}{\pi}$ (d) $\frac{4h}{\pi}$

38. The maximum potential energy due to electrostatic repulsion between two hydrogen nuclei is nearly (radius of the nucleus $= 1.1$ fermi) $\left[\frac{1}{4\pi\varepsilon_0} = 9 \times 10^9 \text{ Nm}^2\text{C}^{-2}\right]$

(a) 0.65 MeV (b) 2.09 MeV
(c) 3.31 MeV (d) 0.92 MeV

39. For the combination of logic gates shown in the figure, the equivalent logic gate is

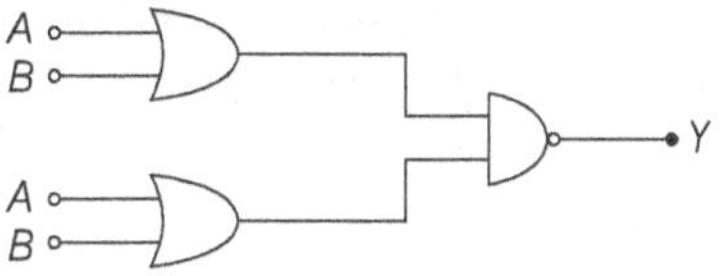

(a) AND (b) NOT (c) NAND (d) NOR

40. A TV transmitter has a range of 50 km. The height of the TV transmitter is ______ (Radius of the earth, $R_e = 6 \cdot 4 \times 10^6$ m)

(a) 195.3 m (b) 186.5 m (c) 206 m (d) 175 m

Answers

1.	(d)	2.	(c)	3.	(c)	4.	(b)	5.	(c)	6.	(b)	7.	(d)	8.	(c)	9.	(d)	10.	(c)
11.	(a)	12.	(c)	13.	(c)	14.	(b)	15.	(b)	16.	(a)	17.	(b)	18.	(c)	19.	(a)	20.	(c)
21.	(d)	22.	(c)	23.	(c)	24.	(a)	25.	(b)	26.	(c)	27.	(c)	28.	(b)	29.	(a)	30.	(a)
31.	(d)	32.	(c)	33.	(a)	34.	(a)	35.	(d)	36.	(b)	37.	(b)	38.	(a)	39.	(d)	40.	(a)

Scan this QR code from your mobile phone to get the explanations of this paper.
Or
Visit : http://tinyurl.com/y6c7bwo9

23 April Shift II
Session 2 (3:00 PM to 6:00 PM)

1. Match the measurements given in List I with the number of significant figures given in List II.

	List I	List II
(A)	74.083	I. 3
(B)	0.029	II. 4
(C)	0.002407	III. 2
(D)	2.74×10^7	IV. 5

The correct answer is

	A	B	C	D
(a)	IV	II	III	I
(b)	IV	III	II	I
(c)	III	IV	II	I
(d)	I	II	III	IV

2. The velocity- displacement (v-s) graph shows the motion of particle moving in a straight line. Velocity-displacement graph is a circle of radius 2 m and centre is at (2, 0) m.

The value of acceleration for this particle at a point $(2 - \sqrt{2}, \sqrt{2})$ m will be ....ms^{-2}.

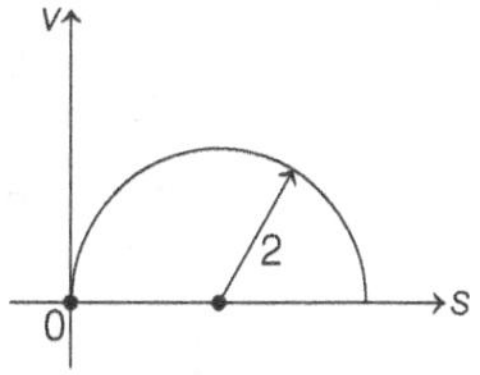

(a) $\sqrt{2}$ (b) 4 (c) 2 (d) 3

3. A body is projected horizontally from the top of a tall tower with a velocity of 30 ms^{-1}. At time t_1, its horizontal and vertical components of the velocity are equal and at time t_2, its horizontal and vertical displacements are equal. Then $t_2 - t_1$ is (take, $g = 10 \text{ ms}^{-2}$)

(a) 1 s (b) 1.5 s
(c) 2 s (d) 3 s

4. A particle is projected at an angle of 60° with the horizontal from the ground with a velocity $10\sqrt{3}\ \text{ms}^{-1}$. The angle between velocity vector after 2s and initial velocity vector is ($g = 10\ \text{ms}^{-2}$)

(a) 0° (b) 30° (c) 60° (d) 90°

5. A bead of mass 100 g is attached to one end of a spring of natural length L and spring constant $k = \dfrac{(\sqrt{3}+1)mg}{L}$, where m is the mass of bead. The other end of the spring is fixed at point A on a smooth vertical ring of radius R as shown in the figure. The normal reaction at B just after it is released to move is (take, $g = 9.8\ \text{ms}^{-2}$)

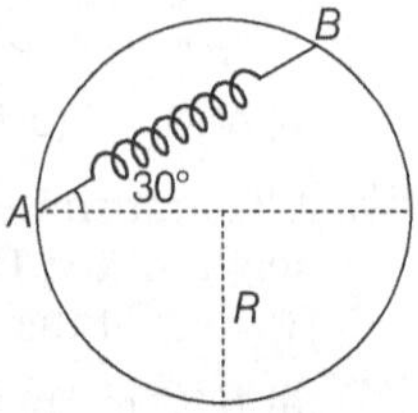

(a) 1.73 N (b) 2.23 N (c) 2.44 N (d) 2.55 N

6. A rocket with an initial mass m_0 is going up with a constant acceleration a by exhausting gases with a velocity v relative to the rocket motion, then the mass of the rocket at any instant of time is (assume that no other forces act on it)

(a) $m = m_0 e^{-\frac{at}{v}}$ (b) $m = m_0 e^{-\frac{2at}{v}}$

(c) $m = m_0 e^{-\frac{at}{2v}}$ (d) $m = m_0 e^{-\frac{a^2t^2}{v^2}}$

7. A particle is released freely from a height H. At a certain height, its kinetic energy is two times of its potential energy. Then, the height and the speed of the particle at that instant are respectively (g = acceleration due to gravity)

(a) $\dfrac{H}{3}, \sqrt{\dfrac{2gH}{3}}$ (b) $\dfrac{H}{3}, 2\sqrt{\dfrac{gH}{3}}$

(c) $\dfrac{2H}{3}, \sqrt{\dfrac{2gH}{3}}$ (d) $\dfrac{H}{3}, \sqrt{2gH}$

8. A uniform chain of length l and mass m lies on the surface of a smooth hemisphere of radius $R(R > l)$ with one end tied to the top of the hemisphere as shown in the figure. Gravitational potential energy of the chain with respect to the base of the hemisphere is

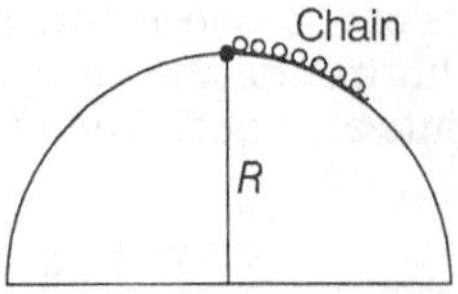

(a) $\dfrac{mgl}{2}$ (b) $\dfrac{mgR^2}{l}\sin\left(\dfrac{l}{R}\right)$

(c) $\dfrac{mgR^2}{l}\sin\left(\dfrac{R}{l}\right)$ (d) $\dfrac{mgl^2}{R}\sin\left(\dfrac{l}{R}\right)$

9. A particle of mass 15 kg is moving with a uniform speed 8ms^{-1} in xy-plane along the line $3y = 4x + 10$, then the magnitude of its angular momentum about the origin in kg-m^2s^{-1} is ... $\left(\sin 53^\circ = \dfrac{4}{5}\right)$

(a) 240 (b) 80 (c) 120 (d) 280

10. An empty bucket of mass 1 kg attached by a light cord passed over a pulley of a water well is released from rest. If the pulley assembly is assumed to be a uniform solid cylinder of mass 8 kg and free to rotate about its axis without any friction, then the speed of the bucket as it hits the water 16 m below is (take, $g = 10\ \text{ms}^{-2}$)

(a) $4\ \text{ms}^{-1}$ (b) $8\ \text{ms}^{-1}$ (c) $16\ \text{ms}^{-1}$ (d) $20\ \text{ms}^{-1}$

11. The displacement of a particle of mass 2 g executing SHM is given by $y = 5\sin\left(4t + \dfrac{\pi}{3}\right)$.Here, y is in metres and t is in seconds. The kinetic energy of the particle, when $t = \dfrac{T}{4}$ is

(a) 0.4 J (b) 0.5 J (c) 3 J (d) 0.3 J

12. Two bodies of equal masses are some distance apart. If 20% of mass is transferred from the first body to the second body, then the gravitational force between them

(a) increases by 4% (b) increases by 14%

(c) decreases by 4% (d) decreases by 14%

13. One end of a long metallic wire of length L, area of cross-section A and Young's modulus Y is tied to the ceiling. The other end is tied to a massless spring of force constant k and a mass m is hung from the free end of the spring. If m is slightly pulled down and released, then its time period of oscillation is

(a) $2\pi\sqrt{\dfrac{m}{k}}$ (b) $2\pi\sqrt{\dfrac{mYA}{kL}}$

(c) $2\pi\sqrt{\dfrac{m(kA+YL)}{kYA}}$ (d) $2\pi\sqrt{\dfrac{m(kL+YA)}{kYA}}$

14. Two solid sphere of radii 2 mm and 4 mm are tied to the two ends of a light string and released in a liquid of specific gravity 1.3 and coefficient of viscosity 1 Pa-s. The string is just taut, when the two spheres are completely in the liquid. If the density of the materials of the two sphere is 2800 kgm^{-3}, then the terminal velocity of the system of the sphere is (take, $g = 10\,ms^{-2}$)

(a) 2 cms^{-1} (b) 4 cms^{-1} (c) 4 ms^{-1} (d) 2 ms^{-1}

15. **Assertion** (A) A room can be cooled by opening the door of a refrigerator in it.

Reason (R) Heat always flows from a body at higher temperature to a body at lower temperature.

(a) (A) and (R) are true and R is the correct explanation of (A).
(b) (A), (R) are true and (R) is not the correct explanation of (A).
(c) (A) is true but (R) is false
(d) (A) is false but (R) is true.

16. A wire of 20 Ω is immersed in ice. If 10 A current is passed through this wire for 1 minute, ice completely melts. The mass of the ice is nearly ($L_{ice} = 79.7\,calg^{-1}$)

(a) 3.5 g (b) 359 g (c) 540 g (d) 3.5 kg

17. A graph drawn between absolute temperature and volume of 3 moles of helium gas as shown in the figure. If 5 cal of heat is used in the process, then the work done is

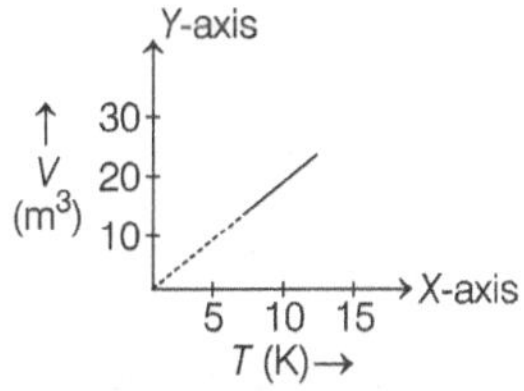

(a) 21.0 J (b) 8.4 J (c) 12.6 J (d) 6.2 J

18. An ideal gas is found to obey $pV^{\frac{3}{2}}$ = constant during an adiabatic process. If such a gas initially at a temperature T is adiabatically compressed to half of its initial volume, then its final temperature is

(a) $\sqrt{2}\,T$ (b) $2T$ (c) $2\sqrt{2}T$ (d) $4T$

19. The rms speed of oxygen molecule at a certain temperature is 600 ms^{-1}. If the temperature is doubled and oxygen molecule dissociates into atomic oxygen atoms, the new rms speed is

(a) 120 ms^{-1} (b) 150 ms^{-1}
(c) 1200 ms^{-1} (d) 600 ms^{-1}

20. A progressive wave of frequency 500 Hz is travelling with a velocity of 360 ms^{-1}. The distance between the two points, having a phase difference of 60° is ....

(a) 1.2 m (b) 12 m (c) 0.12 m (d) 0.012 m

21. A source S emitting sound of frequency 288 Hz is fixed on block B which is attached to the free end of a spring S_2 and an observer O is on block A which is attached to the free end of spring S_1 as shown in the figure. The blocks A and B are simultaneously displaced towards each other through a distance of 0.5 m and then left to oscillate. If the angular velocity of each blocks is 40 rad s^{-1}, then the maximum frequency observed by the observer is (speed of sound in air is 340 ms^{-1})

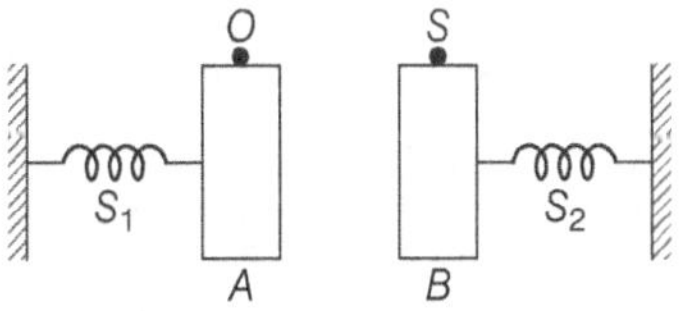

(a) 288 Hz (b) 310 Hz (c) 324 Hz (d) 256 Hz

22. In a compound microscope, the focal lengths of two lenses are 1.5 cm and 6.25 cm. An object is placed at 2 cm from the objective and the final image is formed at 25 cm from the eye lens. The distance between the two lenses is .... (in cm).

(a) 6 (b) 7.75 (c) 9.25 (d) 11

23. In Young's double slit experiment of central fringe is I_0 and fringe width is β. If a point is at a distance x from the central fringe, then the intensity at that point is

(a) $I_0 \cos^2\left(\frac{\pi x}{\beta}\right)$ (b) $I_0 \cos^2\left(\frac{x}{\beta}\right)$
(c) $\frac{I_0}{4} \cos^2\left(\frac{\pi x}{\beta}\right)$ (d) $I_0 \cos^2\left(\frac{\pi \beta}{x}\right)$

24. A proton and an α-particle start from rest in a uniform electric field. The ratio of times taken by them to travel the same distance in the field is

(a) $\sqrt{5} : \sqrt{2}$ (b) $\sqrt{3} : 1$ (c) 2 : 1 (d) 1 : $\sqrt{2}$

25. Two charged balls moving in the same direction with same velocity v are placed in an electric field. After some time, one ball moves with velocity $\frac{v}{2}$ at an angle of 60° with the initial direction and the other ball moves at right angles to the initial direction with a velocity v'. Then, the value of v' is

(a) $\frac{v}{\sqrt{2}}$ (b) $\frac{v}{\sqrt{3}}$ (c) $\frac{v}{2}$ (d) v

26. Electric field vector in a region is given by $\mathbf{E} = (3\hat{\mathbf{i}} + 4y\hat{\mathbf{j}})\,V\text{-}m^{-1}$. The potential at the origin is zero. Then, the potential at a point (2, 1) m is

(a) 7 V (b) 8 V (c) −8 V (d) −7 V

27. In the circuit shown in figure, if the point R is earthed and point P is given a potential of $+1800$ V, then charges on C_2 and C_3 are respectively

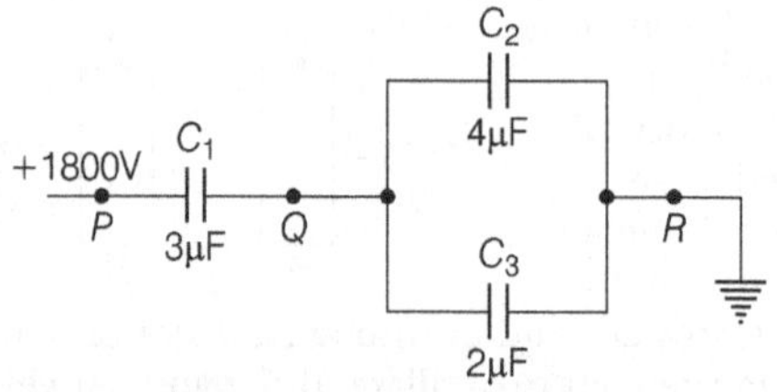

(a) 2.4×10^{-3} C ; 1.2×10^{-3} C
(b) 1.6×10^{-3} C ; 0.8×10^{-3} C
(c) 3.2×10^{-3} C ; 1.6×10^{-3} C
(d) 4.8×10^{-3} C; 2.4×10^{-3} C

28. The bulb which glows with maximum intensity in the given circuit is

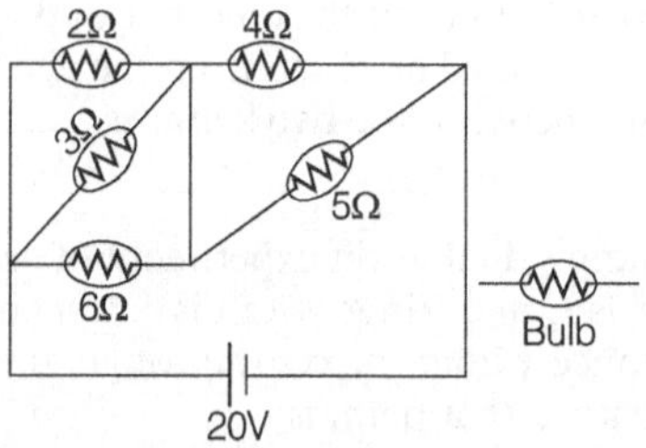

(a) 4 Ω bulb (b) 2 Ω bulb (c) 3 Ω bulb (d) 6 Ω bulb

29. In the circuit shown in figure, power developed across 1 Ω, 2 Ω and 3 Ω resistances are in the ratio.

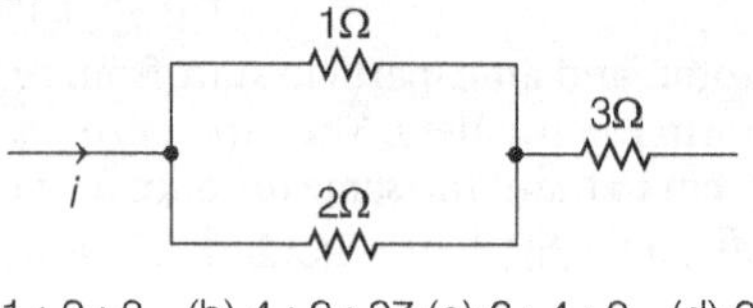

(a) 1 : 2 : 3 (b) 4 : 2 : 27 (c) 6 : 4 : 9 (d) 2 : 1 : 27

30. Two long straight parallel conductors are carrying currents i_1 and i_2 in the same direction. Work done per unit length, when the distance between them is doubled is

(a) $2 \times \frac{\mu_0}{2\pi} i_1 i_2$ (b) $\frac{\mu_0}{2\pi} i_1 i_2 \ln[2]$

(c) $\frac{\mu_0}{2\pi} i_1 i_2 \ln[4]$ (d) 0

31. A straight conductor of length 32 cm carries a current of 30 A. Magnetic induction at a point in air at a perpendicular distance of 12 cm from the mid-point of the conductor is

(a) 0.2 G (b) 0.3 G (c) 0.4 G (d) 0.5 G

32. A sample of a paramagnetic salt containing 3×10^{24} atomic dipoles each of dipole moment 2×10^{-23} A-m^2 is subjected to a uniform magnetic field of 880 mT and cooled to a temperature of 3.5 K. The degree of magnetic saturation achieved is 10%. If the sample is subjected to a magnetic field of 990 mT and cooled to a temperature of 2.1 K, then the total dipole moment of the sample is

(a) 11.25 A-m^2 (b) 23.5 A-m^2
(c) 15 A-m^2 (d) 75 A-m^2

33. A coil of wire of radius r has 600 turns and self inductance of 108 mH. The self inductance of a coil with same radius and 500 turns is

(a) 80 mH (b) 75 mH
(c) 108 mH (d) 90 mH

34. In the AC circuit shown, $E = E_0 \sin(\omega t + \phi)$ and $i = i_0 \sin\left(\omega t + \phi + \frac{\pi}{4}\right)$. Then, the box contains

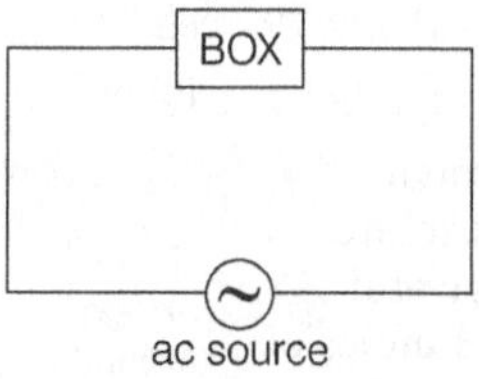

(a) Only C
(b) L and R in series
(c) C and R in series or L, C and R in series
(d) Only R

35. The oscillating electric field of an electromagnetic wave is given by $E_y = 30\sin(2 \times 10^{11} t + 300\pi x)\text{Vm}^{-1}$. Then, the value of wavelength of the electromagnetic wave is

(a) 5.67×10^{-3} m (b) 6.67×10^{-3} m
(c) 66.7×10^{-3} m (d) 7.66×10^{-3} m

36. Photons of wavelength λ emitted by a source of power P incident on a photo cell. If the current produced in the cell is I, then the percentage of incident photons which produce current in the photo cell is. (where, h is Planck's constant and c is the speed of light in vacuum)

(a) $\frac{100ePc}{Ih\lambda}$ (b) $\frac{100eP\lambda}{Ihc}$ (c) $\frac{100Ih\lambda}{ePc}$ (d) $\frac{100Ihc}{eP\lambda}$

37. If λ_1 and λ_2 are the wavelength of the photons emitted, when electrons in the nth orbit of hydrogen atom fall to first excited state and ground state respectively, then the value of n is

(a) $\sqrt{\frac{2(\lambda_2 - \lambda_1)}{2\lambda_2 - \lambda_1}}$ (b) $\sqrt{\frac{2\lambda_2 - \lambda_1}{2(\lambda_2 - \lambda_1)}}$

(c) $\sqrt{\frac{4\lambda_2 - \lambda_1}{4(\lambda_2 - \lambda_1)}}$ (d) $\sqrt{\frac{4(\lambda_2 - \lambda_1)}{(4\lambda_2 - \lambda_1)}}$

38. The number of half lives elapsed before 93.75% of a radioactive sample has decayed is

(a) 6 (b) 4
(c) 2 (d) 8

39. In the common-base configuration, a transistor has current amplification factor 0.95. If the transistor is used in common-emitter configuration and base current changes by 2 μA, then the change in the collector current is

(a) 19 μA (b) 0.91 μA (c) 1.9 μA (d) 38 μA

40. If the height of the transmitting tower is increased by 30%, then the area covered by it increases by

(a) 10% (b) 21% (c) 30% (d) 60%

Answers

1.	(b)	2.	(a)	3.	(d)	4.	(d)	5.	(d)	6.	(a)	7.	(b)	8.	(b)	9.	(a)	10.	(b)
11.	(d)	12.	(c)	13.	(d)	14.	(b)	15.	(d)	16.	(b)	17.	(b)	18.	(a)	19.	(c)	20.	(c)
21.	(c)	22.	(d)	23.	(a)	24.	(d)	25.	(*)	26.	(c)	27.	(a)	28.	(a)	29.	(b)	30.	(b)
31.	(c)	32.	(a)	33.	(b)	34.	(c)	35.	(b)	36.	(d)	37.	(d)	38.	(b)	39.	(d)	40.	(c)

Scan this QR code from your mobile phone to get the explanations of this paper.
Or
Visit : *http://tinyurl.com/y4zoxsbg*

24 April Shift I
Session 1 (10:00 AM to 1:00 PM)

1. If A represents Boltzmann constant, B represents Planck's constant and C represents speed of light in vacuum, then the quantity having the dimensions of $A^4B^{-3}C^{-2}$ is

(a) universal gas constant (b) specific heat capacity
(c) stefan's constant (d) heat energy

2. The motion of a particle along a straight line is described by the function, $x = (2t - 3)^2$ where x is in metres and t is in seconds. The acceleration of the particle at $t = 2$ s is

(a) 1 ms^{-2} (b) 4 ms^{-2} (c) 8 ms^{-2} (d) 7 ms^{-2}

3. A particle moves in the xy- plane with velocity $\mathbf{v} = x\hat{\mathbf{i}} + yt\hat{\mathbf{j}}$. At $t = \frac{x\sqrt{3}}{y}$, the magnitudes of tangential and normal accelerations, respectively are

(a) $\frac{\sqrt{3}y}{2}, \frac{y}{2}$ (b) $\frac{\sqrt{2}y}{3}, \frac{\sqrt{3}y}{2}$

(c) $\frac{\sqrt{3}y}{2}, \frac{5y}{2}$ (d) $2\sqrt{3}y, \frac{11y}{\sqrt{3}}$

4. Assertion (A) The speed of a body in uniform circular motion is constant.

Reason (R) In uniform circular motion, the acceleration of the body is constant.

(a) Both (A) and (R) are true and (R) is the correct explanation of (A).
(b) Both (A) and (R) are true but (R) is not the correct explanation of (A).
(c) (A) is true but (R) is false.
(d) (A) is false but (R) is true.

5. One end of a light string is fixed to a clamp on the ground and the other end passes over a fixed frictionless pulley as shown in the figure. It makes an angle of 30° with the ground. The clamp can tolerate a vertical force of 40 N. If a monkey of mass 5 kg were to climb up the rope, then the maximum acceleration in the upward direction with

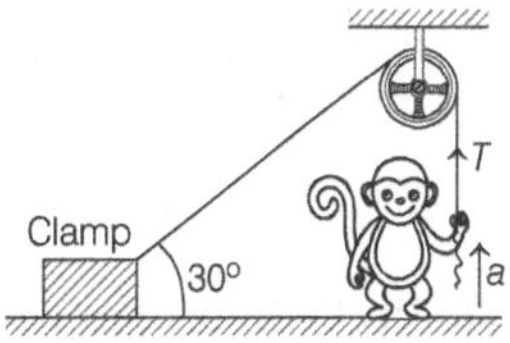

which it can climb safely is ($g = 10\ ms^{-2}$)

(a) $2\ ms^{-2}$ (b) $4\ ms^{-2}$ (c) $6\ ms^{-2}$ (d) $8\ ms^{-2}$

6. In the arrangement shown in the figure, if the blocks of masses m and $2m$ are released from the state of rest, tension in the string is (μ = coefficient of friction, string is massless and inextensible, pulley is frictionless)

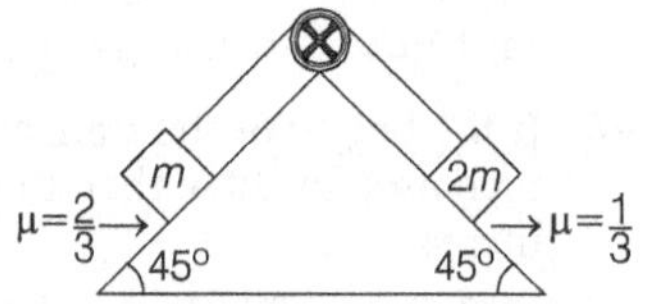

(a) mg (b) $\sqrt{2}\ mg$ (c) $\frac{2\sqrt{2}mg}{3}$ (d) $\frac{\sqrt{2}mg}{3}$

7. A stone of mass 2 kg tied to a light inextensible string of length $\frac{5}{3}$ m is whirling in a circular path in a vertical plane. If the ratio of the maximum tension to the minimum tension in the string is 4, then the speed of the stone at the highest point of the circle is ($g = 10\ ms^{-2}$)

(a) $20\ ms^{-1}$ (b) $10\sqrt{3}\ ms^{-1}$ (c) $\sqrt{50}\ ms^{-1}$ (d) $10\ ms^{-1}$

8. A ball falls freely from a height of 180 m on to a hard horizontal floor and repeatedly bounces. If the coefficient of restitution is 0.5, the average speed and average velocity of the ball before it ceases to rebound are respectively
(acceleration due to gravity = $10\ ms^{-2}$)

(a) $10\ ms^{-1}$, $10\ ms^{-1}$ (b) $50\ ms^{-1}$, $\frac{50}{3}\ ms^{-1}$

(c) $\frac{50}{3}\ ms^{-1}$, $10\ ms^{-1}$ (d) $\frac{20}{3}\ ms^{-1}$, $\frac{50}{3}\ ms^{-1}$

9. A circular disc of radius R is removed from one end of a bigger circular disc of radius $2R$. The centre of mass of the new disc is at a distance αR from the centre of the bigger disc. The value of α is

(a) $\frac{1}{2}$ (b) $\frac{1}{3}$ (c) $\frac{1}{4}$ (d) $\frac{1}{6}$

10. In the figure shown, acceleration with which the mass m falls down when released is (consider the string to be massless, g-acceleration due to gravity)

(a) $\frac{2g}{3}$ (b) $\frac{g}{2}$ (c) $\frac{5g}{6}$ (d) g

11. At $t = 0$, a particle executing SHM with a time period 3 s is in phase with another particle executing SHM. The time period of the second particle is T (less than 3 s). If they are again in the same phase for the third time after 45 s, then the value of T is .... .

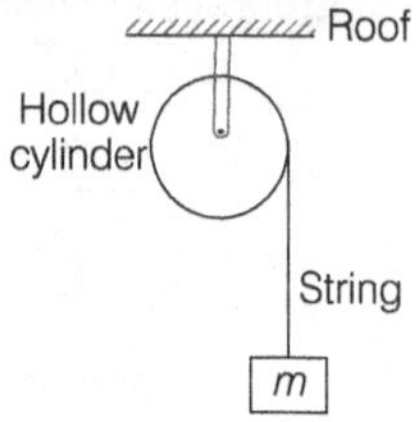

(a) 1 s (b) 1.5 s (c) 2 s (d) 2.5 s

12. A body is projected vertically upwards from the surface of the earth with a velocity sufficient to carry it to infinity. The time taken by it to reach a height of three times the radius of the earth is
(acceleration due to gravity = $9.8\ ms^{-2}$ and radius of the earth = 6400 km)

(a) 44.44 min (b) 22.22 min
(c) 18.76 min (d) 37.52 min

13. A copper wire of cross-sectional area 0.01 cm^2 is under a tension of 22 N. The decrease in the cross-sectional area is
(Young modulus = $1.1 \times 10^{11}\ Nm^{-2}$, Poisson's ratio = 0.32)

(a) $0.128 \times 10^{-6}\ cm^2$ (b) $128 \times 10^{-6}\ cm^2$
(c) $12.8 \times 10^{-6}\ cm^2$ (d) $128 \times 10^{-6}\ cm^2$

14. When a soap bubble of radius 0.2 mm is charged, it experiences an outward electrostatic pressure of magnitude $\frac{\sigma^2}{2\varepsilon_0}$, where $\sigma = 20\ \mu Cm^{-2}$ is the surface charge density. If the excess pressure inside the soap bubble due to the surface tension is same as this electrostatic pressure, then the surface tension of the soap solution is
($\varepsilon_0 = 8.85 \times 10^{-12} C^2 N^{-1} m^{-2}$)

(a) $8.85 \times 10^{-4}\ Nm^{-1}$ (b) $12.4 \times 10^{-4}\ Nm^{-1}$
(c) $11.3 \times 10^{-4}\ Nm^{-1}$ (d) $90 \times 10^{-4}\ Nm^{-1}$

15. The temperature of a spherical black body is inversely proportional to its radius. If its radius is doubled, then the power radiating from it will be

(a) doubled (b) $\frac{1}{4}$ times of initial value
(c) halved (d) four times of initial value

16. A metal sphere immersed in water weighs w_1 at 0°C and w_2 at 50°C. The coefficient of cubical expansion of the metal is less than that of water. Then

(a) $w_1 > w_2$ (b) $w_1 < w_2$ (c) $w_1 = w_2$ (d) $w_1 = 2w_2$

17. A reversible Carnot heat engine converts $\frac{1}{4}$th of its input heat into work. When the temperature of the sink is reduced by 50 K, its efficiency becomes $33\frac{1}{3}$%. The initial temperatures of the source and the sink respectively are

(a) 600 K, 550 K (b) 600 K, 450 K
(c) 300 K, 150 K (d) 450 K, 350 K

18. An ideal monoatomic gas is carried along the cycle *ABCDA* as shown in the figure. The total heat absorbed during this process is

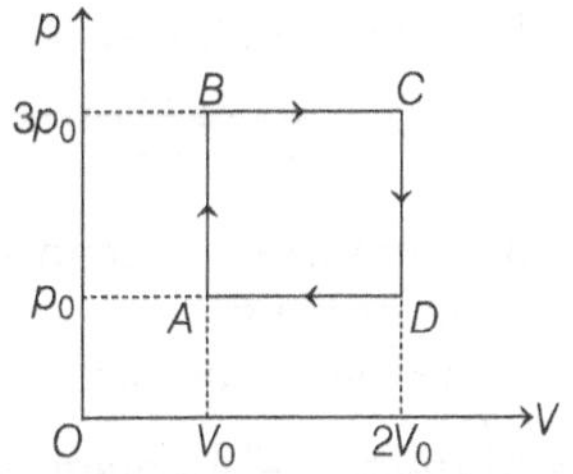

(a) $10.5\,p_0V_0$ (b) $7.5\,p_0V_0$ (c) $2.5\,p_0V_0$ (d) $1.5\,p_0V_0$

19. The ratio of the speed of sound in a monatomic gas at 27°C and rms speed of the molecules of the same gas at a temperature of 127°C is

(a) 1 : 2 (b) $\sqrt{5}:\sqrt{12}$ (c) 3 : 4 (d) $\sqrt{13}:\sqrt{17}$

20. Two uniform stretched steel strings *A* and *B* are vibrating under the same tension. The first overtone of *A* is equal to the second overtone of *B*. If the radius of *A* is twice that of *B*, then the ratio of the lengths of the strings is

(a) 2 : 3 (b) 1 : 2 (c) 1 : 3 (d) 1 : 4

21. A open pipe of length l is vibrating in 3rd overtone with maximum amplitude *A*. The amplitude at a distance of $\frac{l}{16}$ from any open end is

(a) A (b) 0 (c) $\frac{A}{\sqrt{2}}$ (d) $\frac{\sqrt{3}A}{2}$

22. Magnifying power of an astronomical telescope for normal adjustment is 10 and length of the telescope is 110 cm. Magnifying power of the same telescope, when the image is formed at the near point is

(a) 14 (b) 18 (c) 23 (d) 26

23. In Young's double slit experiment, the two slits are illuminated by a light beam consisting of wavelengths 4200 Å and 5040 Å. If the distance between the slits is 2.4 mm and the distance between the slits and the screen is 200 cm, the minimum distance from the central bright fringe to the point where the bright fringes due to both the wavelengths coincide is

(a) 0.7 mm (b) 1.4 mm
(c) 2.1 mm (d) 2.8 mm

24. Flux coming out from a positive charge of 8 C, placed in a medium of dielectric constant 4 is

(a) $\frac{1}{2\varepsilon_0}$ (b) $\frac{2}{\varepsilon_0}$ (c) $8\varepsilon_0$ (d) $32\varepsilon_0$

25. Two charged particles each of mass 9.8 g and charges +20 μC and – 20 μC are attached to the two ends of a massless and rigid uniform non-conducting rod of length 50 cm. This arrangement is held in a uniform electric field of 12.1 NC^{-1}, such that the rod makes a very small angle with the field direction. If the rod is set free, the minimum time needed for the rod to become parallel to the direction of the electric field is .... seconds.

(a) 5 (b) 8 (c) 12 (d) 17

26. Four capacitors of capacitances 2 μF, 3μF, 4μF and xμF are connected to a battery of emf 6 V and of negligible internal resistance, as shown in the figure. If the ratio of the charges on x μF and 4μF capacitances is $\frac{3}{8}$, then the value of x is

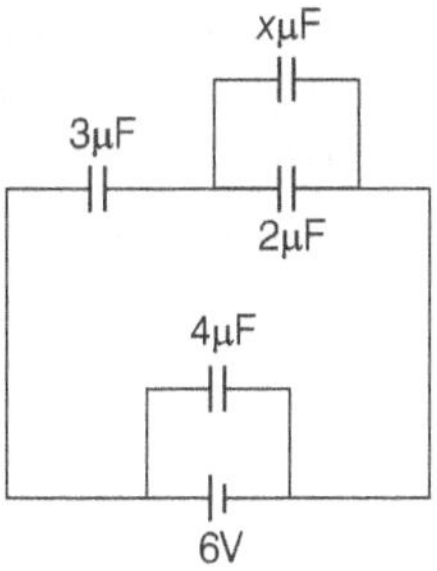

(a) 2 (b) 5
(c) 3 (d) 8

27. The plates of a parallel plate capacitor are charged upto 100 V. A 2 mm thick insulator sheet is inserted between the plates. Then to maintain the same potential difference, the distance between the plates is increased by 1.6 mm. The dielectric constant of the insulator is

(a) 6 (b) 8 (c) 5 (d) 4

28. In the given circuit, current I is independent of the resistance R_6. Then

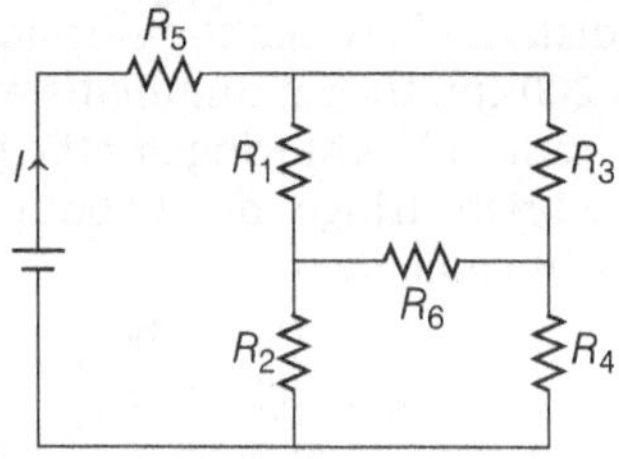

(a) $R_1 R_2 R_5 = R_3 R_4 R_6$

(b) $\frac{1}{R_5} + \frac{1}{R_6} = \frac{1}{R_1 + R_2} + \frac{1}{R_3 + R_4}$

(c) $R_1 R_4 = R_2 R_3$

(d) $R_1 R_3 = R_2 R_4$

29. A fuse wire of radius 0.2 mm blows off with a current of 5 A. The fuse wire of same material but of radius 0.3 mm will blow off with a current of

(a) $\frac{15}{2}$ A (b) $\frac{5\sqrt{3}}{2}$ A (c) $5\sqrt{\frac{27}{8}}$ A (d) 5 A

30. A circular loop and an infinitely long straight conductor carry equal currents, as shown in the figure. The net magnetic field at the centre of the loop is B_1, when the current in the loop is clockwise and B_2 when the current in the loop is anti-clockwise. Then $\frac{B_1}{B_2}$ is

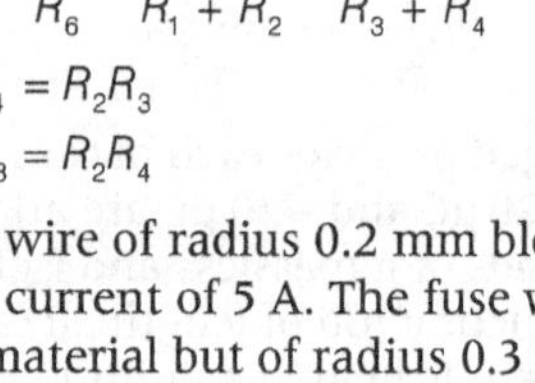

(a) $\frac{15}{19}$ (b) $\frac{13}{15}$ (c) $\frac{13}{17}$ (d) $\frac{17}{19}$

31. Two circular loops of diameters 0.6 cm and 40 cm are kept coaxially with a separation of 15 cm between their centres. If a current 2 A flows through the smaller loop, then the flux linked with the bigger loop is (approximately)

(a) 9×10^{-11} Wb (b) 0.9×10^{-11} Wb
(c) 1.8×10^{-11} Wb (d) 2.7×10^{-11} Wb

32. In the magnetic meridian of a certain place, the vertical component of the earth's magnetic field is 0.3464 G and the dip angle is 30°. The horizontal component of the earth's magnetic field at this location is

(a) 0.4 G (b) 0.6 G
(c) 0.7 G (d) 0.8 G

33. A current carrying circular loop is perpendicular to a magnetic field of induction 10^{-4} T. If the radius of the loop starts shrinking at a uniform rate of 2 mms^{-1}, then the emf induced in the loop at the instant, when its radius is 20 cm will be

(a) 0.02 $\pi\mu$V (b) 0.08 $\pi\mu$V
(c) 0.03 $\pi\mu$V (d) 0.05 $\pi\mu$V

34. A resistor and an inductor are connected in series to an AC source of voltage $150 \sin(100\pi t + \pi)$ volt. If the current in the circuit is $5 \sin\left(100\pi t + \frac{2\pi}{3}\right)$ ampere, then the average power dissipated and the resistance of the resistor are respectively

(a) 187.5 W, 30 Ω (b) 187.5 W, 15 Ω
(c) 375 W, 30 Ω (d) 375 W, 15 Ω

35. An electromagnetic wave of frequency 45 MHz travels in free space along X-axis. At some point and at some instant, the electric field has a maximum value of 750 NC^{-1} along Y-axis. The magnetic field at this position and time is

(a) $2.5 \times 10^{-6}\, \hat{\mathbf{j}}$ (b) $5 \times 10^{-6}\, \hat{\mathbf{k}}$ T
(c) $2.5 \times 10^{-6}\, \hat{\mathbf{k}}$ T (d) $2.5 \times 10^{-6}\, \hat{\mathbf{i}}$ T

36. When light of frequency ν incidents on two metallic plates A and B, photo electrons are emitted. If the work function of A is more than that of B, the correct curve of the following curves drawn between stopping potential V and incident frequency ν is

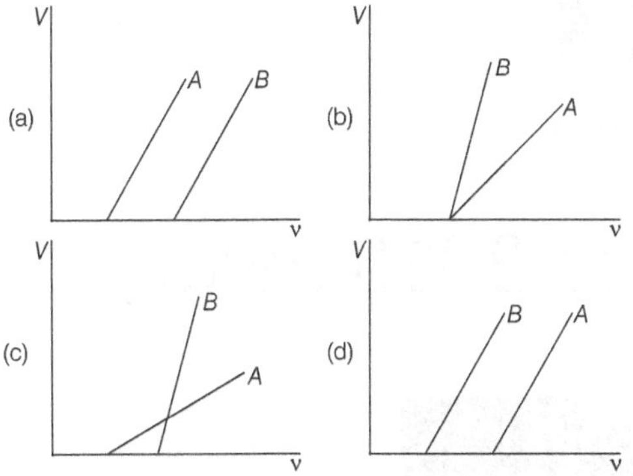

37. The approximate value of principal quantum number for a circular orbit of hydrogen atom of radius 530 nm is

(a) 26 (b) 100 (c) 200 (d) 21

38. A radioactive element X converts into another stable element Y. Half life of X is 2 hours. Initially only X is present. After a time t, if the ratio of atoms of X to Y is $1:4$, then the value of t is

(a) 2 hours (b) 4 hours
(c) between 4 hours and 6 hours (d) 6 hours

39. Match the following List I and List II.

	List I		List II
A.	Small Scale Integration (SSI)	I.	Logic gates < 100
B.	Medium Scale Integration (MSI)	II.	Logic gates > 1000
C.	Large Scale Integration (LSI)	III.	Logic gates ≤ 10
D.	Very Large Scale Integration (VLSI)	IV.	Logic gates < 1000

The correct answer is

	A	B	C	D
(a)	I	III	I	IV
(b)	IV	I	II	III
(c)	I	IV	III	II
(d)	III	I	IV	II

40. A modulated signal is given by $C_m(t) = A_c \sin \omega_c t + \mu A_c \sin \omega_m t \sin \omega_c t$, where μ is modulation index. To keep the signal without distortion, the value of μ should be

(a) >1 (b) ≥ 1
(c) $=1$ (d) ≤ 1

Answers

1.	(c)	2.	(c)	3.	(a)	4.	(c)	5.	(c)	6.	(c)	7.	(c)	8.	(c)	9.	(b)	10.	(b)
11.	(d)	12.	(a)	13.	(d)	14.	(c)	15.	(b)	16.	(b)	17.	(b)	18.	(a)	19.	(b)	20.	(c)
21.	(c)	22.	(a)	23.	(c)	24.	(b)	25.	(a)	26.	(b)	27.	(c)	28.	(c)	29.	(c)	30.	(*)
31.	(*)	32.	(b)	33.	(b)	34.	(b)	35.	(c)	36.	(d)	37.	(b)	38.	(c)	39.	(d)	40.	(d)

Scan this QR code from your mobile phone to get the explanations of this paper.
Or
Visit : http://tinyurl.com/y5zfwad8

TS EAMCET

Engineering Entrance Exam

Online Question Paper 2018 (*Solved*)

04 May Shift I
Session 1 (10:00 AM to 1:00 PM)

1. **Assertion** (A) When we bounce a ball on the ground, it comes to rest after a few bounces, losing all its energy. This is an example of violation of conservation of energy.

Reason (R) Energy can change from one form to another but the total energy is always conserved.

Which of the following is true?

(a) Both (A) and (R) are true and (R) is the correct explanation of (A)
(b) Both (A) and (R) are true, but (R) is not the correct explanation of (A)
(c) (A) is true, but (R) is false
(d) (A) is false, but (R) is true

2. A gas satisfies the relation $pV^{5/3} = k$, where p is pressure, V is volume and k is constant. The dimension of constant k are

(a) $[ML^4T^{-2}]$ (b) $[ML^2T^{-2}]$
(c) $[ML^6T^{-2}]$ (d) $[MLT^{-2}]$

3. A car moves in positive y-direction with velocity v proportional to distance travelled y as $v(y) \propto y^{\beta}$, where β is a positive constant. The car covers a distance L with average velocity $< v >$ proportional to L as $< v > \propto L^{1/3}$. The constant β is given as

(a) $\frac{1}{4}$ (b) $\frac{1}{3}$ (c) $\frac{2}{3}$ (d) $\frac{1}{2}$

4. Consider a particle moving along the positive direction of X-axis. The velocity of the particle is given by $v = \alpha\sqrt{x}$ (α is a positive constant). At time $t = 0$, if the particle is located at $x = 0$, the time dependence of the velocity and the acceleration of the particle are respectively

(a) $\frac{\alpha^2}{2}t$ and $\frac{\alpha^2}{2}$ (b) $\alpha^2 t$ and α^2
(c) $\frac{\alpha}{2}t$ and $\frac{\alpha}{2}$ (d) $\frac{\alpha^2}{4}t$ and $\frac{\alpha^2}{4}$

5. The magnitude of velocity and acceleration and velocity of a particle moving in a plane, whose position vector $\mathbf{r} = 3t^2\hat{\mathbf{i}} + 2t\hat{\mathbf{j}} + \hat{\mathbf{k}}$ at $t = 2$s are respectively

(a) $\sqrt{148}$, 6 (b) $\sqrt{144}$, 6
(c) $\sqrt{13}$, 3 (d) $\sqrt{14}$, 3

Note In the question paper sequence is given, (acceleration and velocity) which is not matching with any of option given.

6. Two objects are located at height 10 m above the ground. At some point of time, the objects are thrown with initial velocity $2\sqrt{2}$ m/s at an angle 45° and 135° with the positive X-axis, respectively. Assuming $g = 10$ m/s^2, the velocity vectors will be perpendicular to each other at time is equal to

(a) 0.2 s (b) 0.4 s
(c) 0.6 s (d) 0.8 s

7. String AB of unstretched length, L is stretched by applying a force F at the mid-point C such that the segments AC and BC make an angle θ with AB as shown in the figure. The string may be considered as an elastic element with a force to elongation ratio K.

The force F is given by

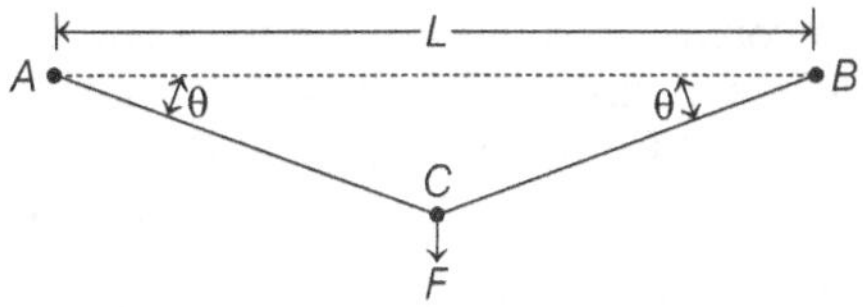

(a) $KL(1 - \tan\theta)\sin\theta$ (b) $2KL(1 - \cos\theta)\tan\theta$
(c) $KL(1 - \cos\theta)\tan\theta$ (d) $2KL(1 - \sin\theta)\tan\theta$

8. A block of mass 5 kg is kept against an accelerating wedge with a wedge angle of 45° to the horizontal. The coefficient of friction between the block and the wedge is $\mu = 0.4$. What is the minimum absolute value of the acceleration of the wedge to keep the block steady? [Assume, $g = 10\ m/s^2$]

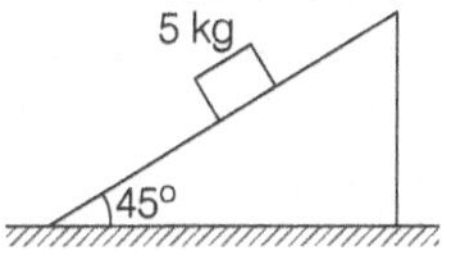

(a) $\frac{60}{7}\ m/s^2$ (b) $\frac{30}{7}\ m/s^2$ (c) $\frac{30}{\sqrt{7}}\ m/s^2$ (d) $\frac{60}{\sqrt{7}}\ m/s^2$

9. An object moves along the circle with normal acceleration proportional to t^{α}, where t is the time and α is a positive constant. The power developed by all the forces acting on the object will have time dependence proportional to

(a) $t^{\alpha-1}$ (b) $t^{\alpha/2}$ (c) $t^{\frac{1+\alpha}{2}}$ (d) $t^{2\alpha}$

10. A ball of mass 1 kg moving along x-direction collides elastically with a stationary ball of mass m. The first ball (mass = 1 kg) recoils at right angle to its original direction of motion. If the second ball starts moving at an angle 30° with the X-axis, then the value of m must be

(a) 0.5 kg (b) 1.5 kg (c) 2.5 kg (d) 2 kg

11. A machine gun can fire 200 bullets/min. If 35 g bullets are fired at a speed of 750 m/s, then the average force exerted by the gun on the bullets is

(a) 87.5 N (b) 26.2 N (c) 78.9 N (d) 110.3 N

12. A solid sphere of radius R makes a perfect rolling down on a plane which is inclined to the horizontal axis at an angle θ. If the radius of gyration is k, then its acceleration is

(a) $\frac{g\sin\theta}{\left(1 + \frac{k^2}{R^2}\right)}$ (b) $\frac{g\sin\theta}{(R^2 + k^2)}$

(c) $\frac{g\sin\theta}{2(R^2 + k^2)}$ (d) $\frac{g\sin\theta}{2\left(1 + \frac{k^2}{R^2}\right)}$

13. A particle of mass m is attached to four springs with spring constant $k, k, 2k$ and $2k$ as shown in the figure. Four springs are attached to the four corners of a square and a particle is placed at the center. If the particle is pushed slightly towards any sides of the square and released, the period of oscillation will be

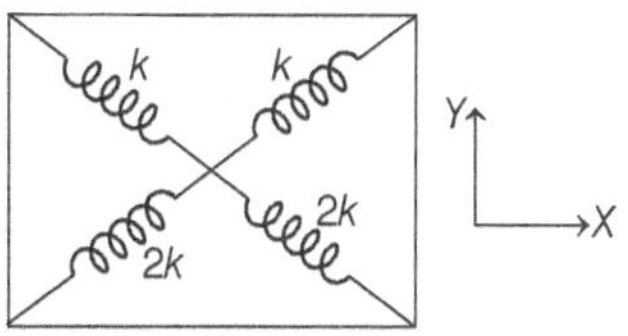

(a) $2\pi\sqrt{\frac{m}{3k}}$ (b) $2\pi\sqrt{\frac{m}{3\sqrt{2}k}}$ (c) $2\pi\sqrt{\frac{m}{6k}}$ (d) $2\pi\sqrt{\frac{m}{2k}}$

14. The ratio of the height above the surface of earth to the depth below, the surface of earth, for gravitational accelerations to be the same (assuming small heights) is

(a) 0.25 (b) 0.5
(c) 1.0 (d) 1.25

15. A steel rod has radius 50 mm and length 2 m. It is stretched along its length with a force of 400 kN. This causes an elongation of 0.5 mm. Find the (approximate) Young's modulus of steel from this information.

(a) $2 \times 0^{10}\ Nm^2$ (b) $10^{11}\ Nm^2$
(c) $2 \times 10^{11}\ Nm^2$ (d) $10^{12}\ Nm^2$

16. Consider a vessel filled with a liquid upto height H. The bottom of the vessel lies in the XY-plane passing through the origin. The density of the liquid varies with Z-axis as $\rho(z) = \rho_0\left[2 - \left(\frac{z}{H}\right)^2\right]$. If p_1 and p_2 are the pressures at the bottom surface and top surface of the liquid, the magnitude of $(p_1 - p_2)$ is

(a) $\rho_0 gH$ (b) $\frac{8}{5}\rho_0 gH$

(c) $\frac{3}{2}\rho_0 gH$ (d) $\frac{5}{3}\rho_0 gH$

17. A one mole of ideal gas goes through a process in which pressure p varies with volume V as $p = 3 - g\left(\frac{V}{V_0}\right)^2$, where, V_0 is a constant. The maximum attainable temperature by the ideal gas during this process is
(all quantities are is SI units and R is gas constant)

(a) $\frac{2V_0}{3R}$ (b) $\frac{2V_0}{R}$
(c) $\frac{3V_0}{2R}$ (d) None of these

18. The internal energy of the air, in a room of volume V, at temperature T and with outside pressure p increasing linearly with time, varies as

(a) increases linearly (b) increases exponentially
(c) decreases linearly (d) remains constant

19. The efficiency of Carnot engine is η, when its hot and cold reservoirs are maintained at temperature T_1 and T_2, respectively. To increase the efficiency to $1.5\,\eta$, the increase in temperature (ΔT) of the hot reservoir by keeping the cold one constant at T_2 is

(a) $\frac{T_1T_2}{(1-\eta)(1-1.5\eta)}$ (b) $\frac{0.5T_2\eta}{(1-1.5\eta)(1-\eta)}$
(c) $\frac{T_1}{(1-\eta)} - \frac{T_2}{(1-1.5\eta)}$ (d) $\frac{(1-\eta)(1-1.5\eta)}{T_1T_2}$

20. An air bubble rises from the bottom of a water tank of height 5 m. If the initial volume of the bubble is 3 mm^3, then what will be its volume as it reaches the surface? Assume that its temperature does not change.
[$g = 9.8$ m/s^2, 1 atm $= 10^5$ Pa, density of water $= 1$ gm/cc]

(a) 1.5 mm^3 (b) 4.5 mm^3
(c) 9 mm^3 (d) 6 mm^3

21. Two harmonic travelling waves are described by the equations $y_1 = a\sin(kx - \omega t)$ and $y_2 = a\sin(-kx + \omega t + \phi)$. The amplitude of the superimposed wave is

(a) $2a\cos\frac{\phi}{2}$ (b) $2a\sin\phi$
(c) $2a\cos\phi$ (d) $2a\sin\frac{\phi}{2}$

22. Where should an object be placed on the axis of a convex lens of focal length 8 cm, so as to achieve magnification of -4? (Distances are measured from optic centre of the lens)

(a) -6 cm (b) -10 cm (c) -12 cm (d) -9 cm

23. A converging mirror is placed on the right hand side of a converging lens as shown in the figure.

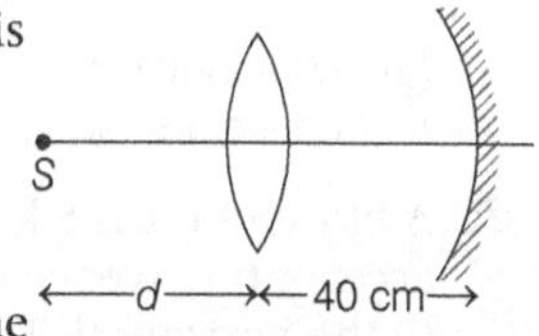

The focal length of the mirror and the lens are 20 cm and 15 cm, respectively. The separation between the lens and the mirror is 40 cm and their principal axis coincide. A point source is placed on the principal axis at a distance d to the left of the lens. If the final beam comes out parallel to the principal axis, then the value of d is

(a) 4 cm (b) 8 cm (c) 12 cm (d) 16 cm

24. Interference fringes are obtained in a Young's double slit experiment using beam of light consisting two wavelengths 500 nm and 600 nm. Bright fringes due to both wavelengths coincide at 2.5 mm from the central maximum. If the separation between the slits is 3 mm, then the distance between the screen and plane of the slits is

(a) 1.2 m (b) 2.8 m (c) 2.5 m (d) 3.2 m

25. A point charge of 50 μC is placed in the XY-plane at a location with radius vector $\mathbf{r}_0 = 2\hat{\mathbf{i}} + 3\hat{\mathbf{j}}$ m. The electric field strength and its magnitude at a point with radius vector $\mathbf{r} = 8\hat{\mathbf{i}} - 5\hat{\mathbf{j}}$ m is ($\varepsilon_0 = 8.85 \times 10^{-12}$ C^2/N-m^2)

(a) 4.5 kV/m (b) 45 kV/m
(c) 0.45 kV/m (d) 450 kV/m

26. The work done to assemble the three charges in a configuration as shown in the figure below is

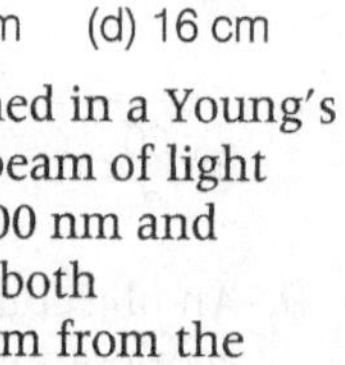

(a) $\frac{-3q^2}{4\pi\varepsilon_0 a}$ (b) $\frac{-2q^2}{4\pi\varepsilon_0 a}$
(c) $\frac{-q^2}{4\pi\varepsilon_0 a}$ (d) 0

27. Consider the following two circuits
[A] 20 bulbs are connected in series to a power supply line.

[B] 20 bulbs identical to [A] are connected in a parallel circuit to an identical power supply line.

Identify which of the following is not true?

(a) If one bulb in [A] blows out, all others will stop glowing
(b) Bulbs in [A] glow brighter, since the current flowing in [A] is higher
(c) If one bulb in [B] blows, other bulbs will still glow
(d) Bulbs in [B] have the highest voltage across each bulb

28. A tapered bar of length L and end diameters D_1 and D_2 is made of a material of electrical resistivity ρ. The electrical resistance of the bar is

(a) $\dfrac{4\rho L}{\pi(D_1 + D_2)^2}$ (b) $\dfrac{4\rho L}{\pi(D_1 - D_2)^2}$
(c) $\dfrac{\rho\pi\sqrt{D_1 D_2}}{4L^2}$ (d) $\dfrac{4\rho L}{\pi D_1 D_2}$

29. Two circular loops L_1 and L_2 of wire carrying equal and opposite currents are placed parallel to each other with a common axis. The radius of loop L_1 is R_1 and that of L_2 is R_2. The distance between the centres of the loops is $\sqrt{3}R_1$. The magnetic field at the centre of L_2 shall be zero, if

(a) $R_2 = 4R_1$ (b) $R_2 = 2R_1$ (c) $R_2 = \sqrt{2}R_1$ (d) $R_2 = 8R_1$

30. A non-conducting thin disc of radius R rotates about its axis with an angular velocity ω. The surface charge density on the disc varies with the distance r from the centre as

$\sigma(r) = \sigma_0\left[1 + \left(\dfrac{r}{R}\right)^{\beta}\right]$, where σ_0 and β are constants. If the magnetic induction at the center is $B = \left(\dfrac{9}{10}\right)\mu_0\sigma_0\omega R$, the value of β is

(a) $\dfrac{1}{4}$ (b) 4 (c) $\dfrac{1}{2}$ (d) 2

31. A bar magnet of magnetic moment M is placed at a distance D with its axis along positive X-axis. Likewise, second bar manget of magnetic moment M is placed at a distance $2D$ on positive Y-axis and perpendicular to it as shown in the figure. The magnitude of magnetic field at the origin is $|\mathbf{B}| = \alpha\left[\dfrac{\mu_0}{4\pi}\dfrac{M}{D^3}\right]$. The value of α must be (assum $D >> l$, where l is the length of magnets)

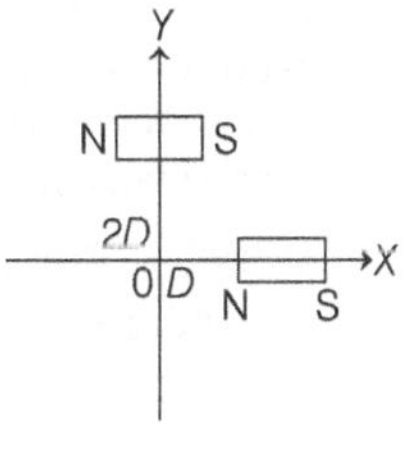

(a) 2 (b) $\dfrac{15}{8}$ (c) $\dfrac{17}{8}$ (d) $\dfrac{9}{8}$

32. A wire loop enclosing a semi-circle of radius R is located on the boundary of a uniform magnetic field of induction $\mathbf{B}$. At time $t = 0$, the loop is set into rotation with angular velocity angular ω about its axis 0, coinciding with a line vector $\mathbf{B}$ on the boundary as shown in the figure. The emf induced in the loop is

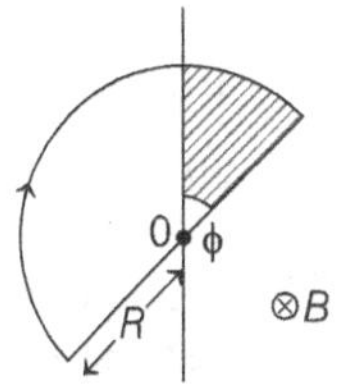

(a) $\dfrac{BR^2}{2}\omega$ (b) $BR\omega$ (c) $BR^2\omega$ (d) $\dfrac{BR^2}{2\omega}$

33. In the circuit given below, the capacitor C is charged by closing the switch S_1 and opening the switch S_2. After charging, the switch S_1 is opened and S_2 is closed, then the maximum current in the circuit

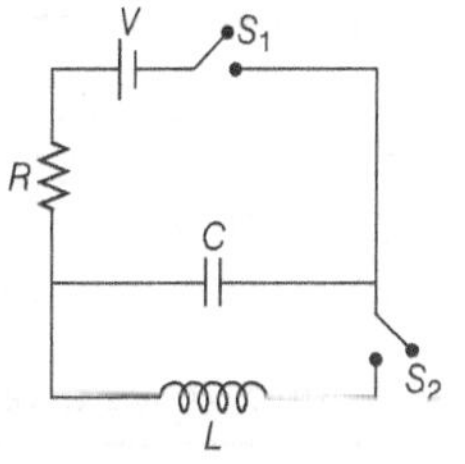

(a) $V\sqrt{\dfrac{L}{C}}$ (b) $V\sqrt{\dfrac{C}{L}}$ (c) $\dfrac{V}{2\pi}\sqrt{\dfrac{L}{C}}$ (d) $2\pi V\sqrt{\dfrac{L}{C}}$

34. A 100 W electric bulb produces electromagnetic radiation with electric field amplitude of $\dfrac{2V}{m}$ at a distance of 10 m. Assuming it as a point source, estimate the efficiency of the bulb.

(a) 4.9% (b) 2.5%
(c) 6.6% (d) 19.7%

35. At an incident radiation frequency of ν_1, which is greater than the threshold frequency, the stoopping potential for a certain metal is V_1. At frequency $2\nu_1$, the stopping potential is $3V_1$. If the stopping potential at frequency $4\nu_1$ is nV_1, then n is

(a) 2 (b) 3 (c) 6 (d) 7

36. The de-Broglie wavelength of an electron of kinetic energy 9 eV is (take, $h = 4 \times 10^{-15}$ eV-s, $c = 3 \times 10^{10}$ cm/s and the mass m_e of electron as $m_e c^2 = 0.5$ MeV)

(a) 4×10^{-8} cm (b) 3×10^{-8} cm
(c) 4×10^{-7} cm (d) 3×10^{-7} cm

37. An active nucleus decays to $\left(\frac{1}{3}\right)$rd in 20 h.

The fraction of original activity remaining after 80 h is

(a) $\frac{1}{16}$ (b) $\frac{1}{81}$ (c) $\frac{1}{36}$ (d) $\frac{1}{54}$

38. Consider an amplifier circuit, where in a transistor is used in common emitter mode. The change in collector current and base current respectively are 4 mA and 20 μA when a signal of 40 mV is added to the base-emitter voltage. If the load resistance is 10 kΩ, then power gain in the circuit is

(a) 1×10^4 (b) 2×10^7 (c) 8×10^5 (d) 1×10^6

39. The output F of the logic circuit given below is

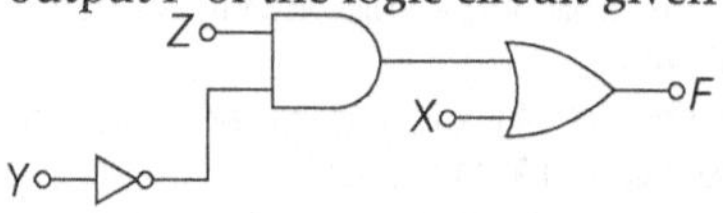

(a) $X + \overline{Y} \cdot Z$ (b) $(Y + Z) \cdot X$
(c) $(\overline{Y} + Z) + X$ (d) $X + \overline{Y} + Z$

40. A carrier wave of peak voltage 20 V is used to transmit a message signal. For getting a modulation index of 60%, the peak voltage of the modulating signal is

(a) 6 V (b) 8 V
(c) 12 V (d) 33.3 V

Answers

1.	(d)	2.	(a)	3.	(b)	4.	(a)	5.	(a)	6.	(b)	7.	(c)	8.	(b)	9.	(a)	10.	(d)
11.	(a)	12.	(a)	13.	(b)	14.	(b)	15.	(c)	16.	(d)	17.	(d)	18.	(a)	19.	(b)	20.	(b)
21.	(d)	22.	(b)	23.	(c)	24.	(c)	25.	(a)	26.	(c)	27.	(b)	28.	(d)	29.	(d)	30.	(a)
31.	(b)	32.	(a)	33.	(b)	34.	(c)	35.	(d)	36.	(a)	37.	(b)	38.	(b)	39.	(a)	40.	(c)

Scan this QR code from your mobile phone to get the explanations of this paper.
Or
Visit : http://tinyurl.com/y6jjapnf

04 May Shift II
Session 2 (3:00 PM to 6:00 PM)

1. Match the entries in List I with those in List II.

List I	List II
A. Unified interaction reducing the number of fundamental forces from four to three	(i) Strong interaction
B. Force between two molecules separated by a distance near about the sum of the molecular radii	(ii) Gravitational force
C. Nuclear binding force	(iii) Electroweak interaction
D. Bodies of astronomical proportions	(iv) Electromagnetic interaction

	A	B	C	D
(a)	(iii)	(iv)	(i)	(ii)
(b)	(iii)	(i)	(ii)	(iv)
(c)	(iii)	(i)	(iv)	(ii)
(d)	(ii)	(i)	(iii)	(iv)

2. Assertion (A) Electromagnetic force is enormously strong as compared to gravitational force. Yet, gravity dominates in the large-scale phenomena (e.g. formation of galaxies).

Reason (R) Existence of positive and negative charges make matter mostly electrically neutral.

Which of the following is true?

(a) Both (A) and (R) are true and (R) is the correct explanation of (A)

(b) Both (A) and (R) are true, but (R) is not the correct explanation of (A)
(c) (A) is true, but (R) is false
(d) (A) is false, but (R) is true

3. An object moves in a straight line with deceleration whose magnitude varies with velocity as $3v^{2/3}$. If at an initial point, the velocity is 8 m/s, then the distance travelled by the object before it stops is
(a) 2 m (b) 4 m (c) 6 m (d) 8 m

4. A particle starts from origin at time $t = 0$ and moves in positive x-direction. Its velocity $\mathbf{v}$ varies with times as $\mathbf{v} = 10t\hat{\mathbf{i}}$ cm/s. The distance covered by the particle in 8 s will be
(a) 320 cm (b) 80 cm
(c) 120 cm (d) 640 cm

5. Consider an object kept at the centre, in the XY-plane, on which five coplanar forces act as shown in the figure. The resultant force on the object is

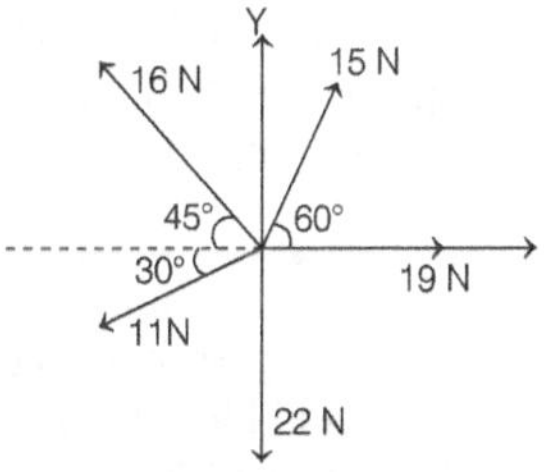

(a) 6.5 N, 330° (b) 6.5 N, 300°
(c) 6.5 N, 30° (d) 5.7 N, 331°

6. Consider an object making uniform motion around a circle of radius 5 m with tangential velocity 2 ms^{-1}. The time it takes to complete 2 revolution and the magnitude of acceleration respectively are
(a) 0.2π s and 0.8 ms^{-2} (b) 0.5π s and 1 ms^{-2}
(c) 10π s and 0.8 ms^{-2} (d) 5π s and 5 ms^{-2}

7. A small block starts sliding down an inclined plane forming an angle 45° horizontal. The coefficient of friction μ, varies with distance s as $\mu = cs^2$ where, c is a constant of appropriate dimensions, then distance covered by the block before it stops is
(a) $\sqrt{\frac{3}{C}}$ (b) $\sqrt{3C}$ (c) $\sqrt{C}$ (d) $\sqrt{\frac{1}{C}}$

8. A movable steel plate is placed between fixed steel and brass plates and the stack of plates is subjected to a weight of 100 N as shown in the figure. The coefficient of kinetic friction for steel on steel is 0.57 and for steel on brass is 0.44. Assuming that the entire weight comes onto the stack and that the weight of the plates is negligible in comparison to the applied weight, the force required to move the middle plate (in N) is
(a) 13 (b) 101 (c) 440 (d) 570

9. A car of mass 1200 kg (together with the driver) is moving with a constant acceleration of 2 m/s^2. How much power does the engine generate at the instance, when the speed reaches 20 m/s? (Assume that the coefficient of friction between the car and the road is 0.5).
(a) 48000 W (b) 120000 W
(c) 168000 W (d) 288000 W

10. A ball moving with a velocity v, collides head on with a stationary second ball of same mass. After the collision, the velocity of the first ball is reduced to 0.15 v. The kinetic energy of the system is decreased nearly by
(a) 20% (b) 25% (c) 30% (d) 40%

11. A uniform disc of mass 100 kg and radius 2 m is rotating at 1 rad/s about a perpendicular axis passing through its centre. A boy of mass 60 kg standing at the centre of the disk suddenly jumps to a point which is 1 m from the centre of the disc. The final angular velocity of the boy (in rad/s) is
(a) 0.77 (b) 0.5 (c) 41 (d) 2

12. A force $\mathbf{F}_1 = A\hat{\mathbf{j}}$ is applied to a point, whose radius vector $\mathbf{r}_1 = a\hat{\mathbf{i}}$, while a force $\mathbf{F}_2 = B\hat{\mathbf{i}}$ is applied to the point whose radius vector $\mathbf{r}_2 = b\hat{\mathbf{j}}$. Both the radius vectors are determined relative to the origin of the coordinate axes O.
The moment of the force relative to O is
(a) $(aA - bB)\hat{\mathbf{k}}$ (b) $(aA - bB)\hat{\mathbf{j}}$
(c) $(ab - AB)\hat{\mathbf{k}}$ (d) $(aB - bA)\hat{\mathbf{j}}$

13. Two springs of spring constant k_1 and k_2 are connected by a mass m as shown in the figure. Under negligible friction, if the mass is displaced by small amount x from its equilibrium position and released, the period of oscillation is

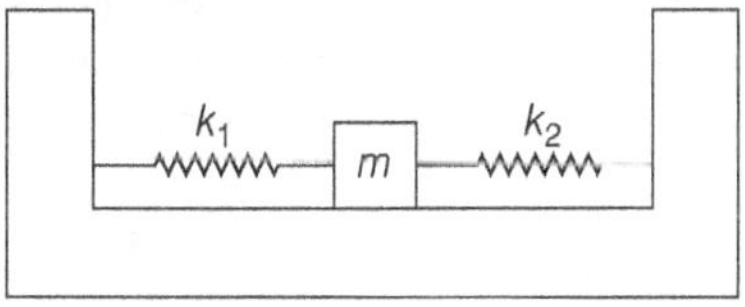

(a) $2\pi\sqrt{\frac{m(k_1+k_2)}{k_1k_2}}$ (b) $2\pi\sqrt{\frac{m}{k_1+k_2}}$

(c) $2\pi\sqrt{\frac{mk_1k_2}{(k_1+k_2)}}$ (d) $2\pi\sqrt{\frac{m(k_1-k_2)}{k_1k_2}}$

14. The density of a solid sphere of radius R is $\rho(r) = 20\frac{r^2}{R^2}$ where, r is the distance from its centre. If the gravitational field due to this sphere at a distance $4R$ from its centre is E and G is the gravitational constant, then the ratio of $\frac{E}{GR}$ is

(a) $\frac{\pi}{5}$ (b) 3π (c) $\frac{3\pi}{2}$ (d) π

15. In a tensile test on a metal bar of diameter 0.015 m and length 0.2 m, the relation between the load and elongation within the proportional limit is found to be $F = 97.2 \times 10^6 (\Delta L)$, where F is the load (in N) and ΔL is the elongation (in m). The Young's modulus of the material in GPa is

(a) 75.5 (b) 85.6 (c) 98.7 (d) 110

16. A tank of height 15 m and cross-section area 10 m^2 is filled with water. There is a small hole of cross-section area a which is much smaller than the container, located at a height of 12 m from the base of the container. How much force should be applied with a piston at the top level, so that the water coming out of the hole hits the ground at a distance of 16 m? (Take, density of water $= 1000 \text{ kg m}^{-3}$)

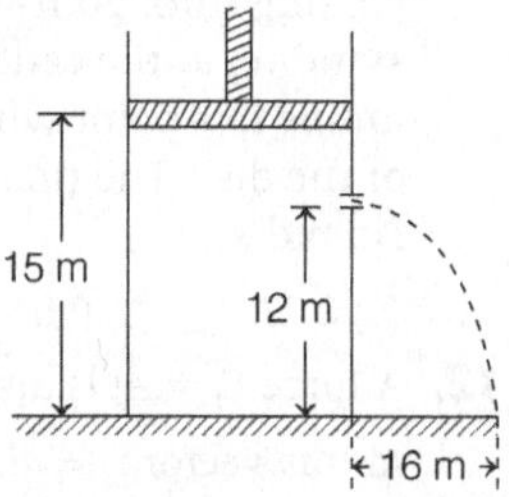

(a) 233 kN (b) 200 kN (c) 320 kN (d) 400 kN

17. An ideal gas has molar heat capacity C_V at constant volume. The gas undergoes a process where in the temperature changes as $T = T_0(1 + \alpha V^2)$, where, T and V are temperature and volume respectively, T_0 and α are positive constants. The molar heat capacity C of the gas is given as $C = C_V + Rf(V)$, where, $f(V)$ is a function of volume. The expression for $f(V)$ is

(a) $\frac{\alpha V^2}{1+\alpha V^2}$ (b) $\frac{1+\alpha V^2}{2\alpha V^2}$

(c) $\alpha V^2(1+\alpha V^2)$ (d) $\frac{1}{2\alpha V^2(1+\alpha V^2)}$

18. A container is filled with a liquid that cools from 100 °C to 70 °C in 5 min, when kept at room temperature of 30 °C. The time that it must have taken to cool down to 80 °C from its initial temperature approximately is

(a) 1.7 min (b) 2.6 min (c) 8.2 min (d) 4.1 min

19. An ideal gas in a cylinder is compressed adiabatically to one-third of its original volume. A work of 45 J is done on the gas by the process. The change in internal energy of the gas and the heat flowed into the gas, respectively are

(a) 45 J and zero (b) −45 J and zero
(c) 45 J and heat flows out of the gas
(d) −45 J and heat flows into the gas

20. In a cubic container of inner side length 10 cm, nitrogen gas of 100 kPa pressure is maintained at 300 K. If the pressure inside the gas is increased to 300 kPa by adding oxygen gas, the ratio of number of N_2 to O_2 molecules in the container is

(a) 0.5 (b) 3.0 (c) 1.5 (d) 0.33

21. A source of sound whose frequency is 1000 Hz is moving with a speed 33 m/s. The waves reflected by a fixed obstacle are registered by a receiver that moves together with the source. The speed of the sound waves is 330 m/s, then the frequency registered by the receiver is

(a) 0.9 kHz (b) 1.1 kHz (c) 1.2 kHz (d) 2.2 kHz

22. Figure shows a ray of light entering and passing through a dense glass slab and emerging from the other side. If the angle $i = 60°$, slab thickness $b = 0.04$ m and the refractive index of glass $= \sqrt{3}$, the parallel shift d between the emerging and entering rays in mm is

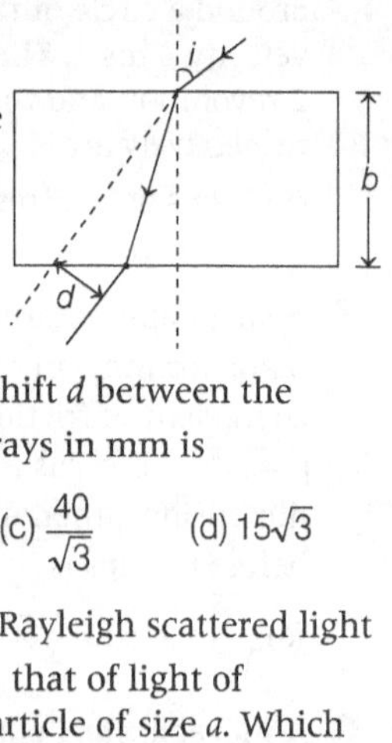

(a) $\sqrt{\frac{3}{4}}$ (b) $\sqrt{\frac{4}{3}}$ (c) $\frac{40}{\sqrt{3}}$ (d) $15\sqrt{3}$

23. Let S_1 be the amount of Rayleigh scattered light of wavelength λ_1 and S_2 that of light of wavelength λ_2 from a particle of size a. Which of the following statement is true?

(a) $\frac{S_1}{S_2} = \left(\frac{\lambda_2}{\lambda_1}\right)^4$, if $\lambda_1, \lambda_2 >> a$

(b) $\dfrac{S_1}{S_2} = \left(\dfrac{\lambda_1}{\lambda_2}\right)^4$, if $\lambda_1, \lambda_2 >> a$

(c) $\dfrac{S_1}{S_2} = \left(\dfrac{\lambda_2}{\lambda_1}\right)^4$, if $\lambda_1, \lambda_2 << a$

(d) $\dfrac{S_1}{S_2} = \left(\dfrac{\lambda_1}{\lambda_2}\right)^4$, If $\lambda_1, \lambda_2 << a$

24. In a Young's double slit experiment, a monochromatic light of wavelength 600 nm is used. If the two slits are covered by transparent sheets of thickness 0.132 mm and 0.1 mm of refractive index 1.5, then the number of fringes that will shift due to introduction of the sheets are

(a) 20 (b) 40 (c) 60 (d) 80

25. The volume charge density in a spherical ball of radius R varies with distance r from the centre as $\rho(r) = \rho_0\left[1 - \left(\dfrac{r}{R}\right)^3\right]$, where, ρ_0 is a constant. The radius at which the field would be maximum is

(a) $\dfrac{R}{2^{1/3}}$ (b) R (c) $\dfrac{R}{2}$ (d) $\dfrac{R^{1/3}}{2}$

26. The potential $\phi(x, y)$ of an electrostatic field $\mathbf{E} = a(y\hat{\mathbf{i}} + x\hat{\mathbf{j}})$ is [a is a constant and $\hat{\mathbf{i}}$ and $\hat{\mathbf{j}}$ are unit vectors along X and Y axes]

(a) $-2axy + c$ (c is a constant)
(b) $axy + c$ (c is a constant)
(c) $a^2xy + c$ (c is a constant)
(d) $a(xy)^2 + c$ (c is a constant)

27. A resistance network is connected to a battery as shown in the figure below. If the internal resistance of the battery is 5Ω, then the value of R (in Ω) for maximum power delivered to the network is

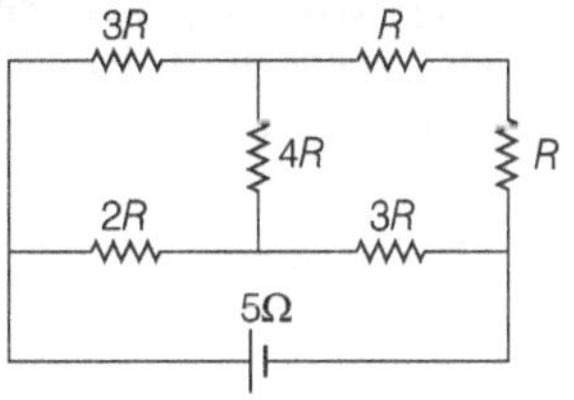

(a) 2 (b) 4 (c) 5 (d) 6

28. Find the voltage V_2 across R_2 for the given circuit

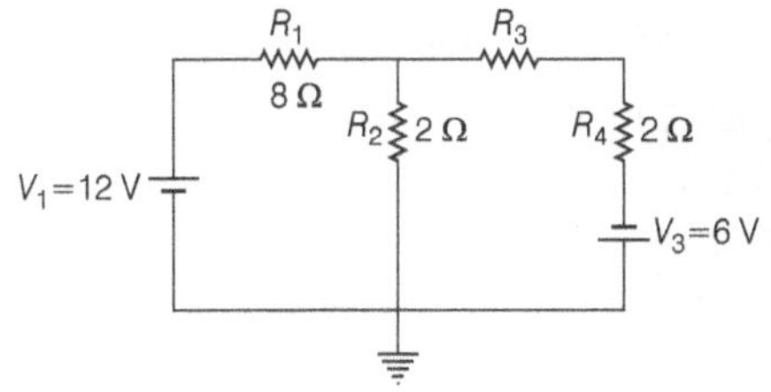

(a) 0.56V (b) 1.61V (c) 0.63V (d) 0.21V

29. A moving coil galvanometer has a rectangular wire coil of enclosed area 0.001 m^2 and 500 turns. The coil operates in a radial magnetic field of 0.2T and carries a current of $6\pi \times 10^{-8}$A. If the torsional spring constant is 6×10^{-7}N - m/ rad, then the angular deflection of the coil in radians is

(a) $\dfrac{\pi}{100}$ (b) $\dfrac{\pi}{200}$ (c) $\dfrac{\pi}{300}$ (d) $\dfrac{\pi}{400}$

30. A charge q enters a region having electric field $\mathbf{E}$ and magnetic field $\mathbf{B}$ with velocity $\mathbf{v}$. If it continues to move with the same velocity, then which of the following statement is not true

(a) $\mathbf{E} \cdot \mathbf{B} = 0$
(b) $\mathbf{E} \cdot \mathbf{v} = 0$
(c) If $\mathbf{v} \cdot \mathbf{B} = 0$, then $\mathbf{v} = \dfrac{\mathbf{E} \times \mathbf{B}}{\mathbf{B} \times \mathbf{B}}$
(d) $\mathbf{v} \times \mathbf{E} = \mathbf{B}$

31. Two identical bar magnets of magnetic moment M each, are placed along X and Y-axes, respectively at a distance d from the origin (as shown in the figure). The origin lies on perpendicular bisector of magnet placed on X-axis and on the magnetic axis of magnet placed on Y-axis. If the magnitude of total magnetic field at the origin is $B = \alpha\left[\dfrac{\mu_0}{4\pi}\dfrac{M}{d^3}\right]$, then the value of constant α will be

($d >> l$, where l is the length of the bar magnets and direction of N to S in magnets is opposite with respect to each other)

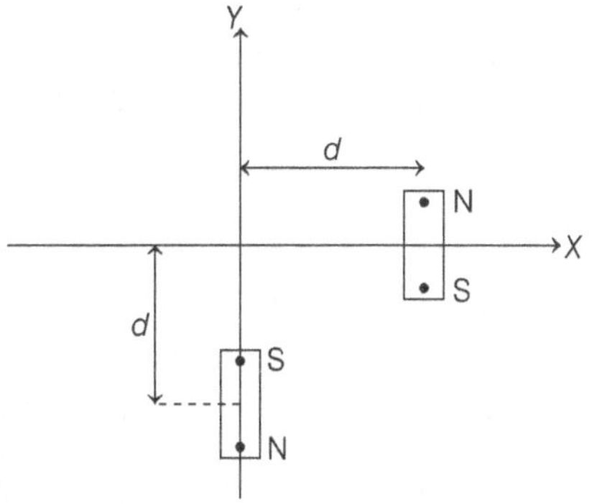

(a) 2 (b) 1 (c) 3 (d) $\sqrt{5}$

32. A conducting rod of length L lies in XY-plane and makes an angle 30° with X-axis. One end of the rod lies at origin initially. A magnetic field also exists in the region pointing along positive Z-direction. The magnitude of the magnetic field varies with y as $B_0\left(\frac{y}{L}\right)^3$, where, B_0 is a constant. At some instant the rod starts moving with a velocity v_0 along X-axis. The emf induced in the rod is

(a) $\frac{B_0v_0L}{64}$ (b) $\frac{B_0v_0L}{16}$ (c) B_0v_0L (d) $64B_0v_0L$

33. An oscillating circuit consisting of a capacitor with capacitance $C = 10\mu F$, a coil with inductance $L = 6.0\mu H$ and active resistance $R = 10\Omega$. The mean power that should be fed to the circuit to maintain undamped harmonic oscillations with an external driving power with 50Hz and a V_m of 280 V is

(a) 3.8 W (b) 48 W (c) 3 mW (d) 48 mW

34. If the magnetic field of a plane electromagnetic wave is given by
$5\times10^{-6}\sin(0.6\times10^2 x + 0.5\times10^{10} t)$, then the speed of the wave is

(a) 0.83×10^7 m/s (b) 0.83×10^8 m/s
(c) 5.24×10^8 m/s (d) 5.24×10^9 m/s

35. An isolated lead ball is charged upon continuous irradiation by EM radiation of wavelength, $\lambda = 221$ nm. The maximum potential attained by the lead ball, if its work function is 4.14 eV is (take, $h = 6.63\times10^{-34}$ J-s, $c = 3\times10^8$ m/s, $e = 1.6\times10^{-19}$C)

(a) 1.49 V (b) 2.67 V
(c) 3.14V (d) 0.51V

36. An energy of 13.6 eV is equal to

(a) 0.518×10^{-25}kcal (b) 6.04×10^{-25}kWh
(c) 2.17×10^{-10}J (d) 2.17×10^{-15}kN-m

37. The frequency of light emitted, when the electron makes transition from the level of principle quantum number $n = 2$ to the level with $n = 1$ is (Take, the ionization energy of hydrogen to be 13.6 eV and $h \simeq 4\times10^{-15}$ eV - s)

(a) 2.55×10^{15}Hz (b) 1.7×10^{15}Hz
(c) 3.4×10^{15}Hz (d) 5.1×10^{15}Hz

38. In a junction transistor, the collector current changes by 6.8 mA, if the emitter current is changed by 7mA. For such transistor, the current amplification factor is

(a) 30 (b) 34
(c) 40 (d) 45

39. In a p-n junction diode, an electric field of magnitude 2×10^5 V / m exists in the depletion region. A particle with charge $-3e$ can diffuse from n-side to p-side, if it has minimum kinetic energy 0.6 eV.
The width of the depletion region of the p-n junction is

(a) 300 nm (b) 600 nm
(c) 1000 nm (d) 1200 nm

40. A person tries to broadcast with the same antenna both the signals at 10^7 Hz and 10^6 Hz. If the receiver at some distance has to receive an equal strength for both the frequencies, then the broadcaster has to approximately increase the signal strength at 10^6 Hz to 10^7 Hz by

(a) $\frac{1}{10}$ times (b) 10 times
(c) 100 times (d) $\frac{1}{100}$ times

Answers

1.	(a)	2.	(a)	3.	(b)	4.	(a)	5.	(a)	6.	(c)	7.	(a)	8.	(b)	9.	(c)	10.	(b)
11.	(a)	12.	(a)	13.	(b)	14.	(d)	15.	(d)	16.	(a)	17.	(b)	18.	(b)	19.	(a)	20.	(a)
21.	(c)	22.	(c)	23.	(a)	24.	(*)	25.	(a)	26.	(*)	27.	(a)	28.	(*)	29.	(a)	30.	(d)
31.	(c)	32.	(a)	33.	(a)	34.	(b)	35.	(a)	36.	(b)	37.	(a)	38.	(b)	39.	(c)	40.	(c)

Scan this QR code from your mobile phone to get the explanations of this paper.
Or
Visit : http://tinyurl.com/y2yg6csk

05 May Shift I

Session 1 (10:00 AM to 1:00 PM)

1. Choose the incorrect statement from the following.

(a) Strong nuclear force is a short range force
(b) Weak nuclear force is weakest among gravitational, electromagnetic, weak and strong nuclear forces
(c) Electromagnetic force is a long range force
(d) Gravitational force acts on all objects

2. If V_0 is the volume of a standard unit cell of germanium crystal containing N_0 atoms, then the expression for the mass m of a volume V in terms of V_0, N_0, M_{mol} and N_A is [here, M is the molar mass of germanium and N_A is the Avogadro's constant]

(a) $M\frac{V}{V_0}\frac{N_A}{N_0}$ (b) $\frac{N_A}{N_0}\frac{V_0}{V}M$
(c) $M\frac{V}{V_0}\frac{N_0}{N_A}$ (d) $M\frac{V_0}{V}\frac{N_0}{N_A}$

3. A stone is dropped from a height of 100 m, while another one is projected vertically upwards from the ground with a velocity of 25 m/s at the same time.

The time in seconds after which they will have the same height is (acceleration due to gravity, $g = 10\,\text{ms}^{-2}$)

(a) 4 (b) 5 (c) 6 (d) 7

4. A car starts from rest and moves with a constant acceleration of 5 m/s^2 for 10 s before the driver applies the brake. It then decelerates for 5 s before coming to rest, then the average speed of the car over the entire journey of the car is

(a) 23 m/s (b) 30 m/s (c) 33 m/s (d) 25 m/s

5. A particle moves in a circle with speed v varying with time as $v(t) = 2t$. The total acceleration of the particle after it completes 2 rounds of cycle is

(a) 16π (b) $2\sqrt{1+64\pi^2}$
(c) $2\sqrt{1+49\pi^2}$ (d) 14π

6. A small object is thrown at an angle 45° to the horizontal with an initial velocity $\mathbf{v}_0$. The velocity is averaged for first $\sqrt{2}$ s and the magnitude of average velocity comes out to be same as that of initial velocity, i.e. $|\mathbf{v}_0|$. The magnitude $|\mathbf{v}_0|$ will be (take, $g = 10\,\text{m/s}^2$)

(a) 3 m/s (b) $3\sqrt{2}$ m/s (c) 4 m/s (d) 5 m/s

7. Consider a wheel rotating around a fixed axis. If the rotation angle θ varies with time as $\theta = at^2$, then the total acceleration of a point A on the rim of the wheel is (v being the tangential velocity)

(a) $\frac{v}{t}\sqrt{1+4a^2t^4}$ (b) $\frac{v}{t}$
(c) $\frac{v}{t}(1+4a^2t^4)$ (d) $\sqrt{(1+4a^2t^4)}$

8. A block of mass 4 m travelling at a velocity v_1 in x-direction on a frictionless horizontal plane makes a head-on collision with another block of mass 2 m travelling in opposite direction with a velocity v_2. After collision, both the blocks travel as a single block along x-direction with a final velocity $5v_2$. The ratio of velocities $\frac{v_1}{v_2}$ is

(a) 2 (b) 3 (c) 5 (d) 8

9. A particle of mass m_1 moving along the X-axis collides with a stationary particle of mass m_2 and deviates by an angle 30° to the X-axis as shown in the figure.

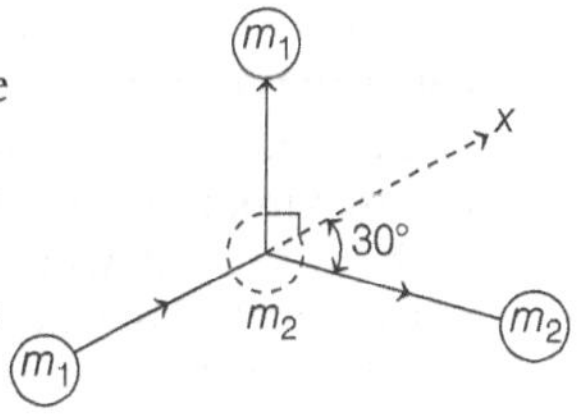

If the percentage change in kinetic energy of the combined system of these two particles reduces by 50%, then the ratio of the masses $\frac{m_2}{m_1}$ is

(a) 8 (b) 6 (c) $\frac{8}{7}$ (d) $\frac{1}{6}$

10. Collision takes place between two solid spheres denoted as 1 and 2. The initial velocities of the spheres are $u_1 = 3$ m/s and $u_2 = 1.5$ m/s and the final velocities are $v_1 = 2.5$ m/s and $v_2 = 3.5$ m/s. The coefficient of restitution between the materials of the spheres is nearly

(a) 0.67 (b) 0.78 (c) 0.83 (d) 0.96

11. A 30 kg boy stands at the far edge of a floating plank, whose near edge is against the shore of a river. The plank is 10 m long and weighs 10 kg. If the boy walks to the near edge of the plank, how far from the shore does the plank move

(a) 7 m (b) 8 m
(c) 7.5 m (d) 15 m

12. A uniform cylinder of radius 1 m, mass 1 kg spins about its axis with an angular velocity 20 rad/s. At certain moment, the cylinder is placed into a corner as shown in the figure. The coefficient of friction between the horizontal wall and the cylinder is μ, whereas the vertical wall is frictionless. If the number of rounds made by the cylinder is 5 before it stops, then the value of μ is (acceleration due to gravity, $g = 10\,\text{m/s}^2$)

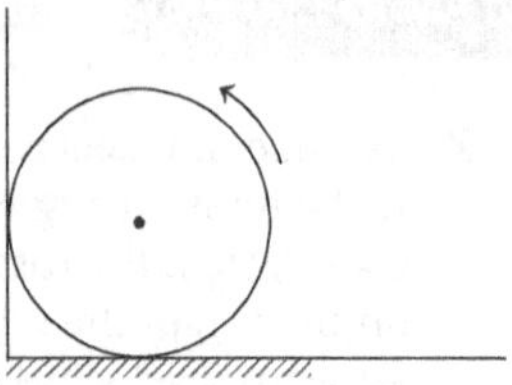

(a) $\frac{3}{\pi}$ (b) $\frac{2}{\pi}$ (c) $\frac{1}{\pi}$ (d) $\frac{0.4}{\pi}$

13. A spring has a natural length l with one end fixed to the ceiling. The other end is fitted with a smooth ring which can slide on a horizontal rod fixed at distance l below the ceiling. Initially, the spring makes an angle of 60° with the vertical, when system is released from rest. Find the angle of the spring with the vertical, when the velocity of the ring reaches half of the maximum velocity, which the ring can attain during the motion.

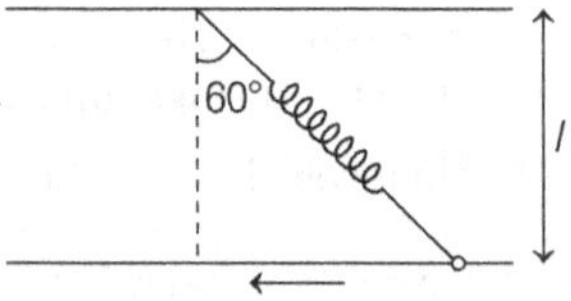

(a) 30° (b) $\cos^{-1}\left(\frac{2}{2+\sqrt{3}}\right)$

(c) $\cos^{-1}\left(\frac{\sqrt{3}-1}{2}\right)$ (d) 45°

14. From the pole of the earth, a body of mass m is imparted a velocity v_0 directed vertically up. If M is the mass of the earth, R its radius and g is the free-fall acceleration on its surface, then the height h to which the body will ascent is (neglect air resistance)

(a) $\frac{Rv_0^2}{(2gR - v_0^2)}$ (b) $\frac{Rv_0^2}{2gR}$

(c) R (d) $\frac{Rv_0^2}{(2gR + v_0^2)}$

15. Young's modulus experiment is performed on a steel wire of 1 m length and 8 mm diameter. The mass required to be added in the experiment to produce 5 mm elongation of the wire is ($Y_{\text{steel}} = 2\times10^9\,\text{Nm}^{-2}$, $g = 10\,\text{m/s}^2$)

(a) 25 kg (b) 50 kg (c) 250 kg (d) 500 kg

16. What is the rate at which a trapped bubble of 2 mm diameter rises slightly through a solution of density $13.6\times10^3\,\text{kg/m}^3$ and coefficient of viscosity 1.5 centipoise? Assume, the density of air is negligible and $g = 10\,\text{m/s}^2$.

(a) 20 m/s (b) 2 m/s (c) 0.2 m/s (d) 0.02 m/s

17. An electric heater with constant heat supply rate is used to convert a certain amount of liquid ammonia to saturated vapour at high pressure. The heater takes 14 minutes to bring the liquid at 15 °C to the boiling point of 50 °C and 92 minutes to convert the liquid at the boiling point wholly to vapour. If the specific heat capacity of liquid ammonia is 4.9 kJ/kg K, the latent heat of vaporisation of ammonia in kJ/kg is

(a) 557 (b) 981 (c) 1127 (d) 2250

18. An aluminium rod of length 1 m and a steel rod of length 2 m both having same cross-sectional area, are soldered together end-to-end. The thermal conductivity of aluminium rod and steel rod is 200 $\text{Js}^{-1}\text{m}^{-1}\text{K}^{-1}$ and 50 $\text{Js}^{-1}\text{m}^{-1}\text{K}^{-1}$ respectively. The temperatures of the free ends are maintained at 300 K and 500 K. What is the temperature of the junction?

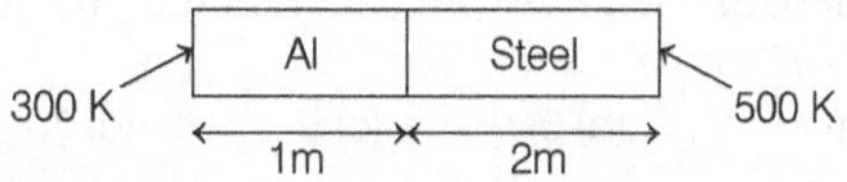

(a) 322 K (b) 350 K
(c) 367 K (d) 400 K

19. One mole of the ideal gas goes through the process $p = p_0\left[1 - \alpha\left(\frac{V}{V_0}\right)^3\right]$, where p and V are pressure and volume, p_0, V_0 and α are constants. If the maximum attainable temperature of the gas is $\left(\frac{3}{4}\right)\frac{p_0V_0}{R}$, then the value of α is

(a) 2 (b) $\frac{1}{2}$ (c) $\frac{1}{4}$ (d) 4

20. A gas mixture contains n_1 moles of a monoatomic gas and n_2 moles of gas of rigid diatomic molecules. Each molecule in monoatomic and diatomic gas has 3 and 5 degrees of freedom respectively. If the adiabatic exponent $\left(\frac{C_p}{C_V}\right)$ for this gas mixture is 1.5, then the ratio $\frac{n_1}{n_2}$ will be

(a) 1 (b) 1.5 (c) 2 (d) 2.5

21. A wire of length 50 cm and weighing 2 gm is attached to a spring at one end and to a fixed wall at the other end. The spring has a spring constant of 50 N/m and is stretched by 1 cm. If a wave pulse is produced on the string near the wall, then how much time will it take to reach the spring?

(a) 0.1 s (b) 0.2 s (c) 0.3 s (d) 0.4 s

22. Consider a point object situated at a distance of 30 cm from the centre of sphere of radius 2 cm and refractive index 1.5 as shown in the figure. If the refractive index of the region surrounding this sphere is 1.4, then the position of the image due to refraction by sphere with respect to the centre is

(a) 30 cm (b) 45 cm
(c) ∞ (d) 28 cm

23. At what distance from a biconvex lens of the focal length F, must be placed an object for the distance between the object and its real image to be minimal?

(a) $2F$ (b) F (c) $\frac{F}{2}$ (d) $4F$

24. In an experiment, light passing through two slits separated by a distance of 0.3 mm is projected on to a screen placed at 1 m from the plane of slits. It is observed that the distance between the central fringe and the adjacent bright fringe is 1.9 mm. The wavelength of light in nm is

(a) 450 (b) 495
(c) 530 (d) 570

25. A solid sphere of radius $r_1 = 1$ cm carries charge distributed uniformly over it with density $\rho_1 = -3\ \text{C/cm}^3$. It is surrounded by a concentric spherical shell of radius $r_2 = 2$ cm carrying uniform charge density $\rho_2 = \frac{1}{2}\ \text{C/cm}^2$. If E_d denotes the magnitude of the electric field at distance d from the common centre of the spheres, then

(a) $E_d = \frac{1}{3\varepsilon_0 d^2}, d \le 1\text{cm}$ (b) $E_d = \frac{1}{\varepsilon_0 d^2}, d \le 1\text{cm}$

(c) $E_d = \frac{d}{3\varepsilon_0}, d \le 1\text{cm}$ (d) $E_d = \frac{d}{\varepsilon_0}, d \le 1\text{cm}$

26. Two isolated, concentric, conducting spherical shells have radii R and $2R$ and uniform charges q and $2q$ respectively. If V_1 and V_2 are potentials at points located at distances $3R$ and $\frac{R}{2}$, respectively, from the centre of shells.

Then the ratio of $\left(\frac{V_2}{V_1}\right)$ will be

(a) 2 (b) 1 (c) $\frac{1}{2}$ (d) 0

27. A battery with internal resistance of 4Ω is connected to a circuit consisting three resistances, R, $2R$ and $4R$ (see following figure). If the power generated in the circuit is highest, then the magnitude of R must be

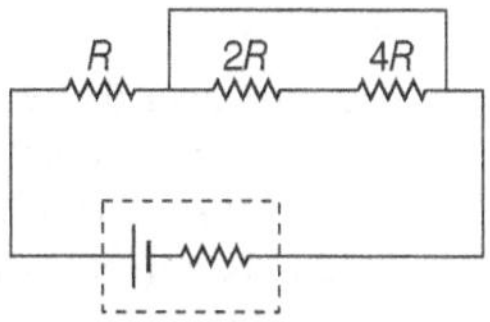

(a) 4 Ω (b) 7 Ω (c) 10 Ω (d) 14 Ω

28. If the resistance of each edge of a cube shaped wire frame as shown in figure below is R, then the resistance between points 1 and 7 is

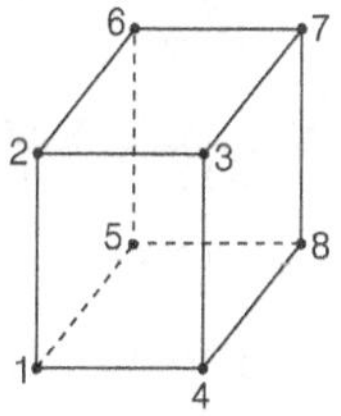

(a) $\frac{5R}{6}$ (b) $\frac{R}{6}$

(c) $5R$ (d) $\frac{6}{5}R$

29. A steady current I flows through a wire with one end at O and the other end extending upto infinity as shown in the figure. The magnetic field at a point P, located at a distance d from O is

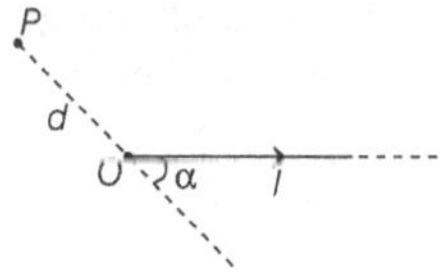

(a) $\frac{\mu_0 I}{4\pi d\cos\alpha}(1-\sin\alpha)$ (b) $\frac{\mu_0 I}{2\pi d\cos\alpha}(1-\sin\alpha)$

(c) $\frac{\mu_0 I}{4\pi d}$ (d) $\frac{\mu_0 I}{4\pi d\sin\alpha}(1-\cos\alpha)$

30. The magnetic induction at point O of the given infinitely long current carrying wire shown in the figure below is

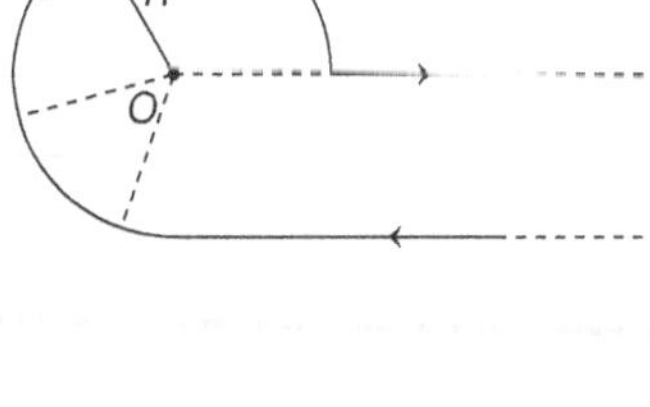

(a) $\frac{\mu_0 I}{4\pi R}\left(1-\frac{3\pi}{2}\right)$ (b) $\frac{\mu_0 I}{2R(1+\pi)}$

(c) $\frac{\mu_0 I}{4\pi R}\left[1+\frac{3\pi}{2}\right]$ (d) $\frac{\mu_0 I}{4\pi R}$

31. At a location, the horizontal component of the earth's magnetic field is 0.3 G in the magnetic meridian and the dip angle is 60°. The earth's magnetic field at this location in G is

(a) 0.3 (b) 0.6 (c) 0.9 (d) 1.2

32. A rectangular loop of wire is placed in the XY-plane with its side of length 3 cm parallel to the X-axis and the side of length 4 cm parallel to the Y-axis. It is moving in the positive X-direction with the speed 10 cm/s. A magnetic field exists in the space with its direction parallel to the Z-axis. The field decreases by 2×10^{-3} T/cm along the positive X-axis and increases in time by 2×10^{-2} T/s. The induced emf in the wire is

(a) -4.8×10^{-5} V (b) 4.8×10^{-5} V

(c) 0 (d) 3.6×10^{-5} V

33. A coil has inductance of 0.4 H and resistance of 8 Ω. It is connected to an AC source with peak emf 4 V and frequency $\frac{30}{\pi}$ Hz. The average power dissipated in the circuit is

(a) 1 W (b) 0.5 W (c) 0.3 W (d) 0.1 W

34. A laser beam is operating at 100 mW. The amount of energy stored by 90 cm length of this laser beam will be

(a) 2×10^{-10} J (b) 3×10^{-10} J

(c) 8×10^{-11} J (d) 6×10^{-11} J

35. A photon of energy 4 eV imparts all its energy to an electron that leaves a metal surface with 1.1 eV of kinetic energy. The work function of the metal is

(a) 2.9 eV (b) 5.1 eV (c) 3.64 eV (d) 4.4 eV

36. Consider an electron revolving in a circular orbit of hydrogen atom, whose quantum number is $n = 2$. The velocity of the electron in that orbit is

(a) 1.1×10^{6} m/s (b) 2.2×10^{7} m/s

(c) 4.4×10^{6} m/s (d) 2.2×10^{5} m/s

37. The half-life of $^{209}_{84}P_0$ is 103 years. The time it takes for 100 g sample of $^{209}_{84}P_0$ to decay to 3.125 g is

(a) 3296 years (b) $103\sqrt{2}$ years

(c) 1648 years (d) 515 years

38. The logic operation performed by the following circuit is

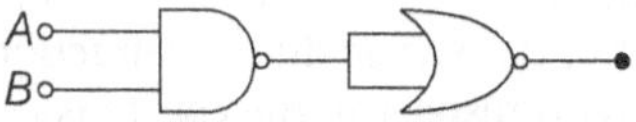

(a) NOR (b) AND (c) NAND (d) OR

39. Which of the following statements is true?

(a) A solid is an insulator or semiconductor, if its conduction band is partially filled

(b) A solid is necessarily an insulator, if its conduction band is empty

(c) A solid is necessarily a semiconductor, if its conduction band is empty

(d) A solid is a conductor, if its conduction band is partially filled

40. A transmitting and receiving antenna have height of d metres each. The maximum distance between them for satisfactory communication in Line-of-Sight mode (LOS) is $2d$ kilometers. If the radius of earth is 6400 km, then the value of d is

(a) 3.2 m (b) 6.4 m (c) 12.8 m (d) 16.0 m

Answers

1.	(b)	2.	(c)	3.	(a)	4.	(d)	5.	(b)	6.	(d)	7.	(a)	8.	(d)	9.	(a)	10.	(a)
11.	(c)	12.	(c)	13.	(*)	14.	(a)	15.	(b)	16.	(a)	17.	(c)	18.	(a)	19.	(c)	20.	(a)
21.	(a)	22.	(a)	23.	(a)	24.	(d)	25.	(d)	26.	(a)	27.	(b)	28.	(a)	29.	(d)	30.	(c)
31.	(b)	32.	(c)	33.	(d)	34.	(b)	35.	(a)	36.	(a)	37.	(d)	38.	(b)	39.	(d)	40.	(c)

Scan this QR code from your mobile phone to get the explanations of this paper.

Or

Visit : http://tinyurl.com/y4c8relv

05 May Shift II
Session 2 (3:00 PM to 6:00 PM)

1. A nucleus of deuterons or deuterium is a bound atomic system best described by

(a) composed of a proton and a neutron
(b) spherical shaped
(c) contains more than two nucleons
(d) proton and neutron are bound by electrostatic forces

2. A wooden cubical block of mass, $m = 20\,\text{kg}$ is measured within an error of 10 g. Its side length, $l = 100\,\text{cm}$ is measured within an error of 1mm. Then, the relative error in the measurement of its density is

(a) 1.8×10^{-2} (b) 2.6×10^{-2} (c) 3.5×10^{-3} (d) 4.8×10^{-3}

3. A vehicle starts moving in a straight line with an acceleration, $a = 4\,\text{m/s}^2$, with initial velocity equal to zero. After accelerating for time t_1, the vehicle moves uniformly and for time t_2, the vehicle finally decelerates for time t_1 eventually coming to a stop. The total time taken during the motion is 10 s and the average velocity during the motion is 5.1m/s. The time taken by the vehicle during acceleration is

(a) 2 s (b) 2.5 s (c) 1.5 s (d) 1.8 s

4. A body travels in a straight line from point A to point B with an initial velocity zero and uniform acceleration, covering 1m during the first second and 39 m during the last second. The distance between A and B in metre is

(a) 50 (b) 100 (c) 390 (d) 400

5. A cricket player can throw a ball with an initial speed of 30 m/s. What is the maximum range of the player can throw the ball? Neglect air resistance. [Take, $g = 10\,\text{m/s}^2$]

(a) 100 m (b) 90 m (c) 80 m (d) $90\sqrt{2}$ m

6. A particle moves in XY-plane with x and y varying with time t as $x(t) = 5t$, $y(t) = 5t(27 - t^2)$. At what time in seconds, the direction of velocity and acceleration will be perpendicular to each other?

(a) $5\sqrt{\frac{27}{2}}$ (b) 5 (c) $5\sqrt{12}$ (d) 3

7. A bullet enters in a piece of wood with velocity v_0 and the resistive force acting on the bullet in the wood is proportional to $v^{\frac{1}{3}}$.

If the total distance travelled by the bullet is proportional to $(v_0)^\beta$, then the value of β is

(a) $\frac{2}{3}$ (b) $\frac{5}{3}$ (c) $\frac{4}{3}$ (d) $-\frac{1}{3}$

8. A mechanical system consists two springs of stiffness coefficients k_1 and k_2 are connected in series. The minimum work to be performed on the system to stretch it by Δl is

(a) $\frac{1}{2}\left(\frac{k_1k_2}{k_1 + k_2}\right)\Delta l^2$ (b) $k_1k_2\Delta l^2$

(c) $\left(\frac{k_1k_2}{k_1 + k_2}\right)\Delta l^2$ (d) $\left(\frac{k_1k_2}{k_1 + k_2}\right)\Delta l$

9. A block of mass 5 kg is pulled by a force F as shown in the figure. If the coefficient of friction is 0.1, then the force needed to accelerate the block to $3\,\text{m/s}^2$ to the right is close to

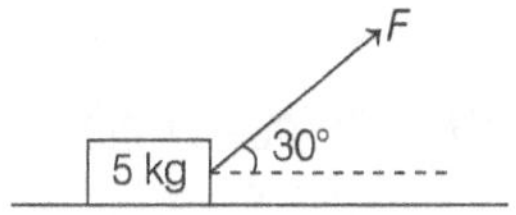

(a) 12N (b) 22N (c) 32N (d) 42N

10. A particle of mass m kg moves along the X-axis with its velocity varying with the distance travelled as $v = kx^\beta$, where k is a positive constant. The total work done by all the forces during displacement of the particle from $x = 0$ to $x = d$ is close to

(a) $\frac{mk^2}{2}$ (b) $\frac{mk^2}{2}d^{2\beta}$ (c) $\frac{mk^2}{2\beta}$ (d) $\frac{mk^2d}{2\beta}$

11. The masses and positions (in rectangular coordinates) of four particles are as follows : 1kg at (a, a), 2kg at $(-a, a)$, 3kg at $(-a, -a)$ and 4kg at $(a, -a)$. The position vector of the centre of mass of the system of four particles is

(a) $-4a\hat{\mathbf{i}}$ (b) $-4a\hat{\mathbf{i}} - 4a\hat{\mathbf{j}}$ (c) 0 (d) $-0.4a\hat{\mathbf{j}}$

12. A solid sphere is rolling without slipping on a semi-circular track of radius 10 m as shown in the figure. The radius of solid sphere is much smaller than the radius of semi-circular track. At the lowest point, it has a velocity

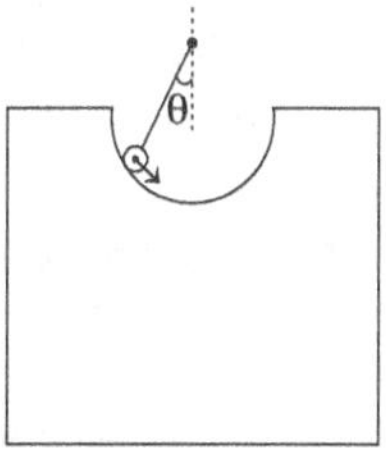

10 m/s. To what maximum angle θ from the vertical will the sphere travel before it comes back down? Neglect the rolling friction between the sphere and the track.

(Take, $g = 10 \text{m/s}^2$)

(a) $\sin^{-1}\left(\frac{3}{5}\right)$ (b) $\sin^{-1}\left(\frac{3}{7}\right)$ (c) $\cos^{-1}\left(\frac{3}{10}\right)$ (d) $\cos^{-1}\left(\frac{1}{3}\right)$

13. A block of mass (10 α)g, where α is a constant is moving with velocity 3m/s to the right collides inelastically with the block on the right with mass 10 g and sticks to it. The right block is connected to three springs as shown in the figure. The spring constant of each spring is 2 N/m. If the amplitude of the resulting simple harmonic motion is $\frac{1}{2\sqrt{2}}$ m, then the value of α is

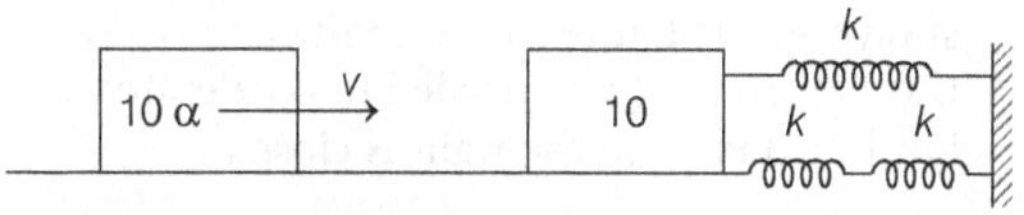

(a) 5 (b) 2.5 (c) 7 (d) 10

14. The mass density inside a solid sphere of radius r varies as $\rho(r) = \rho_0\left(\frac{r}{R}\right)^\beta$, where ρ_0 and β are constants and r is the distance from the centre. Let E_1 and E_2 be gravitational fields due to sphere at distance $\frac{R}{2}$ and $2R$ from the centre of sphere. If $\frac{E_2}{E_1} = 4$, the value of β is

(a) 2 (b) 2.5 (c) 3 (d) 4

15. The pressure to be applied to the ends of a steel cylinder to keep its length constant upon raising its temperature by 100°C is

(thermal expansion coefficient, $\alpha = 11\times10^{-6}$/K, Young's modulus = 200 GPa)

(a) 0.22×10^9Pa (b) 5.5×10^{-6}Pa
(c) 0.22Pa (d) 55Pa

16. The root mean square (rms) velocity of an ideal gas at temperature T is v. If the temperature is increased to $4T$, the rms velocity of the gas is

(a) $\sqrt{3}v$ (b) $\sqrt{2}v$ (c) $2v$ (d) $3v$

17. A glass beaker contains 200 g of carbonated water initially at 20°C. How much ice should be added to obtain the final temperature of 0°C with all ice melted, if the initial temperature of ice is −10°C. Neglect heat capacity of glass.

[Take, $C_{\text{water}} = 4190\,\text{J/kg°C}$,
$C_{\text{ice}} = 2100\,\text{J/kg°C}$, $L_F = 3.34\times10^5\,\text{J/kg}$]

(a) 47g (b) 76 g (c) 200 g (d) 22 g

18. Heat loss takes place from a body maintained at a temperature of 400°C to the surrounding air at 30°C by convection and to the surrounding surfaces at 30°C by radiation. The Newton's cooling coefficient is 20 W/m²K and the Stefan-Boltzmann constant is 5.67×10^{-8} W/m²K⁴. If the rate of heat loss by convection is equal to the rate of heat loss by radiation, the emissivity of the body surface is

(a) 0.35 (b) 0.46 (c) 0.55 (d) 0.66

19. A Carnot engine absorbs heat from a reservoir maintained at temperature 1000 K. The engine rejects heat to a reservoir whose temperature is T. If the magnitude of a absorbed heat is 400J and work performed is 300J, then the value of T is

(a) 250K (b) 500K (c) 750K (d) 1750K

20. The mean kinetic energy of monoatomic gas molecules under standard conditions is $\langle E_1\rangle$. If the gas is compressed adiabatically 8 times to its initial volume, the mean kinetic energy of gas molecules changes to $\langle E_2\rangle$. The ratio $\frac{\langle E_2\rangle}{\langle E_1\rangle}$ is

(a) 2 (b) 4 (c) 6 (d) 8

21. The speed of a transverse wave on a string is 160 m/s. If the three resonant frequencies of this string respectively are 160Hz, 240Hz and 400Hz, the length of the string is

(a) 80 cm (b) 100 cm (c) 160 cm (d) 200 cm

22. Consider a concave mirror of 10 cm focal length illuminated by an object kept at a distance of 25 cm. The distance at which the image is formed and its magnification respectively are

(a) −16.7 cm and −0.67 (b) 7.1 cm and 0.29
(c) −16.7 cm and 0.67 (d) 7.1 cm and −0.29

23. Two objects P and Q are placed at 10 cm and 30 cm infront of a convex lens of focal length 20 cm. The correct option for the image of P and Q is

(a)	P-virtual and inverted	Q-real and upright
(b)	P-virtual and upright	Q-real and inverted
(c)	P-real and inverted	Q-virtual and upright
(d)	P-real and upright	Q-virtual and inverted

24. Calculate the minimum thickness of a soap film (n= 1.33) that results in constructive interference in reflected light, if the film is illuminated with light whose wavelength in free space is 532 nm.

(a) 113 nm (b) 100 nm
(c) 200 nm (d) 226 nm

25. A thin spherical shell encloses a concentric solid sphere. The radius of the shell is $(0.060)^{\frac{1}{2}}$ m and its surface charge density is $-10^{-6}\text{C}/\text{m}^2$. The radius of the solid sphere is $(0.01)^{\frac{1}{3}}$m and its volumetric charge density is $3\times10^{-5}\text{C}/\text{m}^3$. ε_0 is the permittivity of free space in C^2/Nm^2. The electric flux through a spherical surface concentric with the spherical shell and of radius greater than that of the shell in V-m is

(a) $\frac{0.4\pi\times10^{-7}}{\varepsilon_0}$ (b) $\frac{0.8\pi\times10^{-7}}{\varepsilon_0}$ (c) $\frac{1.2\pi\times10^{-7}}{\varepsilon_0}$ (d) $\frac{1.6\pi\times10^{-7}}{\varepsilon_0}$

26. A conducting sphere S_1 of radius r_1 is connected by a conducting wire to another conducting sphere S_2 of radius r_2, where r_1 = 3 cm and r_2 = 2 cm. Before they are connected, S_1 carries charge of 10 units. The electric potential at the point which is at a distance 4 cm from the centre of S_1 and a distance 3 cm from the centre of S_2 is

(a) $\frac{1}{4\pi\varepsilon_0}\frac{17}{6}$ (b) $\frac{1}{4\pi\varepsilon_0}\frac{3}{2}$ (c) $\frac{1}{4\pi\varepsilon_0}\frac{1}{6}$ (d) $\frac{1}{4\pi\varepsilon_0}\frac{17}{12}$

27. A 500Ω resistor connected to an external battery is placed inside a thermally insulated cylinder fitted with a frictionless piston. The cylinder contains an ideal gas. A current i of 200 mA flows through the resistor as shown in the figure. The mass of the piston is 10 kg. Assuming $g = 10\text{m}/\text{s}^2$, the speed at which the piston will move upward, due to heat dissipated by the resistor, so that the temperature of the gas remains unchanged is

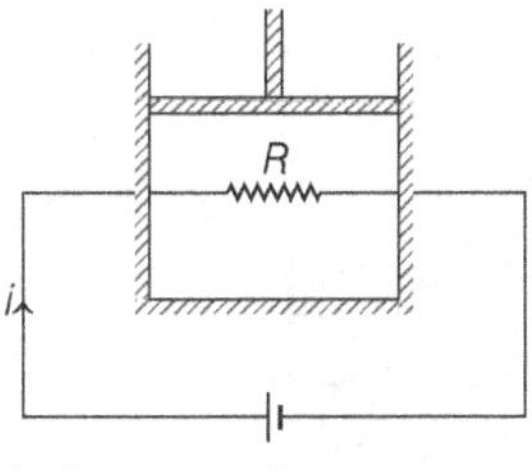

(a) 10 cm/s (b) 15 cm/s
(c) 20 cm/s (d) 30 cm/s

28. A cylindrical shape resistance is connected to a battery with emf 5V. The resistance per unit length varies as $\rho(x) = \rho_0\left(\frac{x}{L}\right)^{\alpha}$, where ρ_0 and α are constants and x is the distance from one end of the resistor. The magnitude or product $\rho_0 L$ is 10 Ω, where L is the length of the resistor. If the thermal power generated by the resistor is 20W, then the value of α is

(a) 3 (b) 5 (c) 7 (d) 9

29. Consider a current carrying wire shown in the figure. If the radius of the curved part of the wire is R and the linear parts are assumed to be very long, then the magnetic induction of the field at the point O is

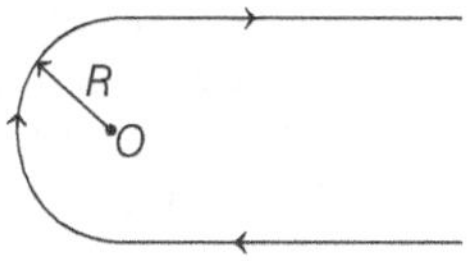

(a) $\frac{\mu_0}{4\pi}\frac{i}{R}(2+\pi)$ (b) $\frac{\mu_0 i}{2\pi R}$ (c) $\frac{\mu_0}{2}\frac{i}{R}$ (d) $\frac{\mu_0}{4}\frac{i}{R}$

30. A charged particle moves with some initial velocity along the direction of external magnetic field B. Now, if we apply uniform field perpendicular to the magnetic field, then the trajectory of the charged particle will be

(a) circle (b) helix
(c) cycloid (d) straight line

31. A magnetic dipole is under the influence of two orthogonal magnetic fields, $B_1 = 0.5\times10^{-3}$T and $B_2 = 0.866\times10^{-3}$T. If the dipole comes to stable equilibrium at an angle θ with respect to B_2 field, then the value of θ is

(a) 45° (b) 30° (c) 60° (d) 90°

32. A wheel with radial metal spokes 1m in length is rotated in a magnetic field of 0.5×10^{-4} T normal to the plane of the wheel. If the induced emf between the rim and axle is $\pi/3000$ V, then the rotational speed of the wheel in revolutions per minute is

(a) 400 (b) 500
(c) 600 (d) 700

33. An initially charged undriven LCR circuit having inductance L, capacitance C and resistance R will be

(a) oscillate with frequency $\frac{1}{\sqrt{LC}}$

(b) oscillate without damping, if $R^2 < \frac{4L}{C}$

(c) oscillate with damping, if $R^2 > \frac{4L}{C}$

(d) oscillate with damping, if $R^2 < \frac{4L}{C}$

34. An electromagnetic wave having frequency 4×10^{14} Hz is passing through a small volume. The energy contained in this volume oscillates with frequency

(a) 0 Hz (b) 4×10^{14} Hz
(c) 8×10^{14} Hz (d) 2×10^{14} Hz

35. Light of frequency 4×10^{14} Hz is incident on a metal surface of work function 2.14 eV, resulting in photoemission of electrons. The maximum kinetic energy of the emitted electrons is [$h = 6.63 \times 10^{-34}$ J-s]

(a) 0.35 eV (b) 0.14 eV
(c) 2.14 eV (d) 0 eV

36. If a proton is accelerated through a potential difference of 1000 V, then its de-Broglie wavelength is (given, $m_p = 1.67 \times 10^{-27}$ kg, $h = 6.63 \times 10^{-34}$ J-s)

(a) 9.1×10^{-13} m (b) $9.1 \times 10^{+13}$ m
(c) 1.09×10^{-15} m (d) $1.09 \times 10^{+15}$ m

37. In uranium radioactive series, initial nucleus $^{238}U_{92}$ decays to final nucleus $^{206}U_{82}$. In this process, the number of α-particles and β-particles emitted are

(a) 8 and 3 (b) 16 and 6
(c) 16 and 3 (d) 8 and 6

38. Determine V_{CE} in the following silicon based transistor circuit

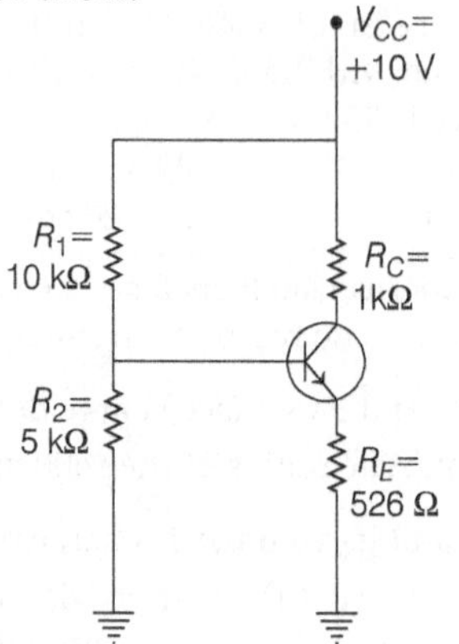

(a) 6.8 V (b) 2.0 V (c) 5.9 V (d) 2.4 V

39. The voltage-current characteristic of a diode during forward bias is given by $I = 7.8 \times 10^{-5} e^{6.5V_D}$, where I is the current in mA and V_D is the diode voltage in V. Find the dynamic resistance of the diode in Ω, when the current is 4mA.

(a) 18.6 (b) 21.7 (c) 28.2 (d) 36.2

40. The height of a transmission antenna is 49m and that of the receiving antenna is 64m. What should be the maximum distance between them for line of sight transmission?

(a) 50.1 km (b) 53.6 km (c) 43.6 km (d) 65.2 km

Answers

1.	(a)	2.	(c)	3.	(c)	4.	(d)	5.	(b)	6.	(d)	7.	(b)	8.	(a)	9.	(b)	10.	(b)
11.	(d)	12.	(c)	13.	(a)	14.	(c)	15.	(a)	16.	(c)	17.	(a)	18.	(d)	19.	(a)	20.	(b)
21.	(b)`	22.	(a)	23.	(b)	24.	(b)	25.	(d)	26.	(a)	27.	(c)	28.	(c)	29.	(a)	30.	(b)
31.	(b)	32.	(a)	33.	(d)	34.	(c)	35.	(d)	36.	(a)	37.	(d)	38.	(d)	39.	(d)	40.	(b)

Scan this QR code from your mobile phone to get the explanations of this paper.
Or
Visit : http://tinyurl.com/y5wpz8ef

07 May Shift I
Session 1 (10:00 AM to 1:00 PM)

1. A tokamak fusion test reactor works on
(a) bombardment of thermal neutrons with uranium-235
(b) magnetic confinement of plasma
(c) electric discharge under high voltage bias
(d) acceleration of charged particles in electromagnetic fields

2. Dimensions of the quantity $\frac{p}{\varepsilon_0 \mu_0}$, where p is the pressure, ε_0 is electric permittivity of free space and μ_0 is permeability of free space, will be
(a) $[MLT^{-4}]$ (b) $[ML^2T^{-2}]$
(c) $[ML^3T^{-3}]$ (d) $[ML^2T^{-4}]$

3. Consider a vechicle moving with a velocity 54 km/h. At a distance of 400 m, from the traffic light brakes are applied. The acceleration of the vehicle, after the application of brakes is $-0.3\ m/s^2$. The vehicle's position relative to the traffic light is
(a) 25 m (b) 375 m (c) 425 m (d) 30 m

4. Two trains A and B travel in two parallel rail tracks in opposite direction with speed v_1 and v_2, respectively. They take 4 s to pass each other at this speed. If the speed of train A is increased by 50%, then they take 3 s to pass each other. The ratio of v_1 / v_2 is
(a) 0:5 (b) 1:5
(c) 2:1 (d) 2:5

5. A small ball is thrown at an angle 45° to the horizontal with an initial velocity of $2\sqrt{2}$ m/s. The magnitude of mean velocity averaged over the first 2 s is [take, acceleration due to gravity, $g = 10\ m/s^2$]
(a) 7.0 m/s (b) 8.2 m/s (c) 7.8 m/s (d) 9 m/s

6. The position vector of a particle moving in a plane is given by $\mathbf{r} = a\cos\omega t\,\hat{\mathbf{i}} + b\sin\omega t\,\hat{\mathbf{j}}$, where $\hat{\mathbf{i}}$ and $\hat{\mathbf{j}}$ are the unit vectors along the rectangular axes X and Y; a, b and ω are constants and t is time. The acceleration of the particle is directed along the vector
(a) $-a\hat{\mathbf{i}} + b\hat{\mathbf{j}}$ (b) $b\hat{\mathbf{i}} + a\hat{\mathbf{j}}$
(c) $-\mathbf{r}$ (d) $\frac{d\mathbf{r}}{dt}$

7. A child is on a merry-go-round, standing at a distance 2 m from the centre. The coefficient of static friction between the child and the surface of merry-go-round is 0.8. At what maximum angular velocity can the merry-go-round be rotated before the child slips? (Take, $g = 10\ m/s^2$)
(a) 0.5 rad/s (b) 1 rad/s (c) 2 rad/s (d) 4 rad/s

8. A ball of mass 0.2 kg is thrown from a height of 1 m and with an initial velocity of $\sqrt{10}$ m/s at an angle of 45° with the horizontal. Assuming, acceleration due to gravity $g = 10\ m/s^2$, then modulus of momentum increment during the total time of motion in kg m/s is
(a) $\frac{2+\sqrt{10}}{\sqrt{10}}$ (b) $\frac{1+\sqrt{10}}{\sqrt{5}}$ (c) $\frac{1+\sqrt{5}}{\sqrt{5}}$ (d) $\frac{\sqrt{5}-1}{\sqrt{5}}$

9. A small body of mass 500 g moves on a rough horizontal surface before finally stops. The initial velocity of the body is 2 m/s and coefficient of friction is 0.3. Then, find absolute value of the average power developed by the frictional force during the time of motion. (Take, $g = 10\ m/s^2$)
(a) 1 W (b) 1.5 W (c) 2 W (d) 2.5 W

10. A 1.5 kg ball is shot upward at an angle of 34° to the horizontal with an initial speed of 20 m/s, then maximum height of the ball reaches is (use $\cos 34° = 0.83$ or $\sin 34° = 0.56$)
(a) 6.3 m (b) 9.4 m (c) 13.8 m (d) 11.2 m

11. If a disc of mass M and radius R rotates with an angular acceleration a, of the torque acting on the disc is
(a) MR^2a (b) $\frac{MR^2a}{2}$ (c) $\frac{2MR^2a}{5}$ (d) $\frac{MR^2a}{12}$

12. Consider a sphere of mass M and radius R centered at origin. The density of material of the sphere is $\rho = Ar^{\alpha}$, where r is the radial distance, α and A are constants. If the moment of inertia of the sphere about the axis passing through centre is $\frac{6}{7}MR^2$, then the value of α is
(a) 3 (b) 6 (c) 9 (d) 12

13. The position of a particle executing simple harmonic motion is given by $x(t) = 2\cos\left(\frac{\pi}{15}t - \frac{\pi}{2}\right)$, where x is in centimetre and t is in seconds. The time period of the kinetic energy of the particle in seconds is

(a) π (b) $\frac{\pi}{15}$ (c) 15 (d) 30

14. An artificial satellite of mass m revolves around the earth at a height h with a speed v. How much power (energy per second) will it require to keep itself moving with constant speed in the orbit of radius r?

(a) $\frac{mv^3}{r}$ (b) $\frac{1}{2}mv^2$ (c) $\frac{6m M_e}{(R_e + h)}$ (d) 0

15. Consider an air bubble of radius 2 mm in a liquid at a depth of 5 cm below the free surface. The density of the liquid is 1000 kg/m^3 and the surface tension is 0.1 N/m. Then, find the pressure inside the air bubble is greater than the pressure at the free surface of the liquid. (Take, $g = 10\,\text{m/s}^2$)

(a) 500 Pa (b) 600 Pa (c) 700 Pa (d) 800 Pa

16. A cylindrical vessel is filled with water upto the height 1 m from the base. A small orifice is opened at some height in the cylinder and the water level is reduced to height of orifice in 20 s. If the base area of the cylinder is 100 times the area of orifice, then the height of orifice from the base is (take, $g = 10\,\text{m/s}^2$)

(a) 80 cm (b) 60 cm (c) 40 cm (d) 20 cm

17. A vessel of volume V contains a mixture of ideal gases at temperature T. The gas mixture contains n_1, n_2 and n_3 moles of three gases. Assuming ideal gas system, the pressure of the mixture is

(a) $\frac{(n_1 + n_2 + n_3)RT}{V}$ (b) $\frac{(n_1 n_2 n_3)RT}{V}$

(c) $\frac{RT}{(n_1 + n_2 + n_3)V}$ (d) $\frac{RT}{V(n_1 n_2 n_3)}$

18. The resistance of a thermometer is 100 Ω at the triple point of water (273 K) and is 300Ω at the melting point of gold (~ 873 K). The temperature at which the resistance of the thermometer is 200 Ω is

(a) 273 K (b) 373 K (c) 473 K (d) 573 K

19. A diesel engine has a compression ratio of 20 : 1. If the initial pressure is 1×10^5 Pa and the initial volume of the cylinder is 1×10^{-3} m^3, then how much work does the gas do during the compression? (Assume the process as adiabatic) ($C_V = 20.8$ J/mol K, $\gamma_{air} = 1.4$, $(20)^{1.4} = 66.3$)

(a) – 880 J (b) – 579 J (c) 220 J (d) 485 J

20. A polyatomic gas has f vibrational degrees of freedom, then the ratio of the specific heat at constant pressure to that at constant volume will be

(a) $\frac{4+f}{3+f}$ (b) $\frac{4-f}{3-f}$ (c) $\frac{3+f}{4+f}$ (d) $\frac{3-f}{4-f}$

21. The speed of sound in air at temperature T and pressure p is v. When the temperature is increased to $2T$ and the pressure is reduced to $\frac{p}{2}$, then the speed is changed to

(a) $2v$ (b) v (c) $\sqrt{2}\,v$ (d) $\frac{v}{\sqrt{2}}$

22. A printed page is kept pressed by a transparent cube of edge t. The refractive index of the cube varies as $\mu(z) = 1 + \frac{z}{t}$, where z is the vertical distance from bottom of the cube. If viewed from top, then the printed letters appear to be shifted by an amount

(a) $(1 - \ln 2)t$ (b) $(2\ln 2 - 1)t$ (c) $\frac{t}{2\ln 2}$ (d) $\frac{2t}{3\ln 2}$

23. A half spherical glass lens with refractive index 1.5 is placed in a liquid with refractive index of 1.3 (see following figure). The radius of the half spherical lens is 10 cm. A parallel beam of light travelling in the liquid is refracted by the glass lens. Then the absolute value of the position of the image from the centre of the glass lens will be

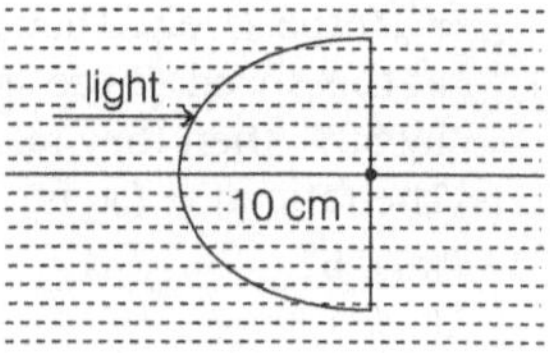

(a) 10 cm (b) 65 cm (c) 5 cm (d) 11.5 cm

24. A light beam of wavelength 800 nm passes through a single slit and projected on a screen kept at 5m away from the slit. What should be the slit width for the ray optics approximation to be valid?

(a) 0.5 mm (b) 2 mm (c) 1.5 mm (d) 0.25 mm

25. Choose the incorrect statement from the following.

(a) The electric field in electrostatics obey principle of superposition

(b) The electric field inside a perfect conductor is zero
(c) The electric dipole will try to orient in a direction opposite to the external electric field
(d) The electric flux passing through any closed surface enclosing the charges remains constant

26. Consider a parallel plate capacitor with plates in the shape of square and in *XY*-plane. The gap between the plates is filled with dielectric material. The dielectric constant *k* varies with *X*-axis as $k(x) = \left[1 + \left(\frac{x}{L}\right)^{\alpha}\right]$, where α is a constant. Let C_d and C_a are capacitance in the presence of dielectric and air, respectively. If the ratio $\frac{C_d}{C_a} = \frac{7}{6}$, then the value of α must be

(a) 3 (b) 5 (c) 7 (d) 9

27. The emfs of three cells connected in parallel are $E_1 = 5\text{ V}, E_2 = 8\text{ V}$ and $E_3 = 10\text{ V}$ and their internal resistances are $R_1 = 1\,\Omega$, $R_2 = 2\,\Omega$ and $R_3 = 3\,\Omega$, respectively. By changing E_3 to E_{3N}, the equivalent emf is doubled, then E_{3N} in *V* is

(a) 12 (b) 34 (c) 47 (d) 82

28. A cell of emf 10 V and internal resistance 3 Ω is connected in parallel with another cell of emf 7 V and internal resistance $\frac{3}{5}\Omega$, such that their positive terminals are joined together and so their are negative terminals. Their positive terminals are joined with the negative terminal and their negative terminal is joined with the positive terminal of a third cell of emf 20 V with internal resistance 2Ω. The combination can be replaced by a battery of emf *E* and internal resistance *r*, then the values of *E* and *R* are respectively

(a) $E = 2\text{ V}, r = 2.5\,\Omega$ (b) $E = 2\text{ V}, r = 0.4\,\Omega$
(c) $E = 5\text{ V}, r = 0.4\,\Omega$ (d) $E = 5\text{ V}, r = 2.5\Omega$

29. A square loop of length *L* is placed with its edges parallel to the *XY*-axes. The loop is carrying the current *I*. If the magnetic field in the region varies as $\mathbf{B} = B_0\left(1 + \frac{xy}{L^2}\right)\hat{\mathbf{k}}$, then the magnitude of the force on the loop will be

(a) IB_0L (b) $\frac{IB_0L}{2}$
(c) $\frac{IB_0L}{\sqrt{2}}$ (d) $\sqrt{2}\,IB_0L$

30. A non-conducting disc of radius *R* has surface charge density which varies with distance from the centre as $\sigma(r) = \sigma_0\left[1 + \sqrt{\frac{r}{R}}\right]$, where σ_0 is a constant. The disc rotates about its axis with angular velocity ω. If *B* is the magnitude of magnetic induction at the centre, then $\frac{B}{\mu_0\sigma_0\omega R}$ will be

(a) $\frac{3}{4}$ (b) $\frac{4}{5}$ (c) $\frac{5}{6}$ (d) $\frac{6}{7}$

31. For a wire, as shown in the figure, carrying a current of 10 A, then the magnetic induction field at the point *O* is [take, $\mu_0 = 4\pi \times 10^{-7}$ H/m]

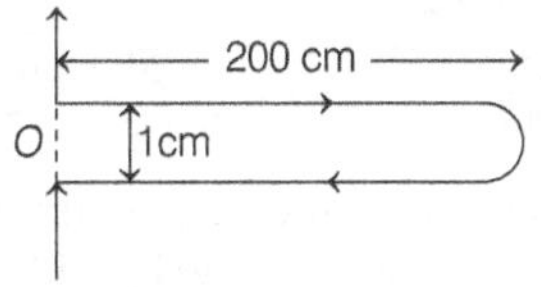

(a) 2×10^{-4} T (b) 4×10^{-4} T
(c) 10×10^{-4} T (d) $4\pi \times 10^{-4}$ T

32. A solenoid of radius *R* has *n* turns per unit length, then the self-inductance of the solenoid per unit length is

(a) $\mu_0 n\pi R^2$ (b) $\mu_0 nR^2$ (c) $\mu_0 n^2R^2$ (d) $\mu_0 n^2\pi R^2$

33. A distribution transformer with an efficiency of 90% supplies to a colony of 10 homes. All the 10 homes have electrical oven running at the same time, that draw 20 A current from 220 V lines. The power dissipated as heat in the transformer is

(a) 12.2 kW (b) 4.9 kW
(c) 8.4 kW (d) 9.9 kW

34. The law not described by any four of the Maxwell's equations is

(a) Gauss' law for electricity
(b) Le-Chatelier's law of equilibrium
(c) Gauss' law for magnetism
(d) Faraday's law of induction

35. Let $\mathbf{E}_0$ and $\mathbf{B}_0$ denote the amplitude of electric and magnetic field of a plane electromagnetic wave in air. The magnitude of the average momentum transferred per unit area and per unit time to a totally absorbing surface is

(a) $\frac{1}{2}\varepsilon_0 E_0^2$ (b) $\frac{1}{2}\mu_0 B_0$
(c) $\varepsilon_0 E_0^2$ (d) $2\frac{B_0^2}{\mu_0}$

36. In a hydrogen sample, if the atoms are excited to states with principal quantum number 20, then the number of different wavelengths which may be observed in the spectrum is

(a) 100 (b) 140
(c) 190 (d) 230

37. Consider a radioactive nuclide which follow decay rate given by $A(t) = A_0 2^{-(t/t_0)}$, where $A(t)$ is the fraction of radioactive material remaining after time t from the initial A_0 at zero time. Let A_1 be the fraction of original activity which remains after 120 hours. Likewise A_2 is the fraction of original activity remaining after 200 hours. If $\frac{A_1}{A_2} = 1.6$, then the half-life (t_0) will be

(a) 10 hours (b) 20 hours
(c) 40 hours (d) 60 hours

38. In the diode-based rectifier circuit given below, if $V_s = V_m \sin \omega t$ and the diode is ideal, then the average value of V_L is

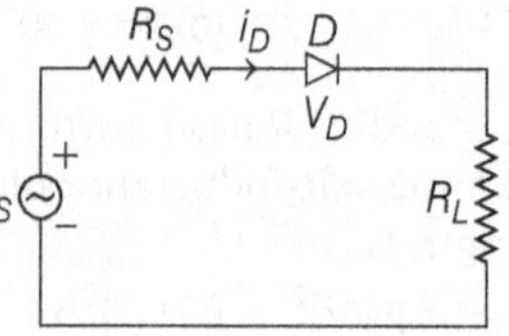

(a) $\frac{R_L}{(R_L + R_S)} \frac{V_m}{\pi}$ (b) $R_L V_m \sin\omega t$

(c) $\frac{R_L}{(R_L + R_S)} V_m$ (d) $\frac{R_L}{(R_L + R_S)} V_m \sin\omega t$

39. Consider the circuit given below

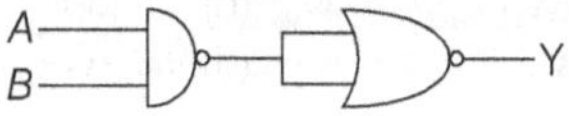

Choose the sketch depicting the output Y of this circuit having inputs A and B as given below

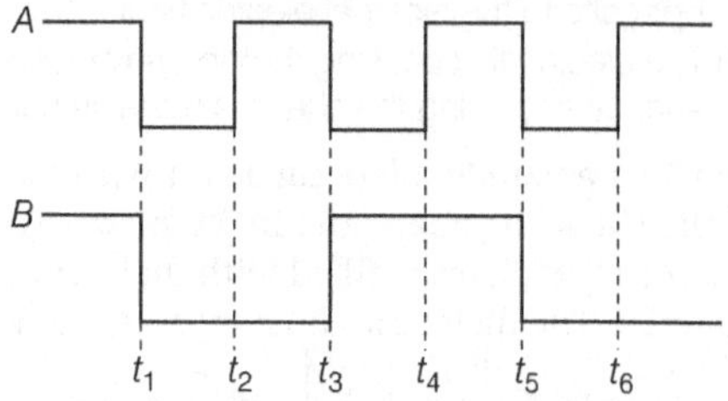

(a)
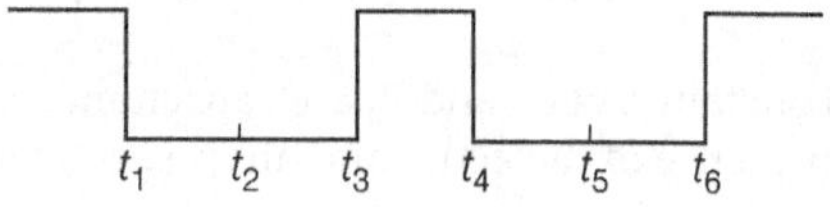

(b)
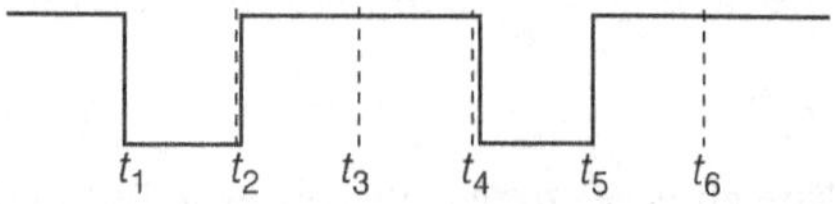

(c)
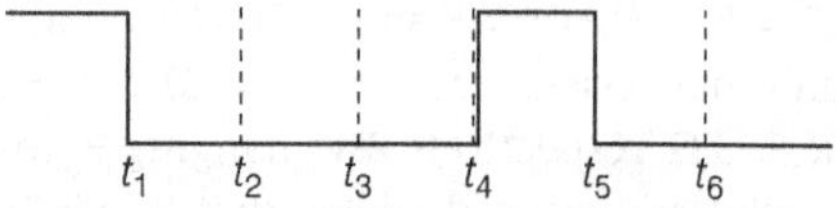

(d)
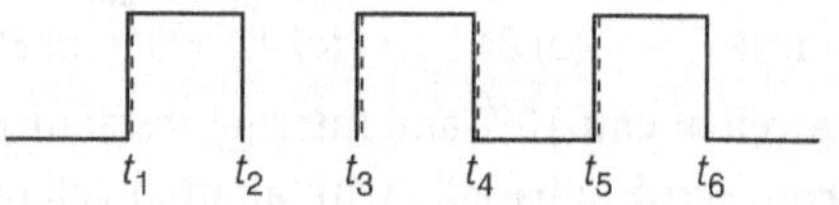

40. For a television network, 5×10^5 channels are granted. If the central frequency of the microwave link is 25 GHz and the alloted bandwidth for each channel is 2 kHz, then how much percentage of the link is used for the network?

(a) 4% (b) 10% (c) 25% (d) 5%

Answers

1.	(b)	2.	(a)	3.	(a)	4.	(c)	5.	(b)	6.	(c)	7.	(c)	8.	(c)	9.	(b)	10.	(a)
11.	(b)	12.	(*)	13.	(c)	14.	(d)	15.	(b)	16.	(a)	17.	(a)	18.	(d)	19.	(b)	20.	(a)
21.	(c)	22.	(a)	23.	(b)	24.	(b)	25.	(c)	26.	(b)	27.	(c)	28.	(b)	29.	(*)	30.	(c)
31.	(b)	32.	(d)	33.	(b)	34.	(b)	35.	(a)	36.	(c)	37.	(b)	38.	(a)	39.	(c)	40.	(a)

Scan this QR code from your mobile phone to get the explanations of this paper.
Or
Visit : http://tinyurl.com/y5bo834u

Fully Solved

AP EAMCET 2017

Engineering Entrance Exam

Physics

1. A monoatomic ideal gas goes through a cyclic process as shown in the figure. The efficiency of this process is

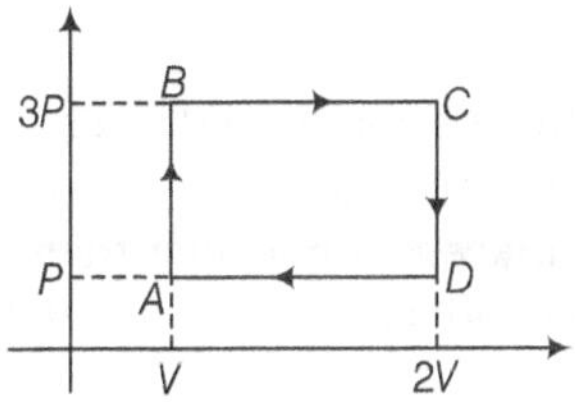

(a) 78%
(b) 42%
(c) 62%
(d) 21%

2. Two situations are shown in fig. (a) and (b).

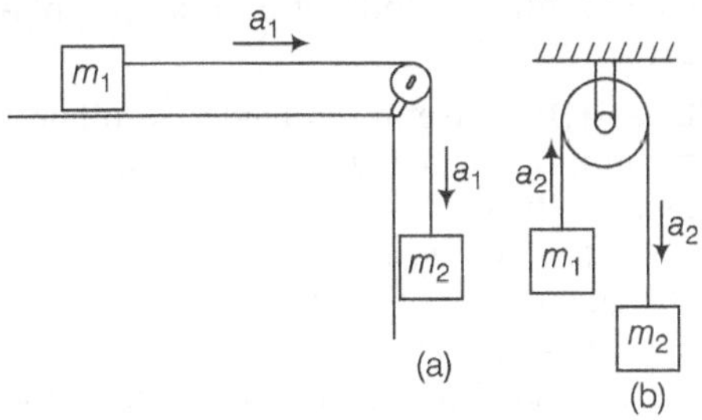

In each case, $m_1 = 3$ kg and $m_2 = 4$ kg. If a_1, a_2 are the respective accelerations of the blocks in these situations, then the values of a_1 and a_2 are respectively [$g = 10 \text{ ms}^{-2}$]

(a) $\frac{20}{7}\text{ ms}^{-2}, \frac{10}{7}\text{ ms}^{-2}$
(b) $\frac{10}{7}\text{ ms}^{-2}, \frac{25}{7}\text{ ms}^{-2}$
(c) $\frac{40}{7}\text{ ms}^{-2}, \frac{10}{7}\text{ ms}^{-2}$
(d) $\frac{30}{7}\text{ ms}^{-2}, \frac{5}{7}\text{ ms}^{-2}$

3. Three uniform thin aluminum rods each of length 2 m form an equilateral triangle PQR as shown in the figure. The mid point of the rod PQ is at the origin of the coordinate system. If the temperature of the system of rods increases by 50°C, the increase in y-coordinate of the centre of mass of the system of the rods is .... mm.

(Coefficient of volume expansion of aluminium $= 12\sqrt{3} \times 10^{-6}\text{ K}^{-1}$)

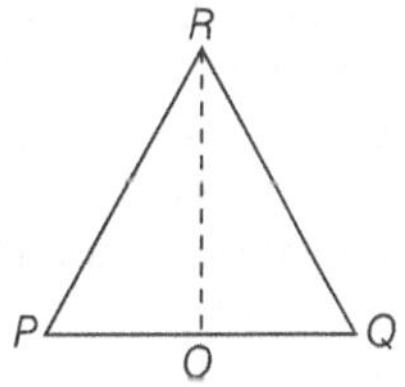

(a) 0.05
(b) 0.8
(c) 0.1
(d) 0.2

4. An infinitely long thin straight wire has uniform linear charge density of $\frac{1}{3}\text{Cm}^{-1}$.

Then the magnitude of the force acting on a charge 3 μC situated at a point of 18 cm away from the wire is

$$\left(\frac{1}{4\pi\varepsilon_0} = 9 \times 10^9 \text{ Nm}^2\text{C}^{-2}\right)$$

(a) 2×10^5 N
(b) 10^5 N
(c) $\frac{1}{3} \times 10^6$ N
(d) 3×10^{11} N

5. An electrostatic paint sprayer has a metal sphere of diameter 18 cm and at a potential of 25 kV. The charge on the metal sphere is

(a) 0.25 μC
(b) 2.5 μC
(c) 0.5 μC
(d) 25 μC

6. A body is projected from the top of a tower with a velocity $\bar{u} = 3\hat{\mathbf{i}} + 4\hat{\mathbf{j}} + 5\hat{\mathbf{k}}$ ms^{-1}, where $\hat{\mathbf{i}}, \hat{\mathbf{j}}$ and $\hat{\mathbf{k}}$ are unit vectors along east, north and vertically upwards respectively. If the height of the tower is 30 m, horizontal range of the body on the ground is ($g = 10$ ms^{-2})

(a) 15 m (b) 25 m
(c) 9 m (d) 12 m

7. Two long parallel conducting wires carrying currents are seperated by a distance 'x'. Work done per unit length in changing the distance between the wires is proportional to

(a) $\dfrac{1}{\log_e x}$ (b) $\dfrac{1}{x}$
(c) $\log_e x$ (d) x

8. A Zener diode voltage regulator operated in the range 120V-180V produces a constant supply of 110 V and 250 mA to the load. If the maximum current is equally shared between the load and the Zener diode, then the values of load resistance (R_L) and series resistance (R_S) are respectively

(a) $R_L = 280\ \Omega$, $R_S = 70\ \Omega$
(b) $R_L = 440\ \Omega$, $R_S = 140\ \Omega$
(c) $R_L = 70\ \Omega$, $R_S = 280\ \Omega$
(d) $R_L = 440\ \Omega$, $R_S = 1400\ \Omega$

9. Equation of a projectile is given by $y = Px - Qx^2$, where P and Q are constants. The ratio of maximum height to the range of the projectile is

(a) $\dfrac{Q^2}{2P}$
(b) $\dfrac{P^2}{Q}$
(c) $4P$
(d) $\dfrac{P}{4}$

10. The transverse displacement of a string of a linear density 0.01 kg m^{-1}, clamped at its ends is given by $Y_{(x,t)} = 0.03 \sin\left(\dfrac{2\pi x}{3}\right) \cos(60\,\pi t)$, where x and y are in metres and time t is in seconds. Tension in the string is

(a) 9 N (b) 36 N
(c) 162 N (d) 81 N

11. A girl of mass 50 kg swinging on a cradle. If she moves with a velocity of 2 ms^{-1} upwards in a direction making an angle 60° with the vertical, then the power generated is ($g = 9.8$ ms^{-2})

(a) 245 W
(b) $490\sqrt{2}$ W
(c) $490\sqrt{3}$ W
(d) 980 W

12. Two point sources S_1 and S_2 are 24 cm apart. Where should a convex lens of focal length 9 cm be placed in between them, so that the images of both sources are formed at the same place?

(a) 8 cm (b) 12 cm
(c) 6 cm (d) 10 cm

13. **Assertion (A)** It is more difficult to push a magnet into a coil with more number of turns.

Reason (R) The emf induced in a coil opposes the motion of a magnet when it is moved towards the coil.

(a) A is false, R is true
(b) Both A and R are true. R is correct explanation of A
(c) A is true, R is false
(d) Both A and R are true. R is not correct explanation of A

14. A wall is made of equally thick layers P and Q of different materials. Thermal conductivity of Q is half of that of the P. In the steady state, If the temperature difference across the wall is 24°C, then the temperature difference across the layer 'P' is ....

(a) 12° C (b) 16°C
(c) 4° C (d) 8°C

15. In the determination of the internal resistance of a cell with a potentiometer, the error in the measurement of the balancing length is ± 1 mm. When the cell alone is connected in the circuit, the balancing length is obtained at 60 cm and when the cell is shunted with a resistance of $10\ \Omega \pm 2\%$, the balancing length is obtained at 50 cm. The error in the determination of the internal resistance of the cell is ....

(a) 2.4% (b) 4.2%
(c) 1.8% (d) 5.6 %

16. The half life of a stream of radioactive particles moving along a straight path with a constant kinetic energy of 4 eV is 1 minute. The percentage of particles which decay before travelling a distance of 3.6 km is (Mass of the radioactive particles $= 3.2 \times 10^{-21}$ kg and charge of the electron $= 1.6 \times 10^{-19}$C).

(a) 87.5 (b) 175
(c) 37.5 (d) 75

17. The process of recovering the modulating signal from the modulated carrier wave is called

(a) amplification (b) detection
(c) rectification (d) noise

18. Two bodies of masses 4m and 9m are seperated by a distance 'r'. The gravitational potential at a point on this line joining them where the gravitational field becomes zero is

(a) $\frac{-25\,Gm}{r}$ (b) $\frac{-4\,Gm}{r}$
(c) $\frac{-9\,Gm}{r}$ (d) $\frac{-13\,Gm}{r}$

19. If the charge on the capacitor is 1 mC in the given circuit,

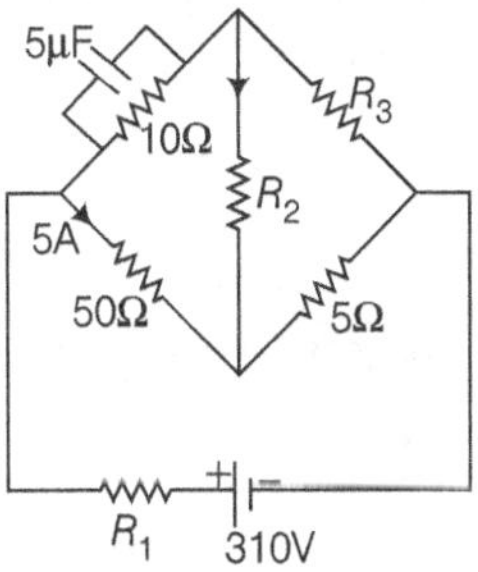

then $\frac{R_1 R_2}{R_3} =$ .... Ω .

(a) 6 (b) 0.4
(c) 0.6 (d) 10

20. The amplitude of electric field in an electromagnetic wave is 60 Vm^{-1}. Then the amplitude of magnetic field is

(a) 2×10^{-7} T (b) 2×10^{7} T
(c) 6×10^{7} T (d) 6×10^{-7} T

21. A bird is tossing (flying to and pro) between two cars moving towards each other on a straight road. One car has speed of 54 kmh^{-1} while the other has the speed of 36 kmh^{-1}. The bird starts moving from first car towards the other and is moving with the speed of 36 kmh^{-1} where the two cars were separated by 36 km. The total distance covered by the bird before the cars meet each other is

(a) 14400 m (b) 1440 m
(c) 244 m (d) 24400 m

22. If the average translational kinetic energy of a molecule in a gas is equal to the kinetic energy of an electron accelerating from rest through 10 V, then the temperature of the gas molecule is

(Boltzmann constant $= 1.38 \times 10^{-23}$ JK^{-1})

(a) 7.73×10^3 K (b) 730 K
(c) 73.7 K (d) 77.3×10^3 K

23. A closed organ pipe of length 'L' and an open organ pipe contain gases of densities ρ_1 and ρ_2 respectively. The compressibility of gases are equal in both the pipes. If the frequencies of their first overtones are same, then the length of the open organ pipe is

(a) $\frac{4L}{3}\sqrt{\frac{\rho_2}{\rho_1}}$

(b) $\frac{4L}{3}\sqrt{\frac{\rho_1}{\rho_2}}$

(c) $\frac{4L}{3}$

(d) $\frac{L}{3}$

24. One mole of a gas expands such that its volume 'V' changes with absolute temperature 'T' in accordance with the relation $V = KT^2$ where 'K' is a constant. If the temperature of the gas changes by 60°C, then work done by the gas is (R is universal gas constant).

(a) $KR \ln 60$ (b) $R \ln 60$ (c) $40 KR$ (d) $120 R$

25. When a coil is connected to AC supply of frequency 50 Hz, a current of 4 A flows in it and it consumes 240 W power. If the potential difference across the coil is 100 V, then the inductance value of the coil is

(a) $L = (5\pi)$ H (b) $L = \frac{\pi}{5}$ H

(c) $L = \frac{1}{5\pi}$ H (d) $L = \frac{1}{25\pi}$ H

26. The uniform electric field intensity between the two plates of a parallel plate capacitor is 1×10^3 Vm^{-1} acting vertically upwards as shown in the figure.

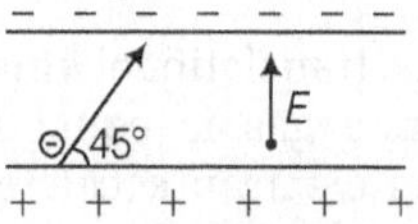

The plates are sufficiently long and have separation 2 cm. A particle of negative charge 1 μC and mass 2 g is projected at an angle 45° with the electric field from the lower plate with a velocity 'u'. The maximum velocity acquired by the particle, if it is not hit the upper plate is

(a) $2 ms^{-1}$ (b) $1 ms^{-1}$ (c) $0.1 ms^{-1}$ (d) $0.2 ms^{-1}$

27. Both an electron and a photon have same de-Broglie wavelength of 1.2 Å. The ratio of their energies is nearly

(a) 1 : 100 (b) 1 : 10 (c) 1 : 1000 (d) 1 : 1

28. When the terminals of a cells are connected by a wire of resistance 4 Ω, the potential difference across the cell is 1.6 V. If a wire of the same resistance is connected in parallel with the first, the potential difference becomes 1.33 V. The emf and internal resistance of the cell are respectively

(a) 1 V, 1 Ω (b) 2 V, 1 Ω

(c) 1 V, 2 Ω (d) 2 V, 2 Ω

29. Two concentric coils of 20 turns each are placed in same plane. Their radii are 30 cm and 60 cm and carry 0.4 A and 0.6 A currents respectively in opposite directions. The magnetic induction at the centre in tesla is ....

(a) $\frac{8}{3}\mu_0$ (b) $\frac{2}{3}\mu_0$

(c) $\frac{5}{3}\mu_0$ (d) $\frac{10}{3}\mu_0$

30. Time period of a simple pendulum of length 'L' is T_1. Time period of a uniform rod of same length 'L' suspended from one end and oscillating in a vertical plane is T_2. Amplitude of oscillation is small in both the cases. Then $\frac{T_1}{T_2}$ is

(a) $\sqrt{\frac{2}{3}}$ (b) $\sqrt{\frac{3}{2}}$

(c) $\sqrt{\frac{4}{3}}$ (d) 1

31. In steady state, a capacitor of capacitance 2μF is charged to 4 μC, as shown in figure. If the internal resistance of the cell is 0.5 Ω, then the emf of the cell is

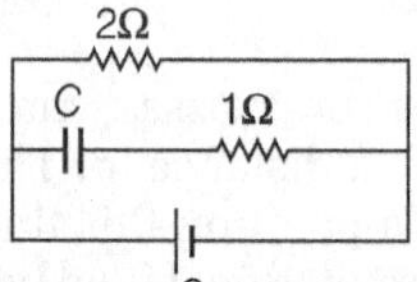

(a) 4 V (b) 5 V (c) 2.5 V (d) 2 V

32. A uniform thin rod of 120 cm length and 1600 g mass is bent as shown in the figure. The moment of inertia of the bent rod about an axis passing through the point 'O' and perpendicular to the plane of the paper is .... kg-m^2.

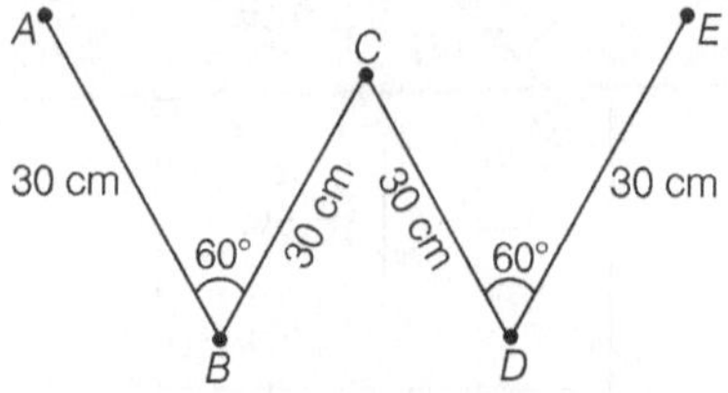

(a) 0.084 (b) 0.360

(c) 0.018 (d) 0.120

33. Two blocks of masses 'M' and 'm' are placed on one another on a smooth horizontal surface as shown in the figure.

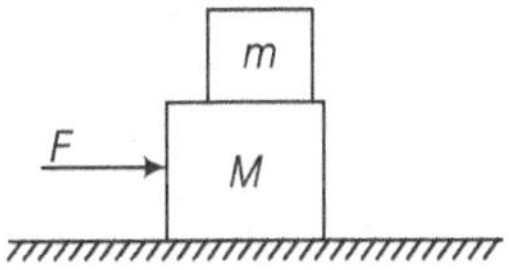

The force 'F' is acting on the mass 'M' horizontally during time interval 't'. Assuming no relative sliding between the blocks, the work done by friction on the blocks is ....

(a) $\frac{Ft}{2(M+m)}$ (b) $\frac{M+m}{mt^2}$

(c) $\frac{mF^2t^2}{2(M+m)^2}$ (d) $\frac{F^2t^2}{(M+m)}$

34. A solid sphere is projected up along an inclined plane of inclination 30° with the horizontal with a speed of 4 ms^{-1}. If it rolls without slipping, the maximum distance traversed by it is .... ($g = 10$ ms^{-2})

(a) 2.24 m (b) 112 m (c) 1.12 m (d) 22.4 m

35. Fully filled open water tank has two holes on either sides of its walls. One is a square hole of side x cm at a depth of 2 m from the top, and the other hole is equilateral triangle of side 4 cm at a depth of 6 m from the top. If the rate of flow of water is same from both the holes, then 'x' is

(a) 1.73 cm (b) 12 cm
(c) 6.92 cm (d) 3.46 cm

36. The radius of orbit of an electron and the speed of electron in the ground state of hydrogen atom are 5.5×10^{-11}m and 4×10^6 ms^{-1} respectively. Then, the orbital period of this electron in the first excited state will be ....

(a) 6.908×10^{-16} s (b) 9.608×10^{-16} s
(c) 7.806×10^{-16} s (d) 8.9068×10^{-16} s

37. Two slits separated by 0.5 mm are illuminated by light of wavelength 500 nm. The screen is at a distance of 120 cm from the slits. The phase difference between the interfering waves at a point 3 mm on the screen from the central bright fringe is ....

(a) 5π (b) π (c) 3π (d) 7π

38. The ratios of lengths, areas of cross-section and Young's modulii of steel to that of brass wires shown in the figure are a, b and c respectively. The ratio of increase in the lengths of brass to that of steel wires is [Assume that the masses of steel and brass wires are negligible]

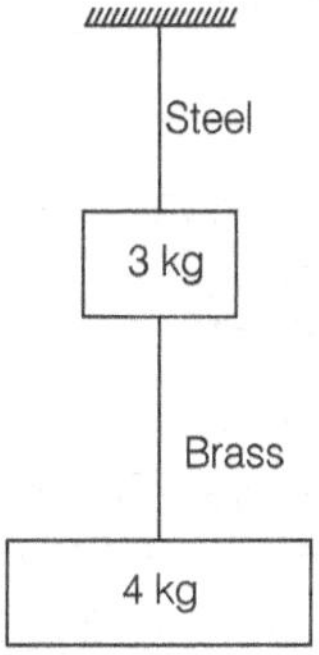

(a) $\frac{4a}{7bc}$ (b) $\frac{7bc}{4a}$ (c) $\frac{4bc}{7a}$ (d) $\frac{7a}{4bc}$

39. A person of 60 kg mass is in a lift which is coming down such that the man exerts a force of 150 N on the floor of the lift. Then the acceleration of the lift is ($g = 10$ ms^{-2})

(a) 7.5 ms^{-2} (b) 40.0 ms^{-2}
(c) 22.5 ms^{-2} (d) 15.0 ms^{-2}

40. Match the following

List-I	List-II
(a) High retentivity	(i) Telephone diaphram
(b) High resistivity	(ii) Diamagnet
(c) Low coercivity	(iii) To decrease eddy current losses
(d) Negative susceptibility	(iv) Permanent magnet

The correct answer is

(a) a-(i), b-(iv), c-(iii), d-(ii)
(b) a-(iv), b-(iii), c-(i), d-(ii)
(c) a-(i), b-(ii), c-(iii), d-(iv)
(d) a-(iv), b-(ii), c-(i), d-(iii)

Answer with Solutions

1. (*) (No options match)

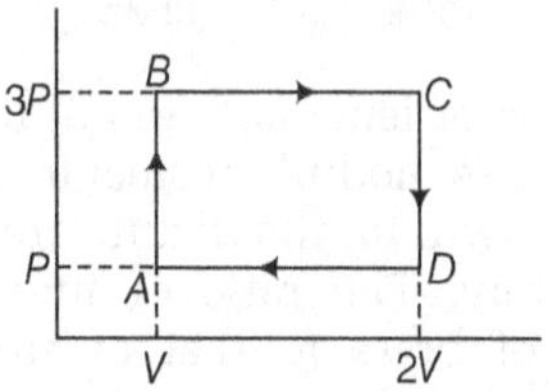

We know that,

$$W = P\Delta V$$

Now,

$$W_{AB} = 0$$
$$W_{BC} = 3P(2V - V) = 3PV$$
$$W_{CD} = 0$$
$$W_{DA} = -PV$$

Total work done,

$$W = W_{AB} + W_{BC} + W_{CD} + W_{DA}$$
$$= 3PV - PV = 2PV$$

Heat given to the system from A to B

$$= nC_V\Delta T$$
$$= n\frac{3}{2}R\Delta T = \frac{3}{2} \times V \times \Delta P$$
$$= \frac{3}{2} \times V \times (3P - P)$$
$$= \frac{3}{2} \times V \times 2P$$
$$= 3PV$$

Similarly,

Heat given to the system from B to C

$$= nC_P\Delta T$$
$$= n\left(\frac{5}{2}R\right)\Delta T$$
$$= \frac{5}{2}(3P)(\Delta V)$$
$$= \frac{5}{2} \times (3P).(2V - V)$$
$$= \frac{5}{2} \times 3P \times V$$
$$= \frac{15}{2}PV$$

The heat is released from C to D and D to A.

$$\text{Efficiency } (\eta) = \frac{\text{Work done by gas}}{\text{Heat given to gas}} \times 100$$

$$= \frac{2PV}{3PV + \frac{15}{2}PV} \times 100$$
$$= \frac{2PV}{PV\left(3 + \frac{15}{2}\right)} \times 100$$
$$= \frac{2}{\left(\frac{6 + 15}{2}\right)} \times 100$$
$$= \frac{2 \times 2}{21} \times 100$$
$$= \frac{4}{21} \times 100$$
$$= 19.04\%$$

2. (c) For fig. (a)

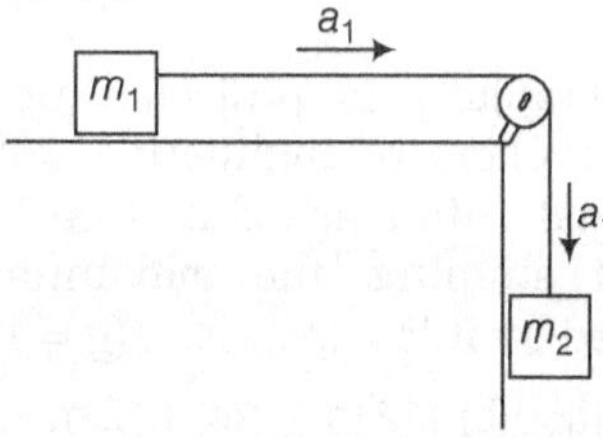

(a)

$$(m_1 + m_2)\,a_1 = m_2 g$$
$$a_1 = \frac{m_2 g}{m_1 + m_2}$$

Given, $m_1 = 3$ kg

$m_2 = 4$ kg

$g = 10$ m/s^2

$$a_1 = \frac{4 \times 10}{3 + 4}$$
$$= \frac{40}{7} \text{ m/s}^2$$

For fig. (b)

$$(m_1 + m_2)\,a = (m_2 - m_1)g$$
$$a = \left(\frac{m_2 - m_1}{(m_1 + m_2)}\right)g$$
$$= \left(\frac{4 - 3}{4 + 3}\right) \times 10$$
$$= \frac{10}{7} \text{ m/s}^2$$

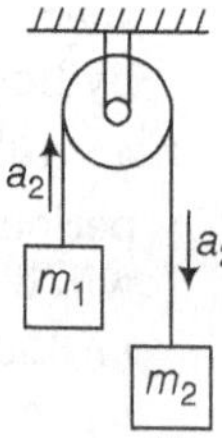

(b)

3. (d)

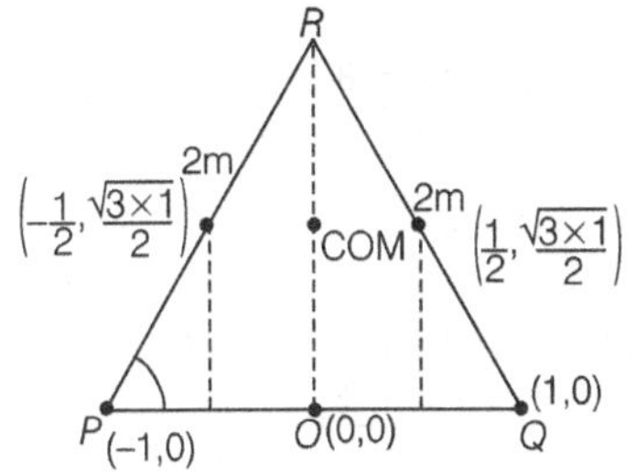

Initially,

$$\mathbf{r}_{COM} = \frac{m_1\mathbf{r}_1 + m_2\mathbf{r}_2 + m_3\mathbf{r}_3}{(m_1 + m_2 + m_3)}$$

$$\mathbf{r}_{COM} = \frac{1}{3}\left(\frac{\sqrt{3}}{2} \times 1 \times 2\right)\hat{j}$$

$$\Rightarrow \qquad \mathbf{r}_{COM} = \frac{1}{\sqrt{3}}\hat{j}$$

Due to expansion each rod length becomes

$$l_f = l_i\,(1 + \alpha\Delta T)$$

$$l_f = l_i\left(1 + \frac{\gamma}{3}\Delta T\right)$$

$$l_f = 2\left(1 + \frac{12\sqrt{3} \times 10^{-6}}{3} \times 50\right)$$

$$l_f = 2\,(1 + 4 \times 50 \times \sqrt{3} \times 10^{-6})$$

$$= 2(1 + 2\sqrt{3} \times 10^{-4})$$

So, $(\mathbf{r}_{COM})_{final} = \frac{1}{3} \times \frac{\sqrt{3}}{2} \times (1 + 2\sqrt{3} \times 10^{-4}) \times 2\,\hat{j}$

$$= \left(\frac{1}{\sqrt{3}} + 2 \times 10^{-4}\right)\hat{j}$$

Hence, $\Delta y = (r_{COM})_{final} - (r_{COM})_{initial}$

$$= 2 \times 10^{-4}\,\text{m} = 0.2\,\text{mm}$$

4. (b) Given,

Linear charge density, $\lambda = \frac{1}{3}\,\text{Cm}^{-1}$

Charge $q = 3\mu\text{C} = 3 \times 10^{-6}\text{C}$

Distance $r = 18\,\text{cm} = 18 \times 10^{-2}\text{m}$

Intensity of the electric field due to infinitely long time at distance r is

$$E = \frac{\lambda}{2\pi\varepsilon_0 \cdot r} = \frac{2\lambda}{4\pi\varepsilon_0 \cdot r} = \frac{9 \times 10^9 \times 2 \times 1}{3 \times 18 \times 10^{-2}}$$

$$= \frac{1}{3} \times 10^{11}\,\text{N/C}$$

Force on charge of $3\,\mu\text{C}$

$$F = qE$$

$$= 3 \times 10^{-6} \times \frac{1}{3} \times 10^{11}$$

$$= 10^5\text{N}$$

5. (a) Given

Radius of sphere, $r = \frac{18}{2} = 9\text{ cm} = 9 \times 10^{-2}\text{ m}$

Potential, $V = 25\,\text{kV} = 25 \times 10^3\text{V}$

$$V = \frac{kq}{r}$$

Charge, $q = \frac{V \times r}{k} = \frac{25 \times 10^3 \times 9 \times 10^{-2}}{9 \times 10^9}$

$$= 25 \times 10^{-8}\text{ C} = 0.25 \times 10^{-6}\text{ C}$$

$$= 0.25\,\mu\text{C}$$

6. (a)

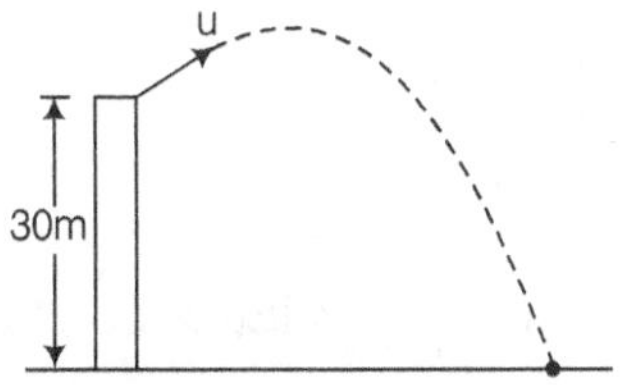

Time in which body is dropped to ground is calculated using following data;

$u = 5\,\text{m/s}$

($\hat{\mathbf{k}}$ is given vertically upward direction)

$a = -10\,\text{m/s}^2$

$h = -30\text{ m}$

Now using the formula

$$h = ut + \frac{1}{2}at^2,$$

$$-30 = 5t - \frac{1}{2} \times 10 \times t^2$$

$$\Rightarrow \qquad t^2 - t - 6 = 0$$

$$\Rightarrow \qquad = t = -2\text{ s (Not possible)}$$

or $\qquad t = 3\text{ s}$

In this time, projectile moving in East and North with speeds 3m/s and 4m/s. Distances covered in these directions are;

In east (x – coordinate).

$$= \text{speed} \times \text{time} = 3 \times 3 = 9\text{m}$$

and in North (y – coordinate)

$$= 4 \times 3 = 12\text{ m}$$

So, Projective lando at $(x, y) \equiv (9\text{m}, 12\text{m})$ mark.

So, horizontal range of body on ground is;

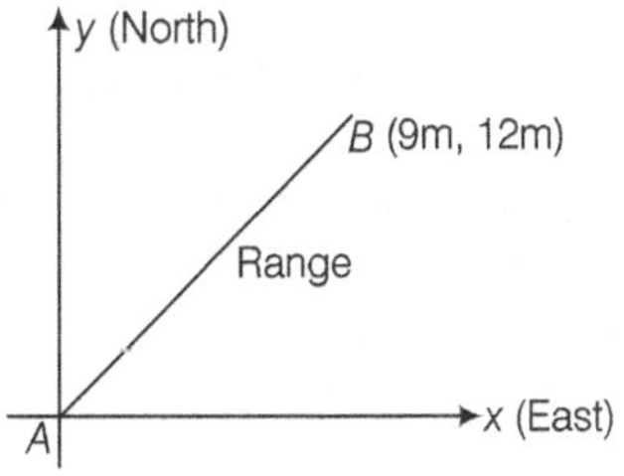

$$\text{Range} = \sqrt{9^2 + 12^2}$$
$$= \sqrt{225}$$
$$= 15 \text{ m}$$

7. (c) We know that

$$\frac{F}{l} = \frac{\mu_0 I_1 I_2}{2\pi x} \quad \text{...(i)}$$

When conducting wire is displaced by (x) dx distance, then work done per unit length is;

$$dW = F \cdot dx$$
$$dW = \frac{\mu_0 I_1 I_2}{2\pi x} dx \quad \text{[From Eq. (i)]}$$
$$\int dW = \int \frac{\mu_0 I_1 I_2}{2\pi x} dx$$
$$W = \frac{\mu_0 I_1 I_2}{2\pi} \int \frac{dx}{x}$$
$$W = \left(\frac{\mu_0 I_1 I_2}{2\pi}\right) \log_e x$$
$$\Rightarrow \quad W \propto \log_e x$$

8. (b)

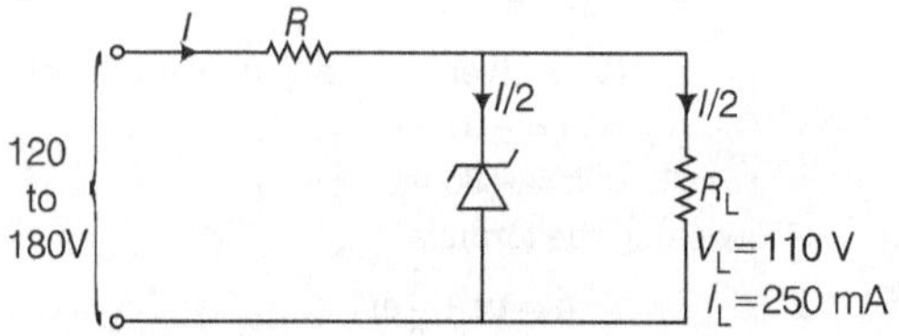

$$R_L = \frac{V_L}{I_L} = \frac{110}{250 \times 10^{-3}} = 440\,\Omega$$

As current is equally shared by Zener diode and resistance R_2

Then,

$$I = 2 \times 250 = 500 \text{ mA}$$
$$= 0.5 \text{ A}$$

So,
$$R_S = \frac{V_S}{I} = \frac{(180 - 110)}{0.5}$$
$$= \frac{70}{0.5} = 140\,\Omega$$

9. (d) Given,

$$y = Px - Qx^2 \quad \text{...(i)}$$

We know that,

$$y = x \tan\theta - \frac{1}{2} g \frac{x^2}{u^2 \cos^2\theta} \quad \text{...(ii)}$$

After comparing Eqs. (i) and (ii), we get

$$P = \tan\theta \quad \text{...(iii)}$$
$$Q = \frac{g}{2u^2 \cos^2\theta} \quad \text{...(iv)}$$

We know that

$$H = \frac{u^2 \sin^2\theta}{2g} \quad \text{...(v)}$$
$$R = \frac{u^2 \sin 2\theta}{g} \quad \text{...(vi)}$$

Dividing Eq. (v) by Eq. (vi), we get

$$\frac{H}{R} = \frac{u^2 \sin^2\theta}{2g} \times \frac{g}{u^2 \sin 2\theta}$$
$$\frac{H}{R} = \frac{\sin^2\theta}{2 \times 2 \sin\theta \cos\theta}$$
$$\frac{H}{R} = \frac{1}{4} \times \tan\theta$$

From Eq. (iii), we have

$$\frac{H}{R} = \frac{P}{4}$$

10. (d) Transverse displacement

$$y_{(x,t)} = 0.03 \sin\left(\frac{2\pi x}{3}\right) \cos 60\pi t$$

Linear density = 0.01 kg/m

The standard equation of transverse displacement of a wave

$$y = a \sin kx \cos \omega t$$

Velocity, $v = \sqrt{\frac{T}{\mu}} = \frac{\omega}{k}$

$\therefore \quad \sqrt{\frac{T}{\mu}} = \frac{\omega}{k}$ [Here, μ = mass per unit length]

Here, $\omega = 60\pi$, $k = 2\pi/3$

$$\sqrt{\frac{T}{0.01}} = \frac{60\pi}{2\pi/3}$$
$$= 90$$
$$\frac{T}{0.01} = 90 \times 90$$
$$T = 90 \times 90 \times 0.01$$
$$= 81 \text{ N}$$

11. (c) Given,

Mass of the girl $(m) = 50$ kg

Velocity $(v) = 2$ m/s

Angle $(\theta) = 60°$

$g = 9.8 \text{ m/s}^2$

Work needed to displace the girl through a small arc of length dS is

$$= mg \sin 60° \times ds$$

But $\quad ds = vdt$

Now, work done in time dt

$$= mg \sin 60° \, vdt$$

Power at that instant $= mg \sin 60°.\, v$

$$= 50 \times 9.8 \times \sin 60° \times 2$$
$$= 50 \times 9.8 \times \frac{\sqrt{3}}{2} \times 2$$
$$= 25 \times 9.8 \times \sqrt{3} \times 2$$
$$= 490\sqrt{3}\text{ W}$$

12. (b)

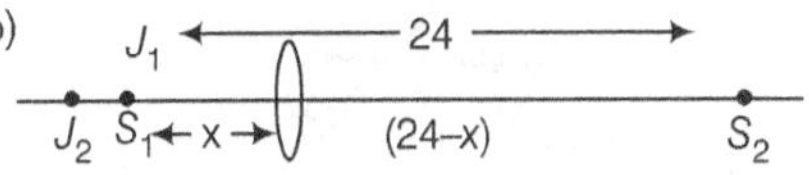

The given condition will be satisfied only if one source (S_1) is placed on one side such that $u < f$ (i.e. it lies under the focus. The other source (S_2) is placed on the other side of the lens such that $u > f$ (i.e. it lies beyond the focus)

If S_1 is the object for the lens, then

$$\frac{1}{f} = \frac{1}{-y} - \frac{1}{-x}$$

$$\Rightarrow \quad \frac{1}{y} = \frac{1}{x} - \frac{1}{-f} \quad \ldots(\text{i})$$

If S_2 is the object for the lens, then

$$\frac{1}{f} = \frac{1}{+y} - \frac{1}{-(24-x)}$$

$$\Rightarrow \quad \frac{1}{-y} = \frac{1}{f} - \frac{1}{(24-x)} \quad \ldots(\text{ii})$$

From the Eqs (i) and (ii), we get

$$\frac{1}{x} - \frac{1}{f} = \frac{1}{f} - \frac{1}{(24-x)}$$
$$\frac{1}{x} + \frac{1}{(24-x)} = \frac{2}{f} = \frac{2}{7}$$
$$x^2 - 24x + 108 = 0$$
$$x = 18\text{ cm and } x = 6\text{ cm}$$

So, the correct answer will be 6 cm.

13. (b) (A) It is more difficult to push a magnet into a coil with large number of turns because of repulsion caused by emf induced.

(B) The emf induced in a coil always opposes the motion of a magnet when it is moved towards the cell. It was experimentally verified by lens.

So both A and R are true. R is correct explanation of A.

14. (d) In the steady state, the rate of flow of heat through layer P and Q is same.

$$\frac{k_P\, a(T_1 - T_0)}{x} = \frac{k_Q\, a(T_0 - T_2)}{x}$$

Here,

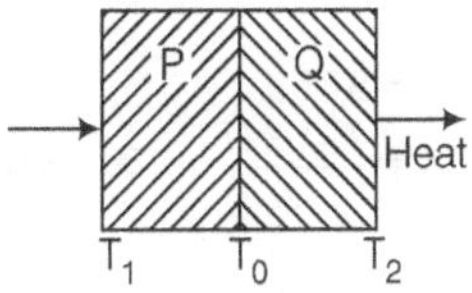

$$K_Q = \frac{K_P}{2}$$
$$K_p = 2K_Q$$
$$\frac{2k_Q\, a(T_1 - T_0)}{x} = \frac{k_Q\, a(T_0 - T_2)}{x}$$
$$2(T_1 - T_0) = T_0 - T_2$$
$$2T_1 - 2T_0 = T_0 - T_2$$
$$2T_1 - 3T_0 + T_2 = 0 \quad \ldots(\text{i})$$

According to the question,

$$T_1 - T_2 = 24°\text{C} \quad \ldots(\text{ii})$$

Now, from Eq. (i),

$$2T_1 - 3T_0 + T_1 - 24 = 0$$
$$3T_1 - 3T_0 = 24$$
$$T_1 - T_0 = 8°\text{C}$$

15. (b) $r = R\left(\frac{l_1}{l_2} - 1\right)$

$$\therefore \quad \frac{\Delta r}{r} \times 100 = \frac{\Delta R}{R} \times 100 + \frac{\Delta\left(\frac{l_1}{l_2}\right)}{\left(\frac{l_1}{l_2}\right)} \times 100$$
$$= 4 + 0.2 = 4.2\%$$

16. (a) Given, KE = 4 eV

$$m = 3.2 \times 10^{-21}\text{ kg}$$
$$e = 1.6 \times 10^{-19}\text{C}$$
$$\text{KE} = \frac{1}{2}mv^2$$
$$\Rightarrow \quad v^2 = \frac{2 \times \text{KE}}{m}$$
$$= \frac{2 \times 4 \times 1.6 \times 10^{-19}}{3.2 \times 10^{-21}} = \frac{2 \times 4}{2 \times 10^{-2}}$$
$$v^2 = 400$$
$$\Rightarrow \quad v = 20\text{ m/s}$$

Time to travel a distance of 3.6 km is

$$t = \frac{D}{v} = \frac{3.6 \times 1000}{20}\text{ s} = \frac{3.6 \times 1000}{20 \times 60}\text{ min}$$
$$= 3\text{ min}$$
$$= 3\text{ half-time}$$

In three half life times, the number of particles decayed

$$\approx 87.5\%$$
$$= \frac{N_0 - N}{N_0} \times 100 \text{ ; where } N = \frac{N_0}{8}$$
$$= \frac{7}{8} \times 100 = 87.5\%$$

17. (b) The process of recovering the modulated signal from the modulated carrier wave is called demodulation or detection.

18. (a) At the position when the gravitational field is zero. (Distance x is measured from 4m mass)

$$\frac{G(4m)}{x} = \frac{G(9m)}{(r-x)}$$
$$\frac{4}{x} = \frac{9}{r-x}$$
$$4(r-x) = 9x$$
$$4r - 4x = 9x$$
$$4r = 9x + 4x$$
$$4r = 13x$$
$$x = \frac{4}{13}r$$

The point P is at a distance $\frac{4}{13}r$ from mass $4m$ and $\left(h - \frac{4}{13}r\right) = \frac{9r}{13}$ from mass m.

$$v = -\frac{G(4m)}{\left(\frac{4}{13}r\right)} - \frac{G(9m)}{\frac{9r}{13}}$$
$$v = -\frac{26Gm}{r}$$

Option (a) is nearest but none of the option is matching.

19. (c)

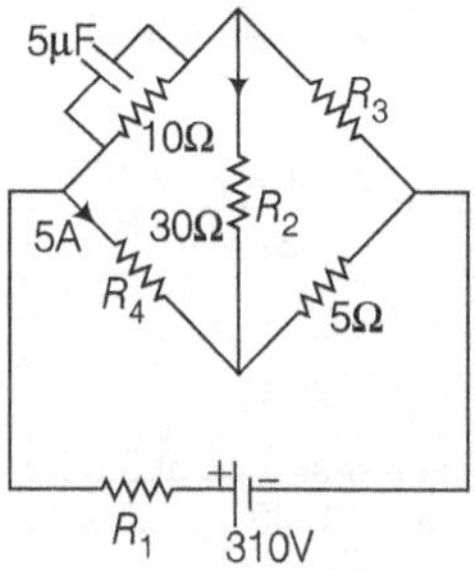

Charge on cap = 1 mC

$$V_{\text{capacitor}} = \frac{Q}{C} = \frac{1 \times 10^{-3}}{5 \times 10^{-6}} = \frac{1000}{5}$$
$$= 200 \text{ V}$$

So, (current throught (R_5),

$$I = \frac{V}{R}$$
$$= \frac{200}{10} = 20 \text{ A}$$

Hence, we have following current distribution.

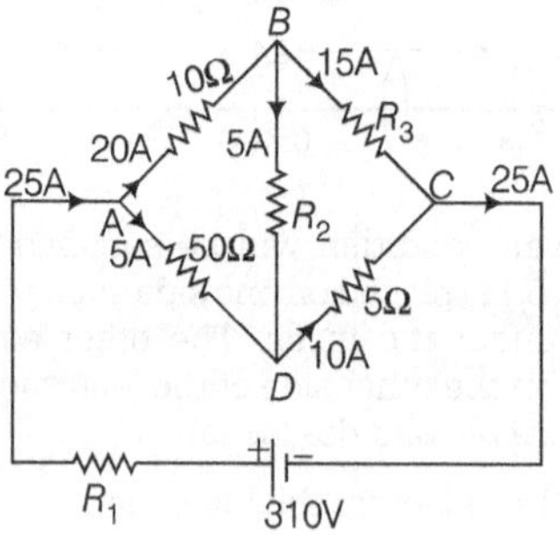

In loop $BCDB$,

$$-15R_3 + 10 \times 5 + 5R_2 = 0 \qquad \text{...(i)}$$

In loop $ABCDA$,

$$-200 - 15R_3 + 50 + 250 = 0$$
$$15R_3 = 100$$
$$R_3 = \frac{100}{15} \Omega$$

From Eq. (i), we get

$$5R_2 = 50$$
$$R_2 = 10 \Omega.$$

and from loop $ADCA$,

$$-250 - 50 + 310 - 25R_1 = 0$$
$$25R_1 = 10 \Rightarrow R_1 = \frac{10}{25} \Omega$$

So, $$\frac{R_1 \times R_2}{R_3} = \frac{\frac{10}{25} \times 10}{\left(\frac{100}{15}\right)}$$
$$= \frac{15}{25} = \frac{3}{5} = 0.6$$

20. (a) Given,

$$E_0 = 60 \text{ V/m}$$
$$B_0 = ?$$

The speed of e.m. wave

$$c = \frac{E_0}{B_0}$$
$$B_0 = \frac{E_0}{c} \quad [\because c = 3 \times 10^8 \text{ m/s}]$$
$$= \frac{60}{3 \times 10^8} = 20 \times 10^{-8}$$
$$= 2 \times 10^{-7} \text{ T}$$

21. (a) The total time duration for the two cars to meet

$$= \frac{\text{Total distance}}{\text{Relative velocity}}$$

$$= \frac{36}{54 + 36}$$

$$T = \frac{36}{90} = 0.4 \text{ h}$$

In this duration, the distance travels

$$= 36 \times 0.4 = 14.4 \text{ km}$$

$$= 14400 \text{ m}$$

The total distance covered by the bird before the cars meet each other is 14400 m.

22. (d) Given,

$$V = 10 \text{ V}$$

$$k = 1.38 \times 10^{-23} \text{ JK}^{-1}$$

According to question, the translation KE of a molecule of gas $= \frac{3}{2} kT$

According to question,

$$\frac{3}{2} kT = eV$$

$$\text{Temperature, } T = \frac{2eV}{3k}$$

$$= \frac{2 \times 1.6 \times 10^{-19} \times 10}{3 \times 1.38 \times 10^{-23}}$$

$$= 7.73 \times 10^4 = 77.3 \times 10^3 \text{ K}$$

23. (b) For closed organ pipe,

$$f = f_2 = 3f_1$$

$$= \frac{3 \times v}{4L} = \frac{3}{4L} \times \sqrt{\frac{\gamma p}{\rho_1}}$$

For open organ pipe,

$$f = f_2 = 2f_1 = \frac{2v}{2L'} = \frac{v}{L'}$$

$$= \frac{1}{L'} \times \sqrt{\frac{\gamma p}{\rho_2}}$$

For same sound frequency,

$$\frac{3}{4L} \times \sqrt{\frac{\gamma P}{\rho_1}} = \frac{1}{L'} \times \sqrt{\frac{\gamma p}{\rho_2}}$$

$$\therefore \quad L' = \frac{4L}{3} \times \sqrt{\frac{\rho_1}{\rho_2}}$$

24. (d) For given gas,

$$pV = RT \text{ and } V = KT^2$$

$$pV = R\left(\frac{V}{K}\right)^{\frac{1}{2}}$$

$$pV^{\frac{1}{2}} = \text{a constant}$$

$$\therefore \quad \gamma = \frac{1}{2} \text{ for this process.}$$

$\therefore$ Work done in this process,

$$W = \frac{nR(T_i - T_f)}{\gamma - 1} = \frac{R(60)}{\frac{1}{2}} = 120R$$

25. (c) $I^2R = 240$ W, $I = 4$ A

$$\therefore \quad R = \frac{240}{16} = 15\ \Omega$$

Now, for the coil (L-R) circuit,

$$V = IZ = I\sqrt{X_L^2 + R^2}$$

$$\Rightarrow \quad \frac{V^2}{I^2} = X_L^2 + R^2$$

$$\text{or} \quad X_L^2 = \frac{100 \times 100}{4 \times 4} - 225$$

$$= 625 - 225 = 400$$

$$\therefore \quad X_L = 20 = L\omega$$

$$\therefore \quad L = \frac{20}{2\pi f} = \frac{20}{2\pi \times 50}$$

$$= \frac{1}{5\pi} \text{ H.}$$

26. (d)

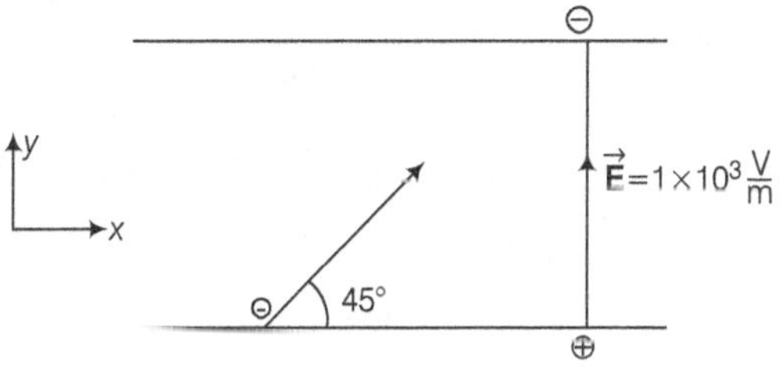

Acceleration of projected charge in y-direction

$$= a_y = -\frac{F}{m} = -\frac{qE}{m}$$

$$= -\frac{1 \times 10^{-6} \times 1 \times 10^3}{2 \times 10^{-3}} = -\frac{1}{2} \text{ms}^{-2}$$

Let projection velocity is u, then its vertical component

$$u_x = u\cos\theta = u \times \cos 45° = \frac{u}{\sqrt{2}} \text{ms}^{-1}$$

If particle is not to hit upper plate, then

$$u_y^2 \le 2a_y(y)$$

$$\Rightarrow \quad \frac{u^2}{2} \le 2 \times \frac{1}{2} \times 2 \times 10^{-2}$$

$\Rightarrow \quad u^2 \leq 4 \times 10^{-2}$

or $\quad u \leq 2 \times 10^{-1}$

or $\quad u \leq 0.2 \text{ ms}^{-1}$

27. (a) The de-Broglie wavelength of electron

$$\lambda_e = \frac{h}{\sqrt{mK_e}}$$

K_e = Kinetic energy of electron

$$\lambda_e^2 = \frac{h^2}{\lambda^2 \times 2\, m_e}$$

De-Broglie wavelength of photon is λ_p

Kinetic energy of photon,

$$K_P = h\nu = \frac{hc}{\lambda_P}$$

$$\therefore \quad \frac{K_e}{K_p} = \frac{h^2 / \lambda_e^2 . 2m_e}{hc / \lambda_p}$$

$$\lambda_e = \lambda_P$$

$$\frac{K_e}{K_P} = \frac{\lambda_P}{hc} \times \frac{h^2}{\lambda_e^2 \times 2m_e}$$

we know taht $m_e = 9.1 \times 10^{-31}$ kg

$h = 6.66 \times 10^{-34}$ J- sec

$\lambda_e = 1.2 \text{Å} = 1.2 \times 10^{-10}$m

and $\quad c = 3 \times 10^8$ m/s

Then, $$\frac{K_e}{K_P} = \frac{h}{c\, \lambda_e \times 2\, m_e}$$

$$= \frac{6.66 \times 10^{-34}}{3 \times 10^8 \times 1.2 \times 10^{-10} \times 2 \times 9.1 \times 10^{-31}}$$

$$\cong \frac{1}{100}$$

$\therefore \quad K_e : K_P :: 1 : 100$

28. (b) $E = V + Ir$

Given, $\quad V = 1.6$ V

$R = 4\,\Omega$

$$I_1 = \frac{1.6}{4} = 0.4 \text{ A}$$

$$E = 1.6 + 0.4r \quad \ldots\text{(i)}$$

When a resistance of 4Ω is connected in parallel, the resultant resistance

$$\frac{1}{R'} = \frac{1}{4} + \frac{1}{4} = \frac{2}{4}$$

$$R' = 2\Omega$$

$$I_2 = \frac{1.33}{2} = 0.66 \text{ A}$$

So, $$E = 1.33 + 0.66r \quad \ldots\text{(ii)}$$

From Eqs. (i) and (ii), we get

$$1.6 + 0.4r = 1.33 + 0.66r$$

$$1.6 - 1.33 = 0.66r - 0.4r$$

$$0 \cdot 27 = 0 \cdot 26r$$

$$r = \frac{0.27}{0.26} = 1$$

Substituting of r in Eq. (i), we get

$$E = 1.6 + 0.4 \times 1$$

$$= 2 \text{ V}$$

29. (d) Given,

$I_1 = 0.4$ A ,

$I_2 = 0.6$ A

$r_1 = 30 \times 1^{-2}$ m

$r_2 = 60 \times 10^{-2}$ m

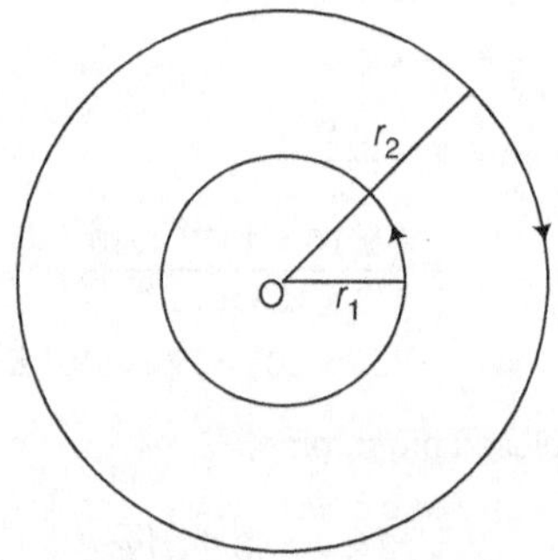

Magnetic field at O,

$$B_O = \frac{\mu_0}{4\pi} . 2\pi \left[\frac{n_1 I_1}{r_1} - \frac{n_2 I_2}{r_2} \right]$$

$$n_1 = n_2 = 20$$

$$B_O = \frac{\mu_0}{4\pi} . 2\pi \times 20 \left[\frac{0.4}{30 \times 10^{-2}} - \frac{0.6}{60 \times 10^{-2}} \right]$$

$$= \frac{\mu_0}{2} \times 20 \left[\frac{0.8 - 0.6}{60 \times 10^{-2}} \right]$$

$$= \frac{\mu_0}{2} \times 20 \times \frac{0.2}{60 \times 10^{-2}}$$

$$= \frac{10}{3} \mu_0$$

30. (b) Given,

Length of pendulum $= L$

Time period $T_1 = 2\pi \sqrt{\frac{L}{g}}$

Length of rod $= L$

Time period of rod;

$$T_2 = 2\pi \sqrt{\frac{2L}{3g}}$$

$$\frac{T_1}{T_2} = \frac{2\pi \sqrt{L/g}}{2\pi \sqrt{2L/3g}} = \sqrt{\frac{3}{2}}$$

31. (c) $V_{cap} = \frac{Q}{C} = \frac{4 \times 10^{-6}}{2 \times 10^{-6}} = 2\text{ v}$

Now $V_{cap} = \text{V (across } 2\Omega \text{ resistor)}$

$\therefore \quad I = \frac{V}{R} = \frac{2}{2} = 1\text{ A}$

Now, using the relation

$$E = V + Ir = 2 + 1 \times 0.5 = 2.5\text{ V}$$

32. (a) There are four rods each of mass $m = 400$ g

$$= \frac{400}{1000} = 0.4\text{ kg}$$

and each having a length of $l = 30$ cm

$$= \frac{30}{100}\text{ m} = 0.3\text{ m}$$

Now, out of therefore two sets of two rods have same m, l.

So, we can calculate moment of inertia as follows

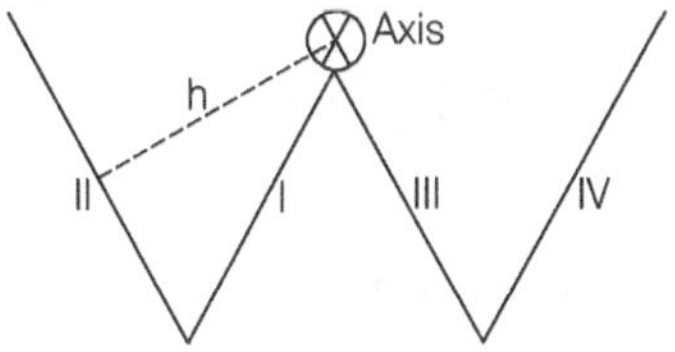

$$h^2 = l^2 - \left(\frac{l}{2}\right)^2 = \frac{3}{4}l^2$$

M.I system $= (\text{MI of I}) \times 2 + (\text{M.I of II}) \times 2$

$$= \frac{ml^2}{3} \times 2 + 2\left(\frac{ml^2}{12} + mh^2\right)$$

$$= \frac{2}{3}ml^2 + 2\left(\frac{ml^2}{12} + \frac{3}{4}ml^2\right)$$

$$= \frac{2}{3}ml^2 + 2ml^2\left[\frac{1}{12} + \frac{3}{4}\right]$$

$$= \frac{2}{3}ml^2 + 2ml^2 \times \frac{10}{12}$$

$$= \frac{2}{3}ml^2$$

$$= \frac{7}{3} \times 0.4 \times 0.3 \times 0.3$$

$$= 0.084\text{ kg - m}^2$$

33. (c)

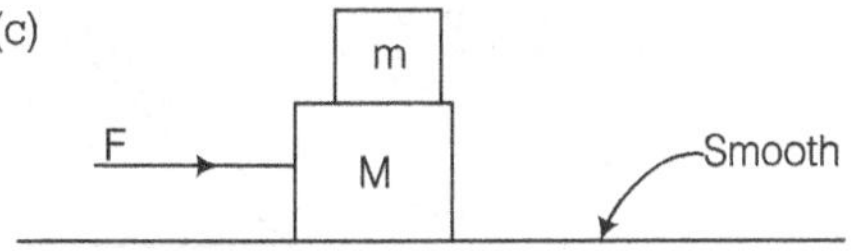

Acceleration of block $= \frac{F}{(M + m)}$

So, friction acting over upper block, f

$$ma = \frac{mF}{(M + m)}$$

Distances moved in time $t = \frac{1}{2}at^2$

$$= \frac{1}{2}\left(\frac{F}{M + m}\right)t^2$$

Work done by friction $= f \times s$

$$= \left(\frac{mF}{M + m}\right) \times \frac{1}{2}\frac{Ft^2}{(M + m)}$$

$$= \frac{mF^2t^2}{2(M + m)^2}$$

34. (a)

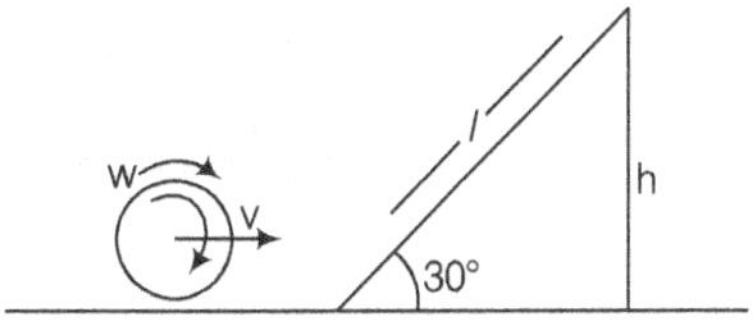

Given, $v = 4\text{ ms}^{-1}$ Also $v = r\omega$

Hence,

KE at bottom

$$= K_{\text{translation}} + K_{\text{rotation}}$$

$$= \frac{1}{2} mv^2 + \frac{1}{2} I\omega^2$$

$$= \frac{1}{2} mv^2 + \frac{1}{2}\left[\frac{2}{5} mr^2 \frac{v^2}{r^2}\right]$$

$$= \frac{1}{2} mv^2 + \frac{1}{2} \times \frac{2}{5} mv^2$$

$$= \frac{1}{2}\left(\frac{7}{5} mv^2\right)$$

At height h, energy conservation gives

$$\frac{1}{2}\left(\frac{7}{5}\right) mv^2 = mgh$$

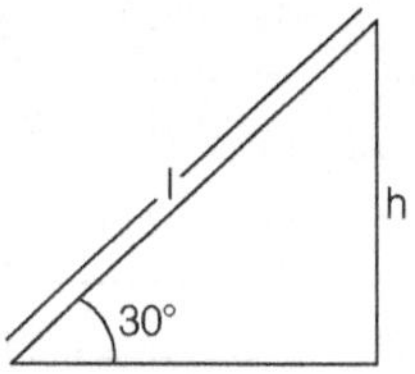

$$\Rightarrow \quad h = \frac{7}{10} \times \frac{v^2}{g}$$

$$= \frac{7}{10} \times \frac{16}{10}$$

$$= 1.12 \text{ m}$$

As, $\quad l = h / \sin 30°$

$\Rightarrow \quad l = 2 \times h$

$= 2.24$ m

35. (a)

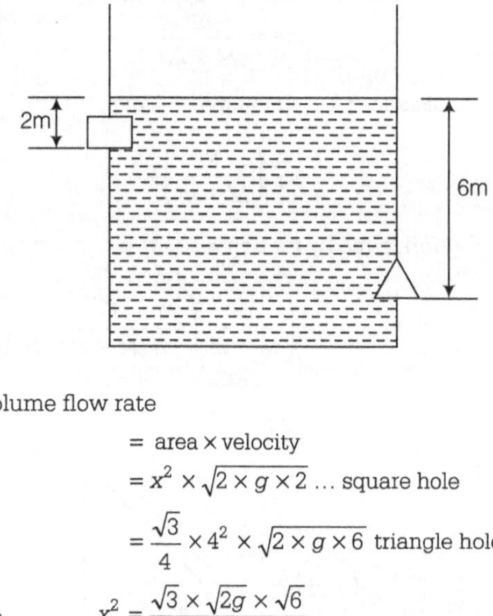

Volume flow rate

$= \text{area} \times \text{velocity}$

$= x^2 \times \sqrt{2 \times g \times 2}$ ... square hole

$= \frac{\sqrt{3}}{4} \times 4^2 \times \sqrt{2 \times g \times 6}$ triangle hole

$$\Rightarrow \quad x^2 = \frac{\sqrt{3} \times \sqrt{2g} \times \sqrt{6}}{\sqrt{2g} \times \sqrt{2}}$$

$$x^2 = \sqrt{3} \times \sqrt{3}$$

$\therefore \quad x = \sqrt{3} \text{ cm} = 1.73 \text{ cm}$

36. (a) Given, in ground state the radius and velocity of electron in hydrogen atom

$$r_1 = 5.5 \times 10^{-11} \text{ m}$$

$$v_1 = 4 \times 10^6 \text{ m/s}$$

In first excited state

$$r_n \propto \frac{n^2}{Z}$$

$$r_n = 5.5 \times 10^{-11} \times 2^2$$

$$= 22.0 \times 10^{-11} \text{m/s}$$

The speed of electron

$$v_n \propto \frac{Z}{n}$$

$$= \frac{4 \times 10^6}{2} = 2 \times 10^6 \text{ m/s}$$

The time period of revolution

$$T = \frac{2\pi r}{v_n} = \frac{2 \times 3.14 \times 22.0 \times 10^{-11}}{2 \times 10^6}$$

$$= 6.908 \times 10^{-16} \text{ s}$$

37. (a) Given,

$$d = 0.5 \times 10^{-9} \text{ m}$$

$$\lambda = 500 \times 10^{-9} \text{ m}$$

$$D = 120 \text{ cm} = 120 \times 10^{-2} \text{ m}$$

The fringe width

$$\beta = \frac{\lambda d}{D}$$

$$= \frac{120 \times 10^{-2} \times 0.5 \times 10^{-9}}{500 \times 10^{-9}}$$

$$= 12 \times 10^{-4} \text{ m}$$

Number of fringe in 3×10^{-3} m distance on screen

$$= \frac{3 \times 10^{-3}}{12 \times 10^{-4}}$$

$$= 2.5 = 3 \text{ rd fringe}$$

The phase difference

$$= 2\pi + 2\pi + \pi = 5\pi$$

38. (c) Let the ratio of length be a, ratio of area be b

Ratio of Young's modulus be c

We know that,

$$Y = \frac{F/A}{\Delta L/L}$$

$$\therefore \quad \Delta L = \frac{FL}{AY}$$

$$\frac{\Delta L_S}{\Delta L_B} = \left(\frac{F_S}{F_B}\right)\left(\frac{L_S}{L_B}\right)\left(\frac{A_B}{A_S}\right)\left(\frac{Y_B}{Y_S}\right)$$

$$= \frac{7}{4} \times (a)\left(\frac{1}{b}\right) \times \left(\frac{1}{c}\right)$$

$$\frac{\Delta L_S}{\Delta L_B} = \frac{7a}{4bc}$$

$$\frac{\Delta L_B}{\Delta L_S} = \frac{4bc}{7a}$$

39. (a) Mass of person, $m = 60$ kg

Force on floor of lift, $F = 150$ N

As lift is coming down the resultant acceleration

$$a' = (g + a)$$

Using Newton's force law

$$F = ma'$$

$$150 = 60\,(10 + a)$$

$$10 + a = \frac{150}{60}$$

$$= 2.5$$

$$a = -7.5 \text{ m/s}^2$$

$$|a| = 7.5 \text{ m/s}^2$$

40. (b)

(a)	High retentivity	(iv)	Permanent magnet
(b)	High resistivity	(iii)	To decrease eddy current losses
(c)	Low coercivity	(i)	Telephone diaphragm
(d)	Negative susceptibility	(ii)	Dimagnet

Fully Solved

TS EAMCET 2017

Engineering Entrance Exam

Physics

1. A force **F** is applied on a square plate of length L. If the percentage error in the determination of L is 3% and in F is 4%, then permissible error in the calculation of pressure is
(a) 13%
(b) 10%
(c) 7%
(d) 12%

2. A positive charge Q is placed on a conducting spherical shell with inner radius R_1 and outer radius R_2. A particle with charge q is placed at the center of the spherical cavity. The magnitude of the electric field at a point in the cavity, a distance r from center is
(a) zero
(b) $\frac{Q}{4\pi\varepsilon_0 r^2}$
(c) $\frac{q}{4\pi\varepsilon_0 r^2}$
(d) $\frac{(q+Q)}{4\pi\varepsilon_0 r^2}$

3. A swimmer wants to cross a 200 m wide river which is flowing at a speed of 2 m/s. The velocity of the swimmer with respect to the river is 1 m/s. How far from the point directly opposite to the starting point does the swimmer reach the opposite bank?
(a) 200 m
(b) 400 m
(c) 600 m
(d) 800 m

4. A coil having n turns and resistance $R\Omega$ is connected with a galvanometer of resistance $4R\Omega$. This combination is moved in time t seconds from a magnetic flux ϕ_1 Weber to ϕ_2 Weber. The induced current in the circuit is
(a) $\frac{\phi_2 - \phi_1}{5Rnt}$
(b) $-\frac{n(\phi_2 - \phi_1)}{5Rt}$
(c) $-\frac{(\phi_2 - \phi_1)}{Rnt}$
(d) $-\frac{n(\phi_2 - \phi_1)}{Rt}$

5. A simple pendulum of length 1 m is freely suspended from the ceiling of an elevator. The time period of small oscillations as the elevator moves up with an acceleration of $2\ \text{m/s}^2$ is (use $g = 10\text{m/s}^2$)
(a) $\frac{\pi}{\sqrt{5}}$ s
(b) $\sqrt{\frac{2}{5}}\pi$ s
(c) $\frac{\pi}{\sqrt{2}}$ s
(d) $\frac{\pi}{\sqrt{3}}$ s

6. Consider a metal ball of radius r moving at a constant velocity v in a uniform magnetic field of induction $\overline{B}$. Assuming that the direction of velocity forms an angle α with the direction of $\overline{B}$, the maximum potential difference between points on the ball is
(a) $r|\overline{B}||\overline{v}|\sin\alpha$
(b) $|\overline{B}||\overline{v}|\sin\alpha$
(c) $2r|\overline{B}||\overline{v}|\sin\alpha$
(d) $2r|\overline{B}||\overline{v}|\cos\alpha$

7. Each of the six ideal batteries of emf 20 V is connected to an external resistance of 4Ω as shown in the figure. The current through the resistance is

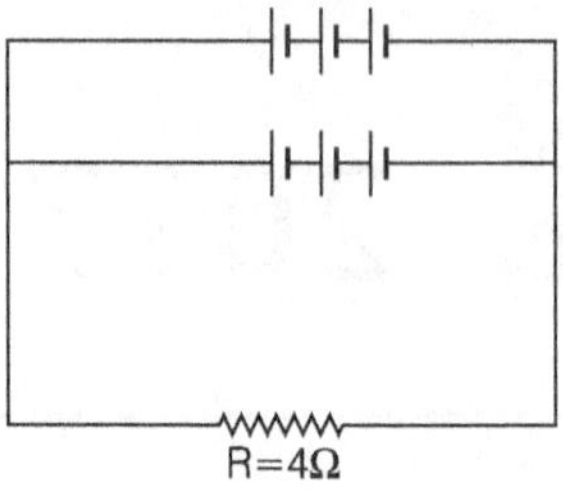

(a) 6 A (b) 3 A (c) 4 A (d) 5 A

8. The energy that should be added to an electron to reduce its de-Broglie wavelength from 1 nm to 0.5 nm is
(a) four-times the initial energy
(b) equal to the initial energy
(c) two-times the initial energy
(d) three-times the initial energy

9. In the given circuit, a charge of +80 μC is given to upper plate of a 4μF capacitor. At steady state, the charge on the upper plate of the 3μF capacitor is

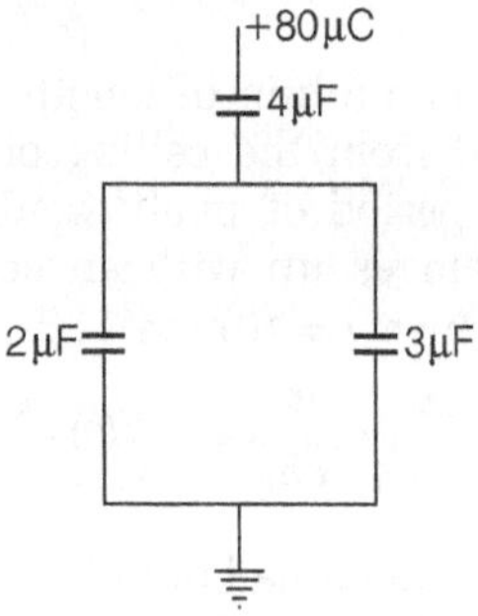

(a) 60 μC (b) 48 μC
(c) 80 μC (d) 0 μC

10. The Young's modulus of a material is 2×10^{11} N/m^2 and its elastic limit is 1×10^8 N/m^2. For a wire of 1 m length of this material, the maximum elongation achievable is
(a) 0.2 mm (b) 0.3 mm
(c) 0.4 mm (d) 0.5 mm

11. A wooden box lying at rest on an inclined surface of a wet wood is held at static equilibrium by a constant force **F** applied perpendicular to the incline. If the mass of the box is 1 kg, the angle of inclination is 30° and the coefficient of static friction between the box and the inclined plane is 0.2, the minimum magnitude of **F** is

(Use $g = 10$ m/s^2)
(a) 0 N, as 30° is less than angle of repose
(b) ≥ 1 N
(c) ≥ 3.3 N
(d) ≥ 16.3 N

12. A meter scale made of steel, reads accurately at 25°C. Suppose in an experiment an accuracy of 0.06 mm in 1 m is required, the range of temperature in which the experiment can be performed with this meter scale is (Coefficient of linear expansion of steel is 11×10^{-6}/°C)
(a) 19° C to 31° C
(b) 25° C to 32° C
(c) 18° C to 25° C
(d) 18° C to 32° C

13. Consider a solenoid carrying current supplied by a DC source with a constant emf containing iron core inside it. When the core is pulled out of the solenoid, the change in current will
(a) remain same (b) decrease
(c) increase (d) modulate

14. A parallel beam of light of intensity I_0 is incident on a coated glass plate. If 25% of the incident light is reflected from the upper surface and 50% of light is reflected from the lower surface of the glass plate, the ratio of maximum to minimum intensity in the interference region of the reflected light is

(a) $\left(\dfrac{\frac{1}{2}+\sqrt{\frac{3}{8}}}{\frac{1}{2}-\sqrt{\frac{3}{8}}}\right)^2$ (b) $\left(\dfrac{\frac{1}{4}+\sqrt{\frac{3}{8}}}{\frac{1}{2}-\sqrt{\frac{3}{8}}}\right)^2$

(c) $\dfrac{5}{8}$ (d) $\dfrac{8}{5}$

15. A thermocol box has a total wall area (including the lid) of 1.0 m^2 and wall thickness of 3 cm. It is filled with ice at 0°C. If the average temperature outside the box is 30°C throughout the day, the amount of ice that melts in one day is

[Use $K_{\text{thermocol}} = 0.03$ W/mK,
$L_{\text{fusion (ice)}} = 3.00 \times 10^5$ J/kg]

(a) 1 kg (b) 2.88 kg
(c) 25.92 kg (d) 8.64 kg

16. Which of the following is emitted, when ${}^{239}_{94}Pu$ decays into ${}^{235}_{92}U$?

(a) Gamma ray
(b) Neutron
(c) Electron
(d) Alpha particle

17. An AC generator 10 V (rms) at 200 rad/s is connected in series with a 50 Ω resistor, a 400mH inductor and a 200 μF capacitor. The rms voltage across the inductor is

(a) 2.5 V (b) 3.4 V
(c) 6.7 V (d) 10.8 V

18. A wire has resistance of 3.1 Ω at 30°C and 4.5Ω at 100°C. The temperature coefficient of resistance of the wire is

(a) 0.0012°C^{-1}
(b) 0.0024°C^{-1}
(c) 0.0032°C^{-1}
(d) 0.0064°C^{-1}

19. An object is thrown vertically upward with a speed of 30 m/s. The velocity of the object half-a-second before it reaches the maximum height is

(a) 4.9 m/s (b) 9.8 m/s
(c) 19.6 m/s (d) 25.1 m/s

20. An electron collides with a hydrogen atom in its ground state and excites it to $n = 3$ state. The energy given to the hydrogen atom in this inelastic collision

(neglecting the recoil of hydrogen atom) is

(a) 10.2 eV (b) 12.1 eV
(c) 12.5 eV (d) 13.6 eV

21. Consider the motion of a particle described by $x = a\cos t$, $y = a\sin t$ and $z = t$. The trajectory traced by the particle as a function of time is

(a) helix
(b) circular
(c) elliptical
(d) straight line

22. Consider a reversible engine of efficiency $\frac{1}{6}$. When the temperature of the sink is reduced by 62°C, its efficiency gets doubled. The temperature of the source and sink respectively are

(a) 372 K and 310 K
(b) 273 K and 300 K
(c) 99°C and 10°C
(d) 200°C and 37°C

23. Consider a light source placed at a distance of 1.5 m along the axis facing the convex side of a spherical mirror of radius of curvature 1 m. The position (s'), nature and magnification (m) of the image are

(a) $s' = 0.375$ m, virtual, upright, $m = 0.25$
(b) $s' = 0.375$ m, real, inverted, $m = 0.25$
(c) $s' = 3.75$ m, virtual, inverted, $m = 2.5$
(d) $s' = 3.75$ m, real, upright, $m = 2.5$

24. An office room contains about 2000 moles of air. The change in the internal energy of this much air when it is cooled from 34°C to 24°C at a constant pressure of 1.0 atm is

[Use $\gamma_{\text{air}} = 1.4$ and universal gas constant $= 8.314$ J/mol-K]

(a) -1.9×10^5 J
(b) $+1.9 \times 10^5$ J
(c) -4.2×10^5 J
(d) $+0.7 \times 10^5$ J

25. A ball is thrown at a speed of 20 m/s at an angle of 30° with the horizontal. The maximum height reached by the ball is

(Use $g = 10 \text{m/s}^2$)

(a) 2 m (b) 3 m
(c) 4 m (d) 5 m

26. A horizontal pipeline carrying gasoline has a cross-sectional diameter of 5 mm. If the viscosity and density of the gasoline are 6×10^{-3} Poise and 720 kg/m^3 respectively, the velocity after which the flow becomes turbulent is

(a) > 1.66 m/s (b) > 3.33 m/s
(c) > 1.6×10^{-3} m/s (d) > 0.33 m/s

27. A piece of copper and a piece of germanium are cooled from room temperature to 80K. Then, which one of the following is correct?

(a) Resistance of each will increase
(b) Resistance of each will decrease
(c) Resistance of copper will decrease while that of germanium will increase
(d) Resistance of copper will increase while that of germanium will decrease

28. A beam of light propagating at an angle α_1 from a medium 1 through to another medium 2 at an angle α_2. If the wavelength of light in medium 1 is λ_1, then the wavelength of light in medium 2, (λ_2), is

(a) $\frac{\sin \alpha_2}{\sin \alpha_1} \lambda_1$ (b) $\frac{\sin \alpha_1}{\sin \alpha_2} \lambda_2$
(c) $\left(\frac{\alpha_1}{\alpha_2}\right) \lambda_1$ (d) λ_1

29. An amplitude modulated signal consists of a message signal of frequency 1 KHz and peak voltage of 5V, modulating a carrier frequency of 1 MHz and peak voltage of 15 V. The correct description of this signal is

(a) $5 [1 + 3 \sin (2\pi 10^6 t)] \sin (2\pi 10^3 t)$
(b) $15 \left[1 + \frac{1}{3} \sin (2\pi 10^3 t) \right] \sin (2\pi 10^6 t)$
(c) $[5 + 15 \sin (2\pi 10^3 t)] \sin (2\pi 10^6 t)$
(d) $[15 + 5 \sin (2\pi 10^6 t)] \sin (2\pi 10^3 t)$

30. Which of the following principles is being used in Sonar Technology?

(a) Newton's laws of motion
(b) Reflection of electromagnetic waves
(c) Law's of thermodynamics
(d) Reflection of ultrasonic waves

31. A particle of mass M is moving in a horizontal circle of radius R with uniform speed v. When the particle moves from one point to a diametrically opposite point, its

(a) momentum does not change
(b) momentum changes by $2Mv$
(c) kinetic energy changes by $\frac{Mv^2}{4}$
(d) kinetic energy changes by Mv^2

32. A billiard ball of mass M, moving with velocity v_1 collides with another ball of the same mass but at rest. If the collision is elastic, the angle of divergence after the collision is

(a) 0° (b) 30°
(c) 90° (d) 45°

33. A planet of mass m moves in a elliptical orbit around an unknown star of mass M such that its maximum and minimum distances from the star are equal to r_1 and r_2 respectively. The angular momentum of the planet relative to the centre of the star is

(a) $m\sqrt{\frac{2GMr_1r_2}{r_1 + r_2}}$
(b) 0
(c) $m\sqrt{\frac{2GM(r_1 + r_2)}{r_1r_2}}$
(d) $\sqrt{\frac{2GMmr_1}{(r_1 + r_2)\, r_2}}$

34. Consider a frictionless ramp on which a smooth object is made to slide down from an initial height h. The distance d necessary to stop the object on a flat track (of coefficient of friction μ), kept at the ramp end is

(a) h/μ (b) μh (c) $\mu^2 h$ (d) $h^2\mu$

35. A generator with a circular coil of 100 turns of area 2×10^{-2} m^2 is immersed in a 0.01 T magnetic field and rotated at a frequency of 50 Hz. The maximum emf which is produced during a cycle is

(a) 6.28 V (b) 3.44 V
(c) 10 V (d) 1.32 V

36. A sound wave of frequency ν Hz initially travels a distance of 1 km in air. Then, it gets reflected into a water reservoir of depth 600 m. The frequency of the wave at the bottom of the reservoir is

$(V_{air} = 340 \text{ m/s } V_{water} = 1484 \text{ m/s})$

(a) $> \nu$ Hz
(b) $< \nu$ Hz
(c) ν Hz
(d) 0 (the sound wave gets attenuated by water completely)

37. Which of the following statement is not true?

(a) the resistance of an intrinsic semiconductor decreases with increase in temperature
(b) doping pure Si with trivalent impurities gives p-type semiconductor
(c) the majority carriers in n-type semiconductors are holes
(d) a $p-n$ junction can act as a semiconductor diode

38. The deceleration of a car traveling on a straight highway is a function of its instantaneous velocity v given by $\omega = a\sqrt{v}$, where a is a constant. If the initial velocity of the car is 60 km/h, the distance of the car will travel and the time it takes before it stops are

(a) $\frac{2}{3}$ m, $\frac{1}{2}$ s
(b) $\frac{3}{2a}$ m, $\frac{1}{2a}$ s
(c) $\frac{3a}{2}$ m, $\frac{a}{2}$ s
(d) $\frac{2}{3a}$ m, $\frac{2}{a}$ s

39. A current carrying wire in its neighbourhood produces

(a) electric field
(b) electric and magnetic fields
(c) magnetic field
(d) no field

40. Consider a particle on which constant forces $\mathbf{F}_1 = \hat{\mathbf{i}} + 2\hat{\mathbf{j}} + 3\hat{\mathbf{k}}$ N and $\mathbf{F}_2 = 4\hat{\mathbf{i}} - 5\hat{\mathbf{j}} - 2\hat{\mathbf{k}}$ N act together resulting in a displacement from position $\mathbf{r}_1 = 20\,\hat{\mathbf{i}} + 15\hat{\mathbf{j}}$ cm to $\mathbf{r}_2 = 7\,\hat{\mathbf{k}}$ cm. The total work done on the particle is

(a) − 0.48 J
(b) + 0.48 J
(c) − 4.8 J
(d) + 4.8 J

Answer with Solutions

1. (b) Given,

Percentage error in length = 3%

Percentage error in force = 4%

We know that,

Pressure, $P = \frac{F}{A}$

Area of square = $(L)^2$

$$P = \frac{F}{L^2}$$

$$\frac{\Delta P}{P} = \frac{\Delta F}{F} + \frac{2\Delta L}{L}$$

$$\left(\frac{\Delta P}{P} \times 100\right) = \left(\frac{\Delta F}{F} \times 100\right) + 2\left(\frac{\Delta L}{L} \times 100\right)$$

$$= 4\% + 2(3\%)$$

$$= 10\%$$

2. (b)

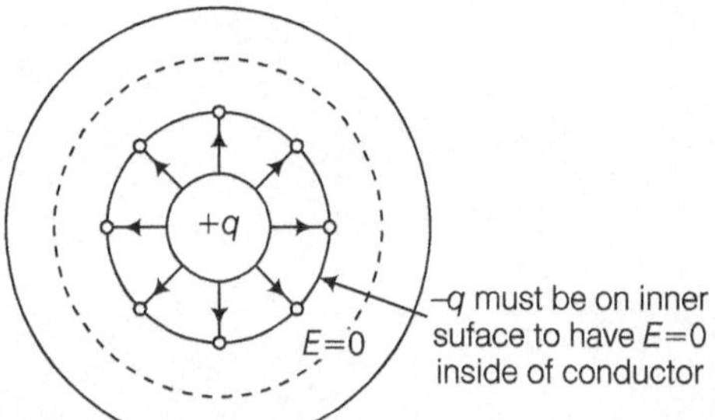

Total charge on shell = $+Q$

Here, total charge on shell is $+Q$. So, the $(-Q)$ is on the inner surface of shell.

Hence, electric field inside the conductor = 0

According the Gauss's law,

$$\oint E ds = \frac{Q}{\varepsilon_0}$$

$$E \oint ds = \frac{Q}{\varepsilon_0}$$

$$E(4\pi r^2) = \frac{Q}{\varepsilon_0}$$

Electric field, $E = \frac{Q}{4\pi r^2 \varepsilon_0}$

3. (b) Given,

Width of river (w) = 200 m

Velocity of river = 2 m/s

Velocity of man = 1 m/s

We know that,

$$\frac{w}{v_{man}} = \frac{d}{v_{strem}}$$

$$d = \frac{w \times v_{strem}}{v}$$

$$d = \frac{200 \times 2}{1}$$

$$d = 400 \text{ m}$$

4. (b) Given,

Number of turns in coil = n

We know that,

Current $(i) = \frac{e}{R'} = \frac{-\Delta\phi}{R'\Delta t}$ $\left[\because e = \frac{-\Delta\phi}{\Delta t}\right]$

$$R' = R + 4R$$

$$i = -\frac{(\phi_2 - \phi_1)}{(R + 4R)\,\Delta t}$$

$$i = \frac{(\phi_2 - \phi_1)}{5R(\Delta t)}$$

Here, coil have n number of turns.

Hence, $i = -\frac{n(\phi_2 - \phi_1)}{5R\,(\Delta t)}$

Induced current, $i = -\frac{n(\phi_2 - \phi_1)}{5Rt}$

5. (d) Given,

Length of simple pendulum (L) = 1 m

Acceleration $(a) = 2 \text{ m/s}^2$

Gravitation acceleration $(g) = 10 \text{ m/s}^2$

We know that,

$$T = 2\pi\sqrt{\frac{l}{g + a}}$$

$$= 2\pi\sqrt{\frac{1}{10 + 2}}$$

$$= 2\pi\sqrt{\frac{1}{12}}$$

$$= \pi\sqrt{\frac{4}{12}}$$

$$I = \frac{\pi}{\sqrt{3}}\ \text{s}$$

6. (c) Given,

Radius of metal ball $= r$

Velocity $= v$

Angle between direction of velocity and magnetic field $(B) = \alpha$

We know that,

$e = Bl\ v \sin\alpha$

Here, $l = 2r$

$e = 2r|B||v| \sin\alpha$

7. (*)Resistance $= 4\Omega$

The equivalent emf of the combination

$$E_{eq} = nE = 3 \times 20 = 60$$

The cell have no internal resistance.

∴Main current flowing through the load

$$i = \frac{nE}{R} = \frac{60}{4} = 15A$$

8. (d) We know that,

We have, $\lambda = \frac{h}{\sqrt{2mk}}$

∴ Kinetic energy $(KE) \propto \frac{1}{\lambda^2}$

Hence,

$$\frac{KE_2}{KE_1} = \left(\frac{\lambda_1}{\lambda_2}\right)^2$$

Here, $\lambda_1 = 1$ nm

$\lambda_2 = 0.5$ nm

$$\frac{KE_2}{KE_1} = \left(\frac{1}{0.5}\right)^2$$

$$KE_2 = 4KE_1$$

Hence, the kinetic energy is increases three times.

$$\Delta KE = 3KE_1$$

9. (b) The net charge on upper plates both capacitor (2μF and 3μF) will be +80 μC, so charge on upper plate of 3μC capacitor will be

$$q = \left(\frac{3}{3+2}\right)(80\ \mu\text{C})$$

$$q = \frac{3}{5} \times 80 = 48\ \mu\text{C}$$

10. (d) Given,

Young's modulus of material $= 2 \times 10^{11}$ N/m^2

Elastic limit or stress $= 1 \times 10^8$ N/m^2

Length of the wire = 1 m

We know that,

$$Y = \frac{\text{Stress}}{\text{Strain}}$$

$$Y = \frac{\text{Stress}}{\frac{\Delta L}{l}}$$

Here, l = original length of the wire

ΔL = charge in the length of the wire

$$\Delta L = \frac{\text{Stress} \times l}{Y}$$

$$= \frac{1 \times 10^8 \times 1}{2 \times 10^{11}}$$

$$= 0.5 \times 10^{-3}$$

$$= 0.5\ \text{mm}$$

11. (d) According to question, we can draw the following diagram.

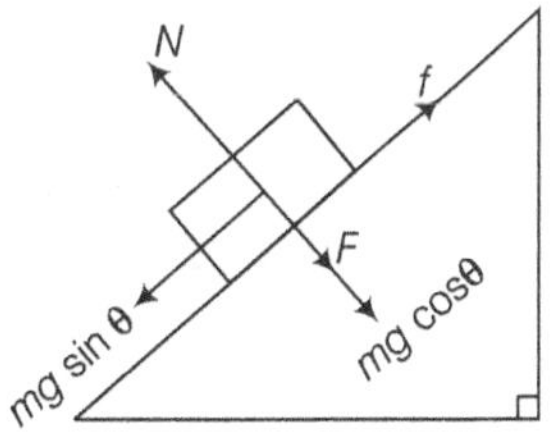

$$mg\sin\theta = \mu\,(F + mg\cos\theta)$$

$$F = \frac{mg\sin\theta}{\mu} - mg\cos\theta$$

$$= mg\left[\frac{\sin\theta}{\mu} - \cos\theta\right]$$

Here,

$$m = 1\text{ kg}, g = 10\text{ m/s}^2, \theta = 30°, \mu = 0.2$$

$$F = 1 \times 10\left[\frac{\sin 30}{0.2} - \cos 30°\right]$$

$$= 10\left[\frac{1}{2 \times 0.2} - \frac{\sqrt{3}}{2}\right]$$

$$= 10\left[\frac{5}{2} - \frac{\sqrt{3}}{2}\right] = 5\,[5 - \sqrt{3}]$$

$$= 5\,[5 - 1.732] = 16.34\text{ N}$$

12. (a) Given,

Coefficient of linear expansion of steel,

$$\alpha = 11 \times 10^{-6}/°\text{C}$$

We know that,

$$\Delta l = l\alpha\Delta t$$

$$\Delta t = \frac{\Delta l}{l\alpha}$$

Here, $\Delta l = 6 \times 10^{-5}$ m

$l = 1$ m

$$\Delta t = \frac{6 \times 10^{-5}}{1 \times 11 \times 10^{-6}} = 5.45°\text{ C}$$

So, the range of temperature in which the experiment can be hence performed him this metre scale will be 19°C to 31°C

Here, option (a) is correct.

13. (a) When the core is pulled out the solenoid, the change in current will remain same.

14. (a) According to question, we can draw the following diagram

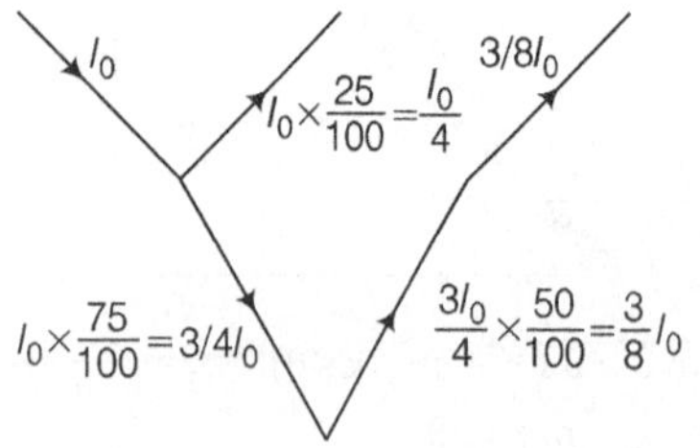

$$I_1 = \frac{I_0}{4}$$

$$I_2 = \frac{3}{8} I_0$$

We know that,

$$\frac{I_{max}}{I_{min}} = \frac{(\sqrt{I_1} + \sqrt{I_2})^2}{(\sqrt{I_1} - \sqrt{I_2})^2}$$

$$= \left(\frac{\frac{1}{2} + \sqrt{\frac{3}{8}}}{\frac{1}{2} - \sqrt{\frac{3}{8}}}\right)^2$$

15. (d) Given,

Total wall area (including the lid) $(A) = 1.0\text{ cm}^2$

Thickness of wall $(l) = 3$ cm

$$= 3 \times 10^{-2}\text{ m}$$

Average temperature outside the box = 30°C

$$\Delta\theta = 30 - 0 = 30°\text{C}$$

$$L_{\text{fusion (ice)}} = 3 \times 10^5\text{ J/kg}$$

$$K_{\text{thermocol}} = 0.03\text{ W/m K}$$

We know that,

$$\frac{Q}{t} = \frac{KA}{l}\Delta\theta$$

For one day, $t = 24 \times 60 \times 60$ s

$$\frac{m \times L_{\text{fusion (ice)}}}{t} = \frac{KA}{l}\Delta Q$$

$$\frac{m \times 3 \times 10^5}{24 \times 60 \times 60} = \frac{0.03 \times 1}{3 \times 10^{-2}} \times 30$$

$$m = \frac{0.03 \times 1 \times 30 \times 24 \times 60 \times 60}{3 \times 10^{-2} \times 3 \times 10^5}$$

$$m = \frac{77760}{9000} = 8.64\text{ kg}$$

16. (d) $^{239}_{94}\text{Pu} \xrightarrow{\alpha} {}^{235}_{92}\text{U}$

When α-particle is emitted that atomic mass is decreases by four and atomic number is decreases by two.

17. (d) Given,

$$E = 10\text{ V}$$

$$\omega = 200\text{ rad/s}$$

$$R = 50\ \Omega$$

$$L = 400\text{ mH}$$

$$C = 200\ \mu\text{F}$$

We know that,

$$Z = \sqrt{R^2 + (X_L - X_C)^2}$$

$$= \sqrt{(50)^2 + (80 - 25)^2}$$

$$= \sqrt{(50)^2 - (55)^2}$$

$$= \sqrt{2500 + 3025}$$

$$Z = \sqrt{5525} = 74.3\ \Omega$$

$$I = \frac{E}{Z} = \frac{10}{74.3} = 0.13459\ \text{A}$$

$$E_L = IX_L = 0.13459 \times 80$$

$$= 10.76\ \text{V or } 10.8\ \text{V}$$

18. (*) Given,

$$t_1 = 30°\text{C}$$

$$R_1 = 3.1\ \Omega$$

$$t_2 = 100°\ \text{C}$$

$$R_2 = 4.5\ \Omega$$

We know that,

Temperature coefficient of resistance,

$$\alpha = \frac{R_2 - R_1}{R_1 t_2 - R_2 t_1}$$

$$= \frac{4.5 - 3.1}{(3.1)(100) - (4.5 \times 30)}$$

$$= \frac{1.4}{310 - 135} = \frac{1.4}{175}$$

$$= 0.008°\text{C}^{-1}$$

19. (a) According to the question,

Velocity of an object half a second before maximum height

= Velocity of an object half a second after maximum height (return journey)

$$= 0 + gt = 0 + 9.8 \times \frac{1}{2}$$

$$= 4.9\ \text{m/s}$$

20. (b) According to the question,

Energy given to hydrogen atom = Difference in energy level from $n_1 = 1$ to $n_2 = 3$ states

$$= 13.6\left(\frac{1}{n_1^2} - \frac{1}{n_2^2}\right)$$

$$= 13.6\left(\frac{1}{1^2} - \frac{1}{3^2}\right)$$

$$= 13.6\left(1 - \frac{1}{9}\right)$$

$$= 13.6 \times \frac{8}{9}$$

$$= 12.08 \approx 12.1\ \text{eV}$$

21. (a) Given,

$$x = a\cos t,$$

$$y = a\sin t$$

and $\quad z = t$

Path is circular in xy- plane,

$$\frac{x^2}{a^2} + \frac{y^2}{a^2} = \cos^2\theta + \sin^2\theta$$

$$\frac{x^2}{a^2} + \frac{y^2}{b^2} = 1$$

In one revolution, the particle move a distance of 1 unit along z-axis.

$$\frac{dz}{dt} = 1$$

Hence, path is helix.

22. (a) Given

$$\eta_1 = \frac{1}{6}$$

According to the question,

$$\eta_1 = \frac{T_1 - T_2}{T_1}$$

$$\frac{T_1 - T_2}{T_1} = \frac{1}{6} \quad \ldots\text{(i)}$$

$$\eta_2 = \frac{T_1 - (T_2 - 62)}{T_1}$$

$$2 \times \eta_1 = \frac{T_1 - T_2 + 62}{T_1}$$

$$2 \times \frac{1}{6} = \frac{T_1 - T_2 + 62}{T_1}$$

$$\frac{1}{3}=\frac{T_1-T_2+62}{T_1} \quad \ldots(ii)$$

From Eq. (i), we get

$$T_1-T_2=\frac{T_1}{6}$$

Substituting this value in Eq. (ii), we get

$$\frac{1}{3}=\frac{\frac{T_1}{6}+62}{T_1}$$

$$\frac{1}{3}=\frac{T_1+372}{6T_1}$$

$$6T_1=3T_1+1116$$

$$3T_1=1116$$

$$T_1=372\text{ K}$$

From Eq. (i), we get

$$\frac{372-T_2}{372}=\frac{1}{6}$$

$$6(372-T_2)=372$$

$$2232-6T_2=372$$

$$6T_2=2232-372$$

$$6T_2=1860$$

$$T_2=\frac{1860}{6}$$

$$T_2=310\text{ K}$$

23. (a) Given,

Distance of light source $(u)=-1.5\text{ m}=-\frac{-3}{2}\text{ m}$

Radius of curvature of mirror $(R)=1\text{ m}$

We know that,

$$\frac{1}{f}=\frac{1}{v}+\frac{1}{u} \qquad \left[\because f=\frac{R}{2}\right]$$

$$\therefore \quad \frac{2}{R}=\frac{1}{v}+\frac{1}{u}$$

$$\frac{2}{1}=\frac{1}{v}+\frac{1}{\frac{-3}{2}}$$

$$\frac{2}{1}=\frac{1}{v}-\frac{2}{3}$$

$$\frac{1}{v}=2+\frac{2}{3}$$

$$\frac{1}{v}=\frac{6+2}{3}$$

$$\frac{1}{v}=\frac{8}{3}$$

$$v=\frac{3}{8}=0.375\text{ m}$$

The image is virtual.

$$\text{Magnification } (m)=\frac{-v}{u}=\frac{\frac{-3}{8}}{\frac{-3}{2}}=\frac{1}{4}=0.25$$

24. (c) Given,

Number of moles of air in room $(n)=2000=2\times10^3$

Temperature difference $(dT)=24-34=-10°\text{C}$

We know that,

$$dQ=nC_v dT$$

$$=2\times10^3\times\frac{R}{0.4}[-10]$$

$$=\frac{-2\times10^3\times8.314\times10}{0.4}$$

$$=\frac{2\times8.314\times10^5}{4}$$

$$=\frac{16.628}{4}\times10^5$$

$$=-4.2\times10^5\text{ J}$$

25. (d) Given,

Speed of ball $(u)=20$ m/s

Angle $(\theta)=30°$

We know that,

$$H=\frac{u^2\sin^2\theta}{2g}$$

$$H=\frac{(20)^2(\sin 30)^2}{2\times10}$$

$$H=\frac{20\times20\times\left(\frac{1}{2}\right)^2}{20}$$

$$H=20\times\frac{1}{4}$$

$$H=5\text{ m}$$

26. (c) Given,

Diameter of pipe $(d) = 5\text{ mm} = 5 \times 10^{-3}$ m

Density of gasoline $(\rho) = 720\text{ kg/m}^3$.

Viscocity of gasoline $(\eta) = 6 \times 10^{-3}$ Poise

We know that, $v_c = \dfrac{\eta}{\rho d} = \dfrac{6 \times 10^{-3}}{720 \times 5 \times 10^{-3}}$

$$= \frac{6 \times 10^{-3}}{3600 \times 10^{-3}} = \frac{1}{600}$$

$$= \frac{1}{6} \times 10^{-2}$$

$$= 1.66 \times 10^{-3}\text{ m/s}$$

27. (c) Copper is a conductor and germanium is semiconductor. When both are cooled from room temperature to 80 K. Then, resistance of copper will decrease while that of germanium will increase.

28. (a) We know that,

$$\lambda = \frac{\lambda_0}{\mu}$$

According to the question,

$$\frac{\sin\alpha_1}{\sin\alpha_2} = \frac{\mu_2}{\mu_1} = \frac{\lambda_1}{\lambda_2}$$

$$\lambda_2 = \lambda_1 \frac{\sin\alpha_2}{\sin\alpha_1}$$

29. (b) Given,

Frequency of message signal $(f_m) = 1$ KHz

$$= 1 \times 10^3\text{Hz}$$

Peak voltage of message signal $(E_m) = 5$ V

Carrier frequency $(f_c) = 1$ MHz

$$= 1 \times 10^6\text{ Hz}$$

Peak voltage of carrier $(E_c) = 15$ V

We know that,

The equation of amplitude modulated wave is given by

$$e(t) = E_c\left[1 + \frac{E_m}{E_c}\sin\omega_m t\right]\sin\omega_c t$$

$$= E_c\left[1 + \frac{E_m}{E_c}\sin(2\pi f_m)t\right]\sin 2\pi f_c t$$

$$= 15\left[1 + \frac{5}{15}\sin(2\pi \times 10^3)t\right]\sin 2\pi \times 10^6 t$$

$$= 15\left[1 + \frac{1}{3}\sin(2\pi\ 10^3 t)\right]\sin(2\pi\ 10^6 t)$$

30. (d) SONAR technology is based on the reflection of ultrasonic waves.

31. (b) Given,

Velocity of particle $= v$

Change in momentum = final momentum – initial momentum

$$= Mv - (-Mv)$$

$$= 2Mv$$

32. (a) When billiard ball collide elastically, they will exchange the kinetic energy, so they may move in straight path or at any angle.

33. (a)

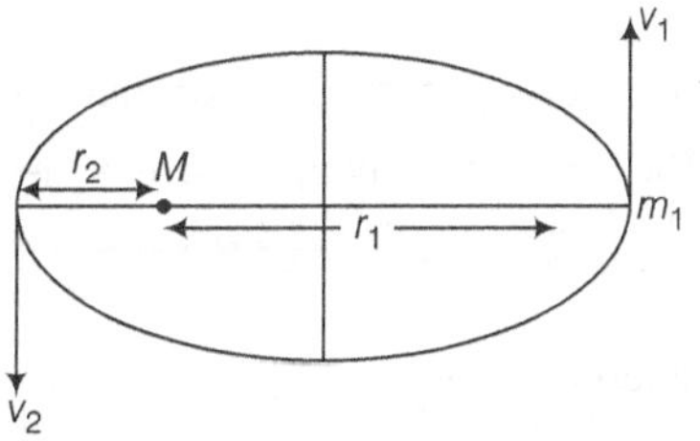

According to the law of conservation of angular momentum,

$$mv_1r_1 = mv_2r_2$$

$$\Rightarrow \quad v_2 = \frac{v_1r_1}{r_2} \quad \ldots\text{(i)}$$

From the law of conservation of total mechanical energy.

$$\frac{-GMm}{r_1} + \frac{1}{2}mv_1^2 = -\frac{GMm}{r_2} + \frac{1}{2}mv_2^2 \quad \ldots\text{(ii)}$$

From Eqs. (i) and (ii), we get

$$v_1 = \sqrt{\frac{2GMr_2}{(r_1 + r_2)r_1}}$$

Angular momentum,

$$L = mv_1r_1$$

$$= m\left(\sqrt{\frac{2GMr_2}{(r_1 + r_2)r_1}}\right) \times r_1$$

$$L = m\sqrt{\frac{2GMr_1r_2}{r_1 + r_2}}$$

34. (a) From the conservation of energy,

$$mgh = \mu mgd$$

$$d = \frac{h}{\mu}$$

35. (a) Given,

Number of turns in circular coil = 100

Area $(A) = 2 \times 10^{-2}\ m^2$

Magnetic field $(B) = 0.01$ T

Frequency of rotation $(f) = 50$ Hz

We know that,

$$e = NBA\omega$$

$$= NBA(2\pi f)$$

$$= 100 \times 0.01 \times 2 \times 10^{-2} \times 2 \times \frac{22}{7} \times 50$$

$$= 6.28 \text{ V}$$

36. (c) The frequency of sound wave remains constant.

37. (c) The majority charge carriers in n-types semiconductor are electrons.

38. (d)

Deceleration $\omega = -a\sqrt{v}$.

But $\omega = \frac{dv}{dt}$

$$\frac{dv}{dt} = -a\sqrt{v}$$

$$\frac{-dv}{\sqrt{v}} = a\,.\,dt$$

$$\int_{v_i}^{0} \frac{dv}{\sqrt{v}} = \int a\,dt$$

$$|2\sqrt{v}|_{v_i}^{0} = at$$

$$t = \frac{2}{a}\sqrt{v_i s}$$

Again,

$$\frac{-dv}{dt} = a\sqrt{v}$$

$$\frac{dv}{dx}\cdot\frac{dx}{dt} = -a\sqrt{v}$$

$$\frac{dv}{dx}\,.\,v = -a\sqrt{v}$$

$$dv\sqrt{v} = -a\,.\,dx$$

$$\int_{v_0}^{0} \sqrt{v}\,dv = -a\int_{0}^{s} ds$$

After solving, we get $s = \frac{2}{3a}\,.\,v_0^{\frac{3}{2}}$

39. (c) A current carrying conductor produces magnetic field in its neighbourhood.

40. (a) Given,

$$\mathbf{F}_1 = (\hat{\mathbf{i}} + 2\hat{\mathbf{j}} + 3\hat{\mathbf{k}})\text{ N}$$

$$\mathbf{F}_2 = (4\hat{\mathbf{i}} - 5\hat{\mathbf{j}} - 2\hat{\mathbf{k}})\text{ N}$$

$$\mathbf{r}_1 = 20\hat{\mathbf{i}} + 15\hat{\mathbf{j}}\text{ cm}$$

$$\mathbf{r}_2 = 7\hat{\mathbf{k}}\text{ cm}$$

Total force on particle, $\mathbf{F} = \mathbf{F}_1 + \mathbf{F}_2$

$$= \hat{\mathbf{i}} + 2\hat{\mathbf{j}} + 3\hat{\mathbf{k}} + 4\hat{\mathbf{i}} - 5\hat{\mathbf{j}} - 2\hat{\mathbf{k}}$$

$$= (5\hat{\mathbf{i}} - 3\hat{\mathbf{j}} + \hat{\mathbf{k}})\text{ N}$$

Displacement of particle, $\mathbf{s} = \mathbf{r}_2 - \mathbf{r}_1$

$$= 7\hat{\mathbf{k}} - 20\hat{\mathbf{i}} - 15\hat{\mathbf{j}}$$

$$= (-20\hat{\mathbf{i}} - 15\hat{\mathbf{j}} + 7\hat{\mathbf{k}})\text{ cm}$$

We know that,

Work $(\omega) = \mathbf{F}\cdot\mathbf{s}$

$$= (5\hat{\mathbf{i}} - 3\hat{\mathbf{j}} + \hat{\mathbf{k}})(-20\hat{\mathbf{i}} - 15\hat{\mathbf{j}} + 7\hat{\mathbf{k}}) \times 10^{-2}$$

$$= (-100 + 45 + 7) \times 10^{-2}$$

$$= -0.48\text{ J}$$

SOLVED PAPER 2016

AP EAMCET

Engineering Entrance Exam

1. Match the List I with List II.

List I	List II
A. Boltzmann constant	I. $[ML^0T^0]$
B. Coefficient of viscosity	II. $[ML^{-1}T^{-1}]$
C. Water equivalent	III. $[MLT^{-3}K^{-1}]$
D. Coefficient of thermal conductivity	IV. $[ML^2T^{-2}K^{-1}]$

The correct match in the following is

(a) A-III; B-I; C-II; D-IV
(b) A-III; B-II; C-I; D-IV
(c) A-IV; B-II; C-I; D-III
(d) A-IV; B-I; C-II; D-III

2. Two trains, which are moving along different tracks in opposite directions are put on the same track by mistake. On noticing the mistake, when the trains are 300 m apart the drivers start slowing down the trains. The graphs given below show decrease in their velocities as function of time. The separation between the trains when both have stopped is

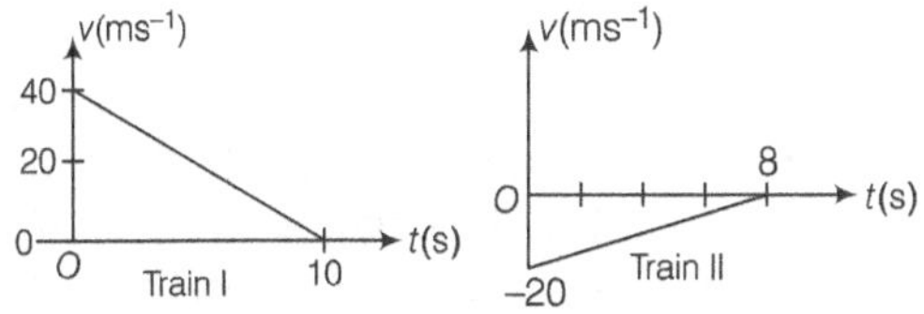

(a) 120 m
(b) 20 m
(c) 60 m
(d) 280 m

3. A point object moves along an arc of a circle of radius R. Its velocity depends upon the distance covered s as $v = K\sqrt{s}$, where K is a constant. If θ is the angle between the total acceleration and tangential acceleration, then

(a) $\tan\theta = \sqrt{\frac{s}{R}}$ (b) $\tan\theta = \sqrt{\frac{s}{2R}}$
(c) $\tan\theta = \frac{s}{2R}$ (d) $\tan\theta = \frac{2s}{R}$

4. A body projected from the ground reaches a point X in its path after 3 seconds and from there it reaches the ground after further 6 seconds. The vertical distance of the point X from the ground is (acceleration due to gravity $= 10\ ms^{-2}$)

(a) 30 m
(b) 60 m
(c) 80 m
(d) 90 m

5. A particle of mass m is suspended from a ceiling through a string of length L. If the particle moves in a horizontal circle of radius r as shown in the figure, then the speed of the particle is

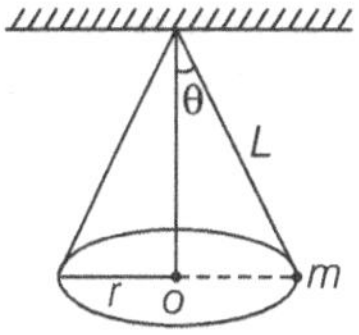

(a) $r\sqrt{\frac{g}{\sqrt{L^2 - r^2}}}$ (b) $g\sqrt{\frac{r}{\sqrt{L^2 - r^2}}}$
(c) $r\sqrt{\frac{g}{\sqrt{L^2 - r^2}}}$ (d) $g\sqrt{\frac{r}{\sqrt{L^2 - r^2}}}$

6. A particle is placed at rest inside a hollow hemisphere of radius R. The coefficient of friction between the particle and the hemisphere is $\mu = \frac{1}{\sqrt{3}}$. The maximum height upto which the particle can remain stationary is

(a) $\frac{R}{2}$

(b) $\left(1-\frac{\sqrt{3}}{2}\right)R$

(c) $\frac{\sqrt{3}}{2}R$

(d) $\frac{3R}{8}$

7. A 1 kg ball moving with a speed of 6 ms^{-1} collides head-on with a 0.5 kg ball moving in the opposite direction with a speed of 9 ms^{-1}. If the coefficient of restitution is $\frac{1}{3}$, then the energy lost in the collision is

(a) 303.4 J (b) 66.7 J
(c) 33.3 J (d) 67.8 J

8. A ball is thrown vertically down from a height of 40 m from the ground with an initial velocity v. The ball hits the ground, loses $\frac{1}{3}$rd of its total mechanical energy and rebounds back to the same height. If the acceleration due to gravity is 10 ms^{-2}, then the value of v is

(a) 5 ms^{-1} (b) 10 ms^{-1}
(c) 15 ms^{-1} (d) 20 ms^{-1}

9. Three identical uniform thin metal rods form the three sides of an equilateral triangle. If the moment of inertia of the system of these three rods about an axis passing through the centroid of the triangle and perpendicular to the plane of the triangle is n times. The moment of inertia of one rod separately about an axis passing through the centre of the rod and perpendicular to its length, the value of n is

(a) 3 (b) 6
(c) 9 (d) 12

10. Two smooth and similar right angled prisms are arranged on a smooth horizontal plane as shown in the figure. The lower prism has a mass 3 times the upper prism. The prisms are held in an initial position as shown and are then released. As the upper prism touches the horizontal plane, the distance moved by the lower prism is

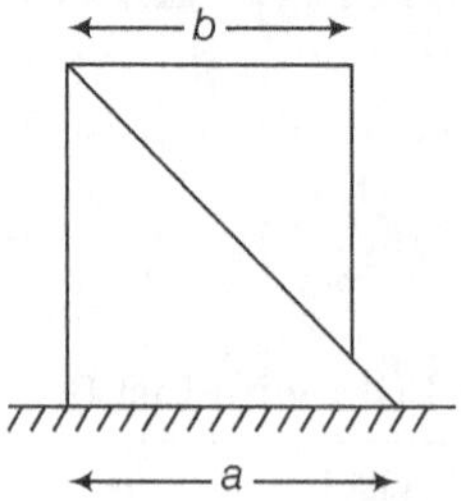

(a) $a - b$ (b) $\frac{a-b}{3}$
(c) $\frac{b-a}{2}$ (d) $\frac{a-b}{4}$

11. A particle is executing simple harmonic motion with an amplitude of 2 m. The difference in the magnitudes of its maximum acceleration and maximum velocity is 4. The time-period of its oscillation and its velocity when it is 1 m away from the mean position are respectively

(a) 2s, $2\sqrt{3}$ ms^{-1} (b) $\frac{7}{22}$ s, $4\sqrt{3}$ ms^{-1}
(c) $\frac{22}{7}$ s, $2\sqrt{3}$ ms^{-1} (d) $\frac{44}{7}$ s, $4\sqrt{3}$ ms^{-1}

12. Two bodies of masses m and $9m$ are placed at a distance r. The gravitational potential at a point on the line joining them, where gravitational field is zero, is (G is universal gravitational constant)

(a) $\frac{-14\,Gm}{r}$ (b) $\frac{-16\,Gm}{r}$ (c) $\frac{-12\,Gm}{r}$ (d) $\frac{-8\,Gm}{r}$

13. When a load of 80 N is suspended from a string, its length is 101 mm. If a load of 100 N is suspended, its length is 102 mm. If a load of 160 N is suspended from it, then length of the string is (Assume the area of cross-section unchanged)

(a) 15.5 cm (b) 13.5 cm (c) 16.5 cm (d) 10.5 cm

14. A sphere of material of relative density 8 has a concentric spherical cavity and just sinks in water. If the radius of the sphere is 2 cm, then the volume of the cavity is

(a) $\frac{76}{3}$ cm^3 (b) $\frac{79}{3}$ cm^3
(c) $\frac{82}{3}$ cm^3 (d) $\frac{88}{3}$ cm^3

15. A hunter fired a metallic bullet of mass m kg from a gun towards an obstacle and it just melts when it is stopped by the obstacle. The initial temperature of the bullet is 300 K. If $\frac{1}{4}$th of heat is absorbed by the obstacle, then the minimum velocity of the bullet is
(Melting point of bullet = 600 K,
Specific heat of bullet = 0.03 cal g^{-1} °C^{-1},
Latent heat of fusion of bullet = 6 cal g^{-1})

(a) 410 ms^{-1} (b) 260 ms^{-1}
(c) 460 ms^{-1} (d) 310 ms^{-1}

16. M kg of water at t °C is divided into two parts so that one part of mass m kg when converted into ice at 0°C would release enough heat to vapourise the other part, then $\frac{m}{M}$ is equal to
(Specific heat of water = 1 cal g^{-1} °C^{-1},
Latent heat of fusion of ice = 80 cal g^{-1},
Latent heat of steam = 540 cal g^{-1})

(a) $640 - t$ (b) $\frac{720 - t}{640}$
(c) $\frac{640 + t}{720}$ (d) $\frac{640 - t}{720}$

17. A diatomic gas ($\gamma = 1.4$) does 300 J work when it is expanded isobarically. The heat given to the gas in this process is

(a) 1050 J (b) 950 J
(c) 600 J (d) 550 J

18. When the absolute temperature of the source of a Carnot heat engine is increased by 25%, its efficiency increases by 80%. The new efficiency of the engine is

(a) 12% (b) 24% (c) 48% (d) 36%

19. A cylinder of fixed capacity 67.2 litres contains helium gas at STP. The amount of heat needed to rise the temperature of the gas in the cylinder by 20°C is ($R = 8.31$ J $mol^{-1}K^{-1}$)

(a) 748 J (b) 374 J
(c) 1000 J (d) 500 J

20. For a certain organ pipe, three successive resonance frequencies are observed at 425, 595 and 765 Hz, respectively. The length of the pipe is (speed of sound in air = 340 ms^{-1})

(a) 0.5 m (b) 1 m
(c) 1.5 m (d) 2 m

21. A student holds a tuning fork oscillating at 170 Hz. He walks towards a wall at a constant speed of 2 ms^{-1}. The beat frequency observed by the student between the tuning fork and its echo is (Velocity of sound = 340 ms^{-1})

(a) 2.5 Hz (b) 3 Hz
(c) 1 Hz (d) 2 Hz

22. An infinitely long rod lies along the axis of a concave mirror of focal length f. The nearer end of the rod is at a distance u, $(u > f)$ from the mirror. Its image will have a length

(a) $\frac{uf}{u + f}$
(b) $\frac{uf}{u - f}$
(c) $\frac{f^2}{u + f}$
(d) $\frac{f^2}{u - f}$

23. In Young's double slit experiment, red light of wavelength 6000 Å is used and the nth bright fringe is obtained at a point P on the screen. Keeping the same setting, the source of light is replaced by green light of wavelength 5000 Å and now $(n + 1)$th bright fringe is obtained at the point P on the screen. The value of n is

(a) 4 (b) 5
(c) 6 (d) 3

24. Two charges each of charge $+10\,\mu C$ are kept on Y-axis at $y=-a$ and $y=+a$, respectively. Another point charge $-20\,\mu C$ is placed at the origin and given a small displacement $x\,(x << a)$ along X-axis. The force acting on the point charge is

$\left(x \text{ and } a \text{ are in metres, } \frac{1}{4\pi\varepsilon_0} = 9\times 10^9 \text{ N-m}^2\,\text{C}^{-2}\right)$

(a) $\frac{3.6x}{a^2}$ N (b) $\frac{2.4x^2}{a}$ N (c) $\frac{3.6x}{a^3}$ N (d) $\frac{4.8x}{a^2}$ N

25. Three identical charges, each $2\,\mu C$ lie at the vertices of a right angled triangle as shown in the figure. Forces on the charge at B due to the charges at A and C respectively are F_1 and F_2. The angle between their resultant force and F_2 is

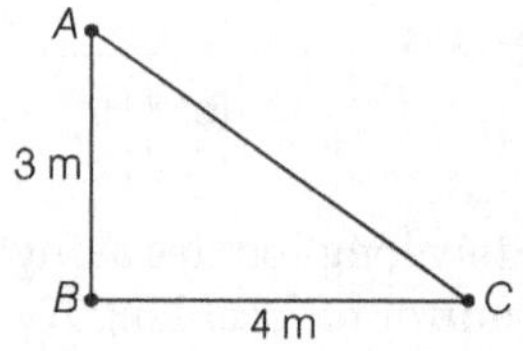

(a) $\tan^{-1}\left(\frac{9}{16}\right)$ (b) $\tan^{-1}\left(\frac{9}{7}\right)$
(c) $\tan^{-1}\left(\frac{16}{9}\right)$ (d) $\tan^{-1}\left(\frac{7}{9}\right)$

26. The figure shows equipotential surfaces concentric at O. The magnitude of electric field at a distance r metres from O is

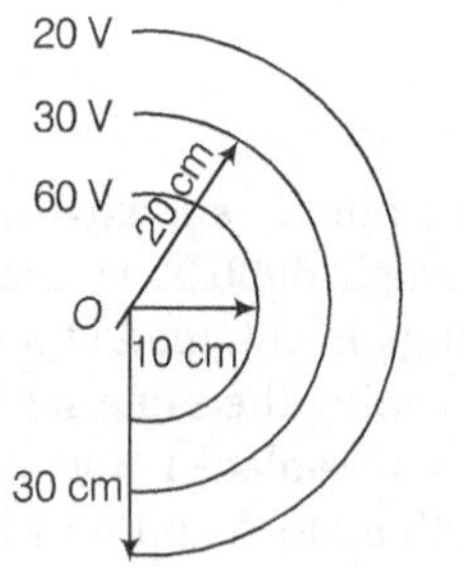

(a) $\frac{9}{r^2}$ Vm^{-1} (b) $\frac{16}{r^2}$ Vm^{-1}
(c) $\frac{2}{r^2}$ Vm^{-1} (d) $\frac{6}{r^2}$ Vm^{-1}

27. A region contains a uniform electric field $\mathbf{E} = (10\hat{\mathbf{i}} + 30\hat{\mathbf{j}})$ Vm^{-1}. A and B are two points in the field at (1, 2, 0) m and (2, 1, 3) m, respectively. The work done when a charge of 0.8 C moves from A to B in a parabolic path is

(a) 8 J (b) 80 J
(c) 40 J (d) 16 J

28. When a long straight uniform rod is connected across an ideal cell, the drift velocity of electrons in it is v. If a uniform hole is made along the axis of the rod and the same battery is used, then the drift velocity of electrons becomes

(a) v (b) $> v$
(c) $< v$ (d) zero

29. In a meter bridge experiment, when a nichrome wire is in the right gap, the balancing length is 60 cm. When the nichrome wire is uniformly stretched to increase its length by 20% and again connected in the right gap, the new balancing length is nearly

(a) 61 cm (b) 31 cm
(c) 51 cm (d) 41 cm

30. A loop of flexible conducting wire lies in a magnetic field of 2.0 T with its plane perpendicular to the field. The length of the wire is 1 m. When a current of 1.1 A is passed through the loop, it opens into a circle, then the tension developed in the wire is

(a) 0.15 N (b) 0.25 N
(c) 0.35 N (d) 0.45 N

31. A charge q is spread uniformly over an isolated ring of radius R. The ring is rotated about its natural axis with an angular velocity ω. Magnetic dipole moment of the ring is

(a) $\frac{q\omega R^2}{2}$

(b) $\frac{q\omega R}{2}$

(c) $q\omega R^2$

(d) $\frac{q\omega}{2R}$

32. A magnetic dipole of moment 2.5 Am^2 is free to rotate about a vertical axis passing through its centre. It is released from East-West direction. Its kinetic energy at the moment, it takes North-South position is $(B_H = 3 \times 10^{-5}\ T)$

(a) 50 μJ (b) 100 μJ
(c) 175 μJ (d) 75 μJ

33. A branch of a circuit is shown in the figure. If current is decreasing at the rate of $10^3\ As^{-1}$, then the potential difference between A and B is

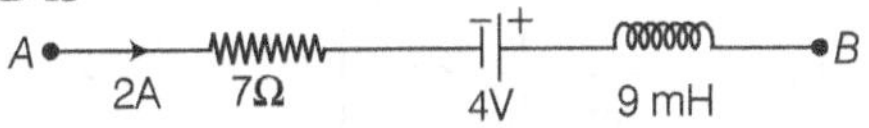

(a) 1 V (b) 5 V
(c) 10 V (d) 2 V

34. The natural frequency of an L-C circuit is 125 kHz. When the capacitor is totally filled with a dielectric material, the natural frequency decreases by 25 kHz. Dielectric constant of the material is nearly

(a) 3.33 (b) 2.12
(c) 1.56 (d) 1.91

35. Choose the correct sequence of the radiation sources in increasing order of the wavelength of electromagnetic waves produced by them.

(a) X-ray tube, Magnetron valve, Radioactive source, Sodium lamp
(b) Radioactive source, X-ray tube, Sodium lamp, Magnetron valve
(c) X-ray tube, Magnetron valve, Sodium lamp, Radioactive source
(d) Magnetron valve, Sodium lamp, X-ray tube, Radioactive source

36. A photo sensitive metallic surface emits electrons when X-rays of wavelength λ fall on it. The de-Broglie wavelength of the emitted electrons is (Neglect the work function of the surface, m is mass of the electron, h is Planck's constant, c is the velocity of light)

(a) $\sqrt{\frac{2mc}{h\lambda}}$ (b) $\sqrt{\frac{h\lambda}{2mc}}$
(c) $\sqrt{\frac{mc}{h\lambda}}$ (d) $\sqrt{\frac{h\lambda}{mc}}$

37. An electron in a hydrogen atom undergoes a transition from a higher energy level to a lower energy level. The incorrect statement of the following is

(a) Kinetic energy of the electron increases
(b) Velocity of the electron increases
(c) Angular momentum of the electron remains constant
(d) Wavelength of de-Broglie wave associated with the motion of electron decreases

38. The radius of germanium (Ge) nuclide is measured to be twice the radius of ${}^9_4Be$. The number of nucleons in Ge will be

(a) 72 (b) 73 (c) 74 (d) 75

39. For a common-emitter transistor amplifier, the current gain is 60. If the emitter current is 6.6 mA, then its base current is

(a) 6.492 mA (b) 0.108 mA
(c) 4.208 mA (d) 0.343 mA

40. If a transmitting antenna of height 105m is placed on a hill, then its coverage area is

(a) 4224 km^2 (b) 3264 km^2
(c) 6400 km^2 (d) 4864 km^2

Answers

1. (c)	**2.** (b)	**3.** (d)	**4.** (d)	**5.** (a)	**6.** (b)	**7.** (c)	**8.** (d)	**9.** (b)	**10.** (d)
11. (c)	**12.** (b)	**13.** (d)	**14.** (d)	**15.** (a)	**16.** (d)	**17.** (a)	**18.** (d)	**19.** (a)	**20.** (b)
21. (d)	**22.** (d)	**23.** (b)	**24.** (c)	**25.** (c)	**26.** (d)	**27.** (d)	**28.** (a)	**29.** (c)	**30.** (c)
31. (a)	**32.** (d)	**33.** (a)	**34.** (c)	**35.** (b)	**36.** (b)	**37.** (c)	**38.** (a)	**39.** (b)	**40.** (a)

Explanations

1. (A) Boltzmann constant = $[ML^2T^{-2}K^{-1}]$

(B) Coefficient of viscosity = $[ML^{-1}T^{-1}]$

(C) Water equivalent = $[ML^0T^0]$

(D) Coefficient of thermal conductivity = $[MLT^{-3}K^{-1}]$

2.

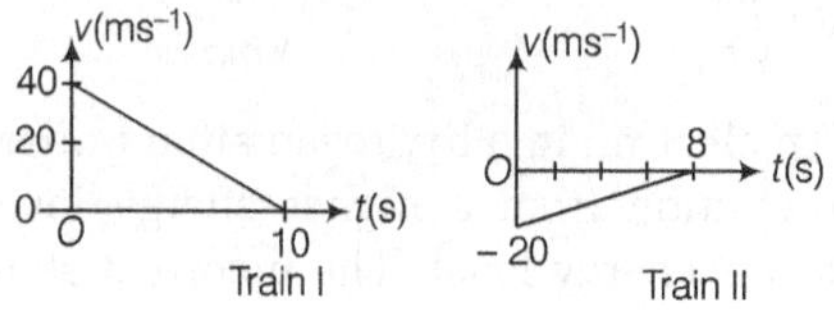

For train I,

$u_1 = 40$ m/s

As, $v_1 = u_1 + a_1 t$

$\Rightarrow \quad 0 = 40 + a_1(10)$

$\Rightarrow \quad a_1 = \frac{-40}{10} = -4 \text{ m/s}^2$

For train II,

$u_2 = -20$ m/s

As, $v_2 = u_2 + a_2 t$

$\Rightarrow \quad 0 = -20 + a_2(8)$

$\Rightarrow \quad a_2 = \frac{20}{8} = \frac{10}{4} \text{ m/s}^2$

For train I,

$v_1^2 = u_1^2 - 2a_1 s_1$

$\Rightarrow \quad 0 = u_1^2 - 2a_1 s_1$

$\Rightarrow \quad s_1 = \frac{u_1^2}{2a_1} = \frac{(40)^2}{2 \times 4}$

$= \frac{1600}{8} = 200$ m

For train II,

$v_2^2 = u_2^2 - 2a_2 s_2$

$\Rightarrow \quad 0 = u_2^2 - 2a_2 s_2$

$\Rightarrow \quad s_2 = \frac{u_2^2}{2a}$

or, $\quad s_2 = \frac{(-20)^2}{2\left(\frac{10}{4}\right)}$

or, $\quad s_2 = \frac{400 \times 2}{10}$

or, $\quad s_2 = 80$ m

Total distance covered by both trains,

$s = s_1 + s_2$

$s = 200 + 80$

$s = 280$ m

$\therefore$ Separation between the trains

= Remaining distance

= 300 – 280 = 20 m

3. Given, velocity depends upon distance covered s as $V = k\sqrt{s}$.

$\because \tan\theta = \frac{a_{\text{radial}}}{a_{\text{tangential}}} = \frac{V^2/R}{a_{\text{tangential}}}$

$\Rightarrow \tan\theta = \frac{1}{a_{\text{tangential}}}\left[\frac{1}{R} \times K^2 s\right]$

$\Rightarrow \tan\theta = \frac{1}{a_{\text{tangential}}}\left[\frac{K^2 s}{R}\right]$ ...(i)

Now, $a_{\text{tangential}} = \frac{dv}{dt} = \frac{d}{dt} = [K\sqrt{s}]$

or, $\quad a_{\text{tangential}} = K \times \frac{1}{2\sqrt{s}} \times \frac{ds}{dt}$

or, $\quad a_{\text{tangential}} = \frac{K}{2\sqrt{s}} \times V$

$= \frac{K}{2\sqrt{s}} \times K\sqrt{s} = \frac{K^2}{2}$ ...(ii)

From Eqs. (i) and (ii), we get

$\tan\theta = \frac{\frac{K^2 s}{R}}{\frac{K^2}{2}} \Rightarrow \tan\theta = \frac{2s}{R}$

4. Given, acceleration due to gravity

$(g) = 10 \text{ ms}^{-2}$

According to the question,

Total time of flight $(t) = \frac{2u}{g}$

where, u is initial vertical velocity.

or, $\quad 9 = \frac{2u}{g} \quad$ or, $u = \frac{9g}{2}$

or, $\quad u = \frac{9 \times 10}{2}$ or, $u = 45$ m/s

Since, in covering the vertical distance, g becomes negative,

$\Rightarrow \quad h = ut - \frac{1}{2}gt^2$

or, $\quad h = 45 \times (3) - \frac{1}{2} \times 10 \times (3)^2$

or, $\quad h = 135 - 45$

or, $\quad h = 90$ m

5.

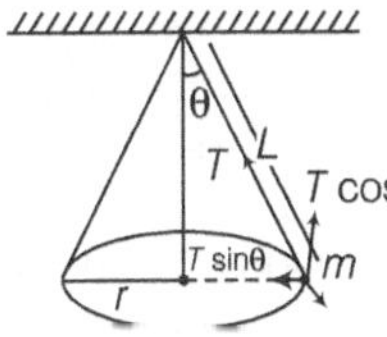

From the diagram,

$$T \sin\theta = \frac{mv^2}{r} \quad \ldots(i)$$

$$T \cos\theta = mg \quad \ldots(ii)$$

Dividing Eq. (i) by Eq. (ii), we get

$$\frac{T\sin\theta}{T\cos\theta} = \frac{mv^2}{r} \times \frac{1}{mg}$$

$$\Rightarrow \quad \tan\theta = \frac{v^2}{rg} \quad \ldots(iii)$$

From the diagram,

$$\tan\theta = \frac{r}{\sqrt{L^2 - r^2}} \quad \ldots(iv)$$

From Eqs. (iii) and (iv), we get

$$\frac{v^2}{rg} = \frac{r}{\sqrt{L^2 - r^2}}$$

$$\Rightarrow \quad v = r\sqrt{\frac{g}{\sqrt{L^2 - r^2}}}$$

6. Given, radius of hollow hemisphere = R

Coefficient of friction between the particle and the hemisphere $(\mu) = \frac{1}{\sqrt{3}}$.

We know that maximum height,

$$h_{max} = \left(1 - \frac{1}{\sqrt{\mu^2 + 1}}\right)R$$

$$= \left(1 - \frac{1}{\sqrt{\left(\frac{1}{\sqrt{3}}\right)^2 + 1}}\right) \times R$$

$$= \left(1 - \frac{1}{\sqrt{\frac{1}{3} + 1}}\right) \times R$$

$$= \left(1 - \frac{1}{\sqrt{\frac{1+3}{3}}}\right) \times R$$

or, $h_{max} = \left(1 - \frac{\sqrt{3}}{2}\right)R$

7. Given, mass of first ball $(m_1) = 1$ kg

Speed of first ball $(u_1) = 6\ ms^{-1}$

Mass of second ball $(m_2) = 0.5$ kg or $\frac{1}{2}$ kg

Speed of second ball $(u_2) = 9\ ms^{-1}$

Coefficient of restitution $(e) = 1/3$

We know that,

$$\Delta KE = \frac{m_1 m_2}{2(m_1 + m_2)}(1 - e^2)(u_1 + u_2)^2$$

$$= \frac{1 \times \frac{1}{2}}{2\left(1 + \frac{1}{2}\right)}\left[1 - \left(\frac{1}{3}\right)^2\right](6 + 9)^2$$

$$= \frac{1}{2} \times \frac{2}{6} \times \frac{8}{9} \times (15)^2$$

$$= \frac{1}{6} \times \frac{8}{9} \times 225$$

$$= 33.33\ J$$

8. Given, height $(h) = 40$ m

Loss of energy = $\frac{1}{3}$rd of total mechanical energy

Acceleration due to gravity $(g) = 10\ ms^{-2}$

Let the total mechanical energy = 1J

Remaining energy $= 1 - \frac{1}{3} = \frac{2}{3}$ J

Now,

$$\frac{2}{3}\left(\frac{1}{2}mv^2 + mgh\right) = mgh$$

$$\Rightarrow \quad \frac{2}{3}\left(\frac{1}{2}v^2 + gh\right) = gh$$

$$\Rightarrow \quad \frac{v^2}{3} = gh - \frac{2gh}{3}$$

$$\Rightarrow \quad \frac{v^2}{3} = \frac{gh}{3} \Rightarrow v = \sqrt{gh}$$

$$\Rightarrow \quad v = \sqrt{400}$$

$$\Rightarrow \quad v = 20\ m/s$$

9. Let the length of the rod be l.

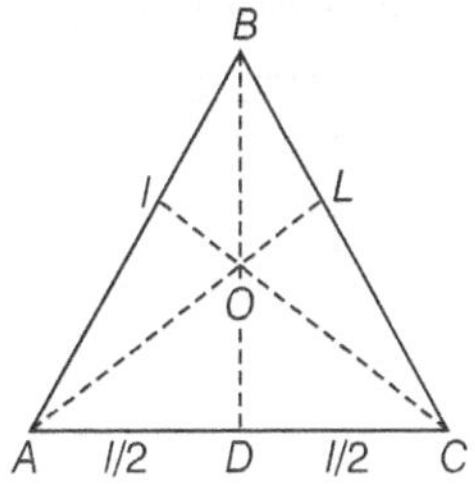

O-centroid of the triangle.

$$AB^2 = BD^2 + \left(\frac{l}{2}\right)^2$$

$$\Rightarrow \quad l^2 = BD^2 + \frac{l^2}{4}$$

or, $$(BD)^2 = l^2 - \frac{l^2}{4} = \frac{3}{4}l^2$$

or, $$BD = \frac{\sqrt{3}}{2}\cdot l$$

$$\Rightarrow \quad OD = \frac{\sqrt{3}}{2}\cdot l \times \frac{1}{3} = \frac{l}{2\sqrt{3}}$$

Moment of inertia about an axis passing through centre and perpendicular to the rod, $I = \frac{ml^2}{12}$

Now applying parallel axes theorem, we get

Moment of inertia about centroid

$$= m\left(\frac{l}{2\sqrt{3}}\right)^2 + I$$

$$= \frac{ml^2}{4\times 3} + \frac{ml^2}{12}$$

$$= \frac{ml^2}{12} + \frac{ml^2}{12}$$

$$= \frac{2ml^2}{12}$$

Moment of inertia of the system of 3 rods

$$= 3 \times \frac{2ml^2}{12} = 6 \times \frac{ml^2}{12} = 6I$$

According to the question, $\frac{6ml^2}{12} = I$

$$= n\cdot\left(\frac{ml^2}{12}\right)$$

$\therefore \quad n = 6$

10. Let m be the mass of upper prism and the mass of lower prism be $3m$.

Let lower prism moves through a horizontal distance x. As, horizontal position of centre of mass of the two prisms system remains unchanged.

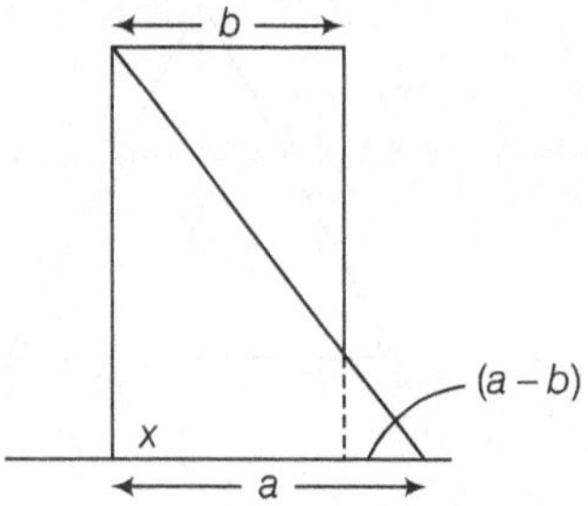

$\therefore \quad 3mx = m[(a-b) - x]$

or, $\quad 3x = (a-b) - x$

or, $\quad 4x = a - b$

or, $\quad x = \frac{a-b}{4}$

11. Amplitude of simple harmonic motion $(A) = 2\,\text{m}$

According to the question,

$$|A\omega^2| - |A\omega| = 4$$

$$\Rightarrow \quad 2\omega^2 - 2\omega - 4 = 0$$

$$\Rightarrow \omega = 2\text{ rad/s} \Rightarrow \frac{2\pi}{T} = 2$$

$$\Rightarrow \quad T = \pi = \frac{22}{7}\text{ s}$$

Velocity, $v = \omega\sqrt{A^2 - y^2} = 2\sqrt{(2)^2 - (1)^2}$

$$= 2\sqrt{4-1} = 2\sqrt{3}\text{ ms}^{-1}$$

12. Mass of first body $(m_1) = m$

Mass of second body $(m_2) = 9m$

Distance between the bodies $(d) = r$

Now, distance of the point from the body of mass m, where gravitational field is zero is given by

$$x = \frac{d}{\sqrt{\frac{m_2}{m_1}} + 1}$$

or, $$x = \frac{r}{\sqrt{\frac{9m}{m}} + 1} \text{ or, } x = \frac{r}{4}$$

Now, $(r - x) = r - \frac{r}{4} = \frac{3r}{4}$

$\therefore$ Potential, $v = v_1 + v_2$

$$= -\frac{Gm_1}{x} - \frac{Gm_2}{(r-x)}$$

$$= -\frac{Gm}{r/4} - \frac{G(9m)}{3r/4}$$

$$= -\frac{4Gm}{r} - \frac{12Gm}{r}$$

$$= -\frac{16\,Gm}{r}$$

13. Given, $T_1 = 80\text{ N}$

$L_1 = 101\text{ mm}$

$T_2 = 100\text{ N}$

$L_2 = 102\text{ mm}$

$T_3 = 160\text{ N}$

$L_3 = ?$

According to the question,

Natural length $(l) = \frac{l_1T_2 - l_2T_1}{T_2 - T_1}$

$$= \frac{101 \times 100 - 102 \times 80}{(100 - 80)}$$

$$= \frac{101 \times 100 - 102 \times 80}{20}$$

$$= \frac{101 \times 100}{20} - \frac{102 \times 80}{20}$$

$$= 505 - 408 = 97 \text{ cm}$$

Now, $\frac{T_1}{T_3} = \frac{4}{l_3 - 97}$

$$\frac{80}{160} = \frac{4}{l_3 - 97}$$

$\Rightarrow l_3 - 97 = 8$

$\Rightarrow l_2 = 105 \text{ mm or } 10.5 \text{ cm}$

14. Relative density of sphere material $(d_B) = 8$

Relative density of water $(d_w) = 1$

Radius of sphere $(R) = 2$ cm

Let the radius of cavity $= r$

Now, $\frac{4}{3}\pi(R^3 - \rho^3)\, d_B g = \frac{4}{3}\pi R^3 d_w g$

$\Rightarrow \frac{8}{1} = \frac{R^3}{R^3 - r^3}$

$\Rightarrow 1 - \frac{R^3}{r^3} = \frac{1}{8} \Rightarrow \frac{R^3}{r^3} = 1 - \frac{1}{8}$

$\Rightarrow \frac{R^3}{r^3} = \frac{7}{8}$

$\Rightarrow r^3 = \frac{8}{7}R^3 = \frac{7}{8}(2)^3 = 7$

$\therefore$ Volume of cavity $= \frac{4}{3}\pi r^3$

$$= \frac{4}{3} \times \frac{22}{7} \times 7 = \frac{88}{3} \text{ cm}^3$$

15. Given, mass of metallic bullet $= m$ kg

Initial temperature of bullet = 300 K

Heat absorbed by the obstacle $= \frac{1}{4}$th of total heat

Let the total heat be one, then

remaining heat $= 1 - \frac{1}{4} = \frac{3}{4}$th part

Melting point of bullet = 600 K

Specific heat of bullet $= 0.03 \text{ cal g}^{-1}\text{°C}^{-1}$

Latent heat of fusion of bullet $= 6 \text{ cal g}^{-1}$

According to the question,

$$\frac{3}{4}\left(\frac{1}{2}mv^2\right) = ms\Delta\theta + mL$$

or, $\frac{3}{4}v^2 = 0.03 \times 4200 \times 300 + 6 \times 4200$

or, $v^2 = \frac{8}{3}[0.01 \times 4200 \times 300 + 2 \times 4200]$

or, $v^2 = 40 \times 4200$

or, $v = \sqrt{168000}$

or, $v = 410$ m/s

16. Given,

Specific heat of water $= 1 \text{ cal g}^{-1}\text{°C}^{-1}$

Latent heat of fusion of ice $= 80 \text{ cal g}^{-1}$

Latent heat of steam $= 540 \text{ cal g}^{-1}$

According to the question,

$$m \times 80 + m \times 1 \times t = (M - m) \times 1 \times (100 - t) + 540\,(M - m)$$

$$\Rightarrow m \times 80 + mt = (M - m) \times 100 - (M - m)t + 540\,M - m \times 540$$

$$\Rightarrow 80m + mt = M \times 100 - m \times 100 - Mt + mt + 540\,M - 540\,m$$

$$\Rightarrow 80m + 100\,m + 540\,m = 640\,M - Mt$$

$$\Rightarrow 720\,m = M(640 - t)$$

$$\Rightarrow \frac{m}{M} = \frac{640 - t}{720}$$

17. Given,

For diatomic gas $(\gamma) = 1.4$

Work done $(dW) = 300$ J

For isobarically expansion,

$$\Rightarrow \frac{dW}{dQ} = 1 - \frac{1}{\gamma}$$

$$\Rightarrow \frac{300}{dQ} = 1 - \frac{1}{1.4}$$

$$\Rightarrow \frac{300}{dQ} = \frac{1.4 - 1}{1.4}$$

$$\Rightarrow \frac{300}{dQ} = \frac{0.4}{1.4}$$

$$\Rightarrow dQ = \frac{300 \times 1.4}{0.4}$$

$$\Rightarrow dQ = 1050 \text{ J}$$

18. Let the initial efficiency of engine be η.

When it is increased by 80%, the new efficiency

$$= \eta + \frac{80}{100}\eta$$

$$= \eta + 0.8\eta = 1.8\,\eta$$

As, $\eta = \frac{T_1 - T_2}{T_1}$

$\therefore$ According to the question,

$$\eta = \frac{100 - T_2}{100} \quad \ldots(i)$$

$$\eta' = \frac{125 - T_2}{125} \quad \text{...(ii)}$$

When the temperature of source is increased by 25%.

From Eqs. (i) and (ii), we get

$$\frac{\eta}{\eta'} = \frac{100 - T_2}{100} \times \frac{125}{125 - T_2}$$

$$\Rightarrow \quad \frac{1}{1.8} = \frac{100 - T_2}{100} \times \frac{125}{125 - T_2}$$

or, $$\frac{5}{9} = \frac{100 - T_2}{4} \times \frac{5}{(125 - T_2)}$$

or, $9(100 - T_2) = 500 - 4T_2$

or, $900 - 9T_2 = 500 - 4T_2$

or, $400 = 5T_2$

or, $T_2 = \frac{400}{5} = 80$

The new efficiency,

$$\eta'' = 1 - \frac{T_2}{T_1} = 1 - \frac{80}{125}$$

$$= \frac{125 - 80}{125} = \frac{45}{125}$$

$$\eta''\% = \frac{45}{125} \times 100 = 36\%$$

19. Given, cylinder is of fixed capacity = 67.2 L

According to the question,

We know that,

$$dQ = \eta C_V dT$$

$$= 3 \times \frac{8.31 \times 3}{2} \times 20$$

$$= 747.9 \approx 748 \text{ J}$$

20. Given, speed of sound in air $(v_0) = 340 \text{ ms}^{-1}$

Also, successive frequencies 425, 595 and 765 Hz are odd frequencies. Thus given organ pipe is "closed organ pipe".

$\therefore$ Fundamental frequency

$$\nu_0 = \frac{595 - 425}{2}$$

$$= \frac{765 - 595}{2} = 85 \text{ Hz}$$

We know that, for a closed organ pipe,

Fundamental frequency is given by

$$\nu_0 = \frac{v_0}{4l}$$

$$\Rightarrow \quad 85 = \frac{340}{4 \times l}$$

$$\Rightarrow \quad l = \frac{340}{4 \times 85}$$

$$\Rightarrow \quad l = 1 \text{ m}$$

21. Given,

frequency of oscillating tuning fork $(n) = 170$ Hz

Speed of tuning fork $(v_0) = 2 \text{ ms}^{-1}$

Velocity of sound $(v) = 340 \text{ ms}^{-1}$

We know that,

$$n' = \left(\frac{v + v_0}{v - v_0}\right) n$$

or, $$n' = \left(\frac{340 + 2}{340 - 2}\right) \times 170$$

or, $$n' = \frac{342}{338} \times 170$$

or, $$n' = 172.01 \approx 172 \text{ Hz}$$

The beat frequency observed by the student between fork and its echo is

$$(172 - 170) = 2 \text{ Hz}$$

22. We know that,

$$\frac{1}{f} = \frac{1}{u} + \frac{1}{v}$$

For concave mirror,

$$u = -u$$

$$f = -f$$

So, $$\frac{-1}{f} = \frac{-1}{u} + \frac{1}{v}$$

$$\Rightarrow \quad \frac{1}{v} = \frac{1}{u} - \frac{1}{f} \Rightarrow \frac{1}{v} = \frac{f - u}{uf}$$

$$v = \frac{uf}{u - f} \quad \text{...(i)}$$

Length of image,

$$L = |v| - |f|$$

From Eq. (i),

$$L = \frac{uf}{u - f} - f$$

$$L = \frac{uf - f(u - f)}{u - f}$$

$$L = \frac{uf - uf + f^2}{u - f}$$

$$L = \frac{f^2}{u - f}$$

23. Given, wavelength of red light

$$= 6000 \text{ Å} = 6000 \times 10^{-10} \text{ m}$$

Wavelength of green light

$$= 5000 \text{ Å} = 5000 \times 10^{-10} \text{ m}$$

Fringe width, $\beta = \frac{\lambda D}{d}$

For n number of fringes,

$$\beta_n = n\frac{\lambda D}{d}$$

For $(n+1)$ th number of fringes,

$$\beta_G = (n+1)\frac{\lambda D}{d}$$

According to the question,

$$\beta_R = \beta_G$$

$$n.\frac{\lambda_R D}{d} = (n+1)\frac{\lambda_G D}{d}$$

$$n.\,6000 \times 10^{-10}\frac{D}{d} = (n+1)5000 \times 10^{-10}\frac{D}{d}\text{or,}$$

$$6n = (n+1)5$$

or, $$6n = 5n + 5$$

or, $6n - 5n = 5$ or $n = 5$

24. Given,

$$q_1 = +10\,\mu\text{C at } y = \pm a$$

$$q_2 = +10\,\mu\text{C}$$

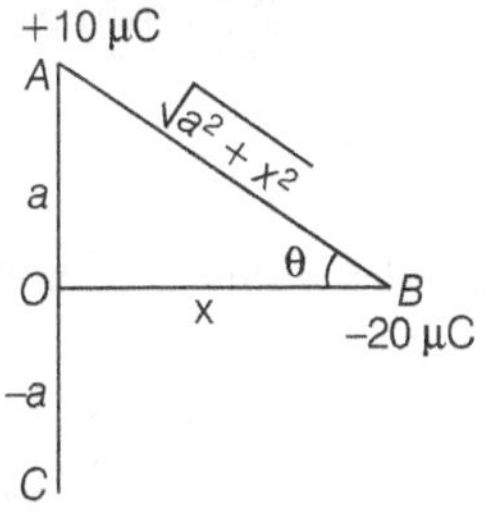

Let the force acting on each charge $+10\,\mu$C be F, x be the displaced position the component of each force will $F\cos\theta$ in x-direction.

So, the net force $F_{\text{net}} = F\cos\theta + F\cos\theta$

$$= 2F\cdot\cos\theta$$

From Coulomb's law,

$$F = k\cdot\frac{q_1 q_2}{r^2}$$

$$k = \frac{1}{4\pi\varepsilon_0} = 9\times 10^9\ \text{Nm}^2/\text{C}^2$$

$$F = 9\times 10^9 \times \frac{10\times 10^{-6}\times 20\times 10^{-6}}{(\sqrt{a^2+x^2})^2}$$

$$= 9\times 10^9\times\frac{200\times 10^{-12}}{(a^2+x^2)}$$

Net force,

$$F_{\text{net}} = 2\times 9\times 10^9\times\frac{200\times 10^{-12}}{(a^2+x^2)}.\cos\theta$$

$$\because \cos\theta = \frac{\text{base}}{\text{hypotenuse}} = \frac{x}{\sqrt{a^2+x^2}}$$

$$\therefore\ F_{\text{net}} = 2\times 9\times\frac{2\times 10^{-1}}{(a^2+x^2)}\left(\frac{x}{\sqrt{a^2+x^2}}\right)$$

$$= 36\times 10^{-1}\frac{x}{(a^2+x^2)^{3/2}}$$

Given, $x << a$

Neglecting x^2.

$$F_{\text{net}} = 3.6\frac{x}{(a^2)^{3/2}} \approx \frac{3.6x}{a^3}\ \text{N}$$

25. According to the question, forces F_1 and F_2 are acting at point B.

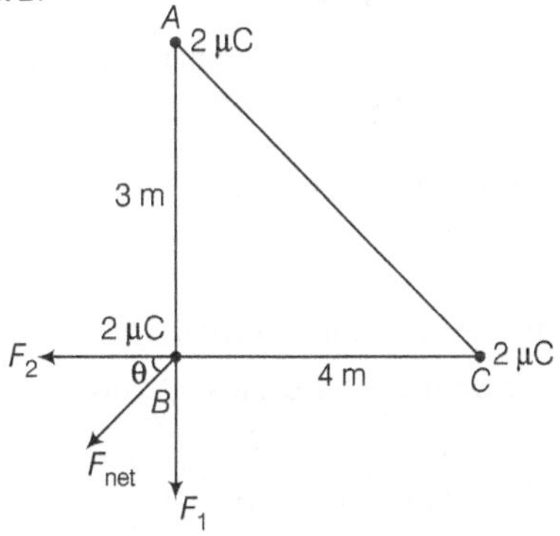

Let the net force F_{net} due to F_1 and F_2 makes an angle θ with force F_2.

From figure, $\tan\theta = \dfrac{F_1}{F_2}$

Also, $$F_1 = k\cdot\frac{q_1 q_2}{(3)^2}$$

$\because$ $$q_1 = q_2 = q_3 = 2\,\mu\text{C}$$

$\Rightarrow$ $$F_2 = k\cdot\frac{q_1 q_3}{(4)^2}$$

$\therefore$ $$\tan\theta = \frac{k\cdot q_1 q_2/(3)^2}{k\cdot q_1 q_3/(4)^2} = \frac{(4)^2}{(3)^2} = \frac{16}{9}$$

$\Rightarrow$ $$\theta = \tan^{-1}\left(\frac{16}{9}\right)$$

26. Potential due to point charge q at distance r is given by

$$V = \frac{Kq}{r}$$

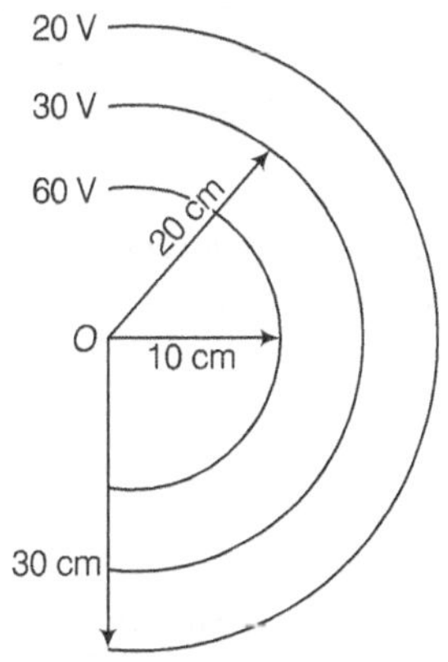

For 60 V equipotential surface,

$60 = \frac{kq}{r}$, here $r = 10 \text{ cm} = 10 \times 10^{-2}$ m

$$60 = \frac{kq}{10 \times 10^{-2}}$$

$$\therefore \quad kq = 60 \times 10 \times 10^{-2} = 6 \quad \ldots(i)$$

The electric field at distance r from charge q,

$$E = \frac{kq}{r^2}$$

Substitution from Eq. (i) gives

$$E = \frac{6}{r^2} \text{ Vm}^{-1}$$

27. Electric field, $\mathbf{E} = (10\hat{\mathbf{i}} + 30\hat{\mathbf{j}})$ V/m

The coordinates of A and B are (1, 2, 0) and (2, 1, 3).

$$\therefore \quad r_A = \hat{\mathbf{i}} + 2\hat{\mathbf{j}} + 0$$

$$r_B = 2\hat{\mathbf{i}} + \hat{\mathbf{j}} + 3\hat{\mathbf{k}}$$

Displacement, $dr = \mathbf{r}_B - \mathbf{r}_A$

$$= (2\hat{\mathbf{i}} + \hat{\mathbf{j}} + 3\hat{\mathbf{k}}) - (\hat{\mathbf{i}} + 2\hat{\mathbf{j}})$$

$$= \hat{\mathbf{i}} - \hat{\mathbf{j}} + 3\hat{\mathbf{k}}$$

We know $E = \frac{dV}{dr}$

$$\Rightarrow \quad dV = \mathbf{E} \cdot dr$$

$$= (10\hat{\mathbf{i}} + 30\hat{\mathbf{j}}) \cdot (\hat{\mathbf{i}} - \hat{\mathbf{j}} + 3\hat{\mathbf{k}})$$

$$= 10\hat{\mathbf{i}} \cdot \hat{\mathbf{i}} - 30\hat{\mathbf{j}} \cdot \hat{\mathbf{j}} + 0$$

$$= 10 - 30 = -20$$

Work done, $W = q \times |dV|$

Here, $q = 0.8$ C

$$\therefore \quad W = 0.8(20) = 16 \text{ joule} = 16 \text{ J}$$

28. The drift velocity,

$$v_d = \frac{I}{neA}$$

$$I = \text{current} = \frac{V}{R}$$

$$\Rightarrow \quad v_d = \frac{V}{RneA}$$

$$\because \quad R = \rho \cdot \frac{l}{A}$$

where, l = length of the wire

ρ = specific resistance

A = cross-sectional area

$$\therefore \quad v_d = \frac{V}{\rho \cdot \frac{l}{A} neA}$$

$$= \frac{V}{\rho l n e}$$

So, v_d does not depend upon the cross-sectional area of the wire. Therefore, option (a) will be correct.

29. The balancing length = 60 cm

Length of remaining wire = 100 − 60 = 40 cm

$$R \propto l$$

$$\Rightarrow \quad \frac{R_L}{R_R} = \frac{60}{40} = \frac{6}{4} = \frac{3}{2} \quad \ldots(i)$$

$$\Rightarrow \quad \frac{R_L}{1.44 R_R} = \frac{l}{100 - l} \quad \ldots(ii)$$

From Eqs. (i) and (ii), we get

$$\frac{1.44 R_R}{R_R} = \frac{3/2}{l/100 - l} = \frac{3}{2} \times \frac{100 - l}{l}$$

$$\Rightarrow \frac{100 - l}{l} = \frac{2}{3} \times 1.44 = 2 \times 0.48 = 0.96$$

$$\therefore \quad 100 - l = 0.96 l$$

or, $\quad 1.96 l = 100$

or, $\quad l = \frac{100}{1.96} = 51.02 \text{ cm} = 51 \text{ cm}$

30. Magnetic field, $B = 2.0$ T

Current, $\quad i = 1.1$ A

When the wire opens in a circle, let the tension developed is T.

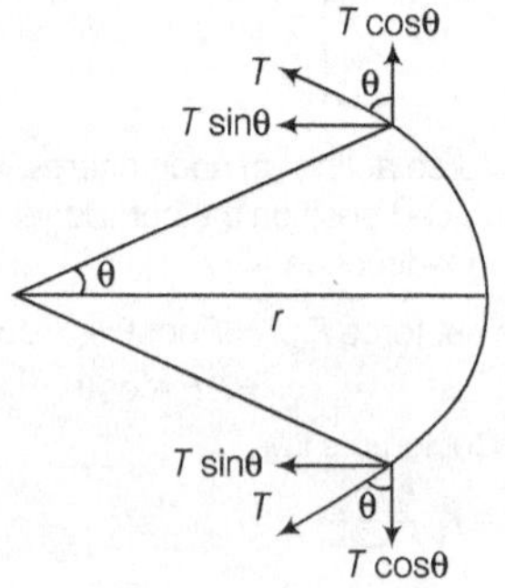

Let radius of loop be r.

For smaller element position.

$$2T \sin\theta = 2r\theta \cdot iB$$

As θ is small, $\sin\theta \approx \theta$

$$2T\theta = 2riB\theta$$

$$T = irB$$

The circumference of the loop = $2\pi r$

$$\Rightarrow \quad 2\pi r = l \Rightarrow r = \frac{l}{2\pi}$$

$$\Rightarrow \quad T = \frac{ilB}{2\pi} = \frac{1.1 \times 1 \times 2.0}{2 \times 3.14}$$

$$= 0.35 \text{ N}$$

31. Given, charge = q

Radius of isolated ring = R

Angular velocity of ring = ω

Magnetic dipole moment of the ring,

$M = niA, n = 1, M = iA$

The current in the ring, $i = q \times f$

where, f = frequency of charge

$$\omega = 2\pi f$$

$$f = \frac{\omega}{2\pi} \Rightarrow i = q \cdot \frac{\omega}{2\pi}$$

Area, $A = \pi R^2$

$$\Rightarrow \quad M = q \cdot \frac{\omega}{2\pi} \cdot \pi R^2 = \frac{1}{2} q\omega R^2$$

32. Given, dipole moment of magnet = 2.5 Am^2

Earth's magnetic field, $B_H = 3 \times 10^{-5}$ T

When the magnetic dipole is released from East-West direction, a torque acts on it. So, in the displacement from *E*-*W* to *N*-*S*, work is done by the torque. The value of torque

$$\tau = \mathbf{M} \times \mathbf{B} = MB \sin\theta$$

$$\text{KE} = \text{work done} = W = \int_{\theta_1}^{\theta_2} \tau \cdot d\theta$$

$$= MB(\cos\theta_1 - \cos\theta_2)$$

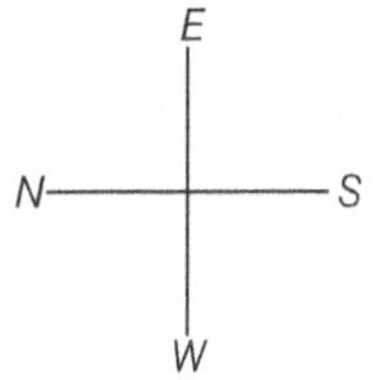

$$\therefore \quad \text{KE} = MB\cos 0°$$

$$= 2.5 \times 3 \times 10^{-5}$$

$$= 7.5 \times 10^{-5}\ \text{J} = 75 \times 10^{-6}\ \mu\text{J}$$

33. According to figure

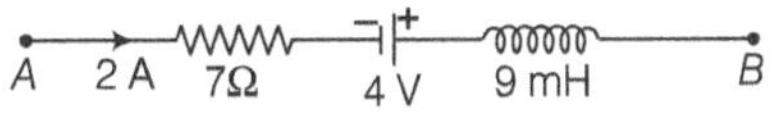

Given, $\frac{dI}{dt} = 10^3$ A/s

$$L = 9\ \text{mH} = 9 \times 10^{-3}\ \text{H}$$

$$V_R = I \cdot R = 2 \times 7 = 14\ \text{V}$$

Voltage of source, $V = 4$ V

$$V_L = L \cdot \frac{dI}{dt}$$

$$= 9 \times 10^{-3} \times 10^3\ \text{V} = 9\text{V}$$

Now, $V_{AB} - V_R + V + V_L = 0$

or, $V_{AB} - 14 + 4 + 9 = 0$

$V_{AB} - 1 = 0$

or, $V_{AB} = 1\text{V}$

34. Given, natural frequency of an *L*-*C* circuit

$$= 125\text{kHz} = 125 \times 10^3\ \text{Hz}$$

Let dielectric constant = K

The natural frequency, $f_N = \frac{1}{2\pi\sqrt{LC}}$

After filling the dielectric material of dielectric constant K

$$f_M = \frac{1}{2\pi\sqrt{KLC}} \quad (\because C' = KC)$$

$$\therefore \quad \frac{f_N}{f_M} = \frac{1/2\pi\sqrt{LC}}{1/2\pi\sqrt{KLC}} = \sqrt{K}$$

$$\Rightarrow \quad \frac{125 \times 10^3}{100 \times 10^3} = \sqrt{K}$$

$[f_M = 125\ \text{kHz} - 25\ \text{kHz} = 100\ \text{kHz} = 100 \times 10^3\ \text{Hz}]$

$$\Rightarrow \quad \frac{5}{4} = \sqrt{K}$$

$$\Rightarrow \quad K = \left(\frac{5}{4}\right)^2 = \frac{25}{16} = 1.562$$

35. Radioactive source $(\sim 10^{-12}\text{m}) \rightarrow$ X-ray tube $(\sim 10^{-10}\text{m}) \rightarrow$ Sodium lamp $(\sim 10^{-9}\text{m}) \rightarrow$ Magnetron valve $(\sim 10^{-3}\text{m})$

36. de-Broglie wavelength associated with electron,

$$\lambda_D = \frac{h}{\sqrt{2mE_k}}$$

Also, $E_k = h\nu = \frac{hc}{\lambda}$

$$\Rightarrow \quad \lambda_D = \frac{h}{\sqrt{2m \times \frac{hc}{\lambda}}} = \sqrt{\frac{\lambda h}{2mc}}$$

37. Angular momentum of the electron will change because the radius of the orbit will change. So, it will not remain constant.

Angular momentum = (mvr)

38. We know that radius of a nucleus, $R \propto A^{1/3}$

where, A = mass number

$$\Rightarrow \quad R_{Ge} \propto (A_{Ge})^{1/3}$$

$$\Rightarrow \quad R_{Be} \propto (A_{Be})^{1/3}$$

$$\Rightarrow \quad \frac{R_{Ge}}{R_{Be}} = \left(\frac{A_{Ge}}{A_{Be}}\right)^{1/3}$$

Given $R_{Ge} = 2R_{Be}$

$$\therefore \quad 2 = \left(\frac{A_{Ge}}{A_{Be}}\right)^{1/3} \text{ or, } 2^3 = \frac{A_{Ge}}{A_{Be}}$$

$$2^3 = \frac{A_{Ge}}{9} \quad [\because A_{Be} = 9]$$

$$\Rightarrow \quad A_{Ge} = 2^3 \times 9 = 8 \times 9 = 72$$

39. Current gain, $\beta = 60$

Emitter current, $I_E = 6.6\text{ mA}$

$$= 6.6 \times 10^{-3}\text{ A}$$

$$\beta = 60 = \frac{I_C}{I_B}$$

$$\Rightarrow \quad I_C = 60 I_B$$

We know, $I_E = I_B + I_C$

$$\Rightarrow \quad I_B = I_E - I_C$$

$$= 6.6 \times 10^{-3} - 60 I_B$$

$$\Rightarrow \quad I_B + 60 I_B = 6.6 \times 10^{-3}$$

$$\Rightarrow \quad 61 I_B = 6.6 \times 10^{-3}$$

$$\Rightarrow \quad I_B = \frac{6.6 \times 10^{-3}}{61}$$

$$= 0.108 \times 10^{-3}$$

$$= 0.108\text{ mA}$$

40. The range of antenna, $d = \sqrt{2Rh}$

where, R = radius of Earth

h = height of antenna

Coverage area, $A = \pi d^2$

$$= \pi(\sqrt{2Rh})^2 = \pi \times 2Rh$$

Here, $h = 105\text{ m}$, $R = 6.4 \times 10^6\text{ m}$

$$\Rightarrow \quad A = 3.14 \times 2 \times 6.4 \times 10^6 \times 105\text{ m}^2$$

$$= 314 \times 2 \times 64 \times 105 \times 10^3\text{ m}^2$$

$$= 4220.6\text{ km}^2 \simeq 4224\text{ km}^2$$

SOLVED PAPER 2016

TS EAMCET

Engineering Entrance Exam

1. Electron microscope is based on the principle of

(a) photoelectric effect
(b) wave nature of electron
(c) superconductivity
(d) laws of electromagnetic induction

2. Force is given by the expression, $F = A\cos(Bx) + C\cos(Dt)$, where x is displacement and t is time. The dimension of $\left(\frac{D}{B}\right)$ is same as that of

(a) velocity
(b) velocity gradient
(c) angular velocity
(d) angular momentum

3. A car accelerates from rest with $2\,\text{m/s}^2$ on a straight line path and then comes to rest after applying brakes. Total distance travelled by the car is 100 m in 20 seconds. Then, the maximum velocity attained by the car is

(a) 10 m/s (b) 20 m/s
(c) 15 m/s (d) 5 m/s

4. A body is falling freely from a point A at a certain height from the ground and passes through points B, C and D (vertically as shown below) so that $BC = CD$. The time taken by the particle to move from B to C is 2 s and from C to D is 1s. Time taken to move from A to B in seconds is

(a) 0.6 (b) 0.5
(c) 0.2 (d) 0.4

5. A particle moves from (1, 0, 3) to the point (−3, 4, 5), when a force $\mathbf{F} = \hat{\mathbf{i}} + 5\hat{\mathbf{k}}$ acts on it. Amount of work done in joules is

(a) 14 (b) 10
(c) 6 (d) 15

6. A particle is projected with velocity $2\sqrt{gh}$ and at an angle 60° to the horizontal so that it just clears two walls of equal height h which are at a distance $2h$ from each other. The time taken by the particle to travel between these two walls is

(a) $2\sqrt{\frac{2h}{g}}$ (b) $\sqrt{\frac{h}{2g}}$
(c) $2\sqrt{\frac{h}{g}}$ (d) $\sqrt{\frac{h}{g}}$

7. A body of mass 20 kg is moving on a rough horizontal plane. A block of mass 3 kg is connected to the 20 kg mass by a string of negligible mass through a smooth pulley as shown in the below figure. The tension in the string is 27 N. The coefficient of kinetic friction between the heavier mass and the surface is $(g = 10\,\text{m/s}^2)$

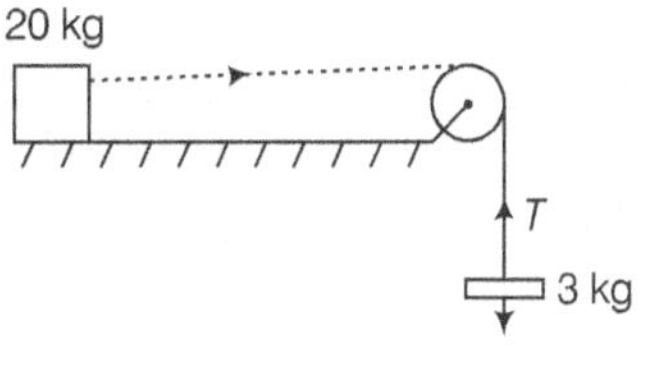

(a) 0.025 (b) 0.035
(c) 0.35 (d) 0.25

8. Two masses m_1 and m_2 are placed on a smooth horizontal surface and are connected by a string of negligible mass. A horizontal force F is applied on the mass m_2 as shown in the figure. The tension in the string is

(a) $\left(\frac{m_1}{m_1+m_2}\right)F$ (b) $\frac{m_2F}{m_1+m_2}$

(c) $\left(\frac{m_1}{m_2}\right)F$ (d) $\frac{m_2F}{m_1}$

9. A body of mass 3 kg moving with a velocity $(2\hat{i}+3\hat{j}+3\hat{k})$ m/s collides with another body of mass 4 kg moving with a velocity $(3\hat{i}+2\hat{j}-3\hat{k})$ m/s. The two bodies stick together after collision. The velocity of the composite body is

(a) $\frac{1}{7}(4\hat{i}+6\hat{j}-3\hat{k})$

(b) $\frac{1}{7}(18\hat{i}+17\hat{j}-3\hat{k})$

(c) $\frac{1}{7}(6\hat{i}+4\hat{j}-6\hat{k})$

(d) $\frac{1}{7}(9\hat{i}+8\hat{j}-6\hat{k})$

10. A simple pendulum of length L carries a bob of mass m. When the bob is at its lowest position, it is given that the minimum horizontal speed necessary for it to move in a vertical circle about the point of suspension. When the string is horizontal, the net force on the bob is

(a) $\sqrt{10}\,mg$ (b) $\sqrt{5}\,mg$

(c) $4\,mg$ (d) $1\,mg$

11. A system of two particles is having masses m_1 and m_2. If the particle of mass m_1 is pushed towards the centre of mass of particles through a distance d, by what distance the particle of mass m_2 should be moved, so as to keep the centre of mass of particles at the original position?

(a) $\left(\frac{m_1}{m_1+m_2}\right)d$ (b) d

(c) $\left(\frac{m_1}{m_2}\right)d$ (d) $\left(\frac{m_2}{m_1}\right)d$

12. A thin uniform circular disc of mass M and radius R is rotating in a horizontal plane about an axis passing through its centre and perpendicular to its plane with an angular velocity ω. Another disc of same thickness and radius but of mass $\frac{1}{8}M$ is placed gently on the first disc coaxially. The angular velocity of the system is now

(a) $\frac{8}{9}\omega$ (b) $\frac{5}{9}\omega$ (c) $\frac{1}{3}\omega$ (d) $\frac{2}{9}\omega$

13. 9 kg solution is poured into a glass U-tube as shown in the figure below. The tube's inner diameter is $2\sqrt{\frac{\pi}{5}}$ m and the solution oscillates freely up and down about its position of equilibrium ($x = 0$). The period of oscillation in seconds is ($1\,m^3$ of solution has a mass $\mu = 900$ kg, $g = 10\,m/s^2$, ignore frictional and surface tension effects)

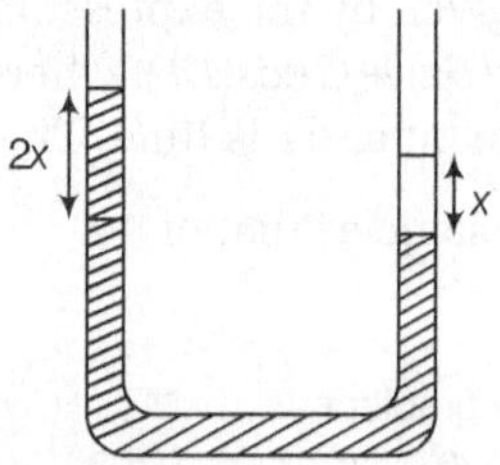

(a) 0.1 (b) 10 (c) $\sqrt{\pi}$ (d) 1

14. The bodies of masses 100 kg and 8100 kg are held at a distance of 1 m. The gravitational field at a point on the line joining them is zero. The gravitational potential at that point in J/kg is ($G = 6.67\times10^{-11}\,Nm^2/kg^2$)

(a) -6.67×10^{-7} (b) -6.67×10^{-10}

(c) -13.34×10^{-7} (d) -6.67×10^{-9}

15. An elastic spring of unstretched length L and force constant k is stretched by a small length x. It is further stretched by another small length y. Work done during the second stretching is

(a) $\frac{ky}{2}(x+2y)$ (b) $\frac{k}{2}(2x+y)$

(c) $ky(x+2y)$ (d) $\frac{ky}{2}(2x+y)$

16. A soap bubble of radius 1.0 cm is formed inside another soap bubble of radius 2.0 cm. The radius of an another soap bubble which has the same pressure difference as that between the inside of the smaller and outside of large soap bubble, in metres is

(a) 6.67×10^{-3}

(b) 3.34×10^{-3}

(c) 2.23×10^{-3}

(d) 4.5×10^{-3}

17. A slab of stone of area 3600 cm^2 and thickness 10 cm is exposed on the lower surface to steam at 100°C. A block of ice at 0°C rests on upper surface of the slab. In one hour 4.8 kg of ice is melted. The thermal conductivity of the stone in $Js^{-1}m^{-1}k^{-1}$ is (Latent heat of ice $= 3.36 \times 10^5$ J/kg)

(a) 12.0 (b) 10.5
(c) 1.02 (d) 1.24

18. The surface of a black body is at a temperature 727°C and its cross-section is 1 m^2. Heat radiated from this surface in one minute in joules is (Stefan's constant $= 5.7 \times 10^{-8}$ W/m^2/k^4)

(a) 34.2×10^5 (b) 2.5×10^5
(c) 3.42×10^5 (d) 2.5×10^6

19. Two moles of a gas is expanded to double its volume by two different processes. One is isobaric and the other is isothermal. If W_1 and W_2 are the works done, respectively then

(a) $W_2 = \frac{W_1}{\log e^2}$

(b) $W_2 = W_1$

(c) $W_2 = W_1 \log e^2$

(d) $W_2 = W_1 \log_e (2)$

20. Uranium has two isotopes of masses 235 and 238 units. If both of them are present in uranium hexafluoride gas, find the percentage ratio of difference in rms velocities of two isotopes to the rms velocity of heavier isotope.

(a) 1.64 (b) 0.064
(c) 0.64 (d) 6.4

21. A source of frequency 340 Hz is kept above a vertical cylindrical tube closed at lower end. The length of the tube is 120 cm. Water is slowly poured in just enough to produce resonance. Then, the minimum height (velocity of sound = 340 m/s) of the water level in the tube for that resonance is

(a) 0.75 m (b) 0.25 m
(c) 0.95 m (d) 0.45 m

22. A thin convex lens of focal length f made of crown glass is immersed in a liquid of refractive index μ_l ($\mu_l > \mu_c$), where μ_c is the refractive index of the crown glass.
The convex lens now is

(a) a convex lens of longer focal length
(b) a convex lens of shorter focal length
(c) a divergent lens
(d) a convex lens of focal length $(\mu_c - \mu_l)f$

23. Two convex lenses of focal lengths f_1 and f_2 form images with magnification m_1 and m_2, when used individually for an object kept at the same distance from the lenses. Then, f_1/f_2 is

(a) $\frac{m_1(1-m_1)}{m_2(1-m_2)}$ (b) $\frac{m_1(1-m_2)}{m_2(1-m_1)}$

(c) $\frac{m_2(1-m_1)}{m_1(1-m_2)}$ (d) $\frac{m_2(1-m_2)}{m_1(1-m_1)}$

24. With the help of a telescope that has an objective of diameter 200 cm, it is proved that light of wavelengths of the order of 6400 Å coming from a star can be easily resolved. Then, the limit of resolution is

(a) 39×10^{-8} deg (b) 39×10^{-8} rad
(c) 19.5×10^{-8} rad (d) 19.5×10^{-8} deg

25. Two charged identical metal spheres A and B repel each other with a force of 3×10^{-5} N. Another identical uncharged sphere C is touched with sphere A and then it is placed mid-way between A and B. Then, the magnitude of net force on C is

(a) 1×10^{-5} N

(b) 3×10^{-5} N

(c) 2×10^{-5} N

(d) 5×10^{-5} N

26. The electrostatic potential inside a charged sphere is given as $V = Ar^2 + B$, where r is the distance from the centre of the sphere, A and B are constants. Then, the charge density in the sphere is

(a) $16\,A\varepsilon_0$ (b) $-6\,A\varepsilon_0$ (c) $20\,A\varepsilon_0$ (d) $-15\,A\varepsilon_0$

27. Three unequal resistances are connected in parallel. Two of these resistances are in the ratio 1:2. The equivalent resistance of these three resistors connected in parallel is 1Ω. What is the highest resistance value among these three resistances if no resistance is fractional?

(a) 10 Ω (b) 8 Ω (c) 15 Ω (d) 6 Ω

28. Two electric resistors have equal values of resistance R. Each can be operated with a power of 320 watts (W) at 220 volts. If the two resistors are connected in series to a 110 volts electric supply, then the power generated in each resistor is

(a) 90 watts (b) 80 watts
(c) 60 watts (d) 20 watts

29. A current of 1 A is flowing along the sides of an equilateral triangle of side 4.5×10^{-2} m. The magnetic field at the centroid of the triangle is ($\mu_0 = 4\pi \times 10^{-7}$ H/m)

(a) 4×10^{-5} T (b) 2×10^{-5} T
(c) 4×10^{-4} T (d) 2×10^{-4} T

30. A charged particle (charge = q; mass = m) is rotating in a circle of radius R with uniform speed V. Ratio of its magnetic moment (μ) to the angular momentum (L) is

(a) $\frac{q}{2m}$ (b) $\frac{q}{m}$
(c) $\frac{q}{4m}$ (d) $\frac{2q}{m}$

31. Two small magnets have their masses and lengths in the ratio 1:2. The maximum torques experienced by them in a uniform magnetic field are the same. For small oscillations, the ratio of their time periods is

(a) $\frac{1}{2\sqrt{2}}$ (b) $\frac{1}{\sqrt{2}}$ (c) $\frac{1}{2}$ (d) $2\sqrt{2}$

32. Two coils have mutual inductance 0.005 H. The current changes in the first coil according to equation $I = I_0 \sin \omega t$, where $I_0 = 10$ A and $\omega = 100\,\pi$ rad s^{-1}. The maximum value of induced emf in the second coil is

(a) 5 (b) $5\,\pi$
(c) $0.5\,\pi$ (d) π

33. A capacitance of $\left(\frac{10^{-3}}{2\pi}\right)$ F and an inductance of $\left(\frac{100}{\pi}\right)$ mH and a resistance of 10 Ω are connected in series with an AC voltage source of 220 V, 50 Hz. The phase angle of the circuit is

(a) 60° (b) 30°
(c) 45° (d) 90°

34. Two equations are given below:

(A) $\oint \mathbf{E} \cdot d\mathbf{A} = \frac{Q}{\varepsilon_0}$

(B) $\oint \mathbf{B} \cdot d\mathbf{A} = 0$

They are

(a) (A) Ampere's law
(B) Gauss law for electricity
(b) (A) Gauss law for electric fields
(B) Gauss law for magnetic fields
(c) (A) Faraday's law
(B) Gauss law for electric fields
(d) Both (A) and (B) represents Faraday's law

35. A charged particle is accelerated from rest through a certain potential difference. The de-Broglie wavelength is λ_1 when it is accelerated through V_1 and is λ_2 when accelerated through V_2. The ratio λ_1/λ_2 is

(a) $V_1^{3/2} : V_2^{3/2}$ (b) $V_2^{1/2} : V_1^{1/2}$
(c) $V_1^{1/2} : V_2^{1/2}$ (d) $V_1^2 : V_2^2$

36. If the first line of Lyman series has a wavelength 1215.4 Å, the first line of Balmer series is approximately

(a) 4864 Å (b) 1025.5 Å
(c) 6563 Å (d) 6400 Å

37. A certain radioactive element disintegrates with a decay constant of 7.9×10^{-10} / s. At a given instant of time, if the activity of the sample is equal to 55.3×10^{11} disintegration/second, then number of nuclei at that instant of time is

(a) 7.0×10^{21} (b) 4.27×10^{13}
(c) 4.27×10^{3} (d) 6×10^{23}

38. The change in current through a junction diode is 1.2 mA when the forward bias voltage is changed by 0.6 V. The dynamic resistance is

(a) 500 Ω (b) 300 Ω
(c) 150 Ω (d) 250 Ω

39. A semiconductor has equal electron and hole concentration of $2 \times 10^{8}\ m^{-3}$. On doping with a certain impurity, the electron concentration increases to $4 \times 10^{10}\ m^{-3}$, then the new hole concentration of the semiconductor is

(a) $10^{6}\ m^{-3}$ (b) $10^{8}\ m^{-3}$
(c) $10^{10}\ m^{-3}$ (d) $10^{12}\ m^{-3}$

40. A message signal of 12 kHz and peak voltage 20 V is used to modulate a carrier wave frequency 12 MHz and peak voltage 30 V. Then, the modulation index is

(a) 0.32 (b) 6.7 (c) 0.67 (d) 67

Answers

1. (b)	**2.** (a)	**3.** (a)	**4.** (b)	**5.** (c)	**6.** (c)	**7.** (b)	**8.** (a)	**9.** (b)	**10.** (a)
11. (c)	**12.** (a)	**13.** (a)	**14.** (a)	**15.** (d)	**16.** (a)	**17.** (d)	**18.** (a)	**19.** (d)	**20.** (c)
21. (d)	**22.** (c)	**23.** (b)	**24.** (b)	**25.** (b)	**26.** (b)	**27.** (d)	**28.** (d)	**29.** (b)	**30.** (a)
31. (a)	**32.** (b)	**33.** (c)	**34.** (b)	**35.** (b)	**36.** (c)	**37.** (a)	**38.** (a)	**39.** (a)	**40.** (c)

Explanations

1. Electron microscope is based on the principle of wave nature of electron.

2. From dimension logic, the quantities of same dimensions can be added or subtracted, so

$[Bx] = [Dt]$ similarly,

$$\Rightarrow \left[\frac{x}{t}\right] = \left[\frac{D}{B}\right] \Rightarrow \left[\frac{D}{B}\right] = \frac{[L]}{[T]}$$

$$\Rightarrow \text{Dimension of } \frac{D}{B} = [LT^{-1}]$$

$[LT^{-1}]$ is the dimension of velocity.

3. Given,

Acceleration of car $(\alpha) = 2 \text{ m/s}^2$

Distance covered by car in 20 seconds $(s) = 100$ m

We know that,

$$s = \frac{1}{2} \cdot \frac{\alpha\beta}{\alpha + \beta} t^2$$

$$100 = \frac{1}{2} \times \frac{2\beta}{(2 + \beta)} \times 20 \times 20$$

$$\frac{100}{400} = \frac{\beta}{(2 + \beta)}$$

$$\Rightarrow \frac{1}{4} = \frac{\beta}{2 + \beta}$$

$$\Rightarrow 4\beta = 2 + \beta$$

$$\Rightarrow 3\beta = 2 \Rightarrow \text{retardation } \beta = \frac{2}{3} \text{m/s}^2$$

$\therefore$ Maximum velocity $(v_{max}) = \dfrac{\alpha\beta t}{\alpha + \beta}$

$$= \frac{2 \times \frac{2}{3} \times 20}{2 + \frac{2}{3}} = \frac{\frac{80}{3}}{\frac{8}{3}} = \frac{80}{3} \times \frac{3}{8}$$

$= 10$ m/s

4.

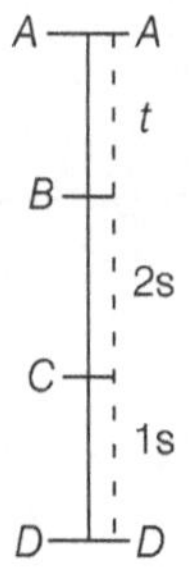

Let velocity of the particle at point B be v.

Now, $$BC = 2v + \frac{1}{2} g \times (2)^2$$

or, $$BC = 2v + 2g \quad \text{...(i)}$$

Similarly, $$2BC = 3v + \frac{1}{2} \times g \times (3)^2$$

$$\Rightarrow 2BC = 3v + \frac{9g}{2} \quad \text{...(ii)}$$

From Eq. (i),

$$2(2v + 2g) = 3v + \frac{9g}{2}$$

$$\Rightarrow 4v + 4g = 3v + \frac{9g}{2}$$

$$\Rightarrow 4v - 3v = \frac{9g}{2} - 4g$$

$$\Rightarrow v = \frac{g}{2} \quad \text{...(iii)}$$

From point A to B,

$v = u + at$

$$\Rightarrow \frac{g}{2} = 0 + g \times t$$

$$\Rightarrow t = \frac{1}{2} \text{ second}$$

$$\Rightarrow t = 0.5 \text{ s}$$

5. Starting point of particle $= \hat{\mathbf{i}} + 3\hat{\mathbf{k}}$

Ending point of particle $= -3\hat{\mathbf{i}} + 4\hat{\mathbf{j}} + 5\hat{\mathbf{k}}$

force $(\mathbf{F}) = \hat{\mathbf{i}} + 5\hat{\mathbf{k}}$

$\therefore$ Displacement of the particle

$$(\mathbf{s}) = (-3\hat{\mathbf{i}} + 4\hat{\mathbf{j}} + 5\hat{\mathbf{k}}) - (\hat{\mathbf{i}} + 3\hat{\mathbf{k}})$$

$$= -4\hat{\mathbf{i}} + 4\hat{\mathbf{j}} + 2\hat{\mathbf{k}}$$

We know that,

Work done, $W = \mathbf{F} \cdot \mathbf{s}$

or, $$W = (\hat{\mathbf{i}} + 5\hat{\mathbf{k}}) \cdot (-4\hat{\mathbf{i}} + 4\hat{\mathbf{j}} + 2\hat{\mathbf{k}})$$

or, $W = -4 + 10$ or, $W = 6$ J

6. Given, velocity of particle $= 2\sqrt{gh}$

Angle $(\theta) = 60°$

Distance covered by particle $= 2h$

Now, $$2h = 2\sqrt{gh} \cos 60° \, t$$

or, $$\sqrt{h} = \sqrt{g} \times \frac{1}{2} t$$

or, $$t = 2\sqrt{\frac{h}{g}}$$

7.

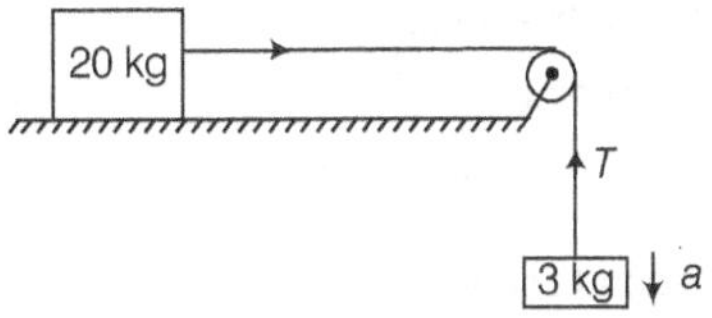

Given, tension in string $(T) = 27\,N$

Mass $(m) = 3\,kg$

Let acceleration of the block be a.

$$3g - T = ma$$

$$\Rightarrow \quad 10 \times 3 - 27 = 3a$$

$$\Rightarrow \quad 30 - 27 = 3a$$

$$\Rightarrow \quad a = \frac{3}{3} = 1\,m/s^2$$

For the body, we have,

$$27 - \mu 20g = 20a$$

$$\Rightarrow \quad 27 - \mu \times 20 \times 10 = 20 \times 1$$

$$\Rightarrow \quad 27 - 200\mu = 20$$

$$\Rightarrow \quad 200\,\mu = 27 - 20$$

$\therefore$ Coefficient of kinetic friction,

$$\mu = \frac{7}{200} = 0.035$$

$\therefore$ Coefficient of kinetic friction is 0.035

8.

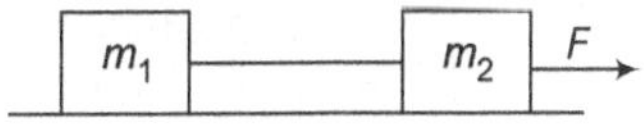

According to the question, force, (F) is applied on m_2 mass.

So, tension in the string,

$T = m_1 \times a$

or, $$T = m_1 \times \frac{F}{(m_1 + m_2)} \qquad \left[\because a = \frac{F}{m_1 + m_2}\right]$$

or, $$T = \left(\frac{m_1}{m_1 + m_2}\right)F$$

9. Given, mass of first body $(m_1) = 3\,kg$

Velocity of first body $(v_1) = (2\hat{i} + 3\hat{j} + 3\hat{k})\,m/s$

Mass of second body $(m_2) = 4\,kg$

Velocity of second body $(v_2) = (3\hat{i} + 2\hat{j} - 3\hat{k})\,m/s$

According to law of conservation of linear momentum,

$$m_1v_1 + m_2v_2 = (m_1 + m_2)v$$

$$\Rightarrow \quad (2\hat{i} + 3\hat{j} + 3\hat{k})3 + (3\hat{i} + 2\hat{j} - 3\hat{k})4 = (4 + 3)v$$

$$\Rightarrow \quad 6\hat{i} + 9\hat{j} + 9\hat{k} + 12\hat{i} + 8\hat{j} - 12\hat{k} = 7v$$

$$\Rightarrow \quad 18\hat{i} + 17\hat{j} - 3\hat{k} = 7v$$

$$\Rightarrow \quad v = \frac{1}{7}(18\hat{i} + 17\hat{j} - 3\hat{k})$$

10. According to the question, the bob is moving in a vertical circle, so the velocity at lowest point $v = \sqrt{5rg}$

Now, applying conservation of mechanical energy, we get

$$\frac{1}{2}m \times 5rg = \frac{1}{2}mv^2 + mgr$$

or, $$\frac{5}{2}rg = \frac{v^2}{2} + rg \quad \text{or,} \quad \frac{3}{2}rg = \frac{v^2}{2}$$

or, $$v^2 = 3rg \qquad \ldots(i)$$

Now, Horizontal force on the bob, $Fx = F_c = \dfrac{mv^2}{r}$

$$= \frac{m \times 3rg}{r} = 3\,mg \qquad \text{[from Eq. (i)]}$$

Vertical force on the bob, $F_y = mg$

$$\therefore \quad F_{net} = \sqrt{F_x^2 + F_y^2}$$

$$= \sqrt{(3mg)^2 + (mg)^2} = \sqrt{10}\,mg$$

11. In two particles system, if the first particle is pushed towards the centre of mass through a distance d. Then to keep the centre of mass at the same position, the second particle should be moved by the distance $= \left(\dfrac{m_1}{m_2}\right)d$.

12. Given, mass of first circular disc $(m_1) = M$

Radius of first circular disc $(r_1) = R$

Mass of second circular disc $(m_2) = \dfrac{1}{8}M$

For first disc,

$$I_1 = \frac{MR^2}{2} \qquad \ldots(i)$$

$$\Rightarrow \quad L_1 = \frac{MR^2\omega_1}{2} \qquad \ldots(ii)$$

For first and second disc system,

$$I_2 = \frac{MR^2}{2} + \frac{M}{8} \cdot \frac{R^2}{2}$$

or, $$I_2 = \frac{9MR^2}{8 \times 2} \qquad \ldots(iii)$$

$$\Rightarrow \quad L_2 = \frac{9MR^2}{8 \times 2}\omega_2 \qquad \ldots(iv)$$

Now from conservation of angular momentum,

$$L_1 = L_2$$

$$\Rightarrow \quad \frac{MR^2\omega_1}{2} = \frac{9\,MR^2}{8 \times 2}\omega_2 \Rightarrow \omega_1 = \frac{9}{8}\omega_2$$

Given, $\omega_2 = \omega$

$$\therefore \quad \omega_2 = \frac{8}{9}\omega_1 = \frac{8}{9}\omega$$

13. Diameter of tube $= 2\sqrt{\frac{\pi}{5}}$ m

$\therefore$ Radius of tube $(r) = \sqrt{\frac{\pi}{5}}$ m

Mass of solution $(u) = 9$ kg

We know that,

$\because$ Mass $(u) = d.v$

$\therefore$ $u = d\pi r^2 L$

or, $9 = 900 \times \pi \times \left(\sqrt{\frac{\pi}{5}}\right)^2 L$

or, $9 = 900 \times \frac{\pi^2}{5} \times L$

or, $L = \frac{5}{100\,\pi^2}$ ...(i)

Now, $T = 2\pi\sqrt{\frac{L}{2g}}$

From Eq. (i),

$$T = 2\pi\sqrt{\frac{5}{200\,\pi^2 \times 10}}$$

or, $T = 2 \times \sqrt{\frac{1}{400}} = \frac{2}{20}$

or, $T = 0.1$ s

14. Mass of first body $(m_1) = 100$ kg

Mass of second body $(m_2) = 8100$ kg

Distance between two bodies = 1 m

Distance of null point from 100 kg

$$x = \frac{d}{\sqrt{\frac{m_2}{m_1}} + 1}$$

or, $x = \frac{1}{\sqrt{\frac{8100}{100}} + 1}$

or, $x = \frac{1}{9+1} = \frac{1}{10}$

$= 0.1$ m

The gravitational potential at that point is given by

$$= -G\left(\frac{m_1}{0.1} + \frac{m_2}{0.9}\right)$$

$$= -6.67 \times 10^{-11}\left(\frac{100}{10^{-1}} + \frac{8100}{9 \times 10^{-1}}\right)$$

$$= -6.67 \times 10^{-11}(1000 + 9000)$$

$$= -6.67 \times 10^{-7} \text{ J/kg}$$

15. According to the question,

In the first condition,

$$W_1 = \frac{1}{2}kx^2 \quad \text{...(i)}$$

In the second condition,

$$W_2 = \frac{1}{2}k(x + y)^2 \quad \text{...(ii)}$$

Work for x to y expansion

$$= \frac{1}{2}k(x + y)^2 - \frac{1}{2}kx^2$$

$$= \frac{1}{2}k[x^2 + y^2 + 2xy - x^2]$$

$$= \frac{1}{2}k[y^2 + 2xy]$$

$$= \frac{1}{2}ky[y + 2x]$$

16. Given, radius of first soap bubble $(R_1) = 2.0$ cm

Radius of second soap bubble $(R_2) = 1.0$ cm

We know that,

Radius of another bubble having same pressure difference,

$$R = \frac{R_1R_2}{R_1 + R_2}$$

or, $R = \frac{2.0 \times 1.0 \times 10^{-4}}{(2.0 + 1.0) \times 10^{-2}}$

or, $R = \frac{2 \times 10^{-4}}{3 \times 10^{-2}}$

or, $R = 6.67 \times 10^{-3}$ m

17. Given, area of slab of stone $(A) = 3600$ cm^2

$= 3600 \times 10^{-4}$ m^2

Thickness of stone slab = 10 cm = 10×10^{-2} m

Temperature difference $(\Delta\theta) = 100°$ C

We know that,

$$\frac{Q}{t} = \frac{KA\Delta\theta}{l}$$

$\Rightarrow$ $\frac{4.8 \times 3.36 \times 10^5}{60 \times 60} = \frac{K \times 3600 \times 10^{-4} \times 100}{10 \times 10^{-2}}$

$\Rightarrow$ $K = \frac{4.8 \times 3.36 \times 10^5 \times 10 \times 10^{-2}}{3600 \times 10^{-4} \times 100 \times 60 \times 60}$

$\Rightarrow$ $K = \frac{161280}{129600}$

$\Rightarrow$ $K = 1.24$ Js^{-1}m^{-1}K^{-1}

18. Given,

Temperature of black body (T) = 727° C

$= 727 + 273 = 1000\,K$

Cross-sectional area of black body (A) = 1 m^2

Stefan's constant (σ) = $5.7 \times 10^{-8}\ W/m^2/K^4$

We know that,

Heat radiated per second

$$E = \sigma A T^4$$

$$= 5.7 \times 10^{-8} \times 1 \times (1000)^4$$

or, $E = 57000\ J$

∴ Heat radiated from this surface in one minute,

$$E = 57000 \times 60$$

or, $E = 3.42 \times 10^6$ or 34.2×10^5 J

19. Given,

In the first condition, work done = W_1

In the second condition, work done = W_2

Now, according to the question,

In the first condition,

$$W_1 = p(2V - V)$$

or, $W_1 = pV$ ...(i)

In the second condition,

$$W_2 = nRT\log_e\left(\frac{V_2}{V_1}\right)$$

or, $W_2 = pV\log_e\left(\frac{2V}{V}\right)$ $[\because pV = nRT]$

From Eq. (i),

$$W_2 = W_1 \log_e(2)$$

20. Given,

Mass of first uranium isotope = 238 units

Mass of second uranium isotope = 235 units

We know that,

$$v_{rms} = \sqrt{\frac{\gamma RT}{M}}$$

$$\Rightarrow \quad v_{rms} \propto \frac{1}{\sqrt{M}}$$

So, the percentage ratio of difference in rms velocity of isotopes is given by

$$\frac{v_{rms_2} - v_{rms_1}}{v_{rms_2}} \times 100$$

$$= \frac{\sqrt{M_1} - \sqrt{M_2}}{\sqrt{M_1}} \times 100$$

$$= \frac{\sqrt{238} - \sqrt{235}}{\sqrt{238}} \times 100$$

$$= \frac{15.427 - 15.329}{15.427} \times 100 = \frac{0.097}{15.427} \times 100$$

$$= 6.34 \times 10^{-3} \times 100 = 0.634 \approx 0.64$$

21. The frequency of source, f_s = 340 Hz

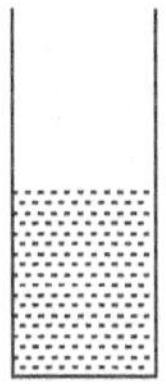

Velocity of sound = 340 m/s

Length of the tube = 120 cm

The minimum height of the tube for resonance, $l_1 = \frac{v}{4f}$

$$= \frac{340}{4 \times 340}\ m$$

$$= \frac{1}{4} = 0.25m = 25\ cm$$

From second resonance condition for closed pipe,

$$h = l_2 - 3l_1$$

Here, $l_2 = 120$ cm

$\Rightarrow$ $h = 120 - 3 \times 25$

$= 120 - 75$

$= 45\ cm = 0.45\ m$

So, for second resonance, 0.45 m should be the height of water level. It will be the minimum height of water in the tube.

22. When the convex lens of focal length f made of crown glass immersed in liquid of refractive index μ_l ($\mu_l > \mu_c$), here μ_c is the refractive index of crown glass, thus from lens maker's formula, we will get focal length of the lens as negative ($\because \mu_e > u_c$). Therefore, the convex lens will behave like a concave lens . So, it will be a divergent lens.

23. The linear magnification of lens in terms of focal length f and u.

$$m = \frac{f}{f + u}$$

For first lens,

$$u_1 = \left(\frac{1 - m_1}{m_1}\right)f_1$$

For second lens,

$$u_2 = \left(\frac{1-m_2}{m_2}\right)f_2$$

According to the question,

$$u_1 = u_2$$

$$\therefore \quad \frac{(m_1-1)}{m_1}f_1 = \frac{(m_2-1)}{m_2}f_2$$

$$\frac{f_1}{f_2} = \frac{m_1}{m_2}\cdot\frac{(m_2-1)}{(m_1-1)} = \frac{m_1(m_2-1)}{m_2(m_1-1)}$$

24. The limit of resolution of a telescope is

$$\theta = \frac{1.22\,\lambda}{d}$$

where, λ = wavelength of light rays

d = aperture of objective lens of telescope.

Here, $\lambda = 6400\text{ Å} = 6400 \times 10^{-10}$ m

$d = 200\text{ cm} = 2\text{ m}$

Substitution of values gives

$$\theta = \frac{1.22 \times 6400 \times 10^{-10}}{2} = \frac{1.22 \times 64 \times 10^{-8}}{2} = 1.22 \times 32 \times 10^{-8} = 39 \times 10^{-8}\text{ rad}$$

25. Spheres A and B have the same charge of same nature. When uncharged sphere C is touched with sphere A, then charge is transferred to C and this charge is equally divided between two spheres.

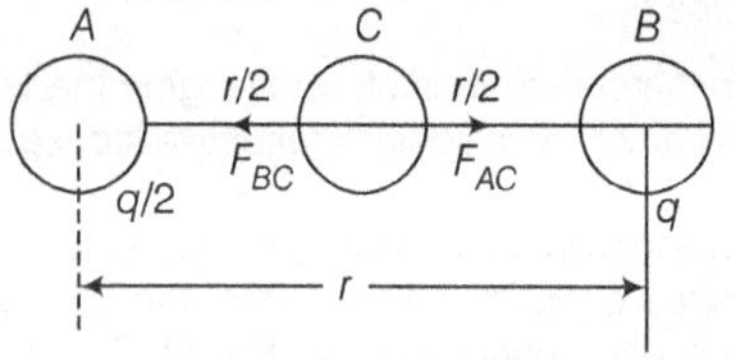

Let initially the charge on spheres A and B is q.

Initially, the repelling force between charged spheres A and B = 3×10^{-5} N

When, sphere C, is placed between charged spheres A and B, then

the force between A and C,

$$F_{AC} = \frac{k\frac{q}{2} \times q/2}{(r/2)^2}$$

Similarly, between B and C

$$F_{BC} = \frac{kq \times q/2}{(r/2)^2}$$

The magnitude of net force on C, $F' = F_{BC} - F_{AC}$

Also $\quad F = \dfrac{kq \times q}{r^2} = 3 \times 10^{-5}$N

$$\text{So,} \quad \frac{F}{F_{BC} - F_{AC}} = \frac{(kq^2/r^2)}{k\left[\frac{q \times q/2}{(r/2)^2} - \frac{q/2 \times q/2}{(r/2)^2}\right]}$$

Here, $\quad F = 3 \times 10^{-5}$ N, $F_{BC} - F_{AC} = F'$

$$\frac{3 \times 10^{-5}}{F'} = \frac{1}{2-1} = \frac{1}{1} = 1$$

$$\therefore \quad F' = 3 \times 10^{-5}\text{ N}$$

26. Let the volume charge density be ρ.

The electric field inside the charged sphere,

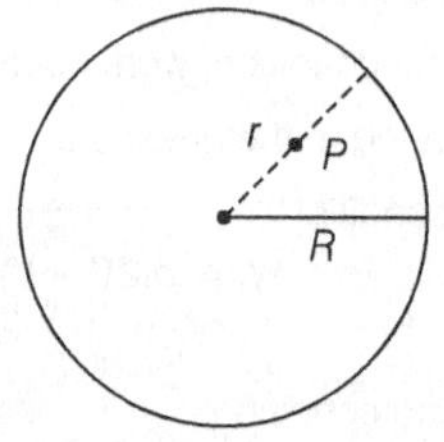

$$E = \frac{K\,qr}{R^3}$$

where, R = Radius of charged sphere

r = Distance of the point (P) inside the sphere

As volume charge density is ρ, then in terms of charge density,

$$E = \frac{\rho r}{3\varepsilon_0}$$

$$\Rightarrow \quad \rho = \frac{3E\varepsilon_0}{r}$$

Now, electric field, $E = -\dfrac{dV}{dr}$

Here, $V = Ar^2 + B$

$$\therefore \quad E = -\frac{dV}{dr} = -2Ar + 0 = -2Ar$$

$$\therefore \quad \rho = \frac{3E\varepsilon_0}{r} = \frac{3(-2Ar\cdot\varepsilon_0)}{r} = -6A\varepsilon_0$$

27. Let the resistances be R_1, R_2 and R_3, respectively.

According to the question, equivalent resistance in parallel = 1 Ω

In parallel combination, the equivalent resistance is given by

$$\frac{1}{R_{eq}} = \frac{1}{R_1} + \frac{1}{R_2} + \frac{1}{R_3}$$

Here, $R_{eq} = 1$

$$\Rightarrow \quad \frac{1}{1} = \frac{1}{R_1} + \frac{1}{R_2} + \frac{1}{R_3}$$

Let $R_3 = 2R_2$

If we check the option given in the question

$$\frac{1}{1} = \frac{1}{R_1} + \frac{1}{R_2} + \frac{1}{2R_2} = \frac{1}{R_1} + \frac{3}{2R_2}$$

If $R_1 = 1\,\Omega, R_2 = 2\,\Omega$

$$\frac{1}{1} = \left(\frac{1}{1} + \frac{3}{2 \times 2}\right) = \frac{1}{1} + \frac{3}{4} = \frac{7}{4}$$

will not hold the condition.

Similarly, if we check the other options only

$$R_1 = 2\Omega, R_2 = 3\Omega$$

$$\frac{1}{1} = \frac{1}{2} + \frac{1}{3} + \frac{1}{R_3}$$

$$= \frac{5}{6} + \frac{1}{R_3} \Rightarrow 1 - \frac{5}{6} = \frac{1}{R_3}$$

or, $\frac{1}{6} = \frac{1}{R_3}$

or, $R_3 = 6\Omega$

So, it will satisfy the equation,

$$\frac{1}{R_{eq}} = \frac{1}{R_1} + \frac{1}{R_2} + \frac{1}{R_3}$$

or, $\frac{1}{R_{eq}} = \frac{1}{2} + \frac{1}{3} + \frac{1}{6} = \frac{6}{6} = \frac{1}{1}$

or, $R_{eq} = 1\Omega$

$R_3 = 6\Omega$ will be highest resistance.

28. Power, $P = \frac{V^2}{R}$

$$R = \frac{V^2}{P}$$

Here, $P = 320$ watts

$V = 220$ volts

When the resistors are connected in series, then power developed across each resistor,

$$P' = \frac{(V')^2}{R} = \frac{\left(\frac{110}{2}\right)^2}{R} = \frac{110 \times 110}{2 \times 2} \times \frac{P}{V^2}$$

$$= \frac{110 \times 110}{2 \times 2} \times \frac{320}{220 \times 220}$$

$$= \frac{1}{4} \times \frac{1}{4} \times 320 = 20 \text{ watts.}$$

29. Let the centroid of the triangle is O, magnetic field due to side AB

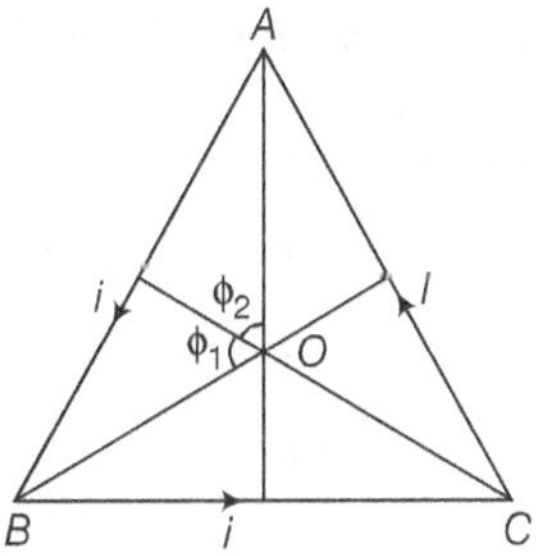

$$B_1 = \frac{\mu_0}{4\pi} \cdot \frac{i}{r} (\sin\phi_1 + \sin\phi_2)$$

where, r is perpendicular distance of AB from centroid O. The magnetic field due to each side is same in magnitude and direction, so the resultant field

$$B = 3B_1$$

$$= 3\frac{\mu_0}{4\pi} \cdot \frac{i}{r} (\sin\phi_1 + \sin\phi_2)$$

(Here, $\mu_0 = 4\pi \times 10^{-7}$ H/m)

$$i = 1 \text{ A}$$

In equilateral triangle, $\phi_1 = \phi_2 = 60^\circ$

$$\therefore \quad B = 3\frac{\mu_0}{4\pi} \cdot \frac{1}{r} (\sin 60^\circ + \sin 60^\circ)$$

Also, $r = 4.5 \times 10^{-2}$ m

$$\Rightarrow \quad B = \frac{3\mu_0}{4\pi} \cdot \frac{1}{4.5 \times 10^{-2}} \left(\frac{\sqrt{3}}{2} + \frac{\sqrt{3}}{2}\right) \text{T},$$

$$= \frac{3\sqrt{3} \cdot \mu_0}{4\pi} \cdot \frac{1}{4.5 \times 10^{-2}} \text{ T}$$

$$= \frac{3\sqrt{3} \times 10^{-7}}{4.5 \times 10^{-2}} \text{ T} \quad \left[\because \frac{\mu_0}{4\pi} = 10^{-7} \text{ N/A}^2\right]$$

$$= \frac{3 \times 1.73}{4.5} \times 10^{-5} \text{ T}$$

$$= 1.15 \times 10^{-5} \text{ T} \approx 2 \times 10^{-5} \text{ T}$$

30. The magnetic moment of charge, $\mu = niA$

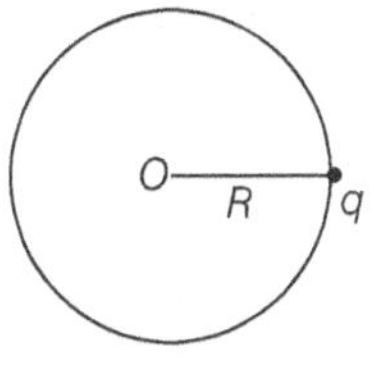

and angular momentum of charge,

$$L = m \cdot v \cdot R$$

Here, $n = 1$

Current, $i = \frac{q}{T}$

Time-period, $T = \frac{2\pi R}{v}$

Equivalent current, $i = \frac{q}{2\pi R / v} = \frac{q \cdot v}{2\pi R}$

Area of loop or circle, $A = \pi R^2$

$\therefore \quad \mu = 1 \times \frac{qv}{2\pi R} \times \pi R^2 = \frac{qvR}{2}$

$\Rightarrow \quad L = I\omega = mR^2 \times \frac{v}{R} = mvR$

I = Moment of inertia of loop

$\therefore \quad \frac{\mu}{L} = \frac{niA}{mvR} = \frac{qvR/2}{mvR} = \frac{q}{2m}$

31. Let the mass of the first magnet = m

$\therefore$ Mass of second magnet = $2m$

The time-period of oscillation of the magnet

$$T = 2\pi\sqrt{\frac{I}{MB_H}}$$

where, I = MI of magnet about the axis passing through its centre

B_H = Earth's magnetic field

M = Magnetic moment of magnet

$$\therefore \quad \frac{T_1}{T_2} = \sqrt{\frac{I_1}{M_1} \times \frac{M_2}{I_2}}$$

Let length of the magnet = L

MI of the magnets about the axis passing through one of the ends is $\frac{mL^2}{3}$

$\therefore \quad I_1 = mL^2/3$ and $I_2 = \frac{(2m)(2L)^2}{3}$

$$\frac{T_1}{T_2} = \sqrt{\frac{mL^2/3}{M_1} \times \frac{M_2}{\frac{2m \times (2L)^2}{3}}}$$

It is given that maximum torques experienced by the magnets are same

$\therefore \quad M \cdot B_H = M_2 B_H \Rightarrow M_1 = M_2 [\because M_1 = M_2 \text{ (given)}]$

$\Rightarrow \quad \frac{T_1}{T_2} = \frac{1}{\sqrt{8}} = \frac{1}{2\sqrt{2}}$

32. Mutual inductance, $M = 0.005\text{H}$

$I = I_0 \sin\omega t$

$I_0 = 10$ A

$\omega = 100\pi$ rad/s

The emf induced in second coil,

$$e = M\frac{dI}{dt} = M\frac{dI}{dt} = 0.005 \times \frac{dI_0 \sin\omega t}{dt}$$

$$= 0.005 \times I_0 \omega\cos\omega t = 0.005 \times I_0 \omega\cos\frac{2\pi}{t}t$$

$\Rightarrow e_{max} = 0.005 \times 10 \times 100\pi \times 1 = 5\pi$ volt

33. Capacitance, $C = \frac{10^{-3}}{2\pi}$ F

Inductance, $L = \left(\frac{100}{\pi}\right)\text{mH} = \frac{100}{\pi} \times 10^{-3}$ H

Resistance, $R = 10\Omega$

Voltage of source = 220 volt

Frequency of source, $f = 50\text{Hz}$

Phase angle ϕ is given by

$$\tan\phi = \frac{X_L - X_C}{R}$$

where, X_L = inductive impedance = ωL

$= 2\pi fL \quad (\because \omega = 2\pi f)$

$\therefore \quad X_L = 2\pi \times 50 \times \frac{100}{\pi} \times 10^{-3}$

$= 10\,\Omega$

and X_C = Capactive impedance

$= \frac{1}{\omega C} = \frac{1}{2\pi fC}$

$= \frac{1 \times 2\pi}{2\pi \times 50 \times 10^{-3}}\Omega = \frac{100}{5} = 20\,\Omega$

$\therefore$ Phase angle,

$$\tan\phi = \frac{X_C - X_L}{R} = \frac{20-10}{10} = 1 \text{ or } \phi = 45^\circ$$

34. (A) $\oint \mathbf{E} \cdot d\mathbf{A} = \frac{Q}{E_0}$

It is Gauss law of electrostatic fields.

(B) $\oint \mathbf{B} \cdot d\mathbf{A} = 0$

Because single pole of a magnet does not exist. So, it is Gauss law for magnetic fields. Option (b) is correct.

35. The de-Broglie wavelength associated with a charged particle is given by

$$\lambda = \frac{h}{\sqrt{mqV}}$$

where, h = planck's constant

m = mass of charged particle

q = charge on the particle

V = potential at which the charged particle is accelerated.

$\therefore \quad \lambda_1 = \frac{h}{\sqrt{m_1 q V_1}}, \lambda_2 = \frac{h}{\sqrt{m_2 q V_2}}$

Here, $m_1 = m_2$

$\Rightarrow \quad \frac{\lambda_1}{\lambda_2} = \sqrt{\frac{m_2 q V_2}{m_1 q V_1}} = \sqrt{\frac{V_2}{V_1}}$

$= V_2^{\frac{1}{2}} \cdot V_1^{\frac{1}{2}}$

36. From hydrogen spectrum, when electron transist from n_2 orbit to n_1 orbit, the emitted wavelength is given by the formula

$$\frac{1}{\lambda_L} = RZ^2\left(\frac{1}{n_1^2} - \frac{1}{n_2^2}\right)$$

Here, R = Rydberg constant.

For Lyman series, $n_1 = 1, n_2 = 2$

For First Lyman line,

$$\frac{1}{\lambda_L} = RZ^2\left(\frac{1}{1^2} - \frac{1}{2^2}\right) \Rightarrow \frac{1}{\lambda_L} = \frac{3}{4}\cdot RZ^2 \quad \ldots\text{(i)}$$

For Balmer series, $n_1 = 2, n_2 = 3, 4 \ldots\ldots$

For first balmer line,

$$\frac{1}{\lambda_B} = RZ^2\left(\frac{1}{2^2} - \frac{1}{3^2}\right) = RZ^2\cdot\frac{5}{36} \quad \ldots\text{(ii)}$$

Dividing Eqs. (i) by (ii), we get

$$\frac{1/\lambda_L}{1/\lambda_B} = \frac{3/4\cdot RZ^2}{5/36\cdot RZ^2} = \frac{3}{4}\times\frac{36}{5} = \frac{27}{5}$$

$$\therefore \quad \frac{\lambda_B}{\lambda_L} = \frac{27}{5}$$

Here, $\lambda_L = 1215.4$ Å

$$\lambda_B = \frac{27}{5}\times 1215.4 \text{ Å}$$

$$= 6563.16 \text{ Å} \approx 6563 \text{ Å}$$

37. Decay constant, $\lambda = 7.9\times10^{-10}$/second

Activity, $A = 55.3\times10^{11}\,\frac{\text{disintegration}}{\text{second}}$

Let the number of nuclei at that instant be N.

We know activity, $A = \lambda N$

$$\therefore \quad N = \frac{A}{\lambda} = \frac{55.3\times10^{11}}{7.9\times10^{-10}} = 7.0\times10^{21}$$

38. Change in current through junction diode,

$$\Delta I = 1.2 \text{ mA} = 1.2\times10^{-3} \text{ A}$$

Change in forward bias voltage, $\Delta V = 0.6$ V

Dynamic resistance,

$$R_{\text{dyn.}} = \frac{\Delta V}{\Delta I} = \frac{0.6}{1.2\times10^{-3}} = 500\,\Omega$$

39. Electron concentration, $n_e = 2\times10^8 \text{m}^{-3}$

Hole concentration, $n_h = 2\times10^8 \text{ m}^{-3}$

After doping with a impurity, the new electron concentration, $n_e' = 4\times10^{10} \text{ m}^{-3}$

New hole concentration, $n_h' = ?$

We know that, $n_e \times n_h = n_i^2$

and $n_e' \times n_h' = n_i^2$

$\therefore \quad n_e \times n_h = n_e' \times n_h'$

$$n'_h = \frac{n_e \times n_h}{n_e'} = \frac{2\times10^8\times2\times10^8}{4\times10^{10}}/\text{m}^3 = 10^6/\text{m}^3$$

$\Rightarrow \quad n_h' = 10^6 \text{m}^{-3}$

40. Given, message signal peak voltage = 20V

$\therefore \quad E_m = 20$V

Carrier voltage, $E_c = 30$ volt

Thus, modulation index,

$$m_a = \frac{E_m}{E_c} = \frac{20}{30} = \frac{2}{3} = 0.67$$

Solved Paper 2015

EAMCET

Engineering Entrance Exam

Physics

1. The pressure on a circular plate is measured by measuring the force on the plate and the radius of the plate. If the errors in measurement of the force and the radius are 5% and 3% respectively, the percentage of error in the measurement of pressure is

(a) 8
(b) 14
(c) 11
(d) 12

2. A body is projected vertically from the surface of the earth of radius R with a velocity equal to half of the escape velocity. The maximum height reached by the body is

(a) $\frac{R}{2}$
(b) $\frac{R}{3}$
(c) $\frac{R}{4}$
(d) $\frac{R}{5}$

3. A particle aimed at a target, projected with an angle 15° with the horizontal is short of the target by 10 m. If projected with an angle of 45° is away from the target by 15 m, then the angle of projection to hit the target is

(a) $\frac{1}{2}\sin^{-1}\left(\frac{1}{10}\right)$
(b) $\frac{1}{2}\sin^{-1}\left(\frac{3}{10}\right)$
(c) $\frac{1}{2}\sin^{-1}\left(\frac{9}{10}\right)$
(d) $\frac{1}{2}\sin^{-1}\left(\frac{7}{10}\right)$

4. A man running at a speed of 5 km/h,find that the rain falls vertically. When he stops running, he finds that the rain is falling at an angle of 60° with the horizontal. The velocity of rain with respect to running man is

(a) $\frac{5}{\sqrt{3}}$ km/h
(b) $\frac{5\sqrt{3}}{2}$ km/h
(c) $\frac{4\sqrt{3}}{2}$ km/h
(d) $5\sqrt{3}$ km/h

5. A horizontal force just sufficient to move a body of mass 4kg lying on a rough horizontal surface, is applied on it. Coefficients of static and kinetic frictions are 0.8 and 0.6 respectively. If the force continues to act even after the body has started moving, the acceleration of the body is (take, $g = 10\ \text{ms}^{-2}$).

(a) 6 ms^{-2}
(b) 8 ms^{-2}
(c) 2 ms^{-2}
(d) 4 ms^{-2}

6. A force $(2\hat{\mathbf{i}} + \hat{\mathbf{j}} - \hat{\mathbf{k}})$ N acts on a body, which is initially at rest. At the end of 20 s the velocity of the body is $(4\hat{\mathbf{i}} + 2\hat{\mathbf{j}} - 2\hat{\mathbf{k}})\ \text{ms}^{-1}$, then the mass of the body is

(a) 8 kg
(b) 10 kg
(c) 5 kg
(d) 4.5 kg

7. A man of weight 50 kg carries an object to a height of 20 m in a time of 10 s. The power used by the man in this process is 2000 W, then find the weight of the object carried by the man (take, $g = 10\ \text{ms}^{-2}$)

(a) 100 kg
(b) 25 kg
(c) 50 kg
(d) 10 kg

8. A ball P moving with a speed of v ms^{-1} collides directly with another identical ball Q moving with a speed 10 ms^{-1}in the opposite direction. P comes to rest after the collision. If the coefficient of restitution is 0.6, the value of v is

(a) 30 ms^{-1}
(b) 40 ms^{-1}
(c) 50 ms^{-1}
(d) 60 ms^{-1}

9. A particle of mass $m = 5$ units is moving with uniform speed $v = 3\sqrt{2}$ units in the XY-plane along the line $Y = X + 4$. The magnitude of the angular momentum about origin is

(a) zero (b) 60 units
(c) 7.5 units (d) 40 units

10. The kinetic energy of a circular disc rotating with a speed of 60 r.p.m. about an axis passing through a point on its circumference and perpendicular to its plane is (mass of circular disc = 5 kg, radius of disc = 1m) approximately.

(a) 170 J (b) 160 J (c) 150 J (d) 140 J

11. The amplitude of a simple pendulum is 10 cm. When the pendulum is at a displacement of 4 cm from the mean position, the ratio of kinetic and potential energies at that point is

(a) 5.25 (b) 2.5
(c) 4.5 (d) 7.5

12. A satellite revolving around a planet has orbital velocity 10 km/s. The additional velocity required for the satellite to escape from the gravitational field of the planet is

(a) 14.14 km/s (b) 11.2 km /s
(c) 4.14 km/s (d) 41.4 km/s

13. The length of a metal wire is l_1 when the tension in it is F_1 and l_2 when the tension is F_2. Then, original length of the wire is

(a) $\dfrac{l_1F_1 + l_2F_2}{F_1 + F_2}$ (b) $\dfrac{l_2 - l_1}{F_2 - F_1}$
(c) $\dfrac{l_1F_2 - l_2F_1}{F_2 - F_1}$ (d) $\dfrac{l_1F_1 - l_2F_2}{F_2 - F_1}$

14. The average depth of Indian ocean is about 3000 m. The value of fractional compression $\left(\dfrac{\Delta V}{V}\right)$ of water at the bottom of the ocean is (given that the bulk modulus of water is 2.2×10^9 Nm^{-2}, $g = 9.8$, $\rho_{H_2O} = 1000$ kg.m^{-3})

(a) 3.4×10^{-2} (b) 1.34×10^{-2}
(c) 4.13×10^{-2} (d) 13.4×10^{-2}

15. The ratio energies of emitted radiation by a black body at 600 K and 933 K when the surrounding temperature is 300 K

(a) $\dfrac{5}{16}$ (b) $\dfrac{7}{16}$ (c) $\dfrac{3}{16}$ (d) $\dfrac{9}{16}$

16. The specific heat of helium at constant volume is 12.6 Jmol^{-1} K^{-1}.The specific heat of helium at constant pressure in Jmol^{-1}K^{-1} is about (Assume the temperature of the gas is moderate, universal gas constant, $R = 8.314$ Jmol^{-1}K^{-1})

(a) 12.6 (b) 16.8
(c) 18.9 (d) 21

17. A gas does 4.5 J of external work during adiabatic expansion. If its temperature falls by 2K, then its internal energy will be

(a) increased by 4.5 J (b) decreased by 4.5 J
(c) decreased by 2.25 J (d) increased by 9.0 J

18. The relation between efficiency η of a heat engine and the coefficient of performance α of a refrigerator is

(a) $\eta = \dfrac{1}{1-\alpha}$ (b) $\eta = \dfrac{1}{1+\alpha}$
(c) $\eta = 1+\alpha$ (d) $\eta = 1-\alpha$

19. A flask contains argon and chlorine in the ratio of 2 : 1 by mass. The temperature of the mixture is 27° C. The ratio of average kinetic energies of two gases per molecule is

(a) 1 :1 (b) 2 : 1
(c) 3 : 1 (d) 6 : 1

20. A transverse wave is represented by the equation $y = 2\sin(30t - 40x)$ and the measurements of distances are in meters, then the velocity of propagation is

(a) 15 ms^{-1} (b) 0.75 ms^{-1}
(c) 3.75 ms^{-1} (d) 300 ms^{-1}

21. Two closed pipes have the same fundamental frequency. One is filled with oxygen and the other with hydrogen at the same temperature. Ratio of their lengths respectively is

(a) 1 : 4 (b) 4 : 1(c) 1 : 2 (d) 2 : 1

22. An image is formed at a distance of 100 cm from the glass surface when light from point source in air falls on a spherical glass surface with refractive index 1.5. The distance of the light source from the glass surface is 100 cm. The radius of curvature is

(a) 20 cm
(b) 40 cm
(c) 30 cm
(d) 50 cm

23. Two coherent sources of intensity ratio 9 : 4 produce interference. The intensity ratio of maxima and minima of the interference pattern is

(a) 13 : 6 (b) 5 : 1
(c) 25 : 1 (d) 3 : 2

24. The energy of a parallel plate capacitor when connected to a battery is E. With the battery still in connection, if the plates of the capacitor are separated, so that the distance between them is twice the original distance, then the electrostatic energy becomes

(a) $2E$ (b) $\frac{E}{4}$ (c) $\frac{E}{2}$ (d) $4E$

25. Two point charges $+8\,\mu$C and $+12\,\mu$C repel each other with a force of 48 N. When an additional charge of $-10\,\mu$C is given to each of these charges (the distance between the charges is unaltered) then the new force is

(a) repulsive force of 24 N
(b) attractive force of 24 N
(c) repulsive force of 12 N
(d) attractive force of 2 N

26. If the dielectric constant of a substance is $K = \frac{4}{3}$, then the electric susceptibility ψ_e is

(a) $\frac{\varepsilon_0}{3}$ (b) $3\,\varepsilon_0$ (c) $\frac{4}{3}\,\varepsilon_0$ (d) $\frac{3}{4}\,\varepsilon_0$

27. In a region of uniform electric field of intensity E, an electron of mass m_e is released from rest. The distance travelled by the electron in a time t is

(a) $\frac{2m_e t^2}{e}$ (b) $\frac{eEt^2}{2m_e}$ (c) $\frac{m_e g t^2}{eE}$ (d) $\frac{2Et^2}{em_e}$

28. A constant potential difference is applied between the ends of the wire. If the length of the wire is elongated 4 times, then the drift velocity of electrons will be

(a) increases 4 times (b) decreases 4 times
(c) increases 2 times (d) decreases 2 times

29. In a meter bridge, the gaps are enclosed by resistances of $2\,\Omega$ and $3\,\Omega$. The value of shunt to be added to $3\,\Omega$ resistor to shift the balancing point by 22.5 cm is

(a) $1\,\Omega$ (b) $2\,\Omega$
(c) $2.5\,\Omega$ (d) $5\,\Omega$

30. Two long straight parallel conductors 10 cm apart, carry equal currents of magnitude 3A in the same direction. Then, the magnetic induction at a point midway between them is

(a) 2×10^{-5} T (b) 3×10^{-5} T
(c) zero (d) 4×10^{-5} T

31. In a crossed field, the magnetic field induction is 2.0 T and electric field intensity is 20×10^3 V/m. At which velocity the electron will travel in a straight line without the effect of electric and magnetic fields?

(a) $\frac{20}{1.6}\times10^3\ \text{ms}^{-1}$ (b) $10\times10^3\ \text{ms}^{-1}$
(c) $20\times10^3\ \text{ms}^{-1}$ (d) $40\times10^3\ \text{ms}^{-1}$

32. A material of 0.25 cm^2 cross-sectional area is placed in a magnetic field of strength (H) 1000 Am^{-1}. Then, the magnetic flux produced is (Susceptibility of material is 313) (Permeability of free space, $\mu_0 = 4\pi\times10^{-7}$ Hm^{-1})

(a) 8.33×10^{-8} Wb (b) 1.84×10^{-6} Wb
(c) 9.87×10^{-6} Wb (d) 3.16×10^{-6} Wb

33. The magnitude of the induced emf in a coil of inductance 30 mH in which the current changes from 6 A to 2 A in 2 s is

(a) 0.06 V (b) 0.6 V (c) 1.06 V (d) 6 V

34. In an AC circuit V and I are given below, then find the power dissipated in the circuit $V = 50\sin(50t)\ v\ I = 50\sin\left(50t\ \frac{\pi}{3}\right)$ mA

(a) 0.625 W (b) 1.25 W
(c) 2.50 W (d) 5.0 W

35. Light with an energy flux of 9 Wcm^{-2} falls on a non-reflecting surface at normal incidence. If the surface has an area of 20 cm^2. The total momentum delivered for complete absorption in one hour is

(a) 2.16×10^{-4} kgms^{-1} (b) 1.16×10^{-3} kgms^{-1}
(c) 2.16×10^{-3} kgms^{-1} (d) 3.16×10^{-4} kgms^{-1}

36. The ratio of the de-Broglie wavelengths for the electron and proton moving with the same velocity is (m_p-mass of proton, m_e-mass of electron)

(a) $m_p : m_e$ (b) $m_p^2 : m_e^2$
(c) $m_e : m_p$ (d) $m_e^2 : m_p^2$

37. The ratio of longest wavelength lines in the Balmer and Paschen series of hydrogen spectrum is

(a) $\frac{5}{36}$ (b) $\frac{7}{20}$ (c) $\frac{7}{144}$ (d) $\frac{5}{27}$

38. In the following nuclear reaction x stands for $n \rightarrow p + e^- + x$

(a) α-particle (b) positron
(c) nutrino (d) antinutrino

39. In the following circuit, the output Y becomes zero for the input combinations.

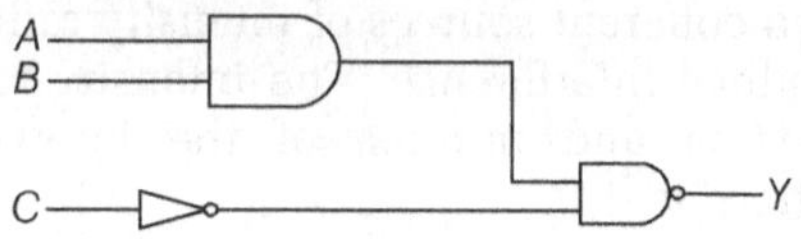

(a) $A = 1, B = 0, C = 0$ (b) $A = 0, B = 1, C = 1$
(c) $A = 0, B = 0, C = 0$ (d) $A = 1, B = 1, C = 0$

40. The maximum amplitude of an amplitude modulated wave is 16 V, while the minimum amplitude is 4 V. The modulation index is

(a) 0.4 (b) 0.5 (c) 0.6 (d) 4

Answers

1. (c)	**2.** (b)	**3.** (d)	**4.** (d)	**5.** (c)	**6.** (b)	**7.** (c)	**8.** (b)	**9.** (b)	**10.** (c)
11. (a)	**12.** (c)	**13.** (c)	**14.** (b)	**15.** (c)	**16.** (d)	**17.** (b)	**18.** (b)	**19.** (a)	**20.** (b)
21. (a)	**22.** (a)	**23.** (c)	**24.** (c)	**25.** (d)	**26.** (a)	**27.** (b)	**28.** (a)	**29.** (b)	**30.** (c)
31. (b)	**32.** (c)	**33.** (a)	**34.** (a)	**35.** (c)	**36.** (a)	**37.** (b)	**38.** (d)	**39.** (d)	**40.** (c)

Solutions

1. The pressure exerted on the circular plate, $p = \frac{F}{A} = \frac{F}{\pi R^2}$

where, R = radius of circular disc
A = area of circular disc
and F = Force on circular disc
Now, percentage error in pressure.

$$\frac{\Delta p}{p} \times 100 = \frac{\Delta F}{F} \times 100 + 2\frac{\Delta R}{R} \times 100$$

$$= 5 + 2(3) = 5 + 6 = 11$$

$$\Rightarrow \quad \frac{\Delta p}{p} \times 100 = 11\,\%$$

2. As, $v = Kv_e$ $(K < 1)$ then

where, v = velocity of projection and
v_e = escape velocity
The maximum height reached by the body is

$$h = \frac{RK^2}{1 - K^2} = \frac{R\left(\frac{1}{4}\right)}{\left(1 - \frac{1}{4}\right)} = \frac{R}{4} \times \frac{4}{3} = \frac{R}{3}$$

$$\Rightarrow \quad h = \frac{R}{3}$$

3. According to question,

$$R_1 = R - 10$$

and again with reference to question,

$$R_2 = R + 15$$

Now as we know that, range $\propto \sin 2\theta$,

So, $$\frac{R - 10}{R + 15} = \frac{\sin 2\theta_1}{\sin 2\theta_2} = \frac{\sin 30°}{\sin 90°} = \frac{1}{2}$$

$$\Rightarrow \quad 2R - 20 = R + 15$$

$$\Rightarrow \quad R = 35$$

For the range to be maximum $\sin 2\theta = \sin 90° = 1$

So, $$R_{max} = \frac{u^2}{g}$$

As, $$R_1 = \frac{u^2 \sin 2\theta}{g} \Rightarrow 50 = \frac{u^2}{g}$$

where, θ = angle of projection.

and $$35 = \frac{50g \times \sin 2\theta}{g} \qquad [\because u^2 = 50g]$$

$$\therefore \quad \sin 2\theta = \frac{35}{50} = \frac{7}{10}$$

$$\Rightarrow \quad 2\theta = \sin^{-1}\left[\frac{7}{10}\right]$$

$$\Rightarrow \quad \theta = \frac{1}{2}\sin^{-1}\left[\frac{7}{10}\right]$$

4. Consider the situational diagram as shown below.

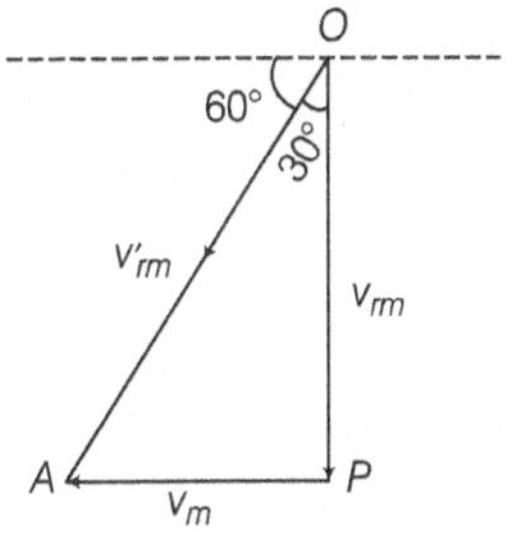

In Δ OAP,

$$\tan 30° = \frac{v_m}{v_{rm}}$$

$$= \frac{\text{Velocity of man}}{\text{Velocity of rain with respect to man}}$$

$$\Rightarrow \quad v_{rm} = \frac{5}{1/\sqrt{3}}$$

$$= 5\sqrt{3} \text{ km/h}$$

5. The net acceleration,

$$a = (\mu_s - \mu_k)\, g$$
$$= (0.8 - 0.6) \times 10$$
$$= 0.2 \times 10$$
$$a = 2 \text{ ms}^{-2}$$

6. The magnitude of force,

$$F = \sqrt{4 + 1 + 1} = \sqrt{6}$$

The speed or magnitude of velocity,

$$v = \sqrt{16 + 4 + 4} = \sqrt{24}$$

As, $$F = \frac{dp}{dt} = m\left(\frac{v - u}{t}\right)$$

where, m = mass of body

$$\Rightarrow \quad \sqrt{6} = m\left(\frac{\sqrt{24} - 0}{20}\right)$$

$$\Rightarrow \quad m = \frac{\sqrt{6} \times 20}{\sqrt{24}} = \frac{20}{2} = 10$$

$$\Rightarrow \quad m = 10 \text{ kg}$$

7. The power used by man,

$$P = (M + m)\, gh / t$$

where, M = mass of man

m = mass of object

t = time

and h = height

$$\Rightarrow \quad 2000 = \frac{(50 + m) \times 10 \times 20}{10}$$

$$\Rightarrow \quad 100 = 50 + x$$

$$\Rightarrow \quad x = 100 - 50 \quad \Rightarrow \quad x = 50 \text{ kg}$$

8. From conservation of momentum,

$$m(v - 10) = mv_2$$
$$v_2 = (v - 10)$$

The coefficient of restitution,

$$e = \frac{\text{Velocity of separation}}{\text{Velocity of approach}}$$

$$= \frac{v_2 - v_1}{u_1 + u_2} = \frac{(v - 10) - 0}{(v + 10)}$$

$$\Rightarrow \quad 0.6 = \frac{v - 10}{v + 10}$$

$$\Rightarrow \quad 0.6v + 6 = v - 10$$

$$\Rightarrow \quad 0.4v = 16$$

$$\Rightarrow \quad v = 40 \text{ ms}^{-1}$$

9. The angular momentum,

$$L = mvb \cos\theta$$

where, m = mass of particle

v = velocity of particle

b = position of particle with respect to origin and θ = angle between momentum vector and position vector.

$$= 5 \times 3\sqrt{2} \times 4 \times \cos 45°$$

$$L = 60 \text{ units}$$

10. The rotational kinetic energy is given by

$$\text{KE} = \frac{1}{2} I\omega^2 = \frac{1}{2} \times \frac{3}{2}\, mr^2 4\pi^2 f^2$$

where, m = mass, r = radius and

f = frequency

$$\Rightarrow \quad \text{KE} = 3mr^2 \times \pi^2 f^2$$

$$= 3 \times 5 \times 1 \times 10 \times 1$$

$$\Rightarrow \quad \text{KE} = 150 \text{ J}$$

11. The kinetic energy is given by $\text{KE} = \frac{1}{2} m\omega^2 (A^2 - x^2)$ while the potential energy is given by $\text{PE} = \frac{1}{2} m\omega^2 x^2$.

Therefore, the ratio,

$$\frac{\text{KE}}{\text{PE}} = \frac{\frac{1}{2} m\omega^2 (A^2 - x^2)}{\frac{1}{2} m\omega^2 x^2}$$

$$\Rightarrow \quad \frac{\text{KE}}{\text{PE}} = \frac{A^2 - x^2}{x^2}$$

$$\Rightarrow \quad \frac{10^2 - 4^2}{4^2} = \frac{84}{16}$$

$$\Rightarrow \quad \frac{\text{KE}}{\text{PE}} = \frac{21}{4} = 5.25$$

12. The relation between two velocities is given by

$$v_e = (\sqrt{2} - 1)\, v_0$$
$$= (1.414 - 1)\, v_0 = 0.414 \times 10$$
$$= 4.14 \text{ km/s}$$

13. As, $F \alpha \Delta l$ where, Δl = change in length Now, suppose the origin length of the metal wire is l then,

$$F_1 \propto (l_1 - l)$$

Similarly, $F_2 \propto (l_2 - l)$

The ratio, $\dfrac{F_1}{F_2} = \dfrac{l_1 - l}{l_2 - l}$

$\Rightarrow$ $F_1 l_2 - F_1 l = F_2\, l_1 - F_2\, l$

$\Rightarrow$ $(F_2 - F_1)\, l = F_2 l_1 - F_1 l_2$

$\Rightarrow$ $l = \dfrac{F_2 l_1 - F_1 l_2}{F_2 - F_1}$

14. The fractional compression or decrease in volume

$$\frac{\Delta V}{V} = \frac{h\rho g}{k}$$

where, h = depth (average)

ρ = density of ocean water

g = gravitational acceleration and

k = bulk modulus

$\Rightarrow$ $\dfrac{\Delta V}{V} = \dfrac{3 \times 10^3 \times 10^3 \times 9.8}{2.2 \times 10^9}$

$= \dfrac{3}{2.2} \times 10^{-4} \times 98$

$= \dfrac{147}{11} \times 10^{-4} = 1.34 \times 10^{-2}$

15. The ratio to energy, $\dfrac{E_1}{E_2} = \dfrac{T_1^4 - T_S^4}{T_2^4 - T_S^4}$

where, T_1, T_S and T_2 are the temperatures

$\Rightarrow$ $\dfrac{E_1}{E_2} = \dfrac{(600)^4 - (300)^4}{(900)^4 - (300)^4} = \dfrac{3}{16}$

16. Given, $C_V = 12.6 \text{ J mol}^{-1}\text{K}^{-1}$

$R = 8.314 \text{ J mol}^{-1} \text{ K}^{-1}$

The specific heat of helium at constant pressure,

$$C_p = C_V + R = 12.6 + 8.314 = 21$$

17. During adiabatic process, no heat transfer takes place,

So, $dQ = 0$

From first law of thermodynamics,

$$dQ = dU + dW$$

$\Rightarrow$ $dU = -dW$

$\Rightarrow$ $dU = -4.5 \text{ J}$

As, the temperature falls so internal energy will decrease i.e. $dU = -4.5 \text{ J}$

18. The efficiency and co-efficient of performance is related as $\eta = \dfrac{1}{1 + \alpha}$

19. The average kinetic energy of molecule is given by $\text{KE}_{\text{av}} = \dfrac{3}{2} KT.$

where, K is Boltzmann's constant.

Independent of nature $\text{KE}_1 : \text{KE}_2 = 1 : 1$

20. The transverse wave is given by

$$y = 2\sin(30t - 40x)$$

The standard transverse wave is

$$y = A\sin(\omega t - kx)$$

On comparing, we get,

$$v = \frac{\omega}{k} = \frac{30}{40} = 0.75 \text{ m/s}$$

21. The fundamental frequency,

$$n = \frac{v}{4l}$$

where, v = wave velocity

$$\frac{v_H}{v_o} = \frac{l_H}{l_o} = \frac{4}{1}$$

$\Rightarrow$ $\dfrac{v_H}{v_o} = \sqrt{\dfrac{M_2}{M_1}} = \dfrac{v_H}{v_o} = \sqrt{\dfrac{32}{2}} = 4$

Here, M_1 and M_2 are molecular weights of hydrogen and oxygen, respectively

$$v_o : v_H = 1 : 4$$

22. The refraction formula is,

$$\frac{\mu_2}{v} - \frac{\mu_1}{u} = \frac{\mu_2 - \mu_1}{R}$$

where, R = radius of curvature

Given, u = 100 cm; v = 100 cm

$\mu_2 = 1.5$, μ_1 (air) = 1.

$\Rightarrow$ $\dfrac{1.5}{100} + \dfrac{1}{100} = \dfrac{1.5 - 1}{R}$

$\dfrac{2.5}{100} = \dfrac{0.5}{R}$

$R = \dfrac{0.5 \times 100}{2.5}$

$\Rightarrow$ $R = 20$ cm

23. Given that the ratio of source intensity

$$\frac{I_1}{I_2} = \frac{9}{4}$$

For the interference pattern,

$$\frac{I_{max}}{I_{min}} = \left(\frac{\sqrt{I_1} + \sqrt{I_2}}{\sqrt{I_1} - \sqrt{I_2}}\right)^2 = \left(\frac{\sqrt{9} + \sqrt{4}}{\sqrt{9} - \sqrt{4}}\right)^2 = \left(\frac{\frac{3}{2} - 1}{\frac{3}{2} + 1}\right)^2 = \frac{25}{1}$$

24. The electrostatic energy stored in a capacitor is

$$E = \frac{1}{2} CV^2$$

$\Rightarrow$ $C \propto \frac{1}{d}$

$\Rightarrow$ $\frac{C_1}{C_2} = \frac{d_2}{d_1} = \frac{2d}{d} = 2$

Now, $\frac{E_1}{E_2} = \frac{C_1}{C_2} = \frac{C}{C/2} = \frac{2}{1}$

$\Rightarrow$ $\frac{E}{E_2} = \frac{2}{1}$

$\Rightarrow$ $E_2 = \frac{E}{2}$

25. Given, $q_1 = +8\,\mu C$, $q_2 = +12\,\mu C$

and $F_1 = 48\,N$

When an amount of charge $-10\mu C$ is added to both of the charges then, these becomes

$$q_1' = -2\mu C \text{ and } q_2' = +2\mu C$$

The force between two charges,

$$F \propto |q_1 q_2|$$

$\Rightarrow$ $F_1 \propto |q_1 q_2|$ and $F_2 \propto |q_1^1\ q_2^1|$

and $\frac{F_1}{F_2} = \frac{q_1 q_2}{q_1' q_2'}$

$\Rightarrow$ $\frac{48}{F_2} = \frac{8 \times 12}{2 \times 2}$

$\Rightarrow$ $F_2 = 2N$

26. The dielectric constant permutating and susceptibility are relative as,

$$K = 1 + \frac{\psi_e}{\varepsilon_0}$$

$$\frac{4}{3} = 1 + \frac{\psi_e}{\varepsilon_0}$$

$\Rightarrow$ $\psi_e = \varepsilon_0 \left(\frac{4}{3} - 1\right) \Rightarrow \psi_e = \frac{\varepsilon_0}{3}$

The electric susceptibility, $\psi_e = \frac{\varepsilon_0}{3}$

27. The force on electron in the electric field

$$F = eE$$

$\therefore$ Acceleration, $a = \frac{F}{m_e} = \frac{eE}{m_e}$

Now, from equation of motion,

$$S = \frac{1}{2} at^2 = \frac{1}{2} \frac{eE}{m_e} t^2$$

where, t = time

28. The drift velocity in inversely proportional to the length(l) of wire

$$v_d \propto \frac{1}{l} \quad \frac{v_{d_1}}{v_{d_2}} = \frac{l_2}{l_1} = \frac{4l}{l}$$

Here, l_1 and l_2 are the lengths of wire in two conditions

$\Rightarrow$ $v_{d_1} : v_{d_2} = 4:1$

29. To obtain the balance point in meter bridge

$$\frac{2(3+x)}{3x} = \frac{62.5}{37.5}$$

$$(6 + 2x)37.5 = 62.5 \times 3x$$

$$225 + 75x = 187.5x$$

$$187.5x - 75x = 225$$

$$112.5x = 225$$

$$x = 2$$

30. At the mid-point of two conductors, the magnetic induction

$$B_1 = B_2 = B.$$

Therefore, the net magnetic induction due to two wire at the mid-point is

$$B_R = B_1 - B_2 = 0$$

31. In case of motion of electron to be unaffected by electric and magnetic field (i.e. E and B) the resultant of both the fields should be zero. Hence, $evB = eE$

where, e = electronic charge and

v = velocity of electron

$\Rightarrow$ $v = \frac{E}{B} v = \frac{20 \times 10^3}{2.0} = 10 \times 10^3\ ms^{-1}$

32. As, we know that

$\Rightarrow$ $\mu = \mu_0 (1 + \chi_m)$

Now, the magnetic flux $\phi = BA = \mu HA$

$$= \mu_0 (1 + \chi)\, HA$$

$$= 4\pi \times 10^{-7}\ (1 + 313) \times 1000 \times 0.25 \times 10^{-4}$$

$$= 9.87 \times 10^{-6} Wb$$

33. The magnitude of induced emf,

$$|e| = -L\frac{di}{dt}$$

$\Rightarrow$ $e = -30 \times 10^{-3} \times \left(\frac{6-2}{2}\right)$

$$= -30 \times 10^{-3} \times \frac{4}{2} = -0.06\ V$$

34. As we know that, the power dissipated in an AC circuit is

$$P = \frac{E_0 i_0 \cos\phi}{2}$$

Here, $E_0 = 50$ V

$i_0 = 50$ mA $= 50 \times 10^{-3}$ A and $\phi = \frac{\pi}{3}$

$\left(\text{i.e. } \cos\frac{\pi}{3} = \frac{1}{2}\right)$

$$\therefore \quad P = \frac{50 \times 50 \times 10^{-3} \times 1}{2 \times 2} = 0.625 \text{ W}$$

35. The total momentum delivered is

$$\Delta p = \left(\frac{IA}{c}\right) t.$$

where, I = intensity,

A = area of surface

c = speed of light and t = time

$$\Delta p = \left(\frac{9 \times 10^4 \times 20 \times 10^{-4}}{3 \times 10^8} \times 3600\right)$$

$$= 2.16 \times 10^{-3} \text{ kgms}^{-1}$$

36. As, we know that de-Broglie wave lengths

$$\lambda = \frac{h}{mv} \Rightarrow \lambda \propto \frac{1}{m}$$

Here, m = mass of charged particle and v = velocity of particle

$$\Rightarrow \quad \frac{\lambda_e}{\lambda_p} = \frac{m_p}{m_e}$$

37. The wavelength of Balmer series is given by

$$\frac{1}{\lambda_B} = R\left[\frac{1}{2^2} - \frac{1}{3^2}\right] = \frac{5}{36} R \quad \ldots\text{(i)}$$

The wavelength for paschen series is given by

$$\frac{1}{\lambda_p} = R\left[\frac{1}{3^2} - \frac{1}{4^2}\right] = \frac{7}{144} R \quad \ldots\text{(ii)}$$

On dividing Eq. (ii) by Eq (i),we get

$$\frac{\lambda_B}{\lambda_p} = \frac{7}{20}$$

38. In the nuclear reaction x stands for an antinutrino number (particle).

39. The output of the circuit can be given by

$$Y = \overline{(AB)\overline{C}} = \overline{A} + \overline{B} + C$$

If the output is zero

i.e. $Y = 0$ then $A = 1$,

$B = 1$ and $C = 0$

40. The modulation index in amplitude modulation is

$$m = \frac{A_m}{A_c} = \frac{E_{max} - E_{min}}{E_{max} + E_{min}}$$

Given that, $E_{max} = 16$ V

and $E_{min} = 4$ V

$$\Rightarrow \quad m = \frac{16 - 4}{16 + 4}$$

$$= \frac{12}{20} = \frac{3}{5} = 0.6$$

Solved Paper 2014

EAMCET

Engineering Entrance Exam

Physics

1. A closed pipe is suddenly opened and changed to an open pipe of same length. The fundamental frequency of the resulting open pipe is less than that of 3rd harmonic of the earlier closed pipe by 55 Hz. Then, the value of fundamental frequency of the closed pipe is

(a) 165 Hz (b) 110 Hz (c) 55 Hz (d) 220 Hz

2. A convex lens has its radii of curvature equal. The focal length of the lens is f. If it is divided vertically into two identical plano-convex lenses by cutting it, then the focal length of the plano-convex lens is (μ = the refractive index of the material of the lens)

(a) f (b) $\frac{f}{2}$ (c) $2f$ (d) $(\mu - 1)f$

3. A thin converging lens of focal length $f = 25$ cm forms the image of an object on a screen placed at a distance of 75 cm from the lens. The screen is moved closer to the lens by a distance of 25 cm. The distance through which the object has to be shifted, so that its image on the screen in sharp again is

(a) 37.5 cm (b) 16.25 cm
(c) 12.5 cm (d) 13.5 cm

4. In a double slit interference experiment, the fringe width obtained with a light of wavelength 5900 Å was 1.2mm for parallel narrow slits placed 2mm apart. In this arrangement, if the slit separation is increased by one-and-half times the previous value, then the fringe width is

(a) 0.9 mm (b) 0.8 mm
(c) 1.8 mm (d) 1.6 mm

5. A charge Q is divided into two charges q and $Q - q$. The value of q such that the force between them is maximum, is

(a) Q (b) $\frac{3Q}{4}$ (c) $\frac{Q}{2}$ (d) $\frac{Q}{3}$

6. Two concentric hollow spherical shells have radii r and R ($R >> r$). A charge Q is distributed on them such that the surface charge densities are equal. The electric potential at the centre is

(a) $\frac{Q(R + r)}{4\pi\varepsilon_0(R^2 + r^2)}$ (b) $\frac{Q(R^2 + r^2)}{4\pi\varepsilon_0(R + r)}$

(c) $\frac{Q}{(R + r)}$ (d) zero

7. Wires A and B have resistivities ρ_A and ρ_B, ($\rho_B = 2\rho_A$) and have lengths l_A and l_B. If the diameter of the wire B is twice that of A and the two wires have same resistance, then $\frac{l_B}{l_A}$ is

(a) 2 (b) 1 (c) $\frac{1}{2}$ (d) $\frac{1}{4}$

8. In the circuit shown, the heat produced in 5 Ω resistance due to current through is 50 J/s. Then, the heat generated per second in 2 Ω resistance is

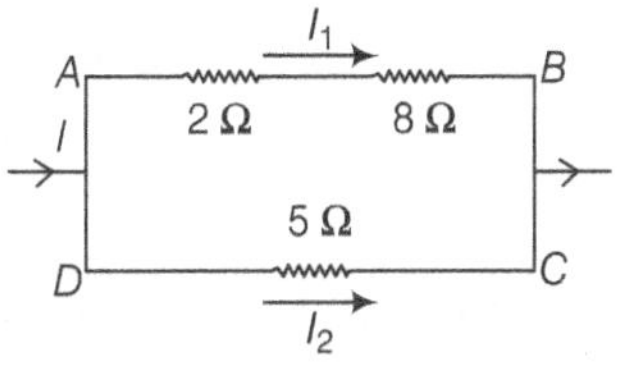

(a) 5J/s (b) 4J/s (c) 9J/s (d) 10J/s

9. A steady current flows in a long wire. It is bent into a circular loop of one turn and the magnetic field at the centre of the coil is B. If the same wire is bent into a circular loop of n turns, the magnetic field at the centre of the coil is

(a) $\frac{B}{n}$ (b) nB (c) nB^2 (d) n^2B

10. An electrically charged particle enters into a uniform magnetic induction field in a direction perpendicular to the field with a velocity v. Then, it travels

(a) in a straight line without acceleration
(b) with force in the direction of the field
(c) in a circular path with a radius directly proportional to v^2
(d) in a circular path with a radius directly proportional to its velocity

11. At a certain place, the angle of dip is 60° and the horizontal component of the earth's magnetic field (B_H) is 0.8×10^{-4} T. The earth's overall magnetic field is

(a) 1.5×10^{-4} T (b) 1.6×10^{-3} T
(c) 1.5×10^{-3} T (d) 1.6×10^{-4} T

12. A coil of wire of radius r has 600 turns and a self inductance of 108 mH. The self inductance of a coil with same radius and 500 turns is

(a) 80 mH (b) 75 mH (c) 108 mH (d) 90 mH

13. A capacitor 50μF is connected to a power source $V = 220\sin 50t$ (V in volt, t in second). The value of rms current (in ampere)

(a) $\frac{\sqrt{2}}{0.55}$ A (b) 0.55 A (c) $\sqrt{2}$ A (d) $\frac{(0.55)}{\sqrt{2}}$ A

14. The electric field for an electromangetic wave in free space is $\mathbf{E} = \mathbf{i}\,30\cos(kz - 5\times 10^8 t)$, where magnitude of E is in V/m. The magnitude of wave vector, k is (velocity of em wave in free space $= 3\times 10^8$ m/s)

(a) 0.46 rad m^{-1} (b) 3 rad m^{-1}
(c) 1.66 rad m^{-1} (d) 0.83 rad m^{-1}

15. The energy of a photon is equal to the kinetic energy of a proton. If λ_1 is the de-Broglie wavelength of a proton, λ_2 the wavelength associated with the proton and if the energy of the photon is E, then (λ_1/λ_2) is proportional to

(a) E^4 (b) $E^{1/2}$
(c) E^2 (d) E

16. The radius of the first orbit of hydrogen is r_H, and the energy in the ground state is -13.6 eV. Considering a μ^--particle with a mass 207 m_e revolving round a proton as in hydrogen atom, the energy and radius of proton and μ^--combination respectively in the first orbit are (assume nucleus to be stationary)

(a) -13.6×207 eV, $\frac{r_H}{207}$
(b) -207×13.6 eV, $207\,r_H$
(c) $-\frac{13.6}{207}$ eV, $\frac{r_H}{207}$
(d) $-\frac{13.6}{207}$ eV, $207\,r_H$

17. If the radius of a nucleus with mass number 125 is 1.5 fermi, then radius of a nucleus with mass number 64 is

(a) 0.48 fermi (b) 0.96 fermi
(c) 1.92 fermi (d) 1.2 fermi

18. A crystal of intrinsic silicon at room temperature has a carrier concentration of $1.6\times 10^{16}/m^3$. If the donor concentration level is $4.8\times 10^{20}/m^3$, then the concentration of holes in the semiconductor is

(a) $53\times 10^{12}/m^3$ (b) $4\times 10^{11}/m^3$
(c) $4\times 10^{12}/m^3$ (d) $5.3\times 10^{11}/m^3$

19. The output characteristics of an $n-p-n$ transistor represent, (I_C = collector current, V_{CE} = potential difference between collector and emitter, I_B = base current, V_{BB} = voltage given to base, V_{BE} = the potential difference between base and emitter)

(a) changes in I_C as I_B and V_{BB} are changed
(b) changes in I_C with changes in V_{CE} (I_B = constant)
(c) changes in I_B with changes in V_{CE}
(d) change in I_C as V_{BE} is changed

20. A TV transmitting antenna is 128m, tall. If the receiving antenna is at the ground level, the maximum distance between, them for satisfactory communication in line of sight mode is (radius of the earth 6.4×10^6m)

(a) $64\times\sqrt{10}$ km (b) $\frac{128}{\sqrt{10}}$ km
(c) $128\times\sqrt{10}$ km (d) $\frac{64}{\sqrt{10}}$ km

21. A wheel which is initially at rest is subjected to a constant angular acceleration about its axis. It rotates through an angle of 15° in time t sec. The increase in angle through which it rotates in the next $2t$ sec is

(a) 90° (b) 120° (c) 30° (d) 45°

22. A thin wire of length l having density ρ is bent into a circular loop with C as its centre, as shown in figure. The moment of inertia of the loop about the line AB is

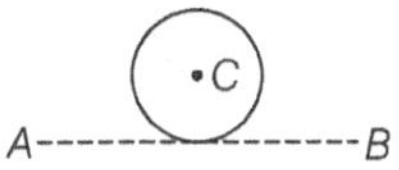

(a) $\frac{5\rho l^3}{16\pi^2}$ (b) $\frac{\rho l^3}{16\pi^2}$

(c) $\frac{\rho l^3}{8\pi^2}$ (d) $\frac{3\rho l^3}{8\pi^2}$

23. The ratio between kinetic and potential energies of a body executing simple harmonic motion, when it is at a distance of $\frac{1}{N}$ of its amplitude from the mean position is

(a) $N^2 + 1$ (b) $\frac{1}{N^2}$ (c) N^2 (d) $N^2 - 1$

24. A satellite is revolving very close to a planet of density ρ. The period of revolution of satellite is

(a) $\sqrt{\frac{3\pi\rho}{G}}$ (b) $\sqrt{\frac{3\pi}{2\rho G}}$

(c) $\sqrt{\frac{3\pi}{\rho G}}$ (d) $\sqrt{\frac{3\pi G}{\rho}}$

25. Two wires of the same material and length but diameters in the ratio 1:2 are stretched by the same force. The elastic potential energy per unit volume for the wires, when stretched by the same force will be in the ratio.

(a) 16 : 1 (b) 1 : 1 (c) 2 : 1 (d) 4 : 1

26. When a big drop of water is formed from n small drops of water, the energy loss is $3E$, where, E is the energy of the bigger drop. If R is the radius of the bigger drop and r is the radius of the smaller drop, then number of smaller drops (n) is

(a) $\frac{4R}{r^2}$ (b) $\frac{4R}{r}$

(c) $\frac{2R^2}{r}$ (d) $\frac{4R^2}{r^2}$

27. A steam at 100°C is passed into 1 kg of water contained in a calorimeter of water equivalent 0.2 kg at 9°C till the temperature of the calorimeter and water in it is increased to 90°C. The mass of steam condensed in kg is nearly (specific heat of water $= 1$ cal/g °C, latent heat of vaporisation $= 540$ cal/g)

(a) 0.81 (b) 0.18 (c) 0.27 (d) 0.54

28. A very small hole in an electric furnace is used for heating metals. The hole nearly acts as a black body. The area of the hole is 200 mm^2. To keep a metal at 727° C, heat energy flowing through this hole per sec, in joules is ($\sigma = 5.67 \times 10^{-8}$ Wm^{-2} K^{-4})

(a) 22.68 (b) 2.268

(c) 1.134 (d) 11.34

29. Five moles of hydrogen initially at STP is compressed adiabatically so that its temperature becomes 673 K. The increase in internal energy of the gas, in kilo joule is ($R = 8.3$ J/mol-K; $\gamma = 1.4$ for diatomic gas)

(a) 80.5 (b) 21.55

(c) 41.50 (d) 65.55

30. The volume of one mole of the gas is changed from V to $2V$ at constant pressure p. If γ is the ratio of specific heats of the gas, change in internal energy of the gas is

(a) $\frac{r.pV}{\gamma-1}$ (b) $\frac{r}{\gamma-1}$

(c) pV (d) $\frac{pV}{\gamma\ 1}$

31. A bus moving on a level road with a velocity v can be stopped at a distance of x, by the application of a retarding force F. The load on the bus is increased by 25% by boarding the passengers. Now, if the bus is moving with the same speed and if the same retarding force is applied, the distance travelled by the bus before it stops is

(a) $1.25x$ (b) x (c) $5x$ (d) $2.5x$

32. A cannon shell fired breaks into two equal parts at its highest point. One part retraces the path to the cannon with kinetic energy E_1 and kinetic energy of the second part is E_2, relation between E_1 and E_2 is

(a) $E_2 = 15\,E_1$ (b) $E_2 = E_1$

(c) $E_2 = 4\,E_1$ (d) $E_2 = 9\,E_1$

33. The force required to move a body up a rough inclined plane is double the force required to prevent the body from sliding down the plane. The coefficient of friction, when the angle of inclination of the plane is 60° is

(a) $\frac{1}{3}$ (b) $\frac{1}{\sqrt{2}}$ (c) $\frac{1}{\sqrt{3}}$ (d) $\frac{1}{2}$

34. A mass M kg is suspended by a weightless string. The horizontal force required to hold the mass at 60° with the vertical is

(a) Mg (b) $Mg\sqrt{3}$

(c) $Mg(\sqrt{3}+1)$ (d) $\frac{Mg}{\sqrt{3}}$

35. A body is projected at an angle θ so that its range is maximum. If T is the time of flight, then the value of maximum range is (acceleration due to gravity = g)

(a) $\frac{g^2T}{2}$ (b) $\frac{gT}{2}$

(c) $\frac{gT^2}{2}$ (d) $\frac{g^2T^2}{2}$

36. The path of a projectile is given by the equation $y = ax - bx^2$, where a and b are constants and x and y are respectively horizontal and vertical distances of projectile from the point of projection. The maximum height attained by the projectile and the angle of projection are respectively

(a) $\frac{2a^2}{b}, \tan^{-1}(a)$ (b) $\frac{b^2}{2a}, \tan^{-1}(b)$

(c) $\frac{a^2}{b}, \tan^{-1}(2b)$ (d) $\frac{a^2}{4b}, \tan^{-1}(a)$

37. Velocity (v) *versus* displacement (x) plot of a body moving along a straight line is as shown in the graph. The corresponding plot of acceleration (a) as a function of displacement (x) is

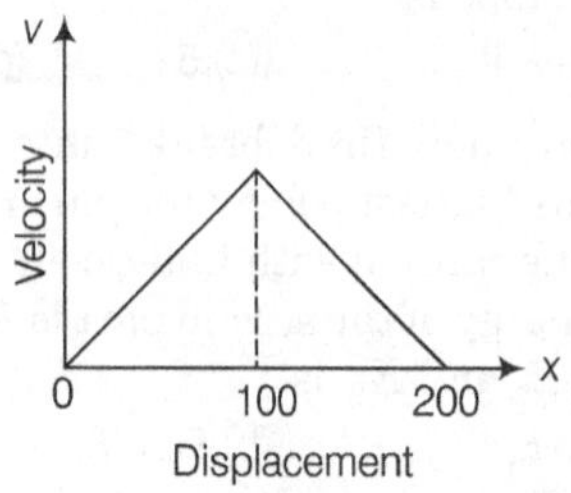

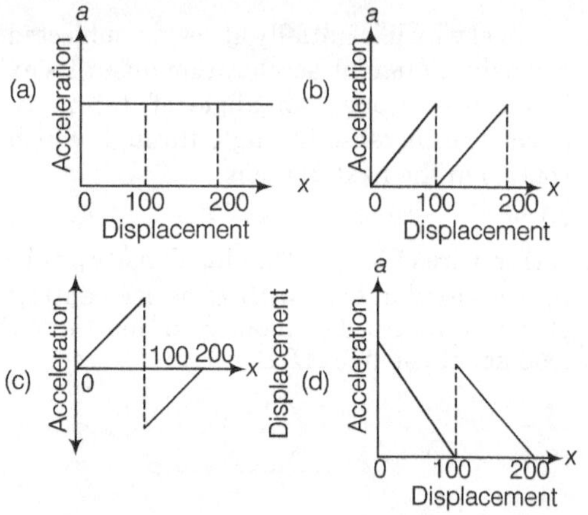

38. A person walks along a straight road from his house to a market 2.5 km away with a speed of 5 km/h and instantly turns back and reaches his house with a speed of 7.5km/h. The average speed of the person during the time interval 0 to 50 min is (in m/s)

(a) $4\frac{2}{3}$ (b) $\frac{5}{3}$

(c) $\frac{5}{6}$ (d) $\frac{1}{3}$

39. If C the velocity of light, h Planck's constant and G gravitational constant are taken as fundamental quantities, then the dimensional formula of mass is

(a) $h^{-1/2}G^{1/2}C^0$ (b) $h^{1/2}C^{1/2}G^{-1/2}$

(c) $h^{-1/2}C^{1/2}G^{-1/2}$ (d) $h^{-1/2}C^{-1/2}G^{-1/2}$

40. Match the following (Take the relative strength of the strongest fundamental forces in nature as one)

I	II
Fundamental forces in nature	**Relative strength**
(A) Strong nuclear force	(e) 10^{-2}
(B) Weak nuclear force	(f) 1
(C) Electromagnetic force	(g) 10^{10}
(D) Gravitational force	(h) 10^{-13}
	(i) 10^{-39}

The correct match is

(a) A-f, B-i, C-e, D-h (b) A-f, B-h, C-e, D-h

(c) A-f, B-h, C-e, D-i (d) A-f, B-e, C-h, D-i

Answers

1. (c)	**2.** (c)	**3.** (c)	**4.** (b)	**5.** (c)	**6.** (a)	**7.** (a)	**8.** (a)	**9.** (d)	**10.** (d)
11. (d)	**12.** (b)	**13.** (d)	**14.** (c)	**15.** (b)	**16.** (a)	**17.** (d)	**18.** (d)	**19.** (b)	**20.** (b)
21. (b)	**22.** (d)	**23.** (d)	**24.** (c)	**25.** (a)	**26.** (d)	**27.** (b)	**28.** (d)	**29.** (c)	**30.** (d)
31. (a)	**32.** (d)	**33.** (c)	**34.** (b)	**35.** (c)	**36.** (d)	**37.** (c)	**38.** (b)	**39.** (b)	**40.** (c)

Hints & Solutions

1. Frequency of first mode of vibration

$$n_1 = \frac{3v}{4l} \quad \text{...(i)}$$

(closed pipe)

and frequency of first mode of vibration

$$n_2 = \frac{v}{2l} \quad \text{...(ii)}$$

(open pipe)

According to the question,

$$n_1 - n_2 = \frac{3v}{4l} - \frac{v}{2l} = 55$$

So $$\frac{3v - 2v}{4l} = 55$$

$\Rightarrow$ $$\frac{v}{4l} = 55\,\text{Hz}$$

2. The given, $R_1 = R, R_2 = -R$

$f = F$

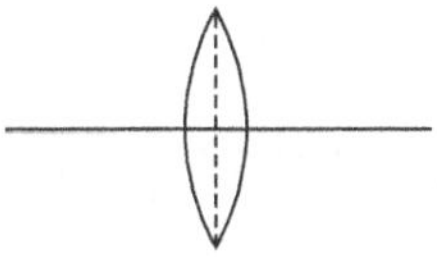

When convex lens is complete

Lens Maker's formula

$$\frac{1}{F} = (\mu - 1)\left[\frac{1}{R_1} - \frac{1}{R_2}\right]$$

$$\frac{1}{f} = (\mu - 1)\left[\frac{1}{R} + \frac{1}{R}\right]$$

$$f = \frac{R}{2(\mu - 1)}$$

$$R = 2f(\mu - 1) \quad \text{...(i)}$$

Now, it is divided vertically into two identical plano convex lens

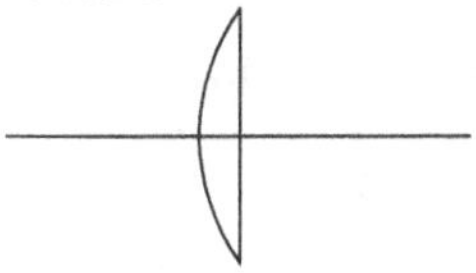

Plano convex lens

$$\frac{1}{f'} = (\mu - 1)\left[\frac{1}{R_1} - \frac{1}{R_2}\right]$$

$[\because R_1 = R, R_2 = \infty]$

$$\frac{1}{f_1} = (\mu - 1)\left[\frac{1}{R} - \frac{1}{\infty}\right]$$

$$f_1 = \frac{R}{(\mu - 1)}$$

$$f_1 = \frac{2f(\mu - 1)}{(\mu - 1)}$$

$$f_1 = 2f$$

3. According to the first condition,

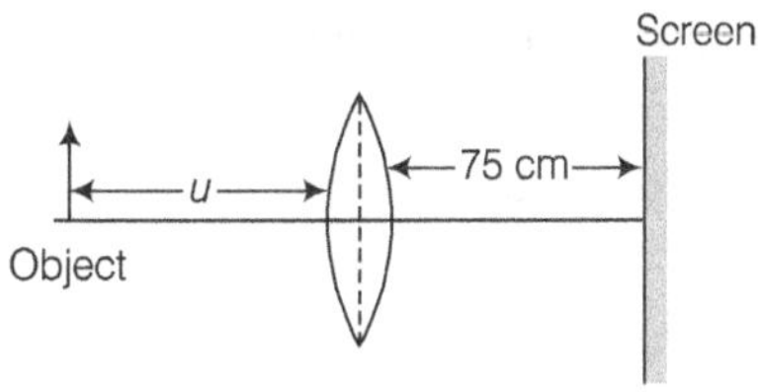

$f = 25\,\text{cm}, v = 75\,\text{cm}$

$u = ?$

$$\frac{1}{f} = \frac{1}{v} - \frac{1}{u}$$

$$\frac{1}{25} = \frac{1}{75} - \frac{1}{u}$$

$$\frac{1}{u}=\frac{1}{75}-\frac{1}{25}$$
$$\frac{1}{u}=\frac{1-3}{75}$$
$$u=-\frac{75}{2}=-37.5 \text{ cm}$$

According to the second condition

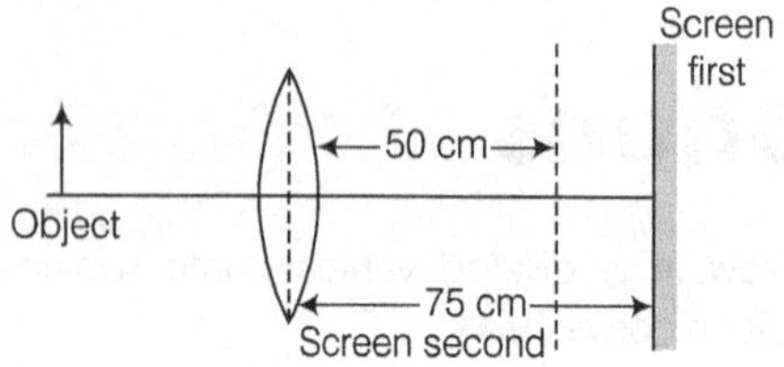

$v_1=50$ cm, $f=25$ cm, $u_1=?$

$$\frac{1}{f}=\frac{1}{v_1}-\frac{1}{u_1}$$
$$\frac{1}{25}=\frac{1}{50}-\frac{1}{u_1}$$
$$\frac{1}{u_1}=\frac{1}{50}-\frac{1}{25}$$
$$\Rightarrow \quad \frac{1}{u_1}=\frac{1-2}{50}$$
$$\Rightarrow \quad u_1=-50 \text{ cm}$$

So, the screen is sharp again is

$$\Delta u=u_1-u$$
$$=50-37.5=12.5 \text{ cm}$$

4. By Young's double slit interference experiment

$$\beta=\frac{\lambda D}{d}$$

The given $\beta_1=1.2$ mm

$$\frac{d_2}{d_1}=1\frac{1}{2}=1.5$$

So, $\beta \propto \frac{1}{d}$

$$\frac{\beta_1}{\beta_2}=\frac{1/d_1}{1/d_2}$$
$$\frac{\beta_1}{\beta_2}=\frac{d_2}{d_1}=1.5 \Rightarrow \frac{1.2}{\beta_2}=1.5$$
$$\Rightarrow \quad \beta_2=\frac{1.2}{1.5}=\frac{4}{5}=0.8 \text{ mm}$$

5. By Coulomb's law,

When charge Q is divided into two charges q and $Q-q$

$$F=\frac{1}{4\pi\varepsilon_0}\cdot\frac{q\cdot(Q-q)}{r^2}$$

The value of q

$$F_{max}=\frac{1}{4\pi\varepsilon_0}\cdot\frac{\frac{Q}{2}\left(Q-\frac{Q}{2}\right)}{r^2}$$

(Putting $q=\frac{Q}{2}$ for the maximum force)

$$=\frac{1}{4\pi\varepsilon_0}\cdot\frac{\frac{Q}{2}\left(\frac{Q}{2}\right)}{r^2}$$
$$=\frac{1}{4\pi\varepsilon_0}\cdot\frac{\frac{Q^2}{4}}{r^2}=\frac{1}{4\pi\varepsilon_0}\cdot\frac{Q^2}{4r^2}$$
$$=\frac{1}{4\pi\varepsilon_0}\cdot\frac{\left(\frac{Q}{2}\right)^2}{r^2}$$

So, option (c) is correct.

6. We know that, the surface charge densities is

$$\sigma=\frac{Q}{4\pi(r^2+R^2)} \quad \text{...(i)}$$

The electric potential at the centre

$$V=\frac{1}{4\pi\varepsilon_0}\left[\frac{\sigma\times 4\pi r^2}{r}+\frac{\sigma\times 4\pi R^2}{R}\right]$$
$$=\frac{1}{4\pi\varepsilon_0}\times\sigma\times 4\pi\left[\frac{r^2}{r}+\frac{R^2}{R}\right]$$
$$=\frac{\sigma}{\varepsilon_0}(r+R)$$

and
$$V=\frac{Q}{\varepsilon_0\cdot 4\pi(r^2+R^2)}\cdot(r+R)$$
$$\Rightarrow \quad V=\frac{Q}{4\pi\varepsilon_0}\cdot\frac{(r+R)}{(r^2+R^2)}$$

7. The given,

$$\rho_B=2\rho_A, R_A=R_B=R$$

Let, $r_A=r$

$r_B=2r$

According to formula,

$$R_A = \rho_A \cdot \frac{l_A}{\pi r_A^2} \quad \text{...(i)}$$

$$R_B = \rho_B \cdot \frac{l_B}{\pi r_B^2} \quad \text{...(ii)}$$

$\because$ $R_A = R_B$

$$\rho_A \cdot \frac{l_A}{\pi r_A^2} = \rho_B \cdot \frac{l_B}{\pi r_B^2}$$

$$\frac{l_B}{l_A} = \frac{r_B^2}{r_A^2} \cdot \frac{\rho_A}{\rho_B}$$

$$= \frac{(2r)^2}{r^2} \cdot \frac{\rho_A}{2\rho_B} = \frac{4r^2}{r^2} \cdot \frac{\rho_A}{2\rho_A}$$

$$= \frac{4}{2} = 2$$

8. The given $P = 50$ J/s

$$P = Vi \Rightarrow P = i^2 R$$

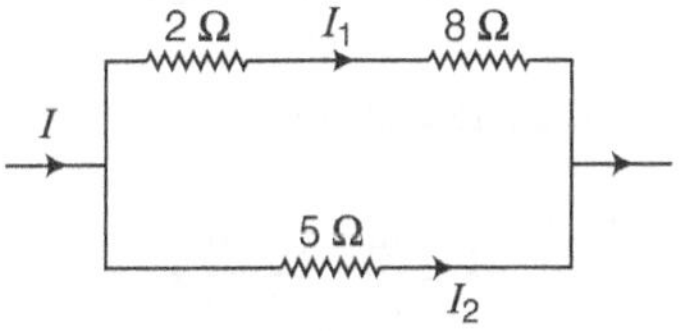

$$\Rightarrow i_2^2 = \frac{P}{R} = \frac{50}{5} = 10 \text{ Amp}^2$$

$$V = i_2 R_{(5\,\Omega)}$$
$$= \sqrt{10} \times 5 = \sqrt{250} \text{ V}$$

and 2 Ω and 8 Ω are in series.

So, the required resistance

$$= 2\,\Omega + 8\,\Omega = 10\,\Omega$$

$$i_1 = \frac{V}{R_{(10\,\Omega)}}$$

$$i_1 = \frac{\sqrt{250}}{10} \text{ A}$$

The heat generated/second in 2 Ω

$$P = Vi_1$$
$$= i_1^2 \times R$$
$$= \left(\frac{\sqrt{250}}{10}\right)^2 \times 2$$
$$= \frac{250}{100} \times 2 = \frac{25}{10} \times 2 = \frac{25}{5} = 5 \text{ J/s}$$

9. The magnetic field a circular coil (for n number of loops)

$$B = \frac{\mu_0 n i}{2r}$$

When, $n_1 = 1, n_2 = 2$

$$2\pi r_1 = n \times 2\pi r_2$$

$$\Rightarrow \frac{r_1}{r_2} = \frac{n}{1}$$

So $$\frac{B_1}{B_2} = \frac{\mu_0 n_1 i / 2r_1}{\mu_0 n_2 i / 2r_2}$$

$$\frac{B}{B_2} = \frac{n_1}{n_2} \cdot \frac{r_1}{r_2}$$

$$\frac{B}{B_2} = \frac{1}{n} \cdot \frac{1}{n} \Rightarrow B_2 = n^2 B$$

10. By motion of charged particles in uniform magnetic field

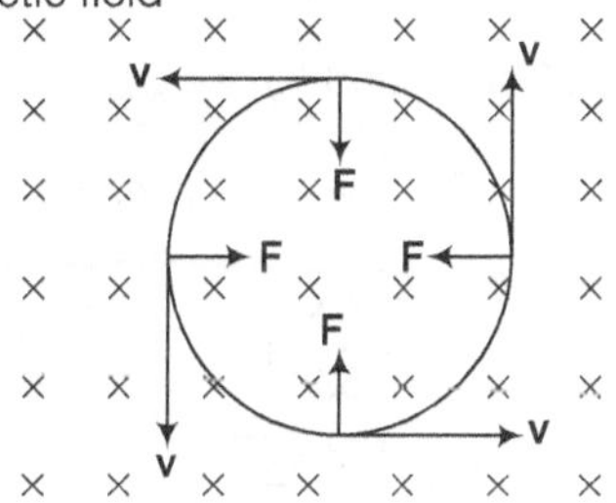

$$r = \frac{mv}{qB}$$

So, $r \propto v$

It travels in a circular path with a radius directly proportional to its velocity.

11. Given,

$$B_H = 0.8 \times 10^{-4} \text{ T}$$
$$\theta = 60°$$
$$B_e = ?$$

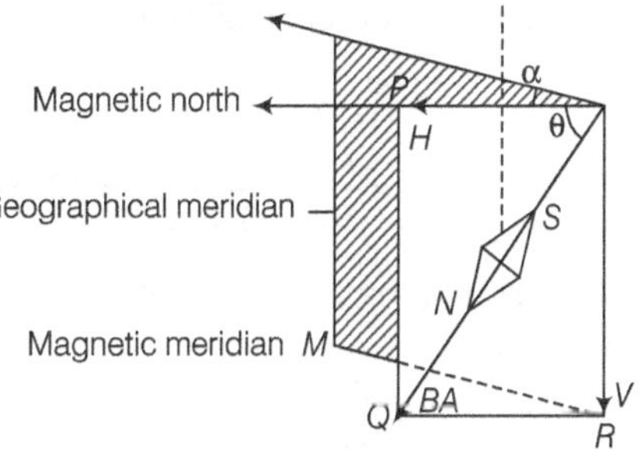

We know that,

$$B_H = B_e \cos\theta$$

$$0.8 \times 10^{-4} = B_e \cos 60°$$

$$B_e = \frac{0.8 \times 10^{-4}}{\frac{1}{2}}$$

$$= 1.6 \times 10^{-4} \text{ T}$$

12. The given,

$L_1 = 108$ mH, $N_1 = 600$ turns, $N_2 = 500$ turns and $L_2 = ?$

By self-inductance of a plane coil

$$L_1 = \frac{\mu_0 \pi N_1^2 a_1}{2} \quad \text{...(i)}$$

$$L_2 = \frac{\mu_0 \pi N_2^2 a_2}{2} \quad \text{...(ii)}$$

From the Eqs. (i) and (ii), we get

$$\frac{L_1}{L_2} = \left(\frac{N_1}{N_2}\right)^2 \quad (\because a_1 = a_2)$$

$$\frac{108}{L_2} = \left(\frac{600}{500}\right)^2$$

$$L_2 = \frac{108 \times 25}{36}$$

$$L_2 = 3 \times 25 = 75 \text{ mH}$$

13. The given

$$C = 50\,\mu\text{F} = 50 \times 10^{-6} \text{ F}$$

$$V = 220 \sin 50t \quad \text{...(i)}$$

But we know that

$$V = V_0 \sin \omega t \quad \text{...(ii)}$$

Comparing both equations

$$V_0 = 220\,V, \omega = 50 \text{ rad/s}$$

The capacitive reactance of the circuit is

$$X_C = \frac{1}{\omega C}$$

$$= \frac{1}{50 \times 50 \times 10^{-6}} = 400\ \Omega$$

The peak and the rms values of current in the circuit are

$$i_0 = \frac{V_0}{X_C} = \frac{220}{400} = \frac{11}{20}$$

and $$i_{rms} = \frac{i_0}{\sqrt{2}}$$

$$= \frac{11/20}{\sqrt{2}} = \frac{0.55}{\sqrt{2}} \text{ A}$$

14. The given

$$\mathbf{E} = \mathbf{i}\,30 \cos(kz - 5 \times 10^8 t) \quad \text{...(i)}$$

We know that,

$$\mathbf{E} = \mathbf{i}V \cos(kz - \omega t) \quad \text{...(ii)}$$

Comparing the both equations,

$$\omega = 5 \times 10^8 \text{ rad/s}$$

But we know that also

$$K = \frac{2\pi}{\lambda} \text{ and } \omega = 2\pi\nu$$

where, λ is wavelength and ν is frequency of the wave

$$\therefore \quad \frac{\omega}{k} = \frac{2\pi\nu}{2\pi/\lambda} = \nu\lambda = C$$

$$\Rightarrow \quad C = \frac{\omega}{k}$$

$$\text{or} \quad k = \frac{\omega}{C} = \frac{5 \times 10^8}{3 \times 10^8}$$

$$\Rightarrow \quad k = \frac{5}{3} = 1.66 \text{ rad/m}$$

15. We know that, de-Broglie wavelength of photon $E = h\nu$

But we know that also

$$E = \frac{1}{2}mv^2 \quad \text{(for proton)}$$

$$\therefore \quad 2E = \frac{P^2}{m}$$

$$\because \quad P = mv$$

$$\frac{P^2}{m} = mv^2$$

$$P = \sqrt{2mE} \quad \text{...(i)}$$

According to the question

$$\lambda_1 = \frac{h}{P} \quad \text{...(ii)}$$

(de-Broglie of matter waves)

$$\text{and} \quad \lambda_2 = \frac{hc}{E} \quad \text{...(iii)}$$

From the Eqs. (ii) and (iii), we get

$$\frac{\lambda_1}{\lambda_2} = \frac{h/P}{hc/E} = \frac{E}{Pc}$$

$$= \frac{E}{\sqrt{2mE}\cdot c} = \frac{\sqrt{E}}{\sqrt{2m}\cdot c}$$

So, $$\frac{\lambda_1}{\lambda_2} = \frac{\sqrt{E}}{\sqrt{2m}\cdot c}$$

$$\frac{\lambda_1}{\lambda_2} \propto \sqrt{E}$$

$\Rightarrow$ $$\lambda_1 : \lambda_2 = E^{1/2}$$

16. The total energy of nth orbit

$$E_n = -\frac{me^4}{8\varepsilon_0^2 h^2}\cdot\frac{1}{n^2}$$

Obviously $E_n \propto m$

$\therefore$ $$\frac{E_\mu}{E_e} = \frac{m_\mu}{m_e}$$

$\Rightarrow$ $$E_\mu = \frac{m_\mu}{m_e} \times E_e$$

Ground state energy of a proton in hydrogen atom,

$$E_\mu = -13.6 \times \frac{207 m_e}{m_e}\text{ eV}$$

$$= -13.6 \times 207\text{ eV}$$

($\because m_\mu = 207 m_e$, where m_e is the mass of electron)

We know that

$$r = \frac{\varepsilon_0 h^2 n^2}{207\pi m_e e^2}$$

For ground state $(n - 1)$ for proton, we have

$$r_\mu = \frac{\varepsilon_0 h^2}{207\pi m_e \cdot e^2}$$

But $\frac{\varepsilon_0 h^2}{\pi m_e \cdot e^2}$ = ground state radius of hydrogen atom

$$\frac{\varepsilon_0 h^2}{\pi m_e \cdot e^2} = r_H$$

$\therefore$ $$r_\mu = \frac{r_H}{207}$$

17. By Rutherford's experiment

$$R_1 = R_0 A_1^{1/3} \quad \text{...(i)}$$

$$R_2 = R_0 A_2^{1/3} \quad \text{...(ii)}$$

Given

$$R_1 = 1.5\text{ fermi}$$
$$A_1 = 125$$
$$A_2 = 64$$
$$R_2 = ?$$

Now, $\frac{R_1}{R_2} = \left(\frac{A_1}{A_2}\right)^{1/3}$ [from the Eqs. (i) and (ii)]

$$\frac{1.5}{R_2} = \left(\frac{125}{64}\right)^{1/3}$$

$\Rightarrow$ $$\frac{1.5}{R_2} = \frac{5}{4}$$

$\Rightarrow$ $$R_2 = \frac{1.5 \times 4}{5} = 0.3 \times 4$$

$$= 1.2\text{ fermi}$$

18. Given $n_1 = 1.6 \times 10^{16}/\text{m}^3$

$$n_e = 4.8 \times 10^{20}/\text{m}^3$$

$$n_h = ?$$

The concentration of holes in the semiconductor

$$n_1^2 = n_e \times n_h$$

$$(1.6 \times 10^{16})^2 = 4.8 \times 10^{20} \times n_h$$

$$n_h = \frac{2.56 \times 10^{32}}{4.8 \times 10^{20}} = 5.3 \times 10^{11}/\text{m}^3$$

19. The potential difference between base and emitter changes in I_C with changes in V_{CE} (when I_B = constant)

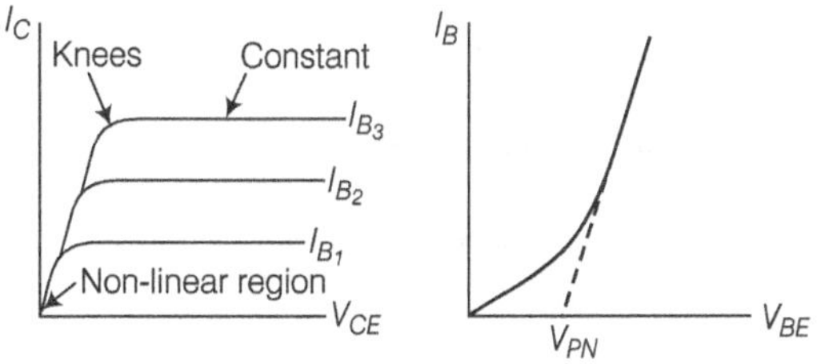

20. Height of transmitting antenna $d \approx \sqrt{2R_e h_T}$

Given $R_e = 6.4 \times 10^6$ m

$$h_T = 128\text{ m}$$

$$d = ?$$

The maximum distance

$$d = \sqrt{2 \times 6.4 \times 10^6 \times 128}$$

$$d = \sqrt{128 \times 10^5 \times 128}$$

$$d = \frac{128 \times 10^2 \sqrt{10}}{\sqrt{10}} \times \sqrt{10}$$

$$d = \frac{128 \times 10^3}{\sqrt{10}} \text{ m} = \frac{128}{\sqrt{10}} \text{ km}$$

21. If angular acceleration is constant, we have

$$\theta = \omega_0 t + \frac{1}{2} \alpha t^2$$

The given $\theta = 15°$

$$\omega_0 = 0$$

For the first conditions (time $= t$ sec)

$$15° = 0 + \frac{1}{2} \alpha t^2$$

$$\Rightarrow \quad 15° = \frac{1}{2} \alpha t^2 \quad \text{...(i)}$$

For the second conditions (time $= 3t$ sec)

$$\theta_1 = \frac{1}{2} \alpha (3t)^2 = \frac{1}{2} (\alpha) 9t^2 \quad \text{...(ii)}$$

So, $$\Delta\theta = \theta_1 - \frac{1}{2} \alpha t^2$$

$$\Delta\theta = 9 \times \frac{1}{2} \alpha t^2 - \frac{1}{2} \alpha t^2$$

$$= 8 \frac{1}{2} \alpha t^2$$

$$= 8 \times 15° = 120° \quad \text{(from Eq. (i))}$$

22. The moment of inertia

$$I = \frac{3}{2} mR^2$$

$$\left[\because \text{Linear density } \rho = \frac{m}{l}\right.$$

$$m = l\rho$$

$$2\pi R = l$$

$$R = \frac{l}{2\pi}$$

$$I = \frac{3}{2} \times l\rho \times \left(\frac{l}{2\pi}\right)^2$$

$$= \frac{3}{2 \times 4} \cdot \frac{l^3 \rho}{\pi^2}$$

$$= \frac{3 l^3 \rho}{8\pi^2}$$

23. The kinetic energy

$$KE = \frac{1}{2} m\omega^2 \left[a^2 - \left(\frac{a}{N}\right)^2\right] \quad \text{...(i)}$$

The potential energy

$$PE = \frac{1}{2} m\omega^2 \frac{a^2}{N^2} \quad \text{...(ii)}$$

From the Eqs. (i) and (ii), we get

$$\frac{KE}{PE} = \frac{\frac{1}{2} m\omega^2 \left[a^2 - \left(\frac{a}{N}\right)^2\right]}{\frac{1}{2} m\omega^2 \frac{a^2}{N^2}}$$

$$= \frac{a^2 - \frac{a^2}{N^2}}{\frac{a^2}{N^2}} = \frac{\frac{a^2}{N^2}(N^2 - 1)}{\frac{a^2}{N^2}} = N^2 - 1$$

24. We know that,

Period of revolution

Let, T be the time of one revolution of the satellite. Then,

$$T = \frac{2\pi r}{v_0} = \frac{2\pi (R_p + h)}{v_0}$$

$$T = \frac{2\pi (R_p + h)}{[GM_e / (R_p + h)]^{1/2}}$$

$$\because \quad v_0 = \sqrt{\frac{GM_p}{(R_p + h)}}$$

$$T = 2\pi \sqrt{\frac{(R_p + h)^3}{GM_p}} \quad \text{...(i)}$$

Again, $$GM_e = gR_e^2$$

$$\therefore \quad T = 2\pi \sqrt{\frac{(R_p + h)^3}{gR_p^2}} \quad \text{...(ii)}$$

If the planet is supposed to be a sphere of mean density ρ, then the mass of the planet is given by

$$M_p = \text{volume} \times \text{density}$$

$$= \frac{4}{3} \pi r_p^3 \cdot \rho$$

So, $$T = \sqrt{\frac{3\pi (R_p + h)^3}{G\rho R_p^3}} \quad \text{...(iii)}$$

If a satellite is orbiting very close to the planet's surface ($h << R_p$), then putting $h = 0$ in eq. (iii), we have

$$T = \sqrt{\frac{3\pi R_p^3}{G\rho R_p^3}}$$

$$\Rightarrow \quad T = \sqrt{\frac{3\pi}{G\rho}}$$

25. We know that,

Elastic potential energy in a stretched wire

$$U = \frac{1}{2} \text{Young's modulus} \times (\text{strain})^2$$

$$U = \frac{1}{2} \times \frac{F}{A} \times \frac{1}{l} \times \frac{Fl}{Y \cdot A}$$

$$U = \frac{1}{2} \frac{F^2}{A^2} \cdot \frac{1}{Y} \Rightarrow U \propto \frac{1}{r^4}$$

So, $$\frac{U_1}{U_2} = \frac{1/r_1^4}{1/r_2^4} = \left(\frac{r_2}{r_1}\right)^4$$

$$\left[\because \frac{d_1}{d_2} = \frac{r_1}{r_2} = \frac{1}{2}\right]$$

$$\frac{U_1}{U_2} = \left(\frac{2}{1}\right)^2 = \frac{16}{1}$$

$$U_1 : U_2 = 16 : 1$$

26. The energy of n small drop – the energy of the bigger drop = Energy loss by bigger drop

$$n \times 4\pi r^2 \times T - 4\pi r^2 \times T = 3 \times 4\pi R^2 \times T$$

$$n \times 4\pi r^2 \times T = 12\pi R^2 \times T + 4\pi R^2 \times T$$

$$n = \frac{16\pi R^2 \times T}{4\pi r^2 \times T}$$

$$n = 4\frac{R^2}{r^2}$$

27. By calorimetry,

Heat lost = Heat gained

$$m \times L + m \times C \times (T_1 - T_2)$$
$$= (m_1 + m_2) \times C \times (T_2 - T_3)$$
$$m \times 540 + m \times 1 \times (100 - 90)$$
$$= (1000\text{ g} + 200\text{ g}) \times 1 \times (90 - 9)$$
$$= m \times 540 + 10m = 1200 \times 81$$
$$550m = 1200 \times 81$$

$$m = \frac{1200 \times 81}{550} = \frac{24 \times 81}{11}\text{ g}$$
$$= \frac{1944}{11}\text{ g} = 176\text{ g} = 0.176\text{ kg}$$

or $m = 0.18$ kg

28. By Stefan's law

If the absolute temperature of a black body is T, then the energy E emitted per second per unit surface area of the body

$$E \propto T^4$$
$$E = \sigma \cdot AT^4$$

Given,

$$\sigma = 5.67 \times 10^{-8}\text{ W/m}^2\text{K}^4$$
$$T = 727 + 273 = 1000\text{ K}$$
$$A = 200 \times 10^{-6}\text{ m}$$
$$E = 5.67 \times 10^{-8} \times (200 \times 10^{-6}) \times (1000)^4$$
$$= 5.67 \times 2 \times 10^{-12} \times 10^{12} = 11.34\text{ J/s}$$

29. Work done by an ideal gas is adiabatic expansion

$$dU = n\frac{R}{\gamma - 1} dT$$
$$dU = n\frac{R}{\gamma - 1}(T_2 - T_1)$$

Given $T_1 = 273\text{K}$
$T_2 = 673\text{K}$
$R = 8.3$ J/mol-K
$n = 5$
$\gamma = 1.4$

$$\therefore dU = 5 \times \frac{8.3}{1.4 - 1}(673 - 273)$$
$$= \frac{41.5}{0.4} \times 400\text{ J}$$
$$= 415 \times 100\text{ J} = 41.50\text{ kJ}$$

30. As, $dU = nC_V dT$

$$= \frac{R}{\gamma - 1}(T_2 - T_1) = \frac{p\,\Delta V}{\gamma - 1}$$

$(\because R\,\Delta T = p\,dV)$

$$= \frac{pV}{\gamma - 1}$$

31. By third's law of motion

$$v^2 = u^2 + 2as$$

$$v^2 - u^2 = -2\left(\frac{F}{m}\right)\cdot s \qquad [\because v = 0]$$

$$-u^2 = -2\frac{F}{m}\cdot s$$

$$u^2 = \frac{2F\cdot s}{m}$$

or $$m = \frac{2F\cdot s}{u^2} \Rightarrow m \propto s$$

Given $s_1 = x$

$$s_2 = ?$$

$$m_1 = m \qquad \text{(Let)}$$

$$m_2 = m \times 25\% + m$$

Now, $$\frac{m_1}{m_2} = \frac{s_1}{s_2}$$

$$\frac{m}{m\times\frac{25}{100} + m} = \frac{x}{s_2}$$

$$s_2 = \frac{x \times m\left(\frac{100+25}{100}\right)}{m}$$

$$s_2 = \frac{125}{100}x$$

$$s_2 = 1.25x$$

32. At highest point

$$mu\cos\theta = -\frac{m}{2}u\cos\theta + \frac{m}{2}v$$

$$mu\cos\theta + \frac{m}{2}u\cos\theta = \frac{m}{2}v$$

$$\frac{2mu\cos\theta + mu\cos\theta}{2} = \frac{m}{2}v$$

$$mv = 3mu\cos\theta$$

$$v = 3u\cos\theta \qquad \text{...(i)}$$

The kinetic energy

$$E_1 = \frac{1}{2}\times\frac{m}{2}u^2\cos^2\theta$$

$$E_1 = \frac{1}{4}mu^2\cos^2\theta \qquad \text{...(ii)}$$

Similarly,

$$E_2 = \frac{1}{2}\times\frac{m}{2}\times 9u^2\cos^2\theta$$

$$E_2 = \frac{9}{4}mu^2\cos^2\theta \qquad \text{...(iii)}$$

The relation between the E_1 and E_2

$$E_2 = 9\times E_1 \qquad \text{(from the Eq. (ii))}$$

$$E_2 = 9E_1$$

33. For upward motion, $F_{up} = mg(\sin\theta + \mu\cos\theta)$ ...(i)

For downward motion, $F_{down} = mg(\sin\theta - \mu\cos\theta)$ ...(ii)

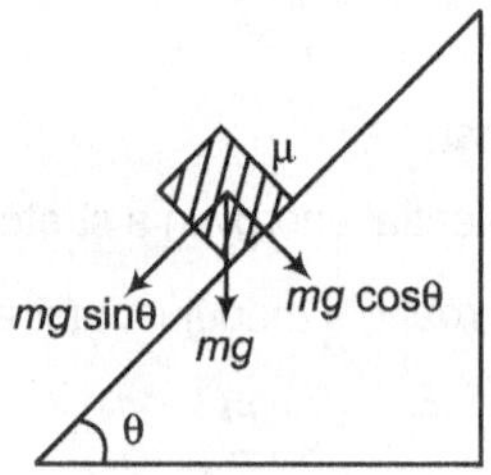

According to the question,

$$F_{up} = 2F_{down}$$

$$mg(\sin\theta + \mu\cos\theta) = 2mg(\sin\theta - \mu\cos\theta)$$

$$\sin\theta + \mu\cos\theta = 2\sin\theta - 2\mu\cos\theta$$

$$3\mu\cos\theta = \sin\theta$$

$$\mu = \frac{1}{3}\tan\theta$$

$$\mu = \frac{1}{3}\times\tan 60^\circ$$

$$\Rightarrow \quad \mu = \frac{1}{3}\sqrt{3} = \frac{1}{\sqrt{3}}$$

34. By Newton's law

$$F = T\sin\theta \qquad \text{...(i)}$$

$$Mg = T\cos\theta \qquad \text{...(ii)}$$

Dividing Eq. (i) by Eq. (ii), we get

$$\frac{F}{Mg} = \frac{T\sin\theta}{T\cos\theta}$$

$$F = Mg\tan\theta \qquad (\because \theta = 60^\circ \text{ given})$$

$$F = Mg\tan 60^\circ$$

$$F = \sqrt{3}\,Mg$$

35. We know that,

Range of projectile

$$R = \frac{u^2\sin 2\theta}{g}$$

As range is maximum, $\theta = 45°$

$$R_{max} = \frac{u^2\sin 2\times 45}{g} = \frac{u^2}{g} \qquad \text{...(i)}$$

Flight time of projectile,

$$T = \frac{2u \sin 45°}{g}$$

$$= \frac{2u}{\sqrt{2} \cdot g} = \frac{\sqrt{2} \cdot u}{g}$$

or $$u = \frac{Tg}{\sqrt{2}}$$

Putting these value of u in Eq. (i), we get

$$R_{max} = \frac{1}{g}\left(\frac{Tg}{\sqrt{2}}\right)^2$$

$$R_{max} = \frac{1}{2} gT^2$$

36. The given equation,

$$y = ax - bx^2 \quad \text{...(i)}$$

and we know that equation of trajectory is

$$y = (\tan\theta)\, x - \frac{1}{2}\frac{g}{u^2 \cos^2\theta} \cdot x^2 \quad \text{...(ii)}$$

Compare both equations, we get

$$a = \tan\theta,\ b = \frac{1}{2} \cdot \frac{g}{u^2 \cos^2\theta}$$

The maximum height

$$\frac{a^2}{b} = \frac{\tan^2\theta}{g} \times 2u^2 \cos^2\theta$$

$$= \frac{\sin^2\theta}{g \cos^2\theta} \cdot 2u^2 \cos^2\theta$$

$$= \frac{2u^2 \sin^2\theta}{g}$$

$$= 4\left(\frac{u^2 \sin^2\theta}{2g}\right)$$

$$H_{max} = \frac{a^2}{4b}$$

and $$a = \tan\theta$$

$$\theta = \tan^{-1}(a)$$

So, required solution is $\frac{a^2}{4b}$, $\tan^{-1}(a)$

37. The given graph

$$v = Kx \quad \text{...(i)}$$

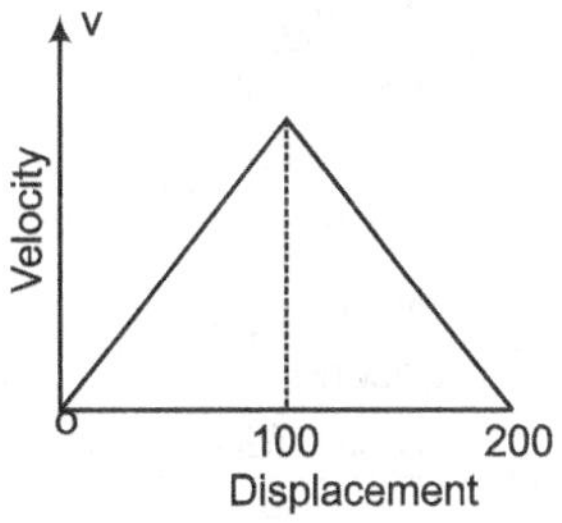

$$\frac{dv}{dt} = K \cdot v \quad \text{(from the Eq. (i))}$$

$$\frac{dv}{dt} = K \cdot (Kx) = K^2 x$$

$$a = K^2 x$$

and $$v = -Kx + v_0$$

$$\frac{dv}{dt} = -K \cdot v = -K(-Kx + v_0)$$

$$a = K^2 x - Kv_0 \quad \text{...(ii)}$$

So, according to the Eq. (ii).

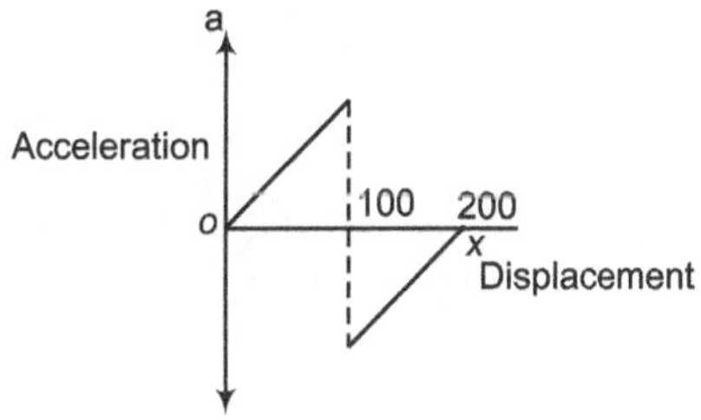

38. A according to question, $t_1 = \frac{2.5}{5} = \frac{1}{2}$ h $= 30$ min

and $t_2 = \frac{2.5}{7.5} = \frac{1}{3}$ h $= 20$ min

So, the average speed

$$= \frac{\text{Total distance (in metre)}}{\text{Total time (in second)}}$$

$$= \frac{(2.5 + 2.5) \times 1000}{(30 + 20) \times 60}$$

$$= \frac{5 \times 1000}{50 \times 60}$$

$$= \frac{50}{30} = \frac{5}{3} \text{ m/s}$$

39. Let, $M = C^a h^b G^c$

$$ML^0T^0 = [LT^{-1}]^a [ML^2T^{-1}]^b [M^{-1}L^3T^{-2}]^a \quad ...(i)$$

where, $h = \frac{\text{Energy}}{\text{Frequency}}$

$$= \frac{[ML^2T^{-2}]}{[T^{-1}]} = [ML^2T^{-1}]$$

$$C = \frac{\text{Metre}}{\text{Second}} = [LT^{-1}]$$

$$G = \frac{\text{Force} \times (\text{distance})^2}{(\text{mass})^2}$$

$$= \frac{[MLT^{-2}]\,[L^2]}{[M^2]} = [M^{-1}L^3T^{-2}]$$

Comparing the coefficients M, L, T, of both sides we get

$$b - c = 1 \quad ...(ii)$$

$$a + 2b + 3c = 0 \quad ...(iii)$$

$$-(a + b + 2c) = 0 \quad ...(iv)$$

Solve the Eqs. (ii), (iii) and (iv), we get

$$a = \frac{1}{2}, b = \frac{1}{2}, c = -\frac{1}{2}$$

So, $M = h^{1/2}C^{1/2}G^{-1/2}$

40.

I Fundamental forces in nature	II Relative strength
(A) Strong nuclear force	(f) 1
(B) Weak nuclear force	(h) 10^{-13}
(C) Electromagnetic force	(e) 10^{-2}
(D) Gravitational force	(i) 10^{-39}

So, A-f, B-h, C-e, D-i

EAMCET

Engineering Entrance Exam

Solved Paper 2013

Physics

1. If E, M, J and G respectively denote energy, mass, angular momentum and universal gravitational constant, the quantity, which has the same dimensions as the dimensions of $\frac{EJ^2}{M^5G^2}$

(a) time (b) angle
(c) mass (d) length

2. The work done in moving an object from origin to a point whose position vector is $\mathbf{r} = 3\hat{\mathbf{i}} + 2\hat{\mathbf{j}} - 5\hat{\mathbf{k}}$ by a force $\mathbf{F} = 2\hat{\mathbf{i}} - \hat{\mathbf{j}} - \hat{\mathbf{k}}$ is

(a) 1 unit (b) 9 units
(c) 13 units (d) 60 units

3. A particle is projected from the ground with an initial speed of v at an angle of projection θ. The average velocity of the particle between its time of projection and time it reaches highest point of trajectory is

(a) $\frac{v}{2}\sqrt{1 + 2\cos^2\theta}$ (b) $\frac{v}{2}\sqrt{1 + 2\sin^2\theta}$
(c) $\frac{v}{2}\sqrt{1 + 3\cos^2\theta}$ (d) $v\cos\theta$

4. Two wooden blocks of masses M and m are placed on a smooth horizontal surface as shown in figure. If a force P is applied to the system as shown in figure such that the mass m remains stationary with respect to block of mass M, then the magnitude of the force P is

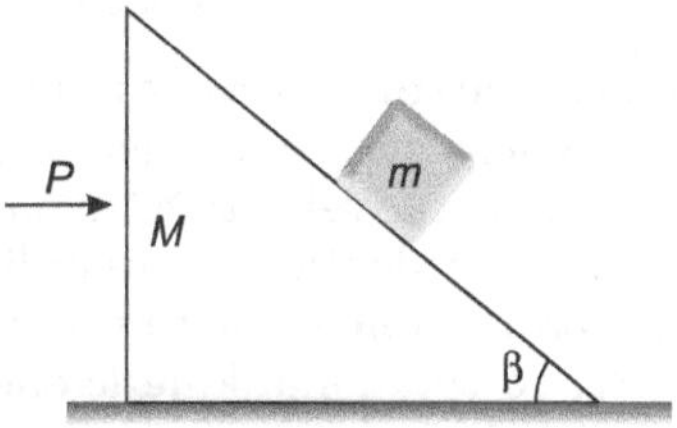

(a) $(M + m)g\tan\beta$ (b) $g\tan\beta$
(c) $mg\cos\beta$ (d) $(M + m)g\,\mathrm{cosec}\,\beta$

5. A ball at rest is dropped from a height of 12. It losses 25% of its kinetic energy on striking the ground and bounces back to a height 'h'. Then value of 'h' is

(a) 3 m (b) 6 m (c) 9 m (d) 12 m

6. Two bodies of mass 4 kg and 5 kg are moving along east and north directions with velocities 5 m/s and 3 m/s respectively. Magnitude of the velocity of centre of mass of the system is

(a) $\frac{25}{9}$ m/s (b) $\frac{9}{25}$ m/s
(c) $\frac{41}{9}$ m/s (d) $\frac{16}{9}$ m/s

7. A mass of 2.9 kg is suspended from a string of length 50 cm and is at rest. Another body of mass 100 g, which is moving horizontally with a velocity of 150 m/s strikes and sticks to it. Subsequently when the string makes an angle of 60° with the vertical, the tension in the string is ($g = 10\,\mathrm{m/s^2}$)

(a) 140 N (b) 135 N (c) 125 N (d) 90 N

8. The upper half of an inclined plane with an angle of inclination ϕ, is smooth while the lower half is rough. A body starting from rest at the top of the inclined plane comes to rest at the bottom of the inclined plane. Then the coefficient of friction for the lower half is

(a) $2 \tan \phi$ (b) $\tan \phi$
(c) $2 \sin \phi$ (d) $2 \cos \phi$

9. Moment of inertia of a body about an axis is 4 kg-m^2. The body is initially at rest and a torque of 8 N-m starts acting on it along the same axis. Work done by the torque in 20 s, in joules, is

(a) 40 (b) 640
(c) 2560 (d) 3200

10. A uniform circular disc of radius R, lying on a frictionless horizontal plane is rotating with an angular velocity 'ω' about is its own axis. Another identical circular disc is gently placed on the top of the first disc coaxially. The loss in rotational kinetic energy due to friction between the two discs, as they acquire common angular velocity is (I is moment of inertia of the disc)

(a) $\frac{1}{8} I\omega^2$ (b) $\frac{1}{4} I\omega^2$
(c) $\frac{1}{2} I\omega^2$ (d) $I\omega^2$

11. The gravitational force acting on a particle, due to a solid sphere of uniform density and radius R, at a distance of $3R$ from the centre of the sphere is F_1. A spherical hole of radius ($R/2$) is now made in the sphere as shown in the figure. The sphere with hole now exerts a force F_2 on the same particle. Ratio of F_1 and F_2 is

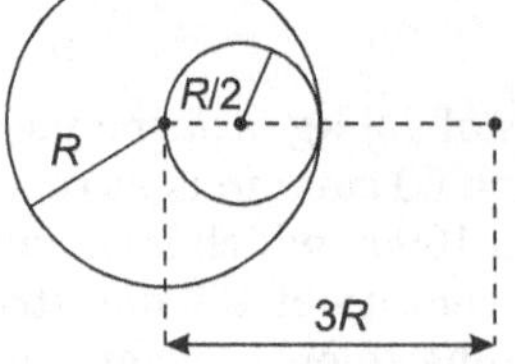

(a) $\frac{50}{41}$ (b) $\frac{41}{50}$ (c) $\frac{41}{42}$ (d) $\frac{25}{41}$

12. Two particles A and B of masses 'm' and '$2m$' are suspended from massless springs of force constants K_1 and K_2. During their oscillation, if their maximum velocities are equal, then the ratio of amplitudes of A and B is

(a) $\sqrt{\frac{K_1}{K_2}}$ (b) $\sqrt{\frac{K_2}{2K_1}}$
(c) $\sqrt{\frac{K_2}{K_1}}$ (d) $\sqrt{\frac{2K_1}{K_2}}$

13. A tension of 20 N is applied to a copper wire of cross sectional area 0.01 cm^2, Young's modulus of copper is 1.1×10^{11} N/m^2 and Poisson's ratio is 0.32. The decrease in cross sectional area of the wire is

(a) 1.16×10^{-6} cm^2 (b) 1.16×10^{-5} m^2
(c) 1.16×10^{-4} m^2 (d) 1.16×10^{-3} cm^2

14. A capillary tube of radius 'r' is immersed in water and water rises to a height of 'h'. Mass of water in the capillary tube is 5×10^{-3} kg. The same capillary tube is now immersed in a liquid whose surface tension is $\sqrt{2}$ times the surface tension of water. The angle of contact between the capillary tube and this liquid is 45°. The mass of liquid which rises into the capillary tube now is, (in kg)

(a) 5×10^{-3} (b) 2.5×10^{-3}
(c) $5\sqrt{2} \times 10^{-3}$ (d) 3.5×10^{-3}

15. The terminal velocity of a liquid drop of radius 'r' falling through air is v. If two such drops are combined to form a bigger drop, the terminal velocity with which the bigger drop falls through air is (ignore any buoyant force due to air)

(a) $\sqrt{2}\, v$ (b) $2\, v$
(c) $\sqrt[3]{4}\, v$ (d) $\sqrt[3]{2}\, v$

16. A glass flask of volume one litre is filled completely with mercury at 0°C. The flask is now heated to 100°C. Coefficient of volume expansion of mercury is 1.82×10^{-4}/°C and coefficient of linear expansion of glass is 0.1×10^{-4}/°C. During this process, amount of mercury which overflows is

(a) 21.2 cc (b) 15.2 cc
(c) 2.12 cc (d) 18.2 cc

17. On a temperature scale Y, water freezes at $-160°\,Y$ and boils at $-50°\,Y$. On this Y scale, a temperature of 340 K is

(a) $-160.3°\,Y$ (b) $-96.3°\,Y$
(c) $-86.3°\,Y$ (d) $-76.3°\,Y$

18. Three moles of an ideal monoatomic gas undergoes a cyclic process as shown in the figure. The temperature of the gas in different states marked as 1, 2, 3 and 4 are 400 K, 700 K, 2500 K and 1100 K respectively. The work done by the gas during the process 1-2-3-4-1 is (universal gas constant is R)

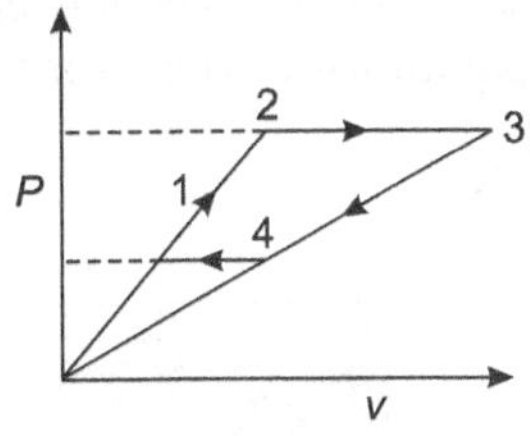

(a) $1650\,R$ (b) $550\,R$
(c) $1100\,R$ (d) $2200\,R$

19. Efficiency of a heat engine whose sink is at temperature of 300 K is 40%. To increase the efficiency to 60%, keeping the sink temperature constant, the source temperature must be increased by

(a) 750 K (b) 500 K
(c) 250 K (d) 1000 K

20. Two bodies A and B of equal surface area have thermal emissivities of 0.01 and 0.81 respectively. The two bodies are radiating energy at the same rate. Maximum energy is radiated from the two bodies A and B at wavelengths λ_A and λ_B respectively. Difference in these two wavelengths is $1\,\mu$m. If the temperature of the body A is 5802 K, then value of λ_B is

(a) $\frac{1}{2}\,\mu$m (b) $1\,\mu$m
(c) $2\,\mu$m (d) $\frac{3}{2}\,\mu$m

21. An air column in a tube 32 cm long, closed at one end, is in resonance with a tuning fork. The air column in another tube, open at both ends, of length 66 cm is in resonance with another tuning fork. When these two tuning forks are sounded together, they produce 8 beats per second. Then the frequencies of the two tuning forks are, (Consider fundamental frequencies only)

(a) 250 Hz, 258 Hz (b) 240 Hz, 248 Hz
(c) 264 Hz, 256 Hz (d) 280 Hz, 272 Hz

22. A source of sound of frequency 640 Hz is moving at a velocity of $\frac{100}{3}$ m/s along a road, and is at an instant 30 m away from a point A on the road (as shown in figure). A person standing at O, 40 m away from the road hears sound of apparent frequency ν'. The value of ν' is (velocity of sound = 340 m/s)

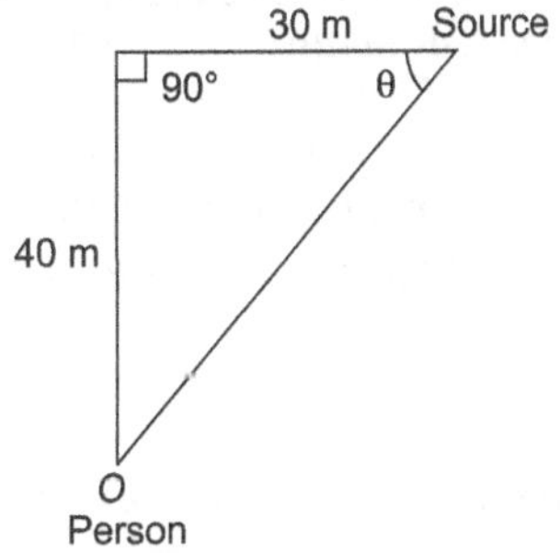

(a) 620 Hz (b) 680 Hz
(c) 720 Hz (d) 840 Hz

23. The two surfaces of a concave lens, made of glass of refractive index 1.5 have the same radii of curvature R. It is now immersed in a medium of refractive index 1.75, then the lens

(a) becomes a convergent lens of focal length $3.5\,R$
(b) becomes a convergent lens of focal length $3.0\,R$
(c) changes as a divergent lens of focal length $3.5\,R$
(d) changes as a divergent lens of focal length $3.0\,R$

24. A microscope consists of an objective of focal length 1.9 cm and eye piece of focal length 5 cm. The two lenses are kept at a distance of 10.5 cm. If the image is to be formed at the least distance of distinct vision, the distance at which the object is to be placed before the objective is (least distance of distinct vision is 25 cm)

(a) 6.2 cm (b) 2.7 cm
(c) 21.0 cm (d) 4.17 cm

25. Fresnel diffraction is produced due to light rays falling on a small obstacle. The intensity of light at a point on a screen beyond an obstacle depends on

(a) the focal length of lens used for observation
(b) the number of half-period zones that superpose at the point
(c) the square of the sum of the number of half period zones
(d) the thickness of the obstacle

26. A short bar magnet having magnetic moment 4 Am^2, placed in a vibrating magnetometer, vibrates with a time period of 8 s. Another short bar magnet having a magnetic moment 8 Am^2 vibrates with a time period of 6 s. If the moment of inertia of the second magnet is 9×10^{-2} kg-m^2, the moment of inertia of the first magnet is (assume that both magnets are kept in the same uniform magnetic induction field.)

(a) 9×10^{-2} kg-m^2 (b) 8×10^{-2} kg-m^2
(c) 5.33×10^{-2} kg-m^2 (d) 12.2×10^{-2} kg-m^2

27. Two short bar magnets have their magnetic moments 1.2 Am^2 and 1.0 Am^2. They are placed on a horizontal table parallel to each other at a distance of 20 cm between their centres, such that their north poles pointing towards geographic south. They have common magnetic equatorial line. Horizontal component of earth's field is 3.6×10^{-5} T. Then, the resultant horizontal magnetic induction at mid point of the line joining their centers is $\left(\frac{\mu_0}{4\pi} = 10^{-7} \text{ N/m}\right)$

(a) 3.6×10^{-5} T (b) 1.84×10^{-4} T
(c) 2.56×10^{-4} T (d) 5.8×10^{-5} T

28. A deflection magnetometer is adjusted and a magnet of magnetic moment M is placed on it in the usual manner and the observed deflection is θ. The period of oscillation of the needle before settling of the deflection is T. When the magnet is removed, the period of oscillation of the needle is T_0 before settling to $0° - 0°$. If the earth's induced magnetic field is B_H, the relation between T and T_0 is

(a) $T^2 = T_0^2 \cos\theta$ (b) $T^2 = \frac{T_0^2}{\cos\theta}$
(c) $T = T_0 \cos\theta$ (d) $T = \frac{T_0}{\cos\theta}$

29. Two metal plates each of area 'A' form a parallel plate capacitor with air in between the plates. The distance between the plates is 'd'. A metal plate of thickness $\frac{d}{2}$ and of same area A is inserted between the plates to form two capacitors of capacitances C_1 and C_2 as shown in the figure. If the effective capacitance of the two capacitors is C' and the capacitance of the capacitor initially is C, then $\frac{C'}{C}$ is

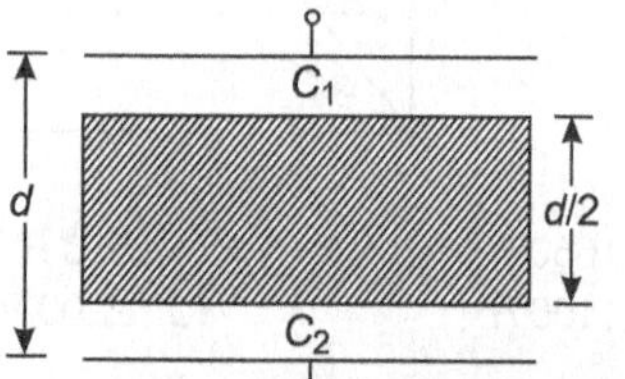

(a) 4 (b) 2
(c) 6 (d) 1

30. In the circuit shown in the figure, the current 'I' is

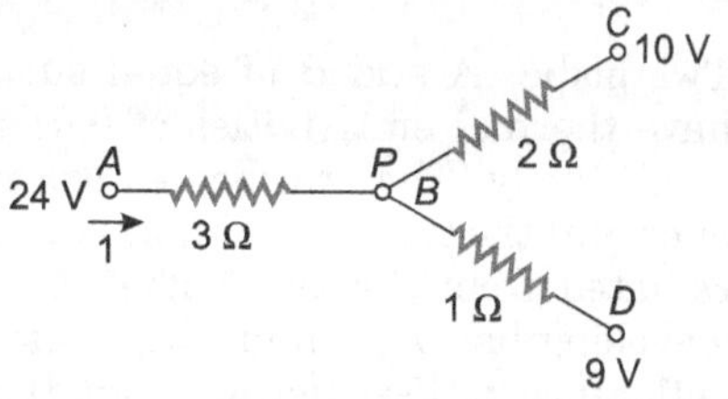

(a) 6 A (b) 2 A
(c) 4 A (d) 7 A

31. In the meter bridge experiment, the length AB of the wire is 1 m. The resistors X and Y have values 5 Ω and 2 Ω respectively. When a shunt resistance S is connected to X, the balancing point is found to be 0.625 m from A. Then, the resistance of the shunt is

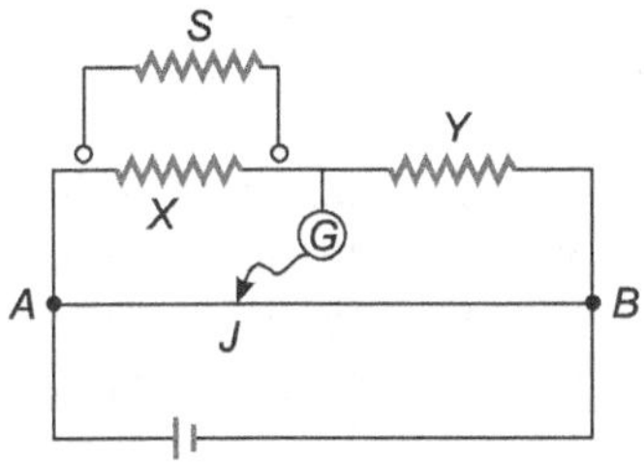

(a) 5 Ω (b) 10 Ω
(c) 7.5 Ω (d) 12.5 Ω

32. The ends of an element of zinc wire are kept at a small temperature difference ΔT and a small current (I) is passed through the wire. Then, the heat developed per unit time

(a) is proportional to ΔT and I
(b) is proportional to I^3 and ΔT
(c) is proportional to Thomson coefficient of the metal
(d) is proportional to ΔT only

33. A series LCR circuit is connected across a source of alternating emf of changing frequency and resonates at frequency f_0. Keeping capacitance constant, if the inductance (L) is increased by $\sqrt{3}$ times and resistance is increased (R) by 1.4 times, the resonant frequency now is

(a) $3^{1/4} f_0$ (b) $\sqrt{3} f_0$
(c) $(\sqrt{3}-1)^{1/4} f_0$ (d) $\left(\frac{1}{3}\right)^{1/4} f_0$

34. The sensitivity of a galvanometer that measures current is decreased by $\frac{1}{40}$ times by using shunt resistance of 10 Ω. Then, the value of the resistance of the galvanometer is

(a) 400 Ω (b) 410 Ω
(c) 30 Ω (d) 390 Ω

35. Initially a photon of wavelength λ_1 falls on photocathode and emits an electron of maximum energy E_1. If the wavelength of the incident photon is changed to λ_2, the maximum energy of the electron emitted becomes E_2. Then value of hc (h = Planck's constant, c = velocity of light) is

(a) $hc = \frac{(E_1 + E_2)\lambda_1\lambda_2}{\lambda_2 - \lambda_1}$

(b) $hc = \frac{E_1 - E_2}{\lambda_2 - \lambda_1} \cdot (\lambda_1\lambda_2)$

(c) $hc = \frac{(E_1 - E_2)(\lambda_2 - \lambda_1)}{\lambda_1\lambda_2}$

(d) $hc = \frac{\lambda_2 - \lambda_1}{\lambda_1\lambda_2 E_2} \cdot E_1$

36. The work function of a metal is 2 eV. If a radiation of wavelength 3000 Å is incident on it, the maximum kinetic energy of the emitted photoelectrons is (Planck's constant $h = 6.6 \times 10^{-34}$ Js; velocity of light $c = 3 \times 10^8$ m/s; $1\,\text{eV} = 1.6 \times 10^{-19}$ J)

(a) 4.4×10^{-19} J (b) 5.6×10^{-19} J
(c) 3.4×10^{-19} J (d) 2.5×10^{-19} J

37. The radius of ${}_{72}\text{Te}^{125}$ nucleus is 6 fermi. The radius of ${}_{13}\text{Al}^{27}$ nucleus in meters is

(a) 3.6×10^{-12} m (b) 3.6×10^{-15} m
(c) 7.2×10^{-8} m (d) 7.2×10^{-15} m

38. A U^{235} nuclear reactor generates energy at a rate of 3.70×10^7 J/s. Each fission liberates 185 MeV useful energy. If the reactor has to operate for 144×10^4 s, then, the mass of the fuel needed is (Assume Avogadro's number $= 6 \times 10^{23}\,\text{mol}^{-1}$, $1\,\text{eV} = 1.6 \times 10^{-19}$ J)

(a) 70.5 kg (b) 0.705 kg
(c) 13.1 kg (d) 1.31 kg

39. The base current in a transistor circuit changes from 45 μA to 140 μA. Accordingly, the collector current changes from 0.2 mA to 0.400 mA. The gain in current is

(a) 9.5 (b) 1
(c) 40 (d) 20

40. Of the following, NAND gate is

(a) 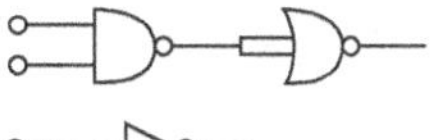

(b) 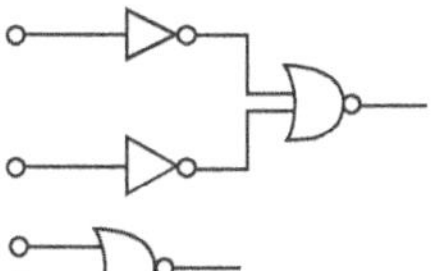

(c) 

(d) 

Answers

1. (b)	**2.** (b)	**3.** (c)	**4.** (a)	**5.** (c)	**6.** (a)	**7.** (b)	**8.** (a)	**9.** (d)	**10.** (b)
11. (a)	**12.** (b)	**13.** (a)	**14.** (a)	**15.** (c)	**16.** (b)	**17.** (c)	**18.** (a)	**19.** (c)	**20.** (d)
21. (c)	**22.** (b)	**23.** (a)	**24.** (b)	**25.** (b)	**26.** (b)	**27.** (c)	**28.** (a)	**29.** (b)	**30.** (a)
31. (b)	**32.** (a)	**33.** (d)	**34.** (d)	**35.** (b)	**36.** (c)	**37.** (b)	**38.** (b)	**39.** (c)	**40.** (d)

Hints & Solutions

1. Given quantity is $\dfrac{EJ^2}{M^5G^2}$ ...(i)

where dimensions of the various given quantities are

Dimensions of $E = [ML^2T^{-2}]$

Dimensions of $J = [ML^2T^{-1}]$

Dimension of $M = [M]$

Dimension of $G = [M^{-1}L^3T^{-2}]$

Now, on putting these dimensions in Eq. (i), we have

$$= \frac{[ML^2T^{-2}][ML^2T^{-1}]^2}{[M^5][M^{-1}L^3T^{-2}]^2}$$

$$= \frac{[M^3L^6T^{-2}]}{[M^3L^6T^{-2}]} = \text{dimensionless}$$

Since, angle is a dimensionless quantity

2. We know, work done $W = \mathbf{F} \cdot \mathbf{d}$

Given, force, $\mathbf{F} = 2\hat{i} - \hat{j} - \hat{k}$,

and position vector, $\mathbf{d} = 3\hat{i} + 2\hat{j} - 5\hat{k}$

Using vector identify $\hat{i} \cdot \hat{i} = \hat{j} \cdot \hat{j} = \hat{k} \cdot \hat{k} = 1$

Hence, $\mathbf{W} = \mathbf{F} \cdot \mathbf{d} = (2\hat{i} - \hat{j} - \hat{k}) \cdot (3\hat{i} + 2\hat{j} - 5\hat{k})$

$$= 6 - 2 + 5 = 9 \text{ units}$$

3. We know, average velocity $= \dfrac{\text{displacement}}{\text{time}}$

$$v_{av} = \frac{\sqrt{\mu^2 + R^2/4}}{T/2} \quad \text{...(i)}$$

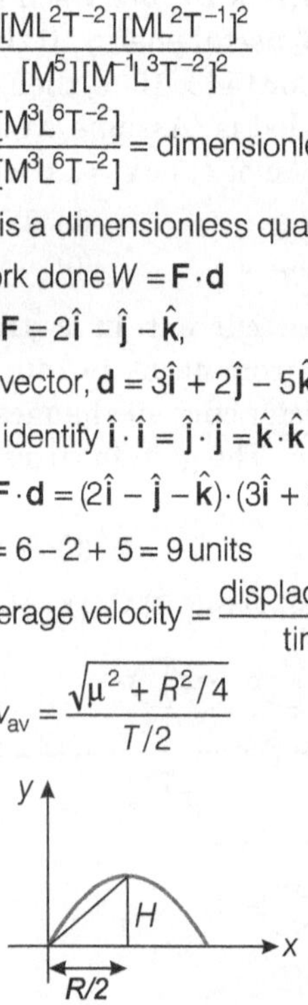

where, H = maximum height $= \dfrac{v^2 \sin^2 \theta}{2g}$ ...(ii)

$$\text{Range } R = \frac{v^2 \sin 2\theta}{g} \quad \text{...(iii)}$$

Time of flight $T = \dfrac{2v \sin \theta}{g}$

Putting the values of Eqs. (ii), (iii) and (iv) in Eq. (i) we have

$$v_{av} = \frac{v}{2}\sqrt{1 + 3\cos^2 \theta}$$

4. The free body diagram of the given situation is

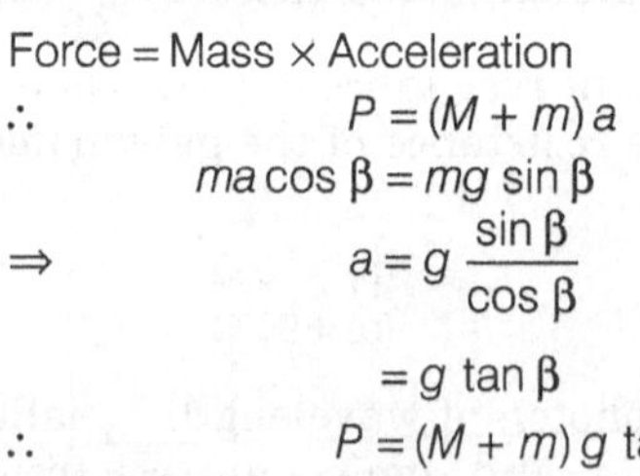

(given)

Force = Mass × Acceleration

$\therefore \quad P = (M + m)\,a$

$$ma \cos \beta = mg \sin \beta$$

$\Rightarrow \quad a = g \dfrac{\sin \beta}{\cos \beta}$

$$= g \tan \beta$$

$\therefore \quad P = (M + m)\,g \tan \beta$

5. Energy of balls at rest, $K_1 = mgh_1$ and $K_2 = mgh_2$

percentage loss in KE $= \dfrac{K_1 - K_2}{K_1} \times 100$

$$\frac{25}{100} = \left(\frac{12 - h^2}{12}\right)$$

$$\Rightarrow \quad \frac{25 \times 12}{100} = 12 - h_2$$

$$\Rightarrow \quad h_2 = 12 - 3 = 9\,\text{m}$$

6. Velocity of centre of mass is

$$\mathbf{v}_{CM} = \frac{m_1\mathbf{v}_1 + m_2\mathbf{v}_2}{m_1 + m_2}$$

Given, $m_1 = 4\,\text{kg}, m_2 = 5\,\text{kg}, v_1 = 5\hat{\mathbf{j}}\,\text{m/s}$
$v_2 = 3\hat{\mathbf{i}}\,\text{m/s}$

$$\therefore \quad \mathbf{v}_{CM} = \frac{4 \times 5\hat{\mathbf{j}} + 5 \times 3\hat{\mathbf{i}}}{5 + 4} = \frac{20\hat{\mathbf{i}}}{9} + \frac{15}{9}\hat{\mathbf{j}}$$

Hence, magnitude $|\mathbf{v}_{CM}| = \sqrt{\left(\frac{20}{9}\right)^2 + \left(\frac{15}{9}\right)^2} = \frac{25}{9}\,\text{m/s}$

7. From law of conservation of momentum, we known,

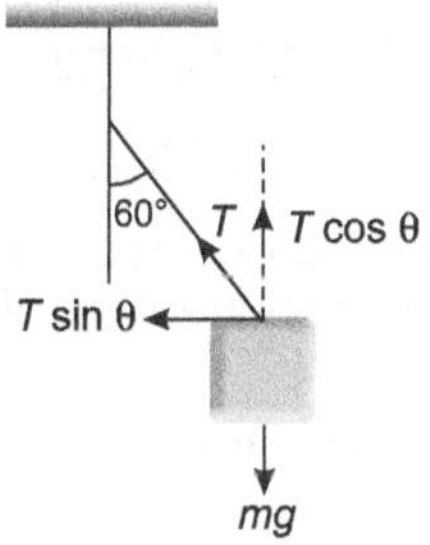

$$m_1u_1 + m_2u_2 = m_1v_1 + m_2v_2$$

$$u_1 = 0, u_2 = 150\,\text{m/s}, m_1 = 2.9\,\text{kg}$$

and $\quad m_2 = 0.1\,\text{kg}$

So, $\quad 2.9 \times 150 = (2.9 + 0.1)\,v$

$$\Rightarrow \quad \frac{2.9 \times 150}{3} = v$$

$$\Rightarrow \quad v = 145\,\text{m/s}$$

Also, $\quad T \sin\theta = \frac{mv^2}{r}$

Putting the values and solving, we get
$T = 135\,\text{N}$.

8. For upper half

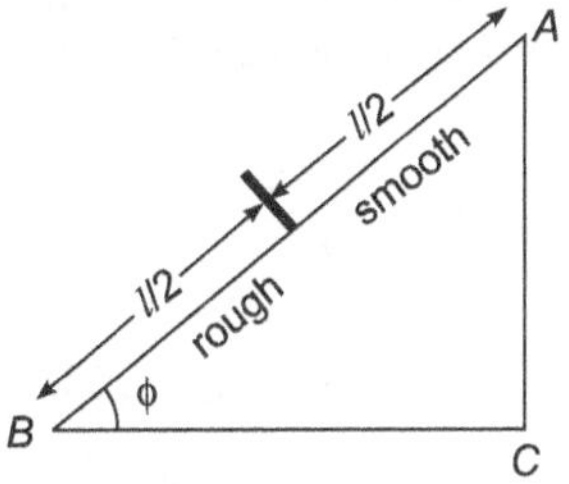

From equation,

$$v^2 = u^2 + 2as$$

we have, $u = 0$ (from rest), $s = l/2$

$$v^2 = 0 + 2\,(g \sin\phi) \cdot \frac{l}{2} \qquad \ldots\text{(i)}$$

For lower half,
$v = 0$ and $a = g\,(\sin\phi - \mu\cos\phi)$,

$$\Rightarrow \quad 0 = u^2 + 2g\,(\sin\phi - \mu\cos\phi) \cdot \frac{l}{2}$$

$$\Rightarrow \; -gl\sin\phi = gl\,(\sin\phi - \mu\cos\phi)$$

$$\Rightarrow \; \mu\cos\phi = 2\sin\phi \quad \Rightarrow \; \mu = 2\tan\phi$$

9. Given, $I = 4\,\text{kg-m}^2, \tau = 8\,\text{N-m}$ and $t = 20\,\text{s}$

$$\tau = I\alpha$$

$$\Rightarrow \quad \alpha = \frac{\tau}{I} = \frac{8}{4} = 2$$

$$\theta = \frac{1}{2}\alpha t^2$$

$$\Rightarrow \quad \theta = \frac{1}{2} \times 2 \times 20 \times 20 = 400$$

$$\omega = \tau\theta = 8 \times 400 = 3200\,\text{J}$$

10. We know the KE of a rotational circular disc

$$\text{KE} = \frac{1}{2}I\omega^2 \quad \text{and} \quad I = \frac{1}{2}MR^2$$

Hence, the resultant loss rotational KE will be the addition of both energy loss is $= \frac{1}{4}I\omega^2$

11. Gravitational force due to solid sphere is

$$F_1 = \frac{GMm}{(3R)^2} = \frac{GMm}{9R^2}$$

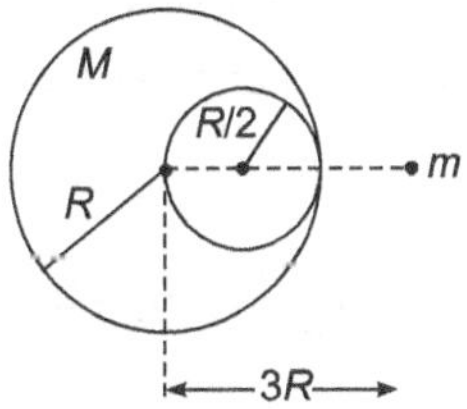

where, M and m are mass of solid sphere and particle respectively. Gravitational force on particle due to sphere with cavity

$$F_2 = \frac{GMm}{9R^2} - \frac{G\left(\frac{M}{8}\right)m}{(5R/2)^2}$$

$$= \frac{GMm}{R^2}\left[\frac{1}{9} - \frac{4}{8 \times 25}\right]$$

$$= \frac{GMm}{R^2}\left[\frac{41}{50 \times 9}\right]$$

$$\therefore \quad \frac{F_1}{F_2} = \frac{50}{41}$$

12. We knows, maximum velocity $V_{max} = A\omega = A\sqrt{\frac{K}{m}}$

Given, $K_1, m_1 = m, K_2, m_2 = 2\,m$

$$(V_{max})_A = (V_{max})_B$$

$$A_A\sqrt{\frac{K_1}{M}} = A_B\sqrt{\frac{K_2}{2m}}$$

$$\Rightarrow \quad \frac{A_A}{A_B} = \sqrt{\frac{K_2}{2K_1}}$$

13. Given, $\sigma = 0.32, F = 20\,N$

$$A = 0.01\,cm^2 = 0.01 \times 10^{-3}\,m$$

and $\quad Y = 1 - 1 \times 10^{11}\,N/m^2$

We know that

$$\frac{\Delta l}{l} = \frac{F}{AY} = \frac{20}{0.01 \times 10^{-3} \times 1.1 \times 10^{11}} = 18.1 \times 10^{-7}$$

and we also known

$$\sigma = \frac{-\Delta r/r}{\Delta l/l}$$

$$-\frac{\Delta r}{r} = 0.32 \times 18.1 \times 10^{-7} = 5.79 \times 10^{-7}$$

Hence, decrease in cross rectional area of wire is

$$\Delta A = 2\frac{\Delta r}{r} \times A = 2 \times 5.79 \times 10^{-7} \times 0.01 \times 10^{-3}$$

$$= 0.158 \times 10^{-10}\,m^2$$

$$= 1.26 \times 10^{-6}\,cm^2$$

14. We knows height of water rise in a capillary tube

$$h = \frac{2T\cos\theta}{rdg}$$

$$h_1 = \frac{2T_1\cos\theta_1}{rdg}, \quad h_2 = \frac{2T_2\cos\theta_2}{rdg}$$

Given, $h_1 = h, T_1 = T, \theta_1 = 0$

$$\therefore \quad h = \frac{2T}{rdg} \quad \ldots(i)$$

Given, $T_2 = \sqrt{2}T, \theta = 45°, \cos 45° = \frac{1}{\sqrt{2}}$

$$\therefore \quad h_2 = \frac{2\sqrt{2}T \times \frac{1}{\sqrt{2}}}{rdg} \quad \ldots(ii)$$

From Eqs. (i) and (ii), we observe

$$h_2 = h.$$

Hence, same mass of liquid rises into the capillary as before 5×10^{-3} kg.

15. Terminal velocity $v = \frac{2}{9}\frac{r^2(\rho - \sigma)g}{\eta}$

When, the two drops of same radius r coalesce then radius of new drop is R.

$$\therefore \quad \frac{4}{3}\pi R^3 = \frac{4}{3}\pi r^3 + \frac{4}{3}\pi r^3$$

$$\Rightarrow \quad R = 2^{1/3} \cdot r$$

Critical velocity $\propto r^2$

$$\therefore \quad \frac{v}{v_1} = \frac{r^2}{2^{2/3} \cdot r^2}$$

$$\Rightarrow \quad v_1 = \sqrt[3]{4} \cdot v$$

16. Due to volume expansion of both mercury and flask, the change in volume of mercury relative to flask is given by

$$\Delta V = V_0\,[\gamma_L - \gamma_g]\,\Delta\theta$$

$$= V\,[\gamma_m - 3\alpha_g]\,\Delta\theta$$

Given, $\gamma_m = 182 \times 10^{-6}/°C, \alpha_g = 10 \times 10^{-6}/°C$

$\Delta\theta = 100°C, \quad V = 1\,L$

$$\therefore \quad \Delta V = 1[(182 \times 10^{-6} - 3 \times 10 \times 10^{-6})] \times 100$$

$$\Delta V = 15.2\,CC$$

17. In given condition

$$\frac{Y + 160}{-50 + 160} = \frac{340 - 273}{373 - 273}$$

$$\frac{Y + 160}{110} = \frac{67}{100}$$

$$Y + 160 = \frac{67 \times 110}{100}$$

$$Y = 73.7 - 160$$

$$Y = -86.3°\,Y$$

18. We knows

$$dQ = du + dw$$

and we also known $du = 0$ for cyclio process so that

$$dQ = dw$$

Here, in given condition the work done during is a basic process

$$W_{2-3} = P_2(V_3 - V_2)$$
$$W_{4-1} = p_1(V_1 - V_4)$$

Total work done $= p_2(V_3 - V_2) + p_1(V_1 - V_4)$

From gas equation $pV = nRT = \frac{3 \times T}{2}$

Hence, total work done

$$= \frac{3R}{2}(400 + 2500 - 700 - 1100)$$
$$= \frac{3}{2}R(2900 - 1800)$$
$$= \frac{3}{2}R(1100) = \frac{3300R}{2}$$
$$= 1650R$$

19. $\frac{T_2}{T_1} = 1 - \eta = 1 - \frac{40}{100} = \frac{3}{5}$

$\Rightarrow \quad T_1 = \frac{5}{3}T_2$

$\Rightarrow \quad T_1 = \frac{5}{3} \times 300 = 500\text{ K}$

New efficiency $\eta' = 60\%$

$$\frac{T_2}{T_1'} = 1 - \eta' = 1 - \frac{60}{100} = \frac{2}{5}$$

$\Rightarrow \quad T_1' = \frac{5}{2} \times 300 = 750\text{ K}$

Increase in temperature $= 750 - 500 = 250\text{ K}$

20. We knows from Stefan's law,

$$E = eA\sigma T^4$$

Here, $\quad E_1 = e_1 A\sigma T_1^4$

$$E_2 = e_2 A\sigma T_2^4$$

so, $\quad E_1 = E_2$

$\therefore \quad e_1 T_1^4 = e_2 T_2^4$

$\Rightarrow \quad T_2 = \left(\frac{e_1}{e_2} T_1^4\right)^{1/4} = \left(\frac{1}{81} \times (5802)^4\right)^{1/4}$

$\Rightarrow \quad T_B = 1934\text{ K}$

From Wein's law, $\lambda_{AT_A} = \lambda_B T_B$

$\Rightarrow \quad \frac{\lambda_A}{\lambda_B} = \frac{T_B}{T_A}$

$\Rightarrow \quad \frac{\lambda_B - \lambda_A}{\lambda_B} = \frac{T_B - T_B}{T_A}$

$\Rightarrow \quad \frac{1}{\lambda_B} = \frac{5802 - 1934}{5802} = \frac{3968}{5802}$

$\Rightarrow \quad \lambda_B = \frac{3}{2}\,\mu\text{m}$

21. We knows frequency of a closed end an column

$$n_1 = \frac{v}{4l_1}$$

We knows frequency of a open end an column

$$n_2 = \frac{v}{2l_2}$$

Given, $l_1 = 32\text{ cm}, l_2 = 66\text{ cm}$

and $\quad n_1 - n_2 = 8\text{ heat/s}$

So, $\quad n_1 = \frac{v}{4 \times 32} = \frac{v}{128}$

and $\quad n_2 = \frac{v}{2 \times 66} = \frac{v}{132}$

In given condition,

$$\frac{v}{128} - \frac{v}{132} = 8$$
$$v = 8448 \times 4$$
$$v = 33792$$

Hence, $\quad n_1 = \frac{33792}{128}$

$$n_1 = 264\text{ Hz}$$

and $\quad n_2 = \frac{33792}{132}$

$$n_2 = 256\text{ Hz}$$

22. We know that,

$$n' = n\left[\frac{v}{v - v_s\cos\theta}\right]$$

Hence, $\quad n' = 640\left[\frac{340}{340 - \frac{100}{3} \times \frac{3}{5}}\right]$

$$n' = 640\left[\frac{340}{340 - \frac{100}{5}}\right]$$

$$n' = 640 \times \frac{340}{320} = 2 \times 340$$

$$= 680\text{ Hz}$$

23. From lens maker's formula

$$\frac{1}{f} = ({}_g^m\mu - 1)\left(\frac{1}{R_1} - \frac{1}{R_2}\right)$$

Now, $${}_g^m\mu = \frac{{}_g\mu}{{}_m\mu} = \frac{1.5}{1.75}$$

For concave lens as shown in the figure, in this case

$$R_1 = -R \quad \text{and} \quad R_2 = +R$$

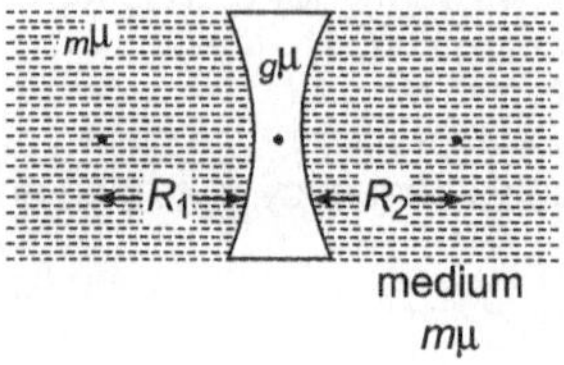

$$\frac{1}{f} = \left(\frac{1.5}{1.75} - 1\right)\left(-\frac{1}{R} - \frac{1}{R}\right) = + \frac{0.25 \times 2}{1.75R}$$

$\Rightarrow$ $$f = +3.5R$$

The positive sign shows that the lens behaves as a convergent lens.

24. For eye piece

$$V_e = -25\,\text{cm}, \quad f_e = 5\,\text{cm}$$

$\Rightarrow$ $$\frac{1}{-25} - \frac{1}{u_e} = \frac{1}{5}$$

$\Rightarrow$ $$u_e = -\frac{25}{6}\,\text{cm}$$

$$v_0 = L - |u_e| = 10.5 - \frac{25}{6} = \frac{38}{6}\,\text{cm}$$

For objective

$$\frac{1}{v_0} - \frac{1}{u_0} = \frac{1}{f_0}$$

$$\frac{1}{38/6} - \frac{1}{u_0} = \frac{1}{1.9}$$

$\Rightarrow$ $$\frac{1}{u_0} = \frac{6}{38} - \frac{1}{1.9}$$

$\Rightarrow$ $$u_0 = 2.7\,\text{cm}$$

25. In Fresnel diffraction, no lenses are required for rendering light rays parallel and also the diffraction pattern may be dark or bright depending upon the number of half-period zones that superpose at the point. Hence, the intensity of light at a point a screen beyond or obstacle depends on the number of half-periods zones that superpose at the point.

26. We know that the time period of a vibrating bar magnet

$$T = 2\pi\sqrt{\frac{I}{MB_H}}$$

Given, $T_1 = 8\,\text{s}, I_1 = I, M = 4\,\text{Am}^2$

$$8 = 2\pi\sqrt{\frac{I}{4 \times B_H}} \quad \ldots\text{(i)}$$

Given, $T_2 = 6\,\text{s}, I_2 = 9 \times 10^{-2}\,\text{kg-m}^2, M = 8\,\text{Am}^2$

$$6 = 2\pi\sqrt{\frac{9 \times 10^{-2}}{8 \times B_H}} \quad \ldots\text{(ii)}$$

Dividing Eqs. (i) and (ii)

$$\frac{8}{6} = \sqrt{\frac{2I}{9 \times 10^{-2}}}$$

Squaring both sides and solving, we have

$$I = 8 \times 10^{-2}\,\text{kg-m}^2$$

27. We knows, $B = \dfrac{\mu_0}{4\pi}\dfrac{M}{r^3}$

Hence the resultant horizontal magnetic induction point of the line joining their conters is

$$B = B_1 + B_2 + B_H$$

$$= \frac{10^{-7} \times 1.2}{(10 \times 10^{-2})^3} + \frac{10^{-7} \times 1}{(10 \times 10^{-2})^3} + 3.6 \times 10^{-5}$$

$$= 1.2 \times 10^{-4} + 1 \times 10^{-4} + 0.36 \times 10^{-4}$$

$$= 2.56 \times 10^{-4}\,\text{T}$$

28. In deflection magnetometer, field due to magnet F and horizontal component B_H of earth's field are perpendicular to each other.

$\therefore$ Net field is $\sqrt{F^2 + B_H^2}$

So the time period

$$T = 2\pi\sqrt{\frac{I}{M\sqrt{F^2 + B_H}}} \quad \ldots\text{(i)}$$

When magnet is removed

$$T_0 = 2\pi\sqrt{\frac{I}{MB_H}} \quad \ldots\text{(ii)}$$

Also, $$\frac{F}{B_H} = \tan\theta$$

Dividing Eqs. (i) by (ii), we get

$$\frac{T}{T_0} = \sqrt{\frac{B_H}{\sqrt{F^2 + B_H^2}}}$$

$$= \sqrt{\frac{B_H}{\sqrt{B_H^2 + \tan^2\theta + B_H^2}}} = \sqrt{\frac{B_H}{B_H\sqrt{\sec^2\theta}}}$$

$$= \sqrt{\cos\theta}$$

$$\Rightarrow \quad T^2 = T_0^2 \cos\theta$$

29. We knows capacitance $C = \frac{\varepsilon_0 A}{d}$

When plate is inserted

$$C' = \frac{\varepsilon_0 A}{d - \frac{d}{2}} = \frac{2\varepsilon_0 A}{d}$$

$$\frac{C'}{C} = \frac{2}{1}$$

30. Applying junction law

We have

$$I = I_1 + I_2$$

$$\frac{24 - V}{3} = \frac{10 - V}{2} + \frac{9 - V}{1}$$

$$\Rightarrow \quad \frac{24 - V}{3} = \frac{28 - 3V}{2}$$

$$\Rightarrow \quad 2(24 - V) = 3(28 - 3V)$$

$$\Rightarrow \quad 48 - 2V = 84 - 9V$$

$$\Rightarrow \quad 7V = 36$$

$$\Rightarrow \quad V = 5.14\,\text{V}$$

From Ohm's law

$$\Delta V = IR$$

$$\Delta V = 24 - 5.14 = 18.86, R = 3\,\Omega$$

$$\therefore \quad I = \frac{18.86}{3} \approx 6\,\text{A}$$

31. Here in given condition, we have

$$\frac{\frac{bx}{b + x}}{2} = \frac{0.625}{0.375}$$

$$\frac{bx}{(b + x)2} = \frac{25}{15}$$

$$\frac{5b}{(b + 5)2} = \frac{5}{3}$$

$$\frac{b}{2b + 10} = \frac{1}{3}$$

$$\Rightarrow \quad 3b - 2b = 10$$

$$b = 10\,\Omega$$

32. The heat developed per unit time in given condition is proportional to ΔT and l.

33. We knows in LCR circuits

$$f = \frac{1}{2\pi\sqrt{LC}}$$

and $$f \propto \frac{1}{\sqrt{L}}$$

Here, in given condition

$$\frac{f_1}{f_2} = \sqrt{\frac{L_1}{L_2}} = \sqrt{\frac{L}{\sqrt{3}L}}$$

$$\Rightarrow \quad f_1 = \left(\frac{1}{3}\right)^{1/4} f_2$$

34.

$$i_g = \frac{S}{S + G} i$$

$$\frac{1}{40} = \frac{10}{10 + x}$$

$$\Rightarrow \quad 10 + x = 400$$

$$\Rightarrow \quad x = 390\,\Omega$$

35. From equation of photoelectric effect, we have

$$E_1 = \frac{hc}{\lambda_1} - W \quad \ldots\text{(i)}$$

$$E_2 = \frac{hc}{\lambda_2} - W \quad \ldots\text{(ii)}$$

where, W is work function.

$$E_1 + W = \frac{hc}{\lambda_1} \quad \ldots\text{(iii)}$$

$$E_2 + W = \frac{hc}{\lambda_2} \quad \ldots\text{(iv)}$$

From Eq. (iv)

$$W = \frac{hc}{\lambda_2} - E_2,$$

$\therefore$ Putting this value in Eq. (iii), we have

$$E_1 + \frac{hc}{\lambda_1} - E_2 - \frac{hc}{\lambda_1}$$

$$\Rightarrow \quad E_1 - E_2 = hc\left(\frac{1}{\lambda_1} - \frac{1}{\lambda_2}\right)$$

$$\Rightarrow \quad E_1 - E_2 = hc\left(\frac{\lambda_2 - \lambda_1}{\lambda_1\lambda_2}\right)$$

$$\Rightarrow \quad hc = \frac{(E_1 - E_2)\lambda_1\lambda_2}{(\lambda_2 - \lambda_1)}$$

36. Maximum KE $= \dfrac{hc}{\lambda} - \phi_0$

Given, $\lambda = 3000\ \text{Å} = 3000 \times 10^{-10}$ m,

$h = 6.6 \times 10^{-34}$ J-s, $c = 3 \times 10^8$ m/s, $\phi = 2$ eV

Maximum KE

$$= \frac{6.6 \times 10^{-34} \times 3 \times 10^8}{3000 \times 10^{-10}} \times \frac{1}{1.6 \times 10^{-12}} - 2$$

$$= 4.13 - 2 = 2.13\,\text{eV}$$

In Joules : $2.13 \times 1.6 \times 10^{-19} = 3.41 \times 10^{-19}$ J

37. The relation between radius (R) and atomic number (A) is

$$\frac{R_1}{R_2} = \left(\frac{A_1}{A_2}\right)^{1/3}$$

Given, $R_1 = 6$ fermi, $A_1 = 125$, $A_2 = 27$

$$\frac{6}{R_2} = \left(\frac{125}{27}\right)^{1/3} = \frac{5}{3}$$

$$\Rightarrow \qquad R_2 = \frac{6 \times 3}{5} = \frac{18}{5} = 3.6\ \text{fermi}$$

$$= 3.6 \times 10^{-15}\ \text{m}$$

38. In 1 s, energy generated is 3.7×10^7 J

In 144×10^4 s, energy generated is

$$= 3.7 \times 10^7 \times 144 \times 10^4\ \text{J}$$

Also energy released in one fission is

$$= 185\,\text{meV}$$

$$= 185 \times 10^6 \times 1.6 \times 10^{-19}\ \text{J}$$

$$\text{Number of fission} = \frac{3.7 \times 10^7 \times 144 \times 10^4}{185 \times 10^6 \times 1.6 \times 10^{-19}}$$

$$= 1.8 \times 10^{24}\ \text{of}\ U^{235}\ \text{atoms.}$$

Mass contained in 1.8×10^{24} atoms of U^{235} is

$$= \frac{235 \times 1.8 \times 10^{24}}{6.023 \times 10^{23}} = 702.3\,\text{g} = 0.70\,\text{kg}$$

39. Current gain $\beta = \dfrac{\Delta i_c}{\Delta i_b}$

$$\Delta i_c = (4 - 0.2)\,\text{mA} = 3.8 \times 10^{-3}\ \text{A}$$

$$\Delta i_b = (140 - 45)\,\mu\text{A} = 95 \times 10^{-6}\ \text{A}$$

$$\therefore \qquad \beta = \frac{3.8 \times 10^{-3}}{95 \times 10^{-5}} = 40$$

40. The logic symbol of NAND gate is

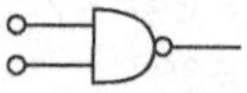

EAMCET

Engineering Entrance Exam

Solved Paper 2012

Physics

1. A uniform rope of mass 0.1 kg and length 2.45 m hangs from a rigid support. The time taken by the transverse wave formed in the rope to travel through the full length of the rope is (Assume $g = 9.8 \text{ m/s}^2$)
(a) 0.5 s (b) 1.6 s
(c) 1.2 s (d) 1.0 s

2. When a vibrating tuning fork is placed on a sound box of a sonometer, 8 beats per second are heard when the length of the sonometer wire is kept at 101 cm or 100 cm. Then the frequency of the tuning fork is (Consider that the tension in the wire is kept constant)
(a) 1616 Hz (b) 1608 Hz
(c) 1632 Hz (d) 1600 Hz

3. The objective and eyepiece of an astronomical telescope are double convex lenses with refractive index 1.5. When the telescope is adjusted to infinity, the separation between the two lenses is 16 cm. If the space between the lenses is now filled with water and again telescope is adjusted for infinity, then the present separation between the lenses is
(a) 8 cm (b) 16 cm
(c) 24 cm (d) 32 cm

4. The dispersive powers of the materials of two lenses forming an achromatic combination are in the ratio of 4 : 3. Effective focal length of the two lenses is + 60 cm then the focal lengths of the lenses should be
(a) – 20 cm, 25 cm (b) 20 cm, – 25 cm
(c) – 15 cm, 20 cm (d) 15 cm, – 20 cm

5. Two coherent point sources S_1 and S_2 vibrating in phase emit light of wavelength λ. The separation between them is 2λ as shown in figure. The first bright fringe is formed at P due to interference on a screen placed at a distance D from S_1 $(D >> \lambda)$, then OP is

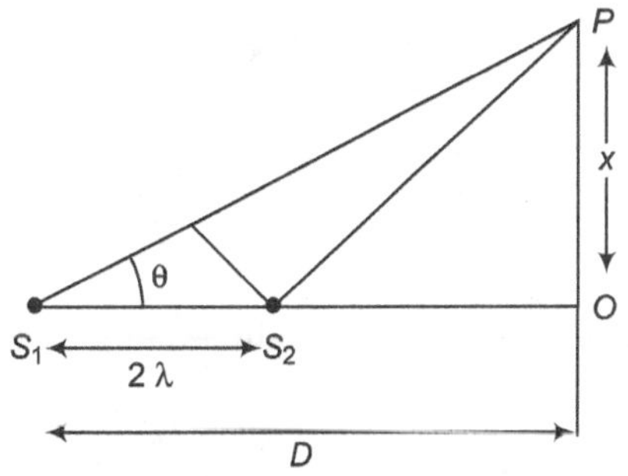

(a) $\sqrt{2}D$ (b) $1.5\,D$ (c) $\sqrt{3}D$ (d) $2\,D$

6. At a certain place a magnet makes 30 oscillations per minute. At another place where the magnetic field is double, its time period will be
(a) 4 s (b) 2 s (c) $\frac{1}{2}$ s (d) $\sqrt{2}$ s

7. A magnetic needle lying parallel to a magnetic field is turned through 60°. The work done on it is W. The torque required to maintain the magnetic needle in the position mentioned above is
(a) $\sqrt{3}W$ (b) $\frac{\sqrt{3}}{2}W$ (c) $\frac{W}{2}$ (d) $2W$

8. A parallel plate capacitor has a capacity 80×10^{-6} F, when air is present between the plates. The volume between the plates is then completely filled with a dielectric slab of dielectric constant 20. The capacitor is now connected to a battery of 30 V by wires. The dielectric slab is then removed. Then, the charge that passes now through the wire is

(a) 45.6×10^{-3}C
(b) 25.3×10^{-3}C
(c) 120×10^{-3}C
(d) 125×10^{-3}C

9. Two small spheres each having equal positive charge Q (Coulomb) on each are suspended by two insulating strings of equal length L (metre) from a rigid hook (shown in figure). The whole set up is taken into satellite where there is no gravity. The two balls are now held by electrostatic forces in horizontal position, the tension in each string is then

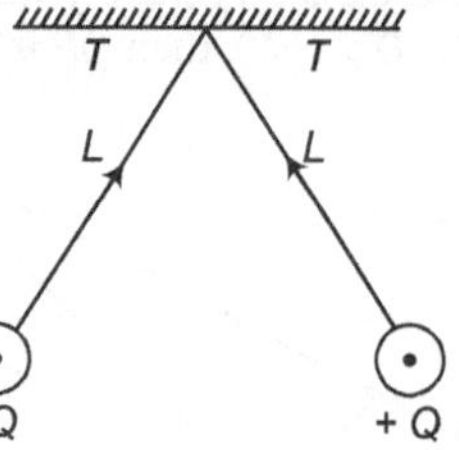

(a) $\dfrac{Q^2}{16\pi\varepsilon_0 L^2}$ (b) $\dfrac{Q^2}{8\pi\varepsilon_0 L^2}$
(c) $\dfrac{Q^2}{4\pi\varepsilon_0 L^2}$ (d) $\dfrac{Q^2}{2\pi\varepsilon_0 L^2}$

10. Three resistances of equal values are arranged in four different configurations as shown below. Power dissipation in the increasing order is

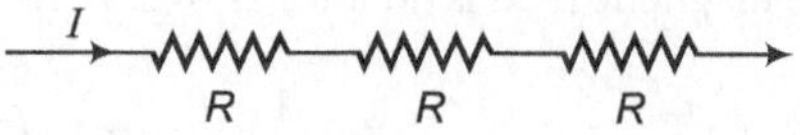

(I)

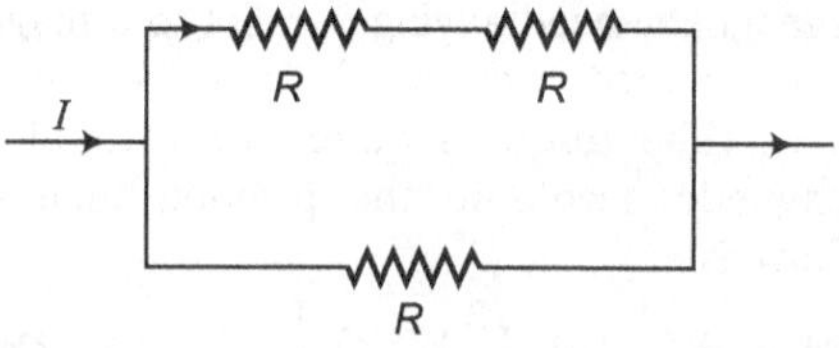

(II)

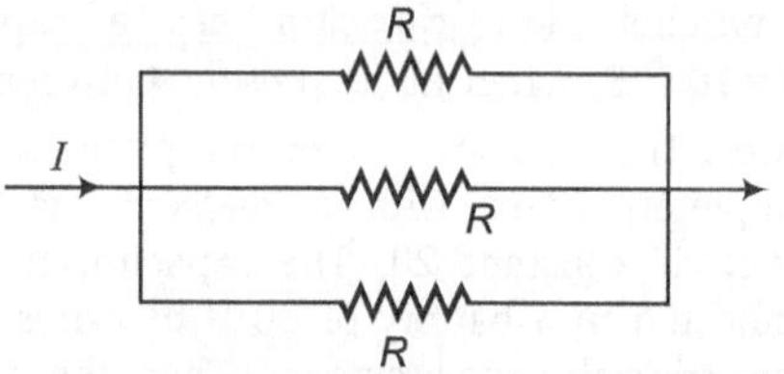

(III)

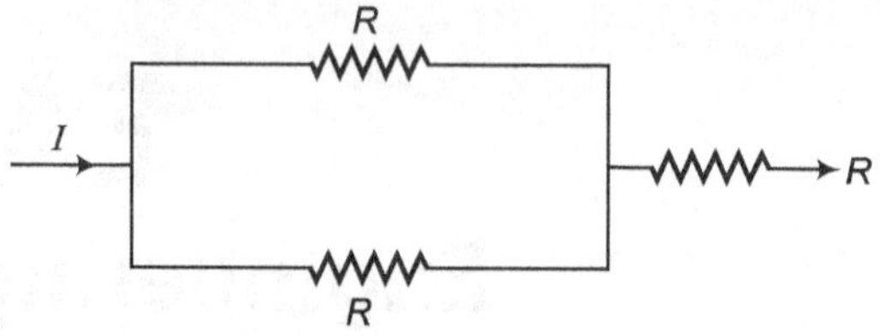

(IV)

(a) (III) < (II) < (IV) < (I)
(b) (II) < (III) < (IV) < (I)
(c) (I) < (IV) < (III) < (II)
(d) (I) < (III) < (II) < (IV)

11. Four resistors A, B, C and D form a Wheatstones bridge. The bridge is balanced, when $C = 100\ \Omega$. If A and B are interchanged, the bridge balances for $C = 121\ \Omega$. The value of D is

(a) $10\ \Omega$ (b) $100\ \Omega$
(c) $110\ \Omega$ (d) $120\ \Omega$

12. Total emf produced in a thermocouple does not depend on
(a) the metals in the thermocouple
(b) thomson coefficients of the metals in the thermocouple
(c) temperature of the junctions
(d) the duration of time for which the current is passed through thermocouple

13. A long curved conductor carries a current **I** (**I** is a vector). A small current element of length **d***l*, on the wire induces a magnetic field at a point, away from the current element. If the position vector between the current element and the point is **r**, making an angle with current element then, the induced magnetic field density; **dB** (vector) at the point is (μ_0 = permeability of free space)

(a) $\dfrac{\mu_0 \mathbf{I} d l \times \mathbf{r}}{4\pi r}$ (perpendicular to the current element $\mathbf{d}l$)

(b) $\dfrac{\mu_0 \mathbf{I} \times \mathbf{r} \times \mathbf{d}l}{4\pi r^2}$ (perpendicular to the current element $\mathbf{d}l$)

(c) $\dfrac{\mu_0 \mathbf{I} \times \mathbf{d}l}{r}$ (perpendicular to the plane containing the current element and position vector **r**)

(d) $\dfrac{\mu_0 \mathbf{I} \times \mathbf{d}l}{4\pi r^2}$ (perpendicular to the plane containing current element and position vector **r**)

14. A primary coil and secondary coil are placed close to each other. A current, which changes at the rate of 25 A in a millisecond, is present in the primary coil. If the mutual inductance is 92×10^{-6} H, then the value of induced emf in the secondary coil is
(a) 4.6 V (b) 2.3 V
(c) 0.368 mV (d) 0.23 mV

15. The de-Broglie wavelength of an electron moving with a velocity of 1.5×10^8 m/s is equal to that of a photon. The ratio of kinetic energy of the electron to that of the photon ($c = 3 \times 10^8$ m/s)
(a) 2 (b) 4 (c) $\frac{1}{2}$ (d) $\frac{1}{4}$

16. A proton when accelerated through a potential difference of V, has a de-Broglie wavelength λ associated with it. If an α-particle is to have the same de-Broglie wavelength λ, it must be accelerated through a potential difference of
(a) $\frac{V}{8}$ (b) $\frac{V}{4}$ (c) $4V$ (d) $8V$

17. The half-life of Ra^{226} is 1620 years. Then the number of atoms decay in one second in 1 g of radium (Avogadro number $= 6.023 \times 10^{23}$)
(a) 4.23×10^9
(b) 3.16×10^{10}
(c) 3.61×10^{10}
(d) 2.16×10^{10}

18. The half-life of a radioactive element is 10 h. The fraction of initial radioactivity of the element that will remain after 40 h is
(a) $\frac{1}{2}$ (b) $\frac{1}{16}$
(c) $\frac{1}{8}$ (d) $\frac{1}{4}$

19. In a transistor if $\frac{I_C}{I_E} = \alpha$ and $\frac{I_C}{I_B} = \beta$. If α varies between $\frac{20}{21}$ and $\frac{100}{101}$, then the value of β lies between
(a) 1-10 (b) 0.95-0.99
(c) 20-100 (d) 200-300

20. Match Column A (layers in the ionosphere for skywave propagation) with Column B (their height range)

	Column A		Column B
A.	D-layer	I.	250-400 km
B.	E-layer	II.	170-190 km
C.	F_1-layer	III.	95-120 km
D.	F_2-layer	IV.	65-75 km

	A	B	C	D
(a)	I	II	III	IV
(b)	IV	III	I	II
(c)	IV	III	II	I
(d)	III	IV	I	II

21. The gravitational field in a region is given by equation $\mathbf{E} = (5\mathbf{i} + 12\mathbf{j})$ N/kg. If a particle of mass 2 kg is moved from the origin to the point (12 m, 5 m) in this region, the change in gravitational potential energy is
(a) − 225 J (b) − 240 J
(c) − 245 J (d) − 250 J

22. The time period of a particle in simple harmonic motion is 8 s. At $t = 0$, it is at the mean position. The ratio of the distances travelled by it in the first and second seconds is
(a) $\frac{1}{2}$ (b) $\frac{1}{\sqrt{2}}$ (c) $\frac{1}{\sqrt{2}-1}$ (d) $\frac{1}{\sqrt{3}}$

23. A tension of 22 N is applied to a copper wire of cross-sectional area 0.02 cm^2 Young's modulus of copper is 1.1×10^{11} N/m^2 and Poisson's ratio 0.32. The decrease in cross-sectional area will be
(a) 1.28×10^{-6} cm^2 (b) 1.6×10^{-6} cm^2
(c) 2.56×10^{-6} cm^2 (d) 0.64×10^{-6} cm^2

24. Drops of liquid of density d are floating half immersed in a liquid of density ρ. If the surface tension of the liquid is T, then the radius of the drop is
(a) $\sqrt{\frac{3T}{g(3d-\rho)}}$ (b) $\sqrt{\frac{6T}{g(2d-\rho)}}$
(c) $\sqrt{\frac{3T}{g(2d-\rho)}}$ (d) $\sqrt{\frac{3T}{g(4d-3\rho)}}$

25. A pipe having an internal diameter D is connected to another pipe of same size. Water flows into the second pipe through 'n' holes, each of diameter d. If the water in the first pipe has speed v, the speed of water leaving the second pipe is
(a) $\frac{D^2 v}{nd^2}$ (b) $\frac{nD^2 v}{d^2}$ (c) $\frac{nd^2 v}{D^2}$ (d) $\frac{d^2 v}{nd^2}$

26. When a liquid is heated in copper vessel its coefficient of apparent expansion is $6 \times 10^{-6}/°C$. When the same liquid is heated in a steel vessel its coefficient of apparent expansion is $24 \times 10^{-6}/°C$. If coefficient of linear expansion for copper is $18 \times 10^{-6}/°C$, the coefficient of linear expansion for steel is

(a) $20 \times 10^{-6}/°C$ (b) $24 \times 10^{-6}/°C$
(c) $36 \times 10^{-6}/°C$ (d) $12 \times 10^{-6}/°C$

27. When the temperature of a body increases from T to $T + \Delta T$, its moment of inertia increases from I to $I + \Delta I$. If α is the coefficient of linear expansion of the material of the body, then $\Delta I / I$ is (neglect higher orders of α)

(a) $\alpha \Delta T$ (b) $2\alpha\Delta T$ (c) $\frac{\Delta T}{\alpha}$ (d) $\frac{2\alpha}{\Delta T}$

28. A sound wave passing through an ideal gas at NTP produces a pressure change of 0.001 dyne/cm^2 during adiabatic compression. The corresponding change in temperature ($\gamma = 1.5$ for the gas and atmospheric pressure is 1.013×10^6 dyne/cm^2) is

(a) 8.97×10^{-4} K (b) 8.97×10^{-6} K
(c) 8.97×10^{-8} K (d) 8.97×10^{-9} K

29. Work done to increase the temperature of one mole of an ideal gas by 30°C, if it is expanding under the condition $V \propto T^{2/3}$ is, ($R = 8.314$ J/mol/K)

(a) 116.2 J (b) 136.2 J
(c) 166.2 J (d) 186.2 J

30. Power radiated by a black body at temperature T_1 is P and it radiates maximum energy at a wavelength λ_1. If the temperature of the black body is changed from T_1 to T_2, it radiates maximum energy at a wavelength $\lambda_1/2$. The power radiated at T_2 is

(a) $2P$ (b) $4P$
(c) $8P$ (d) $16P$

31. Two solid spheres A and B each of radius R are made of materials of densities ρ_A and ρ_B respectively. Their moments of inertia about a diameter are I_A and I_B respectively. The value of I_A/I_B is

(a) $\sqrt{\frac{\rho_A}{\rho_B}}$ (b) $\sqrt{\frac{\rho_B}{\rho_A}}$ (c) $\frac{\rho_A}{\rho_B}$ (d) $\frac{\rho_B}{\rho_A}$

32. **Assertion (A)** The moment of inertia of a steel sphere is larger than the moment of inertia of a wooden sphere of same radius.

Reason (R) Moment of inertia is independent of mass of the body.

The correct one is

(a) Both (A) and (R) are true, and (R) is the correct explanation of (A)
(b) Both (A) and (R) are true, and (R) is not the correct explanation of (A)
(c) (A) is true but (R) is wrong
(d) (A) is wrong but (R) is true

33. When the engine is switched off a vehicle of mass M is moving on a rough horizontal road with momentum p. If the coefficient of friction between the road and tyres of the vehicle is μ_k, the distance travelled by the vehicle before it comes to rest is

(a) $\frac{p^2}{2\mu_k M^2 g}$ (b) $\frac{2\mu_k M^2 g}{p^2}$
(c) $\frac{p^2}{2\mu_k g}$ (d) $\frac{p^2 M^2}{2\mu_k g}$

34. Choose correct statement

(A) The position of centre of mass of a system is dependent on the choice of coordinate system.
(B) Newton's second law of motion is applicable to the centre of mass of the system.
(C) Internal forces can not change the state of centre of mass.
(D) Internal forces can change the state of centre of mass.

(a) Both (A) and (B) are correct
(b) Both (B) and (C) are wrong
(c) Both (A)and (C) are wrong
(d) Both (A) and (D) are wrong

35. A ball A of mass m moving along positive x-direction with kinetic energy K and momentum p undergoes elastic head on collision with a stationary ball B of mass M after collision the ball A moves along negative x-direction with kinetic energy $\frac{K}{9}$, final momentum of B is

(a) p (b) $\frac{p}{3}$ (c) $\frac{4p}{3}$ (d) $4p$

36. A straight conductor of length 4 m moves at a speed of 10 m/s. When the conductor makes on angle of 30° with the direction of magnetic field of induction of 0.1 Wb-m^2, then induced emf is

(a) 8 V (b) 4 V
(c) 1 V (d) 2 V

37. The velocity v reached by a car of mass m at certain distance from the starting point driven with constant power P is such that

(a) $v \propto \frac{3P}{m}$ (b) $v^2 \propto \frac{3P}{m}$
(c) $v^3 \propto \frac{3P}{m}$ (d) $v \propto \left(\frac{3P}{m}\right)^2$

38. It is possible to project a particle with a given velocity in two possible ways so as to make them pass through a point p at a horizontal distance r from the point of projection. If t_1 and t_2 are times taken to reach this point in two possible ways, then the product $t_1 t_2$ is proportional to

(a) $\frac{1}{r}$ (b) r
(c) r^2 (d) $\frac{1}{r^2}$

39. Sum of magnitudes of two forces acting at a point is 16 N. If their resultant is normal to smaller force, and has a magnitude 8 N, then forces are

(a) 6 N, 10 N
(b) 8 N, 8 N
(c) 4 N, 12 N
(d) 2 N, 14 N

40. The length of a pendulum is measured as 1.01 m and time for 30 oscillations is measured as one minute 3 s. Error length is 0.01 m and error in time is 3 s. The percentage error in the measurement of acceleration due to gravity is

(a) 1 (b) 5
(c) 10 (d) 15

Answers

1. (d)	2. (b)	3. (d)	4. (d)	5. (c)	6. (d)	7. (a)	8. (a)	9. (a)	10. (a)
11. (c)	12. (d)	13. (b)	14. (b)	15. (d)	16. (a)	17. (c)	18. (b)	19. (c)	20. (c)
21. (b)	22. (c)	23. (d)	24. (c)	25. (a)	26. (d)	27. (b)	28. (c)	29. (c)	30. (d)
31. (c)	32. (c)	33. (a)	34. (d)	35. (c)	36. (d)	37. (*)	38. (b)	39. (a)	40. (c)

Note '*' None of the given option is correct.

Hints *with* Solutions

1. The time taken by the transverse wave

$$t = 2\sqrt{\frac{l}{g}} = 2\sqrt{\frac{2.45}{9.8}} = 1\text{ s}$$

2. We have, nl = constant

$$n_1 l_1 = n_2 l_2$$

$$(n+8)\,100 = (n-8)\,101$$

or $$\frac{n+8}{n-8} = \frac{101}{100}$$

$$\frac{n}{8} = \frac{201}{1}, \quad n = 1608$$

3. From the lens maker formula

$$\frac{\mu_3}{v} - \frac{\mu_1}{u} = \frac{\mu_2 - \mu_1}{R_1} + \frac{\mu_3 - \mu_2}{R_2}$$

$$\frac{4}{3f_o'} - \frac{1}{\infty} = \frac{1.5-1}{R} + \frac{\frac{4}{3} - 1.5}{-R}$$

$\Rightarrow$ $$f_o' = R = 2f$$

Now, length $= f_o' + f_e'$

$$= 2f_o + 2f_e = 2(f_o + f_e)$$

$$= 2(L) = 2(16) = 32\text{ cm}$$

4. $$P = P_1 + P_2 = \frac{q}{f_1} + \frac{q}{f_2}$$

$$\frac{1}{60} = \frac{q}{f_1} + \frac{q}{f_2}$$

$$\frac{1}{60} = \frac{f_1 + f_2}{f_1 f_2} \quad \text{...(i)}$$

According to question,

$$\frac{\omega_1}{\omega_2} = \frac{f_1}{f_2} \Rightarrow \frac{f_1}{f_2} = \frac{-4}{3}$$

or $$f_1 = -\frac{4}{3} f_2$$

From Eq. (i)

$$\frac{1}{60} = \frac{\frac{4}{3}f_2 + f_2}{(f_2)^2 \frac{4}{3}} \Rightarrow \frac{-\frac{1}{3}}{-\frac{4}{3}f_2}$$

$$f_2 = 15 \text{ cm}$$

$$\therefore \quad f_1 = -\frac{4}{3} \times 15 = -20 \text{ cm}$$

5. From the figure,

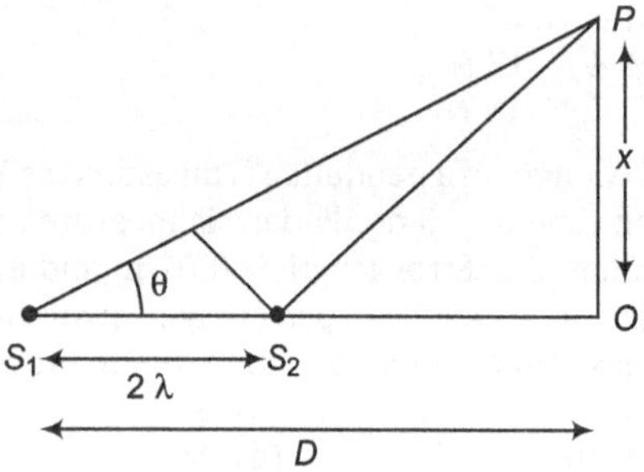

$$(S_1P)^2 = D^2 + x^2$$

and $$(S_2P)^2 = (D - 2\lambda)^2 + x^2$$

So, $$(S_1P)^2 - (S_2P)^2 = D^2 + x^2 - [D^2 + 4\lambda^2 - 4D\lambda + x^2]$$

$$= 4D\lambda - 4\lambda^2$$

$$(S_1P + S_2P)(S_1P - S_2P) = 4D\lambda - 4\lambda^2$$

$$[D >> \lambda]$$

Since, $[D >> \lambda]$ $\therefore S_1P = S_2P$

and neglecting higher power of λ

$$\therefore \quad 2S_1P(S_1P - S_2P) = 4D\lambda$$

$$2(S_1P)(\lambda) = 4D\lambda$$

or $S_1P = 2D$ or $\sqrt{D^2 + x^2} = 2D$

or $x^2 = 3D^2$ or $x = \sqrt{3}D$

Alternative

$$2\lambda \cos\theta = \lambda$$

$$\Rightarrow \quad \cos\theta = \frac{1}{2} \Rightarrow \theta = 60°, \tan\theta = \frac{x}{D}$$

$$\sqrt{3} = \frac{x}{D} \Rightarrow x = \sqrt{3}D$$

6. $T = 2\pi\sqrt{\frac{I}{MB_H}}$

$$\therefore \quad \frac{T_1}{T_2} = \sqrt{\frac{(B_H)_2}{(B_H)_1}}$$

$$T_2 = T_1\sqrt{\frac{(B_H)_1}{(B_H)_2}}$$

$$n_1 = 30 \text{ oscillation/min}$$

$$n_1 = \frac{1}{2} \text{ oscillation/s}$$

$$T_1 = 2 \text{ s}$$

$$T_2 = 2\sqrt{\frac{B_H}{2B_H}} = 2 \times \frac{1}{\sqrt{2}} = \sqrt{2} \text{ s}$$

7. Work done $W = MB(1 - \cos 60°) = \frac{MB}{2}$

The torque required to maintain the magnetic needle

$$\tau = MB\sin\theta = MB\sin 60° = MB\frac{\sqrt{3}}{2}$$

$$\tau = \sqrt{3}W$$

8. Charge that through the wire

$$\Delta q = \Delta CV = (C' - C)V$$

$$= (k - 1)\sigma V = (20 - 1)(80 \times 10^{-6})(30)$$

$$= 4.56 \times 10^{-2} = 45.6 \times 10^{-3} \text{ C}$$

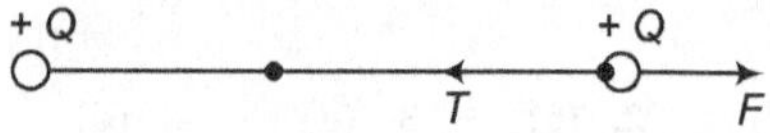

The tension in each string

$$T = F = \frac{1}{4\pi\varepsilon_0}\frac{Q^2}{(2L)^2} = \frac{Q^2}{16\pi\varepsilon_0 L^2}$$

10. For figure I,

Total resistance = $3R$

I power = $I^2(3R)$

For figure II,

Resistance = $\frac{2R}{3}\,\Omega$

II power = $I^2\left(\frac{2R}{3}\right)$

For figure III,

Total resistance = $\frac{R}{3}\,\Omega$

III power = $I^2\left(\frac{R}{3}\right)$

For figure IV,

Total resistance $\frac{3}{2}\,\Omega$

IV power = $I^2\left(\frac{3}{2}R\right)$

Hence, option (a) is correct.

11. Balancing condition of bridge balance

$$\frac{A}{B} = \frac{100}{x}$$

$$\frac{B}{A} = \frac{121}{x}$$

$$\therefore \quad \frac{100}{x} = \frac{x}{121}$$

$$x^2 = 12100$$

$$x = 110\ \Omega$$

12. Total emf produced in a thermocouple does not depend on the duration of time for which the current is passed through thermocouple.

13. The magnetic field

$$dB = \frac{\mu_0 \mathbf{I} \times \mathbf{r} \times \mathbf{d}l}{4\pi r^2}$$

14. The induced emf in secondary coil.

$$e = M\frac{di}{dt} = 92 \times 10^{-6} \times \frac{25}{1 \times 10^{-3}} = 2.3\ \text{V}$$

15. The ratio of kinetic energy of the electron to that of the photon.

$$= \frac{v}{2c} = \frac{1.5 \times 10^8}{2 \times 3 \times 10^8} = \frac{1}{4}$$

16. $\lambda_p = \lambda_\alpha$, $(mqV)_p = (mqV)_\alpha$

Potential difference

$$V_\alpha = \frac{V}{8} \qquad \left[\because \begin{array}{l} m_\alpha = 4m_p \\ q_\alpha = 2q_p \end{array}\right]$$

17. The number of atoms decay in one second

$$\frac{dN}{dt} = \lambda N$$

$$= \frac{0.693}{1620 \times 365 \times 86 \times 400} \times \frac{6.023 \times 10^{23}}{226}$$

$$= 3.61 \times 10^{10}$$

18. After 4 half-lifes $\frac{N_0}{2^4} = \frac{N_0}{16}$

19. $\beta = \dfrac{\alpha}{1-\alpha}$

$$\beta_1 = \frac{\frac{20}{21}}{1 - \frac{20}{21}} = 20, \quad \beta_2 = \frac{\frac{100}{101}}{1 - \frac{100}{101}} = 100$$

The value of β lies between 20 – 100.

20. D-layer — 65 – 75 km

E-layer — 95 – 120 km

F_1-layer — 170 – 190 km

F_2-layer — 250 – 400 km

21. We have,

$$dV = -E \cdot dr = -(5\mathbf{i} + 12\mathbf{j}) \cdot (12\mathbf{i} + 15\mathbf{j})$$

$$= (60 + 60) = -120$$

The change in gravitational potential energy

$$U = mdV = 2 \times (-120) = -240\ \text{J}$$

22. Distance $y_1 = A \sin \dfrac{2\pi}{8} \times 1 = \dfrac{A}{\sqrt{2}}$

and $\qquad y_2 = A - \dfrac{A}{\sqrt{2}}$

The ratio of the distances travelled by it in the first and seconds.

$$\frac{y_1}{y_2} = \frac{1}{\sqrt{2} - 1}$$

23. Young's modulus of materials

$$Y = \frac{F \times l}{A \Delta l}, \frac{\Delta l}{l} = \frac{F}{AY} = \frac{22}{0.02 \times 10^{-4} \times 1.1 \times 10^{11}}$$

$$-10^{-4}$$

Poisson's ratio, $\sigma = \dfrac{\Delta l / l}{\Delta r / r}$

$$\frac{\Delta l}{l} = \sigma \frac{\Delta r}{r} = 0.32 \times \frac{\Delta r}{r}$$

$$= 0.32 \times 10^{-4} = 32 \times 10^{-6}$$

The decrease in cross-sectional area,

$$\frac{\Delta A}{A} = \frac{\Delta A}{0.02} = 0.32 \times \frac{\Delta l}{l}$$

$$\Delta A = 0.64 \times 10^{-6}\ \text{cm}^2$$

24. According to the question,

$$\frac{4}{3}\pi r^3 dg = \frac{2}{3}\pi r^3 \rho g + T \times 2\pi r$$

or $\qquad r = \sqrt{\dfrac{3T}{g(2d - \rho)}}$

25. $\pi\left(\dfrac{D}{2}\right)^2 Xv = n\left(\dfrac{d}{2}\right)^2 Xv', \quad v' = \dfrac{D^2 v}{nd^2}$

26. We have, $\gamma a_1 + 3\alpha_1 = \gamma a_2 + 3\alpha_2$

$$6 \times 10^{-6} + 3(18 \times 10^{-6}) = 24 \times 10^{-6} + 3\alpha_2$$

$$\alpha_2 = 12 \times 10^{-6} / ^\circ\text{C}$$

27. $\dfrac{\Delta I}{I} = 2\dfrac{\Delta k}{k} = 2\alpha\,\Delta T$

$$\frac{\Delta I}{I} = 2\alpha\,\Delta T$$

28. $T^{\gamma} p^{1-\gamma}$ = constant

or $T^{\gamma} = p^{\gamma - 1}$

$$T = p^{\left(\frac{\gamma-1}{\gamma}\right)}$$

$$\therefore \quad \frac{\Delta T}{T} = \frac{\gamma - 1}{\gamma} \times \frac{\Delta p}{p}$$

$$\frac{\Delta T}{T} = \left(\frac{1.5-1}{1.5}\right) \times \frac{0.001}{1.013 \times 10^6}$$

$$\Delta T = 8.98 \times 10^{-8} \text{ K}$$

29. We have, $V \propto T^{2/3}$

and $p \propto \sqrt{V}$

$\therefore \quad p = k\sqrt{V} \Rightarrow p = k\, V^{1/2}$

Work done, $W = \int p\, dV$

$$W = \int kV^{1/2}$$

$$W = \frac{kV^{3/2}}{3/2}$$

$$W = \frac{2}{3}\frac{p}{\sqrt{V}} V^{3/2} = \frac{2}{3} pV \qquad \left[\because V = \frac{p}{\sqrt{V}}\right]$$

$$= \frac{2}{3} nRT = \frac{2}{3} \times 1 \times 8.3 \times 30 = 166.2 \text{ J}$$

30. We have, $P \propto T^4 \propto \frac{1}{\lambda^4} \Rightarrow \frac{P_1}{P_2} = \left(\frac{\lambda_2}{\lambda_1}\right)^4$

$$\frac{P_1}{P_2} = \frac{1}{16} \Rightarrow P_2 = 16P_1 = 16P$$

31. Moment of inertia $I = \frac{2}{3} MR^2$

$$\therefore \quad \frac{I_A}{I_B} = \frac{\frac{2}{5} M_A R^2}{\frac{2}{5} M_B R^2} = \frac{\frac{4}{3}\pi R^3 \rho_A}{\frac{4}{3}\pi R^3 \rho_B} = \frac{\rho_A}{\rho_B}$$

32. Moment of inertia $I = MR^2$

i.e., the moment of inertia depends on the mass of the body.

33. We have, $\mu_k mgs = \frac{p^2}{2M}$ or $s = \frac{p^2}{2M^2 \mu_k g}$

35. Kinetic energy

$$K = \frac{1}{2} mu_1^2, \quad u_1 = \sqrt{\frac{2K}{m}}$$

$$\frac{1}{2} mv_1^2 = \frac{K}{9}, \quad v_1^2 = \frac{2K}{9m}$$

Velocity, $v_1 = \sqrt{\frac{2K}{9m}}$

Kinetic energy $K = \frac{p^2}{2m}$

From conservation of the momentum

$$mu_1 = -mv_1 + p_B$$

$$m(u_1 + v_1) = p_B$$

Final momentum of B

$$p_B = m\left[\sqrt{\frac{2K}{m}} + \sqrt{\frac{2K}{9m}}\right]$$

$$= \sqrt{2mK} + \sqrt{\frac{2mK}{3}} = p + \frac{p}{3} = \frac{4p}{3}$$

36. Induced emf is given by

$$e = Bvl \sin \theta$$

$$= 0.1 \times 10 < 4 \sin 30 = 2 \text{ V}$$

37. $P = \dfrac{\frac{1}{2} mv^2}{t} \Rightarrow v^2 = \dfrac{2Pt}{m} \Rightarrow v^2 \propto \dfrac{2P}{m}$

38. $T_1 = \dfrac{2u \sin \theta}{g}$

and $T_2 = \dfrac{2u \cos \theta}{g}$

$$T_1 T_2 = \frac{2u^2 \sin \theta \cos \theta}{g} = \frac{2r}{g}$$

$$\left[\because R = \frac{v^2 \sin 2\theta}{g}\right]$$

39. $(16 - x)^2 = 8^2 + x^2$

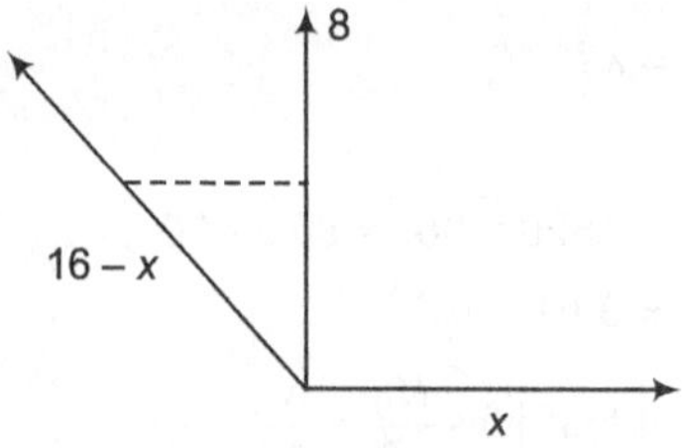

$$256 + x^2 - 32x = 64 + x^2$$

$$32x = 192$$

$$x = \frac{192}{32} = 6$$

$\therefore$ Forces 6 N, 10 N.

40. $\dfrac{\Delta g}{g} = \dfrac{\Delta l}{l} + \dfrac{2\Delta T}{T}$

We get, $\dfrac{\Delta g}{g} \% = 10\%$

EAMCET

Engineering Entrance Exam

Solved Paper 2011

1. Two photons of energy 2.5 eV and 3.5 eV fall on a metal surface of work function 1.5 eV. The ratio of the maximum velocities of the photoelectrons emitted from the metal surface is

(a) 1 : 4 (b) 2 : 1
(c) 1 : 2 (d) $1 : \sqrt{2}$

2. Calculate the wavelength of the K_a line for $z = 31$, when $a = 5 \times 10^7$ $Hz^{1/2}$ for a characteristic X-ray spectrum.

(a) 1.33 Å (b) 1.33 nm
(c) 133×10^{-10} m (d) 133 nm

3. If 200 MeV of energy is released in the fission of one nucleus of $^{236}_{92}U$, the number of nuclei that must undergo fission to release an energy of 1000 J is

(a) 3.125×10^{13} (b) 6.25×10^{13}
(c) 12.5×10^{13} (d) 3.125×10^{14}

4. In a *p-n* junction diode, the thickness of deplection layer is 2×10^{-6} m and barrier potential is 0.3 V. The intensity of the electric field at the junction is

(a) 0.6×10^{-6} Vm^{-1} from n to p side
(b) 0.6×10^{-6} Vm^{-1} from p to n side
(c) 1.5×10^5 Vm^{-1} from n to p side
(d) 1.5×10^5 Vm^{-1} from p to n side

5. The dimensional formula of $\frac{1}{2}\mu_0 H^2$ (μ_0 = permeability of free space and H = magnetic field intensity) is

(a) $[MLT^{-1}]$ (b) $[ML^2T^{-2}]$
(c) $[ML^{-1}T^{-2}]$ (d) $[ML^2T^{-1}]$

6. A certain vector in the *xy*-plane has an *x*-component of 4 m and a *y*-component of 10 m. It is then rotated in the *xy*-plane so that its *x*-component is doubled. Then its new *y*-component is (approximately)

(a) 20 m (b) 7.2 m
(c) 5.0 m (d) 4.5 m

7. A police party is moving in a jeep at a constant speed v. They saw a thief at a distance x on a motorcycle which is at rest. The moment the police saw the thief, the thief started at constant acceleration a. Which of the following relations is true if the police is able to catch the thief?

(a) $v^2 < ax$ (b) $v^2 < 2ax$
(c) $v^2 \geq 2ax$ (d) $v^2 = ax$

8. A 1 N pendulum bob is held at an angle θ from the vertical by a 2 N horizontal force **F** as shown in the figure. The tension in the string supporting the pendulum bob (in newton) is

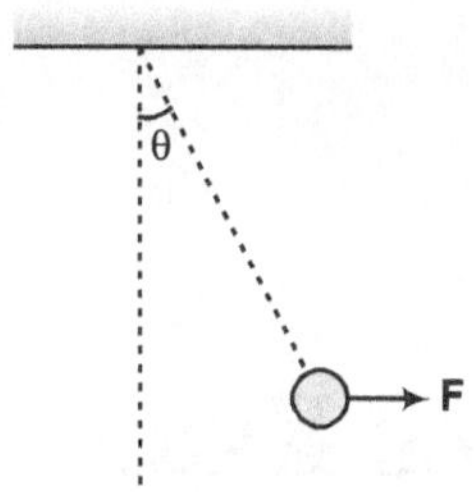

(a) $\cos\theta$ (b) $\dfrac{2}{\cos\theta}$

(c) $\sqrt{5}$ (d) 1

9. The maximum tension a rope can withstand is 60 kg-wt. The ratio of maximum acceleration with which two boys of masses 20 kg and 30 kg can climb up the rope at the same time is

(a) 1 : 2 (b) 2 : 1

(c) 4 : 3 (d) 3 : 2

10. A ball is let fall from a height h_0. It makes n collisions with the earth. After n collisions it rebounds with a velocity v_n and the ball rises to a height h_n, then coefficient of restitution is given by

(a) $e = \left[\dfrac{h_n}{h_0}\right]^{1/2n}$ (b) $e = \left[\dfrac{h_0}{h_n}\right]^{1/2n}$

(c) $e = \dfrac{1}{n}\sqrt{\dfrac{h_n}{h_0}}$ (d) $e = \dfrac{1}{n}\sqrt{\dfrac{h_0}{h_n}}$

11. A circular disc of radius R is removed from a bigger circular disc of radius $2R$ such that the circumferences of the discs touch. The centre of mass of the new disc is at a distance αR from the centre of the bigger disc. The value of α is

(a) $\dfrac{1}{2}$ (b) $\dfrac{1}{3}$

(c) $\dfrac{1}{4}$ (d) $\dfrac{1}{6}$

12. A uniform chain of length L is lying on the horizontal table. If the coefficient of friction between the chain and the table top is μ, what is the maximum length of the chain that can hang over the edge of the table without disturbing the rest of the chain on the table?

(a) $\dfrac{L}{(1+\mu)}$ (b) $\dfrac{\mu L}{(1+\mu)}$

(c) $\dfrac{L}{(1-\mu)}$ (d) $\dfrac{\mu L}{(1-\mu)}$

13. Two uniform circular discs having the same mass and the same thickness but different radii are made from different materials. The disc with the smaller rotational inertia is

(a) the one made from the more dense material

(b) the one made from the less dense material

(c) the disc with the larger angular velocity

(d) the disc with the larger torque

14. A thin hollow sphere of mass m is completely filled with a liquid of mass m. When the sphere rolls with a velocity v, kinetic energy of the system is (neglect friction)

(a) $\dfrac{1}{2}mv^2$ (b) mv^2

(c) $\dfrac{4}{3}mv^2$ (d) $\dfrac{4}{5}mv^2$

15. Assertion A An astronaut inside a massive spaceship orbiting around the earth will experience a finite but small gravitational force.

Reason R The centripetal force necessary to keep the spaceship in orbit around the earth is provided by the gravitational force between the earth and the spaceship.

(a) Both (A) and (R) are true and (R) is the correct explanation of (A)

(b) Both (A) and (R) are true and (R) is not the correct explanation of (A)

(c) (A) is true but (R) is not true

(d) (A) is not true but (R) is true

16. A simple harmonic oscillator consists of a particle of mass m and an ideal spring with spring constant k. The particle oscillates with a time period T. The spring is cut into two equal parts. If one part oscillates with the same particle, the time period will be

(a) $2T$ (b) $\sqrt{2}T$

(c) $\frac{T}{\sqrt{2}}$ (d) $\frac{T}{2}$

17. Two blocks of masses 1 kg and 2 kg are connected by a metal wire going over a smooth pulley. The breaking stress of metal is $\frac{40}{3\pi} \times 10^6 \text{ Nm}^{-2}$. What should be the minimum radius of wire used if it should not break? ($g = 10 \text{ ms}^{-2}$)

(a) 0.5 mm (b) 1 mm

(c) 1.5 mm (d) 2 mm

18. If two soap bubbles of different radii are connected by a tube, then

(a) air flows from bigger bubble to the smaller bubble till sizes become equal

(b) air flows from bigger bubble to the smaller bubble till sizes are interchanged

(c) air flows from smaller bubble to bigger

(d) there is no flow of air

19. A large open tank has two holes in the wall. One is a square hole of side L at a depth y from the top and the other is a circular hole of radius R at a depth $4y$ from the top. When the tank is completely filled with water, the quantities of water flowing out per second from the two holes are the same. Then value of R is

(a) $\frac{L}{\sqrt{2\pi}}$ (b) $2\pi L$

(c) $L\sqrt{\frac{2}{\pi}}$ (d) $\frac{L}{2\pi}$

20. A non-conducting body floats in a liquid at 20°C with $\frac{2}{3}$ of its volume immersed in the liquid. When liquid temperature is increased to 100°C, $\frac{3}{4}$ of body's volume is immersed in the liquid. Then the coefficient of real expansion of the liquid is (neglecting the expansion of container of the liquid)

(a) $15.6 \times 10^{-4}\,°\text{C}^{-1}$

(b) $156 \times 10^{-4}\,°\text{C}^{-1}$

(c) $1.56 \times 10^{-4}\,°\text{C}^{-1}$

(d) $0.156 \times 10^{4}\,°\text{C}^{-1}$

21. An insulated cylindrical vessel filled with an insulated piston of negligible weight and negligible thickness at the mid point of the vessel. The cylinder contains a gas at 0°C. When the gas is heated to 100°C, the piston moves through a length of 5 cm. Length of the cylindrical vessel in cm is

(a) 13.65 (b) 27.3

(c) 38.6 (d) 64.6

22. A reversible engine converts one-sixth of the heat supplied into work. When the temperature of the sink is reduced by 62°C, the efficiency of the engine is doubled. The temperatures of the source and sink are

(a) 99°C, 37°C (b) 80°C, 37°C

(c) 95°C, 37°C (d) 90°C, 37°C

23. During an adiabatic process, the pressure of a gas is proportional to the cube of its temperature. The value of C_p / C_V for that gas is

(a) $\frac{7}{5}$ (b) $\frac{4}{5}$

(c) $\frac{5}{3}$ (d) $\frac{3}{2}$

24. Two slabs A and B of different materials but of the same thickness are joined end to end to form a composite slab. The thermal conductivities of A and B are k_1 and k_2 respectively. A steady temperature difference of 12°C is maintained across the composite slab. If $k_1 = \frac{k_2}{2}$, the temperature difference across slab A is

(a) 4°C (b) 6°C

(c) 8°C (d) 10°C

25. The wavelengths of two sound notes in air are $\frac{40}{195}$ m and $\frac{40}{193}$ m. Each note produces 9 beats per second separately with a third note of fixed frequency. The velocity of sound in air in m/s is

(a) 360 (b) 320
(c) 300 (d) 340

26. Two uniform stretched strings *A* and *B*, made of steel, are vibrating under the same tension. If the first overtone of *A* is equal to the second overtone of *B* and if the radius of *A* is twice that of *B*, the ratio of the lengths of the strings is

(a) 2 : 3 (b) 1 : 2
(c) 1 : 3 (d) 1 : 4

27. The focal length of a lens of dispersive power 0.45 which should be placed in contact with a convex lens of focal length 84 cm and dispersive power 0.21 to make the achromatic combination from the two lenses, in cm is

(a) 45 (b) 90
(c) 180 (d) –180

28. Which of the following statements are true in the context of a Compound Microscope?

(A) Each lens produces a virtual and inverted image.
(B) The objective has a very short focal length.
(C) The eyepiece is used as a simple magnifying glass.
(D) The objective and eyepiece are convex and concave lenses respectively.

(a) (A), (B) and (D) (b) (B) and (C)
(c) (A), (C) and (D) (d) (B) and (D)

29. A ray of light refracts from medium 1 into a thin layer of medium 2, crosses the layer and is incident at the critical angle on the interface between the medium 2 and 3 as shown in the figure. If the angle of incidence of ray is θ, the value of θ is

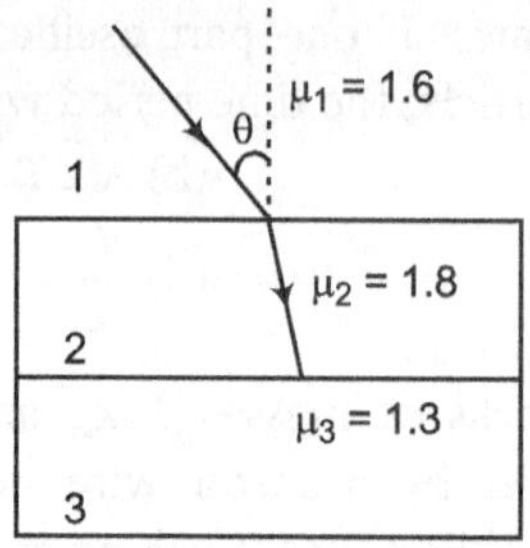

(a) $\sin^{-1}\left(\frac{8}{9}\right)$ (b) $\sin^{-1}\left(\frac{13}{18}\right)$
(c) $\sin^{-1}\left(\frac{13}{16}\right)$ (d) $\sin^{-1}\left(\frac{8}{13}\right)$

30. In the Young's double slit experiment, the resultant intensity at a point on the screen is 75% of the maximum intensity of the bright fringe. Then the phase difference between the two interfering rays at that point is

(a) $\frac{\pi}{6}$ (b) $\frac{\pi}{4}$ (c) $\frac{\pi}{3}$ (d) $\frac{\pi}{2}$

31. If a bar magnet of pole strength *m* and magnetic moment *M* is cut equally 5 times parallel to its axis and again 3 times perpendicular to its axis, then the pole strength and magnetic moment of each piece are respectively

(a) $\frac{m}{20}, \frac{M}{4}$ (b) $\frac{m}{5}, \frac{M}{20}$
(c) $\frac{m}{6}, \frac{M}{24}$ (d) $\frac{m}{5}, \frac{M}{24}$

32. Some physical quantities are given in the List I and the related units are given in the List II. Match the correct pairs in the lists.

List I	List II
(A) Magnetic field intensity	(i) Am
(B) Magnetic flux	(ii) Wb m^{-2}
(C) Magnetic pole strength	(iii) Wb
(D) Magnetic induction	(iv) Am^{-1}
	(v) Am^2

(a) (A)-(i), (B)-(ii), (C)-(iii), (D)-(v)
(b) (A)-(iv), (B)-(iii), (C)-(i), (D)-(ii)
(c) (A)-(iv), (B)-(i), (C)-(v), (D)-(ii)
(d) (A)-(ii), (B)-(iii), (C)-(i), (D)-(iv)

33. A fully charged capacitor has a capacitance C. It is discharged through a small coil of resistance wire, embedded in a block of specific heat s and mass m under thermally isolated conditions. If the temperature of the block is raised by ΔT, the potential difference V across the capacitor initially is

(a) $\left(\frac{2ms\Delta T}{C}\right)^2$ (b) $\left(\frac{2ms\Delta T}{C}\right)^{1/2}$

(c) $\left(\frac{2ms\Delta T}{C}\right)$ (d) $2ms\Delta TC$

34. Two identical condensers M and N are connected in series with a battery. The space between the plates of M is completely filled with a dielectric medium of dielectric constant 8 and a copper plate of thickness $\frac{d}{2}$ is introduced between the plates of N. (d is the distance between the plates). Then potential differences across M and N are, respectively, in the ratio

(a) 1 : 4 (b) 4 : 1

(c) 3 : 8 (d) 1 : 6

35. The electric current i in the circuit shown is

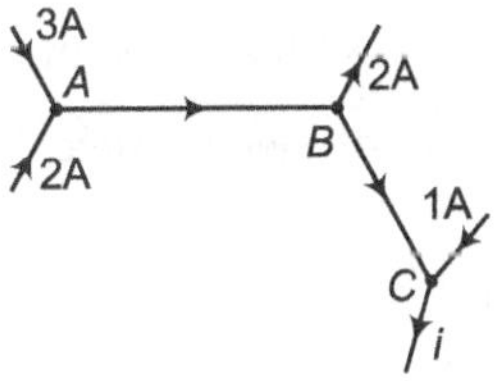

(a) 6 A (b) 2 A (c) 3 A (d) 4 A

36. In the circuit shown below, the ammeter reading is zero. Then the value of the resistance R is

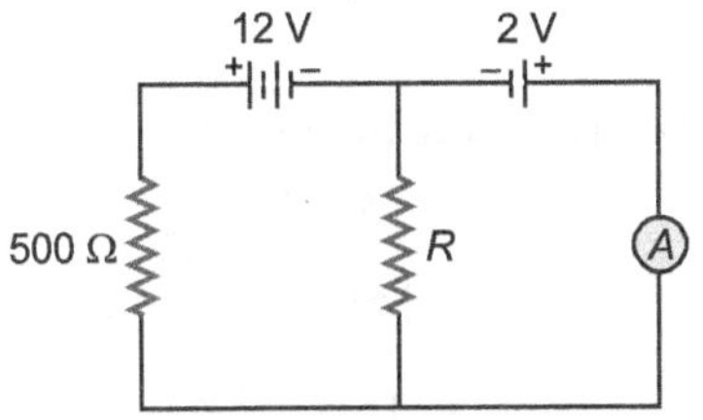

(a) 50 Ω (b) 100 Ω

(c) 200 Ω (d) 400 Ω

37. The thermo emf of a hypothetical thermocouple varies with the temperature θ of hot junction as $E = a\theta + b\theta^2$ in volts, where the ratio a/b is 700°C. If the cold junction is kept at 0°C, then the neutral temperature is

(a) 700°C

(b) 1400°C

(c) 390°C

(d) no neutral temperature is possible for this thermocouple

38. Match the following and find the correct pairs.

List I	List II
(A) Fleming's left hand rule	(i) Direction of induced current
(B) Right hand thumb rule	(ii) Magnitude and direction of magnetic induction
(C) Biot-Savart law	(iii) Direction of force due to magnetic induction
(D) Fleming's right hand rule	(iv) Direction of magnetic lines due to current

(a) (A)-(iii), (B)-(i), (C)-(ii), (D)-(iv)

(b) (A)-(iii), (B)-(iv), (C)-(ii), (D)-(i)

(c) (A)-(ii), (B)-(iv), (C)-(iii), (D)-(i)

(d) (A)-(iv), (B)-(iii), (C)-(i), (D)-(ii)

39. A constant voltage of 25 V is applied to a series L-R circuit at $t = 0$, by closing a switch. What is the potential difference across the resistor and the inductor at time $t = 0$?

(a) 0 V, 25 V (b) 12.5 V, 1.25 V

(c) 10 V, 15 V (d) 25 V, 0 V

40. The sensitivity of a galvanometer is 60 division/A. When a shunt is used, its sensitivity becomes 10 division/A. If the galvanometer is of resistance 20 Ω, the value of shunt used is

(a) 4Ω (b) 5Ω

(c) 20Ω (d) 2Ω

Answers

1. (d)	2. (a)	3. (a)	4. (c)	5. (c)	6. (b)	7. (c)	8. (c)	9. (d)	10. (a)
11. (b)	12. (b)	13. (a)	14. (c)	15. (d)	16. (c)	17. (c)	18. (c)	19. (a)	20. (a)
21. (b)	22. (a)	23. (d)	24. (c)	25. (a)	26. (c)	27. (d)	28. (b)	29. (c)	30. (c)
31. (c)	32. (b)	33. (b)	34. (a)	35. (d)	36. (b)	37. (*)	38. (b)	39. (a)	40. (a)

Hints & Solutions

1. Using the equation

$$\frac{1}{2}mv_1^2 = h\nu_{0_1} - \phi_0 \quad \ldots\text{(i)}$$

and $$\frac{1}{2}mv_2^2 = h\nu_{0_2} - \phi_0 \quad \ldots\text{(ii)}$$

Dividing Eq. (i) by Eq. (ii), we get

$$\frac{\frac{1}{2}mv_1^2}{\frac{1}{2}mv_2^2} = \frac{h\nu_{0_1} - \phi_0}{h\nu_{0_2} - \phi_0}$$

$$\frac{v_1^2}{v_2^2} = \frac{(2.5-1.5)}{(3.5-1.5)} = \frac{1}{2}$$

$$\therefore \quad \frac{v_1^2}{v_2^2} = \frac{1}{2} \text{ or } \frac{v_1}{v_2} = \frac{1}{\sqrt{2}}$$

2. Given, $z = 31$ and $a = 5 \times 10^7 \text{ Hz}^{1/2}$

$$\sqrt{\nu} = a(z-1)$$

or $$\nu = a^2(z-1)^2$$

$$= (5 \times 10^7)^2(31-1)^2$$

$$= 25 \times 10^{14} \times 30 \times 30$$

$$= 2.25 \times 10^{18} \text{ Hz}$$

$$\therefore \quad \nu = \frac{c}{\lambda} \Rightarrow \lambda = \frac{c}{\nu}$$

$$= \frac{3 \times 10^8 \text{ ms}^{-1}}{2.25 \times 10^{18} \text{Hz}}$$

$$= 1.33 \times 10^{-10} \text{ m} = 1.33 \text{ Å}$$

3. Energy released in the fission of one nucleus

$$= 200 \text{ MeV}$$

$$= 200 \times 1.6 \times 10^{-13} \text{ J}$$

$$= 3.2 \times 10^{-11} \text{ J}$$

Energy to be released = 1000 J

3.2×10^{-11} J energy is released due to number of nucleus fissioned = 1

$\therefore$ 1000 J energy is released due to number of nucleus fissioned

$$= \frac{1 \times 1000}{3.2 \times 10^{-11}}$$

$$= 3.125 \times 10^{13} \text{ nucleus}$$

4. Here, the barrier voltage, $V = 0.3$ volt and the width of depletion layer,

$$d = 2 \times 10^{-6} \text{ m}$$

$\therefore$ Electric field at the junction,

$$E = \frac{V}{d} = \frac{0.3 \text{ V}}{2 \times 10^{-6} \text{ m}}$$

$$= 1.5 \times 10^5 \text{ V/m}$$

The direction of electric field is from n-type to p-type.

5. $[\mu_0] = [\text{MLT}^{-2}\text{A}^{-2}]$ and $[H] = [\text{AL}^{-1}]$

$$\therefore \left[\frac{1}{2}\mu_0 H^2\right] = [\text{MLT}^{-2}\text{A}^{-2}][\text{AL}^{-1}]^2 = [\text{ML}^{-1}\text{T}^{-2}]$$

6. Here, $\mathbf{A} = 4\mathbf{i} + 10\mathbf{j}$

$$\therefore \quad |\mathbf{A}| = \sqrt{(4)^2 + (10)^2} = \sqrt{16 + 100}$$

$$= \sqrt{116} \text{ m}$$

Now, according to question,

$$\mathbf{A} = 8\mathbf{i} + n\mathbf{j}$$

So, $$|\mathbf{A}| = \sqrt{(8)^2 + n^2}$$

$$\therefore \quad \sqrt{116} = \sqrt{(8)^2 + n^2}$$

Squaring both sides

$$116 = 64 + n^2$$

or $$n^2 = 116 - 64 = 52$$

or $$n = 7.2 \text{ m}$$

7. Let the police party catch the thief after t second.

$\therefore$ Distance travelled by police party in t seccond $= vt$

and distance travelled by thief $= x + \frac{1}{2}\alpha t^2$

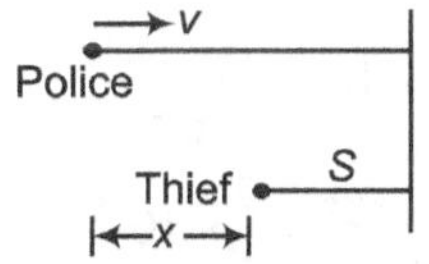

So, $$x + \frac{1}{2}\alpha t^2 \le vt$$

or $$\frac{\alpha t^2}{2} - vt + x = 0 \text{ or } t = \frac{v \pm \sqrt{v^2 - 2\alpha x}}{\alpha}$$

For t to be real, $v^2 \ge 2\alpha x$

8. As the bob is in equilibrium under the effect of three forces — T, F and W

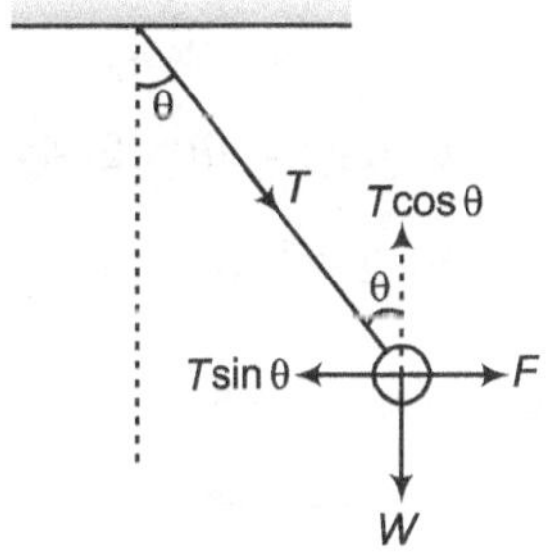

$\therefore$ $$\mathbf{T} + \mathbf{P} + \mathbf{W} = 0$$

From, the figure $$T\cos\theta = W \quad \dots\text{(i)}$$

$$T\sin\theta = F \quad \dots\text{(ii)}$$

From Eqs. (i) and (ii)

$$T^2 = W^2 + F^2$$

or $$T = \sqrt{W^2 + F^2}$$

$$= \sqrt{(1)^2 + (2)^2} = \sqrt{5}$$

9. $60 \text{ kg-wt} = 20(g + a_1) + 30(g + a_2)$

$$= 20 \text{ kg-wt} + 30 \text{ kg-wt} + 20a_1 + 30a_2$$

$$\Rightarrow \quad 20a_1 + 30a_2 = 10 \text{ kg-wt}$$

$$\Rightarrow \quad 2a_1 + 3a_2 = 1$$

$$a_1 = \frac{1}{4}g, \quad a_2 = \frac{1}{6}g$$

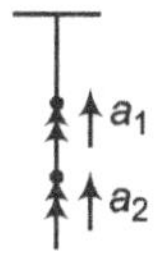

$$a_1 : a_2 = 6 : 4 = 3 : 2$$

10. The velocity of ball after nth rebound will be

$$v_n = e^n v_0 \quad (\text{where } v_0 = \sqrt{2gh_0})$$

Therefore,the height after nth rebound will be

$$h_n = \frac{v_n^2}{2g} = \frac{e^{2n} v_0^2}{2g}$$

$$= \frac{e^{2n} \times 2gh_0}{2g}$$

$$\Rightarrow \quad e^{2n} = \frac{h_n}{h_0} \text{ or } e = \left[\frac{h_n}{h_0}\right]^{1/2n}$$

11. Let centre O_1 of disc be the origin. Due to symmetry the centre of mass of remaining part will lie at x-axis. Let CM of new disc is at point O_2 where, $O_1O_2 = \alpha R$ (given).

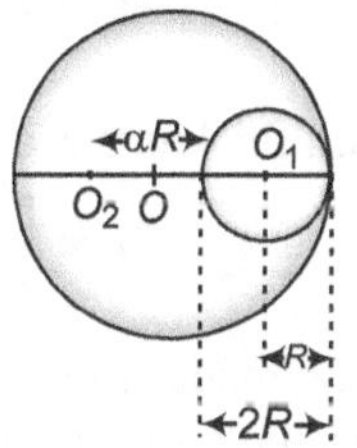

here mass of cut off portion,

$$m = \frac{\pi(R)^2 \cdot M}{\pi(2R)^2} = \frac{M}{4}$$

and position of its centre of mass, $O_1O_1 = R$

Hence, for remaining part (new disc)

$$x_{CM} = \alpha R = \frac{M \times 0 - \left(\frac{M}{4}\right) \times R}{M - \frac{M}{4}}$$

$$= -\frac{R}{3} \Rightarrow \alpha = \frac{1}{3}$$

12. Let l' part of the chain is hanging over the edge of table without sliding.

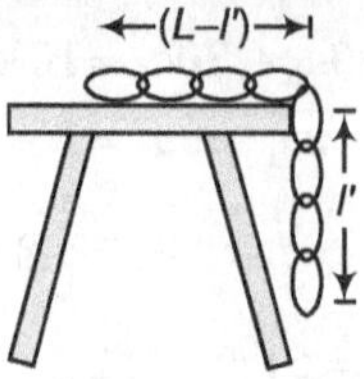

$$\therefore \quad \mu = \frac{\text{Length hanging over the edge}}{\text{Length lying on the table}}$$

(As the chain have uniform linear density)

$$\therefore \quad \mu = \frac{l'}{(L - l')}$$

$$\Rightarrow \quad l' = \frac{\mu L}{(1 + \mu)}$$

13. Moment of inertia of circular disc $= \frac{1}{2} MR^2$

$$= \frac{1}{2} M \left(\frac{M}{\pi t \rho} \right)$$

$$= \frac{1}{2} \frac{M^2}{\pi t \rho}$$

$$\left(\text{As } M = \pi R^2 t \rho \Rightarrow R^2 = \frac{M}{\pi t \rho} \right)$$

If mass and thickness are same, then

$$I \propto \frac{1}{\rho}$$

So, the disc made from more dense material will have smaller rotational inertia.

14. Total energy = KE + rotational KE

$$= \frac{1}{2}(2m)v^2 + \frac{1}{3}mv^2$$

$$= \frac{4}{3}mv^2$$

15. Astronaut would not experience any gravitational force as it is balanced by centrifugal force.

So, A is false and R is true.

16. Mass of the particle $= m$

spring constant $= k$

The time period of oscillator, $T = 2\pi\sqrt{\frac{m}{k}}$

As $k \propto \frac{1}{l}$ (where l is the length of spring)

$$\because \quad k' = 2k$$

$$\therefore \quad T' = 2\pi\sqrt{\frac{m}{2k}} = \frac{1}{\sqrt{2}} T$$

17. Breaking stress $= \frac{F}{A}$

Here, breaking stress $= \frac{40}{3\pi} \times 10^6 \text{ Nm}^{-2}$

$$\Rightarrow \quad \frac{40}{3\pi} \times 10^6 = \frac{3 \times 10}{\pi r^2}$$

$$\Rightarrow \quad r^2 = \frac{9}{4} \times 10^{-6} \text{ or } r = 1.5 \times 10^{-3} \text{m}$$

$$= 1.5 \text{ mm}$$

18. Air flows from smaller bubble to bigger as the pressure in smaller bubble is higher.

19. By the principle of continuity

$$A_1 v_1 = A_2 v_2$$

According to question, $A_1 = L^2$

$$v_1 = \sqrt{2gy} \text{ and } A_2 = \pi R^2$$

$$v_2 = \sqrt{2g\,4y}$$

$$\therefore \quad L^2\sqrt{2gy} = \pi R^2 \sqrt{2g\,4y}$$

or $\quad L^2 = 2\pi R^2$ or $R = \frac{L}{\sqrt{2\pi}}$

20. Coefficient of real expansion

$$\gamma_R = \frac{V_2 - V_1}{V_1(t_2 - t_1)}$$

Here, $\quad V_2 = \frac{3}{4}, V_1 = \frac{2}{3}$

and $\quad (t_2 - t_1) = (100 - 20) = 80°\text{C}$

$$\therefore \quad \gamma_R = \frac{\left(\frac{3}{4} - \frac{2}{3}\right)}{\frac{2}{3}(80)} = \frac{1}{640}$$

$$= 15.6 \times 10^{-4} \text{°C}^{-1}$$

21. According to question,

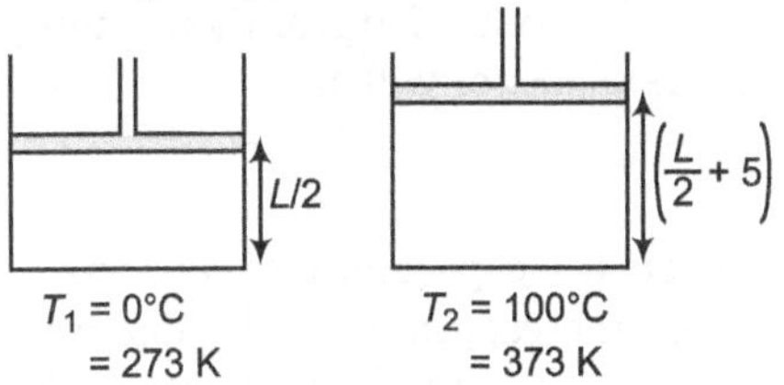

$$\therefore \quad \frac{273}{L/2} = \frac{373}{(L/2)+5}$$

$$\Rightarrow \quad 273\left(\frac{L}{2}+5\right) = 373\left(\frac{L}{2}\right)$$

or $$273 \times 5 = 100\left(\frac{L}{2}\right)$$

or $$L = 27.3 \text{ cm}$$

22. The efficiency of engine, $\eta = \frac{T_1 - T_2}{T_1}$

According to question, $2\eta = \frac{T_1 - (T_2 - 62)}{T_1}$

or $$\frac{1}{2} = \frac{T_1 - T_2}{(T_1 - T_2) + 62}$$

or $$62 = (T_1 - T_2)$$

Only option (a) satisfies the condition.

23. In adiabatic process

$$pV^{\gamma} = k \quad \ldots(i)$$

Given, $p \propto T^3$ or $p = kT^3$

$$= k\left(\frac{pV}{R}\right)^3$$

$$= \left(\frac{k}{R^3}\right)p^3V^3 \text{ or } p = \left(\frac{k}{R^3}\right)p^3V^3$$

$$\Rightarrow \quad p^2V^3 = k$$

$$\Rightarrow \quad pV^{3/2} = k \quad \ldots(ii)$$

Comparing Eqs. (i) and (ii)

we get $$\gamma = \frac{3}{2} = \frac{C_p}{C_V}$$

24. The given situation can be shown as

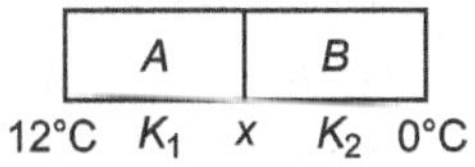

Rate of flow of heat will be equal in both the slabs

$$\therefore \quad (12 - x)K_1 = K_2(x - 0)$$

$$12 - x = 2x \quad \left(\because K_1 = \frac{K_2}{2}\right)$$

$$\Rightarrow \quad x = 4°C$$

The temperature difference across slab

$$A = (12 - x) = (12 - 4)$$
$$= 8°C$$

25. Here, $v_1 = \frac{v}{\left(\frac{40}{195}\right)}$ and $v_2 = \frac{v}{\left(\frac{40}{193}\right)}$

$$\Rightarrow \quad v_1 = \frac{v(195)}{40} \text{ and } v_2 = \frac{v(193)}{40}$$

According to given condition

$$\frac{v}{40}(195) - v = 9 \quad \ldots(i)$$

and $$v - \frac{v\,(193)}{40} = 9 \quad \ldots(ii)$$

Adding Eqs. (i) and (ii)

$$18 = \frac{v}{40}(195 - 193) = \frac{2v}{40} \Rightarrow 18 = \frac{v}{20}$$

or $$v = 360 \text{ m/s}$$

26. Given, 1st overtone of A = 2nd overtone of B

$$\Rightarrow \quad \frac{1}{l_1}\sqrt{\frac{T}{\pi r_1^2 d}} = \frac{3}{2l_2}\sqrt{\frac{T}{\pi r_2^2 d}}$$

$$\Rightarrow \quad \frac{r_2}{r_1} = \frac{3}{2}\left(\frac{l_1}{l_2}\right)$$

But $$r_1 = 2r_2$$

$$\therefore \quad \frac{r_2}{2r_2} = \frac{3}{2}\left(\frac{l_1}{l_2}\right)$$

or $$\frac{l_1}{l_2} = \frac{1}{3} \Rightarrow l_1 : l_2 = 1 : 3$$

27. Here, $\omega_1 = 0.45$

$$\omega_2 = 0.21 \text{ and } f_2 = 84 \text{ cm}$$

As the lens are kept is contact it is achromatic condition.

$$\therefore \quad \frac{\omega_1}{\omega_2} = -\frac{f_1}{f_2}$$

$$\frac{0.45}{0.21} = -\frac{f_1}{84}$$

$$\Rightarrow \quad f_1 = -\frac{45 \times 84}{21} = -180 \text{ cm}$$

28. In compound microscope both objective and eyepiece are convex lenses. An objective lens is of small focal length and eyepiece is of large focal length.
So, option (b) is correct.

29. As the light ray incident at critical angle,

$$\sin C = \frac{\mu_3}{\mu_2} = \frac{1.3}{1.8} \text{ and } C = r$$

$$\therefore \quad \sin r = \frac{1.3}{1.8}$$

$$\Rightarrow \quad \sin \theta = \frac{1.8}{1.6} \times \frac{1.3}{1.8} = \frac{13}{16} \text{ or } \theta = \sin^{-1}\left(\frac{13}{16}\right)$$

30. Given, $I_R = 75\%$ of $I_{\max} = \frac{3}{4} I_{\max}$

$$= \frac{3}{4}(4a^2) = 3a^2 \Rightarrow 4a^2 \cos^2 \frac{\phi}{2} = 3a^2$$

$$\cos^2 \frac{\phi}{2} = \frac{3}{4} \text{ or } \cos \frac{\phi}{2} = \frac{\sqrt{3}}{2}$$

$$\Rightarrow \quad \frac{\phi}{2} = \frac{\pi}{6} \text{ or } \phi = \frac{\pi}{3}$$

31. Given, pole strength $= m$
and magnetic moment $= M$
When it is cut 5 times parallel to its axis,
pole strength, $m' = \frac{m}{6}$
When it is cut 3 times perpendicular to its axis, then length $2l' = \frac{2l}{4}$

$\therefore$ pole strength, $m' = \frac{m}{6}$

and magnetic moment,

$$M' = \left(\frac{m}{6}\right)\left(\frac{2l}{4}\right) = \frac{M}{24}$$

32.

Magnetic field intensity	— Am^{-1}
Magnetic flux	— Wb
Magnetic pole strength	— A-m
Magnetic induction	— Wb-m^{-2}

So, the correct option is (b).

33. Let V be the potential across the capacitor when it is fully charged, then, energy stored in the capacitor will be

$$= \frac{1}{2} CV^2$$

(where C = capacitance of capacitor)
When the capacitor is fully discharged, loss of energy is in the form of heat $= \Delta H$
As the system is thermally isolated so,

$$\Delta H = \frac{1}{2} CV^2$$

Here, $\quad \Delta H = ms\Delta T$

$$\therefore \quad \frac{1}{2} CV^2 = ms\Delta T \text{ or } V = \left(\frac{2ms\Delta T}{C}\right)^{1/2}$$

34. Let the capacitance of condensor, $M = C$
The new capacitance of condensor, $C_M = 8C$
The capacitance of condensor, $N = C$
The new capacitance of condensor, $C_N = \frac{C'}{2}$

where $\quad C' = \frac{A\varepsilon_0}{d/4} = \frac{4A\varepsilon_0}{d} = 4C$

$$\therefore \quad C_N = \frac{C'}{2} = \frac{4C}{2} = 2C$$

Since the two condensers are connected in series

$$\therefore \quad V_M : V_N = \frac{1}{C_M} : \frac{1}{C_N}$$

$$= \frac{1}{8C} : \frac{1}{2C} = 1:4$$

$$\Rightarrow \quad V_M : V_N = 1:4$$

35. Given, situation is predicted as

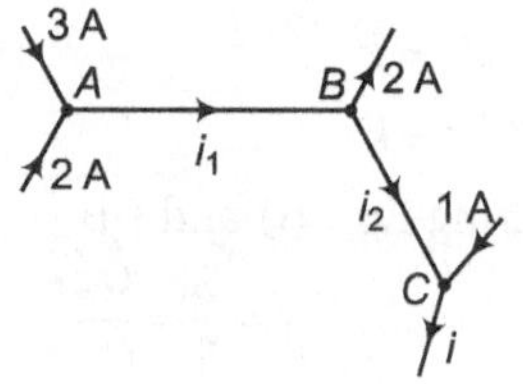

$$i_1 = 3 + 2 = 5 \text{ A}$$

$$i_2 = i_1 - 2 = 5 - 2 = 3 \text{ A}$$

$$i = i_2 + 1 = 3 + 1 = 4 \text{ A}$$

36. Given, circuit

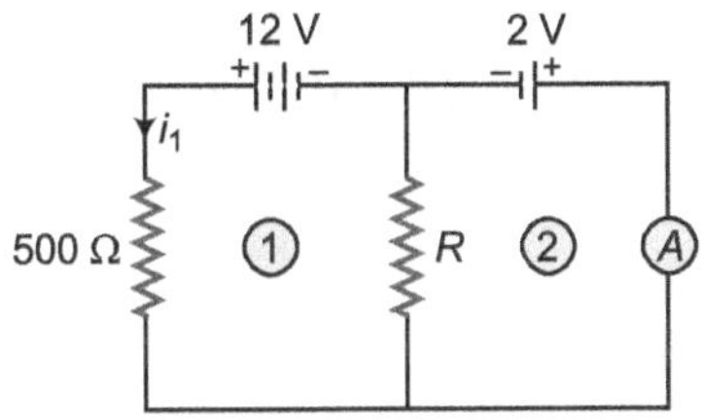

In loop (1)

$$12 - 500i_1 - Ri_1 = 0$$

$$\Rightarrow \quad 12 = i_1(500 + R) \quad \ldots\text{(i)}$$

In loop (2)

$$12 - 500i_1 - 2 = 0$$

$$\Rightarrow \quad 10 = 500i_1$$

$$\text{or} \quad i_1 = \frac{1}{50}\text{ A} \quad \ldots\text{(ii)}$$

From Eqs. (i) and (ii)

$$12 \times \frac{1}{i_1} = (500 + R)$$

$$\Rightarrow \quad 12 \times 50 = 500 + R$$

$$\Rightarrow \quad R = 100\,\Omega$$

37. Given, $E = a\theta + b\theta^2$

$$\therefore \quad p = \frac{dE}{d\theta} = \frac{d}{d\theta}(a\theta + b\theta^2)$$

$$= a + 2b\theta$$

At $\theta = T_n$, $p = 0$

$$\Rightarrow \quad T_n = -\frac{a}{2b}$$

$$= -350°\text{C}$$

No correct option is given.

38.

Fleming's left hand rule	—	Direction of force due to magnetic induction.
Right hand thumb rule	—	Direction of magnetic lines due to current.
Biot-savart law	—	Magnitude and direction of magnetic induction.
Fleming's right hand rule	—	Direction of induced current.

So, the option (b) is correct.

39. At, $t = 0$, switch closes

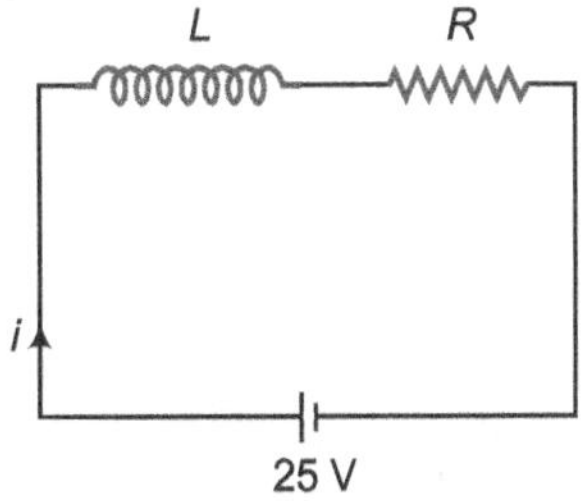

Current $i = i_0[1 - e^{-tR/L}]$

So, at $t = 0, i = 0$

So, potential across inductor = 25 V

and across resistor = 0 V

40. We have, $i_g = i\left(\frac{S}{G + S}\right)$

where i = total current

$$\text{Sensitivity} = \frac{i_g}{i} = \frac{10}{60} = \frac{1}{6}$$

$$\therefore \quad \frac{1}{6} = \frac{S}{G + S}$$

$$\Rightarrow \quad G + S = 6S$$

$$\Rightarrow \quad G = 5S \text{ or } S = \frac{G}{5}$$

$$\Rightarrow \quad S = \frac{20}{5} = 4\,\Omega$$

EAMCET

Engineering Entrance Exam
Solved Paper 2010

Physics

1. A launching vehicle carrying an artificial satellite of mass m is set for launch on the surface of the earth of mass M and radius R. If the satellite is intended to move in a circular orbit of radius $7R$, the minimum energy required to be spent by the launching vehicle on the satellite is
(Gravitational constant $= G$)
(a) $\frac{GMm}{R}$ (b) $-\frac{13\,GMm}{14R}$
(c) $\frac{GMm}{7R}$ (d) $\frac{GMm}{14R}$

2. The displacements of two particles of same mass executing SHM are represented by the equations
$x_1 = 4\sin\left(10t + \frac{\pi}{6}\right)$ and $x_2 = 5\cos(\omega t)$.
The value of ω for which the energies of both the particles remain same is
(a) 16 unit (b) 6 unit
(c) 4 unit (d) 8 unit

3. Match the following

	Column I		Column II
A.	Hooke's law	1.	Tangential strain
B.	Shearing strain	2.	Temporary loss of elastic property
C.	Bulk strain	3.	Elastic limit
D.	Elastic fatigue	4.	3 times the linear strain

	A	B	C	D
(a)	2	1	4	3
(b)	3	4	1	2
(c)	3	1	4	2
(d)	1	2	3	4

4. The excess pressure inside a spherical soap bubble of radius 1 cm is balanced by a column of oil (Specific gravity = 0.8), 2 mm high, the surface tension of the bubble is
(a) 3.92 N/m (b) 0.0392 N/m
(c) 0.392 N/m (d) 0.00392 N/m

5. Water from a tap emerges vertically downwards with initial velocity 4 ms^{-1}. The cross-sectional area of the tap is A. The flow is steady and pressure is constant throughout the stream of water. The distance h vertically below the tap, where the cross-sectional area of the stream becomes $\left(\frac{2}{3}\right)A$, is ($g = 10\ \text{m/s}^2$)
(a) 0.5 m (b) 1 m
(c) 1.5 m (d) 2.2 m

6. A bimetallic strip is formed out of two identical strips, one of copper and the other of brass. The coefficients of linear expansion of the two metals are α_C and α_B. On heating, the temperature of the strip increases by ΔT and the strip bends to form an arc of radius R. Then R is proportional to
(a) ΔT (b) $\frac{1}{\Delta T}$
(c) $\sqrt{\Delta T}$ (d) $\frac{1}{\sqrt{\Delta T}}$

7. Three rods of equal lengths are joined to form an equilateral triangle ABC. D is the mid-point of AB. The coefficient of linear expansion is α_1 for material of rod AB and α_2 for material of rods AC and BC. If the distance DC remains constant for small changes in temperature, then
(a) $\alpha_1 = 2\alpha_2$ (b) $\alpha_1 = 4\alpha_2$
(c) $\alpha_1 = 8\alpha_2$ (d) $\alpha_1 = \alpha_2$

8. An ideal gas expands isothermally from volume V_1 to volume V_2. It is then compressed to the original volume V_1 adiabatically. If p_1, p_2 and

W represent the initial pressure, final pressure and the net work done by the gas respectively during the entire process, then

(a) $p_1 > p_2, W = 0$ (b) $p_1 > p_2, W > 0$
(c) $p_2 > p_1, W > 0$ (d) $p_2 > p_1, W < 0$

9. 3 moles of an ideal monoatomic gas performs $ABCDA$ cyclic process as shown in figure below. The gas temperatures are $T_A = 400$ K, $T_B = 800$ K, $T_C = 2400$ K and $T_D = 1200$ K. The work done by the gas is (approximately) ($R = 8.314$ J/mol K)

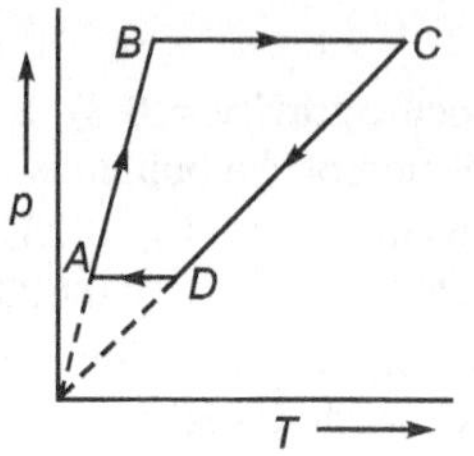

(a) 10 kJ (b) 20 kJ
(c) 40 kJ (d) 100 kJ

10. Three rods AB, BC and BD made of the same material and having the same cross-section have been joined as shown in the figure.

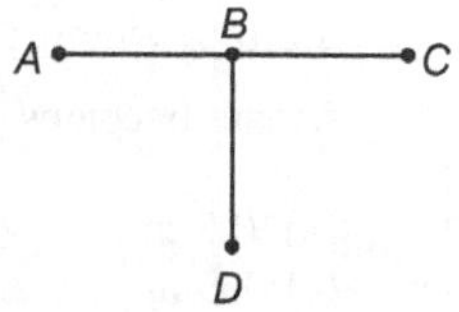

The ends A, C and D are held at temperatures of 20°C, 80°C and 80°C respectively. If each rod is of same length, then the temperature at the junction B of the three rods is

(a) 90°C (b) 60°C
(c) 40°C (d) 30°C

11. An organ pipe P_1, closed at one end and containing a gas of density ρ_1 is vibrating in its first harmonic. Another organ pipe P_2, open at both ends and containing a gas of density ρ_2 is vibrating in its third harmonic. Both the pipes are in resonance with a given tuning fork. If the compressibility of gases is equal in both pipes, the ratio of the lengths of P_1 and P_2 is (assume the given gases to be monoatomic)

(a) $\frac{1}{3}$ (b) 3
(c) $\frac{1}{6}\sqrt{\frac{\rho_1}{\rho_2}}$ (d) $\frac{1}{6}\sqrt{\frac{\rho_2}{\rho_1}}$

12. A sonometer wire has a length of 114 cm, between two fixed ends. Where should two bridges be placed so as to divide the wire into three segments (in cm) whose fundamental frequencies are in the ratio 1: 3 : 4?

(a) $l_1, l_2, l_3 = 18, 24, 72$
(b) $l_1, l_2, l_3 = 24, 18, 72$
(c) $l_1, l_2, l_3 = 72, 18, 24$
(d) $l_1, l_2, l_3 = 72, 24, 18$

13. In an optical fibre, core and cladding were made with materials of refractive indices 1.5 and 1.414 respectively. To observe total internal reflection, what will be the range of incident angle with the axis of optical fibre?

(a) 0°–60° (b) 0–48°
(c) 0°–30° (d) 0°–82°

14. A ray of light passes through an equilateral prism such that the angle of incidence is equal to the angle of emergence and each one is equal to 3/4th the angle of prism. The angle of deviation is

(a) 45° (b) 39°
(c) 20° (d) 30°

15. The diameter of objective of a telescope is 1 m. Its resolving limit for the light of wavelength 4538 Å, will be

(a) 5.54×10^{-7} rad (b) 2.54×10^{-4} rad
(c) 6.54×10^{-7} rad (d) None of these

16. Two coherent sources whose intensity ratio is 64 : 1 produce interference fringes. The ratio of intensities of maxima and minima is

(a) 9 : 7 (b) 8 : 1
(c) 81 : 49 (d) 81 : 7

17. The frequncy of vibration in a vibration magnetometer of the combination of two bar magnets of magnetic moments M_1 and M_2 is 6 Hz when like poles are tied and it is 2 Hz when the unlike poles are tied together, then the ratio $M_1 : M_2$ is

(a) 4 : 5 (b) 5 : 4
(c) 1 : 3 (d) 3 : 1

18. A short magnetic needle is pivoted in a uniform magnetic field of induction 1 T. Now, simultaneously another magnetic field of induction $\sqrt{3}$ T is applied at right angles to the first field; the needle deflects through an angle θ whose value is

(a) 30° (b) 45°
(c) 90° (d) 60°

19. The potential difference between two parallel plates is 10^4 V. If the plates are separated by 0.5 cm, the force on an electron between the plates is

(a) 32×10^{-13} N (b) 0.32×10^{-13} N
(c) 0.032×10^{-13} N (d) 3.2×10^{-13} N

20. Two capacitors of capacities 1 μF and C μF are connected in series and the combination is charged to a potential difference of 120 V. If the charge on the combination is 80 μC, the energy stored in the capacitor of capacity C in μJ is

(a) 1800 (b) 1600
(c) 14400 (d) 7200

21. 6 Ω and 12 Ω resistors are connected in parallel. This combination is connected in series with a 10 V battery and 6 Ω resistor. What is the potential difference between the terminals of the 12 Ω resistor?

(a) 4 V (b) 16 V
(c) 2 V (d) 8 V

22. Charge passing through a conductor of cross-section area $A = 0.3\text{ m}^2$ is given by $q = 3t^2 + 5t + 2$ in coulomb, where t is in second. What is the value of drift velocity at $t = 2\text{s}$? (Given, $n = 2 \times 10^{25}/\text{m}^3$)

(a) 0.77×10^{-5} m/s (b) 1.77×10^{-5} m/s
(c) 2.08×10^{-5} m/s (d) 0.57×10^{-5} m/s

23. The thermo emf of a thermocouple is given by, $E = aT + bT^2$, where $\frac{a}{b} = -200°\text{C}$. If the cold function is kept at 30°C, then the inversion temperature is (ε in volt, T in centigrade)

(a) 103 K (b) 143 K
(c) 333 K (d) 443 K

24. The intensity of the magnetic induction field at the centre of a single turn circular coil of radius 5 cm carrying current of 0.9 A.

(a) $36\pi \times 10^{-7}$ T (b) $9\pi \times 10^{-7}$ T
(c) $36\pi \times 10^{-6}$ T (d) $9\pi \times 10^{-6}$ T

25. A capacitor of capacity 0.1 μF connected in series to a resistor of 10 M Ω is charged to a certain potential and then made to discharge through the resistor. The time in which the potential will take to fall to half its original value is (Given, $\log_{10} 2 = 0.3010$)

(a) 2 s (b) 0.693 s
(c) 0.5 s (d) 1.0 s

26. The time constant of inductance coil is 3 m s. When a 90 Ω resistance is joined in series, then the time constant becomes 0.5 m s. The inductance and the resistance of the coil are

(a) 54 mH, 18 Ω (b) 14 mH, 42 Ω
(c) 42 mH, 14 Ω (d) 14 mH, 60 Ω

27. In Thomson's experiment to determine $\frac{e}{m}$ of an electron, it is found that an electron beam having a kinetic energy of 45.5 eV remains undeflected, when subjected to crossed electric and magnetic fields. If $E = 1 \times 10^3\text{ Vm}^{-1}$, the value of B is (mass of the electron is 9.1×10^{-31} kg)

(a) 2.5×10^{-3} Wb m^{-2}
(b) 5.0×10^{-4} Wb m^{-2}
(c) 2.5×10^{-4} Wb m^{-2}
(d) 1.0×10^{-4} Wb m^{-2}

28. Photoelectric emission is observed from a metallic surface for frequencies ν_1 and ν_2 of the incident light ($\nu_1 > \nu_2$). If the maximum values of kinetic energy of the photoelectrons emitted in the two cases are in the ratio 1 : n, then the threshold frequency of the metallic surface is

(a) $\frac{(\nu_1 - \nu_2)}{(n-1)}$ (b) $\frac{(n\nu_1 - \nu_2)}{(n-1)}$
(c) $\frac{(n\nu_2 - \nu_1)}{(n-1)}$ (d) $\frac{(\nu_1 - \nu_2)}{n}$

29. A proton, a deutron and an α-particle having the same momentum, enters a region of uniform electric field between the parallel plates of a capacitor. The electric field is perpendicular to the initial path of the particles. Then the ratio of deflections suffered by them is

(a) 1 : 2 : 8 (b) 1 : 2 : 4
(c) 1 : 1 : 2 (d) None of these

30. A transistor having a β equal to 80 has a change in base current of 250 μA, then the change in collector current is

(a) 20,000 mA (b) 200 mA
(c) 2000 mA (d) 20 mA

31. If the force is given by $F = at + bt^2$ with t as time. The dimensions of a and b are

(a) [MLT^{-4}], [MLT^{-2}]
(b) [MLT^{-3}], [MLT^{-4}]
(c) [ML^{2}T^{-3}], [ML^{2}T^{-2}]
(d) [ML^{2}T^{-3}], [ML^{3}T^{-4}]

32. $\vec{\mathbf{A}}$ and $\vec{\mathbf{B}}$ are two vectors of equal magnitudes and θ is the angle between them. The angle between $\vec{\mathbf{A}}$ or $\vec{\mathbf{B}}$ with their resultant is

(a) $\frac{\theta}{4}$ (b) $\frac{\theta}{2}$
(c) 2θ (d) zero

33. An athelete completes one round of a circular track of radius R in 40 s. What will be his displacement at the end of 2 min 20 s?
(a) $7R$ (b) $2R$
(c) $2\pi R$ (d) $7\pi R$

34. A ball is falling freely from a height. When it reaches 10 m height from the ground its velocity is v_0. It collides with the ground and loses 50% of its energy and rises back to height of 10 m. Then the velocity v_0 is
(a) 7 m/s (b) 10 m/s
(c) 14 m/s (d) 16 m/s

35. A bomb moving with velocity $(40\hat{\mathbf{i}} + 50\hat{\mathbf{j}} - 25\hat{\mathbf{k}})$ m/s explodes into two pieces of mass ratio 1 : 4. After explosion the smaller piece moves away with velocity $(200\hat{\mathbf{i}} + 70\hat{\mathbf{j}} + 15\hat{\mathbf{k}})$ m/s. The velocity of larger piece after explosion is
(a) $45\hat{\mathbf{j}} - 35\hat{\mathbf{k}}$ (b) $45\hat{\mathbf{i}} - 35\hat{\mathbf{j}}$
(c) $45\hat{\mathbf{k}} - 35\hat{\mathbf{j}}$ (d) $-35\hat{\mathbf{i}} + 45\hat{\mathbf{k}}$

36. A body of mass $m_1 = 4$ kg moves at $5\hat{\mathbf{i}}$ m/s and another body of mass $m_2 = 2$ kg moves at $10\hat{\mathbf{i}}$ m/s. The kinetic energy of centre of mass is
(a) $\frac{200}{3}$ J (b) $\frac{500}{3}$ J
(c) $\frac{400}{3}$ J (d) $\frac{800}{3}$ J

37. A ball falls from a height h and rebounds after striking the floor. The coefficient of restitution is e. The maximum distance covered before it comes to rest is
(a) $\frac{(1-e^2)h}{e^2}$ (b) $\frac{(1+e^2)h}{e^2}$
(c) $\left(\frac{1+e^2}{1-e^2}\right)h$ (d) $\frac{e^2 h}{1-e^2}$

38. An object takes n times as much time as to slide down a 45° rough inclined plane as it takes to slide down a perfectly smooth inclined plane of the same inclination. The coefficient of kinetic friction between the object and the rough incline is given by
(a) $\left(1-\frac{1}{n^2}\right)$ (b) $\left(\frac{1}{1-n^2}\right)$
(c) $\sqrt{1-\frac{1}{n^2}}$ (d) $\sqrt{1+\frac{1}{n^2}}$

39. The moment of inertia of a disc, of mass M and radius R, about an axis which is a tangent and parallel to its diameter is
(a) $\frac{1}{2}MR^2$
(b) $\frac{3}{4}MR^2$
(c) $\frac{1}{4}MR^2$
(d) $\frac{5}{4}MR^2$

40. A fly-wheel of mass 25 kg has a radius of 0.2 m. It is making 240 rpm. What is the torque necessary to bring to rest in 20 s?
(a) 2π Nm (b) 0.4π Nm
(c) $\frac{2}{\pi}$ Nm (d) 4π Nm

Answers

1. (b)	**2.** (d)	**3.** (c)	**4.** (b)	**5.** (b)	**6.** (b)	**7.** (b)	**8.** (d)	**9.** (b)	**10.** (b)
11. (d)	**12.** (d)	**13.** (c)	**14.** (d)	**15.** (a)	**16.** (c)	**17.** (b)	**18.** (d)	**19.** (d)	**20.** (b)
21. (a)	**22.** (b)	**23.** (d)	**24.** (a)	**25.** (b)	**26.** (a)	**27.** (c)	**28.** (b)	**29.** (a)	**30.** (d)
31. (b)	**32.** (b)	**33.** (b)	**34.** (c)	**35.** (a)	**36.** (c)	**37.** (c)	**38.** (a)	**39.** (d)	**40.** (b)

Hints & Solutions

1. The energy of artificial satellite at the surface of the earth

$$E_1 = -\frac{GMm}{R}$$

When the satellite is intended to move in a circular orbit of radius $7R$, then energy of artificial satellite

$$E_2 = -\frac{1}{2}\frac{GMm}{7R}$$

The minimum energy required

$$E = E_1 - E_2$$
$$= -\frac{GMm}{R} + \frac{1}{2}\left(\frac{GMm}{7R}\right)$$
$$= \frac{-14\,GMm + GMm}{14R}$$
$$= -\frac{13\,GMm}{14R}$$

2. The equation of displacement

$$x_1 = 4\sin\left(10t + \frac{\pi}{6}\right)$$

The energy of this equation

$$E_1 = \frac{1}{2}m\omega_1^2 a_1^2$$
$$= \frac{1}{2}m \times 10 \times 10 \times 4 \times 4$$

The second equation of displacement

$$x_2 = 5\cos(\omega t)$$

The energy of this equation

$$E_2 = \frac{1}{2}m\omega_2^2 a_2^2$$
$$= \frac{1}{2}m\,\omega_2^2 \times 5 \times 5$$

$\because$ $E_1 = E_2$

$\therefore$ $\frac{1}{2}m\omega_2^2 \times 5 \times 5$

$$= \frac{1}{2}m \times 10 \times 10 \times 4 \times 4$$
$$\omega_2^2 = \frac{10 \times 10 \times 4 \times 4}{5 \times 5}$$
$$\omega_2 = 8 \text{ unit}$$

3. (i) According to Hooke's law within the elastic limit, stress is proportional to the strain.

(ii) Shearing strain is defined as angle in radian through which a plane perpendicular to the fixed surface of the cubical body gets turned under the effect of tangential force.

(iii) The temporary loss of elastic properties because of the action of repeated alternating deforming force is called elastic fatigue.

Hence option (c) is correct.

4. The excess pressure of soap bubble

$$p = \frac{4T}{R}$$
$$h\rho g = \frac{4T}{R}$$
$$\therefore\ T = \frac{Rh\rho g}{4}$$
$$= \frac{1 \times 10^{-2} \times 2 \times 10^{-3} \times 0.8 \times 10^{3} \times 9.8}{4}$$
$$= 3.92 \times 10^{-2}\ \text{N/m}$$
$$= 0.0392\ \text{N/m}$$

5. The equation of continuity

$$A_1 v_1 = A_2 v_2$$
$$A \times 4 = \frac{2}{3}A \times v_2$$
$$v_2 = 6\ \text{ms}^{-1}$$

From Bernoulli's theorem

$$p + \rho g h_1 + \frac{1}{2}\rho v_1^2 = p + \rho g h_2 + \frac{1}{2}\rho v_2^2$$

or $$g(h_1 - h_2) = \frac{1}{2}(v_2^2 - v_1^2)$$

$$g \times h = \frac{1}{2}[(6)^2 - (4)^2] \quad [\because h_1 - h_2 = h]$$
$$10 \times h = \frac{1}{2}[36 - 16]$$
$$h = \frac{20}{20} = 1\ \text{m}$$

6. Let L_0 be the initial length of each strip before heating. Length after heating will be

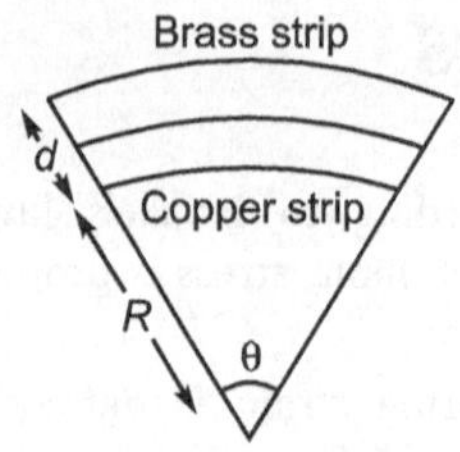

$$L_B = L_0 (1 + \alpha_B \Delta T) = (R + d)\theta$$

$$L_C = L_0 (1 + \alpha_C \Delta T) = R\theta$$

$$\Rightarrow \quad \frac{R + d}{R} = \frac{1 + \alpha_B \Delta T}{1 + \alpha_C \Delta T}$$

$$1 + \frac{d}{R} = 1 + (\alpha_B - \alpha_C)\Delta T$$

$$R = \frac{d}{(\alpha_B - \alpha_C)\Delta T}$$

$$R \propto \frac{1}{\Delta T}$$

7.

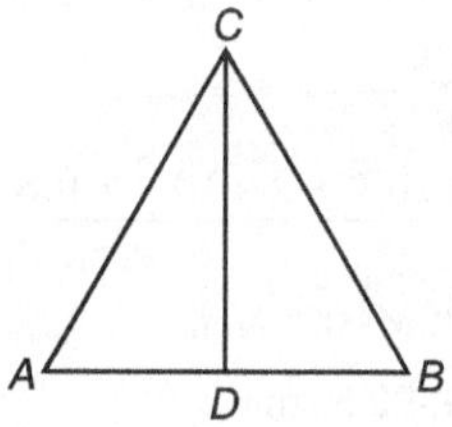

$$CD^2 = (AC)^2 - (AD)^2 = l^2 - \left(\frac{l}{2}\right)^2$$

After small change in temperature

$$CD^2 = (AC)^2 - (AD)^2$$

$$= [l(1 + \alpha_2 t)]^2 - \left[\frac{l}{2}(1 + \alpha_1 t)\right]^2$$

$$\therefore \quad l^2 - \frac{l^2}{4} = l^2 [1 + \alpha_2^2 t^2 + 2\alpha_2 t] - \frac{l^2}{4}[1 + \alpha_1^2 t^2 + 2\alpha_1 t]$$

Neglecting $\alpha_2^2 t^2$ and $\alpha_1^2 t^2$, (because very small quantity)

$$0 = l^2 (2\alpha_2 t) - \frac{l^2}{4}(2\alpha_1 t)$$

or $\quad \alpha_1 = 4\alpha_2$

8.

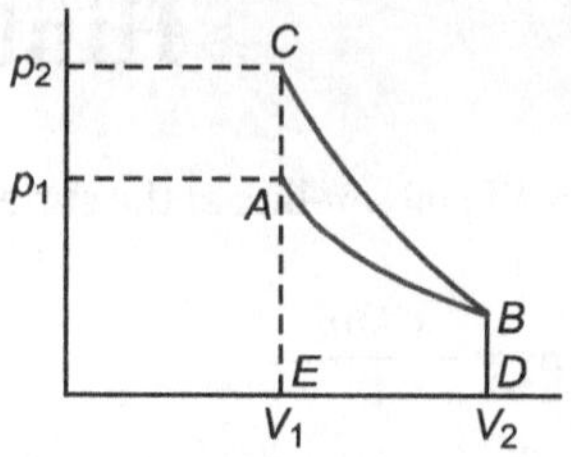

From graph it is clear that, $p_2 > p_1$.

Since, area under adiabatic process ($BCED$) is greater than that of isothermal process ($ABDE$). Therefore, net work done

$\because \quad W_A > W_1$

$\Rightarrow \quad W < 0$

Hence option (d) is correct.

9.

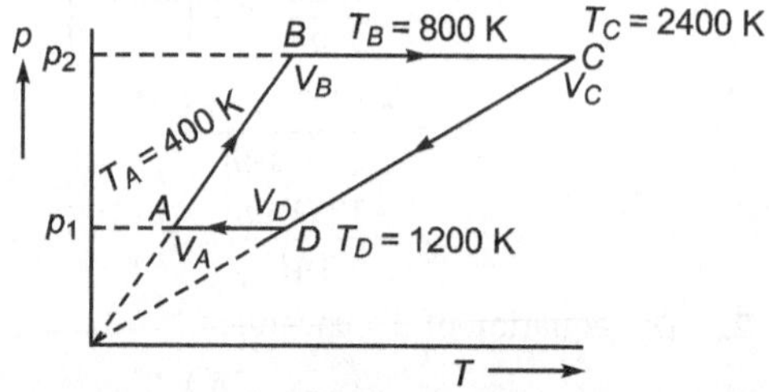

Processes A to B and C to D are parts of straight line graphs of form $y = mx$.

Also, $\quad p = \frac{\mu R}{V} T \ (\mu = 3)$

$$p \propto T$$

So, volume remains constant for the graphs AB and CD.

So, no work is done during processes for A to B and C to D.

$$W_{AB} = W_{CD} = 0$$

and

$$W_{BC} = p_2 (V_C - V_B) = \mu R (T_C - T_B) = 3R(2400 - 800) = 3R \times 1600 = 4800\,R$$

$$W_{DA} = p_1 (V_A - V_D) = \mu R (T_A - T_D) = 3R(400 - 1200) = -2400\,R$$

Work done in complete cycle

$$W = W_{AB} + W_{BC} + W_{CD} + W_{DA}$$

$$= 0 + 4800\,R + 0 + (-2400)\,R$$

$$= 2400\,R$$

$$= 19.944 \text{ J} = 20 \text{ kJ}$$

10. Let the temperature of function θ. Since, rod BC and BD are parallel to each other (because both having the same temperature difference). Hence, given figure can be redrawn as follows (R be the resistance of each rod).

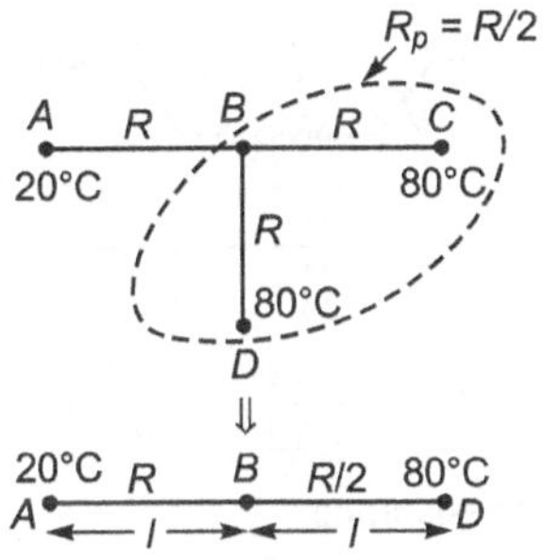

$$\because \frac{Q}{t} = \frac{(\theta_1 - \theta_2)}{R} \text{ and } \left(\frac{Q}{t}\right)_{AB} = \left(\frac{Q}{t}\right)_{BD}$$

$$\Rightarrow \frac{(80 - \theta)}{R/2} = \frac{(\theta - 20°)}{R} \Rightarrow \theta = 60°$$

11. Frequency of closed organ pipe for first harmonic $n_1 = \frac{v_1}{4l_1}$.

Frequency of open organ pipe for third harmonic

$$n_3 = \frac{3v_2}{2l_2}$$

At resonance, $n_1 = n_3$

or $$\frac{v_1}{4l_1} = \frac{3v_2}{2l_2}$$

or $$\frac{l_1}{l_2} = \frac{1}{6}\left(\frac{v_1}{v_2}\right)$$

$$\frac{l_1}{l_2} = \frac{1}{6}\sqrt{\frac{B}{\rho_1}} \times \sqrt{\frac{\rho_2}{B}}$$

$$= \frac{1}{6}\sqrt{\frac{\rho_2}{\rho_1}}$$

12. If length of the wire between the two bridges is l, the frequency of vibration

$$n = \frac{1}{2l}\sqrt{\frac{T}{m}}$$

$$\therefore \quad n \propto \frac{1}{l}$$

Therefore, $n_1 : n_2 : n_3 = \frac{1}{l_1} : \frac{1}{l_2} : \frac{1}{l_3}$

$$n_1 : n_2 : n_3 = \frac{1}{\frac{114 \times 1}{8}} : \frac{1}{\frac{114 \times 3}{8}} : \frac{1}{\frac{114 \times 4}{8}}$$

or $$n_1 : n_2 : n_3 = 8 : \frac{8}{3} : 2$$

or $$n_1 : n_2 : n_3 = 72 : 24 : 18$$

13. The range of incident angle

$$\sin\theta = \frac{\sqrt{\mu_1^2 - \mu_2^2}}{\mu_0}$$

$$\theta = \sin^{-1}\sqrt{(\mu_1)^2 - (\mu_2)^2} \quad [\text{for air } \mu_0 = 1]$$

$$\theta = \sin^{-1}\sqrt{(1.5)^2 - (1.414)^2}$$

$$= \sin^{-1}(0.5006)$$

$$\theta = 30°$$

Hence, option (c) is correct.

14.

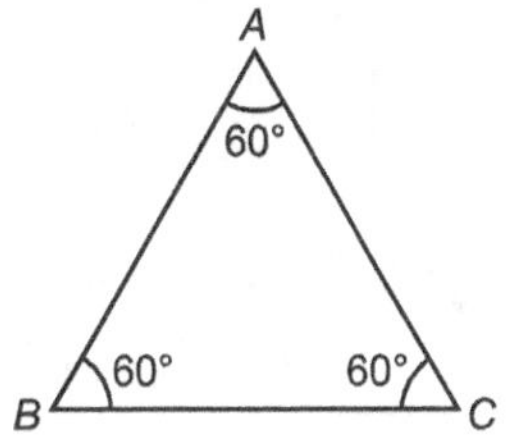

Relation among the (i), (e), (A) and (δ)

$$i + e = A + \delta$$

$$\frac{3}{4} \times 60° + \frac{3}{4} \times 60° = 60° + \delta$$

or $$45° + 45° = 60° + \delta$$

or $$\delta = 30°$$

where, i = angle of incidence
e = angle of emergence
A = angle of prism
δ = angle of deviation

15. Resolving limit

$$d\theta = \frac{1.22\lambda}{a}$$

$$= \frac{1.22 \times 4538 \times 10^{-10}}{1}$$

$$= 5.54 \times 10^{-7} \text{ rad}$$

16. The ratio of intensities of maxima and minima

$$\frac{I_{max}}{I_{min}} = \frac{(\sqrt{I_1} + \sqrt{I_2})^2}{(\sqrt{I_1} - \sqrt{I_2})^2}$$

$$= \frac{(\sqrt{64} + \sqrt{1})^2}{(\sqrt{64} - \sqrt{1})^2}$$

$$\frac{I_{max}}{I_{min}} = \frac{(8+1)^2}{(8-1)^2} = \frac{81}{49}$$

17. In the sum and difference method of vibration magnetometer,

$$\frac{M_1}{M_2}=\frac{T_2^2+T_1^2}{T_2^2-T_1^2}$$

Here, $T_1=\frac{1}{n_1}=\frac{1}{6}\text{s}$

$$T_2=\frac{1}{n_2}=\frac{1}{2}\text{s}$$

$$\frac{M_1}{M_2}=\frac{\frac{1}{4}+\frac{1}{36}}{\frac{1}{4}-\frac{1}{36}}+\frac{\frac{9+1}{36}}{\frac{9-1}{36}}$$

$$=\frac{10}{8}=\frac{5}{4}$$

$$M_1:M_2=5:4$$

18.

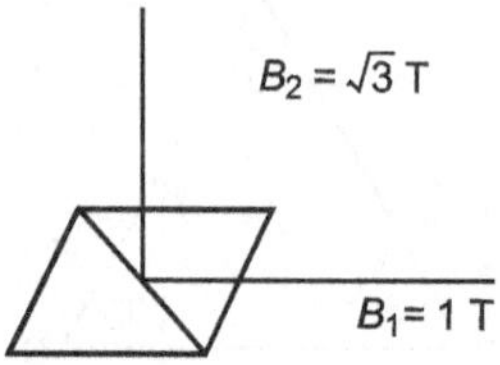

In balance condition

$$B_2=B_1\tan\theta$$

or $\tan\theta=\frac{\sqrt{3}}{1}=\sqrt{3}$

$$\theta=60°$$

19. The force $F=\frac{eV}{d}$

$$=\frac{1.6\times10^{-19}\times10^4}{0.5\times10^{-2}}$$

$$=3.2\times10^{-13}\text{ N}$$

20. Capacitances 1 μF and C μF are connected in series, then

$$C_{eq}=\frac{C}{1+C}$$

Given, $V=120$ V and $q=80$ μC

∵ $q=C_{eq}V$

$$80=\frac{C}{C+1}\times120$$

or $C=2\mu\text{F}$

The energy stored in the capacitor of capacity C

$$U=\frac{1}{2}\frac{q^2}{C}$$

$$=\frac{1}{2}\times\frac{(80\times10^{-6})^2}{2\times10^{-6}}$$

$$=\frac{1}{2}\times\frac{80\times10^{-6}\times80\times10^{-6}}{2\times10^{-6}}$$

$$U=1600\ \mu\text{J}$$

21.

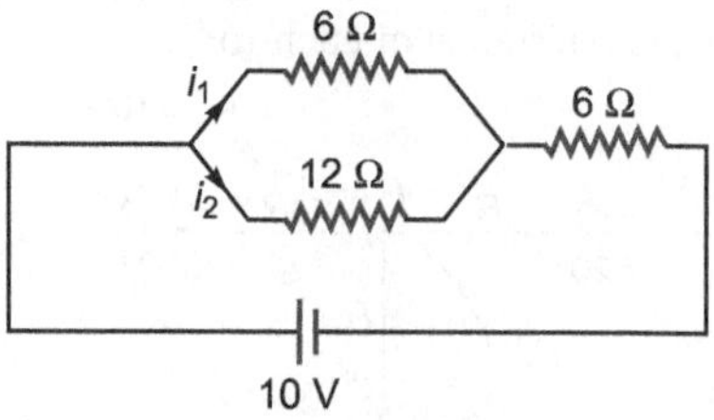

$$R=\frac{6\times12}{6+12}=\frac{6\times12}{18}=4\ \Omega$$

Total resistance,

$$R_{eq}=6+4=10\ \Omega$$

Current, $i=\frac{V}{R}=\frac{10}{10}=1\text{ A}$

The current in 12 Ω resistor is

$$i_2=i\left(\frac{R_1}{R_1+R_2}\right)=1\times\left(\frac{6}{6+12}\right)$$

$$i_2=\frac{1}{3}$$

The potential difference in 12 Ω resistor

$$V=iR=\frac{1}{3}\times12=4\text{ V}$$

22. $A=0.3\text{ m}^2$

$$n=2\times10^{25}/\text{m}^3$$

$$q=3t^2+5t+2$$

$$i=\frac{dq}{dt}=6t+5=17$$

$$i=neAv_d$$

Drift velocity,

$$v_d=\frac{i}{neA}$$

$$=\frac{17}{2\times10^{25}\times1.6\times10^{-19}\times0.3}$$

$$=\frac{17}{0.96\times10^6}$$

$$=1.77\times10^{-5}\text{ m/s}$$

23. At temperature of inversion

$$E=0$$

∵ $E=aT+bT^2$

∴ $0=aT+bT^2$

or $T=-\frac{a}{b}=200°\text{C}$

Because the cold function is kept at 30°C, then the inversion temperature

$$T = 200 - 30 = 170°\text{C}$$

$$T = 273 + 170 = 443\text{ K}$$

24. The intensity of magnetic induction field

$$B = \frac{\mu_0 i}{2r}$$

$$= \frac{4\pi \times 10^{-7} \times 0.9}{2 \times 5 \times 10^{-2}}$$

$$B = 36\pi \times 10^{-7}\text{ T}$$

25. By equation of charging

$$q = q_0 (1 - e^{-t/CR})$$

According to question

$$\frac{q}{q_0} = \frac{1}{2} = 0.50$$

$$\therefore \quad 0.50 = 1 - e^{-t/CR}$$

$$e^{-t/CR} = 1 - 0.50 = 0.50$$

$$e^{t/CR} = 2$$

or $$\frac{t}{CR} = \log_e 2$$

or $$\frac{t}{CR} = 2.3026 \log_{10} 2$$

or $$t = CR \times 2.3026 \log_{10} 2$$

or $$t = 0.1 \times 10^{-6} \times 10 \times 10^6 \times 2.3026 \log_{10} 2$$

or $$t = 2.3026 \times 0.3010$$

or $$t = 0.693\text{ s}$$

26. Time constant $t = \dfrac{L}{R}$

$$3 = \frac{L}{R} \quad \text{...(i)}$$

When a 90 Ω resistance is joined in series the time constant becomes 0.5 m s.

So, $$0.5 = \frac{L}{R + 90} \quad \text{...(ii)}$$

From Eqs. (i) and (ii)

$$\frac{3 \times 10^{-3}}{0.5 \times 10^{-3}} = \frac{R + 90}{R}$$

$$\frac{30}{5} = \frac{R + 90}{R}$$

$$6R = R + 90$$

$$R = 18\ \Omega$$

This value put in Eq. (i)

$$3 \times 10^{-3} = \frac{L}{R}$$

$$3 \times 10^{-3} = \frac{L}{18}$$

or $$L = 54\text{ mH}$$

27. The kinetic energy

$$K = \frac{1}{2} mv^2$$

$$v^2 = \frac{2K}{m}$$

$$v^2 = \frac{2 \times 45.5 \times 1.6 \times 10^{-19}}{9.1 \times 10^{-31}}$$

$$v^2 = 16 \times 10^{12}$$

$$v = 4 \times 10^6$$

Again velocity, $v = \dfrac{E}{B}$

$$4 \times 10^6 = \frac{1 \times 10^3}{B}$$

$$B = \frac{1 \times 10^3}{4 \times 10^6}$$

$$B = 2.5 \times 10^{-4}\text{ Wb m}^{-2}$$

28. By using $h\nu - h\nu_0 = K_{max}$

$$h(\nu_1 - \nu_0) = K_1$$

$$h(\nu_2 - \nu_0) = K_2$$

$$\therefore \quad \frac{\nu_1 - \nu_0}{\nu_2 - \nu_0} = \frac{K_1}{K_2} = \frac{1}{n}$$

or $$\nu_0 = \frac{n\nu_1 - \nu_2}{(n - 1)}$$

29. The deflection suffered by charged particle in an electric field is

$$y = \frac{qELD}{m\mu^2} = \frac{qELD}{p^2/m} \quad (p = mu)$$

$$\Rightarrow \quad y \propto \frac{qm}{p^2}$$

$$\Rightarrow y_p : y_d : y_\alpha = \frac{q_p m_p}{p_p^2} : \frac{q_d m_d}{p_d^2} : \frac{q_\alpha m_\alpha}{p_\alpha^2}$$

Since, $$p_\alpha = p_d = p_p \quad \text{(given)}$$

$$m_p : m_d : m_\alpha = 1 : 2 : 4$$

and $$q_1 : q_d : q_\alpha = 1 : 1 : 2$$

$$\Rightarrow \quad y_b : y_d : y_\alpha = 1 \times 1 : 1 \times 2 : 2 \times 4$$

$$= 1 : 2 : 8$$

30. $\beta = \left(\dfrac{\Delta i_C}{\Delta i_B}\right)$

$$80 = \frac{\Delta i_C}{250 \times 10^{-6}}$$

$$\Delta i_C = 80 \times 250 \times 10^{-6}$$

$$\Delta i_C = 20000 \times 10^{-6}$$
$$= 20 \times 10^{-3} = 20 \text{ mA}$$

31. Dimension of at = Dimension of F

$$[at] = [F]$$
$$[a] = \left[\frac{F}{t}\right]$$
$$[a] = \left[\frac{\text{MLT}^{-2}}{\text{T}}\right]$$
$$[a] = [\text{MLT}^{-3}]$$

Dimension of bt^2 = Dimension of F

$$[bt^2] = [F]$$
$$[b] = \left[\frac{F}{t^2}\right]$$
$$[b] = \left[\frac{\text{MLT}^{-2}}{\text{T}^2}\right]$$
$$[b] = [\text{MLT}^{-4}]$$

32.

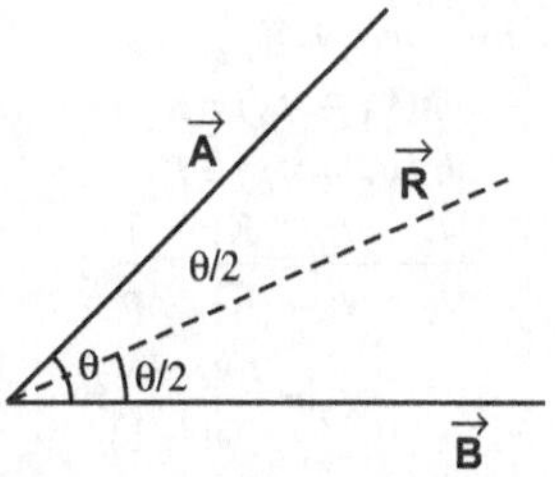

If $\vec{\mathbf{A}}$ and $\vec{\mathbf{B}}$ having equal magnitudes they will make equal angles from resultant $\vec{\mathbf{R}}$.

If angle between $\vec{\mathbf{A}}$ and $\vec{\mathbf{B}}$ is θ.

Then the angle between $\vec{\mathbf{A}}$ or $\vec{\mathbf{B}}$ with their resultant is $\frac{\theta}{2}$.

33. The time = 2 min 20 s

$$= 2 \text{ min} + 20 \text{ s}$$
$$= 2 \times 60 \text{ s} + 20 \text{ s} = 140 \text{ s}$$

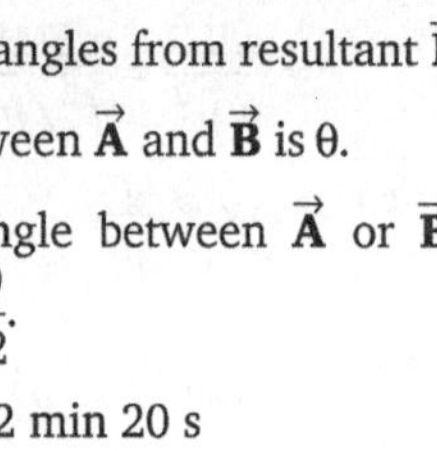

In 40 s athelete completes = 1 round

In 140 s athelete will completes

$$= \frac{140}{40} \text{ round}$$
$$= \frac{120}{40} + \frac{20}{40}$$
$$= 3 + \frac{1}{2} \text{ round}$$

The displacement in 3 round = 0

So displacement in $\frac{1}{2}$ round = $AB = 2R$

34. At height 10 m, the kinetic energy is equal to potential energy then

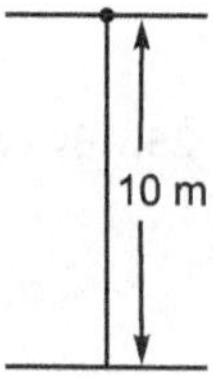

$$\frac{1}{2} mv_0^2 = mgh$$
$$\frac{1}{2} v_0^2 = 9.8 \times 10$$
$$v_0^2 = 2 \times 9.8 \times 10$$
$$v_0 = \sqrt{196}$$
$$v_0 = 14 \text{ m/s}$$

35. From conservation of linear momentum

$$5m(40\hat{\mathbf{i}} + 50\mathbf{j} - 25\hat{\mathbf{k}})$$
$$= m(200\hat{\mathbf{i}} + 70\hat{\mathbf{j}} + 15\hat{\mathbf{k}}) + 4m(x\hat{\mathbf{i}} + y\hat{\mathbf{j}} + z\hat{\mathbf{k}})$$
$$\Rightarrow \quad x\hat{\mathbf{i}} + y\hat{\mathbf{j}} + z\hat{\mathbf{k}} = 45\hat{\mathbf{j}} - 35\hat{\mathbf{k}}$$

36. $$v_{CM} = \frac{m_1 \frac{dr_1}{dt} + m_2 \frac{dr_2}{dt}}{m_1 + m_2}$$
$$= \frac{4 \times 5\hat{\mathbf{i}} + 2 \times 10\hat{\mathbf{i}}}{4 + 2}$$
$$v_{CM} = \frac{40\hat{\mathbf{i}}}{6} = \frac{20}{3}\hat{\mathbf{i}}$$

The kinetic energy

$$K = \frac{1}{2} mv^2$$
$$= \frac{1}{2} \times (4 + 2) \times \frac{20 \times 20}{3 \times 3}$$
$$= \frac{1}{2} \times 6 \times \frac{20 \times 20}{3 \times 3}$$
$$K = \frac{400}{3} \text{ J}$$

37.

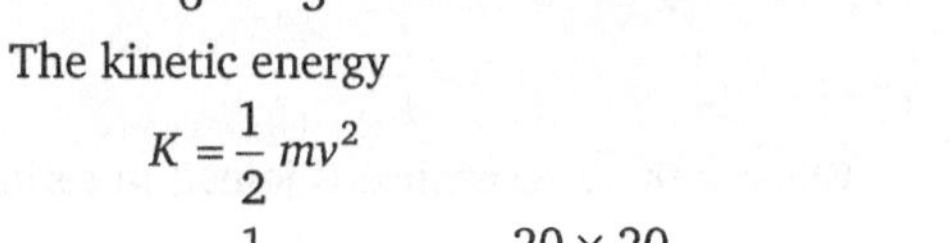

Ball falls from height h then formula for height covered by it in nth rebound is given by

$$h_n = he^{2n}$$

where e = coefficient of restitution

n = number of rebound

Total distance travelled by particle before rebounding has stopped.

$$H = h + 2h_1 + 2h_2 + 2h_n + \ldots$$

$$H = h + 2he^2 + 2he^4 + 2he^6 + 2he^8 + \ldots$$

$$= h + 2h\,(e^2 + e^4 + e^6 + e^8 + \ldots)$$

$$= h + 2h\left[\frac{e^2}{1-e^2}\right]$$

$$= h\left[1 + \frac{2e^2}{1-e^2}\right]$$

$$= h\left[\frac{1+e^2}{1-e^2}\right]$$

38. The coefficient of kinetic friction between the object and the rough incline

$$\mu = \tan\theta\left(1 - \frac{1}{n^2}\right)$$

$$\mu = \tan 45^\circ\left(1 - \frac{1}{n^2}\right)$$

$$= 1 - \frac{1}{n^2}$$

39. The moment of inertia of a disc about axis which is a tangent and parallel to its diameter is $\frac{5}{4}MR^2$.

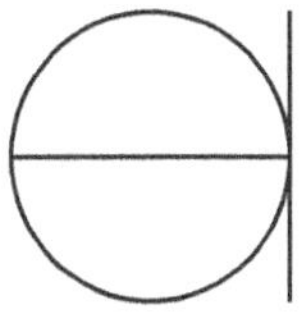

40. $\alpha = \frac{2\pi n}{t} = \frac{2\pi \times \frac{240}{60}}{20}$

$$= \frac{2\pi \times 4}{20}$$

$$\alpha = \frac{2\pi}{5}$$

Torque, $\tau = I\alpha$

$$\tau = MR^2\alpha$$

$$= 25 \times (0.04) \times \frac{2\pi}{5}$$

$$= 0.4\pi \text{ Nm}$$

EAMCET
Engineering Entrance Exam Solved Paper 2009

PHYSICS

1. When a wave traverses a medium, the displacement of a particle located at x at a time t is given by $y = a \sin (bt - cx)$, where a, b and c are constants of the wave, which of the following is a quantity with dimensions?
   (a) $\frac{y}{a}$ (b) bt
   (c) cx (d) $\frac{b}{c}$

2. A body is projected vertically upwards at time $t = 0$ and it is seen at a height H at time t_1 and t_2 second during its flight. The maximum height attained is (g is acceleration due to gravity)
   (a) $\frac{g(t_2 - t_1)^2}{8}$ (b) $\frac{g(t_1 + t_2)^2}{4}$
   (c) $\frac{g(t_1 + t_2)^2}{8}$ (d) $\frac{g(t_2 - t_1)^2}{4}$

3. A particle is projected up from a point at an angle θ with the horizontal direction. At any time t, if p is the linear momentum, y is the vertical displacement, x is horizontal displacement, the graph among the following which does not represent the variation of kinetic energy KE of the particle is

(A)
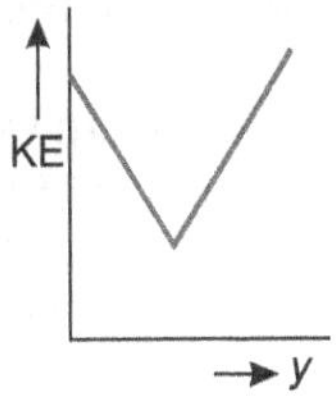

(B)
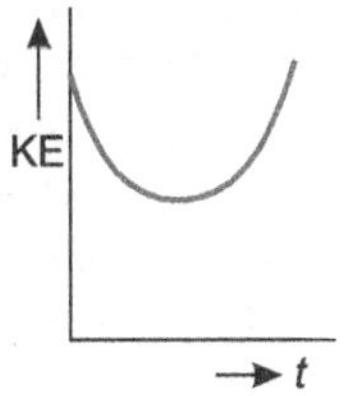

(C)
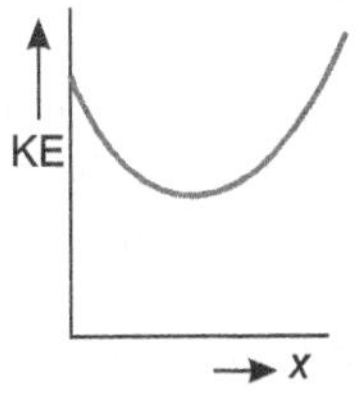

(D)
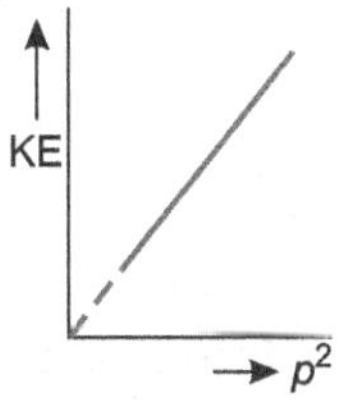

   (a) graph (A) (b) graph (B)
   (c) graph (C) (d) graph (D)

4. A motor of power P_0 is used to deliver water at a certain rate through a given horizontal pipe. To increase the rate of flow of water through the same pipe n times, the power of the motor is increased to P_1. The ratio of P_1 to P_0 is
   (a) $n:1$ (b) $n^2:1$
   (c) $n^3:1$ (d) $n^4:1$

5. A body of mass 5 kg makes an elastic collision with another body at rest and continues to move in the original direction after collision with a velocity equal to $\frac{1}{10}$th of its original velocity. Then the mass of the second body is
   (a) 4.09 kg (b) 0.5 kg
   (c) 5 kg (d) 5.09 kg

6. A particle of mass $4m$ explodes into three pieces of masses m, m and $2m$. The equal masses move along X-axis and Y-axis with velocities 4 ms^{-1} and 6 ms^{-1} respectively. The magnitude of the velocity of the heavier mass is
   (a) $\sqrt{17}$ ms^{-1} (b) $2\sqrt{13}$ ms^{-1}
   (c) $\sqrt{13}$ ms^{-1} (d) $\frac{\sqrt{13}}{2}$ ms^{-1}

7. A body is projected vertically upwards from the surface of the earth with a velocity equal to half the escape velocity. If R is the radius of the earth, maximum height attained by the body from the surface of the earth is
   (a) $\frac{R}{6}$ (b) $\frac{R}{3}$
   (c) $\frac{2R}{3}$ (d) R

8. The displacement of a particle executing SHM is given by
$$y = 5 \sin \left(4t + \frac{\pi}{3}\right).$$
If T is the time period and the mass of the particle is 2 g, the kinetic energy of the particle when $t = \frac{T}{4}$ is given by

(a) 0.4 J (b) 0.5 J
(c) 3 J (d) 0.3 J

9. If the ratio of lengths, radii and Young's modulus of steel and brass wires shown in the figure are a, b and c respectively, the ratio between the increase in lengths of brass and steel wires would be

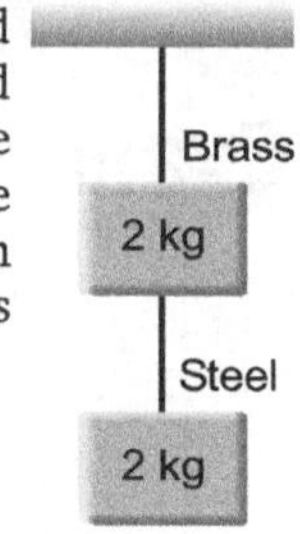

(a) $\frac{b^2a}{2c}$ (b) $\frac{bc}{2a^2}$
(c) $\frac{ba^2}{2c}$ (d) $\frac{a}{2b^2c}$

10. A soap bubble of radius r is blown up to form a bubble of radius $2r$ under isothermal conditions. If T is the surface tension of soap solution, the energy spent in the blowing
(a) $3\pi Tr^2$ (b) $6\pi Tr^2$
(c) $12\pi Tr^2$ (d) $24\pi Tr^2$

11. Eight spherical rain drops of the same mass and radius are falling down with a terminal speed of 6 cm-s^{-1}. If they coalesce to form one big drop, what will be the terminal speed of bigger drop? (Neglect the buoyancy of the air)
(a) 1.5 cm-s^{-1} (b) 6 cm-s^{-1}
(c) 24 cm-s^{-1} (d) 32 cm-s^{-1}

12. A clock pendulum made of invar has a period of 0.5 s, at 20°C. If the clock is used in a climate where the temperature averages to 30°C, how much time does the clock lose in each oscillation? (For invar, $\alpha = 9 \times 10^{-7}/°C$, g = constant)
(a) 2.25×10^{-6} s (b) 2.5×10^{-7} s
(c) 5×10^{-7} s (d) 1.125×10^{-6} s

13. A piece of metal weighs 45 g in air and 25 g in a liquid of density 1.5×10^3 kg-m^{-3} kept at 30°C. When the temperature of the liquid is raised to 40°C, the metal piece weighs 27 g. The density of liquid at 40°C is 1.25×10^3 kg-m^{-3}. The coefficient of linear expansion of metal is
(a) $1.3 \times 10^{-3}/°C$
(b) $5.2 \times 10^{-3}/°C$
(c) $2.6 \times 10^{-3}/°C$
(d) $0.26 \times 10^{-3}/°C$

14. An ideal gas is subjected to a cyclic process $ABCD$ as depicted in the p-V diagram given below

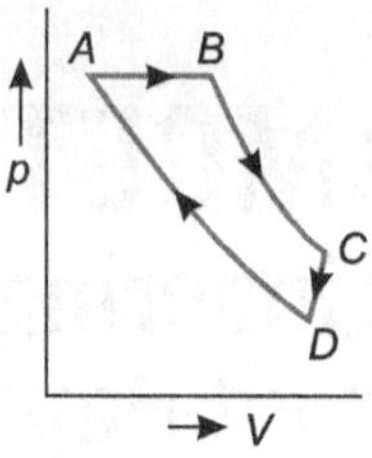

Which of the following curves represents the equivalent cyclic process?

(a)
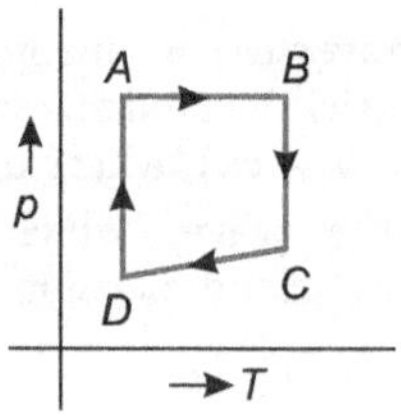

(b)
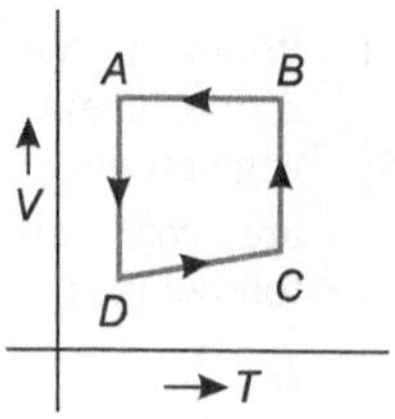

(c)
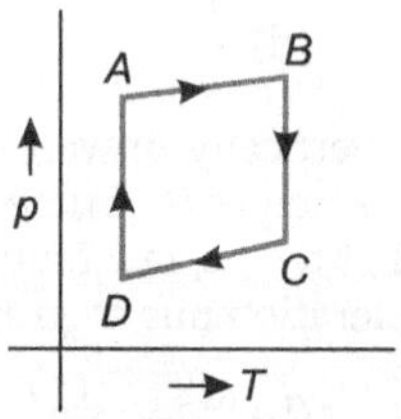

(d)
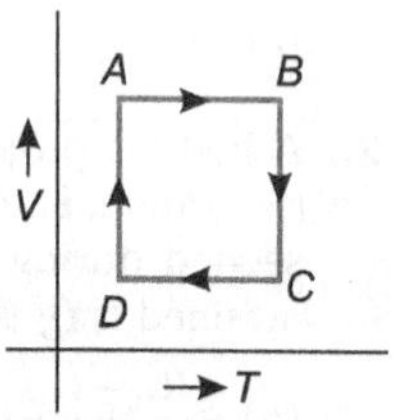

15. An ideal gas is subjected to cyclic process involving four thermodynamic states, the amounts of heat (Q) and work (W) involved in each of these states are
$Q_1 = 6000$ J, $Q_2 = -5500$ J; $Q_3 = -3000$ J; $Q_4 = 3500$ J
$W_1 = 2500$ J; $W_2 = -1000$ J; $W_3 = -1200$ J; $W_4 = x$ J.
The ratio of the net work done by the gas to the total heat absorbed by the gas is η. The values of x and η respectively are
(a) 500; 7.5% (b) 700; 10.5%
(c) 1000; 21% (d) 1500; 15%

16. Two cylinders A and B fitted with pistons contain equal number of moles of an ideal monoatomic gas at 400 K. The piston of A is free to move while that of B is held fixed. Same amount of heat energy is given to the gas in each cylinder. If the rise in temperature of the gas in A is 42 K, the rise in temperature of the gas in B is
(a) 21 K (b) 35 K
(c) 42 K (d) 70 K

17. Three rods of same dimensional have thermal conductivity 3 K, 2 K and K. They are arranged as shown in the figure below

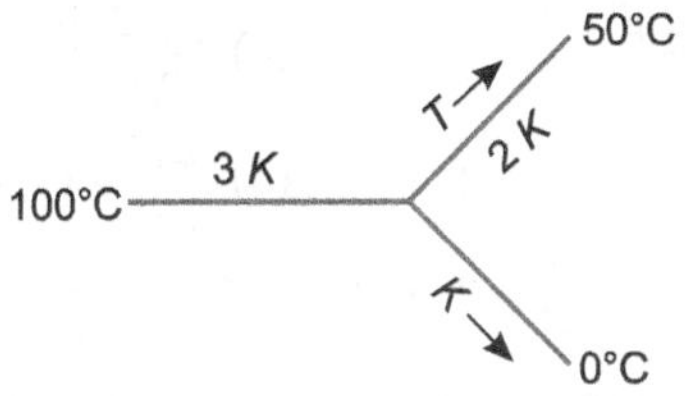

Then, the temperature of the junction in steady state is

(a) $\frac{200}{3}$ °C (b) $\frac{100}{3}$ °C
(c) 75°C (d) $\frac{50}{3}$ °C

18. Two sources A and B are sending notes of frequency 680 Hz. A listener moves from A and B with a constant velocity u. If the speed of sound in air is 340 ms^{-1}, what must be the value of u so that he hears 10 beats per second?

(a) 2.0 ms^{-1} (b) 2.5 ms^{-1}
(c) 3.0 ms^{-1} (d) 3.5 ms^{-1}

19. Two identical piano wires have a fundamental frequency of 600 cycle per second when kept under the same tension. What fractional increase in the tension of one wires will lead to the occurrence of 6 beats per second when both wires vibrate simultaneously?

(a) 0.01 (b) 0.02
(c) 0.03 (d) 0.04

20. In the Young's double slit experiment, the intensities at two points P_1 and P_2 on the screen are respectively I_1 and I_2. If P_1 is located at the centre of a bright fringe and P_2 is located at a distance equal to a quarter of fringe width from P_1, then $\frac{I_1}{I_2}$ is

(a) 2 (b) $\frac{1}{2}$
(c) 4 (d) 16

21. In Young's double slit experiment, the 10th maximum of wavelength λ_1 is at a distance of y_1 from the central maximum. When the wavelength of the source is changed to λ_2, 5th maximum is at a distance of y_2 from its central maximum. The ratio $\left(\frac{y_1}{y_2}\right)$ is

(a) $\frac{2\lambda_1}{\lambda_2}$ (b) $\frac{2\lambda_2}{\lambda_1}$
(c) $\frac{\lambda_1}{2\lambda_2}$ (d) $\frac{\lambda_2}{2\lambda_1}$

22. Four light sources produce the following four waves :

(i) $y_1 = a \sin(\omega t + \phi_1)$
(ii) $y_2 = a \sin 2\omega t$
(iii) $y_3 = a' \sin(\omega t + \phi_2)$
(iv) $y_4 = a' \sin(3\omega t + \phi)$

Superposition of which two waves give rise to interference?

(a) (i) and (ii) (b) (ii) and (iii)
(c) (i) and (iii) (d) (iii) and (iv)

23. The two lenses of an achromatic doublet should have

(a) equal powers
(b) equal dispersive powers
(c) equal ratio of their power and dispersive power
(d) sum of the product of their powers and dispersive power equal to zero

24. Two bar magnets A and B are placed one over the other and are allowed to vibrate in a vibration magnetometer. They make 20 oscillations per minute when the similar poles of A and B are on the same side, while they make 15 oscillations per minute when their opposite poles lie on the same side. If M_A and M_B are the magnetic moments of A and B and if $M_A > M_B$, the ratio of M_A and M_B is

(a) 4 : 3 (b) 25 : 7
(c) 7 : 5 (d) 25 : 16

25. A bar magnet is 10 cm long is kept with its north (N)-pole pointing north. A neutral point is formed at a distance of 15 cm from each pole. Given the horizontal component of earth's field is 0.4 Gauss, the pole strength of the magnet is

(a) 9 A-m (b) 6.75 A-m
(c) 27 A-m (d) 1.35 A-m

26. An infinitely long thin straight wire has uniform linear charge density of $\frac{1}{3}$ Cm^{-1}. Then, the magnitude of the electric intensity at a point 18 cm away is (given $\varepsilon_0 = 8.8 \times 10^{-12}$ C^2Nm^{-2})

(a) 0.33×10^{11} NC^{-1} (b) 3×10^{11} NC^{-1}
(c) 0.66×10^{11} NC^{-1} (d) 1.32×10^{11} NC^{-1}

27. Two point charges $-q$ and $+q$ are located at points (0, 0, $-a$) and (0, 0, a) respectively. The electric potential at a point (0, 0, z), where $z > a$ is

(a) $\frac{qa}{4\pi\varepsilon_0 z^2}$ (b) $\frac{q}{4\pi\varepsilon_0 a}$
(c) $\frac{2qa}{4\pi\varepsilon_0(z^2 - a^2)}$ (d) $\frac{2qa}{4\pi\varepsilon_0(z^2 + a^2)}$

28. In the adjacent shown circuit, a voltmeter of internal resistance R, when connected across B and C reads $\frac{100}{3}$ V. Neglecting the internal resistance of the battery, the value of R is

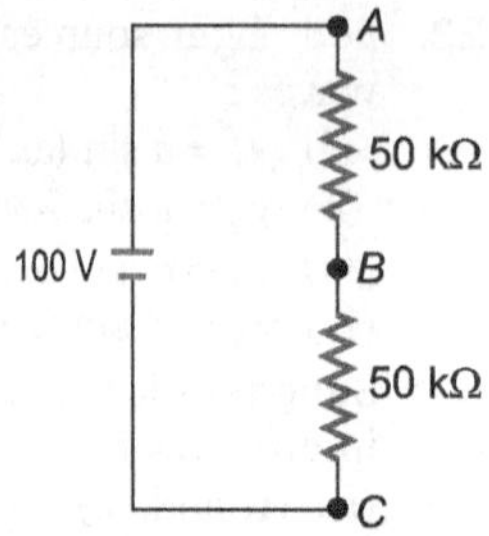

(a) 100 kΩ (b) 75 kΩ
(c) 50 kΩ (d) 25 kΩ

29. A cell in secondary circuit gives null deflection for 2.5 m length of potentiometer having 10 m length of wire. If the length of the potentiometer wire is increased by 1 m without changing the cell in the primary, the position of the null point now is

(a) 3.5 m (b) 3 m
(c) 2.75 m (d) 2.0 m

30. The following series L-C-R circuit, when driven by an emf source of angular frequency 70 kilo-radians per second, the circuit effectively behaves like

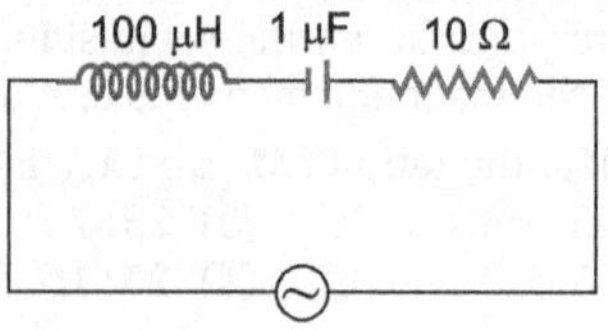

(a) purely resistive circuit
(b) series R-L circuit
(c) series R-C circuit
(d) series L-C circuit with $R = 0$

31. A wire of length l is bent into a circular loop of radius R and carries a current I. The magnetic field at the centre of the loop is B. The same wire is now bent into a double loop of equal radii. If both loops carry the same current I and it is in the same direction, the magnetic field at the centre of the double loop will be

(a) Zero (b) $2B$
(c) $4B$ (d) $8B$

32. An infinitely long straight conductor is bent into the shape as shown below. It carries a current of I ampere and the radius of the circular loop is R metre. Then, the magnitude of magnetic induction at the centre of the circular loop is

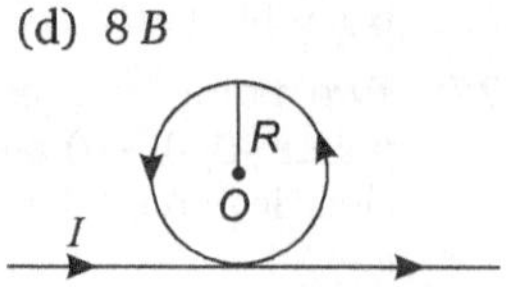

(a) $\frac{\mu_0 I}{2\pi R}$ (b) $\frac{\mu_0 nI}{2R}$

(c) $\frac{\mu_0 I}{2\pi R}(\pi + 1)$ (d) $\frac{\mu_0 I}{2\pi R}(\pi - 1)$

33. The work function of a certain metal is 3.31×10^{-19} J. Then, the maximum kinetic energy of photoelectrons emitted by incident radiation of wavelength 5000 Å is (Given, $h = 6.62 \times 10^{-34}$ J-s, $c = 3 \times 10^8$ ms^{-1}, $e = 1.6 \times 10^{-19}$ C)

(a) 2.48 eV (b) 0.41 eV
(c) 2.07 eV (d) 0.82 eV

34. A photon of energy E ejects a photoelectron from a metal surface whose work function is W_0. If this electron enters into a uniform magnetic field of induction B in a direction perpendicular to the field and describes a circular path of radius r, then the radius r is given by, (in the usual notation)

(a) $\frac{\sqrt{2m(E - W_0)}}{eB}$ (b) $\sqrt{2m(E - W_0)eB}$

(c) $\frac{\sqrt{2e(E - W_0)}}{mB}$ (d) $\frac{\sqrt{2m(E - W_0)}}{eB}$

35. Two radioactive materials X_1 and X_2 have decay constants 10λ and λ respectively. If initially they have the same number of nuclei, then the ratio of the number of nuclei of X_1 to that of X_2 will be $1/e$ after a time

(a) $(1/10\lambda)$ (b) $1/(11\lambda)$
(c) $11/(10\lambda)$ (d) $1/(9\lambda)$

36. Currents flowing in each of the following circuits A and B respectively are

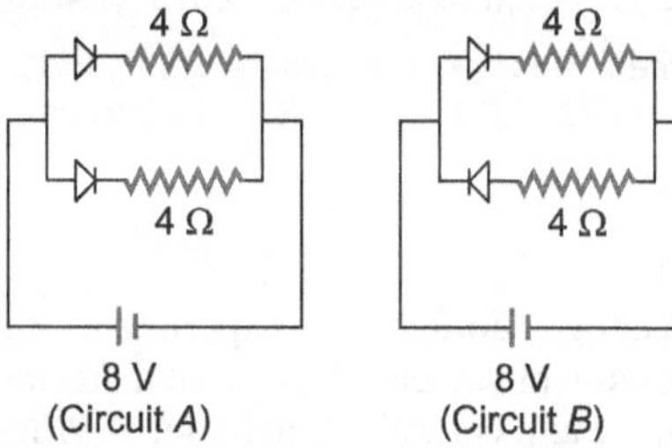

(a) 1 A, 2 A (b) 2 A, 1 A
(c) 4 A, 2 A (d) 2 A, 4 A

37. A bullet of mass 0.02 kg travelling horizontally with velocity 250 ms^{-1} strikes a block of wood of mass 0.23 kg which rests on a rough horizontal surface. After the impact, the block and bullet move together and come to rest after travelling a distance of 40 m. The coefficient of sliding friction of the rough surface is ($g = 9.8$ ms^{-2})

(a) 0.75 (b) 0.61
(c) 0.51 (d) 0.30

38. Two persons A and B are located in X-Y plane at the points (0, 0) and (0, 10) respectively. (The distances are measured in MKS unit). At a time $t = 0$, they start moving simultaneously with velocities $\vec{\mathbf{v}}_A = 2\hat{\mathbf{j}}\ \text{ms}^{-1}$ and $\vec{\mathbf{v}}_B = 2\hat{\mathbf{i}}\ \text{ms}^{-1}$ respectively. The time after which A and B are at their closest distance is

(a) 2.5 s (b) 4 s
(c) 1 s (d) $\frac{10}{\sqrt{2}}$ s

39. A rod of length l is held vertically stationary with its lower end located at a point P, on the horizontal plane. When the rod is released to topple about P, the velocity of the upper end of the rod with which it hits the ground is

(a) $\sqrt{\frac{g}{l}}$ (b) $\sqrt{3gl}$
(c) $3\sqrt{\frac{g}{l}}$ (d) $\sqrt{\frac{3g}{l}}$

40. A wheel of radius 0.4 m can rotate freely about its axis as shown in the figure. A string is wrapped over its rim and a mass of 4 kg is hung. An angular acceleration of 8 rad-s^{-2} is produced in it due to the torque. Then, moment of inertia of the wheel is ($g = 10\ \text{ms}^{-2}$)

(a) 2 kg-m^2 (b) 1 kg-m^2
(c) 4 kg-m^2 (d) 8 kg-m^2

Answers

1. (d)	2. (c)	3. (a)	4. (a)	5. (a)	6. (c)	7. (b)	8. (d)	9. (d)	10. (d)
11. (c)	12. (a)	13. (c)	14. (a)	15. (b)	16. (c)	17. (a)	18. (b)	19. (b)	20. (d)
21. (a)	22. (c)	23. (d)	24. (b)	25. (d)	26. (a)	27. (c)	28. (c)	29. (c)	30. (c)
31. (c)	32. (c)	33. (b)	34. (d)	35. (d)	36. (c)	37. (c)	38. (a)	39. (b)	40. (a)

Solutions

1. Given, $y = a \sin (bt - cx)$

Comparing the given equation with general wave equation

$$y = a \sin \left(\frac{2\pi t}{T} - \frac{2\pi x}{\lambda}\right)$$

we get $b = \frac{2\pi}{T}, c = \frac{2\pi}{\lambda}$

(a) Dimensions of $\frac{y}{a} = \frac{\text{metre}}{\text{metre}} = \frac{[L]}{[L]}$ = Dimensionless

(b) Dimensions of $bt = \frac{2\pi}{T} \cdot t = \frac{[T]}{[T]}$ = Dimensionless

(c) Dimensions of $cx = \frac{2\pi}{\lambda} \cdot x = \frac{[L]}{[L]}$ = Dimensionless

(d) Dimensions of $\frac{b}{c} = \frac{2\pi}{T} \Big/ \frac{2\pi}{\lambda}$

$$= \lambda / T = [LT^{-1}]$$

Thus, option (d) has dimensions.

2. Let time taken by the body to fall from point C to B is t'.

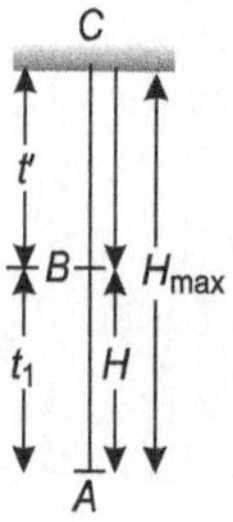

Then $t_1 + 2t' = t_2$

$$t' = \left(\frac{t_2 - t_1}{2}\right) \quad \dots\text{(i)}$$

Total time taken to reach point C

$$T = t_1 + t'$$
$$= t_1 + \frac{t_2 - t_1}{2}$$
$$= \frac{2t_1 + t_2 - t_1}{2}$$
$$= \left(\frac{t_1 + t_2}{2}\right)$$

Maximum height attained

$$H_{max} = \frac{1}{2} g (T)^2$$
$$= \frac{1}{2} g \left(\frac{t_1 + t_2}{2}\right)^2$$
$$= \frac{1}{2} g \cdot \frac{(t_1 + t_2)^2}{4}$$
$$\Rightarrow \quad H_{max} = \frac{1}{8} g \cdot (t_1 + t_2)^2 \text{ m}$$

3. Momentum, $p = m \cdot v$

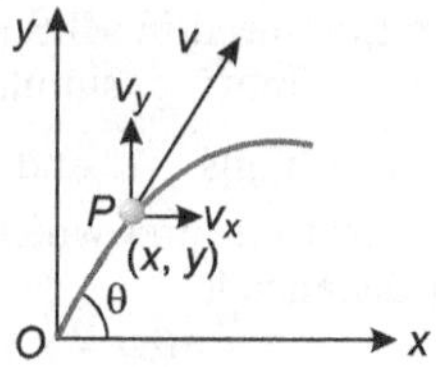

$$\Rightarrow \quad v = \left(\frac{p}{m}\right)$$

Kinetic energy, $KE = \frac{1}{2} mv^2$

$$= \frac{1}{2} m \left(\frac{p^2}{m^2}\right) = \frac{1}{2m} p^2$$

$$\Rightarrow \quad KE \propto p^2 \quad \left(\because \frac{1}{2m} = \text{constant}\right)$$

Hence, the graph between KE and p^2 will be linear as shown below

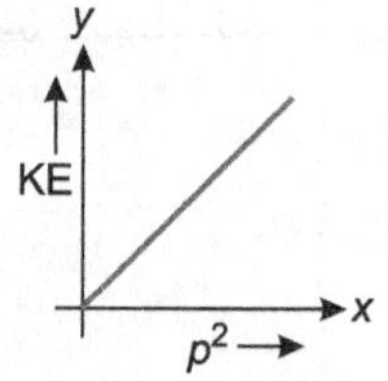

Now, kinetic energy $KE = \frac{1}{2} mv^2$

The velocity component at point P,

$$v_y = (u \sin \theta - gt)$$

and

$$v_x = u \cos \theta$$

Resultant velocity at point P,

$$\vec{\mathbf{v}} = v_y \hat{\mathbf{j}} + v_x \hat{\mathbf{i}}$$
$$= (u \sin \theta - gt) \hat{\mathbf{j}} + u \cos \theta \, \hat{\mathbf{i}}$$
$$|\vec{\mathbf{v}}| = \sqrt{(u \cos \theta)^2 + (u \sin \theta - gt)^2}$$
$$= \sqrt{u^2 \cos^2 \theta + u^2 \sin^2 \theta + g^2 t^2 - 2ugt \sin \theta}$$
$$\therefore \quad = \sqrt{u^2 (\cos^2 \theta + \sin^2 \theta) + g^2 t^2 - 2ugt \sin \theta}$$
$$KE = \frac{1}{2} m (u^2 + g^2 t^2 - 2ugt \sin \theta)$$
$$\Rightarrow KE \propto t^2$$

Hence, graph will be parabolic with intercept on y-axis.

Hence, the graph between KE and t

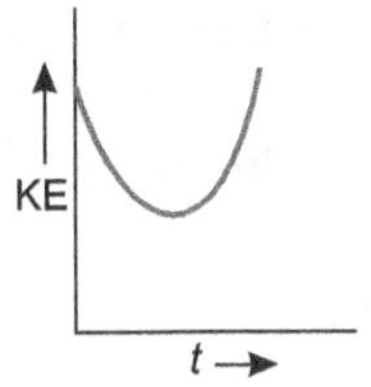

Now, in case of height

$$KE = \frac{1}{2} m(v^2)$$

and $$v^2 = (u^2 - 2gy)$$

$\therefore$ $$KE = \frac{1}{2} m(u^2 - 2gy)$$

$$KE = - mgy + \frac{1}{2} mu^2$$

Intercept on y-axis $= \frac{1}{2} mu^2$

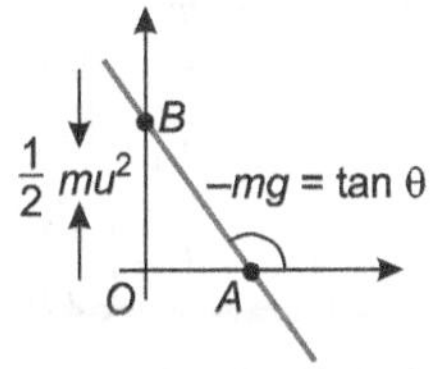

Now, $$KE = \frac{1}{2} mv^2$$

$$KE = \frac{1}{2} m \left(\frac{x}{t}\right)^2$$

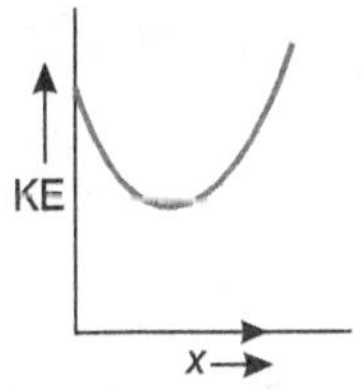

KE $\propto x^2$. Thus graph between KE and x will be parabolic.

4. Power of motor initially $= P_0$
Let, rate of flow of motor $= (x)$

Since, power, $P_0 = \frac{\text{work}}{\text{time}} = \frac{mgy}{t}$

$$= mg\left(\frac{y}{t}\right),$$

$$\frac{y}{t} = x = \text{rate of flow of water}$$

$$= mgx \qquad \text{...(i)}$$

If rate of flow of water is increased by n times, *ie*, (nx).

Increased power $P_1 = \frac{mgy'}{t}$

$$= mg\left(\frac{y'}{t}\right) = mgn \cdot x$$

$$= nmgx \qquad \text{...(ii)}$$

The ratio of power

$$\frac{P_1}{P_0} = \frac{nmgx}{mgx}$$

$$\frac{P_1}{P_0} = \frac{n}{1} \Rightarrow P_1 : P_0 = n : 1$$

5. Mass of the first body $m_1 = 5$ kg, for elastic collision $e = 1$.

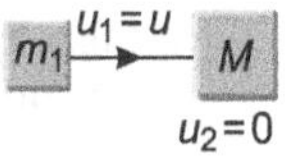

Suppose initially body m_1 moves with velocity v after collision velocity becomes $\left(\frac{u}{10}\right)$.

Let after collision velocity of M block becomes (v_2).
By conservation of momentum

$$m_1u_1 + m_2u_2 = m_1v_1 + m_2v_2$$

or $$5u + M \times 0 = 5 \times \frac{u}{10} + Mv_2$$

or $$5u = \frac{u}{2} + Mv_2 \qquad \text{...(i)}$$

Since, $$v_1 - v_2 = -e(u_1 - u_2)$$

$$\frac{u}{10} - v_2 = -1(u)$$

or $$\frac{u}{10} + u = v_2$$

$$\frac{11u}{10} = v_2 \qquad \text{...(ii)}$$

Substituting value of v_2 in Eq. (i) from Eq. (ii), we get

$$5u = \frac{u}{2} + M\left(\frac{11u}{10}\right)$$

or $$5 - \frac{1}{2} = M\left(\frac{11}{10}\right)$$

or $$M = \frac{9 \times 10}{2 \times 11}$$

or $$M = \frac{45}{11} = 4.09 \text{ kg}$$

6.

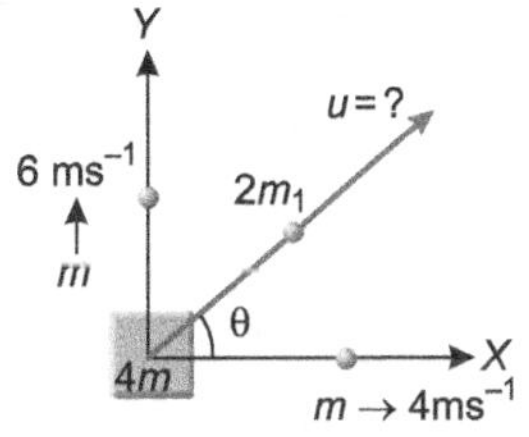

Let third mass particle $(2m)$ moves making angle θ with X-axis.

The horizontal component of velocity of $2m$ mass particle $= u \cos \theta$ and vertical component $= u \sin \theta$

From conservation of linear momentum in X-direction

$$m_1u_1 + m_2u_2 = m_1v_1 + m_2v_2$$

or $\quad 0 = m \times 4 + 2m(u \cos \theta)$

or $\quad -4 = 2u \cos \theta$

or $\quad -2 = u \cos \theta \quad \ldots(\text{i})$

Again, applying law of conservation of linear momentum in Y-direction.

$$0 = m \times 6 + 2m(u \sin \theta)$$

$\Rightarrow \quad -\frac{6}{2} = u \sin \theta$

or $\quad -3 = u \sin \theta \quad \ldots(\text{ii})$

Squaring Eqs. (i) and(ii) and adding, we get

$$(4) + (9) = u^2 \cos^2 \theta + u^2 \sin^2 \theta$$

$$= u^2 (\cos^2 \theta + \sin^2 \theta)$$

or $\quad 13 = u^2$

or $\quad u = \sqrt{13} \text{ ms}^{-1}$

7. Maximum height attained by a projectile

$$h = \frac{v^2R}{2gR - v^2} \quad \ldots(\text{i})$$

Velocity of body = half the escape velocity

$$v = \frac{v_e}{2}$$

or

$$v = \frac{\sqrt{2gR}}{2} \Rightarrow v^2 = \frac{2gR}{4}$$

or $\quad v^2 = \left(\frac{gR}{2}\right)$

Now, putting value of v^2 in Eq. (i), we get

$$h = \frac{\frac{gR}{2} \cdot R}{2gR - \frac{gR}{2}} = \frac{gR^2/2}{3gR/2}$$

or $\quad h = \frac{R}{3}$

8. The displacement of particle, executing SHM

$$y = 5 \sin \left(4t + \frac{\pi}{3}\right) \quad \ldots(\text{i})$$

Velocity of particle

$$\left(\frac{dy}{dt}\right) = \frac{5d}{dt} \sin \left(4t + \frac{\pi}{3}\right)$$

$$= 5 \cos \left(4t + \frac{\pi}{3}\right) \cdot 4$$

$$= 20 \cos \left(4t + \frac{\pi}{3}\right)$$

Velocity at $t = \left(\frac{T}{4}\right)$

$$\left(\frac{dy}{dt}\right)_{t=\frac{T}{4}} = 20 \cos \left(4 \times \frac{T}{4} + \frac{\pi}{3}\right)$$

or $\quad u = 20 \cos \left(T + \frac{\pi}{3}\right) \quad \ldots(\text{ii})$

Comparing the given equation with standard equation of SHM, given by

$$y = a \sin (\omega t + \phi)$$

We get $\quad \omega = 4$

As $\quad \omega = \frac{2\pi}{T}$

$\Rightarrow \quad T = \frac{2\pi}{\omega}$

or $\quad T = \frac{2\pi}{4}$

or $\quad T = \left(\frac{\pi}{2}\right)$

Now, putting value of T in Eq. (ii), we get

$$u = 20 \cos \left(\frac{\pi}{2} + \frac{\pi}{3}\right)$$

$$= -20 \sin \frac{\pi}{3}$$

$$= -20 \times \frac{\sqrt{3}}{2}$$

$$= -10 \times \sqrt{3}$$

The kinetic energy of particle,

$$\text{KE} = \frac{1}{2} mu^2$$

$\because \quad m = 2 \text{ g} = 2 \times 10^{-3} \text{ kg}$

$$= \frac{1}{2} \times 2 \times 10^{-3} \times (-10\sqrt{3})^2$$

$$= 10^{-3} \times 100 \times 3$$

$$= 3 \times 10^{-1}$$

$$\text{KE} = 0.3 \text{ J}$$

9. Free body diagram of the two blocks are

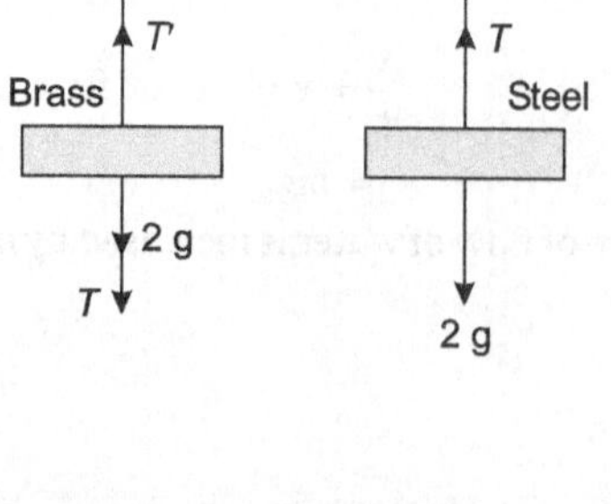

Given, $\frac{l_1}{l_2}=a, \frac{r_1}{r_2}=b, \frac{Y_1}{Y_2}=c$

Let Young's modulus of steel is Y_1 and of brass is Y_2.

$$\therefore \quad Y_1=\frac{F_1 \cdot l_1}{A_1 \cdot \Delta l_1} \quad \ldots (i)$$

$$\text{and} \quad Y_2=\frac{F_2 \cdot l_2}{A_2 \Delta l_2} \quad \ldots (ii)$$

Dividing Eq. (i) by Eq. (ii), we get

$$\frac{Y_1}{Y_2}=\frac{\frac{F_1 \cdot l_1}{A_1 \cdot \Delta l_1}}{\frac{F_2 \cdot l_2}{A_2 \cdot \Delta l_2}}$$

$$\text{or} \quad \frac{Y_1}{Y_2}=\frac{F_1 \cdot A_2 \cdot l_1 \cdot \Delta l_2}{F_2 \cdot A_1 \cdot l_2 \cdot \Delta l_1} \quad \ldots (iii)$$

Force on steel wire from free body diagram

$$T=F_1=(2g) \text{ newton}$$

Force on brass wire from free body diagram

$$F_2=T'=T+2g=(4g) \text{ newton}$$

Now, putting the value of F_1, F_2, in Eq. (iii), we get

$$\frac{Y_1}{Y_2}=\left(\frac{2g}{4g}\right) \cdot \left(\frac{\pi r_2^2}{\pi r_1^2}\right) \cdot \left[\frac{l_1}{l_2}\right] \cdot \left(\frac{\Delta l_2}{\Delta l_1}\right)$$

$$\text{or} \quad c=\frac{1}{2}\left(\frac{1}{b^2}\right) \cdot a\left(\frac{\Delta l_2}{\Delta l_1}\right)$$

$$\text{or} \quad \frac{\Delta l_1}{\Delta l_2}=\left(\frac{a}{2b^2c}\right)$$

10. Initially area of soap bubble

$$A_1=4\pi r^2$$

Under isothermal condition radius becomes $2r$,

Then, area $A_2=4\pi(2r)^2$

$$=4\pi \cdot 4r^2$$
$$=16\pi r^2$$

Increase in surface area

$$\Delta A=2(A_2-A_1)$$
$$=2(16\pi r^2-4\pi r^2)$$
$$=24\pi r^2$$

Energy spent

$$W=T \times \Delta A$$
$$=T \cdot 24\pi r^2$$

$$\text{or} \quad W=24\pi T r^2 \text{ J}$$

11. Let now radius of big drop is R.

Then, $\frac{4}{3}\pi R^3=\frac{4}{3} \times \pi r^3 \cdot 8$

$$R=2r$$

where r is radius of small drops. Now, terminal velocity of drop in liquid.

$$v_e=\frac{2}{9} \times \frac{r^2}{\eta}(\rho-\sigma)g$$

where η is coefficient of viscosity and ρ is density of drop σ is density of liquid.

Terminal speed drop is 6 cm s^{-1}

$$\therefore \quad 6=\frac{2}{9} \times \frac{r^2}{\eta}(\rho-\sigma)g \quad \ldots (i)$$

Let terminal velocity becomes v' after coalesce, then

$$v'=\frac{2}{9}\frac{R^2}{\eta}(\rho-\sigma)g \quad \ldots (ii)$$

Dividing Eq. (i) by Eq. (ii), we get

$$\frac{6}{v'}=\frac{\frac{2}{9}\frac{r^2}{\eta}(\rho-\sigma)g}{\frac{2}{9}\frac{R^2}{\eta}(\rho-\sigma)g}$$

$$\text{or} \quad \frac{6}{v'}=\frac{r^2}{(2r)^2}$$

$$\text{or} \quad v'=24 \text{ cm s}^{-1}$$

12. Time period of oscillation,

$$T=2\pi\sqrt{\frac{l}{g}}$$

$$\Rightarrow \quad \frac{dT}{T}=\frac{1}{2}\frac{dl}{l}$$

$$\text{As,} \quad \frac{dl}{l}=\alpha dt$$

$$\Rightarrow \quad \frac{dT}{T}=\frac{1}{2}\alpha dt$$

$$=\frac{1}{2} \times 9 \times 10^{-7} \times (30-20)$$
$$=4.5 \times 10^{-6}$$

$\therefore$ Loss in time $=4.5 \times 10^{-6} \times 0.5$

$$=2.25 \times 10^{-6} \text{ s}$$

13. The volume of the metal at 30°C is

$$V_{30}=\frac{\text{loss of weight}}{\text{specific gravity} \times g}$$

$$=\frac{(45-25)g}{1.5 \times g}=13.33 \text{ cm}^3$$

Similarly, volume of metal at 40°C is

$$V_{40}=\frac{(45-27)g}{1.25 \times g}=14.40 \text{ cm}^3$$

Now, $V_{40}=V_{30}[1+\gamma(t_2-t_1)]$

or $\gamma = \dfrac{V_{40} - V_{30}}{V_{30}(t_2 - t_1)}$

$= \dfrac{14.40 - 13.33}{13.33\,(40 - 30)}$

$= 8.03 \times 10^{-3}/°C$

$\therefore$ Coefficient of linear expansion of the metal is

$$\alpha = \frac{\gamma}{3} = \frac{8.03 \times 10^{-3}}{3}$$

$$\approx 2.6 \times 10^{-3}/°C$$

14. $A \to B \to C \to D \to A$ is clockwise process. During $A \to B$, pressure is constant and $B \to C$, process follows $p \propto \dfrac{1}{V}$, it means T is constant. During process $C \to D$, both p and V changes and process $D \to A$ follows $p \propto \dfrac{1}{V}$ which means T is constant.

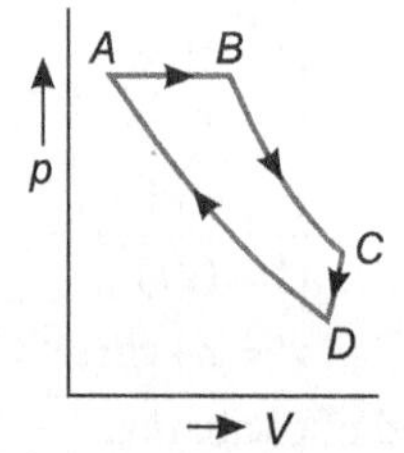

Hence, from above data it is clear that equivalent cyclic process is

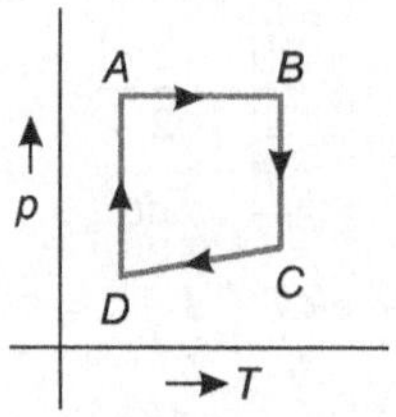

15. From first law of thermodynamics

$$Q = \Delta U + W$$

or $\Delta U = Q - W$

$\therefore$ $\Delta U_1 = Q_1 - W_1 = 6000 - 2500 = 3500$ J

$\Delta U_2 = Q_2 - W_2 = -5500 + 1000 = -4500$ J

$\Delta U_3 = Q_3 - W_3 = -3000 + 1200 = -1800$ J

$\Delta U_4 = Q_4 - W_4 = 3500 - x$

For cyclic process $\Delta U = 0$

$\therefore$ $3500 - 4500 - 1800 + 3500 - x = 0$

or $x = 700$ J

Efficiency, $\eta = \dfrac{\text{output}}{\text{input}} \times 100$

$$= \frac{W_1 + W_2 + W_3 + W_4}{Q_1 + Q_4} \times 100$$

$$= \frac{(2500 - 1000 - 1200 + 700)}{6000 + 3500} \times 100$$

$$= \frac{1000}{9500} \times 100$$

$$\eta = 10.5\%$$

16. From first law of thermodynamics

$$Q = \Delta U + W$$

For cylinder A pressure remains constant

$\therefore$ Work done by a system

$$W = \frac{\mu R}{\gamma - 1}(T_1 - T_2)$$

For monoatomic gases

$$\mu = 1$$

$$\gamma = \frac{5}{3}$$

$\therefore$ $W = \dfrac{1 \times R}{\frac{5}{3} - 1}(442 - 400) = \dfrac{3}{2}R \times 42$

or $W = 63R$

But $\Delta U = 0$, for cylinder A

$\therefore$ $Q = 0 + 63R$

$$Q = 63R$$

For cylinder B volume is constant,

$\therefore$ $W = 0$

and $Q = \mu C_V \Delta T$

For monoatomic gas

$$C_V = \frac{3}{2}R$$

$$Q = 1 \times \frac{3}{2}R\Delta T$$

As heat given to both cylinder is same

$\therefore$ $63R = \dfrac{3}{2}R\,\Delta T$

$$\Delta T = 42\text{ K}$$

17. According to the figure

$$H = H_1 + H_2$$

$\Rightarrow$ $\dfrac{3KA(100 - T)}{l} = \dfrac{2KA(T - 50)}{l} + \dfrac{KA(T - 0)}{l}$

$$300 - 3T = 2T - 100 + T$$

$\Rightarrow$ $6T = 400$

or $T = \dfrac{200}{3}$ °C

18. Listener go from $A \to B$ with velocity (u) let the apparent frequency of sound from source A by listener

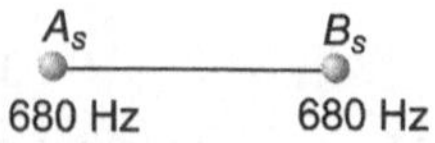

$$n' = n\left(\frac{v - v_o}{v + v_s}\right)$$

or $$n' = 680\left(\frac{340 - u}{340 + 0}\right)$$

The apparent frequency of sound from source B by listener

$$n'' = n\left(\frac{v + v_o}{v - v_s}\right)$$

$$= 680\left(\frac{340 + u}{340 - 0}\right)$$

But listener hear 10 beats per second.

Hence, $$n'' - n' = 10$$

or $$680\left(\frac{340+u}{340}\right) - 680\left(\frac{340-u}{340}\right) = 10$$

or $$2(340 + u - 340 + u) = 10$$

or $$u = 2.5 \text{ m s}^{-1}$$

19. Beats per second when both the wires vibrate simultaneously.

$$n_1 \pm n_2 = 6$$

or $$\frac{1}{2l}\sqrt{\frac{T}{m}} \pm \frac{1}{2l}\sqrt{\frac{T'}{m}} = 6$$

or $$\frac{1}{2l}\sqrt{\frac{T'}{m}} - \frac{1}{2l}\sqrt{\frac{T}{m}} = 6$$

or $$\frac{1}{2l}\sqrt{\frac{T'}{m}} - 600 = 6$$

$$\frac{1}{2l}\sqrt{\frac{T'}{m}} = 606 \qquad \ldots(i)$$

Given that fundamental frequency

$$\frac{1}{2l}\sqrt{\frac{T}{m}} = 600 \qquad \ldots(ii)$$

Dividing Eq. (i) by Eq. (ii), we get

$$\frac{\frac{1}{2l}\sqrt{\frac{T'}{m}}}{\frac{1}{2l}\sqrt{\frac{T}{m}}} = \frac{606}{600}$$

or $$\sqrt{\frac{T'}{T}} = (1.01)$$

or $$\frac{T'}{T} = (1.02)\%$$

or $$T' = T(1.02)$$

Increase in tension

$$\Delta T' = T \times 1.02 - T$$

$$= (0.02T)$$

Hence, $$\Delta T' = 0.02$$

20.

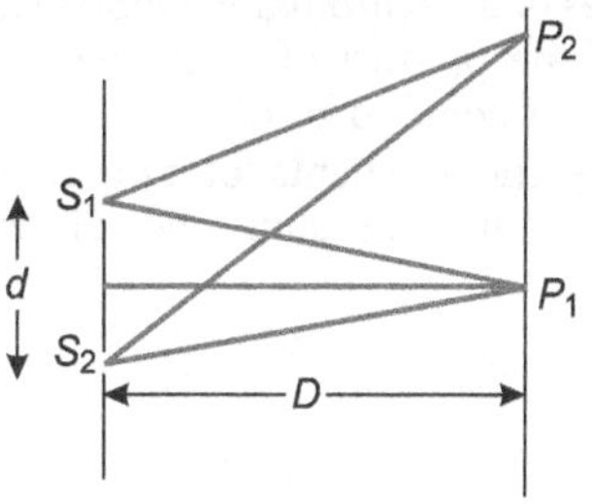

Fringe width $$\beta = \frac{\lambda D}{d}$$

Let the amplitude of that place where constructive inference takes place is a.

The position of fringe at p_2 is

$$x = \frac{n\lambda D}{d}$$

Given, $$\beta' = \left(\frac{\beta}{4}\right)$$

$\therefore$ $$\frac{\lambda D}{4d} = \frac{n\lambda D}{d}$$

or $$n = \frac{1}{4}$$

$\therefore$ $$\frac{I_1}{I_2} = \frac{a^2}{\left(\frac{a}{4}\right)^2}$$

or $$I_1 : I_2 = 16 : 1$$

21. Position fringe from central maxima

$$y_1 = \frac{n\lambda_1 D}{d}$$

Given, $$n = 10$$

$\therefore$ $$y_1 = \frac{10\lambda_1 D}{d} \qquad \ldots(i)$$

For second source

$$y_2 = \frac{5\lambda_2 D}{d} \qquad \ldots(ii)$$

$\therefore$ $$\frac{y_1}{y_2} = \frac{\frac{10\lambda_1 D}{d}}{\frac{5\lambda_2 D}{d}}$$

$\Rightarrow$ $$\frac{y_1}{y_2} = \frac{2\lambda_1}{\lambda_2}$$

22. Interference phenomenon takes place between two waves which have equal frequency and propagate in same direction.

Hence, $$y_1 = a\sin(\omega t + \phi_1)$$

$$y_3 = a'\sin(\omega t + \phi_2)$$

will give rise to interference as the two waves have same frequency ω.

23. The two lenses of an achromatic doublet should have, sum of the product of their powers and dispersive power equal to zero.

24. Ratio of magnetic moments of two magnets of equal size when in sum and difference position is

$$\frac{M_A}{M_B} = \frac{T_d^2 + T_s^2}{T_d^2 - T_s^2} = \frac{v_s^2 + v_d^2}{v_s^2 - v_d^2}$$

$$= \frac{\left(\frac{1}{20}\right)^2 + \left(\frac{1}{15}\right)^2}{\left(\frac{1}{15}\right)^2 - \left(\frac{1}{20}\right)^2}$$

$$= \frac{400 + 225}{400 - 225}$$

$$= \frac{625}{175} = \frac{25}{7}$$

$$\Rightarrow \quad M_A : M_B = 25 : 7$$

25. Length of magnet $= 10 \text{ cm} = 10 \times 10^{-2}$ m,

$$r = 15 \times 10^{-2} \text{ m}$$

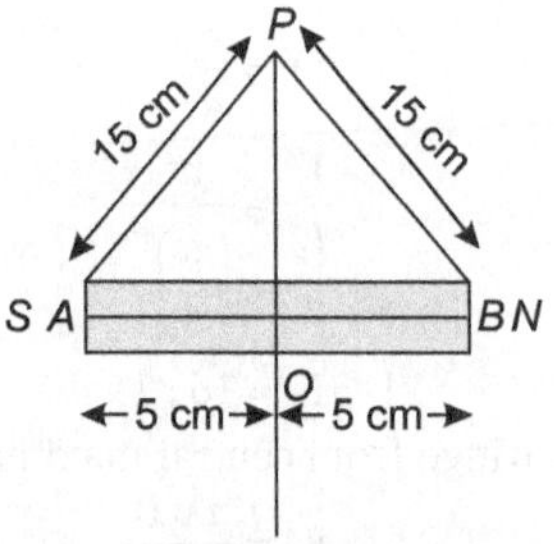

$$OP = \sqrt{225 - 25} = \sqrt{200} \text{ cm}$$

Since, at the neutral point, magnetic field due to the magnet is equal to B_H

$$B_H = \frac{\mu_0}{4\pi} \cdot \frac{M}{(OP^2 + AO^2)^{3/2}}$$

$$0.4 \times 10^{-4} = 10^{-7} \times \frac{M}{(200 \times 10^{-4} + 25 \times 10^{-4})^{3/2}}$$

$$\frac{0.4 \times 10^{-4}}{10^{-7}} \times (225 \times 10^{-4})^{3/2} = M$$

$$0.4 \times 10^3 \times 10^{-6} (225)^{3/2} = M$$

$$M = 1.35 \text{ A-m}$$

26. Charge density of long wire

$$\lambda = \frac{1}{3} \text{ C-m}$$

and $\quad r = 18 \times 10^{-2}$ m

From Gauss theorem

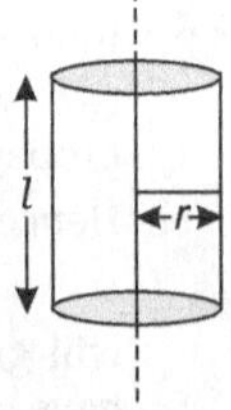

$$\oint \vec{\mathbf{E}} \cdot d\vec{\mathbf{S}} = \frac{q}{\varepsilon_0}$$

$$E \oint dS = \frac{q}{\varepsilon_0}$$

or $\quad E \times 2\pi rl = \dfrac{q}{\varepsilon_0}$

or $\quad E = \dfrac{q}{2\pi\varepsilon_0 rl} = \dfrac{q/l}{2\pi\varepsilon_0 r}$

$$= \frac{\lambda \times 2}{2\pi\varepsilon_0 r \times 2} = \frac{\lambda \times 2}{4\pi\varepsilon_0 r}$$

$$= 9 \times 10^9 \times \frac{1}{3} \times 2 \times \frac{1}{18 \times 10^{-2}}$$

$$= \frac{1}{3} \times 10^{11} = 0.33 \times 10^{11}$$

$$= 0.33 \times 10^{11} \text{ NC}^{-1}$$

27. Potential at P due to $(+q)$ charge

$$V_1 = \frac{1}{4\pi\varepsilon_0} \cdot \frac{q}{(z - a)}$$

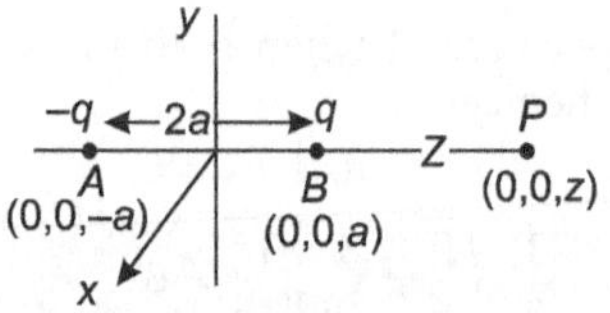

Potential at P due to $(-q)$ charge

$$V_2 = \frac{1}{4\pi\varepsilon_0} \cdot \frac{-q}{(z + a)}$$

Total potential at P due to (AB) electric dipole

$$V = V_1 + V_2$$

$$= \frac{1}{4\pi\varepsilon_0} \cdot \frac{q}{(z - a)} - \frac{1}{4\pi\varepsilon_0} \frac{q}{(z + a)}$$

$$= \frac{q}{4\pi\varepsilon_0} \frac{(z + a - z + a)}{(z - a)(z + a)}$$

$$\Rightarrow \quad V = \frac{2qa}{4\pi\varepsilon_0 (z^2 - a^2)}$$

28.

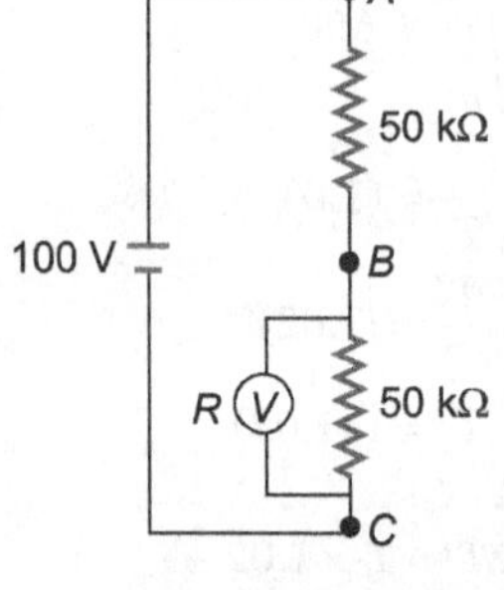

Internal resistance of voltmeter is R.

Therefore effective resistance across B and C, R' is given by

$$\frac{1}{R'} = \frac{1}{R} + \frac{1}{50} = \frac{50+R}{50R}$$

or $$R' = \left(\frac{50R}{50+R}\right)$$

According to Ohm's law

$$V' = IR'$$

or $$\frac{100}{3} = I \cdot \left(\frac{50R}{50+R}\right)$$

or $$\frac{100}{3}\left(\frac{50+R}{50R}\right) = I \qquad \ldots(\text{i})$$

Now, total resistance of circuit

$$R'' = 50 + \frac{50R}{50+R}$$

or $$R'' = \frac{(2500+100R)}{(50+R)}$$

Now, $$V'' = IR''$$

$\Rightarrow$ $$100 = \frac{100}{3}\left(\frac{50+R}{50R}\right)\frac{2500+100R}{(50+R)}$$

or $$150R = 2500 + 100R$$

or $$50R = 2500$$

or $$R = 50\ \text{k}\Omega$$

29. Resistance of potentiometer wire

$$R = \rho \times \frac{l}{A}$$

or $$R = \left(\rho \times \frac{10}{A}\right)$$

The value of 2.5 m length wire

$$R' = \frac{\rho \times 10}{A \times 10} \times 2.5$$

or $$R' = \left(\frac{2.5\rho}{A \times 10}\right)$$

Potential $$V' = I \times R'$$

$$= I\left(\frac{2.5\rho}{A \times 10}\right)$$

Now, again the length of potentiometer wire is increased by 1 m, then resistance of null position wire.

$$R'' = \left(\frac{\rho \times l}{11 \times A}\right)$$

$$V'' = IR''$$

and $$V = V'$$

$$\frac{I \times 2.5\rho}{A \times 10} = \frac{\rho \times l}{11 \times A} \times I$$

or $$\frac{2.5 \times 11}{10} = l = 2.75\ \text{m}$$

30.

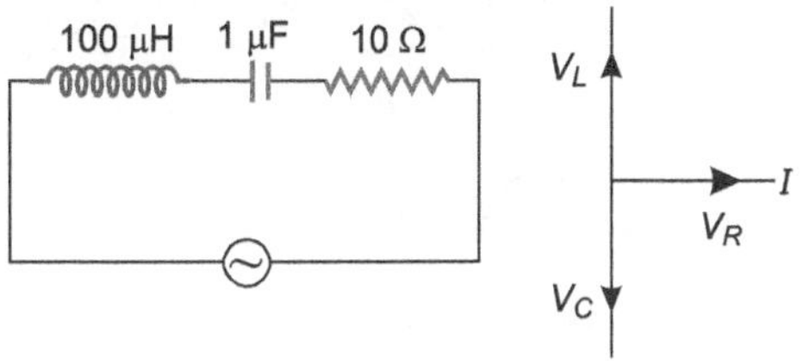

Impedance, $Z = \sqrt{(X_L \sim X_C)^2 + R^2}$

or $$Z = \sqrt{\left(\omega L \sim \frac{1}{\omega C}\right)^2 + R^2}$$

Inductive reactance

$$X_L = \omega L = 70 \times 10^3 \times 100 \times 10^{-6}$$

$$= 7\ \Omega$$

Capacitance reactance

$$X_C = \frac{1}{\omega C} = \frac{1}{70 \times 10^3 \times 1 \times 10^{-6}}$$

$$= \frac{1}{7 \times 10^{-2}} = \frac{10^2}{7} = \frac{100}{7}$$

As $\quad X_C > X_L$

Hence, circuit behave like as R-C circuit.

31. Magnetic field at the centre of the loop

$$B = \frac{\mu_0}{4\pi} \cdot \frac{I \cdot 2\pi R}{R^2} \qquad \ldots(\text{i})$$

For the wire which is looped double let radius becomes r

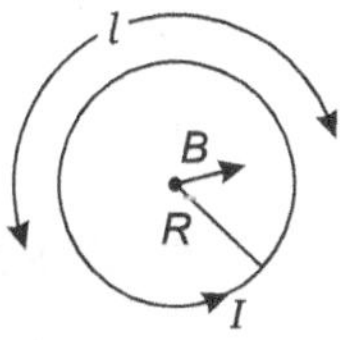

Then, $$\frac{l}{2} = 2\pi r$$

or $$\frac{l}{4\pi} = (r)$$

$\therefore$ $$B' = \frac{\mu_0}{4\pi} \cdot \frac{I \cdot 2\pi r \times 2}{r^2}$$

or $$B' = \frac{\mu_0}{4\pi} \cdot \frac{I \cdot \frac{l}{2} \cdot 2}{\left(\frac{l}{4\pi}\right)^2}$$

or $$B' = \frac{\mu_0}{4\pi} \cdot \frac{Il \times 16\pi^2}{l^2} \qquad \ldots(\text{ii})$$

Now, $$B = \frac{\mu_0}{4\pi} \cdot \frac{I \cdot l}{\left(\frac{l}{2\pi}\right)^2}\left[R = \frac{l}{2\pi}\right] \qquad \ldots(\text{iii})$$

Dividing Eq. (ii) by Eq. (iii), we get

$$\frac{B'}{B} = \frac{\frac{\mu_0}{4\pi} \cdot \frac{I \cdot l \cdot 16\pi^2}{l^2}}{\frac{\mu_0}{4\pi} \cdot \frac{Il \cdot 4\pi^2}{l^2}}$$

or $\quad \frac{B'}{B} = 4$

or $\quad B' = 4B$

32. 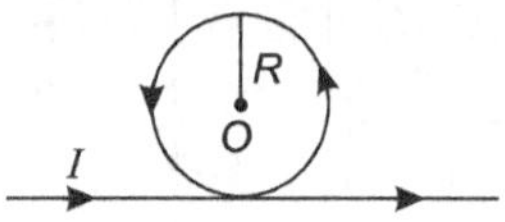

Magnetic field due to long wire at O point

$$B_1 = \frac{\mu_0}{2\pi}\left(\frac{I}{R}\right) \quad \text{(upward direction)}$$

Magnetic field due to loop at O point

$$B_2 = \frac{\mu_0}{4\pi} \cdot \frac{I \cdot 2\pi R}{R^2}$$

$$B_2 = \frac{\mu_0}{2} \cdot \frac{I}{R} \quad \text{(in upward direction)}$$

Hence, resultant magnetic field at centre O

$$B = B_1 + B_2$$

$$B = \frac{\mu_0 I}{2\pi \cdot R}(\pi + 1)\,\text{T}$$

33. Work function $W_0 = 3.31 \times 10^{-19}$ J

Wavelength of incident radiation

$$\lambda = 5000 \times 10^{-10} \text{ m}$$

$$E = W_0 + \text{KE}$$

(According to Einstein equation)

$$\frac{hc}{\lambda} = 3.31 \times 10^{-19} + \text{KE}$$

$$\text{KE} = -3.31 \times 10^{-19} + \frac{6.62 \times 10^{-34} \times 3 \times 10^8}{5000 \times 10^{-10}}$$

$$= -3.31 \times 10^{-19} + \frac{6.62 \times 3}{5} \times 10^{-19}$$

$$= (-3.31 \times 1.324 \times 3) \times 10^{-19}$$

$$= (3.972 - 3.31) \times 10^{-19}$$

$$= 0.662 \times 10^{-19} \text{ J}$$

$$\Rightarrow E = \frac{0.662 \times 10^{-19}}{1.6 \times 10^{-19}} = 0.41 \text{ eV}$$

34. From Einstein's equation

$$E = W_0 + \frac{1}{2}mv^2$$

$$\sqrt{\frac{2(E - W_0)}{m}} = v$$

or A charged particle placed in uniform magnetic field experience a force

$$F = \frac{mv^2}{r}$$

or $\quad evB = \frac{mv^2}{r}$

or $\quad r = \frac{mv}{eB}$

or $\quad r = \frac{m\sqrt{\frac{2(E - W_0)}{m}}}{eB}$

$\Rightarrow \quad r = \frac{\sqrt{2m(E - W_0)}}{eB}$

35. $\quad N_1 = N_0 e^{-10\lambda t}$

and $\quad N_2 = N_0 e^{-\lambda t}$

$\Rightarrow \quad \frac{N_1}{N_2} = \frac{1}{e} = e^{-1} = e^{(-10\lambda + \lambda)t}$

$$= e^{-9\lambda t}$$

$\Rightarrow \quad t = \frac{1}{9\lambda}$

36. In circuit A, both (p-n) junction diode act as forward biasing. Hence, current flows in circuit A.

Total resistance R is given by

$$\frac{1}{R} = \frac{1}{4} + \frac{1}{4}$$

or $\quad \frac{1}{R} = \frac{2}{4}$

or $\quad R = 2\Omega$

According to Ohm' s law

$$V = I_A R$$

or $\quad 8 = I_A \times 2$

or $\quad I_A = 4$ A

In circuit B, lower p-n-junction diode is reverse biased. Hence, no current will flow but upper diode is forward biased so current can flow through it

$$V = I_B R$$

or $\quad 8 = I_B \times 4$

or $\quad I_B = 2$ A

37. After impact the bullet and block move together and comes to rest after covering a distance of 40 m.

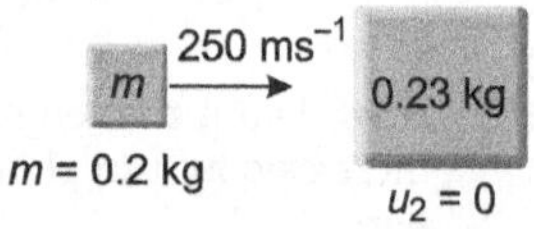

By conservation of momentum

$$m_1u_1 + m_2u_2 = m_1v_1 + m_2v_2$$

or $\quad 0.02 \times 250 + 0.23 \times 0 = 0.02v + 0.23v$

$$5 + 0 = v\,(0.25)$$

$$\frac{500}{25} = v = 20 \text{ ms}^{-1}$$

Now, by conservation of energy

$$\frac{1}{2}Mv^2 = \mu R \cdot d$$

or $\quad \frac{1}{2} \times 0.25 \times 400 = \mu \times 0.25 \times 9.8 \times 40$

$\Rightarrow \quad \mu = \frac{200}{9.8 \times 40} = 0.51$

38. Let after the time (t) the position of A is $(0, v_A t)$ and position of $B = (v_B t, 10)$. Distance between them

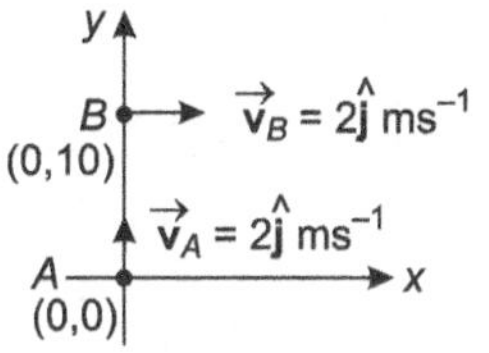

$$y = \sqrt{(0 - v_B t)^2 + (v_A t - 10)^2}$$

or $\quad y^2 = (2t)^2 + (2t - 10)^2$

or $\quad y^2 = l = 4t^2 + 4t^2 + 100 - 40t$

$\Rightarrow \quad l = 8t^2 + 100 - 40t$

Now, $\quad \frac{dl}{dt} = (16t - 40) = 0$

$$t = \frac{40}{16} = 2.5 \text{ s}$$

As $\quad \frac{d^2l}{dt^2} = 16 = (+\text{ve})$

Hence, l will be minimum.

39. In this process potential energy of the metre stick will be converted into rotational kinetic energy.

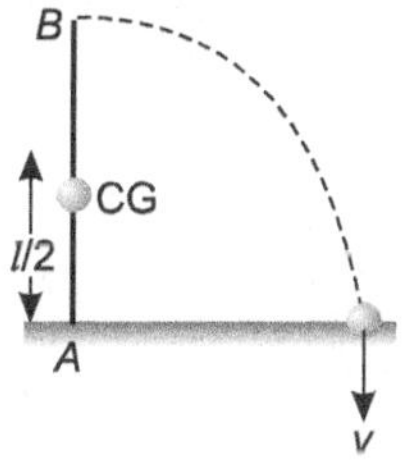

PE of metre stick $= \frac{mgl}{2}$

Because its centre of gravity lies at the middle of the rod.

Rotational kinetic energy $E = \frac{1}{2}I\omega^2$

I = moment of inertia of metre stick about point $A = \frac{ml^2}{3}$.

By the law of conservation of energy

$$mg\left(\frac{l}{2}\right) = \frac{1}{2}I\omega^2$$

$$= \frac{1}{2}\frac{ml^2}{3}\left(\frac{v_B}{l}\right)^2$$

By solving, we get $v_B = \sqrt{3gl}$

40. Given, $\quad r = 0.4$ m,

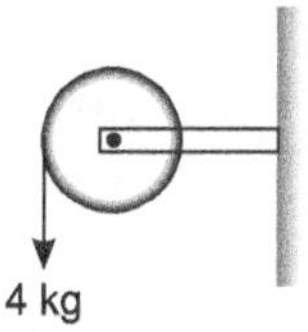

$$\alpha = 8 \text{ rad s}^{-1},$$

$$m = 4 \text{ kg}, \quad I = ?$$

Torque, $\quad \tau = I\alpha$

$$mgr = I \cdot \alpha$$

or $\quad 4 \times 10 \times 0.4 = I \times 8$

$\Rightarrow \quad I = \frac{16}{8} = 2 \text{ kg-m}^2$

or $\quad I = 2 \text{ kg-m}^2$

Chapter

1

Physical World and Measurement

1. The energy (E), angular momentum (L) and universal gravitational constant (G) are chosen as fundamental quantities. The dimensions of universal gravitational constant in the dimensional formula of Planck's constant (h) is

EAMCET | 2008

(a) zero (b) – 1

(c) $\frac{5}{3}$ (d) 1

2. Some physical constants are given in Column I and their dimensional formulae are given in Column. Match the following Columns and choose the correct answer. EAMCET | 2007

Column I	Column II
(A) Planck's constant	(1) $[ML^{-1}T^{-2}]$
(B) Gravitational constant	(2) $[ML^{-1}T^{-1}]$
(C) Bulk modulus	(3) $[ML^{2}T^{-1}]$
(D) Coefficient of viscosity	(4) $[M^{-1}L^{3}T^{-2}]$

Codes

	(A)	(B)	(C)	(D)
(a)	(4)	(3)	(2)	(1)
(b)	(2)	(1)	(3)	(4)
(c)	(3)	(2)	(1)	(4)
(d)	(3)	(4)	(1)	(2)

3. If C, R, L and I denote capacity, resistance, inductance and electric current respectively, the quantities having the same dimensions of time are EAMCET | 2006

(1) CR (2) $\frac{L}{R}$ (3) $\sqrt{LC}$ (4) LI^2

(a) (1) and (2) only

(b) (1) and (3) only

(c) (1) and (4) only

(d) (1), (2) and (3) only

4. Names of units of some physical quantities are given in Column I and their dimensional formulae are given in Column II. Match the following Columns and choose the correct answer. EAMCET | 2005

Column I	Column II
(A) Pa-s	(1) $[L^2T^{-2}K^{-1}]$
(B) Nm-K^{-1}	(2) $[MLT^{-3}K^{-1}]$
(C) J kg^{-1} K^{-1}	(3) $[ML^{-1}T^{-1}]$
(D) $Wm^{-1}K^{-1}$	(4) $[ML^2T^{-2}K^{-1}]$

Codes

	(A)	(B)	(C)	(D)
(a)	(4)	(3)	(1)	(2)
(b)	(3)	(2)	(4)	(1)
(c)	(3)	(1)	(4)	(2)
(d)	(3)	(4)	(1)	(2)

5. The position of a particle at time t is given by the equation $x(t) = \frac{v_0}{A}(1-e^{At})$

v_0 = constant and $A > 0$

Dimensions of v_0 and A respectively are

EAMCET | 2004

(a) $[M^0LT^0]$ and $[M^0L^0T^{-1}]$

(b) $[M^0LT^{-1}]$ and $[M^0LT^{-2}]$

(c) $[M^0LT^{-1}]$ and $[M^0L^0T]$

(d) $[M^0LT^{-1}]$ and $[M^0L^0T^{-1}]$

6. The van der Waals' equation for a gas is

$$\left(p+\frac{a}{V^2}\right)(V-b) = nRT$$

where p, V, R, T and n represent the pressure, volume, universal gas constant, absolute temperature and number of moles of a gas respectively, where a and b are constants. The ratio $\frac{b}{a}$ will have the following dimensional formula EAMCET | 2002

(a) $[M^{-1}L^{-2}T^2]$ (b) $[M^{-1}L^{-1}T^{-1}]$

(c) $[ML^2T^2]$ (d) $[MLT^{-2}]$

7. In the measurement of a physical quantity $X = \frac{A^2B}{C^{1/3}D^3}$. The percentage errors introduced in the measurements of the quantities A, B, C and D are 2%, 2%, 4% and 5% respectively. Then, the minimum amount of percentage error in the measurement of X is contributed by

EAMCET | 2002

(a) A (b) B (c) C (d) D

8. In CGS system the magnitude of the force is 100 dyne. In another system where the fundamental physical quantities are kilogram, metre and minute, the magnitude of the force is **EAMCET | 2001**

(a) 0.036 (b) 0.36 (c) 3.6 (d) 36

9. In an experiment of simple pendulum, the errors in the measurement of length of the pendulum (L) and time period (T) are 3% and 2% respectively. The maximum percentage error in the value of $\frac{L}{T^2}$ is **EAMCET | 2001**

(a) 5% (b) 7% (c) 8% (d) 1%

10. The fundamental physical quantities that have same dimensions in the dimensional formula of torque and angular momentum are **EAMCET | 2000**

(a) mass, time (b) time, length
(c) mass, length (d) time, mole

11. If pressure p, velocity v and time T are taken as fundamental physical quantities the dimensional formula of the force is **EAMCET | 2000**

(a) pv^2T^2 (b) $p^{-1}v^2T^{-2}$
(c) pvT^2 (d) $p^{-1}vT^2$

12. The dimensional formula for latent heat is **EAMCET | 1999**

(a) $[MLT^{-2}]$ (b) $[ML^2T^{-2}]$
(c) $[M^0L^2T^{-2}]$ (d) $[MLT^{-1}]$

13. The SI unit of moment of inertia is **EAMCET | 1999**

(a) kgm^{-2} (b) $kg\ m^2$
(c) Nm^{-2} (d) Nm^2

14. Dimensions of ohm are same as (h = Planck's constant, e = charge) **EAMCET | 1998**

(a) $\frac{h}{e}$ (b) $\frac{h^2}{e}$ (c) $\frac{h}{e^2}$ (d) $\frac{h^2}{e^2}$

15. If M, L, T, and I stand for mass, length, time and electric current respectively, the dimensional formula for capacitance is **EAMCET | 1997**

(a) $[M^{-1}L^2T^{-4}I^2]$ (b) $[M^{-1}L^{-2}T^4I^2]$
(c) $[ML^2T^4I^2]$ (d) $[ML^2T^{-4}I^{-2}]$

16. Which of the following has no dimensions? **EAMCET | 1995**

(a) Angular velocity (b) Momentum
(c) Angular momentum (d) Strain

17. The dimensions of resistance × capacitance are same as for **EAMCET | 1995**

(a) frequency (b) energy
(c) time period (d) current

18. The velocity of a body falling freely under gravitational field varies as g^ph^q, where g is gravitational acceleration and h is height from which the body is released. p and q are given by **EAMCET | 1994**

(a) $p = 2 : q = 1/2$ (b) $p = 1/2 : q = 1/2$
(c) $p = 1/2 : q = 1$ (d) $p = q = 1$

19. The following physical quantities has a ratio of 10^3 between its SI units and CGS units **EAMCET | 1994**

(a) Universal gravitational constant
(b) Boltzmann's constant
(c) Planck's constant
(d) Young's modulus of elasticity

20. The ratio L/R, where L and R stand for inductance and resistance, has the same dimensions as those of **EAMCET | 1994**

(a) velocity (b) acceleration
(c) time (d) force

21. The pair of physical quantities not having the same dimensional formula is **EAMCET | 1993**

(a) acceleration, gravitational field strength
(b) torque, angular momentum
(c) pressure, modulus of elasticity
(d) All of the above

22. If time period t of a drop of liquid of density d vibrating under surface tension s is given by the formula $t = \sqrt{d^ar^bs^c}$ where r is radius of drop. $a = 1$ and $c = -1$, the value of b is **EAMCET | 1993**

(a) 3 (b) – 3 (c) – 4 (d) 4

23. On heating, the length of the side of cube changes by 2%. The volume of the cube changes by **EAMCET | 1992**

(a) 1% (b) 6% (c) 0.5% (d) 3%

24. The dimensional formula of the universal constant of gravitation is **EAMCET | 1992**

(a) $[M^0L^{-3}T^{-2}]$ (b) $[ML^{-3}T^2]$
(c) $[M^{-1}L^3T^{-2}]$ (d) $[M^2L^2T^2]$

25. The pair of physical quantities having the same dimensional formula is **EAMCET | 1991**

(a) energy and torque
(b) torque and entropy
(c) entropy and power
(d) power and angular momentum

26. Siemen is the SI unit for **EAMCET | 1991**

(a) electrical resistivity
(b) electrical conductance
(c) electrical permittivity
(d) electrical capacitance

Answers

1.	(a)	**2.**	(d)	**3.**	(d)	**4.**	(d)	**5.**	(d)	**6.**	(a)	**7.**	(c)	**8.**	(c)	**9.**	(b)	**10.**	(c)
11.	(a)	**12.**	(c)	**13.**	(b)	**14.**	(c)	**15.**	(b)	**16.**	(d)	**17.**	(c)	**18.**	(b)	**19.**	(a)	**20.**	(c)
21.	(b)	**22.**	(a)	**23.**	(b)	**24.**	(c)	**25.**	(a)	**26.**	(b)								

Hints & Solutions

1. $$h \propto G^x L^y E^z$$
$$[ML^2T^{-1}] \propto [M^{-1}L^3T^{-2}]^x [ML^2T^{-1}]^y [ML^2T^{-2}]^z$$
$$[ML^2T^{-1}] = k[M^{-1}L^3T^{-2}]^x [ML^2T^{-1}]^y [ML^2T^{-2}]^z$$

Comparing the powers, we get

$$1 = -x + y + z \quad \text{...(i)}$$
$$2 = 3x + 2y + 2z \quad \text{...(ii)}$$
$$-1 = -2x - y - 2z \quad \text{...(iii)}$$

On solving Eqs. (i), (ii) and (iii), we get

$$x = 0$$

2. (1) Planck's constant

$$[h] = \left[\frac{E}{\nu}\right] = \frac{[ML^2T^{-2}]}{[T^{-1}]} = [ML^2T^{-1}]$$

(2) Gravitational constant

$$[G] = \left[\frac{Fr^2}{m_1 m_2}\right] = \frac{[MLT^{-2}][L^2]}{[M^2]} = [M^{-1}L^3T^{-2}]$$

(3) Bulk modulus

$$[B] = \frac{[\text{Normal stress}]}{[\text{Volumetric strain}]} = [ML^{-1}T^{-2}]$$

(4) Coefficient of viscosity

$$\eta = \frac{[F]}{[A][dv/dy]} = \frac{[MLT^{-2}][L]}{[L^2][LT^{-1}]} = [ML^{-1}T^{-1}]$$

Hence, option (d) is correct.

3. $$[C] = [M^{-1}L^{-2}T^4A^2],\ [R] = [M\,L^2\,T^{-3}A^{-2}]$$
$$[L] = [ML^2T^{-2}A^{-2}] \text{and } [I] = [M^0L^0T^0A]$$

(1) $$[CR] = [M^{-1}L^{-2}T^4A^2][ML^2T^{-3}A^{-2}] = [M^0L^0TA^0]$$

(2) $$\left[\frac{L}{R}\right] = \frac{[ML^2T^{-2}A^{-2}]}{[ML^2T^{-3}A^{-2}]} = [M^0L^0TA^0]$$

(3) $$[\sqrt{LC}] = ([ML^2T^{-2}A^{-2}] \times [M^{-1}L^{-2}T^4A^2])^{1/2} = [M^0L^0TA^0]$$

(4) $$[LI^2] = [ML^2T^{-2}A^{-2}][M^0L^0T^0A^0]^2 = [ML^2T^{-2}A^0]$$

Hence, option (d) is correct.

4. Dimensions of Pa-s is

$$= [ML^{-1}T^{-2}]\cdot[T] = [ML^{-1}T^{-1}]$$

Dimensions of NmK^{-1} is

$$= [MLT^{-2}][L][K]^{-1} = [ML^2T^{-2}K^{-1}]$$

Dimensions of $J\cdot kg^{-1}\,K^{-1}$

$$= [ML^2T^{-2}][M]^{-1}[K]^{-1} = [L^2T^{-2}K^{-1}]$$

Dimensions of $Wm^{-1}K^{-1}$

$$= [ML^2T^{-3}][L]^{-1}[K]^{-1} = [MLT^{-3}K^{-1}]$$

So, the correct option is (d).

5. The dimensions of x = dimensions of $\frac{v_0}{A}$

Therefore, out of the given options v_0 has dimensions equal to $[M^0LT^{-1}]$ and A has dimensions equal to $[M^0L^0T^{-1}]$

So, that $\frac{[v_0]}{[A]} = \frac{[M^0LT^{-1}]}{[M^0L^0T^{-1}]} = [L]$

$= \text{dimension of } x$

6. van der Waals' gas equation is

$$\left(p+\frac{a}{V^2}\right)(V-b) = nRT$$

For principle of homogeneity

Dimensions of $\frac{a}{V^2}$ = dimensions of p

$\therefore$ Dimensions of $a = [V^2] \times [p]$

$[a] = [L^3]^2\,[ML^{-1}T^{-2}]$

$= [ML^5T^{-2}]$

Dimensions of b = dimensions of V

$[b] = [L^3]$

$$\therefore \quad \frac{b}{a} = \frac{[L^3]}{[ML^5T^{-2}]} = [M^{-1}L^{-2}T^2]$$

7. $$x = \frac{A^2B}{C^{1/3}D^3}$$

$$\text{% error in } x, \frac{\Delta x}{x} = 2\frac{\Delta A}{A}+\frac{\Delta B}{B}+\frac{1}{3}\frac{\Delta C}{C}+\frac{3\Delta D}{D}$$

$$= 2\left(\frac{\Delta A}{A}\times 100\%\right)+\left(\frac{\Delta B}{B}\times 100\%\right)$$

$$+\frac{1}{3}\left(\frac{\Delta C}{C}\times 100\%\right)+3\left(\frac{\Delta D}{D}\times 100\%\right)$$

$$\text{Minimum percentage error} = \frac{1}{3}\left(\frac{\Delta C}{C}\times 100\%\right)$$

$$= \frac{1}{3}\times 4 = 1.1\%$$

8. $$n_2 = n_1\left[\left(\frac{m_1}{m_2}\right)^a\left(\frac{L_1}{L_2}\right)^b\left(\frac{T_1}{T_2}\right)^c\right]$$

Dimensions of force are $[MLT^{-2}]$

$\therefore\ a = 1, b = 1, c = -2$

$$\therefore n_2 = 100\left[\left(\frac{\text{g}}{\text{kg}}\right)\left(\frac{\text{cm}}{\text{metre}}\right)\left(\frac{\text{sec}}{\text{min}}\right)^{-2}\right]$$

$$= 100\left[\frac{\text{g}}{1000\text{ g}}\times\frac{\text{cm}}{100\text{cm}}\times\left(\frac{\text{sec}}{60\text{ sec}}\right)^{-2}\right]$$

$$= 100\left[\frac{1}{1000}\times\frac{1}{100}\times(60)^2\right]$$

$$= 100\times\frac{1}{1000}\times\frac{1}{100}\times 3600$$

$= 3.6$

9. Maximum percentage in the value of $\frac{L}{T^2}$

$$= \frac{\Delta L}{L}\times 100\% + 2\frac{\Delta T}{T}\times 100\%$$

$= 3 + 2 \times 2$

$= 7\%$

10. Dimensional formula for torque

$= [ML^2T^{-2}]$

Dimensional formula for angular momentum

$= [ML^2T^{-1}]$

From the above two formulae it is clear that dimensions of mass and length are same.

11. Force = pressure × area

= pressure × (distance)^2

= pressure × (velocity × time)^2

$\therefore$ Dimensional formula of force

$= [pv^2T^2]$

12. Latent heat, $L = \frac{Q\text{ (heat)}}{m\text{ (mass)}}$

Dimensional formula of L

$$= \frac{\text{Dimensional formula of } Q}{\text{Dimensional formula of } m}$$

$$= \frac{[ML^2T^{-2}]}{[M]} = [M^0\,L^2\,T^{-2}]$$

13. SI unit of moment of inertia = kg m^2

14. Dimensional formula of resistance R

$= [M\,L^2\,T^{-3}\,A^{-2}]$

Dimensional formula of Planck's constant (h)

$= [ML^2T^{-1}]$

Dimensional formula of (e^2) = $[A^2\,T^2]$

$$\therefore \quad \frac{h}{e^2} = \frac{[ML^2T^{-1}]}{[A^2T^2]} = [ML^2T^{-3}A^{-2}]$$

15. Capacitance, $C = \frac{q}{V} = \frac{q}{W/q} = \frac{q^2}{W}$

$$= \frac{i^2t^2}{W}$$

Dimensional formula for capacitance

$$= \frac{[I^2][T^2]}{[ML^2T^{-2}]} = [M^{-1}\,L^{-2}\,T^4\,I^2]$$

16. Strain is a ratio of two similar quantities, so it has no dimensions.

17. Resistance, $R = \frac{V}{i} = \frac{W}{q\cdot i} = \frac{W}{i^2t}$

$$[R] = \frac{[ML^2T^{-2}]}{[A^2][T]}$$

$= [ML^2T^{-3}\,A^{-2}]$

Capacitance, $C = \frac{q}{V}$

$$\frac{q}{W/q} = \frac{q^2}{W} = \frac{I^2t^2}{W}$$

$$\therefore \quad [C] = \frac{[A]^2[T^2]}{[ML^2T^{-2}]}$$

$$= [M^{-1}L^{-2}T^4A^2]$$

$$\therefore \quad [R] \times [C] = [ML^2T^{-3}A^{-2}] \times [M^{-1}L^{-2}T^4A^2]$$

$$= [T]$$

= Dimension formula of time period.

18. Velocity $v \propto g^p h^q$

or $v = k g^p h^q$

where k = proportionality constant.

Writing the dimensions on both sides of the equation.

$$[LT^{-1}] = k[LT^{-2}]^p [L]^q$$

On comparing both sides

$$2p = 1$$

$$\Rightarrow \quad p = \frac{1}{2}$$

$$p + q = 1$$

$$\Rightarrow \quad q = 1 - p = 1 - \frac{1}{2} = \frac{1}{2}$$

20. Dimensions of $L/R = \frac{\text{dimensions of } L}{\text{dimensions of } R}$

$$= \frac{[ML^2T^{-2}A^{-2}]}{[ML^2T^{-3}A^{-2}]}$$

$$= [T]$$

= dimension of time

21. The units of acceleration and gravitational field strength is ms^{-2} or Nkg^{-1}, so these have same dimensional formula.

Units of torque and angular momentum are N-m and J-s respectively and their dimensional formulae are $[ML^2T^{-2}]$ and $[ML^2T^{-1}]$, so these quantities do not have same dimensional formula.

22. Time period, $t = \sqrt{d^a r^b s^c}$

where d = density,

r = radius of the drop

s = surface tension of the liquid

Writing the dimension on both sides

$$[M^0L^0T] = [ML^{-3}]^{a/2}[L]^{b/2}[MT^{-2}]^{c/2}$$

$$[M^0L^0T] = [M^{a/2 + c/2}][L^{-3a/2 + b/2}][T^{-c}]$$

On comparing both sides

$$-c = 1$$

$$\Rightarrow \quad c = -1$$

$$\frac{a}{2} + \frac{c}{2} = 0$$

$$\Rightarrow \quad a = -c$$

$$= -(-1) = 1$$

$$-\frac{3a}{2} + \frac{b}{2} = 0$$

$$\Rightarrow \quad b = 3a = 3 \times 1 = 3$$

23. Change in length $\frac{\Delta l}{l} = 2\%$

Volume of cube $V = l^3$

$$\therefore \text{ Change in volume } \frac{\Delta V}{V} = 3\frac{\Delta l}{l}$$

$$= 3 \times 2$$

$$= 6\%$$

24. Universal gravitational constant, $G = \frac{F r^2}{m_1 m_2}$

$\therefore$ Dimensional formula for G

$$= \frac{(\text{Dimensions of } F) \times (\text{Dimensions of } r^2)}{(\text{Dimensions of } m_1) \times (\text{Dimensions of } m_2)}$$

$$= \frac{[MLT^{-2}][L^2]}{[M][M]} = [M^{-1}L^3T^{-2}]$$

25. Unit of energy and torque is J or N-m, so dimensional formula of these quantities will be same.

26. Siemen is the unit for electrical conductance.

Chapter

2

Kinematics

1. The component of vector $\vec{A} = a_x\hat{i}+a_y\hat{j}+a_z\hat{k}$ along the direction of $\hat{i}-\hat{j}$ is **EAMCET | 2008**

(a) $a_x - a_y + a_z$ (b) $a_x - a_y$

(c) $(a_x - a_y)/\sqrt{2}$ (d) $(a_x + a_y + a_z)$

2. A ball thrown vertically up to reach its maximum height in t second. The total time from the time of projection to reach a point at half of its maximum height while returning (in second) is **EAMCET | 2008**

(a) $\sqrt{2}t$ (b) $\left(1+\frac{1}{\sqrt{2}}\right)t$

(c) $\frac{3t}{2}$ (d) $\frac{t}{\sqrt{2}}$

3. If a body is projected with an angle θ to the horizontal, then **EAMCET | 2008**

(a) its velocity is always perpendicular to its acceleration

(b) its velocity becomes zero at its maximum height

(c) its velocity makes zero angle with the horizontal at its maximum height

(d) the body just before hitting the ground, the direction of velocity coincides with the acceleration

4. Velocity and acceleration vectors of charged particle moving perpendicular to the direction of a magnetic field at a given instant of time are $\vec{v} = 2\hat{i}+c\hat{j}$ and $\vec{a} = 3\hat{i}+4\hat{j}$ respectively. Then, the value of c is **EAMCET | 2007**

(a) 3 (b) 1.5 (c) –1.5 (d) – 3

5. A bucket filled with water is tied to a rope of length 0.5 m and is rotated in a circular path in vertical plane. The least velocity it should have at the lowest point of circle so that water does not spill is, (g = 10 ms^{-2}) **EAMCET | 2007**

(a) $\sqrt{5}$ ms^{-1} (b) $\sqrt{10}$ ms^{-1}

(c) 5 ms^{-1} (d) 2 $\sqrt{5}$ ms^{-1}

6. A man standing on a road has to hold his umbrella at 30° with the vertical to keep the rain away. He throws the umbrella and starts running at 10 kmh^{-1}. He finds that raindrops are hitting his head vertically. The actual speed of raindrops is **EAMCET | 2006**

(a) 20 kmh^{-1} (b) $10\sqrt{3}$ kmh^{-1}

(c) $20\sqrt{3}$ kmh^{-1} (d) 10 kmh^{-1}

7. A body is projected from the earth at angle 30° with the horizontal with some initial velocity. If its range is 20 m, the maximum height reached by it is (in metre) **EAMCET | 2006**

(a) $5\sqrt{3}$ (b) $\frac{5}{\sqrt{3}}$ (c) $\frac{10}{\sqrt{3}}$ (d) $10\sqrt{3}$

8. At a given instant of time the position vector of a particle moving in a circle with a velocity $3\hat{i}-4\hat{j}+5\hat{k}$ is $\hat{i}+9\hat{j}-3\hat{k}$. Its angular velocity at that time is **EAMCET | 2005**

(a) $\frac{(13\hat{i}+29\hat{j}-31\hat{k})}{\sqrt{146}}$ (b) $\frac{(13\hat{i}-29\hat{j}-31\hat{k})}{146}$

(c) $\frac{(13\hat{i}+29\hat{j}-31\hat{k})}{\sqrt{146}}$ (d) $\frac{(13\hat{i}+29\hat{j}+31\hat{k})}{146}$

9. A body projected vertically upwards crosses a point twice in its journey at a height h just after t_1 and t_2 second. Maximum height reached by the body is **EAMCET | 2005**

(a) $\frac{g}{4}(t_1+t_2)^2$ (b) $g\left(\frac{t_1+t_2}{4}\right)^2$

(c) $2g\left(\frac{t_1+t_2}{4}\right)^2$ (d) $\frac{g}{4}(t_1t_2)$

10. The equation of trajectory of a projectile is

$$y = 10x-\left(\frac{5}{9}\right)x^2$$

If we assume g = 10 ms^{-2}, the range of projectile (in metre) is **EAMCET | 2005**

(a) 36 (b) 24 (c) 18 (d) 9

11. At a given instant of time two particles are having the position vectors $4\hat{i}-4\hat{j}+7\hat{k}$ metre and $2\hat{i}+2\hat{j}+5\hat{k}$ respectively. If the velocity of the first particle be $0.4\,\hat{i}$ ms^{-1}, the velocity of second particle in metre per second if they collide after 10 s is **EAMCET | 2004**

(a) $6\left(\hat{i}-\hat{j}+\frac{1}{3}\hat{k}\right)$ (b) $0.6\left(\hat{i}-\hat{j}+\frac{1}{3}\hat{k}\right)$

(c) $6\left(\hat{i}+\hat{j}+\frac{1}{3}\hat{k}\right)$ (d) $0.6\left(\hat{i}+\hat{j}-\frac{1}{3}\hat{k}\right)$

12. The horizontal and vertical displacements x and y of a projectile at a given time t are given by $x = 6t$ metre and $y = 8t - 5t^2$ metre. The range of the projectile in metre is **EAMCET | 2004**

(a) 9.6 (b) 10.6 (c) 19.2 (d) 38.4

13. The equations of motion of a projectile are given by $x = 36t$ metre and $2y = 96t - 9.8t^2$ metre. The angle of projection is **EAMCET | 2003**

(a) $\sin^{-1}\left(\frac{4}{5}\right)$ (b) $\sin^{-1}\left(\frac{3}{5}\right)$

(c) $\sin^{-1}\left(\frac{4}{3}\right)$ (d) $\sin^{-1}\left(\frac{3}{4}\right)$

14. A body of mass M kg is on the top point of a smooth hemisphere of radius 5 m. It is released to slide down the surface of the hemisphere. It leaves the surface when velocity is 5 ms^{-1}. At this instant the angle made by the radius vector of the body with the vertical is (acceleration due to gravity = 10 ms^{-2}) **EAMCET | 2002**

(a) 30° (b) 45° (c) 60° (d) 90°

15. The horizontal and vertical displacements of a projectile at time t are $x = 36t$ and $y = 48t - 4.9t^2$ respectively. Initial velocity of the projectile in ms^{-1} is **EAMCET | 2002**

(a) 15 (b) 30 (c) 45 (d) 60

16. An object is projected with a velocity of 20 ms^{-1} making an angle of 45° with horizontal. The equation for the trajectory is $h = Ax - Bx^2$, where h is height, x is horizontal distance A and B are constants. The ratio $A : B$ is (g = 10 ms^{-2}) **EAMCET | 2001**

(a) 1 : 5 (b) 5 : 1 (c) 1 : 40 (d) 40 : 1

17. A body is thrown vertically upwards with an initial velocity u reaches maximum height in 6 s. The ratio of distance travelled by the body in the first and seventh second is **EAMCET | 2000**

(a) 1 : 1 (b) 11 : 1 (c) 1 : 2 (d) 1 : 11

18. A body is thrown horizontally from the top of a tower of 5 m height. It touches the ground at a distance of 10 m from the foot of the tower. The initial velocity of the body is **EAMCET | 2000**

(a) 2.5 ms^{-1} (b) 5 ms^{-1}

(c) 10 ms^{-1} (d) 20 ms^{-1}

19. Four bodies P, Q, R and S are projected with equal velocities having angles of projection 15°, 30°, 45° and 60° with the horizontal respectively. The body having shortest range is **EAMCET | 2000**

(a) P (b) Q (c) R (d) S

20. The speed of a projectile at its maximum height is $\frac{\sqrt{3}}{2}$ times its initial speed. If the range of the projectile is P times the maximum height attained by it, then P equals **EAMCET | 1999**

(a) $\frac{4}{3}$ (b) $2\sqrt{3}$ (c) $4\sqrt{3}$ (d) $\frac{3}{4}$

21. Water drops fall from a tap on the floor 5 m below at regular intervals of time, the first drop striking the floor when the fifth drop begins to fall. The height at which the third drop will be, from ground, at that instant when first drop strikes the ground, will be, (taking g = 10 ms^{-2}) **EAMCET | 1999**

(a) 1.25 m (b) 2.15 m

(c) 2.75 m (d) 3.75 m

22. A car starts from rest and travels with uniform acceleration α, for some time and then with uniform retardation β and comes to rest. If the total time of car is t, the maximum velocity attained by it is given by **EAMCET | 1999**

(a) $\frac{\alpha\beta}{(\alpha+\beta)}t$ (b) $\frac{1}{2}\frac{\alpha\beta}{(\alpha+\beta)}t^2$

(c) $\frac{\alpha\beta}{(\alpha-\beta)}t$ (d) $\frac{1}{2}\frac{\alpha\beta}{(\alpha-\beta)}t^2$

23. The angle between two vectors $6\hat{i}+6\hat{j}-3\hat{k}$ and $7\hat{i}+4\hat{j}+4\hat{k}$ is given by **EAMCET | 1999**

(a) $\cos^{-1}\left(\frac{1}{\sqrt{3}}\right)$ (b) $\cos^{-1}\left(\frac{5}{\sqrt{3}}\right)$

(c) $\sin^{-1}\left(\frac{2}{\sqrt{3}}\right)$ (d) $\sin^{-1}\left(\frac{\sqrt{5}}{3}\right)$

24. The minimum speed for a particle at the lowest point of a vertical circle of radius R, to describe the circle is v. If the radius of circle is reduced to one-fourth its value, the corresponding minimum speed will be **EAMCET | 1999**

(a) $\frac{V}{4}$ (b) $\frac{V}{2}$ (c) 2 v (d) 4 v

25. A car is moving on a circular level road of curvature 300 m. If the coefficient of friction is 0.3 and acceleration due to gravity 10 ms^{-2}, the maximum speed that car can have is **EAMCET | 1999**

(a) 30 kmh^{-1} (b) 81 kmh^{-1}
(c) 108 kmh^{-1} (d) 162 kmh^{-1}

26. A person throws a bottle into a dust-bin at the same height as he is 2 m away at an angle of 45°. The velocity of the throw is **EAMCET | 1998**

(a) g (b) $\sqrt{g}$
(c) $2g$ (d) $\sqrt{2g}$

27. A car starts from rest, attains a velocity of 36 kmh^{-1} with an acceleration of 0.2 ms^{-2}, travels 9 km with this uniform velocity and then comes to half with a uniform deceleration of 0.1 ms^{-2}. The total time of travel of the car is **EAMCET | 1998**

(a) 1050 s (b) 1000 s
(c) 950 s (d) 900 s

28. A stone tied to a string is rotated in a vertical circle. The minimum speed with which the string has to be rotated **EAMCET | 1998**

(a) decreases with increasing mass of the stone
(b) is independent of the mass of the stone
(c) decreases with increasing in length of the string
(d) is independent of the length of the string

29. The maximum speed with which a car can be driven round a curve of radius 18 m without skidding (when g = 10 ms^{-2} and the coefficient of friction between rubber tyres and the roadways is 0.2) is **EAMCET | 1998**

(a) 36.0 kmh^{-1} (b) 18.0 kmh^{-1}
(c) 21.6 kmh^{-1} (d) 14.4 kmh^{-1}

30. For an electron circulating around the nucleus, the centripetal force is supplied by **EAMCET | 1998**

(a) electromagnetic force
(b) electrostatic force
(c) gravitational force
(d) magnetic force

31. A particle is moving east wards with a velocity of 15 ms^{-1}. In a time of 10 s, the velocity changes to 15 ms^{-1} northwards. Average acceleration during this time is (in ms^{-2}) **EAMCET | 1997**

(a) $\frac{3}{\sqrt{2}}$ north-east (b) $3\sqrt{2}$ north-east
(c) $\frac{3}{\sqrt{2}}$ north-west (d) $3\sqrt{2}$ north-west

32. The reaction time for a car driver is 0.9 s. If the car travelling initially with 36 kmh^{-1} is stopped by the driver after observing a signal by the deceleration of 5 ms^{-2}, the total distance travelled by the car before coming to rest is **EAMCET | 1997**

(a) 19 m (b) 9 m (c) 10 m (d) 28 m

33. The angular velocity of the second's-hand of a watch is **EAMCET | 1997**

(a) 0.053 $rads^{-1}$ (b) 0.210 $rads^{-1}$
(c) 0.105 $rads^{-1}$ (d) 0.42 $rads^{-1}$

34. The directions of velocity and acceleration of a projectile at the highest point on the trajectory are **EAMCET | 1996**

(a) parallel to each other
(b) antiparallel to each other
(c) perpendicular to each other
(d) no specific relationship exist between them

35. A bomb is dropped from an aircraft travelling horizontally at 150 ms^{-1} at a height of 490 m. The horizontal distance travelled by the bomb before it hits the ground is (in metre) **EAMCET | 1996**

(a) 1000 (b) 1200
(c) 1500 (d) 1800

36. The angle made by the vector $\vec{A} = \vec{i} + \vec{j}$ with x-axis is **EAMCET | 1996**

(a) 90° (b) 45° (c) 22.5° (d) 30°

37. A fan is making 600 rev/min. If it makes 1200 rev/min, what is the increase in its angular velocity? **EAMCET | 1996**

(a) 10 π rad/s (b) 20 π rad/s
(c) 60 π rad/s (d) 40 π rad/s

38. The angular velocity of a rickshaw wheel is 70 $rads^{-1}$. If the radius of the wheel is 0.5 m, the linear velocity is **EAMCET | 1996**

(a) 10 ms^{-1} (b) 1 ms^{-1}
(c) 35 ms^{-1} (d) 70 ms^{-1}

39. If a particle tied to the end of string is set in circular motion then the tension of the string is **EAMCET | 1996**

(a) always parallel to the velocity of the particle
(b) always perpendicular to the velocity of the particle
(c) perpendicular to the velocity of the particle only at one instant
(d) parallel to the velocity of the particle only at one instant

40. A motor cycle is travelling on a curved track of radius 500 m. If the coefficient of friction between the tyres and road is 0.5, with $g = 10\ ms^{-2}$. What should be the maximum speed to avoid skidding? **EAMCET | 1996**

(a) $500\ ms^{-1}$ (b) $250\ ms^{-1}$

(c) $50\ ms^{-1}$ (d) $10\ ms^{-1}$

41. A body is projected vertically up the speed u takes time T to reach maximum height H. Pick out correct statement. **EAMCET | 1995**

(a) It reaches $H/2$ distance in a time $T/2$

(b) It has speed u at time $T/2$

(c) It has speed $u/2$ at the height $H/2$

(d) It has the same velocity at time $2T$

42. The displacement of a particle moving in a straight line is given by $x = 2t^2 + t + 5$ where x is expressed in metre and t in second. The acceleration at $t = 2$ s is **EAMCET | 1995**

(a) $4\ ms^{-2}$ (b) $8\ ms^{-2}$

(c) $10\ ms^{-2}$ (d) $15\ ms^{-2}$

43. A body falling for 2 s covers a distance s which is equal to that covered in next 1 s. If $g = 10\ ms^{-2}$, the distance s is **EAMCET | 1995**

(a) 30 m (b) 10 m (c) 60 m (d) 20 m

44. A stone tied to a string rotated with uniform speed in a vertical plane. If the mass of the stone is m, length of the string is r and the speed of the stone is v, the tension in the string when the stone is at its lowest point is (g = acceleration due to gravity) **EAMCET | 1995**

(a) mg (b) $\frac{mv^2}{r}$

(c) $\frac{mv^2}{r} - mg$ (d) $\frac{mv^2}{r} + mg$

45. A 2 kg stone tied at the end of a string of 1 m length, is whirled along a vertical circle at a constant speed of $4\ ms^{-1}$. The tension in the string has a value of 52 N when the stone is **EAMCET | 1994**

(a) at the top of the circle

(b) half way down

(c) at the bottom of the circle

(d) None of the above

46. A body A starts from rest with an acceleration a_1. After 2 s another body B starts from rest with an acceleration a_2. If they travel equal distance in the 5th second after the start of A. $a_1 : a_2$ is equal to **EAMCET | 1994**

(a) 5 : 9 (b) 5 : 7 (c) 9 : 5 (d) 9 : 7

47. In the following velocity-time graph, the distance travelled by the body, in metre is **EAMCET | 1994**

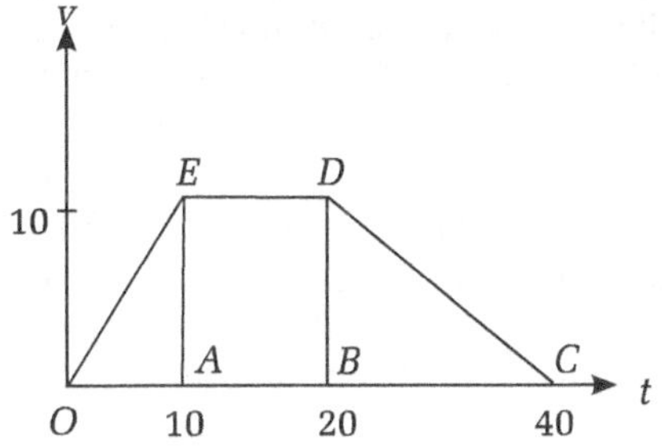

(a) 200 (b) 250 (c) 300 (d) 400

48. A person aiming to reach the exactly opposite point on the bank of a stream is swimming with a speed of $0.5\ ms^{-1}$ at an angle of 120° with the direction of flow of water. The speed of water in the stream, in ms^{-1}, is **EAMCET | 1994**

(a) 1.00 (b) $1/\sqrt{3}$ (c) 0.25 (d) 0.433

49. If a unit vector is represented by $0.5\hat{i} + 0.8\hat{j} + c\hat{k}$, the value of c is **EAMCET | 1994**

(a) 1 (b) $\sqrt{0.11}$

(c) $\sqrt{0.011}$ (d) $\sqrt{0.39}$

50. When two vectors $\vec{A}$ and $\vec{B}$ of magnitude a and b are added, the magnitude of the resultant vector is always **EAMCET | 1993**

(a) equal to $(a + b)$

(b) less than $(a + b)$

(c) greater than $(a + b)$

(d) not greater than $(a + b)$

51. A ball is thrown vertically upwards with a speed of $10\ ms^{-1}$ from the top of a tower 200 m high and another is thrown vertically downwards with the same speed simultaneously. The time difference between them in reaching the ground, in second, if g is taken as $10\ ms^{-2}$, is **EAMCET | 1993**

(a) 12 (b) 6 (c) 2 (d) 1

52. $\vec{A}$ and $\vec{B}$ are vectors such that $|\vec{A}+\vec{B}| = |\vec{A}-\vec{B}|$. Then, the angle between them is **EAMCET | 1993**

(a) 90° (b) 60° (c) 45° (d) 0°

53. A very small particle rests on the top of a hemisphere of radius 20 cm. The smallest horizontal velocity to be given to it, if it is to leave the hemisphere without sliding down its surface, taking $g = 9.8\ ms^{-2}$ is **EAMCET | 1993**

(a) $1.4\ ms^{-1}$ (b) $2.4\ ms^{-1}$
(c) $0.4\ ms^{-1}$ (d) $0.7\ ms^{-1}$

54. A particle starts moving from rest under uniform acceleration. It travels a distance x in the first two seconds and a distance of y in the next two seconds. If $y = n\,x$, then $n =$ **EAMCET | 1993**

(a) 1 (b) 3 (c) 2 (d) 4

55. The resultant of the vectors A and B depends also on the angle θ between them. The magnitude of the resultant is always given by **EAMCET | 1992**

(a) $A + B + 2AB\cos\theta$
(b) $\sqrt{(A+B+2AB\cos\theta)}$
(c) $\sqrt{A^2+B^2+2AB\cos\theta}$
(d) $(A^2 + B^2 + 2AB\cos\theta)^2$

56. A horizontal stream of H_2O leaves an opening in the side of a tank. If the opening is h metre above the ground, and the stream hits the ground D metre away and the acceleration due to gravity is g the speed of H_2O as it leaves the tank in terms of g, h and D is **EAMCET | 1992**

(a) $D\left(\frac{g}{2h}\right)^{3/2}$ (b) $D\left(\frac{g}{2h}\right)^{2}$
(c) $D\left(\frac{g}{2h}\right)^{-1/2}$ (d) $D\sqrt{\frac{g}{2h}}$

57. The banking angle for a curved road of radius 490 m for a vehicle moving at $35\ ms^{-1}$ is **EAMCET | 1992**

(a) $\tan^{-1}(0.25)$ (b) $\tan^{-1}(0.55)$
(c) $\tan^{-1}(0.45)$ (d) $\tan^{-1}(0.75)$

58. Keeping the banking angle same, to increase the maximum speed with which a vehicle can travel on a curved road by 10 percent the radius of curvature of the road has to be changed from 20 m to **EAMCET | 1991**

(a) 6 m (b) 18 m
(c) 24.2 m (d) 30.5 m

59. A wooden block is dropped from the top of a cliff 100 m high. Simultaneously a bullet of mass 10 g is fired from the foot of the cliff upwards with a velocity of $100\ ms^{-1}$. The bullet and wooden block will meet each other after a time **EAMCET | 1991**

(a) 10 s (b) 0.5 s (c) 1 s (d) 7 s

60. If $\vec{A}, \vec{B}$ are perpendicular vectors
$\vec{A} = 5\hat{i} + 7\hat{j} - 3\hat{k}$,
$\vec{B} = 2\hat{i} + 2\hat{j} - c\hat{k}$. The value of c is **EAMCET | 1991**

(a) – 2 (b) 8 (c) – 7 (d) – 8

61. A body falling from rest has a velocity v after it falls through a distance h. The distance it has to fall down further, for its velocity to become double, is .... times h. **EAMCET | 1991**

(a) $5h$ (b) h (c) $2h$ (d) $3h$

62. A body of mass m thrown horizontally with velocity v, from the top of tower of height h, touches the level of ground at a distance of 250 m from the foot of the tower. A body of mass $2m$, thrown horizontally with velocity $v/2$, from the top of a tower of height $4h$ will touch the level ground at a distance in metre from the foot of the tower is **EAMCET | 1991**

(a) 150 m (b) 200 m
(c) 250 m (d) 2500 m

63. A boat is moving with a velocity $3\hat{i} + 4\hat{j}$ with respect to ground the water in the river is moving with a velocity $-3\hat{i} - 4\hat{j}$ w.r.t. ground. The relative velocity of boat w.r.t. water is **EAMCET | 1991**

(a) $5\hat{i} + 6\hat{j}$ (b) $6\hat{i} + 8\hat{j}$
(c) $6\hat{j} + 8\hat{k}$ (d) $5\hat{j} + 6\hat{k}$

Answers

1.	(c)	**2.**	(b)	**3.**	(c)	**4.**	(c)	**5.**	(c)	**6.**	(a)	**7.**	(b)	**8.**	(b)	**9.**	(c)	**10.**	(c)
11.	(b)	**12.**	(a)	**13.**	(a)	**14.**	(c)	**15.**	(d)	**16.**	(d)	**17.**	(b)	**18.**	(c)	**19.**	(a)	**20.**	(c)
21.	(d)	**22.**	(a)	**23.**	(d)	**24.**	(b)	**25.**	(c)	**26.**	(d)	**27.**	(a)	**28.**	(b)	**29.**	(c)	**30.**	(b)
31.	(a)	**32.**	(c)	**33.**	(c)	**34.**	(c)	**35.**	(c)	**36.**	(b)	**37.**	(b)	**38.**	(c)	**39.**	(b)	**40.**	(c)
41.	(d)	**42.**	(a)	**43.**	(a)	**44.**	(d)	**45.**	(c)	**46.**	(a)	**47.**	(b)	**48.**	(c)	**49.**	(b)	**50.**	(d)
51.	(c)	**52.**	(a)	**53.**	(a)	**54.**	(b)	**55.**	(c)	**56.**	(d)	**57.**	(a)	**58.**	(c)	**59.**	(c)	**60.**	(d)
61.	(d)	**62.**	(c)	**63.**	(b)														

Hints & Solutions

1. Let $\vec{B} = \hat{i} - \hat{j}$

Then, component of vector $\vec{A}$ along $\vec{B}$

$$= \frac{\vec{A} \cdot \vec{B}}{|\vec{B}|}$$

$$= \frac{(a_x\hat{i} + a_y\hat{j} + a_z\hat{k}) \cdot (\hat{i} - \hat{j})}{|\hat{i} - \hat{j}|}$$

$$= \frac{a_x - a_y}{\sqrt{2}}$$

2. The ball is thrown vertically upwards then according to equation of motion

$$(0)^2 - u^2 = -2gh \quad \text{...(i)}$$

and $$0 = u - gt \quad \text{...(ii)}$$

From Eqs. (i) and (ii),

$$h = \frac{gt^2}{2}$$

When the ball is falling downwards after reaching the maximum height

$$s = ut' + \frac{1}{2}g(t')^2$$

$$\frac{h}{2} = (0)t' + \frac{1}{2}g(t')^2$$

$$\Rightarrow \quad t' = \sqrt{\frac{h}{g}}$$

$$t' = \frac{t}{\sqrt{2}}$$

Hence, the total time from the time of projection to reach a point at half of its maximum height while returning $= t + t'$

$$= t + \frac{t}{\sqrt{2}}$$

3. Direction of velocity is always tangent to the path so at the top of trajectory, it is in horizontal direction.

4. When a charged particle moves perpendicular to the magnetic field, it follows a circular path. On the circular path its velocity and acceleration will be at right angle to each other.

Given, $\vec{v} = 2\hat{i} + c\hat{j}$, $\vec{a} = 3\hat{i} + 4\hat{j}$

As $\vec{v}$ and $\vec{a}$ are perpendicular, hence

$$\vec{v} \cdot \vec{a} = 0$$

$$(2\hat{i} + c\hat{j}) \cdot (3\hat{i} + 4\hat{j}) = 0$$

$$\Rightarrow \quad 6 + 4c = 0$$

$$\Rightarrow \quad c = -1.5$$

5. For water not to spill out of the bucket,

$$v_{\min} = \sqrt{5gR}$$

$$= \sqrt{5 \times 10 \times 0.5}$$

$$= 5 \text{ ms}^{-1}$$

6. When the man is at rest with respect to the ground, the rain comes to him at an angle 30° with the vertical. This is the direction of the velocity of raindrops with respect to the ground.

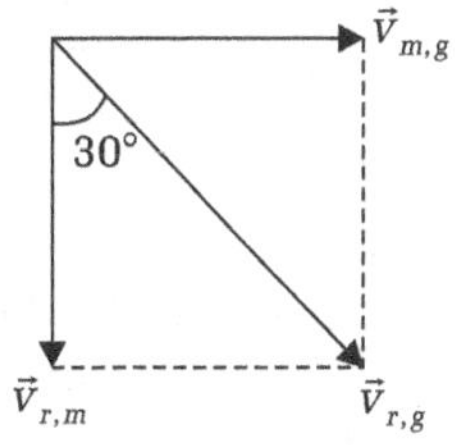

Here, $\vec{v}_{r,g}$ = velocity of the rain with respect to the ground

$\vec{v}_{m,g}$ = velocity of the man with respect to the ground

and $\vec{v}_{r,m}$ = velocity of the rain with respect to the man we have, $\vec{v}_{r,g} + \vec{v}_{r,m} + \vec{v}_{m,g}$ ...(i)

Taking horizontal components, Eq. (i) gives

$v_{r,g} \sin 30° = v_{m,g} = 10 \text{ kmh}^{-1}$

or $v_{r,g} = \dfrac{10}{\sin 30°} = 20 \text{ kmh}^{-1}$

7. $R = \dfrac{u^2 \sin 2\theta}{g}$

$\therefore \quad 20 = \dfrac{u^2 \sin(2 \times 30°)}{g}$

$\Rightarrow \quad \dfrac{u^2}{g} = \dfrac{20}{\sin 60°} = \dfrac{20}{\sqrt{3}} \times 2 = \dfrac{40}{\sqrt{3}}$

Now, $H = \dfrac{u^2 \sin^2 \theta}{2g}$

$= \dfrac{40}{\sqrt{3}} \times \dfrac{\sin^2 30°}{2}$

$= \dfrac{40}{\sqrt{3}} \times \dfrac{\left(\frac{1}{2}\right)^2}{2} = \dfrac{5}{\sqrt{3}}$ m

8. Angular momentum

$\vec{L} = m\vec{r} \times \vec{v}$

but $\vec{L} = I\vec{\omega}$

$\therefore \; mr^2\vec{\omega} = m\vec{r} \times \vec{v}$

$\vec{\omega} = \dfrac{\vec{r} \times \vec{v}}{r^2} = \dfrac{\vec{r} \times \vec{v}}{|\vec{r}|^2}$

$\vec{r} = \hat{i} + 9\hat{j} - 8\hat{k}, \; \vec{v} = 3\hat{i} - 4\hat{j} + 5\hat{k}$

$$\vec{r} \times \vec{v} = \begin{vmatrix} \hat{i} & \hat{j} & \hat{k} \\ 1 & 9 & -8 \\ 3 & -4 & 5 \end{vmatrix}$$

$= 13\hat{i} - 29\hat{j} - 31\hat{k}$

$\therefore \quad \vec{\omega} = \dfrac{13\hat{i} - 29\hat{j} - 31\hat{k}}{[\sqrt{1^2 + 9^2 + (-8)^2}]^2}$

$= \dfrac{13\hat{i} - 29\hat{j} - 31\hat{k}}{146}$

9. Time taken by the body to reach the point A is t_1 (During upward journey).

The body crosses this point again (during downward journey) after t_2, *i.e.*, the body takes the time $(t_2 - t_1)$ to come again at point A.

So, the time taken by the body to reach at point B (at maximum height).

$t = t_1 + \left(\dfrac{t_2 - t_1}{2}\right)$

[$\because$ Time of ascending = Time of descending]

$t = \dfrac{t_1 + t_2}{2}$

So, maximum height $H = \dfrac{1}{2} gt^2$

$= \dfrac{1}{2} g \left(\dfrac{t_1 + t_2}{2}\right)^2$

$= 2g \left(\dfrac{t_1 + t_2}{4}\right)^2$

10. Equation of projectile

$y = 10x - \left(\dfrac{5}{9}\right)x^2$

Standard equation

$y = x \tan\theta - \dfrac{g}{2u^2 \cos^2 \theta} \cdot x^2$

On comparing

$\tan\theta = 10$

and $\dfrac{g}{2u^2 \cos^2 \theta} = \dfrac{5}{9}$

$10\, u^2 \cos^2 \theta = 9g$

$g = 10 \text{ ms}^{-2}$ (given)

$\therefore \quad u^2 \cos^2 \theta = 9$

Range of projectile, $R = \dfrac{2u^2 \sin\theta \cos\theta}{g}$

$= \dfrac{2u^2 \tan\theta \cdot \cos^2 \theta}{g}$

$(\because \sin\theta = \tan\theta \cdot \cos\theta)$

$= \dfrac{2(u^2 \cos^2 \theta) \cdot \tan\theta}{g}$

$= \dfrac{2 \times 9 \times 10}{10} = 18$ m

11. $s_1 + (u_1)t = s_2 + (u_2)t$

$(4\hat{i} - 4\hat{j} + 7\hat{k}) + (0.4\hat{i})\, 10$

$= (2\hat{i} + 2\hat{j} + 5\hat{k}) + (u_2)\, 10$

$\Rightarrow \quad u_2 = \dfrac{(6\hat{i} - 6\hat{j} + 2\hat{k})}{10}$

$= 0.6\left[\hat{i} - \hat{j} + \dfrac{1}{3}\hat{k}\right]$

12. $x = (u \cos\theta)t = 6\,t$

$y = (u \sin\theta)\, t - \dfrac{1}{2} gt^2 = 8t - 5t^2$

Therefore, $u \sin\theta = 8$

$u \cos\theta = 6$

Range, $R = \dfrac{u^2 \sin 2\theta}{g}$

$= \dfrac{u^2 \times 2 \sin\theta \cos\theta}{g}$

$$= \frac{2(u\sin\theta)(u\cos\theta)}{g}$$

$$= \frac{2(8)(6)}{10} = 9.6 \text{ m}$$

13. $x = 36\,t$ metre

$2y = (96\,t - 9.8\,t^2)$ metre

Standard equations are

$$x = (u\cos\theta)\,t$$

$$y = u\sin\theta\, t - \frac{1}{2}g\,t^2$$

$$u\cos\theta = 36$$

$$u\sin\theta = \frac{96}{2} = 48$$

$$\therefore \quad \tan\theta = \frac{u\sin\theta}{u\cos\theta} = \frac{48}{36} = \frac{4}{3}$$

$$\theta = \tan^{-1}\left(\frac{4}{3}\right)$$

or $\quad \theta = \sin^{-1}\left(\frac{4}{5}\right)$

14. Suppose the body leaves the surface of the hemisphere at point P.

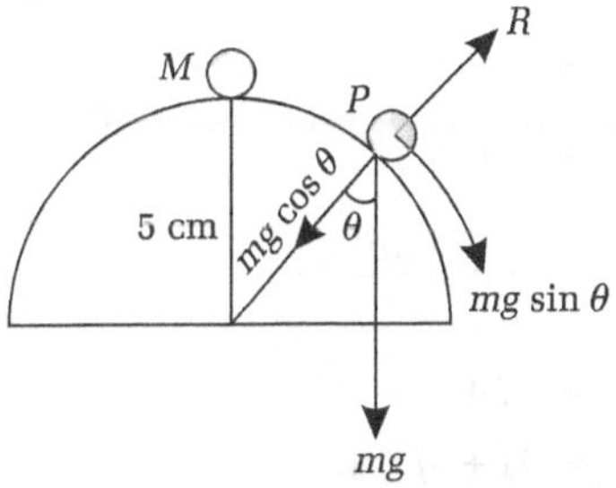

Let at point P radius vector of the body makes an angle θ.

$$\therefore \; m\,g\cos\theta - R = \frac{m\,v^2}{r}$$

When the body leaves the surface then

$$R = 0$$

$$\therefore \quad m\,g\cos\theta = \frac{m\,v^2}{r}$$

$$\cos\theta = \frac{v^2}{r\,g} = \frac{(5)^2}{5\times 10} = \frac{25}{50} = \frac{1}{2}$$

$$= \cos 60°$$

$$\theta = 60°$$

15. $x = 36\,t$

$y = 48\,t - 4.9\,t^2$

Comparing with $x = u\cos\theta\, t$

$$y = u\sin\theta\, t - \frac{1}{2}gt^2$$

where u = initial velocity

$$u\cos\theta = 36,$$

$$u\sin\theta = 48$$

$$(u\cos\theta)^2 + (u\sin\theta)^2 = 36^2 + 48^2$$

$$u^2(\cos^2\theta + \sin^2\theta) = 3600$$

$$u^2 = 3600$$

$$u = 60 \text{ ms}^{-1}$$

16. $u = 20 \text{ ms}^{-1}$, $\theta = 45°$

Equation of trajectory $h = Ax - Bx^2$

Standard equation

$$h = x\tan\theta - \frac{g\,x^2}{2u^2\cos^2\theta}$$

On comparing the two equations

$$A = \tan\theta,\; B = \frac{g}{2u^2\cos^2\theta}$$

$$\frac{A}{B} = \frac{\tan\theta}{g/2\,u^2\cos^2\theta} = \frac{2u^2\cos^2\theta\tan\theta}{g}$$

$$= \frac{2\times(20)^2\cos^2 45°\tan 45°}{10}$$

$$= \frac{2\times 400\times\left(\frac{1}{\sqrt{2}}\right)^2\times 1}{10}$$

$$= 2\times 40\times\frac{1}{2} = 40$$

$$A : B = 40 : 1$$

17. From $v = u - g\,t$

At maximum height, $v = 0$

$$\therefore \quad 0 = u - g\,(6)$$

$$u = 6\,g \text{ ms}^{-1}$$

Distance covered in I[st] sec

$$h_1 = u\,t - \frac{1}{2}g\,t^2$$

$$= 6\,g\,(1) - \frac{1}{2}(g)\times(1)^2$$

$$= 6g - \frac{g}{2} = \frac{11g}{2}$$

Distance covered in 7th sec

$$h_2 = \left[u(7) - \frac{1}{2}g(7)^2\right] - \left[u(6) - \frac{1}{2}g(6)^2\right]$$

$$= u - \frac{13}{2}g = 6g - \frac{13}{2}g = -\frac{g}{2}$$

$$\therefore \quad \frac{h_1}{h_2} = \frac{11g/2}{-g/2} = \frac{-11}{1}$$

$$h_1 : h_2 = -11 : 1 \quad \Rightarrow \quad |h_1 : h_2| = 11 : 1$$

18. Time taken by the body in falling

$$t = \sqrt{\frac{2h}{g}} = \sqrt{\frac{2\times5}{10}} = 1 \text{ s}$$

Horizontal distance covered by the body

$$= 10 \text{ m}$$

$\therefore \quad ut = 10$

$u \times 1 = 10$

$\Rightarrow \quad u = 10 \text{ ms}^{-1}$

19. Horizontal range

$$R = \frac{u^2 \sin 2\theta}{g}$$

$\Rightarrow \quad R \propto \theta$

for the body projected at minimum angle will have shortest range.

So, body *P* will have shortest range.

20. Speed of projectile at maximum height

$$= u \cos\theta = \frac{\sqrt{3}}{2} u$$

where u = initial speed

$$\therefore \quad \cos\theta = \frac{\sqrt{3}}{2} = \cos 30°$$

$$\theta = 30°$$

Range of projectile, $R = \dfrac{u^2 \sin 2\theta}{g}$

According to question

$$R = PH$$

$$\frac{u^2 \sin 2\theta}{g} = P\frac{u^2 \sin^2\theta}{2g}$$

$$\sin 2 \times 30° = P \times \frac{\sin^2\theta}{2}$$

$$\sin 60° = P \times \frac{\sin^2 30°}{2}$$

$$P = \frac{2\sin 60°}{\sin^2 30°}$$

$$= \frac{2\times\frac{\sqrt{3}}{2}}{\left(\frac{1}{2}\right)^2}$$

$$= \sqrt{3}\times 4 = 4\sqrt{3}$$

21. Time taken by the drop to fall

$$h = \frac{1}{2} g t^2$$

$$5 = \frac{1}{2}\times 10\times t^2$$

$\Rightarrow \quad t = 1 \text{ s}$

Time difference between falling the drops

$$= \frac{1}{4} = 0.25 \text{ s}$$

When first drop strikes the ground, then third drop has fallen for a time

$$= 0.25 + 0.25 = 0.5 \text{ s}$$

Height covered by third drop, $h = \dfrac{1}{2} g t^2$

$$= \frac{1}{2}\times 10\times(0.5)^2 = 1.25 \text{ m}$$

Height from the ground = 5 − 1.25 = 3.75 m

22. Let the car accelerates for time t_1

From $\quad v = u + at$

$$v = 0 + \alpha t_1$$

$$v = \alpha t_1$$

$$\therefore \quad t_1 = \frac{v}{\alpha}$$

Now, the car starts to retard till it comes to rest, so

$$v' = v - \alpha t_2$$

$$0 = v - \beta t_2$$

$$t_2 = \frac{v}{\beta}$$

But, $t_1 + t_2 = t$

$$\frac{v}{\alpha} + \frac{v}{\beta} = t$$

$$\therefore \quad v = \frac{\alpha\beta}{\alpha+\beta} t$$

23.

$$\vec{A} = 6\hat{i} + 6\hat{j} - 3\hat{k}$$

$$\vec{B} = 7\hat{i} + 4\hat{j} + 4\hat{k}$$

$$|\vec{A}| = \sqrt{(6)^2 + (6)^2 + (-3)^2}$$

$$= \sqrt{36+36+9} = 9$$

$$|\vec{B}| = \sqrt{(7)^2 + (4)^2 + (-4)^2}$$

$$= \sqrt{49+16+16} = 9$$

$\therefore$ Angle between $\vec{A}$ and $\vec{B}$

$$v = \cos^{-1}\left(\frac{\vec{A}\cdot\vec{B}}{|\vec{A}||\vec{B}|}\right)$$

$$= \cos^{-1}\left\{\frac{(6\hat{i}+6\hat{j}-3\hat{k})\cdot(7\hat{i}+4\hat{j}+4\hat{k})}{9\times 9}\right\}$$

$$= \cos^{-1}\left\{\frac{6\times7+6\times4+(-3)(+4)}{81}\right\}$$

$$= \cos^{-1}\left\{\frac{42+24-12}{81}\right\}$$

$$= \cos^{-1}\left\{\frac{54}{81}\right\} = \cos^{-1}\left(\frac{6}{9}\right)$$

$$= \cos^{-1}\left(\frac{2}{3}\right) = \sin^{-1}\left(\frac{\sqrt{5}}{3}\right)$$

24. Minimum speed at lowest point of a vertical circle.

$$v = \sqrt{5\,Rg}$$

$$\therefore \quad v \propto \sqrt{R}$$

$$\therefore \quad \frac{v_1}{v_2} = \sqrt{\frac{R_1}{R_2}}$$

$$\frac{v}{v_2} = \sqrt{\frac{R}{R/4}}$$

$$\frac{v}{v_2} = 2$$

$$\Rightarrow \quad v_2 = \frac{v}{2}$$

25. Here: $R = 300$ m, $\mu = 0.3$, $g = 10$ ms^{-2}

Maximum speed $v = \sqrt{\mu Rg} = \sqrt{0.3 \times 300 \times 10}$

$$= \sqrt{900} = 30 \text{ ms}^{-1}$$

$$= 30 \times \frac{18}{5}$$

$$= 108 \text{ km-h}^{-1}$$

26. The horizontal range of the bottle $R = 2$ m

$$\therefore \quad R = \frac{u^2 \sin 2\theta}{g}$$

$$2 = u^2 \frac{\sin 2 \times 45°}{g}$$

$$2 = u^2 \frac{\sin 90°}{g}$$

$$\Rightarrow \quad 2 = \frac{u^2}{g}$$

$$\therefore \quad u = \sqrt{2g}$$

27. Here: $u = 0$, $v = 36$ kmh^{-1}

$$= 36 \times \frac{5}{18} = 10 \text{ ms}^{-1},$$

$$s = 9 \text{ km} = 9000 \text{ m}$$

$$a = 0.2 \text{ ms}^{-2}$$

Time taken by the car in which its velocity increases from 0 to 10 ms^{-1}

$$v = u + a\,t$$

$$10 = 0 + 0.2\,t_1$$

$$t_1 = \frac{10}{0.2} = 50 \text{ s}$$

Time taken in covering 9000 m with uniform speed 10 m/s

$$t_2 = \frac{9000}{10}$$

$$\Rightarrow \quad t_2 = 900 \text{ s}$$

Time taken by the car in which it comes rest.

From $\quad v = u - at$

$$0 = 10 - 0.1 \times t_3$$

$$t_3 = \frac{10}{0.1} = 100 \text{ s}$$

Total time taken, $t = t_1 + t_2 + t_3$

$$= 50 + 900 + 100 = 1050 \text{ s}$$

28. Minimum velocity at the highest point of the circle

$$v = \sqrt{lg}$$

Minimum velocity at the lowest point

$$v = \sqrt{5\,lg}$$

Minimum velocity at mid point

$$v = \sqrt{3\,lg}$$

From these formulae it is clear that the velocity is independent of the mass of the stone.

29. $r = 18$ m, $g = 10$ ms^{-2}, $\mu = 0.2$

Maximum speed with which a car can be driven

$$v = \sqrt{\mu\, rg} = \sqrt{0.2 \times 18 \times 10}$$

$$= \sqrt{36} = 6 \text{ ms}^{-1}$$

$$= 6 \times \frac{18}{5} = \frac{108}{5} = 21.6 \text{ kmh}^{-1}$$

30. For an electron circulating around the nucleus, the centripetal force is supplied by the electrostatic force between nuclei and electrons.

31. Here: $v_1 = 15$ ms^{-1},

$$v_2 = 15 \text{ ms}^{-1},$$

$$\Delta t = 10 \text{ s}$$

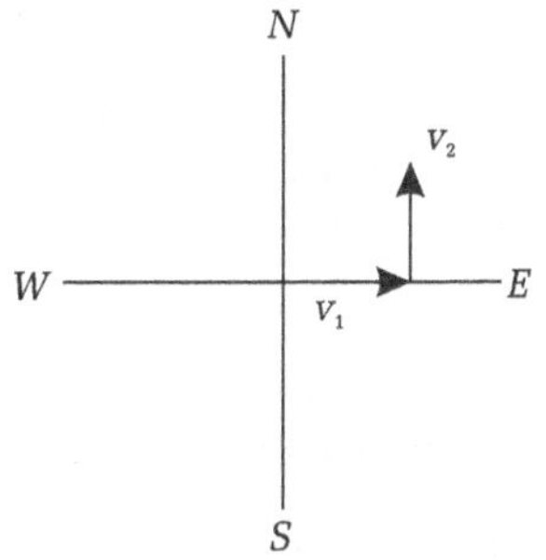

Change in velocity $\Delta v = \sqrt{v_1^2 + v_2^2}$

$= \sqrt{(15)^2 + (15)^2} = 15\sqrt{2}\ ms^{-1}$

$\therefore$ Acceleration, $a = \frac{\Delta v}{\Delta t} = \frac{15\sqrt{2}}{10} = \frac{3\sqrt{2}}{2}$

$= \frac{3}{\sqrt{2}}$ (north-east)

32. Here: $t = 0.9$ s, $u = 36$ kmh^{-1}

$= 36 \times \frac{5}{18} = 10\ ms^{-1}$

$v = 0$

$a = -5\ ms^{-2}$

From $v^2 = u^2 + 2as$

$0 = (10)^2 + 2(-5) \times s$

$10s = 100$

$s = 10$

Distance covered by the car before stopping

$= 10$ m

33. Second hand of a clock rotates by 2π angle in 1 min *i.e.*, in 60 s.

$\therefore$ Angular velocity, $\omega = \frac{2\pi}{60} = \frac{\pi}{30}$

$= \frac{3.14}{30} = 0.105\ rads^{-1}$

34. At the highest point of the projectile there is only horizontal component of velocity, but acceleration (acceleration due to gravity) always acts vertically downwards, so the direction of velocity and acceleration are perpendicular to each other.

$v = 150\ ms^{-1}$, $h = 490$ m

35. Time taken by the bomb to cover the height

$t = \sqrt{\frac{2h}{g}} = \sqrt{\frac{2 \times 490}{9.8}}$

$= \sqrt{100} = 10$ s

$\therefore$ Horizontal distance covered by the bomb

$R = v \times t$

(horizontal velocity of the bomb will be equal to horizontal velocity of plane)

$R = 150 \times 10 = 1500$ m

36. $\vec{A} = \hat{i} + \hat{j}$

Equation of x-axis $\vec{B} = \hat{i}$

Angle between $\vec{A}$ and $\vec{B}$,

$\cos\theta = \frac{\vec{A}\cdot\vec{B}}{(\vec{A})(\vec{B})}$

$= \frac{(\hat{i} + \hat{j})\cdot\hat{i}}{\sqrt{(1)^2 + (1)^2} \times 1}$

$= \frac{1\times1 + 1\times0}{\sqrt{2}} = \frac{1}{\sqrt{2}}$

$= \cos 45°$

$\therefore \quad \theta = 45°$

37. Here : $n_1 = 600$ rev/min

$= \frac{600}{60} = 10$ rev/s

$n_2 = 1200$ rev/min

$= \frac{1200}{60} = 20$ rev/s

Increase in angular velocity $= \omega_2 - \omega_1$

$= 2\pi n_2 - 2\pi n_1$

$= 2\pi(n_2 - n_1)$

$= 2\pi(20 - 10)$

$= 20\pi\ rads^{-1}$

38. Angular velocity, $\omega = 70\ rads^{-1}$

$r = 0.5$ m

Linear velocity, $v = r\omega = 0.5 \times 70 = 35\ ms^{-1}$

39. When the particle tied to the end of string is set in a circular motion, then velocity of the particle is always along the tangent of the circle and acceleration (centripetal acceleration) is always along the radius, so tension is also along the radius, hence tension is always perpendicular to velocity of the particle.

($\because$ Radius and tangent of a circle are always perpendicular to each other)

40. Radius of track $r = 500$ m, coefficient of friction $\mu = 0.5$, $g = 10\ m/s^2$

$\therefore$ Maximum speed to avoid skidding

$v_{max} = \sqrt{\mu r g} = \sqrt{0.5 \times 500 \times 10}$

$= \sqrt{2500} = 50\ ms^{-1}$

41. From $v = u - gt$

At maximum height, $v = 0$

$\therefore \quad 0 = u - gt$

$\therefore \quad T = \frac{u}{g}$

Velocity at time $T/2$

$v = u - gt = u - g\frac{T}{2}$

$= u - g\left(\frac{u}{2g}\right) = u - \frac{u}{2}$

$= \frac{u}{2}$

At time $T/2$ the velocity is $u/2$.
Time taken by the body to reach at maximum height = T

$\therefore$ Time taken by the body to come at the point of projection = T

At the point of projection the body will return with same velocity, so after time $2T = (T + T)$.

It has same velocity.

42. Displacement, $x = 2t^2 + t + 5$

Velocity, $v = \frac{dx}{dt} = \frac{d}{dt}(2t^2 + t + 5)$

$= 4t + 1$

Acceleration, $a = \frac{dv}{dt} = \frac{d}{dt}(4t + 1) = 4 + 0$

$= 4 \text{ m/s}^2$

43. Distance covered by the body in 2 s

$$s = ut + \frac{1}{2}gt^2 = u(2) + \frac{1}{2} \times 10(2)^2$$

$$= 2u + 20 \quad \text{...(i)}$$

Distance covered in next 1 s
= Distance covered in 3 s

(Distance covered in 3 s
– Distance covered in 2 s)

$$s' = \left[u(3) + \frac{1}{2} \times 10(3)^2\right] - [2u + 20]$$

$$= 3u + 45 - 2u - 20$$

$$= u + 25 \quad \text{...(ii)}$$

According to question

$s = s'$

$2u + 20 = u + 25$

$u = 5$

From Eq. (i), we get

$s = 2u + 20$

$= 2 \times 5 + 20 = 10 + 20 = 30 \text{ m}$

44. Tension in the string at any point

$$T = \frac{mv^2}{r} + mg\cos\theta$$

When the stone is at its lowest position

$\theta = 0°$

$$\therefore \quad T = \frac{mv^2}{r} + mg\cos 0°$$

$$= \frac{mv^2}{r} + mg \quad (\because \cos 0° = 1)$$

45. Here: $m = 2 \text{ kg}, r = 1 \text{ m}, v = 4 \text{ ms}^{-1}$

$T = 52 \text{ N}$

Tension at any point in vertical circle

$$T = \frac{mv^2}{r} + mg\cos\theta$$

$$52 = 2\frac{(4)^2}{1} + (2) \times 10\cos\theta$$

$52 = 32 + 20\cos\theta$

$20 = 20\cos\theta$

$\Rightarrow \cos\theta = 1$

$\cos\theta = \cos 0°$

$\therefore \theta = 0°$

46. Distance travelled by a body in n^{th} second

$$s_n = u + \frac{1}{2}a(2n - 1)$$

For first body distance covered in 5th second

$$s_1 = 0 + \frac{1}{2}a_1(2 \times 5 - 1) = \frac{9}{2}a_1$$

The body starts after 2 s to start of A.

$\therefore$ Distance covered by second body in 5th second of motion of A = Distance covered by second body B in 3rd sec

$$\therefore \quad s_2 = 0 + \frac{1}{2}a_2(2 \times 3 - 1)$$

$$= \frac{5}{2}a_2$$

According to question $s_1 = s_2$

$$\therefore \quad \frac{9}{2}a_1 = \frac{5}{2}a_2$$

$$\Rightarrow \quad \frac{a_1}{a_2} = \frac{5}{9}$$

$\Rightarrow a_1 : a_2 = 5 : 9$

47. Total distance covered = area enclosed by velocity-time graph

= Area of Δ OAE + Area of rectangle $ABDE$ + Area of triangle ΔBDC

$$= \frac{1}{2} \times 10 \times 10 + 10 \times 10 + \frac{1}{2} \times 20 \times 10$$

$= 50 + 100 + 100 = 250 \text{ m}$

48. In Δ ABC

$$\sin 30° = \frac{v_r}{v_1}$$

where v_r = speed of water in the stream

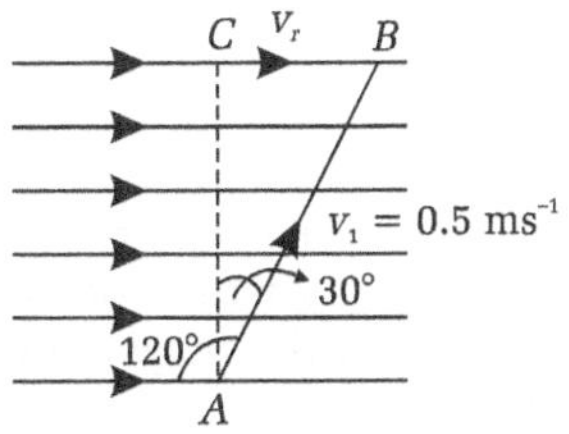

$$\frac{1}{2} = \frac{v_r}{0.5}$$

$$v_r = \frac{0.5}{2} = 0.25 \text{ ms}^{-1}$$

49. Unit vector $= 0.5\hat{i} + 0.8\hat{j} + c\hat{k}$

The magnitude of unit vector = 1

$$\therefore \quad \sqrt{(0.5)^2 + (0.8)^2 + c^2} = 1$$

$$\therefore \quad (0.5)^2 + (0.8)^2 + c^2 = 1$$

$$0.25 + 0.64 + c^2 = 1$$

$$c^2 = 1 - 0.25 - 0.64$$

$$= 1 - 0.89 = 0.11$$

$$c = \sqrt{0.11}$$

50. The sum $(\vec{A} + \vec{B})$ *i.e.*, resultant vector is never greater than the sum of their magnitude *i.e.*, $(a + b)$.

51. For first ball,

Height covered above the top of tower

$$h_1 = \frac{v^2}{2g} = \frac{(10)^2}{2 \times 10} = 5 \text{ m}$$

Time taken in covering 5 m

$$h_1 = \frac{1}{2} g t^2$$

$$\Rightarrow \quad 5 = \frac{1}{2} \times 10 \times t^2$$

$$t = 1 \text{ s}$$

i.e. after 2 s (= 2 × 1) it will again at the top of the tower, so time difference between the two balls in reaching the ground = 2 s.

52. $|\vec{A} + \vec{B}| = |\vec{A} - \vec{B}|$

Squaring both sides

$$|\vec{A} + \vec{B}|^2 = |\vec{A} - \vec{B}|^2$$

$$|\vec{A}|^2 + |\vec{B}|^2 + 2|\vec{A}| \cdot |\vec{B}| = |\vec{A}|^2 + |\vec{B}|^2 - 2|\vec{A}| \cdot |\vec{B}|$$

$$A^2 + B^2 + 2|\vec{A}| \cdot |\vec{B}| = A^2 + B^2 - 2|\vec{A}| \cdot |\vec{B}|$$

$$4|\vec{A}| \cdot |\vec{B}| = 0$$

$$A B \cos\theta = 0$$

$$\therefore \quad \cos\theta = 0$$

$$\cos\theta = \cos 90^\circ$$

$$\Rightarrow \quad \theta = 90^\circ$$

53. Let the velocity is v. The particle will not slide, if centripetal force is not there or the centripetal force is balanced by the weight of the particle.

So, $\frac{mv^2}{R} = mg$

$$\therefore v = \sqrt{R g} = \sqrt{20 \times 10^{-2} \times 9.8}$$

$$= \sqrt{196 \times 10^{-2}} = 1.4 \text{ ms}^{-1}$$

54. The particle starts from rest, so, $u = 0$

Distance travelled in first 2 s

$$s_1 = ut + \frac{1}{2}at^2 = 0 \times 2 + \frac{1}{2} \times a(2)^2$$

$$x = 2a$$

Distance travelled in next 2 s

$$y = \left[0 \times 4 + \frac{1}{2}a(4)^2\right] - 2a = 8a - 2a$$

$$= 6a = 3(2a) = 3x$$

But, $y = nx$ (given)

So, $n = 3$

56. Time taken by the stream to fall through height h

$$\therefore \quad t = \sqrt{\frac{2h}{g}}$$

Horizontal distance travelled by water stream in time t = velocity × t

$$\therefore \quad D = vt$$

$$v = \frac{D}{t}$$

$$= \frac{D}{\sqrt{\frac{2h}{g}}}$$

$$= D\sqrt{\frac{g}{2h}}$$

57. Banking angle, $\theta = \tan^{-1}\frac{v^2}{rg}$

v = velocity of the vehicle

= 35 ms^{-1}

r = radius of curved road

= 490 m

$$\therefore \quad \theta = \tan^{-1}\frac{(35)^2}{490 \times 10}$$

or $\theta = \tan^{-1}(0.25)$

58. Banking angle, $\tan\theta = \frac{v^2}{rg}$

Banking angle remains same, so

$$\frac{v_1^2}{r_1} = \frac{v_2^2}{r_2}$$

$$\frac{v^2}{20} = \frac{\left(v + \frac{v \times 10}{100}\right)^2}{r_2}$$

$$r_2 = \left(\frac{11v}{10}\right)^2 \frac{20}{v^2}$$

$$= \frac{121}{100} \times 20 = 24.2 \text{ m}$$

59. Let the bullet and block meet each other after time t.

Then, distance covered by the block

$$h_1 = \frac{1}{2} g t^2 \qquad \text{(downward motion)}$$

Distance covered by the bullet

$$h_2 = ut - \frac{1}{2} gt^2$$

$$= 100t - \frac{1}{2} gt^2$$

$$\therefore \quad h_1 + h_2 = 100$$

$$\frac{1}{2} g t^2 + 100t - \frac{1}{2} g t^2 = 100$$

$$100\, t = 100$$

$$t = 1 \text{ s}$$

60. $\vec{A} = 5\hat{i} + 7\hat{j} - 3\hat{k}$

$\vec{B} = 2\hat{i} + 2\hat{j} - c\hat{k}$

$\vec{A}$ and $\vec{B}$ are perpendicular to each other, so

$$\vec{A} \cdot \vec{B} = 0$$

$$(5\hat{i} + 7\hat{j} - 3\hat{k}) \cdot (2\hat{i} + 2\hat{j} - c\hat{k}) = 0$$

$$5 \times 2 + 7 \times 2 + (-3)(-c) = 0$$

$$10 + 14 + 3c = 0$$

$$3c = -24$$

$$c = -8$$

61. Body falls from rest, so initial velocity

$$u = 0$$

From equation of motion

$$v^2 = 2\, gh$$

Let at height x velocity becomes double

So, $\quad (2v)^2 = 2\, g\, x$

$$4\, v^2 = 2\, g\, x$$

$$\therefore \quad 4\,(2\, g\, h) = 2\, g\, x$$

$$x = 4\, h$$

Further height $= 4\, h - h = 3\, h$

62. Time taken by the body to reach the ground level $t = \sqrt{\dfrac{2h}{g}}$

$$\Rightarrow \quad t \propto \sqrt{h}$$

Horizontal distance covered

$$R = \text{velocity} \times \text{time}$$

So, $\quad \dfrac{R_1}{R_2} = \dfrac{v_1}{v_2} \times \dfrac{t_1}{t_2} = \dfrac{v_1}{v_2} \times \sqrt{\dfrac{h_1}{h_2}}$

$$\frac{250}{R_2} = \frac{v}{v/2} \sqrt{\frac{h}{4h}} = 2 \times \frac{1}{2} = 1$$

$$\therefore \quad R_2 = 250 \text{ m}$$

63. Velocity of boat $\vec{v}_b = 3\hat{i} + 4\hat{j}$

Velocity of water $\vec{v}_w = -3\hat{i} - 4\hat{j}$

$$= -(3\hat{i} + 4\hat{j})$$

So, the boat and water are moving in opposite directions.

So, relative velocity of boat with respect to water $\sqrt{v_b^2 + v_w^2 + 2v_b v_w \cos\theta}$

$$= \sqrt{v_b^2 + v_w^2 + 2v_b v_w \cos\theta}$$

$$= v_b - v_w$$

$$= (3\hat{i} + 4\hat{j} - [-(3\hat{i} + 4\hat{j})] = 6\hat{i} + 8\hat{j}$$

Chapter

3

Laws of Motion

1. A rifle of 20 kg mass can fire 4 bullet/s. The mass of each bullet is 35×10^{-3} kg and its final velocity is 400 ms^{-1}. Then, what force must be applied on the rifle so that it does not move backwards while firing the bullets? **EAMCET | 2007**

(a) 80 N (b) 28 N
(c) –112 N (d) –56 N

2. An object of mass 2 m is projected with a speed of 100 ms^{-1} at an angle $\theta = \sin^{-1}\left(\frac{3}{5}\right)$ to the horizontal. At the highest point, the object breaks into two pieces of same mass m and the first one comes to rest. The distance between the point of projection and the point of landing of the bigger piece (in metre) is (Given, $g = 10$ ms^{-2}) **EAMCET | 2007**

(a) 3840 (b) 1280
(c) 1440 (d) 960

3. A man slides down on a telegraphic pole with an acceleration equal to one-fourth of acceleration due to gravity. The frictional force between man and pole is equal to in terms of man's weight w **EAMCET | 2007**

(a) $\frac{w}{4}$ (b) $\frac{w}{2}$ (c) $\frac{3w}{4}$ (d) w

4. A man of 50 kg is standing at one end on a boat of length 25 m and mass 200 kg. If he starts running and when he reaches the other end, he has a velocity 2 ms^{-1} with respect to the boat. The final velocity of the boat is (in ms^{-1}) **EAMCET | 2006**

(a) $\frac{2}{5}$ (b) $\frac{2}{3}$ (c) $\frac{8}{5}$ (d) $\frac{8}{3}$

5. The machine gun fires 240 bullet/min. If the mass of each bullet is 10 g and the velocity of the bullet is 600 ms^{-1}, the power (in kW) of the gun is **EAMCET | 2005**

(a) 43200 (b) 432 (c) 72 (d) 7.2

6. A body of mass m is suspended to an ideal spring of force constant k. The expected change in the position of the body due to an additional force F acting vertically downwards is **EAMCET | 2005**

(a) $\frac{3F}{2k}$ (b) $\frac{2F}{k}$ (c) $\frac{5F}{2k}$ (d) $\frac{4F}{k}$

7. Consider the following statements A and B and identify the correct answer.

A. When a person walks on a rough surface the direction of frictional force exerted by the surface on the person is opposite to the direction of his motion.

B. When a cycle is in motion, the force of friction exerted by the ground on the front wheel is in the backward direction. **EAMCET | 2004**

(a) A and B are correct
(b) A is correct, B is wrong
(c) A and B are wrong
(d) A is wrong, B is correct

8. The horizontal acceleration that should be given to a smooth inclined plane of angle $\sin^{-1}\left(\frac{1}{l}\right)$ to keep an object stationary on the plane, relative to the inclined plane is **EAMCET | 2003**

(a) $\frac{g}{\sqrt{l^2-1}}$ (b) $g\sqrt{l^2-1}$
(c) $\frac{\sqrt{l^2-1}}{g}$ (d) $-\frac{g}{\sqrt{l^2+1}}$

9. A body of weight 64 N is pushed with just enough force to start it moving across a horizontal floor and the same force continues to act afterwards. If the coefficients of static and dynamic friction are 0.6 and 0.4 respectively, the acceleration of the body is (acceleration due to gravity $= g$) **EAMCET | 2001**

(a) $\frac{g}{6.4}$ (b) 0.64 g (c) $\frac{g}{32}$ (d) 0.2 g

10. Bullets of 0.03 kg mass each, hit a plate at the rate of 200 bullet/s, with a velocity of 50 ms^{-1} and reflect back with a velocity of 30 ms^{-1}. The average force acting on the plate, in newton, is **EAMCET | 1999**

(a) 120 (b) 180 (c) 300 (d) 480

11. An iron block of sides 50 cm × 8 cm × 15 cm has to be pushed along the floor. The force required will be minimum when the surface in contact with ground is **EAMCET | 1998**

(a) 8 cm × 15 cm surface
(b) 5 cm × 15 cm surface
(c) 8 cm × 5 cm surface
(d) force is same for all surfaces

12. A car of mass 400 kg and travelling at 72 km-h^{-1} crashes into a truck of mass 4000 kg and travelling at 9 km-h^{-1}, in the same direction. The car bounces back at a speed of 18 km-h^{-1}. The speed of the truck after the impact is **EAMCET | 1998**

(a) 9 km-h^{-1} (b) 18 km-h^{-1}
(c) 27 km-h^{-1} (d) 36 km-h^{-1}

13. The relation $\vec{F} = m\vec{a}$, cannot be deduced from Newton's second law, if **EAMCET | 1998**

(a) force depends on time
(b) momentum depends on time
(c) acceleration depends on time
(d) mass depends on time

14. If a body is in equilibrium under a set of non-collinear forces, the minimum number of forces has to be **EAMCET | 1998**

(a) four (b) three (c) two (d) five

15. The weight of a man in a lift moving upwards is 608 N while the weight of the same man in the lift moving downwards, with the same acceleration is 368 N. His normal weight in newton is **EAMCET | 1997**

(a) 498 (b) 588 (c) 480 (d) 240

16. A body of mass 10 kg lies on a rough horizontal surface. When a horizontal force of F newton acts on it, it gets an acceleration of 5 ms^{-2} and when the horizontal force is doubled, it gets an acceleration of 18 ms^{-2}. Then, the coefficient of friction between the body and the horizontal surface is (assume g = 10 ms^{-2}) **EAMCET | 1997**

(a) 0.2 (b) 0.8 (c) 0.4 (d) 0.6

17. A body of weight 50 N is placed on a smooth surface. If the force required to move the body on the rough surface is 30 N the coefficient of friction is **EAMCET | 1996**

(a) 0.6 (b) 1.2 (c) 0.3 (d) 1.67

18. Two forces of equal magnitude F act at a point. If the angle between them is θ, then the magnitude of the resultant force is **EAMCET | 1995**

(a) $F\sqrt{2(1-\sin\theta)}$ (b) $F\sqrt{2(1+\sin\theta)}$
(c) $2F\sin\dfrac{\theta}{2}$ (d) $2F\cos\left(\dfrac{\theta}{2}\right)$

19. A motor car of mass 300 kg is moving with a velocity of 25 ms^{-1}, by applying brakes the car was brought to rest in a distance of 15 m. The force of retardation in newton is **EAMCET | 1994**

(a) 2500 (b) 4500 (c) 6250 (d) 7500

20. A gun is aimed at a target in line with its barrel. The target is released and allowed to fall under gravity, at the instant, the gun is fired. The bullet will **EAMCET | 1994**

(a) pass above the target
(b) pass below the target
(c) hit the target
(d) certainly hit the target

21. A gun fires 50 g bullets with velocity 1000 ms^{-1} each. The soldier holding the gun can exert an average force of 180 N against the gun. The maximum number of bullets, he can fire per minute is **EAMCET | 1993**

(a) 216 (b) 300 (c) 156 (d) 276

22. μ_s, μ_k and μ_r are the coefficients of static, kinetic and rolling friction between two surfaces. In their increasing order of magnitude we can write **EAMCET | 1992**

(a) $\mu_s < \mu_k < \mu_r$ (b) $\mu_r < \mu_k < \mu_s$
(c) $\mu_k < \mu_s < \mu_r$ (d) $\mu_r < \mu_k = \mu_s$

23. A ball of mass 100 g is moving with a velocity of 10 ms^{-1}. On being hit with bat rebounds with a velocity of 10 ms^{-1}. The force of the ball by the bat acts for 0.01 s, then the force exerted on the ball by the bat is **EAMCET | 1992**

(a) 50 N (b) 100 N
(c) 200 N (d) 400 N

24. The average force that is necessary to stop a hammer with 25 Ns^{-1} momentum in 0.05 s is **EAMCET | 1991**

(a) 500 N (b) 125 N (c) 50 N (d) 25 N

25. In deriving Newton's formula for velocity of sound, the changes in volume of air are assumed to be **EAMCET | 1991**

(a) isobaric
(c) adiabatic
(b) isothermal
(d) isochoric

Answers

1. (d)	**2.** (c)	**3.** (c)	**4.** (a)	**5.** (d)	**6.** (b)	**7.** (a)	**8.** (a)	**9.** (d)	**10.** (d)
11. (d)	**12.** (b)	**13.** (d)	**14.** (b)	**15.** (a)	**16.** (b)	**17.** (a)	**18.** (d)	**19.** (c)	**20.** (c)
21. (a)	**22.** (b)	**23.** (c)	**24.** (a)	**25.** (b)					

Hints & Solutions

1. From conservation of momentum

$$MV + (4mv) = 0$$

$$\Rightarrow \quad V = -\frac{4mv}{M}$$

$$= -\frac{4 \times 35 \times 10^{-3} \times 400}{20}$$

$$= -2.8 \text{ ms}^{-1}$$

Force applied on the rifle,

$$F = \frac{MV}{t} = -\frac{20 \times 2.8}{1}$$

$$= -56 \text{ N}$$

2. Horizontal range of the object fired,

$$R = \frac{u^2 \sin 2\theta}{g}$$

At the highest point, when object is exploded into two equal masses, then

$$2mu \cos\theta = m(0) + mv$$

or $\quad v = 2u\cos\theta$

It means, the horizontal velocity becomes double at the highest point, hence it will cover double the distance during the remaining flight.

∴ Total horizontal range of the other part

$$= \frac{R}{2} + R = \frac{3R}{2}$$

$$= \frac{3}{2}\frac{u^2 \sin 2\theta}{g}$$

$$= \frac{3}{2} \times \frac{(100)^2 \times 2\sin\theta\cos\theta}{g}$$

$$= \frac{3}{2} \times \frac{(100)^2 \times 2 \times \frac{3}{5} \times \frac{4}{5}}{10}$$

$$= 1440 \text{ m}$$

3. Man is sliding down the telegraphic pole with acceleration g/4. So,

$$mg - F = \frac{mg}{4}$$

$$\Rightarrow \quad F = mg - \frac{mg}{4}$$

$$\Rightarrow \quad F = \frac{3mg}{4}$$

$$\Rightarrow \quad F = \frac{3w}{4}$$

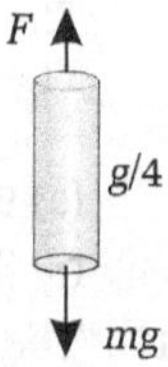

4. Let v be the velocity of the boat with respect to the water, then from conservation of linear momentum.

$$(200 + 50)v + 50 \times 2 = 50 \times 0 + 200 \times 0$$

$$250\,v = -100$$

$$v = -\frac{100}{250} = -\frac{2}{5} \text{ ms}^{-1}$$

5. Work done by the gun

$$= \text{Total kinetic energy of the bullets}$$

$$= n\frac{1}{2}mv^2$$

$$= 240 \times \frac{1}{2} \times 10 \times 10^{-3} (600)^2$$

$$= 120 \times 10 \times 10^{-3} \times 600 \times 600$$

$$\therefore \text{Power of gun} = \frac{\text{work done}}{\text{time taken}}$$

$$= \frac{120 \times 10 \times 10^{-3} \times 600 \times 600}{1 \text{ min}}$$

$$= \frac{120 \times 10 \times 360}{60}$$

$$= 120 \times 10 \times 6 \text{ W}$$

$$= \frac{120 \times 10 \times 6}{1000} \text{ kW}$$

$$= 7.2 \text{ kW}$$

6. Let the change in position of the body due to additional force is x.

So, $\quad F = \frac{1}{2}kx$

$\therefore \quad x = \frac{2F}{k}$

8. Let horizontal acceleration given is a.

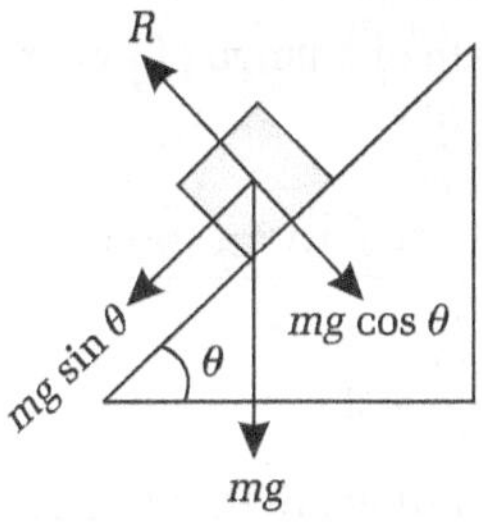

Horizontal force $= m\,a\cos\theta$

$$\therefore \quad ma\cos\theta = mg\sin\theta$$

$$a = g\tan\theta$$

$$= \frac{g}{\sqrt{l^2-1}}$$

9. Here: $w = 64$ N, $\mu_s = 0.6$, $\mu_k = 0.4$

Acceleration of the body $= (\mu_s - \mu_k)g$

$$= (0.6 - 0.4) \times g$$

$$= 0.2\,g \text{ ms}^{-2}$$

10. Initial momentum of the bullet

$$p_1 = n\,m\,v = 200 \times 0.03 \times 50$$

$$= 300 \text{ kg ms}^{-1}$$

Final momentum

$$p_2 = -nmv = -200 \times 0.03 \times 30$$

$$= -180 \text{ kg ms}^{-1}$$

Force acting $= p_2 - p_1 = -180 - (300)$

$$= -480 \text{ N} = 480 \text{ N}$$

11. Force will be same for all the surfaces.

12. Here: $m_1 = 400$ kg,

$$u_1 = 72 \text{ km-h}^{-1} = 72\times\frac{5}{18} = 20 \text{ ms}^{-1}$$

$$m_2 = 4000 \text{ kg},$$

$$u_2 = 9 \text{ km-h}^{-1} = 9\times\frac{5}{18} = 2.5 \text{ ms}^{-1}$$

$$v_1 = -18 \text{ km-h}^{-1} = -18 \times \frac{5}{18} = -5 \text{ ms}^{-1}$$

From law of conservation of momentum total initial momentum = total final momentum

$$\therefore \quad m_1u_1 + m_2u_2 = m_1v_1 + m_2v_2$$

$$400 \times 20 + 4000 \times 2.5 = 400 \times -5 + 400 \times v_2$$

$$8000 + 10000 = -2000 + 4000\,v_2$$

$$v_2 = \frac{20000}{4000}$$

$$= 5 \text{ ms}^{-1}$$

$$= 5\times\frac{18}{5} = 18 \text{ kmh}^{-1}$$

13. The relation $\vec{F} = m\vec{a}$, can only be deduced from Newton's second law, if mass remains constant with time, if mass depends on time then this relation cannot be obtained.

14. If a body is in equilibrium under a set of non-collinear forces, the minimum number of forces has to be three.

15. Apparent weight in a lift moving upwards

$$\omega_1 = 608 \text{ N}$$

$$m(g + a) = 608 \quad \text{...(i)}$$

When lift is moving downwards, then apparent weight = 368 N

$$m(g - a) = 368 \quad \text{...(ii)}$$

From Eqs. (i) and (ii)

$$\frac{m(g+a)}{m(g-a)} = \frac{608}{368}$$

$$\frac{g+a}{g-a} = \frac{38}{23}$$

$$23\,g + 23\,a = 38\,g - 38\,a$$

$$61\,a = 15\,g$$

$$a = \frac{15g}{61} = \frac{15\times10}{61}$$

$$= 2.4 \text{ ms}^{-2}$$

From Eq. (i)

$$m = 49.8 \text{ kg}$$

$\therefore$ Normal weight $= mg = 49.8 \times 10 = 498$ N

16. Here: $m = 10$ kg, $a_1 = 5 \text{ ms}^{-2}$, $F_1 = F$

$a_2 = 18 \text{ ms}^{-2}$, $F_2 = 2F$, $\mu = ?$

Net force on the body $= F - f$

where F = applied force

f = frictional force

From Newton's second law $F - f = ma$

Ist case

$$F_1 - f = ma_1$$

$$F - \mu R = ma_1$$

$$R = \text{normal reaction} = mg$$

$$F - \mu\,mg = ma_1$$

$$F = ma_1 + \mu mg \quad \text{...(i)}$$

$\therefore$ **IInd case** $F_2 - f = ma_2$

$$2F - \mu mg = ma_2$$

$$2F = \mu mg + ma_2 \quad \text{...(ii)}$$

From Eqs. (i) and (ii)

$$2(ma_1 + \mu mg) = \mu mg + ma_2$$

$$\mu mg = ma_2 - 2\,ma_1$$

$$\mu g = a_2 - 2a_1$$
$$\mu \times 10 = 18 - 2 \times 5 = 8$$
$$\Rightarrow \quad \mu = 0.8$$

17. Weight of the body = 50 N

$\therefore$ Normal reaction, $R = 50$ N

Applied force, $F = 30$ N

$\therefore$ Coefficient of friction, $\mu = \dfrac{F}{R} = \dfrac{30}{50} = 0.6$

18. Resultant of two forces

$$R = \sqrt{F_1^2 + F_2^2 + 2F_1 F_2 \cos\theta}$$

Here, $F_1 = F_2 = F$

$\therefore$ Resultant, $R = \sqrt{F^2 + F^2 + 2(F)(F)\cos\theta}$

$$= \sqrt{2F^2 + 2F^2\cos\theta}$$
$$= \sqrt{2F^2(1+\cos\theta)}$$
$$= F\sqrt{2(1+\cos\theta)}$$
$$= F\sqrt{2(1+2\cos^2\theta/2 - 1)}$$
$$= F\sqrt{(4\cos^2\theta/2)}$$
$$= 2F\cos\theta/2$$

19. Here: $m = 300$ kg, $u = 25$ ms^{-1}, $s = 15$ m, $v = 0, F = ?$

From third equation of motion

$$v^2 = u^2 - 2as$$
$$0 = (25)^2 - 2 \times a \times 15$$
$$30a = 625$$
$$a = \frac{625}{30} \text{ ms}^{-2}$$

$\therefore$ Retarding force, $F = ma$

$$= 300 \times \frac{625}{30} = 6250 \text{ N}$$

20. The bullet will hit the target because the vertical velocity of bullet and target will be equal.

21. Let n bullets can be fired per second, from Newton's IInd law

Force = Rate of change of linear momentum

$$180 = \frac{nmv}{t}$$
$$180 = n \times \frac{50 \times 10^{-3} \times 1000}{1}$$
$$n = \frac{180}{50} = 3.6$$

Number of bullets fired per min = 3.6 × 60
= 216

22. We can write the increasing order of magnitudes of static, kinetic and friction coefficients is $\mu_r < \mu_k < \mu_s$.

23. Initial velocity, $v_1 = 10$ ms^{-1}

Final velocity, $v_2 = -10$ ms^{-1}

$\Delta t = 0.01$ s

Mass of ball, $m = 100$ g
$= 100 \times 10^{-3}$ kg
$= 0.1$ kg

Force = Rate of change of momentum

$$= \frac{m(v_1 - v_2)}{\Delta t}$$
$$= 0.1\frac{[10-(-10)]}{0.01}$$
$$= \frac{0.1 \times 20}{0.01}$$
$$= 200 \text{ N}$$

24. Force = rate of change of momentum

$$\frac{\Delta p}{t} = \frac{25}{0.05} = 500 \text{ N}$$

25. In deriving, Newton's formula for velocity of sound, the changes in volume of air are assumed to be isothermal.

Chapter

4

Work, Energy and Power

1. A river of salty water is flowing with a velocity 2 ms^{-1}. If the density of the water is 1.2 g cc^{-1}, then the kinetic energy of each cubic metre of water is **EAMCET | 2008**

(a) 2.4 J (b) 24 J (c) 2.4 kJ (d) 4.8 kJ

2. A ball is dropped from a height h on a floor of coefficient of restitution e. The total distance covered by the ball just before second hit is **EAMCET | 2008**

(a) $h(1 - 2e^2)$ (b) $h(1 + 2e^2)$
(c) $h(1 + e^2)$ (d) he^2

3. A block of mass m = 25 kg sliding on a smooth horizontal surface with a velocity v = 3 ms^{-1} meets the spring of spring constant k = 100 Nm^{-1} fixed at one end as shown in figure. The maximum compression of the spring and velocity of block as it returns to the original position respectively are **EAMCET | 2007**

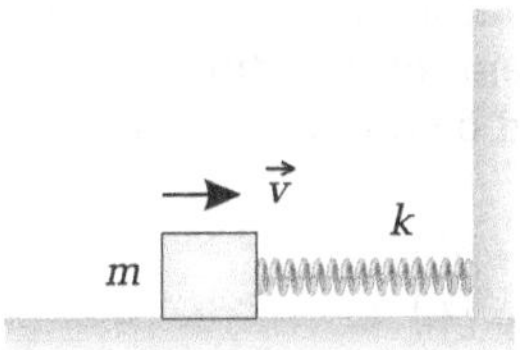

(a) 1.5 m, –3 ms^{-1} (b) 1.5 m, 0.01 ms^{-1}
(c) 1.0 m, 3 ms^{-1} (d) 0.5 m, 2 ms^{-1}

4. In two separate collisions, the coefficient of restitutions e_1 and e_2 are in the ratio 3 : 1. In the first collision the relative velocity of approach is twice the relative velocity of separation, then the ratio between relative velocity of approach and the relative velocity of separation in the second collision is **EAMCET | 2007**

(a) 1 : 6 (b) 2 : 3
(c) 3 : 2 (d) 6 : 1

5. A motor is used to deliver water at a certain rate through a given horizontal pipe. To deliver n-times the water through the same pipe in the same time the power of the motor must be increased as follows **EAMCET | 2006**

(a) n-times (b) n^2-times
(c) n^3-times (d) n^4-times

6. A bullet of mass 10 g is fired horizontally with a velocity 1000 ms^{-1} from a rifle situated at a height 50 m above the ground. If the bullet reaches the ground with a velocity 500 ms^{-1}, the work done against air resistance in the trajectory of the bullet is (g = 10 ms^{-2}) **EAMCET | 2006**

(a) 5005 J (b) 3755 J
(c) 3750 J (d) 17.5 J

7. For a system to follow the law of conservation of linear momentum during a collision, the condition is

(1) total external force acting on the system is zero.
(2) total external force acting on the system is finite and time of collision is negligible.
(3) total internal force acting on the system is zero. **EAMCET | 2006**

(a) (1) only (b) (2) only
(c) (3) only (d) (1) or (2)

8. To the free end of spring hanging from a rigid support, a block of mass m is hung and slowly allowed to come to its equilibrium position. Then, stretching in the spring is d. If the same block is attached to the same spring and allowed to fall suddenly, the amount of stretching is (force constant, k) **EAMCET | 2006**

(a) $\frac{mg}{k}$ (b) 2 d (c) $\frac{mg}{3k}$ (d) 4 d

9. Consider the following statements A and B and identify the correct answer

A. In an elastic collision, if a body suffers a head on collision with another of same mass at rest, the first body comes to rest while the other starts moving with the velocity of the first one.
B. Two bodies of equal mass suffering a head on elastic collision merely exchanges their velocities **EAMCET | 2005**

(a) both A and B are true
(b) both A and B are false
(c) A is true but B is false
(d) A is false but B is true

10. A 2 kg ball moving at 24 ms^{-1} undergoes inelastic head-on collision with a 4 kg ball moving in the opposite direction at 48 ms^{-1}. If the coefficient of restitution is 2/3, their velocities in ms^{-1} after impact are **EAMCET | 2004**

(a) – 56, – 8 (b) – 28, – 4
(c) – 14, – 2 (d) – 7, – 1

11. A block of mass 2 kg is initially at rest on a horizontal frictionless surface. A horizontal force $\vec{F} = (9 - x^2)\hat{i}$ newton acts on it, when the block is at $x = 0$. The maximum kinetic energy of the block between $x = 0$ and $x = 3$m in joule is **EAMCET | 2004**

(a) 24 (b) 20 (c) 18 (d) 15

12. Two identical block A and B, each of mass m resting on smooth floor, are connected by a light spring of natural length L and the spring constant k, with the spring at its natural length. A third identical block C (mass m) moving with a speed v along the line joining A and B collides with A. The maximum compression in the spring is proportional to **EAMCET | 2003**

(a) $\sqrt{\frac{m}{2k}}$ (b) $m\sqrt{\frac{V}{2k}}$

(c) $\sqrt{\frac{mv}{k}}$ (d) $\frac{mv}{2k}$

13. Consider the following statements A and B and identify the correct answer given below

A. A body initially at rest is acted upon by a constant force. The rate of change of its kinetic energy varies linearly with time.

B. When a body is at rest, it must be in equilibrium. **EAMCET | 2003**

(a) A and B are correct
(b) A and B are wrong
(c) A is correct and B is wrong
(d) A is wrong and B is correct

14. Two particles having position vectors $\vec{r}_1 = (3\hat{i} + 5\hat{j})$ m and $\vec{r}_2 = (-5\hat{i} - 3\hat{j})$ m are moving with velocities $\vec{v}_1 = (4\hat{i} + 3\hat{j})$ ms^{-1} and $\vec{v}_2 = (a\hat{i} + 7\hat{j})$ ms^{-1}. If they collide after 2 s, the value of a is **EAMCET | 2003**

(a) 2 (b) 4 (c) 6 (d) 8

15. A body of mass 4 kg is moving with momentum of 8 kg ms^{-1}. A force of 0.2 N acts on it in the direction of motion of the body for 10 s. The increase in kinetic energy in joule is **EAMCET | 2002**

(a) 10 (b) 8.5 (c) 4.5 (d) 4

16. A body is moving up an inclined plane of angle θ with an initial kinetic energy E. The coefficient of friction between the plane and the body is μ. The work done against friction before the body comes to rest is **EAMCET | 2002**

(a) $\frac{\mu\cos\theta}{E\cos\theta + \sin\theta}$ (b) E

(c) $\frac{\mu E\cos\theta}{\mu\cos\theta - \sin\theta}$ (d) $\frac{\mu E\cos\theta}{\mu\cos\theta + \sin\theta}$

17. A body of mass 2 kg starts from rest and moves with uniform acceleration. It acquires a velocity 20 ms^{-1} in 4 s. The power exerted on the body in 2 s in watt is **EAMCET | 2002**

(a) 50 (b) 100 (c) 150 (d) 200

18. A heavy nucleus at rest breaks into two fragments which fly off with velocities in the ratio 3 : 1. The ratio of radii of the fragments is **EAMCET | 2001**

(a) 1 : $3^{1/3}$ (b) $3^{1/3}$: 4
(c) 4 : 1 (d) 2 : 1

19. A particle falls from a height h upon a fixed horizontal plane and rebounds. If e is the coefficient of restitution, the total distance travelled before rebounding has stopped is **EAMCET | 2001**

(a) $h\left(\frac{1+e^2}{1-e^2}\right)$ (b) $h\left(\frac{1-e^2}{1+e^2}\right)$

(c) $\frac{h}{2}\left(\frac{1-e^2}{1+e^2}\right)$ (d) $\frac{h}{2}\left(\frac{1+e^2}{1-e^2}\right)$

20. A body of mass 6 kg is under a force which causes displacement in it given by $s = \frac{t^2}{4}$ metre where t is time. The work done by the force in 2 s is **EAMCET | 2001**

(a) 12 J (b) 9 J (c) 6 J (d) 3 J

21. A force applied by an engine on a train of mass 2.05×10^6 kg changes its velocity from 5 ms^{-1} to 25 ms^{-1} in 5 min. The power of the engine is **EAMCET | 2001**

(a) 1.025 MW (b) 2.05 MW
(c) 5 MW (d) 6 MW

22. A force of 5 N making an angle θ with the horizontal acting on an object displaces it by 0.4 m along the horizontal direction. If the object gains kinetic energy of 1 J the horizontal component of the force is EAMCET | 2000

(a) 1.5 N (b) 2.5 N (c) 3.5 N (d) 4.5 N

23. A body of mass m_1 moving with a velocity 10 ms^{-1} collides with another body at rest of mass m_2. After collision the velocities of the two bodies are 2 ms^{-1} and 5 ms^{-1} respectively, along the direction of motion of m_1. The ratio $\frac{m_1}{m_2}$ is EAMCET | 2000

(a) $\frac{5}{12}$ (b) $\frac{5}{8}$ (c) $\frac{8}{5}$ (d) $\frac{12}{5}$

24. A ball is projected vertically down with an initial velocity from a height of 20 m on to a horizontal floor. During the impact it loses 50% of the energy and rebounds to the same height, the initial velocity of its projection is

EAMCET | 2000

(a) 20 ms^{-1} (b) 15 ms^{-1}

(c) 10 ms^{-1} (d) 5 ms^{-1}

25. A 1.0 HP motor pumps out water from a well of 30 m and fills a water tank of volume 2238 L at a height of 10 m from the ground. The running time of the motor to fill the empty water tank is EAMCET | 2000

(a) 5 min (b) 10 min

(c) 15 min (d) 20 min

26. An object initially at rest explodes into 3 fragments *A*, *B* and *C*. The momentum of *A* of $p\hat{i}$ and that of *B* is $\sqrt{3}p\hat{j}$ where *p* is a positive number. The momentum of *C* will be

EAMCET | 1999

(a) $(1+\sqrt{3})p$ in a direction of making 120° with that of *A*

(b) $(1+\sqrt{3})p$ in a direction of making 150° with that of *B*

(c) 2 *p* in a direction making 150° with that of *A*

(d) 2 *p* in a direction making 150° with that of *B*

27. A ball *A* moving with a speed of 99 ms^{-1} collides directly with another identical ball *B* moving with a speed *v* in the opposite direction, *A* comes to rest after the collision. If the coefficients of restitution is 0.8, the speed of *B* before collision, is EAMCET | 1999

(a) 10 ms^{-1} (b) 81 ms^{-1}

(c) 22.5 ms^{-1} (d) 90 ms^{-1}

28. A mass of 12 kg at rest explodes into two pieces of masses 4 kg and 8 kg which move in opposite directions. If the velocity of 8 kg piece is 6 ms^{-1}, then the kinetic energy of the other piece is (in joule) EAMCET | 1997

(a) 64 (b) 128 (c) 144 (d) 288

29. A force $\vec{F} = 3\hat{i} + c\hat{j} + 2\hat{k}$ acting on a particle causes a displacement $\vec{s} = -4\hat{i} + 2\hat{j} + 3\hat{k}$ in its own direction. If the work done is 6 J, the value of *c* is EAMCET | 1997

(a) zero (b) 1 (c) 12 (d) 6

30. A solid wooden block resting on a frictionless surface is hit by a bullet. The bullet gets embedded. During this process

EAMCET | 1996

(a) only kinetic energy is conversed

(b) only momentum is conserved

(c) both momentum and kinetic energy are conserved

(d) neither momentum nor kinetic energy is conserved

31. Two bodies with kinetic energies in the ratio of 4 : 1 are moving with equal linear momentum. The ratio of their masses is EAMCET | 1996

(a) 1 : 2 (b) 1 : 1

(c) 4 : 1 (d) 1 : 4

32. A uniform chain of length *L* hangs partially from table and held in equilibrium by friction. If greatest length of chain that hangs without slipping is *l* then the coefficient of friction between chain and table is EAMCET | 1995

(a) $\frac{l}{2}$ (b) $\frac{l}{L+l}$ (c) $\frac{l}{L-l}$ (d) $\frac{l}{L+1}$

33. At high altitude, a body explodes at rest into two equal fragments with one of the fragments receiving horizontal velocity 10 ms^{-1}. The time when the radius vectors connecting point of explosion to fragments make 90° is ($g = 10\ ms^{-2}$)

EAMCET | 1995

(a) 10 s (b) 4 s (c) 2 s (d) 1 s

34. Two bodies have masses 2*m* and *m*. Their kinetic energies are in the ratio 8 : 1, their linear momentum are in the ratio of

EAMCET | 1995

(a) 1 : 1 (b) 2 : 1 (c) 4 : 1 (d) 8 : 1

35. Two trolleys of masses *m* and 3*m* are connected by a spring. The spring is compressed and released the trolleys move off in opposite directions and come to rest after travelling distances s_1 and s_2 respectively. Assuming coefficient of friction is same for both the ratio of s_1 to s_2 is **EAMCET | 1995**

(a) 1 : 9 (b) 1 : 3 (c) 3 : 1 (d) 9 : 1

36. A 2 kg mass moving on a smooth frictionless surface with a velocity of 10 ms^{-1}, hits another 2 kg mass kept at rest in an elastic collision. After collision, if they move together **EAMCET | 1994**

(a) they travel with a velocity of 5 ms^{-1} in the same direction

(b) they travel with a velocity of 10 ms^{-1} in the same direction

(c) they travel with a velocity of 10 ms^{-1} in the opposite direction

(d) they travel in the opposite direction with a velocity of 5 ms^{-1}

37. A 2 kg body and 3 kg body have equal momentum. If the kinetic energy of 3 kg body is 10 J, the kinetic energy of 2 kg body will be, (in joule) **EAMCET | 1993**

(a) 6.66 (b) 15 (c) 22.5 (d) 45

38. A bullet of mass x moves with a velocity y, hits a wooden block of mass z, at rest and gets embedded in it. After collision, if the wooden block with bullet in it moves, the velocity is **EAMCET | 1993**

(a) $\frac{x}{x+z}y$ (b) $\frac{x+z}{x}y$

(c) $\frac{z}{x+y}y$ (d) $\frac{x+y}{z}y$

39. A ball of mass m moving with a velocity $\vec{v}$ collides head on elastically with another of the same mass m but moving with a $-\vec{v}$ (in the opposite direction). After the collision **EAMCET | 1992**

(a) the velocities are exchanged between the two balls

(b) both the balls come to rest

(c) both of them move at right angles to the original line of motion

(d) one ball comes to rest and the other ball travels back with velocity $2v$

40. The work done on a particle moving round a horizontal circular path of radius r with uniform speed v under a centripetal force F is equal to **EAMCET | 1992**

(a) mvr (b) 0 (c) $m\omega r^2$ (d) $\frac{mv^2}{r}$

41. A railway truck of mass $m = 2 \times 10^4$ kg travelling at 0.5 ms^{-1} collides with another of half of its mass moving in opposite direction with a velocity 0.4 ms^{-1}. If they collide each other the combined velocity is **EAMCET | 1991**

(a) 0.1 ms^{-1} (b) 0.4 ms^{-1}

(c) 0.2 ms^{-1} (d) 0.5 ms^{-1}

42. A particle of mass 4 m which is at rest explodes into three fragments. Two of the fragments each of mass m are found to move with a speed of v each in mutually perpendicular direction. The total energy released in the process is **EAMCET | 1991**

(a) $\frac{1}{2}mv^2$ (b) mv^2

(c) $\frac{5}{3}mv^2$ (d) $\frac{3}{2}mv^2$

Answers

1.	(c)	2.	(b)	3.	(a)	4.	(d)	5.	(c)	6.	(c)	7.	(a)	8.	(b)	9.	(a)	10.	(a)
11.	(c)	12.	(a)	13.	(c)	14.	(d)	15.	(c)	16.	(b)	17.	(b)	18.	(a)	19.	(a)	20.	(d)
21.	(b)	22.	(b)	23.	(b)	24.	(a)	25.	(d)	26.	(d)	27.	(a)	28.	(d)	29.	(d)	30.	(b)
31.	(d)	32.	(c)	33.	(d)	34.	(c)	35.	(c)	36.	(a)	37.	(b)	38.	(a)	39.	(a)	40.	(b)
41.	(c)	42.	(d)																

Hints & Solutions

1. Given, velocity of river, $v = 2\ ms^{-1}$

Density of water, $\rho = 1.2\ g\ cc^{-1}$

Mass of each cubic metre

$$m = \frac{1.2\times10^{-3}}{(10^{-2})^3} = 1.2\times10^3\ kg$$

$\therefore$ Kinetic energy $= \frac{1}{2}mv^2$

$$= \frac{1}{2}\times1.2\times10^3\times(2)^2$$

$$= 2.4\times10^3\ J = 2.4\ kJ$$

2.

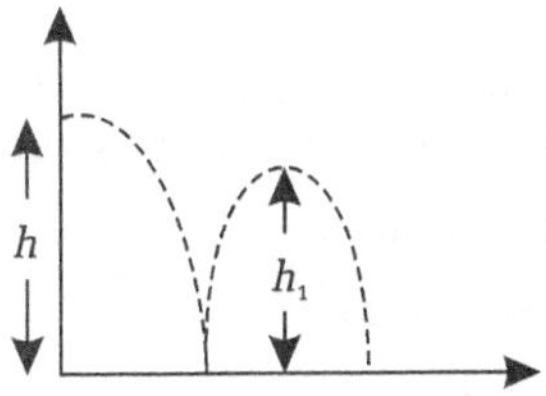

Total distance travelled by the ball before its second hit is

$$H = h + 2h_1$$

$$= h[1 + 2e^2] \qquad [\because h_1 = he^2]$$

3. When block strikes the spring, the kinetic energy of block converts into potential energy of spring, *i.e.*,

$$\frac{1}{2}mv^2 = \frac{1}{2}kx^2$$

where x is compression in spring.

$$\Rightarrow \quad x = \sqrt{\frac{mv^2}{k}}$$

$$= \sqrt{\frac{25\times(3)^2}{100}} = \sqrt{\frac{9}{4}} = \frac{3}{2} = 1.5\ m$$

When block returns to the original position, again potential energy converts into kinetic energy of the block, so velocity of the block is same as before but its sign changes as it goes to mean position.

Hence, $v = -3\ ms^{-1}$

4. Coefficient of restitution is given by

$$e = \frac{\text{relative velocity of separation}}{\text{relative velocity of approach}}$$

we have

$$e_1 = \frac{1}{2}$$

and $$e_2 = \left(\frac{\text{relative velocity of separation}}{\text{relative velocity of approach}}\right)_2$$

Given, $$\frac{e_1}{e_2} = \frac{3}{1}$$

$$\Rightarrow \quad \frac{e_2}{e_1} = \frac{1}{3}$$

$$\Rightarrow \left(\frac{\text{relative velocity of separation}}{\text{relative velocity of approach}}\right)_2 = \frac{1}{3}\times\frac{1}{2}$$

$$= \frac{1}{6}$$

$$\Rightarrow \left(\frac{\text{relative velocity of approach}}{\text{relative velocity of separation}}\right)_2 = \frac{6}{1}$$

5. If the motor pumps water (density $= \rho$) continuously through a pipe of area of cross-section A with velocity v, then mass flowing out per second,

$$m = A\,v\,\rho \qquad ...(i)$$

Rate of increase of kinetic energy

$$= \frac{1}{2}mv^2 = \frac{1}{2}(A\,v\,\rho)v^2 \qquad ...(ii)$$

Mass m, flowing out per sec, can be increased to m' by increasing v to v', then power increases from P to P'.

$$\frac{P'}{P} = \frac{\frac{1}{2}A\rho v'^3}{\frac{1}{2}A\rho v^3}$$

or $$\frac{P'}{P} = \left(\frac{v'}{v}\right)^3$$

Now, $$\frac{m'}{m} = \frac{A\rho v'}{A\rho v} = \frac{v'}{v}$$

As $m' = nm,\ v' = nv$

$$\therefore \quad \frac{P'}{P} = n^3$$

$$\Rightarrow \quad P' = n^3P$$

6. From equation of motion,

$$v^2 = u^2 - 2\,a\,s$$

$$(500)^2 = (1000)^2 - 2\times a\times s$$

$$s = \frac{(1000)^2-(500)^2}{2\,a} = \frac{375000}{a}$$

$\therefore$ Work done against air resistance

$$= Fs$$

$$= ma\times s$$

$$= \frac{10}{1000}a\times\frac{375000}{a}$$

$$= 3750\ J$$

7. From Newton's second law,

$$F = \frac{dp}{dt}$$

If $\quad F = 0$, then $\frac{dp}{dt} = 0$

$\Rightarrow \quad p = \text{constant}.$

Thus, if total external force acting on the system is zero, then linear momentum of the system remains conserved.

8. To leave the block, it oscillates in vertical plane. If maximum extension in spring in extreme position of block is x_1, then

Work done by weight of the block

= potential energy stored in spring

$$mg\,x = \frac{1}{2}k\,x^2$$

$$\therefore \quad x = 2\frac{mg}{k} = 2\,d \qquad \left(\because d = \frac{mg}{k}\right)$$

9. Both statements A and B given in the system are true.

10.
$$v_1' = \left[\frac{m_1 - em_2}{m_1 + m_2}\right]v_1 - \left[\frac{(1+e)m_2}{m_1+m_2}\right]v_2$$

$$= \left[\frac{2-\left(\frac{2}{3}\right)4}{2+4}\right]24 - \left[\frac{\left(1+\frac{2}{3}\right)4}{2+4}\right]48$$

$$= -56\,\text{ms}^{-1}$$

and
$$v_2' = \left[\frac{(1+e)m_1}{m_1+m_2}\right]v_1 - \left[\frac{m_2 - em_1}{m_1+m_2}\right]v_2$$

$$= \left[\frac{\left(1+\frac{2}{3}\right)2}{2+4}\right]24 - \left[\frac{4-\left(\frac{2}{3}\right)2}{2+4}\right]48$$

$$= -8\,\text{ms}^{-1}$$

11.
$$\text{KE} = \int F dx$$

$$\text{KE} = \int_{x=0}^{x=3}(9-x^2)dx$$

$$= 9\int_{x=0}^{x=3}dx - \int_{x=0}^{x=3}x^2dx$$

$$= 9[x]_0^3 - \left[\frac{x^3}{3}\right]_0^3$$

$$= 27 - 9 = 18\text{ J}$$

12.
$$T = 2\pi\sqrt{\frac{m}{2k}}$$

Compression, $x = vT = v \times 2\pi\sqrt{\frac{m}{2k}}$

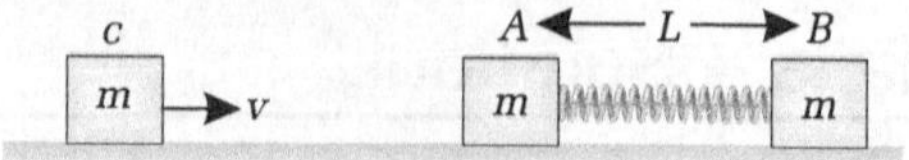

$$\therefore \quad x \propto \sqrt{\frac{m}{2k}}$$

13. $\text{KE} = \frac{1}{2}mv^2 = \frac{1}{2}m\,(at)^2 = \frac{1}{2}m\,a^2t^2$

Rate of change of KE,

$$\frac{dk}{dt} = \frac{d}{dt}\left(\frac{1}{2}ma^2\,t^2\right) = m\,a^2\,t$$

$$\therefore \quad \frac{dk}{dt} \propto t$$

So, statement A is correct.

When the body is at rest then it may be or may not be in equilibrium, so statement B is wrong.

14. Here: $\vec{r}_1 = (3\hat{i}+5\hat{j})$ m

$\vec{r}_2 = (-5\hat{i}-3\hat{j})$ m

$\vec{v}_1 = (4\hat{i}+3\hat{j})\ \text{ms}^{-1}$,

$\vec{v}_2 = (a\hat{i}+7\hat{j})\ \text{ms}^{-1}$

Time taken in collision, $t = \frac{r}{v}$

where $\quad r$ = resultant position vector

$= \vec{r}_1 - \vec{r}_2$

$= 8\hat{i}+8\hat{j}$

v = resultant velocity

$$\vec{v}_2 - \vec{v}_1 = (a-4)\hat{i}+4\hat{j}$$

$$\therefore \quad 2 = \frac{8\hat{i}+8\hat{j}}{(a-4)\hat{i}+4\hat{j}}$$

$$(a-4)\hat{i}+4\hat{j} = 4\hat{i}+4\hat{j}$$

$$a - 4 = 4$$

$$a = 8$$

15. Here: $\quad m = 4$ kg, p = kg ms^{-1},

$F = 0.2$ N, $t = 10$ s

From Newton's IInd law

Force = rate of change of momentum

$$F = \frac{p_2 - p_1}{t}$$

$$0.2 = \frac{mv-}{10}$$

$$2 = 4 \times v - 8$$

$$4\,v = 10$$

$$\Rightarrow \quad v = \frac{5}{2}\ \text{ms}^{-1}$$

$\therefore$ Final momentum $p_2 = mv = 4 \times \frac{5}{2}$

$= 10 \text{ kg ms}^{-1}$

Increase in KE $= \frac{p_2^2 - p_1^2}{2m}$

$= \frac{(10)^2 - (8)^2}{2 \times 4}$

$= \frac{100 - 64}{8} = \frac{36}{8}$

$= 4.5 \text{ J}$

16. Acceleration of a body up a rough inclined plane

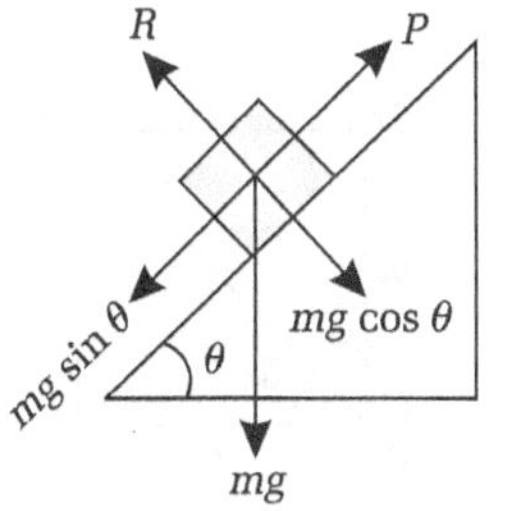

$a = g(\mu \cos\theta + \sin\theta)$

From equation of motion

$v^2 = u^2 - 2as$

$0 = u^2 - 2as$

$u^2 = 2as$

Initial KE, $E = \frac{1}{2} m u^2$

$E = \frac{1}{2} m (2as)$

$s = \frac{E}{ma}$

Work done, $W = F \cdot s$

$= (mg \sin\theta + \mu R) \cdot \frac{E}{ma}$

$= (mg \sin\theta + \mu\, m\, g \cos\theta) \cdot \frac{E}{m(\mu \cos\theta + \sin\theta)}$

$= g(\sin\theta + \mu \cos\theta) \cdot \frac{E}{g(\mu \cos\theta + \sin\theta)}$

$= E$

17. Here: $m = 2$ kg, $u = 0$, $v = 20 \text{ ms}^{-1}$, $t = 4$ s

Acceleration, $a = \frac{v - u}{t} = \frac{20 - 0}{4} = 5 \text{ ms}^{-2}$

$\therefore$ Force applied, $F = m\,a = 2 \times 5 = 10$ N

Velocity at the end of 2 s

$v = u + a\,t = 0 + 5 \times 2$

$= 10 \text{ ms}^{-1}$

$\therefore$ Power, $P = Fv = 10 \times 10 = 100$ W

18. From law of conservation of momentum

$m\,v = \text{constant}$

$V \rho\, v = k$

$\frac{4}{3}\pi R^3 \rho v = k$

$\left(\frac{R_1}{R_2}\right)^3 = \frac{v_2}{v_1}$

$\Rightarrow \quad \frac{R_1}{R_2} = \left(\frac{v_2}{v_1}\right)^{1/3} = \left(\frac{1}{3}\right)^{1/3}$

$= 1 : 3^{1/3}$

20. Work done, $W = \text{Force} \times \text{displacement}$

$= m\,a \times s$

Displacement, $s = \frac{t^2}{4}$

Acceleration, $a = \frac{dv}{dt} = \frac{d}{dt}\left(\frac{ds}{dt}\right)$

$= \frac{d}{dt}\left[\frac{d}{dt}\left(\frac{t^2}{4}\right)\right]$

$= \frac{d}{dt}\left(\frac{2t}{4}\right) = \frac{1}{2}$

$\therefore \quad W = 6 \times \frac{1}{2} \times \frac{t^2}{4} = \frac{3}{4}t^2 = \frac{3}{4}(2)^2$

$= \frac{3}{4} \times 4 = 3 \text{ J}$

21. $m = 2.05 \times 10^6$ kg, $v_1 = 5 \text{ ms}^{-1}$

$v_2 = 25 \text{ ms}^{-1}$, $t = 5$ min

$= 5 \times 60 = 300$ s

Power $= \frac{W}{t} = \frac{\text{change in KE}}{t}$

$= \frac{1}{2} \frac{m(v_2^2 - v_1^2)}{300}$

$= \frac{1}{2} \times \frac{2.05 \times 10^6 [(25)^2 - (5)^2]}{300}$

$= \frac{1}{2} \times \frac{2.05 \times 10^6 \times 600}{300}$

$= 2.05 \times 10^6$ W

$= 2.05$ MW

22. Work done by the force

$W = F s \cos\theta$

$= 5 \times 0.4 \cos\theta = 2\cos\theta$

From work energy theorem

work done = change in kinetic energy

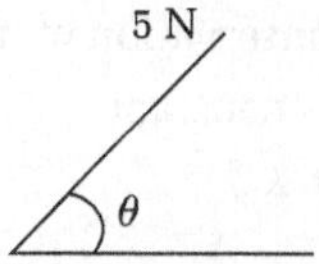

$2 \cos\theta = 1$ J

$\cos\theta = \frac{1}{2}$

∴ Horizontal component

$= F\cos\theta = 5 \times \frac{1}{2} = 2.5$ N

23. From law of conservation of linear momentum
Total initial momentum
= total final momentum

$$m_1 u_1 + m_2 u_2 = m_1 v_1 + m_2 v_2$$
$$m_1 \times 10 + m_2 \times 0 = m_1 \times 2 + m_2 \times 5$$
$$10\, m_1 = 2\, m_1 + 5\, m_2$$
$$8\, m_1 = 5\, m_2$$
$$\frac{m_1}{m_2} = \frac{5}{8}$$

24. Final velocity, $v^2 = u^2 + 2\,g\,h$

$$= u^2 + 2\,g\,(20)$$
$$v = \sqrt{u^2 + 40\,g}$$

Loss in energy = 50%

Remaining energy = (100 – 50)

= 50% of initial energy

$= \frac{1}{2}$ of initial energy

$$= \frac{1}{2}\left(\frac{1}{2} m\, v^2\right)$$
$$= \frac{1}{4} m \times (u^2 + 50g)$$

The ball rebounds to same height.

$$\therefore \text{ Remaining energy} = \frac{1}{2} m v'^2 = \frac{1}{2} m(2\,g\,h)$$
$$= m\,g\,h$$
$$\therefore \quad m\,g\,h = \frac{1}{4} m(u^2 + 40\,g)$$
$$m\,g\,(20) = \frac{1}{4} m(u^2 + 40\,g)$$
$$80\,g - 40\,g = u^2$$
$$u = \sqrt{40\,g}$$
$$u = \sqrt{40 \times 10} = 20 \text{ ms}^{-1}$$

25. Here: $P = 1$ HP = 746 W,
$V = 2238$ L,
$h_1 = 30$ m, $h_2 = 10$ m.

$\therefore\ m = V\rho = 2238 \times 1 = 2238$ kg

Total height lift by the pump

$= h_1 + h_2 = 30 + 10 = 40$ m

Power, $P = \frac{m\,g\,h}{t}$

$$\Rightarrow \quad t = \frac{m\,g\,h}{P} = \frac{2238 \times 10 \times 40}{746}$$
$$= 1200 \text{ s}$$
$$= \frac{1200}{60} = 20 \text{ min}$$

26. Momentum of $A = p_A = p\hat{i}$

Momentum of $B = p_B = \sqrt{3}p\hat{j}$

i.e., $p_A \perp p_B$

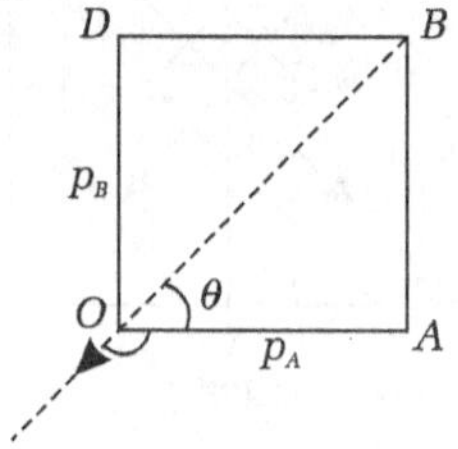

Momentum of C will equal and opposite to the resultant of p_A and p_B

Resultant of p_A and $p_B = \sqrt{p_A^2 + p_B^2}$

$$= \sqrt{p^2 + 3p^2}$$
$$= 2\,p$$

Angle between p_A and p_B

$$\theta = \tan^{-1}\frac{p_B}{p_A} = \tan^{-1}\frac{\sqrt{3}p}{p} = 60^\circ$$

∴ Third part will move with a momentum $2\,p$ and $(180 - 60 + 30) = 150^\circ$ from the direction of B.

27. Coefficient of restitution $e = \frac{v_2 - v_1}{u_1 - u_2}$

Here: $u_1 = 90$ ms^{-1}, $u_2 = -v$

$v_1 = 0$

$$\therefore \quad 0.8 = \frac{v_2 - 0}{90 - (-v)}$$
$$0.8 = \frac{v_2 - 0}{90 + v}$$
$$90 + v = \frac{v_2}{0.8} \qquad \text{...(i)}$$

Applying law of conservation of linear momentum

$$m_1 u_1 + m_2 u_2 = m_1 v_1 + m_2 v_2$$
$$m \times 90 + m(-v) = m \times 0 + m v_2$$
$$90 - v = v_2$$

From Eq. (i)

$$90 + v = \frac{90 - v}{0.8}$$

$$72 + 0.8\,v = 90 - v$$

$$1.8\,v = 18$$

$$v = 10\text{ ms}^{-1}$$

28. From law of conservation of momentum

Initial momentum = Final momentum

$$Mv = m_1v_1 + m_2v_2$$

$$12 \times 0 = 8 \times 6 + 4\,(-v)$$

$$\Rightarrow \quad 4v = 48$$

$$\Rightarrow \quad v = 12\text{ ms}^{-1}$$

$\therefore$ KE of other piece $= \frac{1}{2}m_2v^2$

$$= \frac{1}{2} \times 4 \times (12)^2$$

$$= 2 \times 144 = 288\text{ J}$$

29. Force, $\vec{F} = 3\hat{i} + c\hat{j} + 2\hat{k}$

Displacement, $\vec{s} = -4\hat{i} + 2\hat{j} + 3\hat{k}$

Work done, $W = \vec{F} \cdot \vec{s}$

$$6 = (3\hat{i} + c\hat{j} + 2\hat{k}) \cdot (-4\hat{i} + 2\hat{j} + 3\hat{k})$$

$$= (3 \times -4) + (c \times 2) + (2 \times 3)$$

$$6 = -12 + 2c + 6$$

$$6 = -6 + 2c$$

$$\Rightarrow \quad 2c = 12$$

$$c = 6$$

30. The bullet gets embedded in the block, so the collision is inelastic, therefore only momentum will remain conserve.

31. Ratio of kinetic energies

$$K_1 : K_2 = 4 : 1$$

Kinetic energy, $K = \frac{p^2}{2\,m}$

where p = momentum of the body

Both bodies are moving with equal momentum, so

$$K \propto \frac{1}{m}$$

$$\frac{K_1}{K_2} = \frac{m_2}{m_1}$$

or $\frac{m_1}{m_2} = \frac{K_2}{K_1}$

$\therefore \quad m_1 : m_2 = 1 : 4$

32. Let mass per unit length of the chain is m.

Then, mass of whole chain $= Lm$

Mass of hanging part $= lm$

Mass of part of chain which is kept on table $= (L - l)m$

Force will be applied by the hanging part.

$\therefore \quad F = l\,m\,g$

Coefficient of friction, $\mu = \frac{F}{R}$

R = normal reaction of the table

= weight of part of the chain kept on the table

$= (L - l)\,m\,g$

$$\therefore \quad \mu = \frac{l\,m\,g}{(L - l)\,m\,g} = \frac{l}{(L - l)}$$

33. The radius vector makes 90° *i.e.*, the motion is vertical, so initial horizontal velocity of the body will zero. Initial velocity of body, $u = 0$

final velocity, $v = 10\text{ ms}^{-1}$

$$v = u + g\,t$$

$$10 = 0 + 10\,t$$

$$t = \frac{10}{10} = 1\text{ s}$$

34. $m_1 = 2\,m,\ m_2 = m$

Ratio of kinetic energies, $K_1 : K_2 = 8 : 1$

Linear momentum $p = \sqrt{2\,m\,K}$

$$\therefore \quad \frac{p_1}{p_2} = \sqrt{\frac{m_1}{m_2} \cdot \frac{K_1}{K_2}}$$

$$= \sqrt{\frac{2m}{m} \times \frac{8}{1}} = \sqrt{\frac{16}{1}}$$

$$= \frac{4}{1}$$

$\therefore \quad p_1 : p_2 = 4 : 1$

35. Work done by a body on a horizontal rough surface

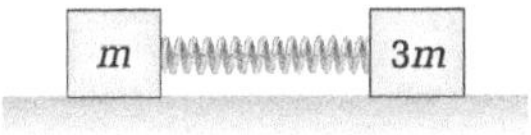

$$w = \mu\,m\,g\,s$$

For first body, $w = \mu\,m\,g\,s_1$

For second body, $w = \mu\,(3\,m)g\,s_2$

$$\therefore \quad \mu\,m\,g\,s_1 = \mu\,(3\,m)g\,s_2$$

$$\frac{s_1}{s_2} = \frac{3}{1}$$

$$\Rightarrow \quad s_1 : s_2 = 3 : 1$$

36. From law of conservation of linear momentum

$$m_1u_1 + m_2u_2 = (m_1 + m_2)\,v$$

$$2 \times 10 + 2 \times 0 = (2 + 2)v$$

$$v = \frac{2 \times 10}{4} = 5 \text{ ms}^{-1}$$

i.e., they travel with velocity 5 ms^{-1} in same direction.

37. Kinetic energy of a body, $KE = \frac{p^2}{2m}$

where p = momentum of the body.

Here the momentum is kept same, so

$$(KE) \propto \frac{1}{m}$$

$$\frac{(KE)_1}{(KE)_2} = \frac{m_2}{m_1}$$

$$\frac{10}{(KE)_2} = \frac{2}{3}$$

$$(KE)_2 = \frac{10 \times 3}{2} = 15 \text{ J}$$

38. From law of conservation of linear momentum

$$m_1u_1 + m_2u_2 = (m_1 + m_2)\,v$$

$$x \times y + z \times 0 = (x + z)v$$

$$\therefore \quad v = \frac{xy}{(x+z)}$$

39. When two bodies of same mass suffer elastic collision, then their velocities are exchanged between them.

41. Here: $m_1 = 2 \times 10^4$ kg, $m_2 = \frac{m_1}{2} = 1 \times 10^4$ kg

$u_1 = 0.5 \text{ ms}^{-1}$, $u_2 = -0.4 \text{ ms}^{-1}$

Combined velocity, v = ?

From law of conservation of linear momentum.

Total initial momentum

= total final momentum

$$m_1u_1 + m_2u_2 = (m_1 + m_2)\,v$$

$$2 \times 10^4 \times 0.5 + (1 \times 10^4)(-0.4) = (2 \times 10^4 + 1 \times 10^4)\,v$$

$$0.6 \times 10^4 = 3 \times 10^4\,v$$

$$v = 0.2 \text{ ms}^{-1}$$

42. From law of conservation of momentum

Momentum of third fragment = Resultant momentum of two mutually perpendicular fragments

$$p_3 = \sqrt{p_1^2 + p_2^2}$$

$$(4m - m - m)\,v' = \sqrt{(mv)^2 + (mv)^2}$$

$$2\,mv' = mv\sqrt{2}$$

$$v' = \frac{v\sqrt{2}}{2}$$

Energy released

$$= \frac{1}{2}mv^2 + \frac{1}{2}mv^2 + \frac{1}{2}(2m)v'^2$$

$$= mv^2 + m\left(\frac{v\sqrt{2}}{2}\right)^2$$

$$= mv^2 + m\left(\frac{2v^2}{4}\right)$$

$$= mv^2 + \frac{mv^2}{2} = \frac{3}{2}mv^2$$

Chapter

5

Rotational Motion

1. Two particles A and B initially at rest, move towards each other, under mutual force of attraction. At an instance when the speed of A is v and speed of B is $2v$, the speed of centre of mass (CM) is **EAMCET | 2008**

(a) zero (b) v (c) $2.5v$ (d) $4v$

2. Starting from rest, the time taken by a body sliding down on a rough inclined plane at 45° with the horizontal is, twice the time taken to travel on a smooth plane of same inclination and same distance. Then, the coefficient of kinetic friction is **EAMCET | 2008**

(a) 0.25 (b) 0.33 (c) 0.50 (d) 0.75

3. The moment of inertia of a thin circular disc about an axis passing through its centre and perpendicular to its plane is I. Then, the moment of inertia of the disc about an axis parallel to its diameter and touching the edge of the rim is **EAMCET | 2008**

(a) I (b) $2I$ (c) $\frac{3}{2}I$ (d) $\frac{5}{2}I$

4. Two bodies of 6 kg and 4 kg masses have their velocity $5\hat{i}-2\hat{j}+10\hat{k}$ and $10\hat{i}-2\hat{j}+5\hat{k}$ respectively. Then, the velocity of their centre of mass is **EAMCET | 2007**

(a) $5\hat{i}+2\hat{j}-8\hat{k}$ (b) $7\hat{i}+2\hat{j}-8\hat{k}$

(c) $7\hat{i}-2\hat{j}+8\hat{k}$ (d) $5\hat{i}-2\hat{j}+8\hat{k}$

5. Two solid spheres (A and B) are made of metals of different densities ρ_A and ρ_B respectively. If their masses are equal, the ratio of their moments of inertia (I_A/I_B) about their respective diameter is **EAMCET | 2007**

(a) $\left(\frac{\rho_B}{\rho_A}\right)^{2/3}$ (b) $\left(\frac{\rho_A}{\rho_B}\right)^{2/3}$

(c) $\frac{\rho_A}{\rho_B}$ (d) $\frac{\rho_B}{\rho_A}$

6. When the angle of inclination of an inclined plane is θ, an object slides down with uniform velocity. If the same object is pushed up with a initial velocity u on the same inclined plane; it goes up the plane and stops at a certain distance on the plane. Thereafter the body **EAMCET | 2006**

(a) slides down the inclined plane and reaches the ground with velocity u.

(b) slides down the inclined plane and reaches the ground with velocity less than u.

(c) slides down the inclined pane and reaches the ground with velocity greater than u.

(d) stays at rest on the inclined plane and will not slide down.

7. A uniform rod of length $8a$ and mass $6m$ lies on a smooth horizontal surface. Two point masses m and $2m$ moving in the same plane with speed $2v$ and v respectively strike the rod perpendicular at distances a and $2a$ from the mid point of the rod in the opposite directions and stick to the rod. The angular velocity of the system immediately after the collision is **EAMCET | 2006**

(a) $\frac{6v}{32a}$ (b) $\frac{6v}{33a}$

(c) $\frac{6v}{40a}$ (d) $\frac{6v}{41a}$

8. Assume the earth's orbit around the sun as circular and the distance between their centres as D. Mass of the earth is M and its radius is R. If earth has an angular velocity ω_0 with respect to its centre and ω with respect to the centre of the sun, the total kinetic energy of earth is **EAMCET | 2006**

(a) $\frac{MR^2\omega_0^2}{5}\left[1+\left(\frac{\omega}{\omega_0}\right)^2+\frac{5}{2}\left(\frac{D\omega}{R\omega_0}\right)^2\right]$

(b) $\frac{MR^2\omega_0^2}{5}\left[1+\frac{5}{2}\left(\frac{D\omega}{R\omega_0}\right)^2\right]$

(c) $\frac{2}{5}MR^2\omega_0^2\left[1+\frac{5}{2}\left(\frac{D\omega}{R\omega_0}\right)^2\right]$

(d) $\frac{2}{5}MR^2\omega_0^2\left[1+\left(\frac{\omega}{\omega_0}\right)^2+\frac{5}{2}\left(\frac{D\omega}{R\omega_0}\right)^2\right]$

9. The centre of mass of three particles of masses 1 kg, 2 kg and 3 kg is at (2, 2, 2). The position of the fourth mass of 4 kg to be placed in the system as that the new centre of mass is at (0, 0, 0) is **EAMCET | 2005**

(a) (– 3, – 3, – 3) (b) (– 3, 3, – 3)
(c) (2, 3, – 3) (d) (2, – 2, 3)

10. The minimum force required to move a body up an inclined plane is three times the minimum force required to prevent it from sliding down the plane. If the coefficient of friction between the body and the inclined plane is $\frac{1}{2\sqrt{3}}$, the angle of the inclined plane is **EAMCET | 2005**

(a) 60° (b) 45° (c) 30° (d) 15°

11. The instantaneous velocity of a point B of the given rod of length 0.5 m is 3 ms^{-1} in the represented direction. The angular velocity of the rod for minimum velocity of end A is **EAMCET | 2005**

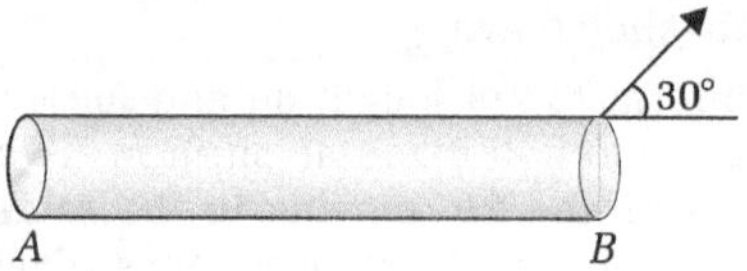

(a) 1.5 rads^{-1} (b) 5.2 rads^{-1}
(c) 2.5 rads^{-1} (d) None of these

12. Identify the increasing order of the angular velocities of the following **EAMCET | 2005**

1. Earth rotating about its own axis
2. Hour's hand of a clock
3. Second's hand of a clock
4. Flywheel of radius 2 m making 300 rpm

(a) 1, 2, 3, 4 (b) 2, 3, 4, 1
(c) 3, 4, 1, 2 (d) 4, 1, 2, 3

13. Two particles of equal mass have velocities $\vec{v}_1 = 4\hat{i}$ ms^{-1} and $\vec{v}_2 = 4\hat{j}$ ms^{-1}. First particle has an acceleration $\vec{a}_1 = (5\hat{i} + 5\hat{j})$ ms^{-2} while the acceleration of the other particle is zero. The centre of mass of the two particles moves in a path of **EAMCET | 2004**

(a) straight line (b) parabola
(c) circle (d) ellipse

14. A thin uniform square lamina of side a is placed in the xy-plane with its sides parallel to x and y-axes and with its centre coinciding with origin. Its moment of inertia about an axis passing through a point on the y-axis at a distance $y = 2a$ and parallel to x-axis is equal to its moment of inertia about an axis passing through a point on the x-axis at a distance $x = d$ and perpendicular to xy-plane. Then, value of d is **EAMCET | 2004**

(a) $\frac{7}{3}a$ (b) $\sqrt{\frac{47}{12}}\,a$ (c) $\frac{9}{5}a$ (d) $\sqrt{\frac{51}{12}}\,a$

15. A particle of mass 1 kg is projected with an initial velocity 10 ms^{-1} at an angle of projection 45° with the horizontal. The average torque acting on the projectile, between the time at which it is projected and the time at which it strikes the ground, about the point of projection in newton-metre is **EAMCET | 2004**

(a) 25 (b) 50 (c) 75 (d) 100

16. Two objects of masses 200 g and 500 g possess velocities $10\hat{i}$ ms^{-1} and $3\hat{i} + 5\hat{j}$ ms^{-1} respectively. The velocity of their centre of mass in ms^{-1} is **EAMCET | 2003**

(a) $5\hat{i} - 25\hat{j}$ (b) $\frac{5}{7}\hat{i} - 25\hat{j}$
(c) $5\hat{i} + \frac{25}{7}\hat{j}$ (d) $25\hat{i} - \frac{5}{7}\hat{j}$

17. The moment of inertia of a meter scale of mass 0.6 kg about an axis perpendicular to the scale and located at the 20 cm position on the scale in kg-m^2 is (Breadth of the scale is negligible) **EAMCET | 2003**

(a) 0.078 (b) 0.104
(c) 0.148 (d) 0.208

18. A circular disc of radius R and thickness $\frac{R}{6}$ has moment of inertia I about an axis passing through its centre and perpendicular to its plane. It is melted and recasted into a solid sphere. The moment of inertia of the sphere about its diameter as axis of rotation is **EAMCET | 2003**

(a) I (b) $\frac{2I}{3}$ (c) $\frac{I}{5}$ (d) $\frac{I}{10}$

19. If A is the areal velocity of a planet of mass M, its angular momentum is **EAMCET | 2002**

(a) $\frac{M}{A}$ (b) $2\,MA$ (c) $A^2 M$ (d) AM^2

20. Moment of inertia of a uniform horizontal solid cylinder of mass M about an axis passing through its edge and perpendicular to the axis of the cylinder when its length is 6 times its radius R is **EAMCET | 2002**

(a) $\frac{39\,MR^2}{4}$ (b) $\frac{30\,MR^2}{4}$
(c) $\frac{49\,MR}{4}$ (d) $\frac{49\,MR^2}{4}$

21. A body is sliding down a rough inclined plane. The coefficient of friction between the body and the plane is 0.5. The ratio of the net force required for the body to slide down and the normal reaction on the body is 1 : 2. Then, the angle of the inclined plane is EAMCET | 2002

(a) 15° (b) 30° (c) 45° (d) 60°

22. Particles of masses m, $2m$, $3m$ ... nm gram are placed on the same line at distance l, $2l$, $3l$ ..... nl cm from a fixed point. The distance of centre of mass of the particles from the fixed point in cm is EAMCET | 2002

(a) $\frac{(2n+1)l}{3}$ (b) $\frac{l}{n+1}$

(c) $\frac{n(n^2+1)l}{2}$ (d) $\frac{2l}{n(n^2+1)}$

23. The diameter of a flywheel is 1 m. It has a mass of 20 kg. It is rotating about its axis with a speed of 120 rotations in 1 min. Its angular momentum in kg-m^{2}s^{-1} is EAMCET | 2002

(a) 13.4 (b) 31.4 (c) 41.4 (d) 43.4

24. The velocities of three particles of masses 20 g, 30 g and 50 g are $10\hat{i}, 10\hat{j}$ and $10\hat{k}$ respectively. The velocity of the centre of mass of the three particles is EAMCET | 2001

(a) $2\hat{i}+3\hat{j}+5\hat{k}$ (b) $10(\hat{i}+\hat{j}+\hat{k})$

(c) $20\hat{i}+30\hat{j}+5\hat{k}$ (d) $2\hat{i}+30\hat{j}+50\hat{k}$

25. A particle is projected up along a rough inclined plane of inclination 45° with the horizontal. If the coefficient of friction is 0.5, the acceleration is EAMCET | 2001

(a) $\frac{g}{2}$ (b) $\frac{g}{2\sqrt{2}}$ (c) $\frac{3g}{2\sqrt{2}}$ (d) $\frac{g}{\sqrt{2}}$

26. A uniform metal rod of length L and mass M is rotating about an axis passing through one of the ends and perpendicular to the rod with angular speed ω. If the temperature increases by t°C, then the change in its angular velocity is proportional to which of the following? (coefficient of linear expansion of rod = α) EAMCET | 2001

(a) $\sqrt{\omega}$ (b) ω (c) ω^2 (d) $\frac{1}{\omega}$

27. From a uniform wire, two circular loops are made (i) P of radius r and (ii) Q of radius nr. If the moment of inertia of Q about an axis passing through its centre and perpendicular to its plane is 8 times that of P about a similar axis, the value of n is (diameter of the wire is very much smaller than i or nr) EAMCET | 2001

(a) $8\sqrt{2}$ (b) $6\sqrt{2}$ (c) $4\sqrt{2}$ (d) $2\sqrt{2}$

28. A body is sliding down an inclined plane having coefficient of friction 0.5. If the normal reaction is twice that of the resultant downward force along the inclination the angle between the inclined plane and the horizontal is EAMCET | 2000

(a) 15° (b) 30° (c) 45° (d) 60°

29. The radius of gyration of a sphere of mass M and radius R about the axis parallel to the axis passing through its centre and tangent to the sphere is EAMCET | 2000

(a) $\frac{7}{5}R$ (b) $\frac{3}{5}R$

(c) $\left(\sqrt{\frac{7}{5}}\right)R$ (d) $\left(\sqrt{\frac{3}{5}}\right)R$

30. A wheel has a speed of 1200 rev/min and is made to slow down at a rate of 4 rads^{-2}. The number of revolutions it makes before coming to rest is EAMCET | 2000

(a) 143 (b) 272 (c) 314 (d) 722

31. Two particles of mass 1 kg and 3 kg have position vectors $2\hat{i}+3\hat{j}+4\hat{k}$ and $-2\hat{i}+3\hat{j}-4\hat{k}$ respectively. The centre of mass, has a position vector EAMCET | 1999

(a) $\hat{i}+3\hat{j}-2\hat{k}$ (b) $-\hat{i}-3\hat{j}-2\hat{k}$

(c) $-\hat{i}+3\hat{j}+2\hat{k}$ (d) $-\hat{i}+3\hat{j}-2\hat{k}$

32. A stone is projected vertically up to reach maximum height h. The ratio of its kinetic energy to its potential energy, at a height $\frac{4}{5}h$, will be EAMCET | 1999

(a) 5 : 4 (b) 4 : 5 (c) 1 : 4 (d) 4 : 1

33. A body takes $1\frac{1}{3}$ times as much time to slide down a rough inclined plane as it takes to slide down an identical but smooth inclined plane. If the angle of inclined plane is 45°, the coefficient of friction is EAMCET | 1999

(a) $\frac{7}{16}$ (b) $\frac{9}{16}$ (c) $\frac{7}{9}$ (d) $\frac{3}{4}$

34. The moment of inertia of a thin uniform rod of mass M and length L about an axis perpendicular to the rod, through its centre is I. The moment of inertia of the rod about axis perpendicular to the rod through its end point is EAMCET | 1999

(a) $\frac{I}{4}$ (b) $\frac{I}{2}$ (c) $2I$ (d) $4I$

35. The position of a particle is given by $\vec{r} = (\hat{i}+2\hat{j}-\hat{k})$ momentum $\vec{p} = (3\hat{i}+4\hat{j}-2\hat{k})$. The angular momentum is perpendicular to EAMCET | 1998

(a) x-axis
(b) y-axis
(c) z-axis
(d) line at equal angles to all the three axes

36. A thin metal disc of radius 0.25 m and mass 2 kg starts from rest and rolls down an inclined plane. If its rotational kinetic energy is 4 J at the foot of the inclined plane, then its linear velocity at the same point is **EAMCET | 1997**

(a) 1.2 ms^{-1} (b) $2\sqrt{2}$ ms^{-1}
(c) 20 ms^{-1} (d) 2 ms^{-1}

37. A constant torque of 1000 N-m, turns a wheel of moment of inertia 200 kg-m^2 about an axis through its centre. Its angular velocity after 3 s is, (in rad/s) **EAMCET | 1997**

(a) 1 (b) 5 (c) 15 (d) 10

38. A wheel of mass 10 kg has a moment of inertia of 160 kg-m^2 about its own axis. The radius of gyration is **EAMCET | 1996**

(a) 10 m (b) 4 m (c) 5 m (d) 6 m

39. The moment of inertia of a solid sphere of mass M and radius R about the tangent is **EAMCET | 1995**

(a) $\frac{2}{5}MR^2$ (b) $\frac{7}{5}MR^2$
(c) $\frac{2}{3}MR^2$ (d) $\frac{-5}{3}MR^2$

40. A bomb travelling in a parabolic path under the effect of gravity, explodes in mid-air. The centre of mass of the fragments will **EAMCET | 1993**

(a) move vertically upwards and then vertically downwards
(b) move vertically downwards
(c) move in irregular path
(d) move in the parabolic path the unexploded bomb would have travelled

41. A solid cylinder at rest at top of an inclined plane of height 2.7 m, rolls down without slipping. If the same cylinder has to slide down a frictionless inclined plane and acquire the same velocity as that acquired by centre of mass of rolling cylinder, at the bottom of inclined plane, the height of the inclined plane should be **EAMCET | 1993**

(a) 5 ms^{-1}, 1.5 m (b) 7 ms^{-1}, 2.5 m
(c) 6 ms^{-1}, 1.8 m (d) 3 ms^{-1}, 1.2 m

42. The moment of inertia of thin uniform circular disc about one of the diameter is I. Its moment of inertia about an axis perpendicular to the circular surface and passing through its centre is **EAMCET | 1992**

(a) $\sqrt{2}I$ (b) $2I$ (c) $\frac{I}{2}$ (d) $\frac{I}{\sqrt{2}}$

43. Two particles P and Q located at distance r_P and r_Q respectively from the centre of a rotating disc such that $r_P > r_Q$ **EAMCET | 1992**

(a) both P and Q have the same acceleration
(b) both P and Q do not have any acceleration
(c) P has greater acceleration than Q
(d) Q has greater acceleration than P

44. A ball of 1 g released down an inclined plane describes a circle of radius 10 cm in the vertical plane on reaching the bottom. The minimum height of the inclined plane is **EAMCET | 1991**

(a) 10 cm (b) 15 cm
(c) 20 cm (d) 25 cm

Answers

1.	(a)	**2.**	(d)	**3.**	(d)	**4.**	(c)	**5.**	(a)	**6.**	(d)	**7.**	(d)	**8.**	(b)	**9.**	(a)	**10.**	(c)
11.	(b)	**12.**	(a)	**13.**	(a)	**14.**	(b)	**15.**	(b)	**16.**	(c)	**17.**	(a)	**18.**	(c)	**19.**	(b)	**20.**	(d)
21.	(c)	**22.**	(a)	**23.**	(b)	**24.**	(a)	**25.**	(c)	**26.**	(b)	**27.**	(d)	**28.**	(c)	**29.**	(c)	**30.**	(c)
31.	(d)	**32.**	(c)	**33.**	(a)	**34.**	(d)	**35.**	(a)	**36.**	(b)	**37.**	(c)	**38.**	(b)	**39.**	(b)	**40.**	(d)
41.	(c)	**42.**	(b)	**43.**	(c)	**44.**	(d)												

Hints & Solutions

1. As initially both the particles were at rest therefore velocity of centre of mass was zero and there is no external force on the system so speed of centre of mass remains constant *i.e.*, it should be equal to zero.

2. $$\mu = \tan\theta\left[1-\frac{1}{n^2}\right]$$

Here: $\theta = 45°$ and $n = 2$

$$\therefore \quad \mu = \tan 45°\left[1-\frac{1}{2^2}\right]$$

$$= 1-\frac{1}{4} = \frac{3}{4} = 0.75$$

3. Moment of inertia of a circular disc about an axis passing through centre of gravity and perpendicular to its plane

$$I = \frac{1}{2}MR^2 \qquad \text{...(i)}$$

From Eq. (i) $MR^2 = 2I$

Then, moment of inertia of disc about tangent in a plane $= \frac{5}{4}MR^2$

$$= \frac{5}{4}(2I)$$

$$= \frac{5}{2}I$$

4. Given, $m_1 = 6$ kg, $m_2 = 4$ kg

$$\vec{v}_1 = 5\hat{i}-2\hat{j}+10\hat{k}, \quad \vec{v}_2 = 10\hat{i}-2\hat{j}+5\hat{k}$$

The velocity of centre of mass is

$$\vec{v} = \frac{m_1\vec{v}_1+m_2\vec{v}_2}{m_1+m_2}$$

$$= \frac{6(5\hat{i}-2\hat{j}+10\hat{k})+4(10\hat{i}-2\hat{j}+5\hat{k})}{6+4}$$

$$= \frac{70\hat{i}-20\hat{j}+80\hat{k}}{10}$$

$$= 7\hat{i}-2\hat{j}+8\hat{k}$$

5. As two solid spheres are equal in masses, so

$$m_A = m_B$$

$$\Rightarrow \quad \frac{4}{3}\pi R_A^3\rho_A = \frac{4}{3}\pi R_B^3\rho_B$$

$$\Rightarrow \quad \frac{R_A}{R_B} = \left(\frac{\rho_B}{\rho_A}\right)^{1/3}$$

The moment of inertia of sphere about diameter

$$I = \frac{2}{5}mR^2$$

$$\Rightarrow \quad \frac{I_A}{I_B} = \left(\frac{R_A}{R_B}\right)^2 \qquad (\text{as } m_A = m_B)$$

$$\Rightarrow \quad \frac{I_A}{I_B} = \left(\frac{\rho_B}{\rho_A}\right)^{2/3}$$

7. Applying conservation of angular momentum about point O.

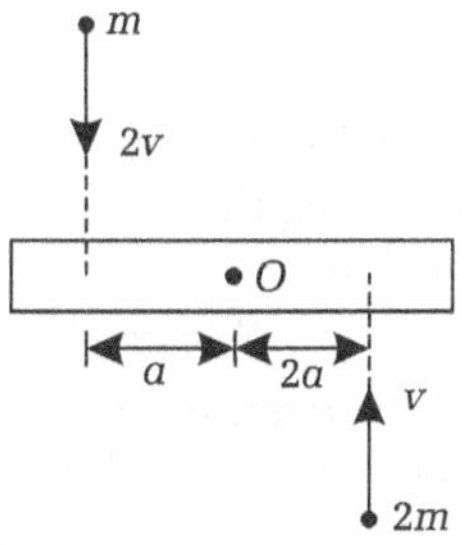

$$m(a)(2v) + 2m(2a)(v) = I\omega$$

or $$\omega = \frac{6m\,av}{I} \qquad \text{...(i)}$$

Now, $$I = \frac{6m(8a)^2}{12}+m(a^2)+2m(2a)^2$$

$$= 32ma^2 + ma^2 + 8ma^2$$

$$= 41ma^2$$

Hence, from Eq. (i)

$$\omega = \frac{6mav}{41ma^2} = \frac{6v}{41a}$$

8. $$(\text{KE})_{\text{total}} = \frac{1}{2}\times\frac{2}{5}MR^2\omega_0^2+\frac{1}{2}MR^2\left(\frac{D^2}{R^2}\right)\omega^2$$

$$= \frac{MR^2\omega_0^2}{5}\left[1+\frac{5}{2}\left(\frac{D\omega}{R\omega_0}\right)^2\right]$$

9. Given, $m_1 = 1$ kg, $m_2 = 2$ kg, $m_3 = 3$ kg

Position of centre of mass (2, 2, 2)

$$m_4 = 4 \text{ kg}$$

New position of centre of mass (0, 0, 0).

For initial position

$$X_{CM} = \frac{m_1x_1+m_2x_2+m_3x_3}{m_1+m_2+m_3}$$

$$2 = \frac{m_1x_1+m_2x_2+m_3x_3}{1+2+3}$$

$$m_1 x_1 + m_2 x_2 + m_3 x_3 = 12$$

Similarly,

$$m_1 y_1 + m_2 y_2 + m_3 y_3 = 12$$

and $m_1 z_1 + m_2 z_2 + m_3 z_3 = 12$

For new position,

$$X'_{CM} = \frac{m_1x_1 + m_2x_2 + m_3x_3 + m_4x_4}{m_1 + m_2 + m_3 + m_4}$$

$$0 = \frac{12 + 4 \times x_4}{1+2+3+4}$$

$$4x_4 = -12$$

$$x_4 = -3$$

Similarly, $y_4 = -3$

$$z_4 = -3$$

$\therefore$ Position of fourth mass $(-3, -3, -3)$.

10. Minimum force required to move a body up a rough inclined plane

$$F_1 = mg (\sin\theta + \mu \cos\theta)$$

Minimum force required to prevent the body form sliding down the rough inclined plane

$$F_2 = \mu m g \cos\theta$$

According to question,

$$F_1 = 3F_2$$

$$\therefore mg (\sin\theta + \mu \cos\theta) = 3 (\mu mg \cos\theta)$$

$$\sin\theta + \mu \cos\theta = 3 \mu \cos\theta$$

$$\sin\theta = 2 \mu \cos\theta$$

$$\tan\theta = 2\mu$$

$$= 2 \times \frac{1}{2\sqrt{3}}$$

$$= \frac{1}{\sqrt{3}}$$

$$= \tan 30°$$

$$\therefore \quad \theta = 30°$$

11. If rod is rotated about end A, then vertical component of velocity $v \perp$ of end A will be zero.

$$\therefore \quad \omega = \frac{v \cos 60°}{l} = \frac{\sqrt{3}v}{2l}$$

$$= \frac{\sqrt{3} \times 3}{2 \times 0.5} = 5.2 \text{ rads}^{-1}$$

12. (1) Angular velocity of earth

$$\omega_1 = \frac{2\pi}{T} = \frac{2\pi}{24 \times 60 \times 60}$$

$$= \frac{2\pi}{86400} \text{ rads}^{-1}$$

(2) Angular velocity of hour's hand of a clock

$$\omega_2 = \frac{2\pi}{T}$$

$$= \frac{2\pi}{12 \times 60 \times 60} = \frac{2\pi}{43200} \text{ rads}^{-1}$$

(3) Angular velocity of second's hand of a clock

$$\omega_3 = \frac{2\pi}{T}$$

$$= \frac{2\pi}{1 \times 60} = \frac{2\pi}{60} \text{ rads}^{-1}$$

(4) Angular velocity of flywheel

$$\omega_4 = 2 \pi n$$

$$= 2\pi \times \frac{300}{60}$$

$$= 2\pi \times 5 \text{ rad/s}$$

So, the increasing order is

$$1 < 2 < 3 < 4$$

13. $\vec{v}_{CM} = \dfrac{m_1\vec{v}_1 + m_2\vec{v}_2}{m_1 + m_2} = \dfrac{\vec{v}_1 + \vec{v}_2}{2}$ (as $m_1 = m_2$)

and $\vec{a}_{CM} = \dfrac{m_1\vec{a}_1 + m_2\vec{a}_2}{m_1 + m_2} = \dfrac{\vec{a}_1 + 0}{2} = \dfrac{\vec{a}_1}{2}$

The centre of mass of two particles will move with the mean velocity of two particles having common acceleration $\dfrac{\vec{a}}{2}$. Hence, path of CM will be a straight line.

14. $\dfrac{ma^2}{12} + m(4a^2) = \dfrac{ma^2}{6} + md^2$

or $\quad d^2 = \dfrac{47a^2}{12}$

$$d = \sqrt{\frac{47}{12}}\, a$$

15. $\tau = \dfrac{dL}{dt} = m[u^2 \cos^2\theta]$

$$= (1)(10)^2 \cos^2 45° = 50 \text{ N-m}$$

16. Given, $m_1 = 200$ g, $m_2 = 500$ g

$$v_1 = 10\hat{i} \text{ ms}^{-1}, \; v_2 = (3\hat{i} + 5\hat{j}) \text{ ms}^{-1}$$

Velocity of centre of mass

$$v_{CM} = \frac{m_1v_1 + m_2v_2}{m_1 + m_2}$$

$$= \frac{200 \times 10\hat{i} + 500(3\hat{i} + 5\hat{j})}{200 + 500}$$

$$= \frac{2000\hat{i} + 1500\hat{i} + 2500\hat{j}}{700}$$

$$= \frac{3500\hat{i} + 2500\hat{j}}{700}$$

$$= 5\hat{i} + \frac{25}{7}\hat{j}$$

17. $m = 0.6$ kg

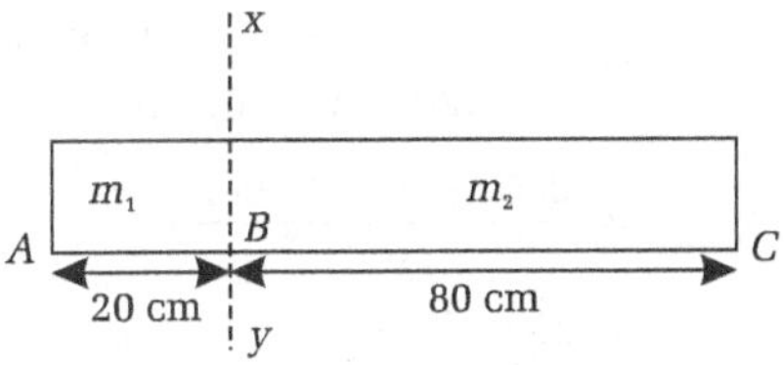

$$\text{Mass per unit length} = \frac{0.6}{100} \text{ kgcm}^{-1}$$

$$\text{Mass of part } AB,\ m_1 = \frac{0.6}{100} \times 20 = \frac{0.6}{5} \text{ kg}$$

$$\text{Mass of part } BC,\ m_2 = \frac{0.6}{100} \times 80$$

$$= \frac{0.6 \times 4}{5} = \frac{2.4}{5} \text{ kg}$$

Moment of inertia

$$I = m_1\left(\frac{AB}{2}\right)^2 + m_2\frac{(BC)^2}{2}$$

$$= \frac{0.6}{5} \times \left(\frac{20}{2} \times 10^{-2}\right)^2 + \frac{2.4}{5} \times \left(\frac{80}{2} \times 10^{-2}\right)^2$$

$$= \frac{0.6}{5} \times 10^{-2} + \frac{2.4}{5} \times (4 \times 10^{-1})^2$$

$$= \frac{0.6}{5} \times 10^{-2} + \frac{2.4}{5} \times 16 \times 10^{-2}$$

$$= \left(\frac{0.6 + 38.4}{5}\right) \times 10^{-2}$$

$$= 7.8 \times 10^{-2} \text{ kg-m}^2$$

$$= 0.078 \text{ kg-m}^2$$

18. Moment of inertia of a disc

$$I = \frac{1}{2}MR^2$$

Disc is melted and recasted into a solid sphere.

$\therefore$ Volume of sphere = Volume of disc

$$\frac{4}{3}\pi R_1^3 = \pi R^2 \times \frac{R}{6}$$

$$\frac{4}{3}R_1^3 = \frac{R^3}{6}$$

$$R_1^3 = \frac{R^3}{8}$$

$$\Rightarrow \quad R_1 = \frac{R}{2}$$

$\therefore$ Moment of inertia of sphere

$$I' = \frac{2}{5}MR_1^2 = \frac{2}{5}M\left(\frac{R}{2}\right)^2 = \frac{2}{5}\frac{MR^2}{4}$$

$$= \frac{1}{5}\left(\frac{1}{2}MR^2\right)$$

$$= \frac{I}{5}$$

19. Areal velocity, $A = \frac{1}{2}R^2\omega$

$\therefore$ Multiplying by M on both sides

$$MA = \frac{1}{2}MR^2\omega$$

$$MA = \frac{1}{2}I\omega$$

where, I = moment of inertia

$$MA = \frac{1}{2}L$$

where, L = angular momentum

$$= I\omega$$

$$\therefore \quad L = 2\,MA$$

20. Moment of inertia of solid cylinder, about the axis passing through its centre of mass and perpendicular to its plane

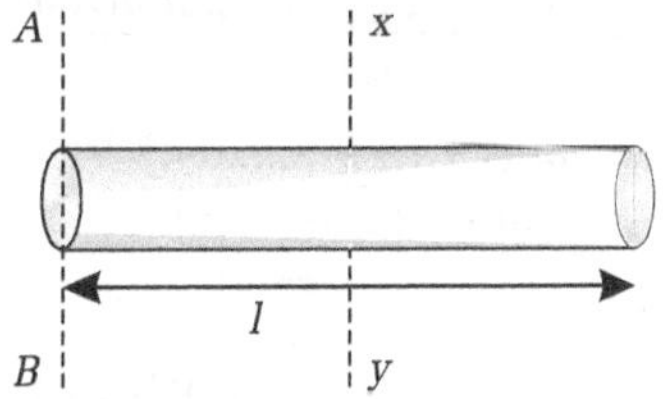

$$I_{xy} = M\left(\frac{l^2}{12} + \frac{R^2}{4}\right)$$

From theorem of parallel axis, moment of inertia of cylinder about an axis passing through its edge and perpendicular to it plane

$$I_{AB} = I_{XY} + M\left(\frac{l}{2}\right)^2$$

$$\therefore \quad I_{AB} = M\left(\frac{l^2}{12} + \frac{R^2}{4}\right) + M\frac{l^2}{4}$$

$$= M\left(\frac{l^2}{3} + \frac{R^2}{4}\right)$$

But, $l = 6\,R$

$$\therefore \quad I_{AB} = M\left[\frac{(6\,R)^2}{3} + \frac{R^2}{4}\right] = M\left[12R^2 + \frac{R^2}{4}\right]$$

$$= M\left(\frac{49\,R^2}{4}\right) = \frac{49\,M\,R^2}{4}$$

21. $\mu = 0.5, \frac{F}{R} = \frac{1}{2}$

Net force acting downward

$= mg \sin\theta - f$

where f = frictional force

$= \mu R$ (R = Normal reaction)

$= \mu mg \cos\theta$

$$\frac{F}{R} = \frac{1}{2}$$

$$\frac{mg\sin\theta - \mu mg\cos\theta}{mg\cos\theta} = \frac{1}{2}$$

$$\tan\theta - \mu = \frac{1}{2}$$

$$\Rightarrow \tan\theta = \frac{1}{2} + \mu$$

$$= \frac{1}{2} + 0.5 = 1$$

$$\tan\theta = \tan 45$$

$$\therefore \theta = 45°$$

22. Distance of centre of mass

$$X_{CM} = \frac{m_1x_1 + m_2x_2 + ...m_nx_n}{m_1 + m_2 + ...m_n}$$

$$= \frac{m\,l + 2\,m\,2\,l + ...n\,m \times n\,l}{m + 2\,m + 3\,m + ...n\,m}$$

$$= \frac{ml(1+4+9+.......n^2)}{m(1+2+3+.....n)}$$

$$1 + 4 + 9 + ... n^2 = \sum n^2$$

$$= \frac{n(n+1)(2n+1)}{6}$$

$$1 + 2 + 3 + ... n = \sum n = \frac{n(n+1)}{2}$$

$$\therefore X_{CM} = \frac{\frac{ln(n+1)(2n+1)}{6}}{n\frac{(n+1)}{2}}$$

$$= \frac{l(2n+1)}{3}$$

23. Given, $r = \frac{1}{2}$m $= 0.5$ m, $m = 20$ kg,

$n = 120$ rotation/min $= 2$ rotation/s

Angular momentum $L = I\omega$

$$= \frac{M\,r^2}{2} 2\pi n = \frac{20 \times (0.5)^2}{2} \times 2 \times 3.14 \times 2$$

$= 5 \times 3.14 \times 2$

$= 31.4$ kg-m²s⁻¹

24. Given, $m_1 = 20$ g, $m_2 = 30$ g, $m_3 = 50$ g

$$\vec{v}_1 = 10\hat{i}\,,\ \vec{v}_2 = 10\hat{j}\,,\ \vec{v}_3 = 10\hat{k}$$

$$v_{CM} = \frac{m_1\vec{v}_1 + m_2\vec{v}_2 + m_3\vec{v}_3}{m_1 + m_2 + m_3}$$

$$= \frac{20 \times 10^{-3} \times 10\hat{i} + 30 \times 10^{-3} \times 10\hat{j} + 50 \times 10^{-3} \times 10\hat{k}}{(20+30+50) \times 10^{-3}}$$

$$= \frac{200\hat{i} + 300\hat{j} + 500\hat{k}}{100}$$

$$= 2\hat{i} + 3\hat{j} + 5\hat{k}$$

25. Acceleration of an object up a rough inclined plane

$a = g(\sin\theta + \mu\cos\theta) = g(\sin 45° + 0.5\cos 45°)$

$$= g\left(\frac{1}{\sqrt{2}} + \frac{1}{2}\cdot\frac{1}{\sqrt{2}}\right) = \frac{g}{\sqrt{2}}\left(1 + \frac{1}{2}\right) = \frac{3\,g}{2\sqrt{2}}$$

26. From law of conservation of angular momentum

L = constant

$$\therefore I_1\omega_1 = I_2\omega_2 = L$$

$$\omega_1 = \frac{L}{I_1}, \omega_2 = \frac{L}{I_2}$$

Change in angular velocity

$$\Delta\omega = \omega_2 - \omega_1 = \frac{L}{I_2} - \frac{L}{I_1} = L\left(\frac{1}{I_2} - \frac{1}{I_1}\right)$$

$$= L\left(\frac{I_1 - I_2}{I_1I_2}\right) = \frac{L}{I_1}\left(\frac{I_1}{I_2} - 1\right)$$

$$= \omega_1\left(\frac{I_1}{I_2} - 1\right)$$

$$\therefore \Delta\omega \propto \omega_1$$

$$\Delta\omega \propto \omega$$

27. Moment of inertia of circular loop

$$I = m\,r^2$$

Given, $I_Q = 8\,I_P$

$$mr_Q^2 = 8\,m_Pr_P^2$$

$$m_P \times (nr_P)^2 = 8m_P \times r_P^2$$

$$n^2 = 8$$

$$\Rightarrow n = 2\sqrt{2}$$

28. Coefficient of friction $\mu = 0.5$

Net force acting on a body moving downward a rough inclined plane

$$F = mg\sin\theta - \mu R$$

where R = normal reaction.

According to question, $R = 2\,F$

$\therefore \quad R = 2\,(mg \sin\theta - \mu R)$

$R = 2\,mg \sin\theta - 2\,\mu R$

$R = 2\,mg \sin\theta - 2 \times 0.5\,R$

$2\,R = 2\,mg \sin\theta$

But, $\quad R = mg\cos\theta$

$\therefore \; mg\cos\theta = mg\sin\theta$

$\tan\theta = 1$

$\Rightarrow \quad \theta = 45°$

29. Moment of inertia of the sphere about the centre

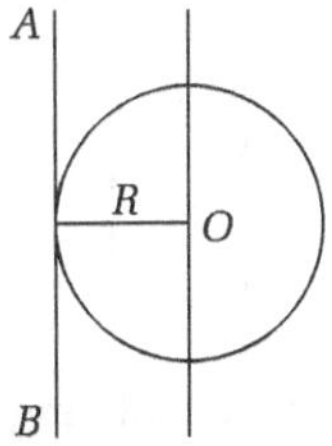

$$I_O = \frac{2}{5}MR^2$$

$\therefore$ Moment of inertia of the sphere about the required axis

$$I_{AB} = I_O + MR^2$$

(From theorem of parallel axis)

$$= \frac{2}{5}MR^2 + MR^2 = \frac{7}{5}MR^2$$

If radius of gyration is K, then

$$MK^2 = \frac{7}{5}MR^2$$

$$\therefore \quad K = \sqrt{\frac{7}{5}}R$$

30. Given, $n = 1200$ rev/min

$$= \frac{1200}{60}\text{ rev/s}$$

$$= 20\text{ rev/s}$$

$$\omega = 2\,\pi\,n = 2\,\pi(20) = 40\,\pi\text{ rads}^{-1}$$

Angular acceleration, $\alpha = 4\text{ rads}^{-2}$

From equation of rotational motion

$$\omega^2 = \omega_0^2 - 2\,\alpha\,\theta$$

$= 0,\ \omega$

$$\therefore \quad \theta = \frac{\omega_0^2}{2\alpha} = \frac{(40\,\pi)^2}{2 \times 4} = 200\,\pi^2$$

$$\therefore \text{Number of revolutions} = \frac{200\,\pi^2}{2\,\pi}$$

$$= 100\,\pi$$

$$= 100 \times 3.14$$

$$= 314$$

31. Given, $m_1 = 1$ kg, $m_2 = 3$ kg

$$\vec{r}_1 = 2\hat{i} + 3\hat{j} + 4\hat{k},$$

$$\vec{r}_2 = -2\hat{i} + 3\hat{j} - 4\hat{k}$$

Position vector of centre of mass

$$\vec{r}_{CM} = \frac{m_1\vec{r}_1 + m_2\vec{r}_2}{m_1 + m_2}$$

$$= \frac{1(2\hat{i} + 3\hat{j} + 4\hat{k}) + 3(-2\hat{i} + 3\hat{j} - 4\hat{k})}{1+3}$$

$$= \frac{-4\hat{i} + 12\hat{j} - 8\hat{k}}{4}$$

$$= -\hat{i} + 3\hat{j} - 2\hat{k}$$

32. Total energy of the stone $= mgh$

$\therefore$ PE at $\frac{4\,h}{5}$,

$$\text{PE} = mg\left(\frac{4}{5}h\right)$$

$$= \frac{4}{5}mgh$$

$\therefore$ KE at $\frac{4}{5}h$,

$$\text{PE} = mgh - \frac{4}{5}mgh = \frac{1}{5}mgh$$

(From law of conservation of energy)

$$\frac{\text{KE}}{\text{PE}} = \frac{\frac{1}{5}mgh}{\frac{4}{5}mgh} = \frac{1}{4}$$

33. Coefficient of friction $\mu = 1 - \frac{1}{n^2}$

n = comparison of time between smooth and rough plane

$$= 1\frac{1}{3} = \frac{4}{3}$$

$$\therefore \quad \mu = 1 - \frac{1}{(4/3)^2} = 1 - \frac{1}{16/9}$$

$$= 1 - \frac{9}{16} = \frac{7}{16}$$

34. Moment of inertia of the thin uniform rod about an axis perpendicular to rod and through its centre

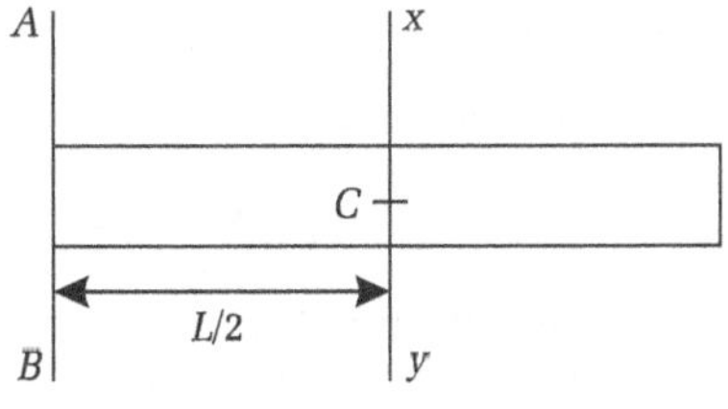

$$I_{XY} = \frac{ML^2}{12}$$

$\therefore$ Moment of inertia about axis perpendicular to rod and through its end point

$$I_{AB} = I_{XY} + M\left(\frac{L}{2}\right)^2 = \frac{ML^2}{12} + \frac{ML^2}{4}$$

$$= \frac{ML^2}{3} = 4\left(\frac{ML^2}{12}\right)$$

$$= 4I$$

35. Given, $\vec{r} = (\hat{i} + 2\hat{j} - \hat{k})$

$$\vec{p} = (3\hat{i} + 4\hat{j} - 2\hat{k})$$

Angular momentum, $\vec{L} = \vec{r} \times \vec{p}$

$$= \begin{vmatrix} \hat{i} & \hat{j} & \hat{k} \\ 1 & 2 & -1 \\ 3 & 4 & -2 \end{vmatrix}$$

$$= \hat{i}[(2\times -2) - (4\times -1)] - \hat{j}[(1\times -2) - (3\times -1)] + \hat{k}[(1\times 4) - (3\times 2)]$$

$$= 3\hat{j} - 2\hat{k}$$

In this expression there is no $\hat{i}$ (unit vector along x-axis) therefore angular momentum is perpendicular to x-axis.

36. Given, $r = 0.25$ m, $m = 2$ kg

Rotational kinetic energy, $K_r = 4$ J

$$\frac{1}{2}I\omega^2 = 4$$

I = moment of inertia of disc $= \frac{1}{2}mr^2$

$$\therefore \quad \frac{1}{2}\left(\frac{1}{2}mr^2\right)\left(\frac{v^2}{r^2}\right) = 4$$

$$\frac{1}{4}mv^2 = 4$$

$$\Rightarrow \quad \frac{1}{4}\times 2v^2 = 4$$

$$v^2 = \frac{4\times 4}{2}$$

$$v^2 = 8$$

$$v = \sqrt{8}$$

$$= 2\sqrt{2}\ \text{ms}^{-1}$$

37. Given, $\tau = 1000$ N-m, $I = 200$ kg-m^2, $t = 3$ s

Angular acceleration, $\alpha = \frac{\tau}{I}$

$$= \frac{1000}{200} = 5\ \text{rads}^{-2}$$

$\therefore$ Angular velocity after 3 s

$$\omega = \alpha t = 5 \times 3 = 15\ \text{rads}^{-1}$$

38. Mass, $m = 10$ kg,

Moment of inertia, $I = 160$ kg-m^2

Radius of gyration, $K = \sqrt{\frac{I}{m}} = \sqrt{\frac{160}{10}}$

$$= \sqrt{16} = 4\ \text{m}$$

39. The moment of inertia of sphere about its centre

$$I_O = \frac{2}{5}MR^2$$

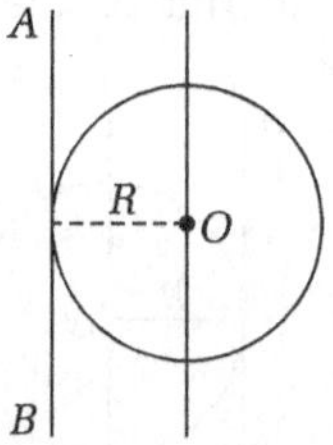

Moment of inertia about tangent $= I_{AB}$

From theorem of parallel axis

$$I_{AB} = I_O + MR^2$$

$$= \frac{2}{5}MR^2 + MR^2$$

$$= \frac{2MR^2 + 5MR^2}{5} = \frac{7}{5}MR^2$$

40. When a bomb explodes in mid air on travelling a parabolic path under the effect of gravity, the centre of mass of the fragments are move in the parabolic path the unexploded bomb would have travelled.

41. Ist case When cylinder rolls down the inclined plane, in this case it will have rotational and linear kinetic energies both. From law of conservation of energy

$$\frac{1}{2}Mv^2 + \frac{1}{2}I\omega^2 = Mgh$$

Moment of inertia of cylinder, $I = \frac{1}{2}MR^2$

and angular velocity, $(\omega) = \frac{v}{R}$

$$\therefore \quad \frac{1}{2}Mv^2 + \frac{1}{2}\left(\frac{1}{2}MR^2\right)\frac{v^2}{R^2} = Mgh$$

$$\frac{1}{2}Mv^2 + \frac{1}{4}Mv^2 = Mgh$$

$$\frac{3}{4}Mv^2 = Mgh$$

$$v = \sqrt{\frac{4gh}{3}} = \sqrt{\frac{4\times 10\times 2.7}{3}} = 6\ \text{ms}^{-1}$$

IInd case When cylinder slides than it has only linear kinetic energy.

$$\therefore \quad \frac{1}{2}Mv^2 = Mgh'$$

$$h' = \frac{v^2}{2g} = \frac{(6)^2}{2 \times 10} = 1.8 \text{ m}$$

42. Moment of inertia of uniform circular disc about its diameter $I = \frac{1}{4}MR^2$. Moment of inertia of this uniform circular disc about an axis through its centre and perpendicular to its plane $I' = \frac{1}{2}MR^2$

$$= 2I$$

43. In case of rotation,
angular acceleration, $a = r\omega^2$
As $r_P > r_Q$ so, $a_P > a_Q$

44. Let v is the velocity of the ball at the bottom of the plane (*i.e.*, at the lowest point of the circle).

$\therefore$ From law of conservation of energy

$$\frac{1}{2}mv^2 = mgh$$

$$\therefore \quad v = \sqrt{2gh}$$

But, at the lowest point of the circle

$$v = \sqrt{5\,Rg}$$

$$\therefore \quad 5\,Rg = 2\,gh$$

$$h = \frac{5}{2}R = \frac{5}{2} \times 10 = 25 \text{ cm}$$

Chapter

6

Gravitation

1. The orbit of geostationary satellite is circular, the time period of satellite depends on
   (i) mass of the satellite
   (ii) mass of the earth
   (iii) radius of the orbit
   (iv) height of the satellite from the surface of earth

   Which of the following is correct?

   EAMCET | 2008

   (a) (i) only (b) (i) and (ii)
   (c) (i), (ii) and (iii) (d) (ii), (iii) and (iv)

2. The mass of a planet is half that of the earth and the radius of the planet is one-fourth that of earth. If we plan to send an artificial satellite from the planet, the escape velocity will be, (escape velocity on earth v_e = 11 km- s^{-1})

   EAMCET | 2007

   (a) 11 km-s^{-1} (b) 5.5 km-s^{-1}
   (c) 15.55 km-s^{-1} (d) 7.78 km-s^{-1}

3. **Assertion (A)** A particle of mass m dropped into a hole made along the diameter of the earth from one end to the other and possess simple harmonic motion.

   Reason (R) Gravitational force between any two particles is inversely proportional to the square of the distance between them.

   EAMCET | 2006

   (a) Both (A) and (R) are true and (R) is the correct explanation of (A)
   (b) Both (A) and (R) are true but (R) is not the correct explanation of (A)
   (c) (A) is true but (R) is false
   (d) (A) is false but (R) is true

4. The escape velocity of a body on the earth's surface is v_e. A body is thrown up with a speed $\sqrt{5}\, v_e$. Assuming that the sun and planets do not influence the motion of the body, velocity of the body at infinite distance, is

   EAMCET | 2004

   (a) zero (b) v_e (c) $\sqrt{2}\, v_e$ (d) $2\, v_e$

5. A satellite is launched into a circular orbit of radius R around earth while a second satellite is launched into a orbit of radius 1.02 R. The percentage difference in the time periods of the two satellites is **EAMCET | 2003**

   (a) 0.7 (b) 1.0 (c) 1.5 (d) 3

6. A body is projected up with a velocity equal to $\frac{3}{4}$ th of the escape velocity from the surface of the earth. The height it reaches is (Radius of the earth = R) **EAMCET | 2002**

   (a) $\frac{10\,R}{9}$ (b) $\frac{9\,R}{7}$ (c) $\frac{9\,R}{8}$ (d) $\frac{10\,R}{3}$

7. Mass M is divided into two parts xm and $(1 - x)m$. For a given separation the value of x for which the gravitational attraction between the two pieces becomes maximum is

   EAMCET | 2001

   (a) $\frac{1}{2}$ (b) $\frac{3}{5}$ (c) 1 (d) 2

8. R and r are the radii of the earth and moon respectively, ρ_e and ρ_m are densities of earth and moon respectively. The ratio of the acceleration due to gravity on the surfaces of the moon and earth, is **EAMCET | 2000**

   (a) $\frac{R}{r}\cdot\frac{\rho_e}{\rho_m}$ (b) $\frac{r}{R}\cdot\frac{\rho_e}{\rho_m}$
   (c) $\frac{r}{R}\cdot\frac{\rho_m}{\rho_e}$ (d) $\frac{R}{r}\cdot\frac{\rho_m}{\rho_e}$

9. The height of the point vertically above the earth's surface at which acceleration due to gravity becomes 1% of its value at the surface is (Radius of the earth = R) **EAMCET | 2000**

   (a) $8R$ (b) $9R$ (c) $10R$ (d) $20R$

10. Taking that earth revolves round the sun in a circular orbit of radius 15×10^{10} m, with a time period of 1 yr the time taken by another planet, which is at a distance of 540×10^{10} m, to revolve round the sun in circular orbit once, will be **EAMCET | 1999**

    (a) 216 yr (b) 144 yr
    (c) 72 yr (d) 36 yr

11. If R is the radius of earth, the height, at which the weight of a body becomes $\frac{1}{4}$ of its weight on the surface of earth, is **EAMCET | 1999**

(a) $2R$ (b) R (c) $\frac{R}{2}$ (d) $\frac{R}{4}$

12. Value of g is **EAMCET | 1998**

(a) maximum at poles
(b) maximum at equator
(c) same everywhere
(d) minimum at poles

13. A satellite is revolving near the earth's surface. Its orbit velocity is **EAMCET | 1998**

(a) 5.8 km-s^{-1} (b) 18.4 km-s^{-1}
(c) 11.2 km-s^{-1} (d) 8.0 km-s^{-1}

14. The mass of a planet is 1/9 of the mass of the earth and its radius is half that of the earth. If a body weighs 9 N on the earth, its weight on the planet would be **EAMCET | 1997**

(a) 6 N (b) 4 N (c) 2 N (d) 1 N

15. The escape velocity of a body from the earth is u. What is the escape velocity from a planet whose mass and radius are twice those of the earth? **EAMCET | 1996**

(a) 2 u (b) u (c) 4 u (d) 16 u

16. The orbital speed for an earth satellite near the surface of the earth is 7 km-s^{-1}. If the radius of the orbit is 4 times the radius of the earth the orbital speed would be **EAMCET | 1998**

(a) 3.5 km-s^{-1} (b) 7 km-s^{-1}
(c) $7\sqrt{2}$ km-s^{-1} (d) 14 km-s^{-1}

17. A geostationary satellite has an orbital period of **EAMCET | 1994**

(a) 2 h (b) 5 h
(c) 24 h (d) 12 h

18. The escape velocity of an object on a planet whose radius is 4 times that of the earth and value of g is same as that on the earth, in km-s^{-1} is **EAMCET | 1994**

(a) 33.6 (b) 22.4 (c) 16.8 (d) 25.2

19. If the earth suddenly stops rotating, the value of g at equator would **EAMCET | 1993**

(a) decrease (b) remain unchanged
(c) increase (d) become zero

20. If the acceleration due to gravity g at the earth's surface is 9.8 ms^{-2} and mass of earth is 80 times that of moon and radius of earth 4 times that of moon, the value of g at the moon's surface will be **EAMCET | 1993**

(a) 1.96 ms^{-2} (b) 2.96 ms^{-2}
(c) 0.96 ms^{-2} (d) 3.96 ms^{-2}

21. Two satellites A and B go around the earth in circular orbits at a height of R_A and R_B respectively from the surface of the earth. Assume earth to be a uniform sphere of radius R_e. The ratio of the magnitude of the velocities of the satellites v_A/v_B **EAMCET | 1992**

(a) $\sqrt{\frac{R_B}{R_A}}$ (b) $\frac{R_B+R_e}{R_A+R_e}$
(c) $\sqrt{\frac{R_B+R_e}{R_A+R_e}}$ (d) $\left(\frac{R_A}{R_B}\right)^2$

22. Let A be the area swept out by the line joining the earth and the sun during Feb, 1991. The area swept out by the line during a typical week in Feb, 1992 is **EAMCET | 1992**

(a) equal (b) high
(c) reduce (d) cannot say

23. Earth is flattened at poles and bulging at the equator. This is due to **EAMCET | 1991**

(a) centrifugal force is less at the equator than at poles
(b) angular velocity is more at poles
(c) centrifugal force is more at the equator than at poles
(d) None of the above

24. If the escape velocity on earth is 11.2 km-s^{-1}, its value for a planet having double the radius and 8 times the mass of earth is **EAMCET | 1991**

(a) 11×10^3 ms^{-1} (b) 22.4 ms^{-1}
(c) 1100 ms^{-1} (d) 22.4×10^3 ms^{-1}

25. The acceleration due to gravity at a height (take g = 10 ms^{-2} on earth surface) above earth's surface is 9 ms^{-2}. It value at a point, at an equal distance below the surface of the earth is **EAMCET | 1991**

(a) 9.5 ms^{-2} (b) 8.5 ms^{-2}
(c) 7.5 ms^{-2} (d) 5.5 ms^{-2}

■ Answers

1.	(d)	**2.**	(c)	**3.**	(a)	**4.**	(d)	**5.**	(d)	**6.**	(b)	**7.**	(a)	**8.**	(a)	**9.**	(b)	**10.**	(a)
11.	(b)	**12.**	(a)	**13.**	(d)	**14.**	(b)	**15.**	(b)	**16.**	(d)	**17.**	(c)	**18.**	(b)	**19.**	(c)	**20.**	(a)
21.	(c)	**22.**	(a)	**23.**	(c)	**24.**	(d)	**25.**	(a)										

■ Hints & Solutions

1. Time period of satellite

$T \propto \frac{1}{M^{1/2}}$, where M is mass of earth.

$\propto (R+h)^{3/2}$ where R is radius of the orbit, h is the height of satellite from the earth's surface.

2. Escape velocity

$$v_{es} = \sqrt{\frac{2GM}{R}}$$

$$\Rightarrow \frac{v_1}{v_2} = \sqrt{\frac{M_1}{M_2} \times \frac{R_2}{R_1}}$$

$$\Rightarrow \frac{v_1}{v_2} = \sqrt{\frac{M_1}{\frac{M_1}{2}} \times \frac{\frac{R_1}{4}}{R_1}} = \frac{1}{\sqrt{2}}$$

$$\Rightarrow v_2 = \sqrt{2} \times 11 = 15.55 \text{ km-s}^{-1}$$

4. Since, velocity of projection (v) is greater than the escape velocity (v_e), therefore at infinite distance the body moves with a velocity

$$v' = \sqrt{v^2 - v_e^2}$$

$$v' = \sqrt{(\sqrt{5}v_e)^2 - v_e^2}$$

$$= 2v_e$$

5. From Kepler's law

$$T^2 \propto R^3$$

$$\Rightarrow \frac{T_1^2}{T_2^2} = \frac{R_1^3}{R_2^3}$$

$$\frac{T_1}{T_2} = \left(\frac{R_1}{R_2}\right)^{3/2}$$

$$= \left(\frac{R}{1.02R}\right)^{3/2}$$

$$= \left(\frac{50}{51}\right)^{3/2}$$

$$= \frac{50}{51}\left(\frac{50}{51}\right)^{\frac{1}{2}}$$

$$= \frac{50}{51} \times 0.99$$

$$\frac{T_1}{T_2} = \frac{0.97}{1}$$

$$\Rightarrow T_1 = 0.97\,x \qquad (\because T_2 = x)$$

$$\text{Difference} = T_2 - T_1 = x - 0.97\,x = 0.03\,x$$

$$\%\text{ difference} = \frac{0.03x}{x} \times 100 = 3\%$$

6. Velocity of projection, $v = \frac{3}{4}v_e$

where, v_e = escape velocity = $\sqrt{2\,g\,R}$

Maximum height attained by the body

$$h = \frac{v^2 R}{2\,g\,R - v^2}$$

$$= \frac{\left(\frac{3}{4}\sqrt{2\,g\,R}\right)^2 \times R}{2\,g\,R - \left(\frac{3}{4}(\sqrt{2\,g\,R})\right)^2}$$

$$= \frac{\frac{9}{16} \times 2\,g\,R \times R}{2\,g\,R - \frac{9}{16} \times 2\,g\,R}$$

$$= \frac{\frac{9}{16} \times 2\,g\,R^2 \times R}{2\,g\,R\left(1 - \frac{9}{16}\right)} = \frac{\frac{9}{16}R}{\frac{7}{16}}$$

$$= \frac{9}{7}R$$

7. Force of gravitation $F \propto m_1\,m_2$

$$F = k\,m_1\,m_2$$

$$F = k\,(x\,m)\,(1-x) \times m$$

For F to be maximum $\frac{dF}{dx} = 0$

$$\frac{d}{dx}[k(x\,m)(1-x)\times m] = 0$$

$$m^2 - 2\,x\,m^2 = 0$$

$$\therefore \quad x = \frac{1}{2}$$

8. Acceleration due to gravity

$$g = \frac{GM}{R^2} = \frac{GV\rho}{R^2}$$

$$= \frac{G\frac{4}{3}\pi R^3\rho}{R^2}$$

$$= \frac{4}{3}\pi GR\rho$$

$$\therefore \quad \frac{g_e}{g_m} = \frac{R_e}{R_m}\times\frac{\rho_e}{\rho_m}$$

$$= \frac{R}{r}\times\frac{\rho_e}{\rho_m}$$

9. At the surface of earth $g = \frac{GM}{R^2}$

Above the surface of earth $g' = \frac{GM}{(R+h)^2}$

But, $g' = 1\%$ of $g = \frac{1\times g}{100}$

$$\therefore \quad \frac{g}{100} = \frac{GM}{(R+h)^2}$$

$$\therefore \quad \frac{1}{100}\frac{GM}{R^2} = \frac{GM}{(R+h)^2}$$

$$(R+h)^2 = 100\,R^2$$

$$R + h = 10\,R$$

$$\therefore \quad h = 10\,R - R = 9\,R$$

10. Here: $R_1 = 15\times10^{10}$ m, $T_1 = 1$ yr

$R_2 = 540\times10^{10}$ m, $T_2 = ?$

From Kepler's third law

$$T^2 \propto R^3$$

$$\left(\frac{T_1}{T_2}\right)^2 = \left(\frac{R_1}{R_2}\right)^3$$

$$\left(\frac{1}{T_2}\right)^2 = \left(\frac{15\times10^{10}}{540\times10^{10}}\right)^3$$

$$\frac{1}{T_2^2} = \left(\frac{1}{36}\right)^3$$

$$\Rightarrow \quad T_2 = (36)^{3/2}$$

$$= (6^2)^{3/2} = (6)^3 = 216 \text{ yr}$$

11. Acceleration due to gravity at height h

$$g' = \frac{g}{\left(1+\frac{h}{R}\right)^2}$$

$$\therefore \quad mg' = \frac{mg}{\left(1+\frac{h}{R}\right)^2}$$

$$w' = \frac{w}{\left(1+\frac{h}{R}\right)^2}$$

$$w' = \frac{w}{4} \quad \text{(given)}$$

$$\therefore \quad \frac{w}{4} = \frac{w}{\left(1+\frac{h}{R}\right)^2}$$

$$\Rightarrow \quad \frac{1}{4} = \frac{w}{\left(1+\frac{h}{R}\right)^2}$$

$$1+\frac{h}{R} = 2$$

$$\Rightarrow \quad \frac{h}{R} = 1$$

$$\Rightarrow \quad h = R$$

12. Value of g (acceleration due to gravity) is maximum at poles, because at the poles radius of earth is minimum (due to flattening of earth at poles).

13. Orbital velocity of satellite revolving near the earth

$$v = \sqrt{gR_e}$$

where, R_e = radius of the earth.

$$v = \sqrt{10\times6.4\times10^6} = 8 \text{ kms}^{-1}$$

14. Mass of planet, $M_p = \frac{1}{9}M_e$

Radius of planet, $R_p = \frac{1}{2}R_e$

∴ Acceleration due to gravity at earth

$$g_e = \frac{G\,M_e}{R_e^2}$$

Acceleration due to gravity at planet

$$g_p = \frac{G\,M_p}{R_p^2} = \frac{G\,M_e/9}{(R_e/2)^2}$$

$$= \frac{G\,M_e/9}{R_e^2/4}$$

$$= \frac{4}{9}\frac{GM_e}{R_e^2} = \frac{4}{9}g_e$$

$\therefore \quad \dfrac{\text{Weight on planet}}{\text{Weight on earth}} = \dfrac{m\,g_p}{m\,g_e}$

$$\frac{w'}{9} = \frac{g_p}{g_e}$$

$$= \frac{4}{9} \times \frac{g_e}{g_e}$$

$$w = \frac{4}{9} \times 9$$

$$= 4\text{ N}$$

15. Mass of planet, $M = 2\,M_e$

Radius of planet, $R = 2\,R_e$

Escape velocity from earth

$$u = \sqrt{\frac{2\,G\,M_e}{R_e}}$$

Escape velocity from the planet

$$v = \sqrt{\frac{2\,G\,M}{R}} = \sqrt{\frac{2\,G\,(2M_e)}{2\,R_e}}$$

$$= \sqrt{\frac{2\,G\,M_e}{R_e}}$$

$$= u$$

16. Orbit speed near the surface of earth

$$v_o = \sqrt{g\,R} \Rightarrow 7\text{ km-s}^{-1}$$

Orbital speed in the new orbit

$$v'_o = \sqrt{g\,(4R)} = 2\sqrt{gR}$$

$$= 2 \times 7 = 14\text{ km-s}^{-1}$$

17. The orbital period of geostationary satellite is equal to the time period of earth on its own axis, *i.e.*, 24 h.

18. Escape velocity from earth, $v_e = \sqrt{2gR_e}$

For planet, $v_p = \sqrt{2g(4R_e)} = 2(\sqrt{2gR_e})$

$$= 2 \times v_e$$

[For earth, escape velocity, $v_e = 11.2\text{ km-s}^{-1}$]

$\therefore \quad v_p = 2 \times 11.2 = 22.4\text{ km-s}^{-1}$

19. Value of g at equator

$$g_e = g - R\omega^2$$

If earth stops rotating then $\omega = 0$

So, $\quad g_e = g$

i.e., Value of g on the equator increases.

20. At earth's surface, $g_e = \dfrac{GM_e}{R_e^2}$

At moon surface, $g_m = \dfrac{GM_m}{R_m^2}$

But, $\quad M_e = 80\,M_m$

and $\quad R_e = 4\,R_m$

$$\therefore \quad g_e = \frac{G\,(80\,M_m)}{(4\,R_m)^2}$$

$$= 5\left(\frac{G\,M_m}{R_m^2}\right) = 5\,g_m$$

$$\therefore \quad g_m = \frac{g_e}{5} = \frac{9.8}{5}$$

$$= 1.96\text{ ms}^{-2}$$

21. Orbital velocity of satellite

$$v_o = \sqrt{\frac{GM_e}{(R_e + h)}}$$

For I[st] satellite

$$v_A = \sqrt{\frac{GM_e}{R_e + R_A}}$$

Similarly, $v_B = \sqrt{\dfrac{GM_e}{R_e + R_B}}$

$$\therefore \quad \frac{v_A}{v_B} = \sqrt{\frac{R_e + R_B}{R_e + R_A}}$$

22. According to Kepler's second law areal velocity of the planet remain constant.

23. Earth is flattened at poles and bulging at the equator because centrifugal force is more at the equator than at poles.

24. Escape velocity from earth's surface

$$v_e = \sqrt{\frac{2\,GM_e}{R_e}} = 11.21\text{ km-s}^{-1}$$

Here: $\quad M_e$ = mass of earth

R_e = radius of earth

M_p = mass of planet = $8\,M_e$

R_p = radius of planet = $2\,R_e$

$\therefore$ Escape velocity from planet's surface

$$v_p = \sqrt{\frac{2GM_p}{R_p}} = \sqrt{\frac{2G(8M_e)}{2R_e}}$$

$$= 2\sqrt{\frac{2GM_e}{R_e}}$$

$$= 2 \times 11.2 = 22.4\text{ kms}^{-1}$$

$$= 22.4 \times 10^3\text{ ms}^{-1}$$

25. Above the earth's surface

$$g_1 = g\left(1 - \frac{2h}{R_e}\right) \quad \text{...(i)}$$

where h = Height above the earth's surface

Below the earth surface

$$g_2 = g\left(1-\frac{d}{R_e}\right) \quad \text{...(ii)}$$

where d = depth below the earth's surface

At surface of earth, $g = 10 \text{ ms}^{-2}$

From Eq. (i)

$$9 = 10\left(1-\frac{2h}{R_e}\right)$$

$$\frac{9}{10} = 1-\frac{2h}{R_e}$$

$$\frac{2h}{R_e} = 1 - \frac{9}{10}$$

$$\Rightarrow \quad \frac{2h}{R_e} = \frac{1}{10}$$

$$h = \frac{R_e}{20}$$

According to question, $d = h$

So, from Eq. (ii)

$$g_2 = g\left(1-\frac{h}{R_e}\right)$$

$$= 10\left(1-\frac{R_e/20}{R_e}\right)$$

$$= 10\left(1-\frac{1}{20}\right)$$

$$= 10 \times \frac{19}{20}$$

$$= 9.5 \text{ ms}^{-2}$$

Chapter

7

Oscillations

1. A particle is executing simple harmonic motion with an amplitude A and time period T. The displacement of the particles after $2T$ period from its initial position is
EAMCET | 2008
(a) A (b) $4A$
(c) $8A$ (d) zero

2. The magnitude of maximum acceleration is π times that of maximum velocity of a simple harmonic oscillator. The time period of the oscillator in second is EAMCET | 2007
(a) 4 (b) 2 (c) 1 (d) 0.5

3. The time period of a simple pendulum is T. When the length is increased by 10 cm, its period is T_1. When the length is decreased by 10 cm, its period is T_2. Then, relation between T, T_1 and T_2 is EAMCET | 2004
(a) $\frac{2}{T^2} = \frac{1}{T_1^2} + \frac{1}{T_2^2}$ (b) $\frac{2}{T^2} = \frac{1}{T_1^2} - \frac{1}{T_2^2}$
(c) $2T^2 = T_1^2 + T_2^2$ (d) $2T^2 = T_1^2 - T_2^2$

4. When a body of mass 1.0 kg is suspended from a certain light spring hanging vertically, its length increases by 5 cm. By suspending 2.0 kg block to the spring and if the block is pulled through 10 cm and released, the maximum velocity in it in ms^{-1} is (Acceleration due to gravity = 10 ms^{-1}) EAMCET | 2003
(a) 0.5 (b) 1 (c) 2 (d) 4

5. An object is attached to the bottom of a light vertical spring and set vibrating. The maximum speed of the object is 15 cm s^{-1} and the period is 628 m-s. The amplitude of the motion in cm is EAMCET | 2003
(a) 3.0 (b) 2.0 (c) 1.5 (d) 1.0

6. If the displacement (x) and velocity (v) of a particle executing simple harmonic motion are related through the expression $4v^2 = 25 - x^2$, then time period is EAMCET | 2002
(a) π sec (b) 2π sec (c) 4π sec (d) 6π sec

7. A body executes simple harmonic motion under the action of a force F_1 with a time period $\frac{4}{5}$s. If the force is changed to F_2 it executes SHM with time period $\frac{3}{5}$s. If both the forces F_1 and F_2 act simultaneously in the same direction on the body, its time period in second is
EAMCET | 2002
(a) $\frac{12}{25}$ (b) $\frac{24}{25}$ (c) $\frac{35}{24}$ (d) $\frac{25}{12}$

8. Two particles P and Q start from origin and execute simple harmonic motion along X-axis with the same amplitude but with period 3 s and 6 s respectively. The ratio of the velocities of P and Q when they meet is EAMCET | 2001
(a) 1 : 2 (b) 2 : 1
(c) 2 : 3 (d) 3 : 2

9. A body is executing simple harmonic motion. At a displacement x its potential energy is E_1 and at a displacement y it potential energy is E_2. The potential energy (E) at displacement ($x + y$) is EAMCET | 2001
(a) $\sqrt{E} = \sqrt{E_1} - \sqrt{E_2}$
(b) $\sqrt{E} = \sqrt{E_1} + \sqrt{E_2}$
(c) $E = E_1 + E_2$
(d) $E = E_1 - E_2$

10. A body of mass 1 kg is executing simple harmonic motion. Its displacement y cm at t sec is given by $y = 6\sin\left(100t + \frac{\pi}{4}\right)$ its maximum kinetic energy is EAMCET | 2000
(a) 6 J (b) 18 J (c) 24 J (d) 36 J

11. A particle executing simple harmonic motion has an amplitude of 6 cm. Its acceleration at a distance from the mean position 2 cm is 8 cm s^{-2}. The maximum speed of the particle is
EAMCET | 2000
(a) 8 cm s^{-1} (b) 12 cm s^{-1}
(c) 16 cm s^{-1} (d) 24 cm s^{-1}

12. The maximum velocity of a particle executing SHM is v. If the amplitude is doubled and the time period of oscillation decreased to $\frac{1}{3}$ of its

original value, the maximum velocity becomes **EAMCET | 1999**

(a) 18 v (b) 12 v (c) 6 v (d) 3 v

13. Two simple pendulums of lengths $16l$ and l are in phase at the mean position at a certain time. If T is the time period of shorter pendulum, the minimum time after which they will be again in phase **EAMCET | 1999**

(a) $\frac{1}{3}T$ (b) $\frac{2}{3}T$ (c) $\frac{3}{2}T$ (d) $\frac{4}{3}T$

14. A simple pendulum hanging freely and at rest is vertical because in that position **EAMCET | 1998**

(a) kinetic energy is zero

(b) kinetic energy is minimum

(c) potential energy is zero

(d) potential energy is minimum

15. The equation of motion of a particle is given by $\frac{dp}{dt} + m\omega^2 n = 0$, where p is the momentum and n is the position. Then, the particle **EAMCET | 1998**

(a) moves along a straight line

(b) moves along a parabola

(c) execute simple harmonic motion

(d) falls freely under gravity

16. Average energy in one time period of a simple harmonic oscillator whose amplitude is A, angular velocity is ω and mass is m is **EAMCET | 1996**

(a) $m\omega^2A^2$ (b) $2\,m\omega^2A^2$

(c) $m\omega^2A^2/2$ (d) zero

17. A simple harmonic oscillator has an amplitude A. The potential energy is one-fourth of the total energy. When the displacement is **EAMCET | 1995**

(a) $\frac{A}{\sqrt{2}}$ (b) $\frac{A}{2}$

(c) $\frac{A}{4}$ (d) $\frac{A}{2\sqrt{2}}$

18. The time period of a simple pendulum measured inside a stationary lift is found to be T. If the lift starts accelerating upwards with an acceleration of $g/3$, the time period of the pendulum will be **EAMCET | 1994**

(a) $\sqrt{3}T$ (b) $\frac{\sqrt{3}}{2}T$

(c) $T/\sqrt{3}$ (d) $T/3$

19. A spring of force constant k is cut into two equal parts. The force constant of each part is **EAMCET | 1994**

(a) $k/2$ (b) k (c) $2\,k$ (d) $4\,k$

20. The displacement of a particle executing SHM is given by $y = 10 \sin (6\,t + \pi/3)$ in metre and time t in second. The initial displacement and the velocity of the particle are respectively **EAMCET | 1992**

(a) $5\sqrt{3}$ m and 30 ms^{-1}

(b) 15 m and $5\sqrt{3}$ ms^{-1}

(c) $15\sqrt{3}$ m and 30 ms^{-1}

(d) $20\sqrt{3}$ m and 30 ms^{-1}

21. The total mechanical energy of a harmonic oscillator of $A = 1$ m and force constant 200 Nm^{-1} is 150 J. Then **EAMCET | 1991**

(a) the minimum PE is zero

(b) the minimum PE is 100 J

(c) the minimum PE is 50 J

(d) the maximum KE is 150 J

22. A simple harmonic oscillation is represented by the equation $y = 0.40 \sin \left(\frac{40\,t}{7} + 0.61\right)$ where y and t are in metre and second respectively. The value of time period is **EAMCET | 1991**

(a) $\frac{7\pi}{20}$ sec (b) $\frac{5\pi}{20}$ sec

(c) $\frac{4\pi}{15}$ sec (d) $2\,\pi$ sec

Answers

1.	(d)	**2.**	(b)	**3.**	(c)	**4.**	(b)	**5.**	(c)	**6.**	(a)	**7.**	(a)	**8.**	(b)	**9.**	(b)	**10.**	(b)
11.	(b)	**12.**	(c)	**13.**	(d)	**14.**	(d)	**15.**	(c)	**16.**	(c)	**17.**	(b)	**18.**	(b)	**19.**	(c)	**20.**	(a)
21.	(d)	**22.**	(a)																

■ Hints & Solutions

1. It is the least interval of time after which the periodic motion of a body repeats itself. Therefore, displacement will be zero.

2. Maximum acceleration

$$= \text{Maximum velocity} \times \pi$$

i.e., $\omega^2 A = \pi\omega A$

where A is amplitude and ω is angular velocity.

$\Rightarrow \quad \omega = \pi$

$\Rightarrow \quad \frac{2\pi}{T} = \pi$

$\Rightarrow \quad T = 2\text{ s}$

3. $T^2 = 4\pi^2\left(\frac{l}{g}\right)$ ...(i)

$T_1^2 = 4\pi^2\left(\frac{l+10}{g}\right)$ ...(ii)

$T_2^2 = 4\pi^2\left(\frac{l-10}{g}\right)$ ...(iii)

Adding Eqs. (ii) and (iii), we get

$$T_1^2 + T_2^2 = 4\pi^2\left[\frac{2l}{g}\right]$$

$$= 2(4\pi^2)\left(\frac{l}{g}\right)$$

$$= 2T^2$$

4. Here: $m_1 = 1$ kg,

extension $l_1 = 5\text{ cm} = 5 \times 10^{-2}$ m

$\therefore \quad m_1 g = k l_1$

where, k = force constant of the spring.

$$k = \frac{m_1 g}{l_1} = \frac{1\times10}{5\times10^{-2}}$$

$$= 200\text{ Nm}^{-1}$$

Time period of the block of mass 2 kg

$$T = 2\pi\sqrt{\frac{m}{k}}$$

$$= 2\pi\sqrt{\frac{2}{200}}$$

$$= 2\pi\times\frac{1}{10} = \frac{\pi}{5}\text{ s}$$

Maximum velocity, $v_{max} = A\omega$

where A = amplitude

$= 10\text{ cm} = 10 \times 10^{-2}$ m

$$v_{max} = A\times\frac{2\pi}{T}$$

$$= 10 \times 10^{-2} \times \frac{2\pi}{\pi/5}$$

$$= 10^{-1} \times 2 \times 5$$

$$= 1\text{ ms}^{-1}$$

5. $v_{max} = 15\text{ cm s}^{-1} = 15 \times 10^{-2}\text{ ms}^{-1}$

$T = 628\text{ ms} = 628 \times 10^{-3}$ s

$\therefore \quad v_{max} = A\omega$

$\Rightarrow \quad v_{max} = A \times \frac{2\pi}{T}$

$$15 \times 10^{-2} = A \times \frac{2\times3.14}{628\times10^{-3}}$$

$$A = \frac{15\times10^{-2}\times628\times10^{-3}}{2\times3.14}$$

$$= 15 \times 10^{-3}\text{ m}$$

$$= 1.5\text{ cm}$$

6. $4v^2 = 25 - x^2$

Differentiating both the sides, we have

$$4(2v)\frac{dv}{dt} = 0 - 2x\frac{dx}{dt}$$

$$\frac{dv}{dt} = A\text{ (acceleration)}$$

$$\frac{dx}{dt} = v\text{ (velocity)}$$

$\therefore \quad 8v \times A = -2x$

$$4A = -x$$

$$\frac{x}{A} = -\frac{1}{4}$$

$\Rightarrow \quad \frac{\text{Displacement}}{\text{Acceleration}} = \frac{1}{4}$

Time period, $T = 2\pi\sqrt{\frac{\text{displacement}}{\text{acceleration}}}$

$$= 2\pi\sqrt{\frac{1}{4}}$$

$$= 2\pi \times \frac{1}{2}$$

$$= \pi\text{ sec}$$

7. If both force acts simultaneously, then time period, $T = t_1 t_2$

$$= \frac{4}{5}\times\frac{3}{5}$$

$$= \frac{12}{25}\text{ s}$$

8. Ratio of velocities $\frac{v_1}{v_2} = \frac{A\omega_1}{A\omega_2} = \frac{\omega_1}{\omega_2}$

$$= \frac{2\pi / T_1}{2\pi / T_2}$$

$$= \frac{T_2}{T_1}$$

$$= \frac{6}{3}$$

$$v_1 : v_2 = 2 : 1$$

9. Potential energy of a body executing SHM

$$U = \frac{1}{2} m\,\omega^2\, y^2$$

$$\therefore \quad U_1 = \frac{1}{2} m\,\omega^2\, x^2$$

$$\Rightarrow \quad x = \sqrt{\frac{2\,U_1}{m\omega^2}}$$

$$\text{and} \quad U_2 = \frac{1}{2} m\,\omega^2\, y^2$$

$$\Rightarrow \quad y = \sqrt{\frac{2\,U_2}{m\,\omega^2}}$$

At displacement $(x + y)$

$$U = \frac{1}{2} m\omega^2 (x + y)^2$$

$$(x + y) = \sqrt{\frac{2\,U}{m\,\omega^2}}$$

$$\sqrt{\frac{2\,U_1}{m\,\omega^2}} + \sqrt{\frac{2\,U_2}{m\,\omega^2}} = \sqrt{\frac{2\,U}{m\,\omega^2}}$$

$$\therefore \quad \sqrt{U_1} + \sqrt{U_2} = \sqrt{U}$$

i.e., $$\sqrt{E} = \sqrt{E_1} + \sqrt{E_2}$$

10. $y = 6\sin\left(100\,t + \frac{\pi}{5}\right)$

Comparing with standard equation

$y = a \sin (\omega t + \theta)$

Amplitude, $a = 6 \text{ cm} = 6 \times 10^{-2} \text{ m}$

$\omega = 100 \text{ rads}^{-1}$

$$\text{Maximum, KE} = \frac{1}{2} m\,\omega^2\, a^2$$

$$= \frac{1}{2} \times 1 \times (100)^2 \times (6 \times 10^{-2})^2$$

$$= \frac{1}{2} \times 10^4 \times 36 \times 10^{-4}$$

$$= 18 \text{ J}$$

11. Amplitude, $a = 6$ cm

Displacement, $y = 2$ cm

Acceleration, $A = 8 \text{ cm s}^{-2}$

$$A = \omega^2\, y$$

$$8 = \omega^2 \times 2$$

$$\Rightarrow \quad \omega = 2 \text{ rads}^{-1}$$

Maximum speed, $v_{max} = a\,\omega = 6 \times 2$

$$= 12 \text{ cm s}^{-1}$$

12. Maximum velocity $= v$

But, $v_{max} = A\omega$

$\therefore \quad v = A\omega$

where A = amplitude,

ω = angular velocity

$$v = A\frac{2\pi}{T}$$

New maximum velocity

$$v'_{max} = A'\omega = A'\frac{2\pi}{T'}$$

$$= 2\,A \times \frac{2\pi}{T/3}$$

$$= 6\left(A \times \frac{2\pi}{T}\right) = 6\,v$$

14. The simple pendulum hanging freely and rest in vertical position, because in this position its potential energy is minimum.

$$\text{PE} = \frac{1}{2} m\omega^2 y^2$$

[In vertical position $y = 0$ $\therefore$ PE = 0 (min)]

15. $$\frac{dp}{dt} = -\, m\omega^2 n$$

$\frac{dp}{dt}$ = rate of change of momentum

$= F$ (force)

$\therefore \quad F = -\, m\omega^2 n$

m and ω are constants

$\therefore \quad F \propto -\,n$

Force $\propto$ displacement

So, this is the condition for simple harmonic motion, so the particle will execute simple harmonic motion.

16. Average energy in one time period of simple harmonic oscillator $= \frac{1}{2} m\omega^2 A^2$

17. The total energy of simple harmonic oscillator

$$E = \frac{1}{2} m\omega^2 A^2$$

PE of simple harmonic oscillator

$$U = \frac{1}{2}m\omega^2 y^2$$

According to question, $U = \frac{E}{4}$

$$\therefore \quad \frac{1}{2}m\omega^2 y^2 = \frac{1}{4}\left(\frac{1}{2}m\omega^2 A^2\right)$$

$$y^2 = \frac{A^2}{4}$$

$$\Rightarrow \quad y = \frac{A}{2}$$

18. Time period of simple pendulum (in stationary lift)

$$T = 2\pi\sqrt{\frac{l}{g}}$$

In moving lift

$$T' = 2\pi\sqrt{\frac{l}{g'}}$$

$$\therefore \quad \frac{T'}{T} = \sqrt{\frac{g}{g'}}$$

Lift is accelerating upwards with acceleration $g/3$.

$$\therefore \quad g' = g + \frac{g}{3} = \frac{4g}{3}$$

So, $$\frac{T'}{T} = \sqrt{\frac{g}{4g/3}}$$

$$\Rightarrow \quad \frac{T'}{T} = \sqrt{\frac{3}{4}}$$

$$T' = \frac{\sqrt{3}}{2}T$$

19. Force constant of spring is inversely proportional to the length of the spring. So, force constant of each part will be $2\,k$.

20. $$y = 10 \sin (6t + \pi/3)$$

For initial displacement we have to put $t = 0$

$\therefore$ Initial displacement

$$y = 10 \sin (6 \times 0 + \pi/3)$$

$$= 10 \sin\frac{\pi}{3}$$

$$= 10 \times \frac{\sqrt{3}}{2} = 5\sqrt{3} \text{ m}$$

Velocity, $v = \frac{dy}{dt} = 10 \cos (6\,t + \pi/3) \times 6$

For initial velocity, $t = 0$

$\therefore$ Initial velocity, $u = 60 \cos\left(6 \times 0 + \frac{\pi}{3}\right)$

$$= 60 \cos\frac{\pi}{3}$$

$$= 60 \times \frac{1}{2} = 30 \text{ ms}^{-1}$$

21. Total energy is 150 J, so maximum potential or maximum kinetic energy will be 150 J.

22. Equation of SHM

$$y = 0.40 \sin\left(\frac{40t}{7} + 0.61\right)$$

Comparing with standard equation

$$y = a \sin (\omega\, t + \phi)$$

$$\omega = \frac{40}{7}$$

$$\frac{2\pi}{T} = \frac{40}{7}$$

$$\Rightarrow \quad T = \frac{2\pi \times 7}{40} = \frac{7\pi}{20} \text{ sec}$$

Chapter

8

General Properties of Matter

1. A steel wire can withstand a load up to 2940 N. A load of 150 kg is suspended from a rigid support. The maximum angle through which the wire can be displaced from the mean position, so that the wire does not break when the load passes through the position of equilibrium, is **EAMCET | 2008**

(a) 30° (b) 60° (c) 80° (d) 85°

2. A load of 1 kg weight is a attached to one end of a steel wire of area of cross-section 3 mm^2 and Young's modulus 10^{11} Nm^{-2}. The other end is suspended vertically from a hook on a wall, then the load is pulled horizontally and released. When the load passes through its lowest position the fractional change in length is ($g = 10$ ms^{-2}) **EAMCET | 2008**

(a) 0.3×10^{-4} (b) 0.3×10^{-3}
(c) 0.3×10^{3} (d) 0.3×10^{4}

3. The surface tension of soap solution is 0.03 Nm^{-1}. The work done in blowing to form a soap bubble of surface area 40 cm^2, (in J), is **EAMCET | 2008**

(a) 1.2×10^{-4} (b) 2.4×10^{-4}
(c) 12×10^{-4} (d) 24×10^{-4}

4. Two rain drops reach the earth with different terminal velocities having ratio 9 : 4. Then, the ratio of their volumes is **EAMCET | 2008**

(a) 3 : 2 (b) 4 : 9
(c) 9 : 4 (d) 27 : 8

5. 1 L of oxygen at a pressure of 1 atm and 2 L of nitrogen at a pressure of 0.5 atm, are introduced into a vessel of volume 1 L. If there is no change in temperature, the final pressure of the mixture of gas (in atm) is **EAMCET | 2008**

(a) 1.5 (b) 2.5 (c) 2 (d) 4

6. There is some change in length when a 33000 N tensile force is applied on a steel rod of area of cross-section 10^{-3} m^2. The change of temperature required to produce the same elongation, if the steel rod is heated, is (The modulus of elasticity is 3×10^{11} Nm^{-2} and the coefficient of linear expansion of steel is 1.1×10^{-5}/°C). **EAMCET | 2008**

(a) 20° C (b) 15° C (c) 10° C (d) 0° C

7. When a wire of length 10 m is subjected to a force of 100 N along its length, the lateral strain produced is 0.01×10^{-3} m. The Poisson's ratio was found to be 0.4. If the area of cross-section of wire is 0.025 m^2, its Young's modulus is **EAMCET | 2007**

(a) 1.6×10^{8} Nm^{-2} (b) 2.5×10^{10} Nm^{-2}
(c) 1.25×10^{11} Nm^{-2} (d) 16×10^{9} Nm^{-2}

8. A liquid does not wet the solid surface if the angle of contact is **EAMCET | 2007**

(a) zero (b) equal to 45°
(c) equal to 90° (d) greater than 90°

9. A horizontal pipe of non-uniform cross-section allows water to flow through it with a velocity 1 ms^{-1} when pressure is 50 kPa at a point. If the velocity of flow has to be 2 ms^{-1} at some other point, the pressure at that point should be **EAMCET | 2007**

(a) 50 kPa (b) 100 kPa
(c) 48.5 kPa (d) 24.25 kPa

10. Two gases A and B having same pressure p, volume V and absolute temperature T are mixed. If the mixture has the volume and temperature as V and T respectively, then the pressure of the mixture is **EAMCET | 2007**

(a) $2p$ (b) p (c) $\frac{p}{2}$ (d) $4p$

11. **Assertion (A)** Ductile metals are used to prepare thin wires.

Reason (R) In the stress-strain curve of ductile metals, the length between the points representing elastic limit and breaking point is very small. **EAMCET | 2006**

(a) Both (A) and (R) are true and (R) is the correct explanation of (A)
(b) Both (A) and (R) are true but (R) is not the correct explanation of (A)
(c) (A) is true but (R) is false
(d) (A) is false but (R) is true

12. Two soap bubbles combine to form a single bubble. In this process, the change in volume and surface area are respectively V and A. If p is the atmospheric pressure, and T is the surface tension of the soap solution, the following relation is true. **EAMCET | 2006**

(a) $4pV + 3TA = 0$ (b) $3pV - 4TA = 0$

(c) $4pV - 3TA = 0$ (d) $3pV + 4TA = 0$

13. An air bubble of radius 1 cm rises from the bottom portion through a liquid of density 1.5 g cc^{-1} at a constant speed of 0.25 cm s^{-1}. If the density of air is neglected, the coefficient of viscosity of the liquid is approximately, (in Pa-s) **EAMCET | 2006**

(a) 13000 (b) 1300 (c) 130 (d) 13

14. Two blocks of masses 1 kg and 2 kg are connected by a metal wire going over a smooth pulley as shown in figure. The breaking stress of the metal is 2×10^9 Nm^{-2}. What should be the minimum radius of the wire used if it is not to break? (Take $g = 10$ m/s^2) **EAMCET | 2006**

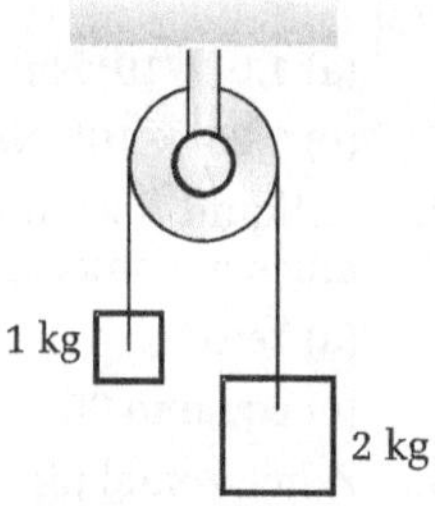

(a) 4.6×10^{-5} m (b) 4.6×10^{-6} m

(c) 2.5×10^{-6} m (d) 2.5×10^{-5} m

15. The radii and Young's moduli of two uniform wires A and B are in the ratio 2 : 1 and 1 : 2 respectively. Both wires are subjected to the same longitudinal force. If the increase in length of the wire A is one percent, the percentage increase in length of the wire B is **EAMCET | 2005**

(a) 1.0 (b) 1.5 (c) 2.0 (d) 3.0

16. The heat evolved for the rise of water when one end of the capillary tube of radius r is immersed vertically into water is (Assume surface tension = T and density of water to be ρ) **EAMCET | 2005**

(a) $\frac{2\pi T}{\rho g}$ (b) $\frac{\pi T^2}{\rho g}$

(c) $\frac{2\pi T^2}{\rho g}$ (d) None of these

17. An iron sphere of mass 20×10^{-3} kg falls through a viscous liquid with terminal velocity 0.5 ms^{-1}. The terminal velocity (in ms^{-1}) of another iron sphere of mass 54×10^{-2} kg is **EAMCET | 2005**

(a) 4.5 (b) 3.5 (c) 2.5 (d) 1.5

18. The relation between the coefficient of real expansion (γ_r) and coefficient of apparent expansion (γ_a) of a liquid and the coefficient of linear expansion (α_g) of the material of the container is **EAMCET | 2005**

(a) $\gamma_r = \alpha_g + \gamma_a$ (b) $\gamma_r = \alpha_g + 3\gamma_a$

(c) $\gamma_r = 3\alpha_g + \gamma_a$ (d) $\gamma_r = 3(\alpha_g + \gamma_a)$

19. The difference between volume and pressure coefficients of an ideal gas is **EAMCET | 2005**

(a) $\frac{1}{273}$ (b) 273 (c) $\frac{2}{273}$ (d) zero

20. The tyre of a motor car contains air at 15°C. If the temperature increases to 35°C, the approximate percentage increase in pressure is (ignore to expansion of tyre) **EAMCET | 2005**

(a) 7 (b) 9 (c) 11 (d) 13

21. A metallic ring of radius r and cross-sectional area A is fitted into a wooden circular disc of radius R ($R > r$). If the Young's modulus of the material of the ring is Y, the force with which the metal ring expands is **EAMCET | 2004**

(a) $\frac{AYR}{r}$ (b) $\frac{AY(R-r)}{r}$

(c) $\frac{Y(R-r)}{Ar}$ (d) $\frac{YR}{AR}$

22. One end of a uniform glass capillary tube of radius $r = 0.025$ cm is immersed vertically in water to a depth $h = 1$ cm. The excess pressure in Nm^{-2} required to blow an air bubble out of the tube
(Surface tension of water = 7×10^{-2} Nm^{-1}
Density of water = 10^3 kg m^{-3}
Acceleration due to gravity = 10 ms^{-2}) **EAMCET | 2004**

(a) 0.0048×10^5 (b) 0.0066×10^5

(c) 1.0048×10^5 (d) 1.0066×10^5

23. Water in a river 20 m deep is flowing at a speed of 10 ms^{-1}. The shearing stress between the horizontal layers of water in the river in Nm^{-2} is (Coefficient of viscosity of water = 10^{-3} SI units) **EAMCET | 2004**

(a) 1×10^{-2} (b) 0.5×10^{-2}

(c) 1×10^{-3} (d) 0.5×10^{-3}

24. There are two holes one each along the opposite sides of a wide rectangular tank. The cross-section of each hole is 0.01 m^2 and the vertical distance between the holes is 1 m. The tank is filled with water. The net force on the tank in newton when the water flows out of the holes is (Density of water = 1000 kg m^{-3})

EAMCET | 2004

(a) 100 (b) 200 (c) 300 (d) 400

25. Two identical vessels A and B with frictionless pistons contain the same ideal gas at the same temperature and the same volume V. The masses of gas in A and B and m_A and m_B respectively. The gases are allowed to expand isothermally to the same final volume $2V$. The change in pressures of the gas in A and B are found to be Δp and $1.5\ \Delta p$ respectively. Then

EAMCET | 2004

(a) $9m_A = 4m_B$ (b) $3m_A = 2m_B$

(c) $2m_A = 3m_B$ (d) $4m_A = 9m_B$

26. Bulk modulus of water is 2×10^9 Nm^{-2}. The pressure required to increase the volume of water by 0.1% in Nm^{-2} is EAMCET | 2003

(a) 2×10^9 (b) 2×10^0

(c) 2×10^6 (d) 2×10^4

27. Two spherical soap bubbles of radii r_1 and r_2 in vacuum combine under isothermal conditions. The resulting bubble has a radius equal to

EAMCET | 2003

(a) $\frac{r_1 + r_2}{2}$ (b) $\frac{r_1 r_2}{r_1 + r_2}$

(c) $\sqrt{r_1 r_2}$ (d) $\sqrt{r_1^2 + r_2^2}$

28. The rate of steady volume flow of water through of capillary tube of length l and radius r, under a pressure difference of p is V. This tube is connected with another tube of the same length but half the radius, in series. Then, the rate of steady volume flow through them is (The pressure difference across the combination is p) EAMCET | 2003

(a) $\frac{V}{16}$ (b) $\frac{V}{17}$ (c) $\frac{16V}{17}$ (d) $\frac{17V}{16}$

29. A large tank filled with water to a height h is to be emptied through a small hole at the bottom. The ratio of times taken for the level of water to fall from h to $h/2$ and $h/2$ to zero is

EAMCET | 2003

(a) $\sqrt{2}$ (b) $\frac{1}{\sqrt{2}}$

(c) $\sqrt{2}-1$ (d) $\frac{1}{\sqrt{2}-1}$

30. A horizontal uniform glass tube of 100 cm, length sealed at both ends contains 10 cm mercury column in the middle. The temperature and pressure of air on either side of mercury column are respectively 31°C and 76 cm of mercury. If the air column at one end is kept at 0°C and the other end at 273°C, the pressure of air which is at 0°C is (in cm of Hg)

EAMCET | 2003

(a) 76 (b) 88.2 (c) 102.4 (d) 122

31. Tanks A and B open at the top contain two different liquids upto certain height in them. A hole is made to the wall of each tank at a depth h from the surface of the liquid. The area of the hole in B is twice that of in A. If the liquid mass flux through each hole is equal, then the ratio of the densities of the liquids respectively, is

EAMCET | 2002

(a) 1 (b) $\frac{3}{2}$ (c) $\frac{2}{3}$ (d) $\frac{1}{2}$

32. A water barrel having water upto a depth d is placed on a table of height h. A small hole is made on the wall of the barrel at its bottom. If the stream of water coming out of the hole falls on the ground at a horizontal distance R from the barrel, then the value of d is

EAMCET | 2002

(a) $\frac{4h}{R^2}$ (b) $4hR^2$ (c) $\frac{R^2}{4h}$ (d) $\frac{h}{4R^2}$

33. A glass capillary tube of inner diameter 0.28 mm is lowered vertically into water in a vessel. The pressure to be applied on the water in the capillary tube so that water level in the tube is same as that in the vessel (in Nm^{-2}) is Surface tension of water = 0.07 Nm^{-1} Atmospheric pressure = 10^5 Nm^{-2}

EAMCET | 2002

(a) 10^3 (b) 99×10^3

(c) 100×10^3 (d) 101×10^3

34. The Poisson's ratio of a material is 0.4. If a force is applied to a wire of this material, there is a decrease of cross-sectional area by 2%. The percentage increase in its length is

EAMCET | 2002

(a) 3% (b) 2.5% (c) 1% (d) 0.5%

35. The mass of oxygen gas occupying a volume of 11.2 L at a temperature 27°C and a pressure of 760 nm of mercury in kilogram is
[Molecular weight of oxygen = 32]

EAMCET | 2002

(a) 0.001456 (b) 0.01456
(c) 0.1456 (d) 1.1456

36. When an air bubble of radius r rises from the bottom to the surface of a lake. Its radius becomes $\frac{5r}{4}$ (the pressure of the atmosphere is equal to the 10 m height to water column). If the temperature is constant and the surface tension is neglected the depth of the lake is **EAMCET | 2001**

(a) 5.53 m (b) 6.53 m
(c) 9.53 m (d) 12.53 m

37. A closed hollow insulated cylinder is filled with gas at 0°C and also contains, an insulated piston of negligible weight and negligible thickness at the middle point. The gas in one side of the piston is heated to 100°C. If the piston moves 5 cm. The length of the hollow cylinder is **EAMCET | 2001**

(a) 15.65 cm (b) 27.3 cm
(c) 38.6 cm (d) 64.6 cm

38. The length of an elastic string is a metres when the longitudinal tension is 4 N and b meters when the longitudinal tension is 5 N. The length of the string in metres when the longitudinal tension is 9 N is **EAMCET | 2001**

(a) $a - b$ (b) $5b - 4a$
(c) $2b - \frac{1}{4}a$ (d) $4a - 3b$

39. A mercury drop of radius 1 cm is sprayed into 10^6 drops of equal size. The energy expended in joule is (Surface tension of mercury is 460×10^{-3} Nm^{-1}) **EAMCET | 2001**

(a) 0.057 (b) 5.7
(c) 5.7×10^{-4} (d) 5.7×10^{-3}

40. Water is conveyed through a uniform tube of 8 cm in diameter and 3140 m in length at the rate 2×10^{-3} m^3s^{-1}. The pressure required in maintain the flow is (Viscosity of water = 10^{-3} SI units) **EAMCET | 2001**

(a) 6.25×10^3 Nm^{-2} (b) 0.625 Nm^{-2}
(c) 0.0625 Nm^{-2} (d) 0.00625 Nm^{-2}

41. A tank with vertical walls is mounted so that its base is at a height H above the horizontal ground. The tank is filled with water to a depth h. A hole is punched in the side wall of the tank at a depth x below the water surface. To have maximum range of the emerging stream, the value of x is **EAMCET | 2001**

(a) $\frac{H+h}{4}$ (b) $\frac{H+h}{2}$
(c) $\frac{H+h}{3}$ (d) $\frac{3(H+h)}{4}$

42. When a uniform wire of radius r, is stretched by a 2 kg weight the increase in its length is 2.00 mm. If the radius of the wire is $\frac{r}{2}$ and other conditions remaining the same, the increase in its length is **EAMCET | 2001**

(a) 2.00 mm (b) 4.00 mm
(c) 6.00 mm (d) 8.00 mm

43. 8000 identical water drops are combined to form a big drop. Then, the ratio of final surface energy to the initial surface energy of all the drops together is **EAMCET | 2000**

(a) 1 : 10 (b) 1 : 15 (c) 1 : 20 (d) 1 : 25

44. When a liquid in a glass vessel, is heated its apparent expansion is 10.30×10^{-4}/°C same liquid when heated in a metal its apparent expansion 10.06×10^{-4}/°C. The coefficient of linear expansion of the metal is (Coefficient of linear expansion of glass = 9×10^{-6}/°C) **EAMCET | 2000**

(a) 51×10^{-6}/°C (b) 43×10^{-6}/°C
(c) 25×10^{-6}/°C (d) 17×10^{-6}/°C

45. A vessel is filled with an ideal gas at a pressure of 10 atm and temperature 27°C. Half of the mass of the gas is removed from the vessel and temperature of the remaining gas is increased to 87°C. Then, the pressure of the gas in the vessel will be **EAMCET | 2000**

(a) 5 atm (b) 24 atm (c) 7 atm (d) 8 atm

46. A flask is filled with 1.3 g of an ideal gas at 27°C and its temperature is raised to 52°C. The mass of the gas that has to be released to maintain the temperature of the gas in the flask at 52°C and the pressure remaining the same is **EAMCET | 2000**

(a) 2.5 g (b) 20 g (c) 1.5 g (d) 0.1 g

47. The mass of a balloon with its contents is 1.5 kg. It is descending with an acceleration equal to half that of acceleration due to gravity. If it is to go up with the same acceleration keeping the volume same, its mass should be decreased by **EAMCET | 1999**

(a) 1.2 kg (b) 1 kg (c) 0.75 kg (d) 0.5 kg

48. The elongation of a steel wire stretched by a force is e. If a wire of the same material of double the length, and half the diameter is subjected to double the force, its elongation will be **EAMCET | 1999**

(a) 16 e (b) 4 e (c) $\frac{e}{4}$ (d) $\frac{e}{16}$

49. When a cylindrical tube is dipped vertically into a liquid then the angle of contact is 140°, if the tube is dipped, with an inclination of 40° then angle of contact is **EAMCET | 1999**

(a) 100° (b) 140° (c) 180° (d) 60°

50. In a compensated pendulum two rods of different metals are used with their lengths in ratio of 2 : 3. The coefficients of linear expansions for metals in the ratio is **EAMCET | 1999**

(a) 1 : 1 (b) 2 : 3 (c) 3 : 2 (d) 9 : 4

51. For a perfect gas, if α, β are the volume and pressure coefficients of expansions, then **EAMCET | 1999**

(a) $\alpha = \beta$ (b) $\alpha > \beta$
(c) $\alpha < \beta$ (d) $\alpha > \beta, \alpha < \beta$

52. The Poisson's ratio σ should satisfy the relation **EAMCET | 1998**

(a) $-1 < \sigma < 0.5$ (b) $-0.5 < \sigma < 1.0$
(c) $0.5 < \sigma < 1.0$ (d) $-1.0 < \sigma < 0.5$

53. Neglecting gravity, the potential energy of a molecule of a liquid on the surface of the liquid when compared to the potential energy of a molecule inside the liquid is **EAMCET | 1998**

(a) greater
(b) less
(c) equal
(d) depending on the liquid, sometimes less sometimes more

54. A real gas can be approximated to an ideal gas at **EAMCET | 1998**

(a) low density (b) high pressure
(c) high density (d) low temperature

55. One litre of helium gas at a pressure of 76 cm-Hg and temperature 27 °C is heated till its pressure and volume are doubled. The final temperature attained by the gas is **EAMCET | 1998**

(a) 900 °C (b) 927 °C
(c) 627 °C (d) 327 °C

56. A copper solid cube of 60 mm side is subjected to a pressure of 2.5×10^7 Pa. If the bulk modulus of copper is 1.25×10^{11} Nm^{-2}, the change in the volume of cube is **EAMCET | 1997**

(a) -43.2 m^3 (b) -43.2 mm^3
(c) -43.2 cm^3 (d) -432 mm^3

57. A gas at temperature 27°C and pressure 30 atm is allowed to expand to atmospheric pressure. If the volume becomes 10 times its initial volume, the final temperature becomes **EAMCET | 1997**

(a) 100 °C (b) 373 °K
(c) 373 °C (d) −173 °C

58. The modulus of elasticity dimensionally equivalent to **EAMCET | 1996**

(a) stress
(b) surface tension
(c) strain
(d) coefficient of viscosity

59. If the temperature of a liquid is increased, then its surface tension **EAMCET | 1996**

(a) decreases
(b) increases
(c) remains the same
(d) increases and then decreases

60. The variation of density of a solid with temperature is given by the formula **EAMCET | 1996**

(a) $d_2 = \frac{d_1}{1+\gamma(t_2 - t_1)}$ (b) $d_2 = \frac{d_1}{1-\gamma(t_2 - t_1)}$
(c) $d_2 = \frac{d_1}{1-2\gamma(t_2 - t_1)}$ (d) $d_2 = \frac{d_1}{1+2\gamma(t_2 - t_1)}$

61. A wire whose cross-sectional area is 2 mm^2 is stretched by 0.1 mm by a certain load. If a similar wire of triple the area of cross-section is stretched by the same load, the elongation of the second wire would be **EAMCET | 1996**

(a) 0.33 mm (b) 0.033 mm
(c) 3.3 mm (d) 0.0033 mm

62. The pressure of a gas in a closed vessel is increased by 0.4% when heated by 1°C, the initial temperature of the gas is **EAMCET | 1995**

(a) 23°C (b) 250°C
(c) − 23°C (d) 300 K

63. A cube is subjected to a uniform volume compression if the side of the cube decreases by 1% the bulk strain is **EAMCET | 1995**

(a) 0.01 (b) 0.06 (c) 0.02 (d) 0.03

64. A wire stretches by 0.01 m when it is stretched by a certain force. Another wire of the same material but double the length and double the diameter is stretched by the same force. The elongation is **EAMCET | 1995**

(a) 0.005 m (b) 0.01 m

(c) 0.02 m (d) 0.04 m

65. When the temperature increases the surface tension of a liquid **EAMCET | 1995**

(a) increases

(b) decreases

(c) remains unchanged

(d) varies depending upon the nature of the liquid

66. A diatomic gas molecule has translational, rotational and vibrational degrees of freedom. The ratio of specific heats $\frac{C_p}{C_V}$ is **EAMCET | 1995**

(a) 1.67 (b) 1.4 (c) 1.29 (d) 1.33

67. One mole of a gas occupies 100 ml at 50 mm pressure. The volume of 2 mole of the gas at 100 mm pressure and same temperature is **EAMCET | 1995**

(a) 50 ml (b) 100 ml

(c) 200 ml (d) 500 ml

68. Under the application of force, a steel wire ($Y = 19 \times 10^{10}$ Nm^{-2}) of 5 m in length suffers an elongation of 1 mm. The potential energy stored per unit volume in this process, in J/m^3 is **EAMCET | 1994**

(a) 1.9×10^3 (b) 9.4×10^3

(c) 9.5×10^3 (d) 3.8×10^3

69. Water film of thickness 0.5 mm exists between two flat circular glass plates of diameter 10 cm each. If the surface tension of water is 7×10^{-4} Nm^{-1}, the force in newton required to pull the plates aparts is **EAMCET | 1994**

(a) $1.75\,\pi \times 10^{-6}$ (b) $7\,\pi \times 10^{-3}$

(c) $7/\pi \times 10^{-5}$ (d) $7/10 \times 10^{-4}$

70. The extension of a wire by application of a load is 0.3 cm. The extension in a wire of same material, but of double the length and half the radius of cross-section, by the same load will be, in cm **EAMCET | 1993**

(a) 0.3 (b) 0.6 (c) 1.2 (d) 2.4

71. A quantity of heat Q is supplied to a monoatomic ideal gas which expands at constant pressure. The fraction of heat that goes into work done by the gas is **EAMCET | 1993**

(a) 2/5 (b) 3/5 (c) 2/3 (d) 1

72. If for a material
Young's modulus $= 6.6 \times 10^{10}$ Nm^{-2} and
Bulk modulus $= 11 \times 10^{10}$ Nm^{-2}, its Poisson's ratio is **EAMCET | 1993**

(a) 0.1 (b) 0.2 (c) 0.3 (d) 0.4

73. A spherical soap bubble of radius 1 cm is formed inside another of radius 3 cm. The radius of a single soap bubble which maintains the same pressure difference as inside the smaller and outside the larger soap bubble is **EAMCET | 1993**

(a) 0.5 cm (b) 1.0 cm (c) 1.5 cm (d) 2.0 cm

74. A plastic tube containing few stones is floating in a tank of water. If the stones are unloaded, the water level **EAMCET | 1992**

(a) remains same

(b) rises

(c) falls

(d) rises or falls depending on the number of stones unloaded

75. A vessel is filled with an ideal gas at a pressure of 20 atm and is at a temperature of 27°C. One-half of the mass is removed from the vessel and the temperature of the remaining gas is increased to 87°C. At this temperature the pressure of the gas will be **EAMCET | 1992**

(a) 10 atm (b) 12 atm

(c) 14 atm (d) 8 atm

76. If the work done in stretching a wire by 1 mm is 2 J, the work necessary for stretching another wire of same material but with double radius of cross-section and half the length by 1 mm (in joule) is **EAMCET | 1991**

(a) 16 (b) 8 (c) 4 (d) 1/4

77. The work done to get n smaller equal size spherical drops from a bigger size spherical drop of water is proportional to **EAMCET | 1991**

(a) $\left(\frac{1}{n^{2/3}}-1\right)$ (b) $\left(1-\frac{1}{n^{1/3}}\right)$

(c) $\left(n^{2/3}-1\right)$ (d) $\left(n^{4/3}-1\right)$

78. If surface tension of H_2O is 7.3×10^{-2} Nm^{-1}. The excess pressure inside spherical drop of radius 1 mm is **EAMCET | 1991**

(a) 146 Nm^{-2} (b) 126 Nm^{-2}

(c) 256 Nm^{-2} (d) 746 Nm^{-2}

79. A car tyre has air at 1.5 atm at 300 K. If p increases to 1.75 atm with V same. The temperature will be **EAMCET | 1991**

(a) 150 K (b) 350 K

(c) 250 K (d) 376 K

Answers

1.	(b)	**2.**	(a)	**3.**	(b)	**4.**	(d)	**5.**	(c)	**6.**	(c)	**7.**	(a)	**8.**	(d)	**9.**	(c)	**10.**	(a)
11.	(c)	**12.**	(d)	**13.**	(c)	**14.**	(a)	**15.**	(c)	**16.**	(c)	**17.**	(a)	**18.**	(c)	**19.**	(d)	**20.**	(a)
21.	(b)	**22.**	(b)	**23.**	(d)	**24.**	(b)	**25.**	(b)	**26.**	(c)	**27.**	(d)	**28.**	(b)	**29.**	(c)	**30.**	(c)
31.	(a)	**32.**	(c)	**33.**	(d)	**34.**	(b)	**35.**	(b)	**36.**	(c)	**37.**	(d)	**38.**	(b)	**39.**	(a)	**40.**	(a)
41.	(b)	**42.**	(d)	**43.**	(c)	**44.**	(d)	**45.**	(b)	**46.**	(d)	**47.**	(b)	**48.**	(a)	**49.**	(b)	**50.**	(c)
51.	(a)	**52.**	(a)	**53.**	(a)	**54.**	(a)	**55.**	(b)	**56.**	(b)	**57.**	(d)	**58.**	(a)	**59.**	(a)	**60.**	(a)
61.	(b)	**62.**	(c)	**63.**	(d)	**64.**	(a)	**65.**	(b)	**66.**	(b)	**67.**	(b)	**68.**	(d)	**69.**	(b)	**70.**	(d)
71.	(a)	**72.**	(d)	**73.**	(c)	**74.**	(c)	**75.**	(b)	**76.**	(a)	**77.**	(b)	**78.**	(a)	**79.**	(b)		

Hints & Solutions

1. Now, at B

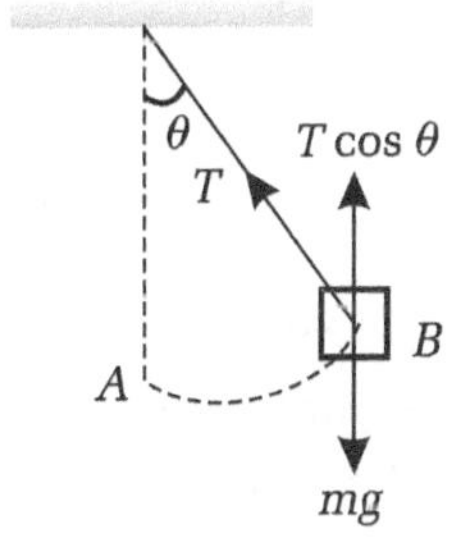

$$T\cos\theta = mg$$

$$T\cos\theta = \frac{150 \times 9.8}{2940}$$

$$\Rightarrow \cos\theta = 0.5$$

$$\Rightarrow \theta = 60°$$

2.

$$Y = \frac{mgl}{A\Delta l}$$

$$\Rightarrow \frac{\Delta l}{l} = \frac{mg}{AY}$$

$$\therefore \frac{\Delta l}{l} = \frac{1 \times 10}{3 \times 10^{-6} \times 10^{11}}$$

$$= 0.3 \times 10^{-4}$$

3. In case of soap bubble

$$W = T \times 2 \times \Delta A$$

$$= 0.03 \times 2 \times 40 \times 10^{-4}$$

$$= 2.4 \times 10^{-4} \text{ J}$$

4. Terminal velocity, $v_T \propto r^2$

or $$\frac{v_{T_1}}{v_{T_2}} = \frac{r_1^2}{r_2^2}$$

$$\therefore \sqrt{\frac{9}{4}} = \frac{r_1}{r_2}$$

or $$\frac{r_1}{r_2} = \frac{3}{2}$$

$$\therefore V = \frac{4}{3}\pi r^3$$

or $$\frac{V_1}{V_2} = \frac{r_1^3}{r_2^3} = \frac{27}{8}$$

5. Ideal gas equation is given by

$$pV = nRT \qquad \text{...(i)}$$

For oxygen, p = 1 atm, V = 1 L, $n = n_O$

Therefore Eq. (i) becomes

$$\therefore 1 \times 1 = n_{O_2}RT$$

$$\Rightarrow n_{O_2} = \frac{1}{RT}$$

For nitrogen $p = 0.5$ atm, $V = 2$ L, $n = n_N$

$\therefore \quad 0.5 \times 2 = n_{N_2} RT$

$\Rightarrow \quad n_{N_2} = \dfrac{1}{RT}$

For mixture of gas

$$p_{mix} V_{mix} = n_{mix} RT$$

Here, $\quad n_{mix} = n_O + n_{N_2}$

$\therefore \quad \dfrac{p_{mix} V_{mix}}{RT} = \dfrac{1}{RT} + \dfrac{1}{RT}$

$\Rightarrow \quad p_{mix} V_{mix} = 2$

6. Modulus of elasticity $= \dfrac{\text{Force}}{\text{Area}} \times \dfrac{l}{\Delta l}$

$$3 \times 10^{11} = \frac{33000}{10^{-3}} \times \frac{l}{\Delta l}$$

$$\frac{\Delta l}{l} = \frac{33000}{10^{-3}} \times \frac{1}{3 \times 10^{11}}$$

$$= 11 \times 10^{-5}$$

Change in length, $\dfrac{\Delta l}{l} = \alpha \Delta T$

$$11 \times 10^{-5} = 1.1 \times 10^{-5} \times \Delta T$$

$\Rightarrow \quad \Delta T = 10$ K or $10°$C

7. Poisson's ratio $= \dfrac{\text{lateral strain}}{\text{longitudinal strain}}$

i.e., $\quad 0.4 = \dfrac{0.01 \times 10^{-3}}{\Delta L / L}$

or $\quad \dfrac{L}{\Delta L} = \dfrac{0.4}{0.01 \times 10^{-3}} = 4 \times 10^4$

Young's modulus

$$Y = \frac{FL}{A \Delta l}$$

$$= \frac{100}{0.025} \times 4 \times 10^4$$

$$= 1.6 \times 10^8 \text{ Nm}^{-2}$$

8. A liquid does not wet the solid surface if the angle of contact is obtuse *i.e.,* greater than 90°. In this case cohesive forces will be greater than adhesive forces and so, the liquid does not wet the surface of solid.

9. According to Bernoulli's equation for horizontal pipe,

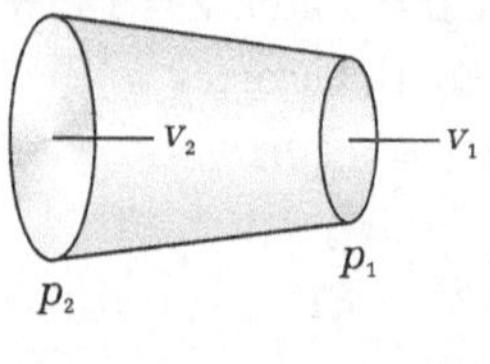

$$p_1 + \frac{1}{2}\rho v_1^2 = p_2 + \frac{1}{2}\rho v_2^2$$

$$\Rightarrow p_1 + \frac{1}{2}\rho(v_1^2 - v_2^2) = p_2$$

$$\Rightarrow \quad p_2 = 50 \times 10^3 + \frac{1}{2} \times 10^3 \times (1^2 - 2^2)$$

$$\Rightarrow \quad p_2 = 50 \times 10^3 - 1.5 \times 10^3$$

$$= 48.5 \text{ kPa}$$

10. The total pressure exerted by a mixture of non-reacting gases occupying a vessel is equal to the sum of the individual pressures which each gas exert if it alone occupied the same volume at a given temperature.

For two gases

$$p = p_1 + p_2 = p + p = 2p$$

12. Let radii of two soap bubbles are a and b respectively and radius of single larger bubble is c.

As excess pressure for a soap bubble is $\dfrac{4T}{r}$ and external pressure p.

$$p_i = p + \frac{4T}{r}$$

So, $\quad p_a = p + \dfrac{4T}{a}$

$$p_b = p + \frac{4T}{b}$$

and $\quad p_c = p + \dfrac{4T}{c} \quad$ ...(i)

and $\quad V_a = \dfrac{4}{3}\pi a^3, \; V_b = \dfrac{4}{3}\pi b^3$

and $\quad V_c = \dfrac{4}{3}\pi c^3 \quad$ ...(ii)

Now as mass is conserved.

$$\mu_a + \mu_b = \mu_c$$

i.e., $\quad \dfrac{p_a V_a}{RT_a} + \dfrac{p_b V_b}{RT_b} = \dfrac{p_c V_c}{RT_c} \quad$ (as $pV = \mu RT$)

As temperature is constant, *i.e.,* $T_a = T_b = T_c$

So, $\quad p_a V_a + p_b V_b = p_c V_c$

which in the light of Eqs. (i) and (ii) becomes,

$$\left(p + \frac{4T}{a}\right)\left(\frac{4}{3}\pi a^3\right) + \left(p + \frac{4T}{a}\right)\left(\frac{4}{3}\pi b^3\right)$$

$$= \left(p + \frac{4T}{c}\right)\left(\frac{4}{3}\pi c^3\right)$$

i.e., $4T(a^2 + b^2 - c^2) = p(c^3 - a^3 - b^3) \quad$ ...(iii)

Now, $\quad V = \dfrac{4}{3}\pi(a^3 + b^3 - c^3)$

and $\quad A = 4\pi(a^2 + b^2 - c^2)$

$\therefore \quad \frac{TA}{\pi} = -\frac{3}{4\pi}Vp$

or $\quad 4TA + 3pV = 0$

13. $v = \frac{2}{9}\frac{r^2\rho g}{\eta}$

$\Rightarrow \quad \eta = \frac{2}{9}\cdot\frac{r^2\rho g}{v}$

$= \frac{2}{9}\frac{(1\times10^{-2})^2\times(1.5\times10^3)\times9.8}{0.25\times10^{-2}}$

$= 130$ Pa-s

14. The stress in the wire $= \frac{\text{tension}}{\text{area of cross-section}}$

To avoid breaking, this stress should not exceed the breaking stress.

Let the tension in the wire be T. The equations of motion of the two blocks are,

$T - 10 = 1\,a$

and $20\text{ N} - T = 2\,a$

Eliminating a from these equations,

$T = \left(\frac{40}{3}\right)\text{N}$

Stress, $\quad T = \frac{\left(\frac{40}{3}\right)}{\pi r^2}$

If the minimum radius needed to avoid breaking is r,

$2\times10^9 = \frac{\left(\frac{40}{3}\right)}{\pi r^2}$

Solving this,

$r = 4.6\times10^{-5}$ m

15. Increase in length $\Delta l = \frac{Fl}{AY}$

or $\quad \Delta l = \frac{Fl}{\pi r^2 Y}$

Percent increase in length

$\Delta x = \frac{\Delta l}{l}\times100 = \frac{F}{\pi r^2 Y}$

Here, same longitudinal force is applied.

So, $\quad \frac{\Delta x_1}{\Delta x_2} = \left(\frac{r_2}{r_1}\right)^2\cdot\left(\frac{Y_2}{Y_1}\right)$

$\frac{1}{\Delta x_2} = \left(\frac{1}{2}\right)^2\cdot\left(\frac{2}{1}\right)$

$= \frac{1}{4}\times\frac{2}{1}$

$\frac{1}{\Delta x_2} = \frac{1}{2}$

$\Delta x_2 = 1\times2 = 2\%$

16. Water rise to height $h = \frac{2T}{\rho g r}$

Potential energy of water column

$U = \frac{mgh}{2} = \frac{2\pi T^2}{\rho g}$

The work performed by force of surface tension is

$W = 2\pi r\,Th$

$= \frac{2\pi T^2}{\rho g}$

From conservation of energy the heat evolved

$Q = W - U$

$= \frac{2\pi T^2}{\rho g}$

17. Terminal velocity $v \propto r^2$

or $\quad \frac{v_1}{v_2} = \left(\frac{r_1}{r_2}\right)^2 = \left[\left(\frac{r_1}{r_2}\right)^3\right]^{\frac{2}{3}}$

$\frac{v_1}{v_2} = \left(\frac{M_1}{M_2}\right)^{2/3}$

$\therefore \quad \frac{0.5}{v_2} = \left(\frac{20\times10^{-3}}{54\times10^{-2}}\right)^{2/3}$

$\frac{0.5}{v_2} = \frac{1}{9}$

$\Rightarrow \quad v_2 = 4.5\text{ ms}^{-1}$

18. Coefficient of real expansion

= coefficient of apparent expansion

+ coefficient of expansion of material of container

$\gamma_r = \gamma_a + \gamma_g$

but, $\gamma = 3\alpha$

So, $\gamma_g = 3\alpha_g$

$\therefore \quad \gamma_r = \gamma_a + 3\,\alpha_g$

19. For an ideal gas the pressure and volume coefficients are exactly equal to each other, so, their difference will be zero.

20. $T_1 = 15°\text{C} = 15 + 273 = 288$ K

$T_2 = 35°\text{C} = 35 + 273 = 308$ K

Volume remains constant.

So, $\quad \frac{p_1}{T_1} = \frac{p_2}{T_2}$

$\frac{p_1}{p_2} = \frac{T_1}{T_2}$

$$\Rightarrow \quad \frac{p_1}{p_2} = \frac{288}{308}$$

$$\frac{p_2}{p_1} = \frac{308}{288}$$

$$\% \text{ increase in pressure} = \frac{p_2 - p_1}{p_1} \times 100$$

$$= \frac{308 - 288}{288} \times 100$$

$$\approx 7\%$$

21. $$Y = \frac{F}{A} \cdot \frac{L}{l}$$

$$\therefore \text{ Force, } \quad F = \frac{AYl}{L} = \frac{AY[2\pi(R-r)]}{2\pi r}$$

$$\Rightarrow \quad F = \frac{AY(R-r)}{r}$$

22. Excess pressure

$$p = hdg + h'dg$$

$$\Rightarrow \quad p = dg(h + h')$$

where h is capillary rise $= \frac{2T}{rdg}$

$$= \frac{2 \times 7 \times 10^{-2}}{25 \times 10^{-5} \times 10^3 \times 10}$$

$$= 0.056 \text{ m}$$

$$\therefore \quad p = 10^3 \times 10[0.056 + 0.01]$$

$$= 0.066 \times 10^4$$

$$= 0.0066 \times 10^5 \text{ Nm}^{-2}$$

23. Shearing stress $= \eta\left(\frac{dv}{dx}\right)$

$$= 10^{-3}\left(\frac{10}{20}\right)$$

$$= 0.5 \times 10^{-3} \text{ Nm}^{-2}$$

24. The net force on the tank

where, $F = 2A\rho gh$

A = area of cross-section of the hole

ρ= density of water

h = vertical distance between the holes

$$\therefore \quad F = 2 \times 0.01 \times 1000 \times 10 \times 1$$

$$= 200 \text{ N}$$

25. Let p_1 and p_2 are the initial and final pressures of the gas filled in A. Then

$$p_1 = \frac{\mu_A RT}{V} \text{ and } p_2 = \frac{\mu_A RT}{2V}$$

$$\therefore \quad \Delta p = p_2 - p_1 = -\frac{\mu_A RT}{2V}$$

$$= -\left(\frac{m_A}{M}\right)\frac{RT}{2V} \quad \text{...(i)}$$

where M is the atomic weight of the gas.

Similarly, $1.5\,\Delta p = -\left(\frac{m_B}{M}\right)\frac{RT}{2V}$ ...(ii)

Dividing Eq. (ii) by Eq. (i), we get

$$1.5 = \frac{m_B}{m_A}$$

or $$\frac{3}{2} = \frac{m_B}{m_A}$$

or $$3m_A = 2m_B$$

26. Bulk modulus, $K = 2 \times 10^9 \text{ Nm}^{-2}$

Change in volume ΔV = 0.1% of initial volume

$$= 0.1\% \text{ of } V = \frac{V \times 0.1}{100}$$

$$= V \times 10^{-3}$$

$$\therefore \quad K = \frac{pV}{\Delta V}$$

$$2 \times 10^9 = \frac{p \times V}{V \times 10^{-3}}$$

$$p = 2 \times 10^9 \times 10^{-3}$$

$$= 2 \times 10^6 \text{ Nm}^{-2}$$

27. Excess of pressure, inside the first bubble

$$p_1 = \frac{4T}{r_1}$$

Similarly, $p_2 = \frac{4T}{r_2}$

Let the radius of the large bubble be R. Then, excess of pressure inside the large bubble

$$p = \frac{4T}{R}$$

Under isothermal condition, temperature remains constant.

So, $$pV = p_1 V_1 + p_2 V_2$$

$$\frac{4T}{R}\left(\frac{4}{3}\pi R^3\right) = \frac{4T}{r_1}\left(\frac{4}{3}\pi r_1^3\right) + \frac{4T}{r_2}\left(\frac{4}{3}\pi r_2^3\right)$$

$$R^2 = r_1^2 + r_2^2$$

$$\Rightarrow \quad R = \sqrt{r_1^2 + r_2^2}$$

28. The rate of flow of water inside a capillary

$$V = \frac{\pi p r^4}{8nl}$$

Pressure difference, $p = \frac{V(8\,n\,l)}{\pi\, r^4}$

In series combination

$$p = p_1 + p_2$$

where p_1 and p_2 are the pressure difference in the two tubes.

$$\therefore \quad \frac{V\,(8\,n\,l)}{\pi\,r^4} = \frac{V'\,(8\,n\,l)}{\pi\,r^4} + \frac{V'\,(8\,n\,l)}{\pi\,(r/2)^4}$$

In series combination, rate of flow of water (V') will be same in both the tubes.

$$\therefore \quad \frac{V}{r^4} = \frac{V'}{r^4} + \frac{V' \times 16}{r^4}$$

$$V = V' + 16\,V'$$

$$V' = \frac{V}{17}$$

29. Time taken $t = \sqrt{\dfrac{2h}{g}}$

Time taken for the level of water to fall from h to $h/2$.

$$t_1 = \sqrt{\frac{2}{g}}\,[\sqrt{h_1} - \sqrt{h_2}]$$

$$= \sqrt{\frac{2}{g}}\left[\sqrt{h} - \sqrt{\frac{h}{2}}\right]$$

$$= \sqrt{\frac{2h}{g}}\left(1 - \frac{1}{\sqrt{2}}\right)$$

Similarly, time taken for the level of water to fall from $h/2$ to 0.

$$t_2 = \sqrt{\frac{2}{g}}\left(\sqrt{\frac{h}{2}} - 0\right)$$

$$\Rightarrow \quad t_2 = \sqrt{\frac{2h}{g}} \cdot \frac{1}{\sqrt{2}}$$

$$\therefore \quad \frac{t_1}{t_2} = \frac{\sqrt{\dfrac{2h}{g}}\left(1 - \dfrac{1}{\sqrt{2}}\right)}{\sqrt{\dfrac{2h}{g}}\,\dfrac{1}{\sqrt{2}}}$$

$$= \frac{\left(\dfrac{\sqrt{2}-1}{\sqrt{2}}\right)}{1/\sqrt{2}} = \sqrt{2} - 1$$

30. On keeping the temperature of the ends of tube at 0°C and 273°C.

Applying ideal gas equation

$$\frac{p_1 V_1}{T_1} = \frac{p_2 V_2}{T_2} = \frac{p_3 V_3}{T_3}$$

$$\frac{76 \times 45}{(273+31)} = \frac{p_2 \times l}{(273+0)} = \frac{p_3(90-l)}{273+273}$$

$$\underset{\text{I}}{\frac{76 \times 45}{304}} = \underset{\text{II}}{\frac{p_2 \times l}{273}} = \underset{\text{III}}{\frac{p_3(90-l)}{546}}$$

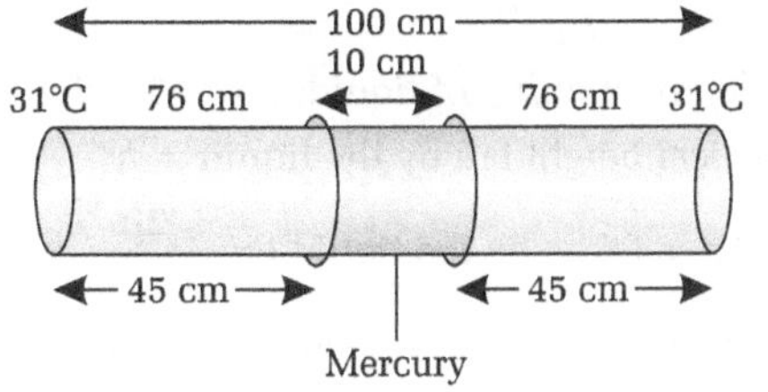

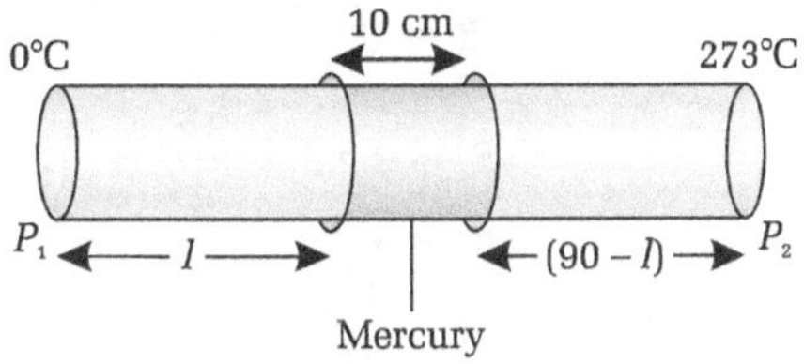

From II and III

$$\frac{p_2 \times l}{273} = \frac{p_3(90-l)}{546}$$

(Mercury column is at rest, so pressure difference $p_2 - p_3 = 0 \Rightarrow p_2 = p_3$)

$$\therefore \quad \frac{p_2 \times l}{273} = \frac{p_2(90-l)}{546}$$

$$2\,l = 90 - l$$

$$\Rightarrow \quad l = 30 \text{ cm}$$

From I and II

$$\frac{76 \times 45}{304} = \frac{p_2 \times 30}{273}$$

$$\Rightarrow \quad p_2 = \frac{76 \times 45 \times 273}{30 \times 304}$$

$$p_2 = 102.4$$

31. Let the velocity of liquid from hole in A is v_1 and velocity of liquid from hole in B is v_2, then from equation of continuity

$$A_1 v_1 = A_2 v_2$$

$$A\,v_1 = 2\,A\,v_2$$

$$v_2 = \frac{v_1}{2}$$

Volume of liquid coming out per second from hole in tank $A = A_1\,v_1 = A\,v_1$

$\therefore$ Mass, $\quad m_1 = A\,v_1\,\rho_1$

Similarly, $\quad m_2 = A_2\,v_2\,\rho_2$

$$= 2A \cdot \frac{v_1}{2}\,\rho_2$$

$$= A\,v_1\,\rho_2$$

But, $m_1 = m_2$

$$A v_1 \rho_1 = A v_1 \rho_1$$

$$\frac{\rho_1}{\rho_2} = 1$$

32. Velocity of efflux of liquid, $v = \sqrt{2 g d}$

Vertical height fall by the liquid $= h$

$\therefore$ Time taken by the liquid $t = \sqrt{\dfrac{2h}{g}}$

$\therefore$ Horizontal range = velocity × time

$$R = \sqrt{2 g d} \times \sqrt{\frac{2h}{g}}$$

$$R^2 = 2 g d \times \frac{2h}{g}$$

$$\Rightarrow \quad R^2 = 4 d h$$

$$d = \frac{R^2}{4h}$$

33. Diameter, $d = 0.28$ mm

$= 0.28 \times 10^{-3}$ m

Radius, $r = \dfrac{d}{2} = 0.14 \times 10^{-3}$ m

Surface tension, $T = 0.07\ \text{Nm}^{-1}$

$$T = \frac{r h d g}{2 \cos \theta}$$

For water $\theta = 0°$

$\therefore \quad \cos \theta = 1$

$$T = \frac{r (h d g)}{2}$$

$$= \frac{r p}{2}$$

$$p = \frac{2T}{r} = \frac{2 \times 0.07}{0.14 \times 10^{-3}}$$

$= 1 \times 10^3\ \text{Nm}^{-2}$

Total pressure = p + atmospheric pressure

$= 1 \times 10^3 + 10^5$

$= 1 \times 10^3 + 100 \times 10^3$

$= 101 \times 10^3\ \text{Nm}^{-2}$

34. Poission's ratio, $\sigma = \dfrac{\Delta R / R}{\Delta l / l}$

$$\frac{\Delta l}{l} = \frac{\Delta R}{R} \times \frac{1}{\sigma}$$

$$= \frac{\Delta R}{R} \times \frac{1}{0.4}$$

$\therefore$ Increase in length $= \left(\dfrac{\Delta R}{R} \times \dfrac{1}{0.4}\right) \times 100$

$$= \frac{2}{2} \times \frac{1}{0.4} = 2.5\%$$

35. At STP (273 K and at 760 mm of Hg) the mass of oxygen = 32 g

From $\dfrac{p_1 V_1}{m_1 T_1} = \dfrac{p_2 V_2}{m_1 T_2}$

$p_1 = 760$ mm, $V_1 = 22.41$ (at STP),

$T_1 = 273$ K,

$p_2 = 760$ mm (given)

$V_2 = 11.2$ it (given)

$T_2 = 27 + 273 = 300$ K

$$\therefore \quad \frac{760 \times 22.4}{32 g \times 273} = \frac{760 \times 11.2}{m_2 \times 300}$$

$$m_2 = \frac{32 \times 273}{300 \times 2} = 14.56 \text{ g}$$

$= 0.01456$ kg

36. Initial pressure, p_1 = atmospheric pressure + pressure of liquid column

$= hdg + h_1 dg$

$h = 10$ m of water

h_1 = depth of lake

$p_1 = dg(h + h_1)$

From, $p_1 V_1 = p_2 V_2$

$$dg\,(10 + h) \times \frac{4}{3}\pi r_1^2 = hdg \times \frac{4}{3}\pi r_2^3$$

$$(10 \times h) \times r^3 = 10 \times \left(\frac{5}{4} r\right)^3$$

$$(10 + h) = 10 \times \frac{125}{64}$$

$$h = \frac{1250}{64} - 10$$

$$\Rightarrow \quad h = \frac{610}{64} = 9.53 \text{ m}$$

37. From Charles' law, $\dfrac{V_1}{V_2} = \dfrac{T_1}{T_2}$

Volume (V) is proportional to the length of hollow cylinder.

$$\therefore \quad \frac{l_1}{l_2} = \frac{T_1}{T_2}$$

$$\frac{l + 5}{l - 5} = \frac{273 + 100}{273 + 0}$$

$$\frac{l + 5}{l - 5} = \frac{373}{273}$$

$$\frac{2l}{10} = \frac{646}{100}$$

$$= \frac{646 \times 10}{2 \times 100} = 32.3 \text{ cm}$$

$\therefore$ Length of cylinder $= 2l = 2 \times 32.3 = 64.6$ cm.

38. Let the initial length of the string be l.

Tension $\propto$ elongation of the string

$$\frac{T_1}{T_2} = \frac{a-l}{b-l}$$

$$\Rightarrow \frac{4}{5} = \frac{a-l}{b-l}$$

$$4b - 4l = 5a - 5l$$

$$l = 5a - 4b$$

Again, $\frac{T_1}{T_3} = \frac{a-l}{x-l}$

x = length of the string at tension T (= 9 N)

$$\frac{4}{9} = \frac{a-(5a-4b)}{x-(5a-4b)}$$

$$\frac{4}{9} = \frac{-4a+4b}{x-(5a-4b)}$$

$$\frac{4}{9} = \frac{4(-a+b)}{x-(5a-4b)}$$

$$\Rightarrow x - (5a - 4b) = 9a + 9b$$

$$x = -9a + 9b + 5a - 4b$$

$$= 5b - 4a$$

39. Total volume of small drops

= volume of big drop

$$10^6 \times \frac{4}{3}\pi r^3 = \frac{4}{3}\pi R^3$$

$$\Rightarrow 10^6 r^3 = R^3$$

$$r = \frac{R}{10^2}$$

Energy expended = work done

$$= \Delta A \times T$$

$$= (n\, 4\pi r^2 - 4\pi R^2)\, T$$

$$= 4\pi (n r^2 - R^2)\, T$$

$$= 4\pi\left[n\left(\frac{R}{10^2}\right)^2 - R^2\right]T$$

$$= 4\pi R^2\left[n\frac{1}{10^4} - 1\right]T$$

$$= 4 \times 3.14 \times (1 \times 10^{-2})^2 \times \left[10^6 \times \frac{1}{10^4} - 1\right] \times 460 \times 10^{-3}$$

$$= 4 \times 3.14 \times 10^{-4} \times (10^2 - 1) \times 460 \times 10^{-3}$$

$$= 4 \times 3.14 \times 10^{-4} \times 99 \times 460 \times 10^{-3} = 0.057 \text{ J}$$

40. Radius $r = \frac{8}{2}$ cm = 4 cm = 4×10^{-2} m,

Rate of flow of water

$$Q = 2 \times 10^{-3} \text{ m}^3\text{s}^{-1}$$

$$Q = \frac{\pi p r^2}{8\eta l}$$

$$\Rightarrow p = \frac{Q(8\eta l)}{\pi r^4}$$

η = coefficient of viscosity of water

= 10^{-3} SI units

$$\therefore p = \frac{2 \times 10^{-3} \times 8 \times 10^{-3} \times 3140}{3.14 \times (4 \times 10^{-2})^4}$$

$$= \frac{2 \times 8 \times 3140 \times 10^{-6}}{3.14 \times 256 \times 10^{-8}}$$

$$= \frac{3140 \times 10^2}{3.14 \times 16}$$

$$= \frac{100 \times 10^3}{16}$$

$$= 6.25 \times 10^3 \text{ Nm}^{-2}$$

41. Total height of water level from the ground

$= (h + H)$

From Torrcelli's theorem we know that to have maximum range, the depth of hole.

$$x = \frac{(h+H)}{2}$$

42. Increase in length of the wire

$$\Delta l = \frac{mgl}{\pi r^2 Y}$$

where Y = Young's modulus of elasticity of the material of the wire.

$$\Delta l \propto \frac{1}{r^2}$$

$$\therefore \frac{\Delta l_1}{\Delta l_2} = \left(\frac{r_2}{r_1}\right)^2$$

$$\Rightarrow \frac{2}{\Delta l_2} = \left(\frac{r/2}{r}\right)^2$$

$$\Rightarrow \frac{2}{\Delta l_2} = \frac{1}{4}$$

$$\Rightarrow \Delta l_2 = 8 \text{ mm}$$

43. Volume of big drop

= 8000 × volume of small drop

$$\frac{4}{3}\pi R^3 = 8000\left(\frac{4}{3}\pi r^3\right)$$

$$R = 20\, r$$

Initial surface energy of all the drops together

$$U_1 = n\,(4\pi r^2)\, T$$

where, T = surface tension, $n = 8000$

Final surface energy of big drop

$$U_2 = 4\pi R^2 T$$

$$\therefore \quad \frac{U_2}{U_1} = \frac{4\pi R^2 T}{n(4\pi r^2)T}$$

$$= \frac{R^2}{nr^2} = \frac{(20r)^2}{8000r^2}$$

$$= \frac{400r^2}{8000r^2} = \frac{1}{20}$$

44. From the relation, $\gamma_r = \gamma_a + \gamma_g$

γ_r = coefficient of real expansion

γ_a = coefficient of apparent expansion

γ_g = coefficient of volume expansion of material of vessel = 3α

For glass, $\gamma_r = 10.30 \times 10^{-4} + 3 \times 9 \times 10^{-6}$
$= 10.30 \times 10^{-4} + 0.27 \times 10^{-4}$
$= 10.57 \times 10^{-4}/°C$

For metal, $\gamma_r = \gamma'_a + \gamma_m$

$10.57 \times 10^{-4} = 10.06 \times 10^{-4} + 3(\alpha_m)$

$0.51 \times 10^{-4} = 3\alpha_m$

$\therefore \quad \alpha_m = 0.17 \times 10^{-4}$
$= 17 \times 10^{-6}/°C$

45. From ideal gas equation

$$\frac{p_1 V_1}{T_1} = \frac{p_2 V_2}{T_2}$$

$$\frac{p_1(m_1)}{T_1 \rho} = \frac{p_2(m_2)}{T_2 \rho}$$

$$\therefore \quad \frac{p_1 m_1}{T_1} = \frac{p_2 m_2}{T_2}$$

$$\frac{10 \times m}{(273+27)} = \frac{p_2 m/2}{(273+87)}$$

$$\frac{10 \times m}{300} = \frac{p_2 \times m}{2 \times 360}$$

$$p_2 = \frac{10 \times 2 \times 360}{300} = 24 \text{ atm}$$

46. From the equation

$$\frac{p_1}{m_1 T_1} = \frac{p_2}{m_2 T_2}$$

But, $\quad p_1 = p_2$ (given)

$$\therefore \quad \frac{1}{m_1 T_1} = \frac{1}{m_2 T_2}$$

$$\frac{1}{1.3 \times (273+27)} = \frac{1}{m_2(273+52)}$$

$$m_2 = \frac{1.3 \times 300}{325} = 1.2 \text{ g}$$

$\therefore$ Gas to be expelled = 1.3 – 1.2 = 0.1 g

47. Acceleration of balloon $= \frac{g}{2}$

$\therefore$ Upthrust acting on the balloon

$$= \frac{mg}{2} = \frac{1.5\,g}{2}$$

Let x kg of mass be removed from the balloon, then from Archimedes' principle.

Upthurst-wt. of the balloon = Force

$$1.5 \times \frac{g}{2} - (1.5 - x)g = (1.5 - x)\frac{g}{2}$$

$$1.5\frac{g}{2} = \frac{3}{2}(1.5 - x)g$$

$$0.5 = 1.5 - x$$

$$x = 1 \text{ kg}$$

48. Young's modulus, $Y = \frac{Fl}{\pi r^2 \Delta l}$

In both the case the wire is of same material. So, Young's modulus will be same.

$$\therefore \quad \frac{F_1 l_1}{r_1^2 \Delta l_1} = \frac{F_2 l_2}{r_2^2 \Delta l_2}$$

$$\frac{Fl}{r^2 \cdot e} = \frac{(2F)(2l)}{(r/2)^2 \Delta l_2}$$

$$\frac{1}{e} = \frac{16}{\Delta l_2}$$

$$\Delta l_2 = 16\,e$$

49. Angle of contact does not depend on inclination of tube, so it will remain 140°.

50. For compensated pendulum, we have the relation

$$\alpha_1 l_1 = \alpha_2 l_2$$

where α_1 and α_2 are the coefficients of linear expansion of the rods.

$$\therefore \quad \frac{\alpha_1}{\alpha_2} = \left(\frac{l_2}{l_1}\right) = \left(\frac{3}{2}\right)$$

$$\alpha_1 \alpha_2 = 3 : 2$$

51. For a perfect gas the coefficients of volume and pressure expansion are equal.

$$\therefore \quad \alpha = \beta$$

52. The value of σ (Poisson's ratio) lies between –1 and 0.5

$$\therefore \quad -1 < \sigma < 0.5$$

53. Potential energy of molecule of a liquid on the surface of the liquid is greater than that of inside the liquid. When the molecule is inside the liquid then it is attracted uniformly by all the molecules.

54. A real gas can be approximated to an ideal gas at low density.

55. Here: $V_1 = 1$ L, $p_1 = 76$ cm of Hg

$T_1 = 27°C = 27 + 273 = 300K,$

$p_2 = 2p, V_2 = 2V_1$

From gas equation

$$\frac{p_1V_1}{T_1} = \frac{p_2V_2}{T_2}$$

$$\frac{76 \times 1}{300} = \frac{2(76) \times 2 \times 1}{T_2}$$

$$T_2 = 1200 \text{ K} = 1200 - 273 = 927°C$$

56. Side of cube, $a = 60$ mm

Pressure, $p = 2.5 \times 10^7$ Pa

$B = 1.25 \times 10^{11}$ Nm^{-2}

Initial volume of cube

$= a^3 = (60)^3 = 216 \times 10^3$

$= 2.16 \times 10^5$ mm^3

Bulk modulus, $B = -\dfrac{pV}{\Delta V}$

∴ Change in volume

$$\Delta V = \frac{-pV}{B} = -\frac{2.5 \times 10^7 \times 2.16 \times 10^5}{1.25 \times 10^{11}}$$

$$= -\frac{2.5 \times 2.16 \times 10}{1.25} = -4.32 \times 10$$

$= -43.2$ mm^3

57. Here: $T_1 = 27°C, T_2 = ?$

$T_1 = 27 + 273 = 300$ K

$p_1 = 30$ atm, $p_2 = 1$ atm,

$V_1 = V, V_2 = 10V$

From gas equation

$$\frac{p_1V_1}{T_1} = \frac{p_2V_2}{T_2}$$

$$\Rightarrow \frac{30 \times V}{300} = \frac{1 \times 10V}{T}$$

$$T_2 = \frac{300 \times 10}{30}$$

$= 100 \text{ K} = 100 - 273 = -173°C$

58. Unit of modulus of elasticity = Nm^{-2}

Unit of stress = Nm^{-2}

∴ Modulus of elasticity and stress are dimensionally same.

59. On increasing the temperature the surface tension of the liquid decreases.

60. Variation of density of α solid with temperature

$$d_2 = \frac{d_1}{1+\gamma(t_2 - t_1)}$$

61. Here: $A_1 = 2$ mm^2, $\Delta l_1 = 0.1$ mm

$A_2 = 3A_1 = 6$ mm^2

$\Delta l_2 = ?$

Elongation of wire, $\Delta l = \dfrac{F \cdot l}{AY}$

where, Y = Young's modulus of elasticity. Both the wire are similar, so l and Y are same.

$$\therefore \quad \frac{\Delta l_1}{\Delta l_2} = \frac{F_1}{F_2} \times \frac{A_2}{A_1}$$

$$\frac{0.1}{\Delta l_2} = \frac{F}{F} \times \frac{6}{2}$$

$$\Delta l_2 = \frac{0.1}{3} = 0.033 \text{ mm}$$

62. Let initial temperature is T.

∴ $T_1 = T$

Final temperature, $T_2 = T + 1$

From Gay-Lussac's law

$$\frac{p_1}{T_1} = \frac{p_2}{T_2}$$

$$\Rightarrow \frac{p_1}{p_2} = \frac{T_1}{T_2}$$

$$\frac{100}{100.4} = \frac{T}{T+1}$$

$100T + 100 = 100.4T$

$0.4T = 100$

$T = 250$ K

$= 250 - 273 = -23°C$

64. Elongation of wire

$$\Delta l = \frac{F \cdot l}{Y\pi r^2}$$

F = applied force

l = initial length

Y = Young's modulus,

πr^2 = area of cross-section

Ist case $0.01 = \dfrac{F \cdot l}{Y\pi r^2}$

IInd case $\Delta l' = \dfrac{F \cdot (2l)}{Y\pi(2r)^2}$

[In second case same force (F) is applied, initial length and diameter (or radius) are double than that in case I]

$$\frac{\Delta l'}{0.01} = \frac{2l}{l}\times\frac{r^2}{(2r)^2} = 2\times\frac{r^2}{4r^2} = \frac{1}{2}$$

$$l' = \frac{0.01}{2} = 0.005 \text{ m}$$

66. For diatomic gas, $C_p = \frac{7}{2}R$

$$C_p = \frac{5}{2}R$$

$$\therefore \quad \frac{C_p}{C_V} = \frac{7/2\,R}{5/2\,R} = 1.4$$

67. Ist case $p_1V_1 = n_1RT_1$

IInd case $p_2V_2 = n_2RT_2$

$$\therefore \quad \frac{p_1}{p_2}\cdot\frac{V_1}{V_2} = \frac{n_1}{n_2}\cdot\frac{T_1}{T_2}$$

$$\frac{50}{100}\times\frac{100}{V_2} = \frac{1}{2}\times 1 \qquad (\because T_1 = T_2)$$

$$V_2 = 100 \text{ ml}$$

68. Potential energy stored per unit volume

$$U = \frac{1}{2}\times\text{stress}\times\text{strain} = \frac{1}{2}\times Y\times(\text{strain})^2$$

$$\left[\because \text{Young's modulus, } Y = \frac{\text{stress}}{\text{strain}}\right]$$

$$U = \frac{1}{2}\times 19\times 10^{10}\left(\frac{\Delta l}{l}\right)^2$$

$$= \frac{1}{2}\times 19\times 10^{10}\left(\frac{1\times 10^{-3}}{5}\right)^2$$

$$= 3.8 \times 10^9 \times 10^{-6}$$

$$= 3.8 \times 10^3 \text{ Jm}^{-3}$$

69. Radius of plate, $r = \frac{10}{2} = 5 \text{ cm} \times 10^{-2} \text{ m}$

Area of film, $A = \pi r^2 = \pi\,(5 \times 10^{-2})^2$

$$= \pi \times 25 \times 10^{-4} \text{ m}^2$$

$\therefore$ Work done, $W = 2TA$

(water film has two free surfaces)

$$= 2 \times 7 \times 10^{-4} \times \pi \times 25 \times 10^{-4}$$

$$= 350\,\pi \times 10^{-8} = 3.5\,\pi \times 10^{-6} \text{ J}$$

$\therefore$ Force required, $F = \frac{W}{s} = \frac{3.5\pi\times 10^{-6}}{0.5\times 10^{-3}}$

$$= 7\pi \times 10^{-3} \text{ N}$$

70. The extension of wire

$$\Delta l = \frac{F\,l}{\pi r^2 Y}$$

where F = load applied

l = initial length of the wire

r = radius of the wire

Y = Young's modulus of material of wire.

Here, both the wires are of same material and same load is applied on them.
So, F and Y will be equal

$$\therefore \quad \frac{\Delta l_1}{\Delta l_2} = \frac{l_1}{l_2}\times\left(\frac{r_2}{r_1}\right)^2$$

$$\frac{0.2}{\Delta l_2} = \frac{l}{2l}\times\left(\frac{r/2}{r}\right)^2$$

$$= \frac{1}{2}\times\left(\frac{1}{2}\right)^2 = \frac{1}{8}$$

$$\Delta l_2 = 0.3 \times 8 = 2.4 \text{ cm}$$

71. Heat is given at constant pressure, so

$$Q = nC_p\cdot\Delta t$$

From Ist law of thermodynamics

$$= \Delta U + \Delta W$$

$$n\,C_p\,\Delta t = nC_V\,\Delta t + \Delta W$$

$$\Delta W = n(C_p - C_V)\,\Delta t$$

$$= nR\,\Delta t$$

Required fraction $= \frac{\Delta W}{Q} = \frac{nR\Delta T}{nC_p\Delta T}$

$$= \frac{C_p - C_V}{C_p} = 1 - \frac{C_V}{C_p}$$

$$= 1 - \frac{1}{\gamma} = 1 - \frac{1}{5/3}$$

$$= 1 - \frac{3}{5} = \frac{2}{5}$$

72. Young's modulus, $Y = 6.6 \times 10^{10} \text{ Nm}^{-2}$

Bulk modulus, $B = 11 \times 10^{10} \text{ Nm}^{-2}$

Poison's ratio, $\sigma = \frac{1}{2}\left(1 - \frac{Y}{3B}\right)$

$$= \frac{1}{2}\left(1 - \frac{6.6\times 10^{10}}{3\times 11\times 10^{10}}\right)$$

$$= \frac{1}{2}(1 - 0.2) = \frac{1}{2}\times 0.8$$

$$= 0.4$$

73. Pressure difference inside smaller soap bubble and outside the larger soap bubble

$$= \frac{4T}{r_1} - \frac{4T}{r_2}$$

Let the radius of single soap bubble which maintains the same pressure difference as inside the smaller and outside the larger, is R

Then, $\frac{4T}{R} = \frac{4T}{r_1} - \frac{4T}{r_2}$

$\frac{1}{R} = \frac{1}{r_1} - \frac{1}{r_2}$

$R = \frac{r_1 r_2}{r_2 - r_1} = \frac{1 \times 3}{3-1}$

$= \frac{3}{2} = 1.5 \text{ cm}$

74. When stones are unloaded then tube will rise up in the water level, so the water level falls.

75. Volume of the gas will remain same.

So, $\frac{p_1}{T_1} = \frac{p_2}{T_2}$

$\frac{20}{(27+273)} = \frac{p_2}{(273+87)}$

$\frac{20}{300} = \frac{p_2}{360}$

$p_2 = \frac{20}{300} \times 360$

$= 24 \text{ atm}$

But mass of the gas is halved.

So, final pressure $= \frac{p_2}{2}$

$= \frac{24}{2} = 12 \text{ atm}$

76. Stretching force $F = \frac{Y\pi r^2 \Delta l}{l}$

Both wires are of same material, so Y will be equal, extension in both the wire is same, so Δl will be equal.

So, $F \propto \frac{r^2}{l}$

$\frac{F_1}{F_2} = \left(\frac{r_1}{r_2}\right)^2 \times \left(\frac{l_2}{l_1}\right)$

$\frac{F_1}{F_2} = \left(\frac{r}{2r}\right)^2 \times \left(\frac{l}{2l}\right) = \frac{1}{8}$

$F_2 = 8F_1$

Work done in first case $W_1 = F_1 \Delta l$

In second case $W_2 = F_2 \Delta l$

$\therefore \frac{W_1}{W_2} = \frac{F_1}{F_2}$

$\frac{2}{W_2} = \frac{1}{8}$

$\Rightarrow W_2 = 16 \text{ J}$

77. Let radius of smaller drops be r and radius of bigger drops be R.

$\therefore n \times \frac{4}{3}\pi r^3 = \frac{4}{3}\pi R^3$

$R = n^{1/3} r$

Change in surface area, $\Delta A = A_2 - A_1$

$= n4\pi r^2 - 4\pi R^2$

$= n4\pi r^2 - 4\pi (n^{1/3} r)^2$

$= n4\pi r^2 \left(1 - \frac{1}{n^{1/3}}\right)$

$\therefore \Delta A \propto \left(1 - \frac{1}{n^{1/3}}\right)$

Work done, $W \propto \Delta A$

So, $W \propto \left(1 - \frac{1}{n^{1/3}}\right)$

78. Excess of pressure inside the spherical drop

$p = \frac{2T}{r}$

where, T = surface tension of the liquid

$= 7.3 \times 10^{-2} \text{ Nm}^{-1}$

r = radius of drop

$= 1 \text{ mm}$

$= 1 \times 10^{-3} \text{ m}$

$\therefore p = \frac{2 \times 7.3 \times 10^{-2}}{1 \times 10^{-3}}$

$= 146 \text{ Nm}^{-2}$

79. Initial pressure, $p_1 = 1.5$ atm

Initial temperature, $T_1 = 300$ K

Final pressure, $p_2 = 1.75$ atm

Volume (V) is kept constant.

So, $\frac{p_1}{T_1} = \frac{p_2}{T_2}$

$\frac{1.5}{300} = \frac{1.75}{T_2}$

$T_2 = \frac{1.75 \times 300}{1.5} = 350 \text{ K}$

Chapter

9

Heat and Thermodynamics

1. In the adiabatic compression, the decrease in volume is associated with EAMCET | 2008
(a) increase in temperature and decrease in pressure
(b) decrease in temperature and increase in pressure
(c) decrease in temperature and decrease in pressure
(d) increase in temperature and increase in pressure

2. Which of the following is true in the case of an adiabatic process, where $\gamma = C_p/C_V$? EAMCET | 2008
(a) $p^{1-\gamma}T^{\gamma}$ = constant (b) $p^{\gamma}T^{1-\gamma}$ = constant
(c) pT^{γ} = constant (d) $p^{\gamma}T$ = constant

3. Two slabs A and B of equal surface area are placed one over the other such that their surfaces are completely in contact. The thickness of slab A is twice that of B. The coefficient of thermal conductivity of slab A is twice that of B. The first surface of slab A is maintained at 100° C, while the second surface of slab B is maintained at 25° C. The temperature at the correct of their surfaces is EAMCET | 2008
(a) 62.5° C (b) 45° C
(c) 55° C (d) 85° C

4. A clock which keeps correct time at 20°C, is subjected to 40°C. If coefficient of linear expansion of the pendulum is 12×10^{-6}/°C. How much will it gain or lose time? EAMCET | 2007
(a) 10.3 s/day (b) 20.6 s/day
(c) 5 s/day (d) 20 min/day

5. The temperature of the system decreases in the process of EAMCET | 2007
(a) free expansion
(b) adiabatic expansion
(c) isothermal expansion
(d) isothermal compression

6. Two cylinders A and B fitted with pistons, contain equal number of moles of an ideal monoatomic gas at 400 K. The piston of A is free to move while that of B is held fixed. Same amount of heat energy is given to the gas in each cylinder. If the rise in temperature of the gas in A is 42 K, the rise in temperature of the gas is B is ($\gamma = 5/3$) EAMCET | 2007
(a) 25.2 K (b) 35 K
(c) 42 K (d) 70 K

7. A black body radiates energy at the rate of E W/m² at a high temperature T K. When the temperature is reduced to $\left(\frac{T}{2}\right)$ K, the radiant energy is EAMCET | 2007
(a) $\frac{E}{2}$ (b) $2E$ (c) $\frac{E}{4}$ (d) $\frac{E}{16}$

8. The temperature of a thin uniform circular disc, of 1 m diameter is increased by 10°C. The percentage increase in moment of inertia of the disc about an axis passing through its centre and perpendicular to the circular face (linear coefficient of expansion = 11×10^{-6} /°C) EAMCET | 2006
(a) 0.0055 (b) 0.011
(c) 0.022 (d) 0.044

9. A given mass of a gas is compressed isothermally until its pressure is doubled. It is then allowed to expand adiabatically until its original volume is restored and its pressure is then found to be 0.75 of its initial pressure. The ratio of the specific heats of the gas is approximately EAMCET | 2006
(a) 1.20 (b) 1.41 (c) 1.67 (d) 1.83

10. Two solid spheres A and B made of the same material have radii r_A and r_B respectively. Both the spheres are cooled from the same temperature under the conditions valid for Newton's law of cooling. The ratio of the rate of change of temperature of A and B is EAMCET | 2006
(a) $\frac{r_A}{r_B}$ (b) $\frac{r_B}{r_A}$ (c) $\frac{r_A^2}{r_B^2}$ (d) $\frac{r_B^2}{r_A^2}$

11. A cyclic process $ABCD$ is shown below in the given p-V diagram. In the following answers the one that represents the same process as in p-V diagram **EAMCET | 2006**

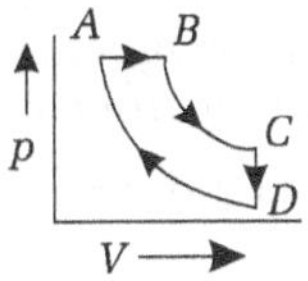

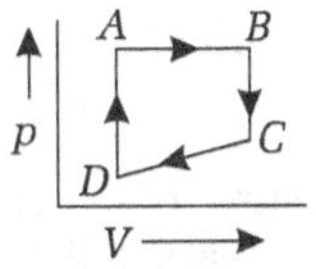
(a)

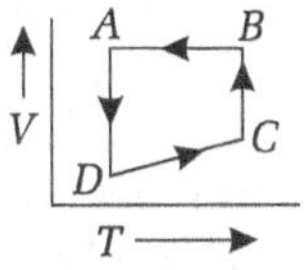
(b)

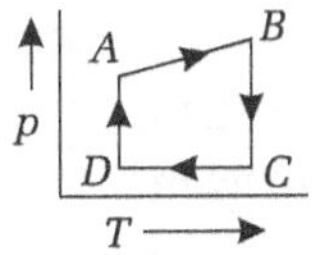
(c)

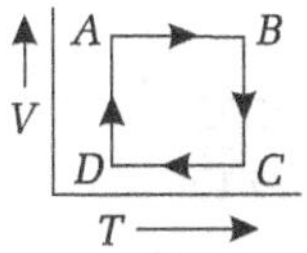
(d)

12. The ratio of specific heats of a gas is γ. The change in internal energy of one mole of the gas, when the volume changes from V to $2V$ at constant pressure p is **EAMCET | 2005**

(a) $\frac{\gamma-1}{pV}$ (b) pV

(c) $\frac{pV}{\gamma-1}$ (d) $\frac{pV}{\gamma}$

13. Two identical bodies have temperatures 277°C and 67°C. If the surroundings temperature is 27°C, the ratio of loss of heats of the two bodies during the same interval of time is (approximately) **EAMCET | 2005**

(a) 4 : 1 (b) 8 : 1

(c) 12 : 1 (d) 19 : 1

14. A metallic solid sphere is rotating about its diameter as axis of rotation. If the temperature is increased by 200°C, the percentage increase in its moment of inertia is (Coefficient of linear expansion of the metal = 10^{-5}/°C) **EAMCET | 2004**

(a) 0.1% (b) 0.2% (c) 0.3% (d) 0.4%

15. The pressure and density of a given mass of a diatomic gas $\left(\gamma = \frac{7}{5}\right)$ change adiabatically from (p, d) to (p', d'). If $\frac{d'}{d} = 32$, then $\frac{p'}{p}$ is (γ = ratio of specific heat) **EAMCET | 2004**

(a) 1/28 (b) 1/64 (c) 64 (d) 128

16. If 4 moles of an ideal monoatomic gas at temperature 400 K is mixed with 2 moles of another ideal monoatomic gas at temperature 700 K, the temperature of the mixture is **EAMCET | 2004**

(a) 550°C (b) 500°C

(c) 550 K (d) 500 K

17. A black body of mass 34.38 g and surface area 19.2 cm^2 is at an initial temperature of 400 K. It is allowed to cool inside an evacuated enclosure kept at constant temperature 300 K. The rate of cooling is 0.04 °C/s. The specific heat of the body in J kg^{-1}K^{-1} is (Stefan's constant, $\sigma = 5.73 \times 10^{-8}$ Wm^{-2}K^{-4}) **EAMCET | 2004**

(a) 2800 (b) 2100

(c) 1400 (d) 1200

18. The temperature of 5 moles of a gas at constant volume is changed from 100°C to 120°C. The change in internal energy is 80 J. The total heat capacity of the gas at constant volume will be in J/K **EAMCET | 2003**

(a) 8 (b) 4 (c) 0.8 (d) 0.4

19. The radiation emitted by a star A is 10,000 times that of the sun. If the surface temperatures of the sun and the star A are 6000 K and 2000 K respectively, the ratio of the radii of the star A and the sun is **EAMCET | 2003**

(a) 300 1 (b) 600 1

(c) 900 1 (d) 1200 1

20. The densities of a liquid at 0°C and 100°C are respectively 1.0127 and 1. A specific gravity bottle is filled with 300 g of the liquid at 0°C upto the brim and it is heated to 100°C. Then, the mass of the liquid expelled in gram is (Coefficient of linear expansion of glass = 9×10^{-6}/°C) **EAMCET | 2003**

(a) $\frac{3}{10.1}$ (b) $\frac{3}{1.01}$

(c) $\frac{3.81}{1.0127}$ (d) $\frac{3.81}{0.0127}$

21. The coefficients of apparent expansion of a liquid when determined using two different vessels A and B are y_1 and y_2 respectively. If the coefficient of linear expansion of the vessel A is α, the coefficient of linear expansion of the vessel B is **EAMCET | 2002**

(a) $\frac{\alpha\gamma_1\gamma_2}{\gamma_1+\gamma_2}$ (b) $\frac{\gamma_1-\gamma_2}{2\alpha}$

(c) $\frac{\gamma_1-\gamma_2+\alpha}{3}$ (d) $\frac{\gamma_1-\gamma_2}{3}+\alpha$

22. A metal sphere of radius r and specific heat s is rotated about an axis passing through its centre at a speed of n rotation/s. It is suddenly stopped and 50% of its energy is used in increasing its temperature. Then, the rise in temperature of the sphere is **EAMCET | 2002**

(a) $\frac{2\pi^2n^2r^2}{5s}$ (b) $\frac{1\pi^2n^2}{10r^2s}$

(c) $\frac{7}{8}\pi r^2n^2s$ (d) $\frac{5(\pi rn)^2}{14s}$

23. 5 moles of Hydrogen $\left(\gamma=\frac{7}{5}\right)$ initially at STP are compressed adiabatically so that its temperature becomes 400°C. The increase in the internal energy of the gas in kilo-joule is (R = 8.30 J mol^{-1}K^{-1}) **EAMCET | 2002**

(a) 21.56 (b) 41.55

(c) 65.55 (d) 80.55

24. When the temperature of a black body increases, it is observed that the wavelength corresponding to maximum energy changes from 0.26 μm to 0.13 μm. The ratio of the emissive power of the body at the respective temperature is **EAMCET | 2002**

(a) $\frac{16}{1}$ (b) $\frac{4}{1}$ (c) $\frac{1}{4}$ (d) $\frac{1}{16}$

25. The wavelength of maximum intensity of radiation emitted by a star is 289.8 nm. The radiation intensity of the star is (Stefan's constant = 5.67×10^{-8} Wm^{-2} K^{-4}, constant b = 2898 μmK) **EAMCET | 2001**

(a) 5.67×10^8 W/m^2 (b) 5.67×10^{12} W/m^2

(c) 10.67×10^7 W/m^2 (d) 10.67×10^{14} W/m^2

26. A lead bullet of mass 10 g travelling at 300 m/s strikes against a block of wood and comes to rest. Assuming 50% of heat is absorbed by the bullet, the increase in its temperature is (specific heat of lead = 150 J/kg °C) **EAMCET | 2001**

(a) 100°C (b) 125°C

(c) 150°C (d) 200°C

27. Thomson coefficient of a conductor is 10 μ VK. The two ends of it are kept at 50°C and 60°C respectively. Amount of heat absorbed by the conductor when a charge of 10 C flows through it, is **EAMCET | 2001**

(a) 1000 J (b) 100 J

(c) 100 mJ (d) 1 mJ

28. During an adiabatic process, if the pressure of an ideal gas is proportional to the cube of its temperature the ratio $\gamma=\frac{C_p}{C_V}$ is (Specific heat at constant volume = C_V specific heat at constant pressure = C_p) **EAMCET | 2000**

(a) $\frac{1}{5}$ (b) $\frac{4}{3}$ (c) $\frac{5}{3}$ (d) $\frac{3}{2}$

29. An ideal gas at a pressure of 1 atm and temperature of 27°C is compressed adiabatically until its pressure becomes 8 times the initial pressure, then final temperature is (γ = 3/2) **EAMCET | 2000**

(a) 627°C (b) 527°C

(c) 427°C (d) 327°C

30. The liquids at temperature 60°C and 30°C respectively have masses in the ratio 3 : 4 and their specific heats in the ratio 4 : 5. If the two liquids are mixed, the resultant temperature is **EAMCET | 2000**

(a) 70°C (b) 50°C

(c) 40°C (d) 41.25°C

31. Two metal rods A and B of equal lengths and equal cross-sectional areas are joined end to end. The coefficients of thermal conductivities of A and B are in the ratio 2 3, when the free end of A is maintained at 100° C and the free end of B is maintained at 0° C, the temperature of the junction is **EAMCET | 2000**

(a) 30° C (b) 40° C (c) 50° C (d) 60° C

32. If on heating liquid through 80°C, the mass expelled is $\left(\frac{1}{100}\right)^{th}$ of mass still remaining, the coefficient of apparent expansion of liquid is **EAMCET | 1999**

(a) 126.5×10^{-4}/°C (b) 0.8×10^{-4}/°C

(c) 1.25×10^{-6}/°C (d) 1.25×10^{-4}/°C

33. When heat energy of 1500 J is supplied to a gas at constant pressure, 2.1×10^5 Nm^{-2}, there was an increase in its volume equal to 2.5×10^{-3} m^3. The increase in its internal energy in joule is **EAMCET | 1999**

(a) 450 (b) 525 (c) 975 (d) 2025

34. A liquid of mass M and specific heat s is at temperature $2t$. If another liquid of thermal capacity 1.5 times at a temperature of $\frac{t}{3}$ is added to it, the resultant temperature will be
EAMCET | 1999

(a) $\frac{4}{3}t$ (b) t (c) $\frac{t}{2}$ (d) $\frac{2t}{3}$

35. The relation between melting point of ice and pressure is shown by ice line, which will be
EAMCET | 1999

(a) with a positive slope
(b) with a negative slope
(c) parallel to pressure axis
(d) parallel to temperature axis

36. A steel bridge in a town is 200 m long. Where minimum temperature in winter is 10°C and maximum in summer is 40°C. The change in length of the bridge from winter to summer is [for steel $\alpha = 11 \times 10^{-6}$/°C] EAMCET | 1998

(a) 3.3 cm (b) 6.6 cm (c) 6.6 m (d) 8.3 m

37. A glass flask of volume 200 cm^3 is completely filled with mercury at 20°C. The amount of mercury that spilt over when the flask is heated to 80°C is (coefficient of volume expansion for glass 27×10^{-8} /°C, mercury 0.18×10^{-8} /°C)
EAMCET | 1998

(a) zero (b) 0.32 cm^3
(c) 1.84 cm^3 (d) 2.40 cm^3

38. The first law of thermodynamics states that
EAMCET | 1998

(a) system can do the work
(b) system has temperature
(c) system has pressure
(d) heat is a form of energy

39. A lead bullet of mass 21g travelling at a speed of 100 m/s comes to rest in a wooden block. If no heat is taken away by the wood, the rise in temperature of the bullet in the wood nearly is (specific heat of lead = 30 cal/kg °C)
EAMCET | 1998

(a) 25 °C (b) 28 °C (c) 33 °C (d) 39 °C

40. In order that heat is conducted from one part of a solid to another part, what is required is?
EAMCET | 1998

(a) Uniform density
(b) Uniform temperature
(c) Temperature gradient
(d) Density gradient

41. The coefficient of real expansion of mercury is 18×10^{-5} /°C. The thermometer bulb has a volume of 10^{-6} m^3 and the cross-section of the stem is 0.002 cm^2. Assuming that the bulb is filled with mercury at 0°C, the length of the mercury column at 100°C will be
EAMCET | 1997

(a) 9 cm (b) 18 cm (c) 9 mm (d) 18 mm

42. A clock with an iron pendulum keeps correct time at 15°C. If the room temperature rises to 20°C, the error in second per day will be (coefficient of linear expansion of iron is 0.000012/°C) EAMCET | 1997

(a) 2.5 s (b) 2.6 s (c) 2.4 s (d) 2.2 s

43. Certain amount of heat supplied to an ideal gas under isothermal conditions will result in
EAMCET | 1997

(a) a rise in temperature
(b) doing external work and a change in temperature
(c) doing external work
(d) an increase in the internal energy of the gas

44. 30 g of water at 300°C is in a breaker. Which of the following, when added to water, will have greater cooling effect? (specific heat of copper = 0.1 cal/g°C) EAMCET | 1997

(a) 100 g of water at 10°C
(b) 15 g of water at 0°C
(c) 3 g of ice at 0°C
(d) 18 g of copper at 0°C

45. Two cylindrical conductors A and B of same metallic material have their diameters in the ratio 1 : 2 and lengths in the ratio 2 : 1. If the temperature difference between their ends is same, the ratio of heats conducted respectively by A and B per sec is EAMCET | 1997

(a) 1 : 2 (b) 1 : 4
(c) 1 : 16 (d) 1 : 8

46. For a constant volume gas thermometer one should fill the gas at EAMCET | 1996

(a) high temperature and high pressure
(b) high temperature and low pressure
(c) low temperature and low pressure
(d) low temperature and high pressure

47. A body does not emit heat energy at
EAMCET | 1996

(a) 0°C (b) 0 K (c) 273°C (d) 373°C

48. A piece of lead falls from a height of 100 m on a fixed non-conducting slab which brings it to rest. The temperature of the piece immediately after collision increases by (specific heat of lead is 30.6 cal $kg^{-1}°C^{-1}$ and $g = 9.8\ ms^{-2}$) **EAMCET | 1996**

(a) 0 K (b) 27°C (c) 7.63°C (d) 4.2K

49. An amount of water of mass 20 g at 0°C is mixed with 40 g of water at 10°C. Final temperature of mixture is **EAMCET | 1996**

(a) 20°C (b) 6.67°C (c) 5°C (d) 0°C

50. Coefficient of real expansion of mercury is 0.18×10^{-3}/°C. If the density of mercury at 0°C is 13.6 g/cc, its density at 473 K will be **EAMCET | 1996**

(a) 13.11 g cc^{-1} (b) 13.65 g cc^{-1}
(c) 13.51 g cc^{-1} (d) 13.22 g cc^{-1}

51. A glass vessel just holds 50 g of a liquid at 0°C. If the coefficient of linear expansion of glass is 8×10^{-4} /°C. The mass of the liquid, it holds at 50° C is **EAMCET | 1996**

(a) 46 g (b) 48 g (c) 56 g (d) 42 g

52. An iron ball of mass 0.2 kg is heated to 100°C and put into a block of ice at 0°C. 25 g of ice melts, then specific heat of iron (in cal $kg^{-1}°C^{-1}$) is [Latent heat of fusion of ice = 80 cal g^{-1}] **EAMCET | 1995**

(a) 1 (b) 0.1 (c) 0.8 (d) 0.08

53. Work done by 0.1 mole of gas at 27°C when it expands to double its volume at constant pressure is (assume R = 2 cal/mol-K) **EAMCET | 1994**

(a) 600 cal (b) 42 cal (c) 60 cal (d) 546 cal

54. A pyknometer weight 40 g when empty and 1040 g when filled with mercury at 0°C. On heating to 100°C, 10 g of mercury overflows. If the coefficient of real expansion of mercury is 0.0002/°C, the coefficient of expansion of glass is **EAMCET | 1994**

(a) 0.00001/°C (b) 0.0002/°C
(c) 0.0002/°C (d) 0.0001/°C

55. In an isothermal change, an ideal gas obeys **EAMCET | 1994**

(a) Boyle's law (b) Charles' law
(c) Gay-Lusac law (d) None of these

56. A compound slab is made with two different materials A and B with coefficient of thermal conductivity $K_A = 2K_B$ and thickness $x_A = \frac{1}{2}x_B$. If the face of the A surface is at 100°C and that of the B surface is at 25°C the temperature of the common surface will be **EAMCET | 1993**

(a) 85°C (b) 45°C (c) 40°C (d) 15°C

57. Boiling point of a liquid can be defined as that temperature at which .... the liquid becomes equal to atmospheric pressure. **EAMCET | 1993**

(a) due point
(b) surface vapour pressure
(c) internal energy of liquid
(d) None of the above

58. When a liquid is taken in a long cylindrical vessel of material, with linear coefficient of expansion α, is heated, the level of liquid did not change. The volume coefficient of expansion of liquid is **EAMCET | 1993**

(a) α (b) 2α (c) 3α (d) $1.5\,\alpha$

59. A liquid of mass m and specific heat s is heated to a temperature T. Another liquid of mass $m/2$ and specific heat $2\,s$ is heated to temperature $2\,T$. If these two liquids are mixed, the resultant temperature of the mixture will be **EAMCET | 1992**

(a) $\frac{2}{3}T$ (b) $\frac{8}{5}T$ (c) $\frac{3}{4}T$ (d) $\frac{3}{2}T$

60. When an ice cube melts and becomes water, the ice water system undergoes **EAMCET | 1992**

(a) the entropy of the system increases and the internal energy increases
(b) the entropy of the system decreases and the internal energy decreases
(c) the entropy of the system deceases and the internal energy increases
(d) the entropy of the system increases and the internal energy deceases

61. A 2 m long Al pipe at 27°C is heated until it is 2.0024 m, at 77°C. The coefficient of linear expansion of Al is **EAMCET | 1992**

(a) 2.4×10^{-5} /°C (b) 1.4×10^{-5} /°C
(c) 2.4×10^{-3} /°C (d) 1.4×10^{-3} /°C

62. Assume that heat capacity of H_2O to be 4.2×10^3 $Jkg^{-1}K^{-1}$ and the latent heat of vaporisation of H_2O to be 22.5×10^5 Jkg^{-1}. The amount of heat in joule required to heat 1 kg of water from 50°C to 100°C and then to convert into steam at 100°C is **EAMCET | 1992**

(a) 12.3×10^5 J (b) 24.6×10^5 J
(c) 20.0×10^5 J (d) 18.6×10^5 J

63. The spheres of different materials one with double the radius and one-fourth wall thickness of the other are filled with ice. If the time taken for complete melting of ice in the larger radius one is 25 min and that for smaller one is 16 min, the ratio of thermal conductivities of materials of larger sphere to smaller sphere is **EAMCET | 1991**

(a) 4 : 5 (b) 5 : 4 (c) 25 : 8 (d) 1 : 25

64. Ice contracts on melting when subjected to pressure and the pressure is increased the melting point **EAMCET | 1991**

(a) increase

(b) decrease

(c) remains same

(d) first increase than decrease

■ Answers

1.	(d)	**2.**	(a)	**3.**	(a)	**4.**	(a)	**5.**	(b)	**6.**	(a)	**7.**	(d)	**8.**	(c)	**9.**	(b)	**10.**	(b)
11.	(a)	**12.**	(c)	**13.**	(d)	**14.**	(d)	**15.**	(d)	**16.**	(d)	**17.**	(c)	**18.**	(b)	**19.**	(c)	**20.**	(b)
21.	(d)	**22.**	(a)	**23.**	(b)	**24.**	(d)	**25.**	(a)	**26.**	(c)	**27.**	(d)	**28.**	(d)	**29.**	(d)	**30.**	(d)
31.	(b)	**32.**	(d)	**33.**	(c)	**34.**	(b)	**35.**	(b)	**36.**	(b)	**37.**	(a)	**38.**	(d)	**39.**	(d)	**40.**	(c)
41.	(a)	**42.**	(b)	**43.**	(c)	**44.**	(a)	**45.**	(d)	**46.**	(b)	**47.**	(b)	**48.**	(c)	**49.**	(b)	**50.**	(a)
51.	(c)	**52.**	(b)	**53.**	(b)	**54.**	(d)	**55.**	(a)	**56.**	(a)	**57.**	(b)	**58.**	(c)	**59.**	(d)	**60.**	(a)
61.	(a)	**62.**	(b)	**63.**	(d)	**64.**	(a)												

■ Hints & Solutions

1. In adiabatic compression temperature and hence internal energy of the gas increases. In compression pressure will increase.

2. For adiabatic change equation of state is

$$pV^{\gamma} = \text{constant}$$

It can also be re-written as

$$TV^{\gamma-1} - \text{constant} \qquad \left[\text{as } p = \frac{nRT}{V}\right]$$

and $p^{1-\gamma}T^{\gamma}$ = constant $\left[\text{as } V = \frac{nRT}{p}\right]$

3. The temperature at the contact of the surface

$$= \frac{K_1 d_2 \theta_1 + K_2 d_1 \theta_2}{K_1 d_2 + K_2 d_1}$$

$$= \frac{2K_2 d_2 \times 100 + 2d_2 \times K_2 \times 25}{2K_2 d_2 + K_2 2d_2}$$

$$= \frac{200 + 50}{4} = 62.5^\circ \text{ C}$$

4.

$$T = 2\pi\sqrt{\frac{l}{g}}$$

$$\frac{\Delta T}{T} = \frac{1}{2}\frac{\Delta l}{l}$$

$$= \frac{1}{2}\alpha\Delta\theta$$

$$= \frac{1}{2} \times 62 \times 10^{-6}(40 - 20)$$

$$= 12 \times 10^{-5}$$

$$\Delta T = T \times 12 \times 10^{-5}$$

$$= 24 \times 60 \times 60 \times 12 \times 10^{-5}$$

$$= 10.3 \text{ s/day}$$

5. In adiabatic expansion of a gas system, gas expands, so temperature of the system decreases.

6. Given, $T = 400$ K, V = constant,

$$\Delta T = 42 \text{ K}$$

Heat supplied, $\Delta Q = \Delta U + \Delta W$

or $\Delta Q = n\times\frac{3R}{2}\times 42+0$

In second process, when piston is free to move

$$\Delta Q = nC_p\Delta T'$$

$$n\times\frac{3R}{2}\times 42 = n\times\frac{5R}{2}\times\Delta T'$$

or $\Delta T' = \frac{126}{5} = 25.2\text{ K}$

7. According to Stefan's law,

$$E \propto T^4$$

or $\frac{E_2}{E_1} = \left(\frac{T_2}{T_1}\right)^4$

or $\frac{E_2}{E} = \left(\frac{T/2}{T}\right)^4 = \left(\frac{1}{2}\right)^4$

or $E_2 = \frac{E}{16}$

8. Increase in area of disc

$$\Delta A = A\,(2\alpha)\Delta t$$
$$= \pi(0.5)^2\,(2\times 11\times 10^{-6})\times 10$$
$$= 0.000055\,\pi$$

New area of the disc,

$$A' = A + \Delta A$$
$$A' = \pi(0.5)^2 + 0.000055\,\pi$$

or $\pi r'^2 = 0.250055\,\pi\text{ m}^2$

or $r' = 0.500055\text{ m}$

Increase in moment of inertia.

$$\frac{I'-I}{I} = \frac{(0.500055)^2-(0.5)^2}{(0.5)^2}$$
$$= 0.00022$$
$$= 0.022\%$$

9. In isothermal process, temperature of the gas remains constant, so the gas obeys Boyle's law. That is,

$$p \propto \frac{1}{V}$$

$\Rightarrow$ $\frac{p_2}{p_1} = \frac{V_1}{V_2}$

$\Rightarrow$ $\frac{2p}{p} = \frac{V_1}{V_2}$

$\therefore$ $\frac{V_1}{V_2} = 2$ ...(i)

Now, the gas is expanded adiabatically, so

$$pV^\gamma = \text{constant}$$

$$\frac{p_1}{p_2} = \left(\frac{V_2}{V_1}\right)^\gamma$$

$\Rightarrow$ $\frac{2p}{0.75p} = \left(\frac{2}{1}\right)^\gamma$

(since volume is restored)

$\Rightarrow$ $\log\left(\frac{8}{3}\right) = \gamma\log 2$

$\Rightarrow$ $\log 8 - \log 3 = \gamma\log 2$

$$\gamma = 1.41$$

10. $\frac{4\pi}{3}r^3\rho c\left(-\frac{dT}{dt}\right) = \sigma 4\pi r^2(T^4 - T_0^4)$

$\therefore$ $\left(-\frac{dT}{dt}\right) = \frac{3\sigma}{\rho rc}(T^4 - T_0^4) = H\text{ (say)}$

Ratio of rates of fall of temperature

$$\frac{H_A}{H_B} = \frac{r_B}{r_A}$$

11. In *p-V* diagrams process *AB* is isothermal process in which pressure remains constant *i.e*, p = constant at all temperatures.
Process *BC* is isothermal process in which, temperature remains constant *i.e.*,
T = constant.
Process *CD* is isochoric process in which volume remains constant *i.e.*, *p-T* diagram *CD* is a straight line passing through origin.
Process *AD* is adiabatic process which corresponds to process *AD* in *p-T* diagram.
Hence, the correct *p-T* diagram is shown in option (a).

12. Change in internal energy

$$dU = dQ - dW$$

At constant pressure

$$dU = C_p dT - pdV$$
$$= C_p dT - RdT$$
$$= (C_p - R)dT = C_V dT$$
$$= \frac{R}{\gamma-1}dT$$
$$= \frac{R}{\gamma-1}\times\frac{pV}{R}$$
$$= \frac{pV}{\gamma-1}$$

13. Given, $T_1 = 277°\text{C} = 277 + 273 = 550\text{ K}$
$T_2 = 67°\text{C} = 67 + 273 = 340\text{ K}$

Temperature of surrounding

$$T = 27°\text{C} = 27 + 273 = 300\text{ K}$$

Ratio of loss of heat $= \frac{T_1^4 - T^4}{T_2^4 - T^4}$

$$= \frac{\left(\frac{T_1}{T_2}\right)^4 - 1}{\left(\frac{T_2}{T_1}\right)^4 - 1} = \frac{\left(\frac{550}{300}\right)^4 - 1}{\left(\frac{340}{300}\right)^4 - 1}$$

$$= \frac{9.5}{0.5} = \frac{19}{1}$$

14. The moment of inertial of a solid sphere about the axis along its diameter is

$$I = \frac{2}{5}mR^2$$

$\Rightarrow \quad I \propto R^2$

$\therefore \quad \frac{\Delta I}{I} \times 100 = 2\left[\frac{\Delta R}{R}\right]100$

but, $\quad \alpha = \frac{\Delta R}{R \times \Delta t}$

$\Rightarrow \quad \frac{\Delta R}{R} = \alpha \Delta T$

$\therefore \quad \frac{\Delta I}{I} \times 100 = 2\,(\alpha)\,(\Delta t)\,100$

$= 2(10^{-5})\,(200)\,(100)$

$= 0.4\%$

15. $\quad pV^\gamma = \frac{p}{\rho^\gamma} = \text{constant}$

$\therefore \quad \frac{p'}{p} = \left(\frac{\rho'}{\rho}\right) = (32)^{7/5}$

$= 32 \times 4 = 128$

16. Temperature of the mixture

$$T = \frac{m_1 T_1 + m_2 T_2}{m_1 + m_2}$$

$$= \frac{4(400) + 2(700)}{4 + 2}$$

$= 500$ K

17. $\frac{d\theta}{dt} = \frac{\sigma A(T^4 - T_0^4)}{ms}$

$\therefore$ Specific heat, $s = \frac{\sigma A(T^4 - T_0^4)}{m\left(\frac{d\theta}{dt}\right)}$

Substituting the values

$$\therefore s = \frac{(5.73 \times 10^{-8})(19.2 \times 10^{-4})[(4)^4 - (3)^4] \times 10^8}{(34.38 \times 10^{-3})(4 \times 10^{-2})}$$

$= 1400$ Jkg^{-1}K^{-1}

18. Given, $n = 5$ moles, $T_1 = 100°C$

$T_2 = 120°C$, $\Delta U = 80$ J

Rise in temperature, $\Delta t = 120 - 100 = 20°C$

$\Delta U = m\, s\, \Delta t$

$\frac{80}{5} = 1 \times s \times 20$

$s = 0.8$ J

$\therefore$ For 5 moles, $\quad s = 0.8 \times 5$

$= 4$ J/K

19. Energy radiated per unit time

$$E = \sigma A T^4$$

where, $\quad \sigma$ = Stefan's constant

$\therefore$ For sun, $E_{sun} = \sigma A_{sun} T_{sun}^4$

According to question

$E_{star} = 10{,}000\, E_{sun}$

$\sigma\, A_{star} \times T_{star}^4 = 10{,}000 \times \sigma\, A_{sun} \times T_{sun}^4$

$\pi\, R_{star}^2 T_{star}^4 = 10{,}000 \times \pi\, R_n^2 \times T_{sun}^4$

$\left(\frac{R_{star}}{R_{sun}}\right)^2 = 10{,}000\left(\frac{T_{sun}}{T_{star}}\right)^4$

$= 10{,}000\left(\frac{6000}{2000}\right)^4$

$\Rightarrow \quad \frac{R_{star}}{R_{sun}} = \sqrt{10000 \times (3)^4}$

$= 100 \times 3^2 = 900$

$R_{star} : R_{sun} = 900 : 1$

20. Density at 0°C, $\quad \rho_0 = 1.0127$

Density at 100°C, $\rho_{100} = 1$

Coefficient of real expansion of liquid

$$\gamma_{real} = \frac{\rho_0 - \rho_{100}}{\rho_{100} \times \Delta t}$$

$$= \frac{1.0127 - 1}{1 \times 100}$$

$= 0.0127 \times 10^{-2}$

$= 1.27 \times 10^{-4}$

$\gamma_{real} = \gamma_{app} + \gamma_g$

γ_g = coefficient of volume expansion of glass $= 3\,\alpha$

$\therefore \quad 1.27 \times 10^{-4} = \gamma_{app} + 3\alpha$

$1.27 \times 10^{-4} = \gamma_{app} + 3 \times 9 \times 10^{-6}$

$\gamma_{app} = 1.27 \times 10^{-4} - 27 \times 10^{-6}$

$= 1.27 \times 10^{-4} - 0.27 \times 10^{-4}$

$= 1 \times 10^{-4}$

$$\therefore \quad \gamma_{app} = \frac{\text{mass expelled}}{\text{remaining mass} \times \Delta t}$$

$$1 \times 10^{-4} = \frac{m_1 - m_2}{m_2 \times 100}$$

$$\left(\frac{m_1}{m_2} - 1\right) = 1 \times 10^{-4} \times 100 = 10^{-2}$$

$$\frac{m_1}{m_2} = 1 + 10^{-2} = 1.01$$

$$m_2 = \frac{m_1}{1.01} = \frac{300}{1.01}$$

Mass expelled $= m_1 - m_2$

$$= 300 - \frac{300}{1.01}$$

$$= \frac{3}{1.01}$$

21. Coefficient of apparent expansion of liquid for vessel $(A) = \gamma_1$

Coefficient of apparent expansion of liquid for vessel $(B) = \gamma_2$

For vessel A

$$\gamma_{real} = \gamma_{app} + \gamma_{vessel}$$

For vessel, $\gamma_{vessel} = 3\,\alpha_A = 3\,\alpha$

$$\because \quad \gamma_{real} = \gamma_1 + 3\alpha$$

For vessel, B

$$\gamma_{real} = \gamma_2 + 3\alpha_B$$

$$\therefore \quad \gamma_1 + 3\,\alpha = \gamma_2 + 3\,\alpha_B$$

$$\alpha_B = \frac{\gamma_1 - \gamma_2 + 3\alpha}{3}$$

$$= \frac{\gamma_1 - \gamma_2}{3} + \alpha$$

22. Rotational KE of sphere $= \frac{1}{2} I\omega^2$

For sphere, $I = \frac{2}{5} mr^2$

$$\therefore \quad \text{KE} = \frac{1}{2} \times \frac{2}{5} mr^2 (2\pi n)^2$$

$$= \frac{1}{5} mr^2 \times 4\pi^2 n^2$$

$$= \frac{4}{5} mr^2 \pi^2 n^2 \text{J}$$

$\therefore$ Heat produced, $\Delta Q = \frac{1}{2}\text{KE}$

$$= \frac{1}{2}\left(\frac{4}{5} mr^2 \pi^2 n^2\right)$$

$$= \frac{2}{5} mr^2 \pi^2 n^2$$

$$\therefore \quad \Delta Q = m\,s\,\Delta t$$

$\therefore$ In temperature

$$\Delta t = \frac{\Delta Q}{ms} = \frac{2}{5} \frac{mr^2 \pi^2 n^2}{m \cdot s}$$

$$= \frac{2}{5} \frac{r^2 \pi^2 n^2}{s}$$

23. Initial temperature, $T_1 = 0°\,\text{C}$

Final temperature, $T_2 = 400°\text{C}$

Work done, $W = \frac{\mu R}{\gamma - 1} \times \Delta t$

$$= \frac{5 \times 8.31}{\frac{7}{5} - 1} \times (400 - 0)$$

$$= \frac{5 \times 8.31 \times 400}{2/5} \text{J}$$

$$= \frac{5 \times 5 \times 8.31 \times 400}{2} \text{kJ}$$

$= 41.55$ kJ

For adiabatic process

Increase in internal energy = work done

$= 41.55$ kJ

24. Given, $\lambda_1 = 0.26\,\mu\text{m}, \lambda_2 = 0.13\,\mu\text{m}$

From Wien's displacement law

$$\lambda T = \text{constant}$$

$$\lambda_1 T_1 = \lambda_2 T_2$$

$$\frac{T_1}{T_2} = \frac{\lambda_2}{\lambda_1} = \frac{0.13}{0.26} = \frac{1}{2}$$

Ratio of emissive powers, $\frac{E_1}{E_2} = \left(\frac{T_1}{T_2}\right)^4 = \left(\frac{1}{2}\right)^4$

$= 1 : 16$

25. Given, $\lambda_m = 289.8$ nm $= 289.8 \times 10^{-9}$ m

From Wien's law

$\lambda_m T = b$ (constant)

Temperature of star, $T = \frac{b}{\lambda_m} = \frac{2898 \times 10^{-6}}{289.8 \times 10^{-9}}$

$$= \frac{2898 \times 10^{-6}}{2898 \times 10^{-10}}$$

$= 10^4$ K

Radiation intensity, $E = \sigma T^4$

$= 5.67 \times 10^{-8} (10^4)^4$

$= 5.67 \times 10^{-8} \times 10^{16}$

$= 5.67 \times 10^8$ W/m^2

26. Given, $m = 10\text{ g} = 10 \times 10^{-3}\text{ kg}, v = 300\text{ ms}^{-1}$

Heat produced $= \frac{1}{2} \times \text{KE}$ of the bullet

$$= \frac{1}{2}\left(\frac{1}{2}mv^2\right)$$

$$= \frac{1}{4} \times 10 \times 10^{-3} \times (300)^2$$

$$= 2.5 \times 10^{-3} \times 9 \times 10^4$$

$$= 225\text{ J}$$

From $Q = m\, s\, \Delta t$

$$225 = 10 \times 10^{-3} \times 150 \times \Delta t$$

$$\Delta t = \frac{225}{10 \times 10^{-3} \times 150}$$

$$= \frac{225}{1.5} = 150°\text{C}$$

27. Amount of heat absorbed, $H = \sigma\, q\, \Delta t$

$$= 10 \times 10^{-6} \times 10 \times (60 - 50)$$

$$= 10 \times 10^{-6} \times 10 \times 10$$

$$= 10^{-3}\text{ J} = 1\text{ mJ}$$

28. According to question $p \propto T^3$

$$\therefore \quad \frac{p}{T^3} = \text{constant}$$

or $\frac{T^3}{p} = \text{constant}$

But, standard equation

$$\frac{T^\gamma}{p^{\gamma-1}} = \text{constant}$$

On comparing $= \frac{\gamma}{\gamma - 1} = \frac{3}{1}$

$$\Rightarrow \quad \gamma = (3\gamma - 3)$$

$$\gamma = \frac{3}{2}$$

29. Given, $p_1 = 1\text{ atm}$,

$T_1 = 27°\text{C} = (273 + 27) = 300\text{ K}$

$p_2 = 8\,p_1 = 8 \times 1 = 8\text{ atm}$

For adiabatic process $\frac{T^\gamma}{p^{\gamma-1}} = \text{constant}$

$$\therefore \quad \frac{T_1^\gamma}{p_1^{\gamma-1}} = \frac{T_2^\gamma}{p_2^{\gamma-1}}$$

$$\frac{(300)^{3/2}}{(1)^{\frac{3}{2}-1}} = \frac{T_2^{3/2}}{(8)^{\frac{3}{2}-1}}$$

$$T_2^{3/2} = (300)^{\frac{3}{2}} \times (8)^{\frac{1}{2}}$$

$$= (300^3 \times 8)^{\frac{1}{2}}$$

$$T_2 = \left[(300^3 \times 8)^{\frac{1}{2}}\right]^{\frac{2}{3}}$$

$$= [300^3 \times 8]^{\frac{1}{3}} = 300 \times 2 = 600\text{ K}$$

$$= 600 - 273 = 327°\text{C}$$

30. Given, $t_1 = 60°\text{C}, m_1 = 3\,k$,

$m_2 = 4\,k, t_2 = 30°\text{C}$

$s_1 = 4x, s_2 = 5x$

Heat given by hot liquid = Heat taken by cool liquid

$$m_1\, s_1\, (t_1 - t) = m_2\, s_2\, (t - t_2)$$

where, t = temperature of mixture

$$3\,k \times 4\,x\,(60 - t) = 4\,k \times 5\,x\,(t - 30)$$

$$12\,(60 - t) = 20\,(t - 30)$$

$$3\,(60 - t) = 5\,(t - 30)$$

$$180 - 3\,t = 5\,t - 150$$

$$330 = 8\,t$$

$$\Rightarrow \quad t = \frac{330}{8}$$

$$= 41.25°\text{C}$$

31. Given, $K_1 : K_2 = 2 : 3$

$$\Rightarrow \quad K_1 = 2\,x, K_2 = 3\,x$$

$$l_1 = l_2, A_1 = A_2,$$

$$\theta_1 = 100°\text{C}, \theta_2 = 0°\text{C}$$

Temperature of junction

$$\theta = \frac{K_1\theta_1 l_2 + K_2\theta_2 l_1}{K_1 l_2 + K_2 l_1}$$

$$= \frac{2x \times 100 \times l + 3x + 0 \times l}{2x \times l + 3x \times l}$$

$$= \frac{200\,x\,l}{5\,x\,l} = 40°\text{C}$$

32. Coefficient of apparent expansion

$$\gamma_a = \frac{\Delta V}{V \times \Delta t} = \frac{\Delta m / \rho}{m / \rho \times \Delta t}$$

where, ρ = density of liquid

$$\gamma_a = \frac{\Delta m}{m \times \Delta t} = \frac{\frac{1}{100}m}{m \times 80}$$

$$= \frac{1}{8000}$$

$$= 0.125 \times 10^{-3}$$

$$= 1.25 \times 10^{-4}\text{ /°C}$$

33. Given, $dQ = 1500\text{ J}, dV = 2.5 \times 10^{-3}\text{ m}^3$,

$p = 2.1 \times 10^5\text{ Nm}^{-2}$

From first law of thermodynamics

$$dQ = dU + dW$$

dU = change in internal energy

dW = external work

$$= pdV = 2.1 \times 10^5 \times 2.5 \times 10^{-3}$$

$$= 5.25 \times 10^2 = 525 \text{ J}$$

$$dU = dQ - dW = 1500 - 525 = 975 \text{ J}$$

34. Heat given by hot liquid = Heat taken by cold liquid

$$m_1 s_1 (t_1 - T) = m_2 s_2 (T - t_2)$$

where T = temperature of mixture.

or, $c_1 (t_1 - T) = c_2 (T - t_2)$

where c_1 and c_2 are the thermal capacities of the liquids.

$$\therefore \quad c(2t - T) = 1.5\, c\left(T - \frac{t}{3}\right)$$

$$2t - T = 1.5\,T - 0.5\,t$$

$$2.5\,t = 2.5\,T$$

$$T = t$$

35. On increasing the pressure, melting point of ice will decrease, so ice line will be with a negative slope.

36. $l = 200$ m, $\Delta t = (40 - 10)°\text{C} = 30°$ C,

$\alpha = 11 \times 10^{-6}$/°C

$$\Delta l = l\alpha\Delta t = 200 \times 11 \times 10^{-6} \times 30$$

$$= 6000 \times 11 \times 10^{-6}$$

$$= 66 \times 10^{-3}$$

$$= 6.6 \times 10^{-2} \text{ m}$$

$$= 6.6 \text{ cm}$$

37. $\Delta t = 80°\text{C} - 20°\text{C} = 60°\text{C}$

Increase in volume of the flask

$$\Delta V = V\gamma\Delta t s = 200 \times 27 \times 10^{-8} \times 60$$

$$= 12000 \times 27 \times 10^{-8}$$

$$= 324 \times 10^{-5}$$

$$= 3.24 \times 10^{-3} \text{ cm}^3$$

Increase in volume of the mercury

$$\Delta V = V\gamma\Delta t = 200 \times 0.18 \times 10^{-8} \times 60$$

$$= 12000 \times 10^{-8} \times 0.18$$

$$= 2.16 \times 10^{-5} \text{ cm}^3$$

Increase in volume of flask is more than the increase in volume of mercury, so mercury will not split out.

38. First law of thermodynamics tells that when heat is given to the system then it can do some work *i.e.*, heat is a form of energy.

39. Given, $m = 21 \text{ g} = 21 \times 10^{-3}$ kg, $v = 100 \text{ ms}^{-1}$

KE of bullet $= \frac{1}{2}mv^2$

$$= \frac{1}{2} \times 21 \times 10^{-3} \times (100)^2$$

$$= \frac{1}{2} \times 21 \times 10^{-3} \times 10^4$$

$$= \frac{210}{2} = 105 \text{ J} = \frac{105}{4.2} \text{ cal}$$

$\therefore$ Heat produced $= \text{KE} = \frac{105}{4.2}$ cal

$$m\,s\,\Delta t = \frac{105}{4.2}$$

$$21 \times 10^{-3} \times 30 \times \Delta t = \frac{105}{4.2}$$

$$\Rightarrow \quad \Delta t = \frac{105}{21 \times 10^{-3} \times 30 \times 4.2}$$

$$= \frac{5}{4.2 \times 30 \times 10^{-3}}$$

$$= \frac{500}{12.6} \simeq 39°\text{C}$$

40. For conduction of heat from one part to other part of the solid, we require temperature difference per unit length *i.e.*, temperature gradient.

41. Coefficient of real expansion

$$\gamma_r = 13 \times 10^{-5} \text{ /°C}$$

Initial volume, $V = 10^{-6} \text{ m}^3$

$\therefore$ Increase in volume of mercury

$$\Delta V = \gamma_r V \Delta t$$

$$= 18 \times 10^{-5} \times 10^{-6} \times (100 - 0)$$

$$= 18 \times 10^{-11} \times 100$$

$$= 18 \times 10^{-9} \text{ m}^3 = 0.018 \times 10^{-6} \text{ m}^3$$

$$= 0.018 \text{ cm}^3$$

$\therefore$ Length of mercury column

$$= \frac{\text{Increase in volume}}{\text{Cross-sectional area}}$$

$$= \frac{0.018}{0.002}$$

$$= 9 \text{ cm}$$

42. Time period $T = 2\pi\sqrt{\frac{l}{g}}$

On charging the temperature the length will change

Change in length, $\frac{\Delta l}{l} = \alpha\,\Delta t$

∴ Change in time period

$$\frac{\Delta T}{T} = \frac{1}{2}\frac{\Delta l}{l} = \frac{1}{2}\times(\alpha\times\Delta t) \text{ sec}$$

∴ Change in time period per day

$$= \frac{1}{2}(\alpha\times\Delta t)\times 86400$$

(∵ 1 day has 86400 s)

$$= \frac{1}{2}\times 0.000012\times(20-15)\times 86400$$

$$= 2.59 \approx 2.6 \text{ s}$$

43. From first law of thermodynamics

$$\Delta Q = \Delta U + \Delta W$$

For isothermal process $\Delta U = 0$

(∵ Internal energy of ideal gas depends only on the temperature)

i.e., amount of heat supplied to an ideal gas will result in doing external work.

44. Amount of heat taken by 100 g of water at 10°C will be maximum, so it will have greatest cooling effect.

45. $r_1 : r_2 = 1 : 2$

(ratio of radius is equal to the ratio of diameter)

$$l_1 : l_2 = 2 : 1$$

$$\Rightarrow l_2 : l_1 = 1 : 2$$

Heat conducted through a conductor

$$Q = \frac{K\,A\,\Delta\theta}{l} = \frac{K\,\pi\,r^2\,\Delta\theta}{l}$$

Both conductors are of same material, so K is same. Hence, temperature difference $\Delta\theta$ is same.

$$\therefore \quad \frac{Q_1}{Q_2} = \left(\frac{r_1}{r_2}\right)^2\left(\frac{l_2}{l_1}\right)$$

$$\frac{Q_1}{Q_2} = \left(\frac{1}{2}\right)^2\left(\frac{1}{2}\right) = \frac{1}{4}\times\frac{1}{2}$$

$$Q_1 : Q_2 = 1 : 8$$

46. In a constant volume gas thermometer, gas is filled at low pressure and high temperature, so that it obey gas laws.

47. At absolute zero temperature *i.e.*, at 0 K a body does not emit heat energy.

48. $h = 100$ m

Energy of lead piece = mgh joule

Heat produced, $R = \dfrac{mgh}{J}$ cal

J = mechanical equivalent of heat = 4.2 J/cal

If rise in temperature is Δt

Then, $Q = m\,s\,\Delta t$

s = specific heat of lead

$$m\,s\,\Delta t = \frac{mgh}{J}$$

$$30.6\times\Delta t = \frac{9.8\times 100}{4.2}$$

$$\Delta t = \frac{9.8\times 100}{4.2\times 30.6}$$

$$= 7.63^\circ\text{C}$$

49. Given, $m_1 = 20$ g, $t_1 = 0^\circ$C, $m_2 = 40$ g, $t_2 = 10^\circ$C.

From principle of calorimetry

Heat given by hot water = Heat taken by cold water

$$m_2\,s\,(t_2 - t) = m_1\,s\,(t - t_1)$$

where, t = final temperature or temperature of mixture

$$40\,(10 - t) = 20\,(t - 0)$$

$$2\,(10 - t) = t$$

$$20 - 2\,t = t$$

$$\Rightarrow \quad 3\,t = 20$$

$$t = \frac{20}{3} = 6.67^\circ\text{C}$$

50. Given, $\gamma_r = 0.18\times 10^{-3}$ /°C, $d_0 = 13.6$ g cc^{-1}

$t_1 = 0^\circ\text{C} = 273$ K, $t_2 = 473$ K

$$\therefore \quad \Delta t = t_2 - t_1$$

$$= 473 - 273$$

$$= 200 \text{ K} = 200^\circ\text{C}$$

Density at 200°C

$$d' = d_0\,(1 - \gamma_r\,\Delta t)$$

$$= 13.6\,[1 - 0.18\times 10^{-3}\,(200 - 0)]$$

$$= 13.6\,[1 - 0.36\times 10^{-1}]$$

$$= 13.6\,[1 - 0.036]$$

$$= 13.11 \text{ g cc}^{-1}$$

51. Linear expansion coefficient

$$\alpha = 8\times 10^{-4}/^\circ\text{C}$$

∴ Volume expansion coefficient, $\gamma = 3\,\alpha$

$$= 3\times 8\times 10^{-4} = 24\times 10^{-4}\ /^\circ\text{C}$$

Volume of glass vessel at 50°C.

$$V' = V\,[1 + \gamma\Delta t]$$

$$\frac{m'}{\rho} = \frac{m}{\rho}(1+\gamma\Delta t)$$

$$m' = m(1 + \gamma \Delta t)$$
$$= 50[1 + 24 \times 10^{-4} \times (50 - 0)]$$
$$= 50[1 + 24 \times 10^{-4} \times 50]$$
$$= 50[1 + 1200 \times 10^{-4}]$$
$$= 50[1.12]$$
$$= 56 \text{ g}$$

52. Given, $m = 0.2$ kg, $\Delta t = 100°C$

Heat taken by the ice in melting

$$Q = mL$$
$$L = \text{latent heat of ice} = 80 \text{ cal g}^{-1}$$
$$\therefore \quad Q = 25 \times 80$$
$$= 2000 \text{ cal}$$

Heat given by iron ball, $Q = m_1 s \Delta t$

From principle of calorimetery

Heat given = Heat taken

$$m_1 s \Delta t = 2000$$
$$0.2 \times 10^3 \times s \times 100 = 2000$$
$$s = \frac{2000}{100 \times 0.2 \times 10^3}$$
$$= 0.1 \text{ cal/g°C}$$

53. Given, $n = 0.1$, $T = 27°C = 27 + 273 = 300$ K

Work done at constant pressure.

$$W = 2.3026\, nRT \log_{10} \frac{V_2}{V_1}$$
$$= 2.3026 \times 0.1 \times 2 \times 300 \log_{10} \frac{2V}{V}$$
$$= 2.3026 \times 0.1 \times 600 \times \log_{10} 2$$
$$= 2.3026 \times 0.1 \times 600 \times 0.3010$$
$$\approx 42 \text{ cal}$$

54. Weight of empty pyknometer = 40 g

Weight of pyknometer with mercury = 1040 g

∴ Weight of mercury = 1040 – 40 = 1000 g

Weight of mercury left after heating

$$W' = 1000 - 10 = 990 \text{ g}$$

Coefficient of apparent expansion of mercury

$$\gamma_a = \frac{W - W'}{W' \times \Delta t}$$
$$= \frac{(1000 - 990)}{990 \times 1(100 - 0)}$$
$$= \frac{10}{990 \times 100}$$
$$= \frac{1}{9900} = 0.0001/°C$$

Coefficient of real expansion

$$\gamma_r = \gamma_a + \gamma_g$$
$$\gamma_g = \text{coefficient of expansion of glass}$$
$$\gamma_g = \gamma_r - \gamma_a = 0.0002 - 0.0001 = 0.0001/°C$$

55. In an isothermal change, an ideal gas obeys the Boyle's law.

56. The heat will flow from point P to point Q. Let the temperature of the common surface is θ, then

Rate of flow of heat in A

= Rate of flow of heat in B

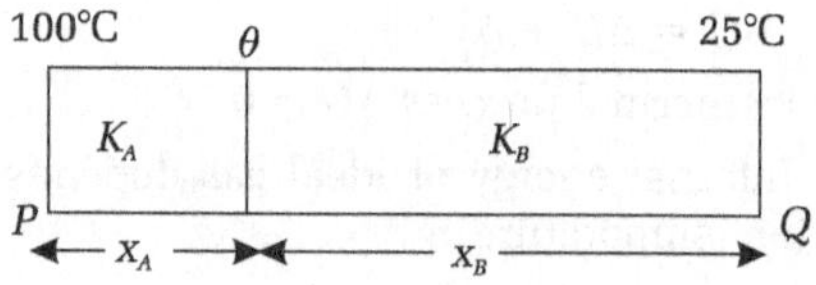

$$K_A \frac{A(100 - \theta)}{x_A} = K_B \frac{A(\theta - 25)}{x_B}$$
$$\frac{2K_B(100 - \theta)}{x_A} = \frac{K_B(\theta - 25)}{2x_B}$$
$$4(100 - \theta) = (\theta - 25)$$
$$5\theta = 425°$$
$$\Rightarrow \quad \theta = \frac{425°}{5}$$
$$= 85°C$$

57. Boiling point of a liquid can be defined as that temperature at which of the liquid becomes equal to atmospheric pressure and surface vapour pressure.

58. The level of liquid did not change in the vessel. So, the volume expansion coefficient of liquid = volume expansion coefficient of material of vessel = 3α

[∵ Volume expansion coefficient of material is three times the linear expansion coefficient of the material]

59. From calorimetry's principle

Heat given by hot liquid

= Heat taken by cold liquid

$$m_1 s_1 (t_1 - t) = m_2 s_2 (t - t_2)$$

where, t = resultant temperature

$$\therefore \quad \frac{m}{2} \times 2s(2T - t) = m \times s(t - T)$$
$$\because \quad t_1 = T, t_2 = 2T$$
$$2T - t = t - T$$
$$3T = 2t$$
$$\Rightarrow \quad t = \frac{3}{2}T$$

60. When ice cube melts *i.e.*, convert from solid to liquid, then disorder increases, so entropy of the system increases and for conversion from solid to liquid state temperature is given, so internal energy increases.

61. Increase in length

$$\Delta l = l_2 - l_1 = 2.0024 - 2$$
$$= 0.0024 \text{ m}$$

Rise in temperature

$$\Delta t = t_2 - t_1$$
$$= 77 - 27 = 50°C$$

∴ Coefficient of linear expansion

$$\alpha = \frac{\Delta l}{l_1 \times \Delta t} = \frac{0.0024}{2 \times 50}$$
$$= \frac{0.0024}{100}$$
$$= 0.000024 = 2.4 \times 10^{-5}/°C$$

62. Mass of water, $m = 1$ kg

Heat capacity of water

$$c = 4.2 \times 10^3 \text{ Jkg}^{-1}\text{-K}^{-1}$$

Latent heat of vaporization of water

$$L = 22.5 \times 10^5 \text{ Jkg}^{-1}$$

Amount of heat required to raise temperature of water from 50°C to 100°C.

$$Q_1 = m\,c\,\Delta t$$
$$= 1 \times 4.2 \times 10^3\,(100 - 50)$$
$$= 210 \times 10^3 \text{ J}$$
$$= 2.1 \times 10^5 \text{ J}$$

Amount of heat required to convert the water into steam at 100°C, $Q_2 = mL$

$$= 1 \times 22.5 \times 10^5$$
$$= 22.5 \times 10^5 \text{ J}$$

∴ Total heat required, $Q = Q_1 + Q_2$

$$= 2.1 \times 10^5 + 22.5 \times 10^5$$
$$= 24.6 \times 10^5 \text{ J}$$

63. Ratio of thermal conductivities

$$\frac{K_1}{K_2} = \left(\frac{r_2}{r_1}\right)^2 \times \left(\frac{t_2}{t_1}\right) \times \frac{x_1}{x_2}$$
$$= \left(\frac{r}{2r}\right)^2 \times \frac{16}{25} \times \left(\frac{x}{4x}\right)$$
$$= \frac{1}{4} \times \frac{16}{25} \times \frac{1}{4}$$
$$= \frac{1}{25} = 1 : 25$$

Chapter

10

Waves

1. When a sound wave of wavelength λ is propagating in a medium, the maximum velocity of the particle is equal to the wave velocity. The amplitude of wave is

EAMCET | 2008

(a) λ (b) $\frac{\lambda}{2}$ (c) $\frac{\lambda}{2\pi}$ (d) $\frac{\lambda}{4\pi}$

2. A car is moving with a speed of 72 kmh^{-1} towards a hill. Car blows horn at a distance of 1800 m from the hill. If echo is heard after 10 s, the speed of sound (in m s) is EAMCET | 2008

(a) 300 (b) 320 (c) 340 (d) 360

3. A whistle of frequency 540 Hz rotates in a horizontal circle of radius 2 m at an angular speed of 15 rad/s. The highest frequency heard by a listener at rest with respect to the centre of circle (velocity of sound in air = 330 ms^{-1})

EAMCET | 2007

(a) 590 Hz (b) 594 Hz

(c) 598 Hz (d) 602 Hz

4. A segment of wire vibrates with a fundamental frequency of 450 Hz under a tension of 9 kg-wt. Then, tension at which the fundamental frequency of the same wire becomes 900 Hz is

EAMCET | 2007

(a) 36 kg-wt (b) 27 kg-wt

(c) 18 kg-wt (d) 72 kg-wt

5. Two strings A and B of lengths, L_A = 80 cm and $L_B = x$ cm respectively are used separately in a sonometer. The ratio of their densities (d_A/d_B) is 0.81. The diameter of B is one-half that of A. If the strings have the same tension and fundamental frequency the value of x is

EAMCET | 2006

(a) 33 (b) 102 (c) 144 (d) 130

6. An observer is standing 500 m away from a vertical hill. Starting between the observer and the hill, a police van sounding a siren of frequency 1000 Hz moves towards the hill with a uniform speed. If the frequency of the sound heard directly from the siren is 970 Hz, the frequency of the sound heard after reflection from the hill (in Hz) is about, (velocity of sound = 300 ms^{-1})

EAMCET | 2006

(a) 1042 (b) 1032 (c) 1022 (d) 1012

7. A vehicle sounding a whistle of frequency 256 Hz is moving on a straight road, towards a hill with a velocity of 10 ms^{-1}. The number of beats per second observed by a person travelling in the vehicle is (velocity of sound = 330 ms^{-1})

EAMCET | 2005

(a) zero (b) 10 (c) 14 (d) 16

8. A transverse wave propagating on a stretched string of linear density 3×10^{-4} kg-m^{-1} is represented by the equation

$$y = 0.2 \sin (15x + 60t)$$

where x is in metre and t is in second. The tension in the string (in newton) is

EAMCET | 2005

(a) 0.24 (b) 0.48 (c) 1.20 (d) 1.80

9. The wavelengths of two nodes in air are $\frac{36}{195}$ m and $\frac{36}{193}$ m. Each node produces 10 beats/s separately with a third node of fixed frequency. The velocity of sound in air in m/s is

EAMCET | 2004

(a) 330 (b) 340 (c) 350 (d) 360

10. An iron load of 2 kg is suspended in air from the free end of a sonometer wire of length 1 m. A tuning fork of frequency 256 Hz, is in resonance with $\frac{1}{\sqrt{7}}$ times the length of the sonometer wire. If the load is immersed in water, the length of the wire in metre that will be in resonance with the same tuning fork is (specific gravity of iron = 8) EAMCET | 2004

(a) $\sqrt{8}$ (b) $\sqrt{6}$ (c) $\frac{1}{\sqrt{6}}$ (d) $\frac{1}{\sqrt{8}}$

11. Two uniform strings A and B made of steel are made to vibrate under the same tension. If the first overtone of A is equal to the second overtone of B and if the radius of A is twice that

of B, the ratio of the lengths of the strings is
EAMCET | 2003

(a) 1 : 2 (b) 1 : 3 (c) 1 : 4 (d) 1 : 5

12. If the length of a stretched string is shortened by 40% and the tension is increased by 44% then the ratio of the final and initial fundamental frequencies is EAMCET | 2003

(a) 2 : 1 (b) 3 : 2 (c) 3 : 4 (d) 1 : 3

13. An auditorium has volume of $10^5 m^3$ and surface area of absorption 2×10^4 m^2. Its average absorption coefficient is 0.2. The reverberation time of the auditorium in second is
EAMCET | 2002

(a) 6.5 (b) 5.5 (c) 4.25 (d) 3.25

14. A metallic wire with tension T and at temperature 30°C vibrates with its fundamental frequency of 1 kHz. The same wire with the same tension but at 10°C temperature vibrates with a fundamental frequency of 1.001 kHz. The coefficient of linear expansion of the wire is EAMCET | 2002

(a) 2×10^{-4}/°C (b) 1.5×10^{-4}/°C
(c) 1×10^{-4}/°C (d) 0.5×10^{-4}/°C

15. The sound waves of wavelengths 5 m and 6 m formed 30 beats in 3 s. The velocity of sound is
EAMCET | 2001

(a) 300 ms^{-1} (b) 310 ms^{-1}
(c) 320 ms^{-1} (d) 330 ms^{-1}

16. In order to double the frequency of the fundamental note emitted by a stretched string, the length is reduced to $\frac{3}{4}$th of the original length and the tension is changed. The factor by which the tension is to be changed is
EAMCET | 2001

(a) $\frac{3}{8}$ (b) $\frac{2}{3}$ (c) $\frac{8}{9}$ (d) $\frac{9}{4}$

17. A steel meter scale is to be ruled so that millimetre intervals are accurate within about 5×10^{-5} m at a certain temperature. The maximum temperature variation allowable during the ruling is (coefficient of linear expansion of steel = 10×10^{-6} K^{-1})
EAMCET | 2001

(a) 2°C (b) 5°C (c) 7°C (d) 10°C

18. The frequency of a stretched uniform wire under tension is in resonance with the fundamental frequency of a closed tube. If the tension in the wire is increased by 8 N, it is in resonance with the first overtone of the closed tube. The initial tension in the wire is
EAMCET | 2000

(a) 1 N (b) 4 N (c) 8 N (d) 16 N

19. If vibrating tuning fork of frequency 255 Hz is moving with a velocity 4 ms^{-1} towards the wall the number of beats heard per second is (speed of sound in air = 340 ms^{-1}) EAMCET | 2000

(a) 3 (b) 4 (c) 5 (d) 6

20. A source producing sound of frequency 170 Hz is approaching a stationary observed with a velocity of 17 ms^{-1}. The apparent change in the wavelength of sound heard by the observer is (speed of sound in air = 340 ms^{-1})
EAMCET | 2000

(a) 0.1 m (b) 0.2 m (c) 0.4 m (d) 0.5 m

21. In a medium, in which a transverse progressive wave is travelling to the phase difference between two points with a distance of separation is 1.25 cm is $\frac{\pi}{4}$. If the frequency of wave is 1000 Hz, its velocity will be
EAMCET | 1999

(a) 10^4 ms^{-1} (b) 125 ms^{-1}
(c) 100 ms^{-1} (d) 10 ms^{-1}

22. A glass tube 1.5 m long and open at both ends is immersed vertically in a water tank completely. A tuning fork of 600 Hz is vibrated and kept at the upper end of tube and tube is gradually raised out of water. The total number of resonances heard before when the tube comes out of water, taking v = 330 ms^{-1}
EAMCET | 1999

(a) 12 (b) 6 (c) 8 (d) 4

23. A car with a horn of frequency 620 Hz, travels towards a large wall with a speed 20 ms^{-1}. If velocity of sound is 330 ms^{-1} the frequency of echo of sound of horn as heard by driver
EAMCET | 1999

(a) 700 Hz (b) 660 Hz
(c) 620 Hz (d) 550 Hz

24. A person standing on the edge of a well throws a stone vertically upwards with an initial velocity 5 ms^{-1}. The stone goes up, comes down and falls in the well making a sound. If the person hears the sound 3 s after throwing, the water is at a depth from ground given by (neglect time of travel for the sound and take g = 10 ms^{-2}) EAMCET | 1998

(a) 1.25 m (b) 21.25 m
(c) 30 m (d) 32.50 m

25. The equation of wave is

$y = 1.0 \cos 2\pi\left(\frac{t}{0.02} - \frac{x}{10}\right)$ where t is in second.

The frequency of the wave is **EAMCET | 1998**

(a) 50 Hz (b) 315 Hz (c) 10 Hz (d) 63 Hz

26. A string a musical instrument is 50 cm long and its fundamental frequency is 270 Hz. If the desired frequency of 1000 Hz is to be produced, the required string length is **EAMCET | 1998**

(a) 13.5 cm (b) 2.7 cm
(c) 5.4 cm (d) 10.8 cm

27. A man stands in front of a hillock and fires a gun. He hears an echo after 1.5 s. The distance of the hillock from the man is (velocity of sound in air is 330 ms^{-1}) **EAMCET | 1998**

(a) 220 m (b) 247.5 m
(c) 268.5 m (d) 292.5 m

28. An organ pipe P_1 closed at one end vibrating in its first overtone and another pipe P_2, open at both ends vibrating in its third overtone are in resonance with a given tuning fork. Then, the ratio of lengths of P_1 and P_2 respectively are given by **EAMCET | 1997**

(a) 1 : 2 (b) 1 : 3 (c) 3 : 8 (d) 3 : 4

29. A source and an observer move away from each other, each with a velocity of 10 m/s, with respect to ground. If the observer find the frequency of sound coming from the source as 1950 Hz, the original frequency of the source is (assume velocity of sound in air = 340 ms^{-1}) **EAMCET | 1997**

(a) 1950 Hz (b) 2068 Hz
(c) 1832 Hz (d) 2186 Hz

30. The length of the closed pipe whose fundamental frequency is equal to that of open pipe of 60 cm, length is **EAMCET | 1996**

(a) 20 cm (b) 24 cm (c) 28 cm (d) 30 cm

31. An observer is moving away from a sound source of frequency 100 Hz. If the observer is moving with a velocity 49 ms^{-1} and the speed of sound in air is 330 ms^{-1}. The observed frequency is **EAMCET | 1996**

(a) 85 Hz (b) 91 Hz (c) 100 Hz (d) 149 Hz

32. A wave is given by the equation

$$y = A \sin 2\pi\,(ft - x/\lambda)$$

Its maximum particle velocity is four times the wave velocity, when λ is **EAMCET | 1995**

(a) πA (b) $\pi A/2$ (c) $\pi A/4$ (d) $\pi A/8$

33. Stationary waves are setup in an air column. If the velocity of sound in air is 330 ms^{-1} and frequency is 165 Hz, the distance between the nodes is **EAMCET | 1995**

(a) 2 m (b) 1 m (c) 0.5 m (d) 4 m

34. An observer is moving away from a source of sound of frequency 100 Hz at a speed of 33 ms^{-1}. If the speed of the sound in air is 330 ms^{-1} and the observed frequency is **EAMCET | 1995**

(a) 90 Hz (b) 100 Hz (c) 91 Hz (d) 110 Hz

35. Which of the following statements is not true for the velocity of sound in gas? **EAMCET | 1995**

(a) Independence of pressure
(b) Increases with increasing temperature
(c) Dependent on molecular weight
(d) Greater in dry gas than in moist gas

36. Two identical stringed instruments have a frequency of 100 Hz. The tension in one of them is increased by 4%. If they are now sounded together the number of beat/s is **EAMCET | 1995**

(a) 1 (b) 8 (c) 4 (d) 2

37. The phase difference between two vibrating particles separated by a distance of 11 m into medium through which a progressive wave is travelling is 1320°. If the frequency of the disturbance is 105 Hz, the phase velocity of the progressive wave in ms^{-1} **EAMCET | 1994**

(a) 315 (b) 330 (c) 350 (d) 300

38. A closed pipe 1 m long, emitting its second overtone, is in unison with an open pipe emitting its third overtone. The length of the open pipe will be **EAMCET | 1994**

(a) 1.2 m (b) 1.6 m (c) 2.5 m (d) 3.2 m

39. When a wave travels in a medium the particles displacement is given by the equation

$$y(x, t) = 0.03 \sin \pi\,(2t - 0.01\,x)$$

where y and x are in metre and t in second. The wavelengths of the wave is **EAMCET | 1994**

(a) 10 m (b) 20 m (c) 100 m (d) 200 m

40. A tuning fork of frequency 392 Hz, resonates with 50 cm length of a string under tension T. If the length of the string is decreased by

2% keeping the tension constant the number of beats heard when the string and the tuning fork are made to vibrate simultaneously is **EAMCET | 1994**

(a) 8 (b) 12 (c) 4 (d) 6

41. In resonance column experiment with a closed pipe, the first, second and third resonance lengths l_1, l_2, l_3 respectively bear the relationship **EAMCET | 1993**

(a) $l_3 = 2l_2 = 4l_1$ (b) $(l_3 - l_2) = (l_2 - l_1)$

(c) $l_3 = \frac{5}{3} l_2 = 5l_1$ (d) $(l_3 - l_2) = 2(l_2 - l_1)$

42. The wavelength of a wave represented by equation $y = 0.03 \sin \pi (2t - 0.01x)$ where y and x are in metre and t in second is **EAMCET | 1993**

(a) 200 m (b) 100 m (c) 300 m (d) 400 m

43. Using the same tuning fork first resonance lengths were observed with an organ pipe open at both ends and also with an organ pipe closed at one end, as l_1 and l_2 respectively. The ratio $l_1 : l_2$ will be **EAMCET | 1993**

(a) 1 : 1 (b) 2 : 1 (c) 1 : 2 (d) 3 : 1

44. A source of sound emitting sound with frequency 540 Hz approaches a stationary observer with a speed of 30 ms^{-1}. If velocity of sound is taken as 330 ms^{-1}, the frequency as heard by the observer will be **EAMCET | 1993**

(a) 194 Hz (b) 294 Hz

(c) 394 Hz (d) 594 Hz

45. The velocity of propagation of sound is 330 ms^{-1}, in air. If the third harmonic of the fundamental that can be exerted in an open ended tube is 450 Hz, the length of the tube is **EAMCET | 1992**

(a) 3.3 m (b) 1.1 m (c) 2.2 m (d) 4.5 m

46. Let v_s be the speed of the source emitting waves, n the actual frequency of the source of sound, v the speed of the sound in the medium and n' the frequency of sound waves as perceived by a stationary observer to whom the source of sound is approaching. The formula for calculate for n' is **EAMCET | 1992**

(a) $n' = n\left(1 - \frac{v_s}{v}\right)$ (b) $n' = n/\left(1 - \frac{v_s}{v}\right)$

(c) $n' = n/\left(1 + \frac{v_s}{v}\right)$ (d) $n' = n$

47. A certain number of beats are heard when two tuning forks of natural frequencies n_1 and n_2 are sounded together. The number of beats heard when one of the fork is loaded **EAMCET | 1992**

(a) increases
(b) decreases
(c) remains constant
(d) may increase or decrease

48. A body vibrating with a certain frequency sends waves of wavelength 15 cm in a medium A and 20 cm in medium B. If v of waves in A is 120 ms^{-1}. That in B will be **EAMCET | 1991**

(a) 196 ms^{-1} (b) 160 ms^{-1}

(c) 360 ms^{-1} (d) 260 ms^{-1}

Answers

1.	(c)	**2.**	(c)	**3.**	(b)	**4.**	(a)	**5.**	(c)	**6.**	(b)	**7.**	(d)	**8.**	(b)	**9.**	(d)	**10.**	(d)
11.	(b)	**12.**	(a)	**13.**	(c)	**14.**	(d)	**15.**	(a)	**16.**	(d)	**17.**	(b)	**18.**	(a)	**19.**	(c)	**20.**	(a)
21.	(c)	**22.**	(b)	**23.**	(a)	**24.**	(c)	**25.**	(a)	**26.**	(a)	**27.**	(b)	**28.**	(c)	**29.**	(b)	**30.**	(d)
31.	(a)	**32.**	(b)	**33.**	(b)	**34.**	(a)	**35.**	(d)	**36.**	(d)	**37.**	(a)	**38.**	(b)	**39.**	(d)	**40.**	(a)
41.	(b)	**42.**	(a)	**43.**	(b)	**44.**	(d)	**45.**	(b)	**46.**	(b)	**47.**	(d)	**48.**	(b)				

■ Hints & Solutions

1. $$v_{max} = v$$
$$\Rightarrow A\omega = v$$
$$\Rightarrow A \times 2\pi\nu = \nu\lambda$$
or $$A = \frac{\lambda}{2\pi}$$

2. The speed of the car is 72 kmh^{-1}
$$= 72 \times \frac{5}{18} = 20 \text{ ms}^{-1}$$
The distance travelled by car in 10 s
$$= 10 \times 20 = 200 \text{ m}$$
Hence, the distance travelled by sound in reaching the hill and coming back to the moving driver
$$= 1800 + (1800 - 200)$$
$$= 3400 \text{ m}$$
So, the speed of sound $= \frac{3400}{10} = 340 \text{ ms}^{-1}$

3. Velocity of source
$$v_s = r\omega = 2 \times 15 = 30 \text{ ms}^{-1}$$
The highest frequency heard by the stationary listener
$$f' = f\left(\frac{v}{v - v_s}\right)$$
or $$f' = 540\left(\frac{330}{330 - 30}\right)$$
$$= 594 \text{ Hz}$$

4. Fundamental frequency of wire
$$f = \frac{1}{2\pi}\sqrt{\frac{T}{m}}$$
or $$f \propto \sqrt{T}$$
or $$\frac{f_2}{f_1} = \sqrt{\frac{T_2}{T_1}}$$
or $$\frac{900}{450} = \sqrt{\frac{T_2}{9}}$$
or $$T_2 = 4 \times 9$$
$$= 36 \text{ kg-wt}$$

5. Given, $\frac{T_A}{T_B} = 1, \frac{L_A}{L_B} = \frac{80}{x}$
$$\frac{D_A}{D_B} = \frac{2}{1}$$
$$\frac{d_A}{d_B} = \frac{0.81}{1}$$
Let μ_1 and μ_2 be the linear densities.
$$\therefore \frac{\mu_A}{\mu_B} = \left(\frac{D_A}{D_B}\right)^2 \times \frac{d_A}{d_B}$$
$$= \left(\frac{2}{1}\right)^2 \times 0.81$$
$$= 4 \times 0.81 = 3.24$$
$$\therefore \frac{f_1}{f_2} = \frac{L_B}{L_A} \times \sqrt{\frac{T_A}{T_B} \times \frac{\mu_B}{\mu_A}}$$
$$1 = \frac{x}{80} \times \sqrt{1 \times \frac{1}{3.24}}$$
$$\therefore x = 80 \times \sqrt{3.24}$$
or $$x = 144$$

6. Sound heard directly
$$f_1 = f_0\left(\frac{v}{v + v_s}\right)$$
$$\therefore 970 = 1000\left(\frac{330}{330 + v_s}\right)$$
or $$v_s = 10.2 \text{ ms}^{-1}$$
The frequency of reflected sound is given by
$$f_2 = f_0\left(\frac{v}{v - v_s}\right)$$
$$= 1000\left(\frac{330}{330 - 10.2}\right)$$
$$= \frac{1000 \times 330}{319.8}$$
$$\approx 1032 \text{ Hz}$$

7. Apparent frequency heard by the observer
$$n' = \left(\frac{v + v}{v - v_s}\right) \times n$$
$$= \left(\frac{330 + 10}{330 - 10}\right) \times 256$$
$$= \frac{340}{320} \times 256$$
$$= 272 \text{ Hz}$$
$\therefore$ Number of beats heard by the observer
$$= 272 - 256 = 16$$

8. Equation of wave, $y = 0.2 \sin (1.5\,x + 60t)$
Comparing with standard equation
$$y = A \sin (kx + \omega t)$$
$$k = 1.5, \omega = 60$$

$\therefore$ Velocity of wave, $v = \dfrac{\omega}{k}$

$$= \frac{60}{1.5} = 40\ \text{ms}^{-1}$$

Velocity of wave in a stretched string

$$v = \sqrt{\frac{T}{m}}$$

where, m = linear density

T = tension in the string

So, $T = v^2 m$

$$= (40)^2 \times 3 \times 10^{-4}$$

$$= 0.48\ \text{N}$$

9. Beat frequency = $n_1 \sim n_2$

Let the frequency of third node be n.

Then, $\dfrac{195v}{36} - n = 10$ ...(i)

and $n - \dfrac{193v}{36} = 10$ ...(ii)

Adding Eqs. (i) and (ii)

$$\frac{v}{18} = 20$$

$\Rightarrow$ $v = 360\ \text{ms}^{-1}$

10. We know, $l \propto \sqrt{T}$

$\therefore$ $\dfrac{l_{\text{air}}}{l_{\text{water}}} = \sqrt{\dfrac{T_{\text{air}}}{T_{\text{water}}}}$

But, specific gravity

$$8 = \frac{T_{\text{air}}}{T_{\text{air}} - T_{\text{water}}}$$

$\Rightarrow$ $T_{\text{water}} = \dfrac{7}{8} T_{\text{air}}$

$\therefore$ $\dfrac{l_{\text{air}}}{l_{\text{water}}} = \sqrt{\dfrac{8}{7}}$

but, $l_{\text{air}} = \dfrac{1}{\sqrt{7}} l$ (given)

$\therefore$ $l_{\text{water}} = \dfrac{1}{\sqrt{8}} l$

11. Fundamental frequency of string

$$n = \frac{1}{2l}\sqrt{\frac{T}{m}}$$

where, m = mass per unit length of the string

$= \pi r^2 \rho$

$\therefore$ $n = \dfrac{1}{2l}\sqrt{\dfrac{T}{\pi r^2 \rho}}$

For string A first overtone

$$n_A = \frac{1}{l_1}\sqrt{\frac{T_1}{m_1}} = \frac{1}{l_1}\sqrt{\frac{T_1}{\pi r_1^2 \rho}}$$

For string B second overtone

$$n_B = \frac{3}{2l_2}\sqrt{\frac{T_2}{\pi r_2^2 \rho}}$$

According to question

$$n_A = n_B$$

$$\frac{1}{l_1}\sqrt{\frac{T_1}{\pi r_1^2 l_1}} = \frac{3}{2l_2}\sqrt{\frac{T_2}{\pi r_2^2 l_2}}$$

but, $T_1 = T_2$

$\therefore$ $\dfrac{2l_2}{3l_1} = \sqrt{\dfrac{\pi r_1^2 \rho}{\pi r_2^2 \rho}}$

$$\frac{4l_2^2}{9l_1^2} = \frac{r_1^2}{r_2^2}$$

$$\left(\frac{l_1}{l_2}\right)^2 = \frac{4r_2^2}{9r_1^2}$$

$$\frac{2l_2}{3l_1} = \frac{r_1}{r_2}$$

$$\frac{l_2}{l_1} = \frac{3r_1}{2r_2}$$

$$\frac{l_1}{l_2} = \frac{2r_2}{3r_1}$$

but, $r_1 = 2\,r_2$

$\therefore$ $\dfrac{l_1}{l_2} = \dfrac{2r_2}{3(2r_2)}$

$$l_1 : l_2 = 1 : 3$$

12. Fundamental frequency, $n = \dfrac{1}{2l}\sqrt{\dfrac{T}{m}}$

Initial frequency, $n_1 = \dfrac{1}{2l}\sqrt{\dfrac{T'}{m}}$

New length, $l' = l - \dfrac{l \times 40}{100} = 0.6\,l$

New tension, $T' = T + \dfrac{T \times 44}{100}$

$= 1.44\,T$

$\therefore$ New frequency, $n_2 = \dfrac{1}{2l}\sqrt{\dfrac{T'}{m}}$

$$\frac{n_2}{n_1} = \frac{l}{l_1}\sqrt{\left(\frac{T'}{T}\right)}$$

$$= \frac{l}{0.6l}\sqrt{\frac{1.44T}{T}}$$

$$= \frac{1}{0.6}\times 1.2 = 2$$

$n_2 : n_1 = 2 : 1$

13. Reverberation time, $T = \frac{0.017v}{as}$

where, a = average absorption coefficient $= 0.2$

$$T = \frac{0.17\times 10^5}{0.2\times 2\times 10^4} = 4.25 \text{ s}$$

14. Frequency of wire, $n = \frac{1}{2l}\sqrt{\frac{T}{m}}$

where, m = mass per unit length

In both the condition same wire is kept same tension.

So, $\frac{n_1}{n_2} = \frac{l_2}{l_1}$

$$\Rightarrow \quad \frac{1}{1.001} = \frac{l_2}{l_1}$$

$$l_2 = \frac{l_1}{1.001}$$

Fall in temperature, $\Delta t = 30 - 10 = 20°C$

$$\therefore \quad l_2 = l_1(1 - \alpha\,\Delta t)$$

$$\frac{l_1}{1.001} = l_1(1 - \alpha \times 20)$$

$$1 - \alpha \times 20 = \frac{1}{1.001} = \frac{0.001}{1.001}$$

$$\alpha = \frac{1}{1001\times 20}$$

$$= 0.5 \times 10^{-4} /°C$$

15. Given, $\lambda_1 = 5$ m, $\lambda_2 = 6$ m

Frequency of first, $n_1 = \frac{v}{\lambda_1}$

Similarly, $n_2 = \frac{v}{\lambda_2}$

Number of beats per sec, $(n_1 - n_2) = \frac{30}{3}$

$$\frac{v}{\lambda_1} - \frac{v}{\lambda_2} = 10$$

$$\Rightarrow \quad v\left(\frac{1}{\lambda_1} - \frac{1}{\lambda_2}\right) = 10$$

$$v\left(\frac{1}{5} - \frac{1}{6}\right) = 10$$

$$v\left(\frac{1}{30}\right) = 10$$

$$\Rightarrow \quad v = 300 \text{ ms}^{-1}$$

16. Frequency of stretched string

$$n = \frac{1}{2l}\sqrt{\frac{T}{m}}$$

where, m = mass per unit length

String is same in both the cases, so

$$n \propto \frac{\sqrt{T}}{l}$$

$$\frac{n_1}{n_2} = \frac{l_2}{l_1}\sqrt{\frac{T_1}{T_2}}$$

$$\frac{n}{2n} = \frac{3l}{4}\sqrt{\frac{T_1}{T_2}}$$

$$\frac{1}{2} = \frac{3}{4}\sqrt{\frac{T_1}{T_2}}$$

$$\Rightarrow \quad \sqrt{\frac{T_1}{T_2}} = \frac{2}{3}$$

$$\therefore \quad \frac{T_1}{T_2} = \frac{4}{9}$$

$$T_2 = \frac{9}{4}T_1$$

$\therefore$ Tension should be changed by the factor $\frac{9}{4}$.

17. Change in length, $\Delta L = 5 \times 10^{-5}$ m

Initial length, $L = 1$ m,

$\alpha = 10 \times 10^{-6} /°C$

$\therefore$ Change in temperature

$$\Delta t = \frac{\Delta L}{\alpha L} = \frac{5\times 10^{-5}}{10\times 10^{-6}\times 1}$$

$$= 5°C$$

18. Frequency of stretched wire

$$n_1 = \frac{1}{2l}\sqrt{\frac{T}{m}}$$

Fundamental frequency of closed tube

$$n_2 = \frac{v}{4l}$$

Frequency of first overtone of closed tube

$$n_3 = \frac{3v}{4l}$$

1st condition $n_1 = n_2$

$$\frac{1}{2l}\sqrt{\frac{T}{m}} = \frac{v}{4l} \quad \text{...(i)}$$

IInd condition $\frac{1}{2l}\sqrt{\frac{T+8}{m}} = \frac{3v}{4l}$ ...(ii)

Equation (i) ÷ (ii)

$$\frac{\sqrt{T/m}}{\sqrt{(T+8)/m}} = \frac{1}{3}$$

$$\frac{T/m}{(T+8)/m} = \frac{1}{9}$$

$$\Rightarrow \quad \frac{T}{m}\times\frac{m}{T+8} = \frac{1}{9}$$

$$9T = T + 8$$

$$\Rightarrow \quad T = 1\text{ N}$$

19. Given, $n = 255$ Hz, $v_s = 4\text{ms}^{-1}$

Apparent frequency when turning fork move towards the wall

$$n' = \frac{v}{v-v_s}\times n$$

$$= \frac{340}{340-4}\times 255 = 258\text{ Hz}$$

Number of beats heard per second is

$$= 258 - 253 = 5$$

20. Velocity of source, $v_s = 17\text{ ms}^{-1}$

Apparent frequency, $n' = \dfrac{v}{v-v_s}\times n$

$$= \frac{340}{340-17}\times 170$$

$$= \frac{340}{323}\times 170 = 179\text{ Hz}$$

Initial wavelength, $\lambda_1 = \dfrac{v}{n} = \dfrac{340}{170}$

$$= 2\text{ m}$$

New wavelength, $\lambda_2 = \dfrac{v}{n'}$

$$= \frac{340}{179} = 1.9\text{ Hz}$$

∴ Change in wavelength $= 2 - 1.9 = 0.1$ m

21. Phase difference, $\Delta\phi = \dfrac{\pi}{4}$

Path difference, $\Delta x = 1.25$ cm

$$= 1.25 \times 10^{-2}\text{ m}$$

$$\Delta\phi = \frac{2\pi}{\lambda}\times\Delta x$$

$$\frac{\pi}{4} = \frac{2\pi}{4}\times 1.25\times 10^{-2}$$

$$\lambda = 4 \times 2 \times 1.25 \times 10^{-2}$$

$$= 10 \times 10^{-2} = \frac{1}{10}\text{m}$$

∴ Velocity, $v = n\lambda$

$$= 1000\times\frac{1}{10} = 100\text{ ms}^{-1}$$

22. Suppose when the tube is x m above the water, the first resonance is head.

Frequency of tube $= \dfrac{v}{4l}$

(The tube will behave as a closed organ pipe)

For resonance, $\dfrac{v}{4l} = 600$

$$\frac{330}{4\times x} = 600$$

$$x = \frac{330}{4\times 600}\text{m} = 0.1375\text{ m}$$

Other resonance will occur at $3x$, $5x$, $7x$, $9x$...

i.e., at 0.4125 m, 0.6875 m, 0.9625 m, 1.2375 m, 1.5125 m.

i.e., Total 6 resonance will be obtained.

23. The wall will behave like a source of sound, so source and observer are coming towards each other.

∴ Apparent frequency

$$n' = \left(\frac{v+v_o}{v-v_s}\right)n = \left(\frac{330+20}{330-20}\right)\times 620$$

$$= \frac{350}{310}\times 620 = 700\text{ Hz}$$

24. At maximum height $v = 0$

From $\quad v = u - gt$

$$0 = 5 - 10 \times t$$

$$t = \frac{1}{2}\text{s}$$

Time taken by the stone to reach the edge of the well $= \dfrac{1}{2}+\dfrac{1}{2} = 1$ s

∴ Time taken by stone to reach the water level

$$= 3 - 1 = 2\text{ s}$$

Depth of water level, $h = ut + \dfrac{1}{2}gt^2$

$$= 5 \times 2 + \frac{1}{2}\times 10 \times (2)^2$$

$$= 10 + 5 \times 4 = 30\text{ m}$$

25. Equation of wire

$$y = 1.0\cos 2\pi\left(\frac{t}{0.02}-\frac{x}{10}\right)$$

Standard equation

$$y = A\cos 2\pi\left(\frac{t}{T}-\frac{x}{\lambda}\right)$$

On comparing the two equations

Time period, $T = 0.02$ s

∴ Frequency, $n = \dfrac{1}{T} = \dfrac{1}{0.02} = 50$ Hz

26. $l = 50$ cm, $n = 270$ Hz

Fundamental frequency of string

$$n = \frac{v}{2l}$$

where, v = velocity of sound

$$\therefore \quad n \propto \frac{1}{l}$$

$$\therefore \quad \frac{n_1}{n_2} = \frac{l_2}{l_1}$$

$$l_2 = \frac{270 \times 50}{1000} = 13.5 \text{ cm}$$

27. Time taken by the sound

$$t = \frac{2d}{v}$$

where, d = distance of the hillock from the man

$$\therefore \quad d = \frac{vt}{2} = \frac{330 \times 1.5}{2}$$

$$= 247.5 \text{ m}$$

28. Frequency of first overtone of closed pipe

$$n_1 = \frac{3v}{4l_1}$$

where, v = velocity of sound

Frequency of third overtone of open pipe

$$n_2 = \frac{4v}{2l_2}$$

For resonance, $n_1 = n_2$

$$\frac{3v}{4l_2} = \frac{4v}{2l_2}$$

$$\frac{l_1}{l_2} = \frac{3 \times 2}{4 \times 4} = \frac{3}{8}$$

$$l_1 : l_2 = 3 : 8$$

29. Given, $v_s = v_o = 10 \text{ ms}^{-1}$

Apparent frequency $n' = 1950$ Hz,

$n = ?$

When observer and source are moving away from each other, then apparent frequency

$$n' = \frac{v - v_o}{v + v_s} \times n$$

$$1950 = \frac{340 - 10}{340 + 10} \times n$$

$$1950 = \frac{330}{350} \times n$$

$$\therefore \quad n = 1950 \times \frac{350}{330} = 2068 \text{ Hz}$$

30. Fundamental frequency of closed pipe

$$n_1 = \frac{v}{4l_1}$$

Fundamental frequency of open pipe

$$n_2 = \frac{v}{2l_2}$$

According to question, $n_1 = n_2$

$$\therefore \quad \frac{v}{4l_1} = \frac{v}{2l_2}$$

(v = velocity of sound)

$$\frac{1}{2l_1} = \frac{1}{l_2}$$

$$\frac{1}{2l_1} = \frac{1}{60}$$

$$l_1 = \frac{60}{2} = 30 \text{ cm}$$

31. $n = 100$ Hz, velocity of observer, $v_o = 49 \text{ ms}^{-1}$

Velocity of sound, $v = 330 \text{ ms}^{-1}$

When observer moves away from the source, then apparent frequency

$$n' = \frac{v - v_o}{v} \times n$$

$$= \frac{330 - 49}{330} \times 100$$

$$= \frac{281}{330} \times 100 = 85 \text{ Hz}$$

32. Equation of wave

$$y = A \sin 2\pi (ft - x/\lambda)$$

$$= A \sin \frac{2\pi}{\lambda}(f\lambda t - x)$$

$$= A \sin 2\pi (vt - x)$$

$\therefore$ Wave velocity $= v$

Maximum particle velocity, $v_p = 2\pi f A$

Here, $v_p = 4v$

$$2\pi f A = 4 f \lambda$$

$$\lambda = \frac{\pi A}{2}$$

33. Velocity of sound, $v = 330 \text{ ms}^{-1}$

Frequency, $n = 165$ Hz

$$\therefore \text{ Wavelength, } \lambda = \frac{v}{n} = \frac{330}{165} = 2 \text{ m}$$

$\therefore$ Distance between any two consecutive nodes

$$= \frac{\lambda}{2} = \frac{2}{2}$$

$$= 1 \text{ m}$$

34. Actual frequency, $n = 100$ Hz

Speed of observer, $v_o = 33\ ms^{-1}$

Speed of sound, $v = 330\ ms^{-1}$

The observer is moving away from source. So, apparent frequency

$$n' = \frac{v - v_o}{v} n$$

$$= \frac{330 - 33}{330} \times 100$$

$$= \frac{297}{330} \times 100 = 90 \text{ Hz}$$

35. The velocity of sound is greater in moist air than in dry air, so statement (d) is not correct.

36. Frequency of stretched string

$$n = \frac{p}{2l}\sqrt{\frac{T}{m}}$$

Where, p = number of loops in which the string is vibrating

T = tension in string

m = mass per unit length of the string

Ist case $$100 = \frac{p}{2l}\sqrt{\frac{T}{m}} \quad \text{...(i)}$$

IInd case $$n_2 = \frac{p}{2l}\sqrt{\frac{T + \frac{T \times 4}{100}}{m}}$$

$$n_2 = \frac{p}{2l}\sqrt{\frac{1.04\,T}{m}} \quad \text{...(ii)}$$

Dividing Eq. (ii) by Eq. (i)

$$\frac{n_2}{100} = \sqrt{\frac{1.04T}{T}}$$

$$\frac{n_2^2}{(100)^2} = \frac{(1.04)}{1}$$

$\Rightarrow$ $$n_2^2 = 100 \times 104$$

$$n_2 = \sqrt{100 \times 104} = 102$$

$\therefore$ Number of beats $= n_2 - n_1 = 102 - 100 = 2$

37. Phase difference, $\Delta\phi = 1320° = 1320 \times \frac{\pi}{180}$

$$= \frac{66}{9}\pi = \frac{22}{3}\pi$$

Phase difference

$$\Delta\phi = \frac{2\pi}{\lambda} \times \Delta x$$

(where, Δx = path difference)

$$\frac{22\pi}{3} = \frac{2\pi}{\lambda} \times 11$$

$$\lambda = \frac{2\pi \times 11 \times 3}{22\pi} = 3 \text{ m}$$

$\therefore$ Phase velocity, $v = n\lambda = 105 \times 3$

$= 315\ ms^{-1}$

38. Frequency of second overtone for closed pipe,

$$n_1 = \frac{5\,v}{4\,l_1}$$

Frequency of third overtone for open pipe

$$n_2 = \frac{4\,v}{2\,l_2}$$

According to question, $n_1 = n_2$

$$\frac{5\,v}{2\,l_1} = \frac{4\,v}{2\,l_2}$$

$$\frac{5}{4 \times l} = \frac{4}{2 \times l_2}$$

$$l_2 = \frac{4 \times 4}{2 \times 5} = 1.6 \text{ m}$$

39. Equation of wave

$$y = 0.03 \sin \pi(2\,t - 0.01\,x)$$

$$y = 0.03 \sin 2\pi\left(\frac{2t}{2} - \frac{0.01x}{2}\right)$$

Comparing with standard equation

$$y = a \sin 2\,\pi\left(\frac{t}{T} - \frac{x}{\lambda}\right)$$

On comparing the two equations, we get

$$\frac{x}{\lambda} = \frac{0.01x}{2}$$

$\Rightarrow$ $$\lambda = \frac{2}{0.01}$$

$\Rightarrow$ $$\lambda = 200 \text{ m}$$

40. Initial frequency of string

$$n = \frac{1}{2l}\sqrt{\frac{T}{m}}$$

$$392 = \frac{1}{2l}\sqrt{\frac{T}{m}}$$

New frequency, $$n' = \frac{1}{2l'}\sqrt{\frac{T}{m}}$$

$\therefore$ $$\frac{392}{n'} = \frac{l'}{l}$$

(Because other factors are kept same)

$\therefore$ $$\frac{392}{n'} = \frac{l - \frac{l \times 2}{100}}{l} = \frac{98}{100}$$

$$n' = \frac{392 \times 100}{98} = 400 \text{ Hz}$$

$\therefore$ Number of beats $= n' - n = 400 - 392 = 8$

42. Equation of given wave

$$y = 0.03 \sin \pi(2t - 0.01x)$$

$$y = 0.03 \sin 2\pi\left(t - \frac{0.01x}{2}\right)$$

Comparing this equation with standard equation

$$y = a \sin 2\pi\left(\frac{t}{T} - \frac{x}{\lambda}\right)$$

$$\therefore \quad \frac{x}{\lambda} = \frac{0.01x}{2}$$

$$\lambda = \frac{2}{0.01} = 200 \text{ m}$$

44. Actual frequency, $n = 540$ Hz

Velocity of source, $v_s = 30 \text{ ms}^{-1}$

Velocity of sound, $v = 330 \text{ ms}^{-1}$

When source approaches a stationary observer then, apparent frequency

$$n' = \frac{v}{v - v_s} \times n$$

$$= \frac{330}{330 - 30} \times 540$$

$$= \frac{330}{300} \times 540 = 594 \text{ Hz}$$

45. Frequency of third harmonic in open pipe

$$n = 3\frac{v}{2l}$$

where, v = velocity of sound = 330 ms^{-1}

l = length of the tube

$$\therefore \quad 450 = \frac{3 \times 330}{2l}$$

$$l = \frac{3 \times 330}{2 \times 450}$$

$$= \frac{990}{900} = 1.1 \text{ m}$$

46. When source approaches the observer, then apparent frequency

$$n' = n\frac{v}{v - v_s}$$

$$n' = \frac{n}{(v - v_s)/v}$$

$$= \frac{n}{\left(1 - \frac{v_s}{v}\right)}$$

48. Wavelength in medium A,

$$\lambda_A = 15 \text{ cm}$$

$$= 15 \times 10^{-2} \text{ m}$$

Similarly, $\lambda_B = 20 \text{ cm} = 20 \times 10^{-2}$ m

Velocity in medium A,

$$v_A = 120 \text{ ms}^{-1}$$

When a wave goes from one medium to other then its frequency does not change.

Frequency, $n = \frac{v}{\lambda}$

$$\therefore \quad \frac{v_A}{\lambda_A} = \frac{v_B}{\lambda_B}$$

$$\frac{120}{15 \times 10^{-2}} = \frac{v_B}{20 \times 10^{-2}}$$

$$v_B = \frac{120 \times 20}{15}$$

$$= 160 \text{ ms}^{-1}$$

Chapter

11

Electrostatics

1. A charge of 1 μC is divided into two parts such that their charges are in the ratio of 2 : 3. These two charges are kept at a distance 1 m apart in vacuum. Then, the electric force between them (in N) is **EAMCET | 2008**

(a) 0.216 (b) 0.00216

(c) 0.0216 (d) 2.16

2. Two charges $+q$ and $-q$ are kept apart. Then at any point on the right bisector of line joining the two charges **EAMCET | 2008**

(a) the electric field strength is zero

(b) the electric potential is zero

(c) both electric potential and electric field strength are zero

(d) both electric potential and electric field strength are non-zero

3. Along the x-axis, three charges $\frac{q}{2}$, $-q$ and $\frac{q}{2}$ are placed at $x = 0$, $x = a$ and $x = 2a$ respectively. The resultant electric potential at a point P located at a distance r from the charge $-q(a << r)$ is (ε_0 is the permittivity of free space) **EAMCET | 2007**

(a) $\frac{qa}{4\pi\varepsilon_0 r^2}$ (b) $\frac{qa^2}{4\pi\varepsilon_0 r^3}$

(c) $\frac{q\left(\frac{a^2}{4}\right)}{4\pi\varepsilon_0 r^3}$ (d) $\frac{q}{4\pi\varepsilon_0 r}$

4. Two unit negative charges are placed on a straight line. A positive charge q is placed exactly at the mid point between these unit charges. If the system of these three charges is in equilibrium, the value of q (in C) is **EAMCET | 2007,06**

(a) 1.0 (b) 0.75 (c) 0.5 (d) 0.25

5. The bob of simple pendulum is hanging vertically down from a fixed identical bob by means of a string of length l. If both bobs are charged with a charge q each, time period of the pendulum is (ignore the radii of the bobs) **EAMCET | 2006**

(a) $2\pi\sqrt{\frac{l}{g+\left(\frac{q^2}{l^2 m}\right)}}$ (b) $2\pi\sqrt{\frac{l}{g-\left(\frac{q^2}{l^2 m}\right)}}$

(c) $2\pi\sqrt{\frac{l}{g}}$ (d) $2\pi\sqrt{\frac{l}{g-\left(\frac{q^2}{l}\right)}}$

6. One end each of a resistance r, capacitor C and resistance $2r$ are connected together. The other ends are respectively connected to the positive terminals of batteries. P, Q, R having respectively emf's E, E and $2E$. The negative terminals of the batteries are then connected together. In this circuit, with steady current the potential drop across the capacitor is **EAMCET | 2006**

(a) $\frac{E}{3}$ (b) $\frac{E}{2}$ (c) $\frac{2E}{3}$ (d) E

7. A 4 μF capacitor is charged by a 200 V battery. It is then disconnected from the supply and is connected to another uncharged 2 μF capacitor. During the process, loss of energy (in J) is **EAMCET | 2005**

(a) 3.43×10^{-2} (b) 2.67×10^{-2}

(c) 2.67×10^{-4} (d) 3.43×10^{-4}

8. Two charges 2 C and 6 C are separated by a finite distance. If a charge of -4 C is added to each of them, the initial force of 12×10^3 N will change to **EAMCET | 2005**

(a) 4×10^3 N (repulsion)

(b) 4×10^2 N (repulsion)

(c) 6×10^3 N (attraction)

(d) 4×10^3 N (attraction)

9. A particle of mass 1×10^{-26} kg and charge 1.6×10^{-19} C travelling with a velocity 1.28×10^6 ms^{-1} along the positive x-axis enters a region in which a uniform electric field $\vec{E}$ and a uniform magnetic field of induction $\vec{B}$ are present. If $\vec{E} = -102.4 \times 10^3\ \hat{k}$ NC^{-1} and $B = 8 \times 10^{-2}\ \hat{j}$ Wbm^{-2}, the direction of motion of the particle is **EAMCET | 2005**

(a) along the positive x-axis
(b) along the negative x-axis
(c) at 45° to the positive x-axis
(d) at 135° to the positive x-axis

10. The plates of a parallel plate capacitor are charged upto 200 V. A dielectric slab of thickness 4 mm is inserted between its plates. Then, to maintain the same potential difference between the plates of the capacitor, the distance between the plates is increased by 3.2 mm. The dielectric constant of the dielectric slab is

EAMCET | 2004

(a) 1 (b) 4 (c) 5 (d) 6

11. Three point charges 1C, – 2C and – 2C are placed at the vertices of an equilateral triangle of side 1 m. The work done by an external force to increase the separation of the charges to 2 m in joule is (ε_0 = permittivity of air)

EAMCET | 2004

(a) $\frac{1}{4\pi\varepsilon_0}$ (b) $\frac{1}{8\pi\varepsilon_0}$
(c) $\frac{1}{16\pi\varepsilon_0}$ (d) zero

12. A parallel plate capacitor of capacity C_0 is charged to a potential V_0. (i) The energy stored in the capacitor when the battery is disconnected and the plate separation is doubled is E_1. (ii) The energy stored in the capacitor when the charging battery is kept connected and the separation between the capacitor plates is doubled is E_2. Then, E_1/E_2 value is

EAMCET | 2003

(a) 4 (b) 3/2 (c) 2 (d) 1/2

13. An infinite number of electric charges each equal to 5 n-C (magnitude) are placed along x-axis at x = 1 cm, x = 2 cm, x = 4 cm, x = 8 cm ..... and so on. In this set up if the consecutive charges have opposite sign, then the electric field in newton/coulomb at x = 0 is

$\left(\frac{1}{4\pi\varepsilon_0} = 9\times10^9 \text{ N-m}^2\text{C}^{-2}\right)$ **EAMCET | 2003**

(a) 12×10^4 (b) 24×10^4
(c) 36×10^4 (d) 48×10^4

14. A body of mass 1g and carrying a charge 10^{-8}C passes from two points P and Q. P and Q are at electric potentials 600 V and 0 V respectively. The velocity of the body at Q is 20 cms^{-1}. It velocity in ms^{-1} at P is **EAMCET | 2002**

(a) $\sqrt{0.028}$ (b) $\sqrt{0.056}$
(c) $\sqrt{0.56}$ (d) $\sqrt{5.6}$

15. A parallel plate capacitor of capacity 100 μF is charged by a battery of 50 V. The battery remains connected and if the plates of the capacitor are separated so that the distance between them becomes double the original distance, the additional energy given by the battery to the capacitor in joule is

EAMCET | 2002

(a) $\frac{125}{2}\times10^{-3}$ (b) 12.5×10^{-3}
(c) 1.25×10^{-3} (d) 0.125×10^{-3}

16. The time in second required to produce a potential difference of 20 V across a capacitor of 1000 μF when it is charged at the steady rate of 200 μC/s is **EAMCET | 2002**

(a) 50 (b) 100 (c) 150 (d) 200

17. If the charge on a body is increased by 2 C, the energy stored in it increases by 21%. The original charge on the body in coulomb is

EAMCET | 2001

(a) 10 (b) 20 (c) 30 (d) 40

18. Two electric charges of 9 μC and – 3μC are placed 0.16 m apart in air. There will be a point P at which electric potential is zero on the line joining two charges and in between them. The distance of P from 9 μC is **EAMCET | 2001**

(a) 0.14 m (b) 0.12 m
(c) 0.08 m (d) 0.06 m

19. A 20 F capacitor is charged to 5 V and isolated. It is then connected in parallel with an uncharged 30 F capacitor. The decrease in the energy of the system will be **EAMCET | 2001**

(a) 25 J (b) 100 J (c) 125 J (d) 150 J

20. There is a uniform electric field of strength 10^3 V m^{-1} along y-axis. A body of mass 1 g and charge 10^{-6} C is projected into the field from origin along the positive X-axis with a velocity 10 ms^{-1}. Its speed in ms^{-1} after 10 s is (Neglect gravitation) **EAMCET | 2001**

(a) 10 (b) $5\sqrt{2}$ (c) $10\sqrt{2}$ (d) 20

21. A body of capacity 4 μF is charged to 80 V and another body of capacity 6 μF is charged to 30 V. When they are connected the energy lost by 4 μF capacitor is **EAMCET | 2001**

(a) 9.8 mJ (b) 4.6 mJ
(c) 3.2 mJ (d) 2.5 mJ

22. A charged particle of mass 3×10^{-6} kg is held stationary in spacing in an electric field of strength 10^6 NC^{-1} directed vertically downwards. The charge on the particle is ($g = 10\ ms^{-2}$) **EAMCET | 2000**

(a) $-20 \times 10^{-3}\ \mu C$

(b) $-3 \times 10^{-5}\ \mu C$

(c) $5 \times 10^{-5}\ \mu C$

(d) $20 \times 10^{-5}\ \mu C$

23. Electric charges of 1 μC, 1μC and 2μC are placed in air at the corners of A, B and C respectively of an equilateral triangle ABC having the length of the side 10 cm. The resultant forces at C is

$\left(\frac{1}{4\pi\varepsilon_0} = 9\times10^9 \frac{\text{N-m}^2}{\text{C}^2}\right)$ **EAMCET | 2000**

(a) 0.9 N (b) $1.8\sqrt{3}$ N

(c) 2.7 N (d) 3.6 N

24. Two electric charges 12 μC and -6 μC are placed 20 cm apart in air, there will be a point P at which electric potential is zero on the line joining these two charges and out side excluding the region between them. The distance of P from $-6\ \mu$C charge is **EAMCET | 2000**

(a) 0.10 m (b) 0.15 m

(c) 0.20 m (d) 0.25 m

25. The displacement r of a charge Q in an electric field $\vec{E} = c_1\hat{i} + c_2\hat{j} + c_3\hat{k}$ is $\vec{r} = a\hat{i} + b\hat{j}$. The work done is **EAMCET | 2000**

(a) $Q(ac_1 + bc_2)$ (b) $Q\sqrt{(ac_1)^2 + (bc_2)^2}$

(c) $Q(c_1 + c_2)\sqrt{a^2 + b^2}$ (d) $Q\left(\sqrt{c_2^2 + c_1^2}\right)(a + b)$

26. Two charges 8 C and -6 C are placed at a distance of separation d between them and exerts a force of magnitude F on each other. If a charge 8 C is added to each of these and they are brought nearer to by a distance $d/3$, the magnitude of force between them will be **EAMCET | 1999**

(a) $\frac{F}{3}$ (b) $\frac{9F}{4}$ (c) $6F$ (d) $\frac{2F}{3}$

27. The electric field intensity in air at a point 20 cm from a point charge Q coulombs is 4.5×10^5 N/C. The magnitude of Q is **EAMCET | 1999**

(a) 0.1 μC (b) 0.2 μC

(c) 1 μC (d) 2 μC

28. A parallel plate capacitor filled with a dielectric of relative permittivity 5 between its plates is charged to acquire an energy E and isolated. If the dielectric is replaced by another of relative permittivity 2, its energy becomes **EAMCET | 1999**

(a) E (b) $0.4\ E$ (c) $2.5\ E$ (d) $6.25\ E$

29. The charges $+5\ \mu$C and $+10\ \mu$C are placed 20 cm apart. The electric field at the mid point between the two charges is **EAMCET | 1998**

(a) 4.5×10^6 N/C directed towards $+5\ \mu$C

(b) 4.5×10^6 N/C directed towards $+10\ \mu$C

(c) 13.5×10^6 N/C directed towards $+5\ \mu$C

(d) 13.5×10^6 N/C directed towards $+10\ \mu$C

30. A parallel plate condenser with oil between the plates (dielectric constant of oil $K = 2$) has a capacitance C. If the oil is removed, the capacitance of the capacitor becomes **EAMCET | 1998**

(a) $\sqrt{2}C$ (b) $2\ C$ (c) $\frac{C}{\sqrt{2}}$ (d) $\frac{C}{2}$

31. A charge q is placed at the centre of the line joining two equal charges Q to establish equilibrium. The system of three charges will be in equilibrium if q is equal to **EAMCET | 1997**

(a) $+Q/4$ (b) $+Q/2$

(c) $-Q/2$ (d) $-Q/4$

32. The capacity of a parallel plate capacitor with no dielectric but with a separation 0.4 cm is 2 μF. The separation is reduced to half and it is filled with a dielectric of value 2.8. The final capacity of the capacitor is **EAMCET | 1997**

(a) 11.2 μF (b) 5.6 μF

(c) 4.0 μF (d) 22.4 μF

33. When a dielectric material is introduced between the plates of a charged condenser the electric field between the plates **EAMCET | 1996**

(a) decreases

(b) increases

(c) does not change

(d) may increase or decrease

34. A parallel plate condenser is charged and disconnected from the battery. If the plates of the capacitor are moved further apart by means of insulating handles **EAMCET | 1996**

(a) the charge in the capacitor becomes zero
(b) the capacitance becomes infinite
(c) the charge in the capacitor increases
(d) the voltage across the plates increases

35. An infinite number of charges of equal magnitude q, but of opposite sign are placed along the x-axis at $x = 1, x = 2, x = 4, x = 8$ and so on. The electric potential at the point $x = 0$ due to these charges will be proportional to **EAMCET | 1996**

(a) $\frac{q}{2}$ (b) $\frac{q}{3}$ (c) $\frac{2q}{3}$ (d) $\frac{3q}{2}$

36. Two capacitors 2 μF and 4μF are connected in series and a potential of 100 V is applied across the combination. Energy stored in the capacitors is **EAMCET | 1996**

(a) 0.0067 J (b) 0.067 J
(c) 0.0033 J (d) 0.057 J

37. The electric potential at the centre of a charged conductor is **EAMCET | 1995**

(a) zero
(b) twice that on the surface
(c) half that on the surface
(d) same as on the surface

38. The energy stored in a capacitor is given by (V = voltage, C = capaitance, q = charge) **EAMCET | 1995**

(a) qV (b) $\frac{1}{2}qV$
(c) $1-\frac{1}{2}CV$ (d) $\frac{1}{2}\frac{q}{C}$

39. A parallel plate capacitor has a capacitance of 10 μF without dielectric. A dielectric of dielectric constant 2 is used to fill exactly half the thickness between the plates. The capacitance in μF, now is **EAMCET | 1995**

(a) 10 (b) 20 (c) 15 (d) 13.33

40. When a dielectric slab of the same area of cross-section and thickness equal to 2/3 of the separation is introduced between the plates of a parallel plate capacitor, its capacitance becomes 2.25 times the original value. The dielectric constant of the material of the slab is **EAMCET | 1994**

(a) 1.5 (b) 4.5 (c) 5.0 (d) 6.0

41. In a parallel plate air capacitor of capacitance 4 F if the lower half of air space is filled with a material of dielectric constant 3, its capacitance changes to **EAMCET | 1993**

(a) $\frac{4}{3}$ F (b) $\frac{8}{3}$ F (c) 8 F (d) 12 F

42. A charge $+2\ \mu$C is placed at $x = 0$ and a charge of $-$ 32 μC at x = 60 cm where must a third charge $+Q$ be placed on the x-axis such that it experiences no force? The distance of the point is **EAMCET | 1992**

(a) 20 cm left (b) 20 cm right
(c) 30 cm left (d) 30 cm right

43. If 3 capacitors of values 1, 2 and 3 μF are available, the maximum and minimum values of capacitances one can obtain by different combinations of the 3 capacitors together are respectively **EAMCET | 1992**

(a) $\frac{6}{5}\mu$F (b) $\frac{6}{11}\mu$F (c) $\frac{11}{6}\ \mu$F (d) $\frac{11}{8}\ \mu$F

44. A 2 μF condenser is charged to 500 V and then the plates are joined through a resistance. The heat produced in the resistance (in joule) is **EAMCET | 1992**

(a) 0.10 J (b) 0.15 J (c) 0.25 J (d) 0.30 J

45. A charged bead is capable of sliding freely through a string held vertically in tension. An electric field is applied parallel to the string, so that the bead stays at rest at middle of the string. If the electric field is switched off momentarily and switched on **EAMCET | 1991**

(a) the bead moves downwards and stops as soon the field is switched on
(b) The bead moves downwards when the field is off and moves upwards when the field is switched on
(c) the bead moves downwards with constant acceleration till it reaches the bottom of the string
(d) the bead moves downwards with constant velocity till it reaches the bottom of the string

46. A change q is placed at the centre of line joining two equal charges Q. The system of 3 charges will be in equilibrium if q is equal to **EAMCET | 1991**

(a) $-Q/2$ (b) $-Q/4$ (c) $Q/4$ (d) $Q/2$

47. A parallel plate capacitor is charged and the charging battery is then disconnected. If the plates of the capacitor are moved further apart by means of insulating handles **EAMCET | 1991**

(a) the charge in the capacitor becomes zero
(b) the capacitance becomes infinite
(c) the capacitance in increases
(d) the voltage across the plates increases

48. Five equal capacitors connected in series have a resultant capacitance of 4 μF. The total energy stored in these when these are connected in parallel and charged to 400 V, is

EAMCET | 1991

(a) 1 J (b) 8 J (c) 16 J (d) 4 J

49. If 4×10^{20} eV of energy is required to move a charge of 6.25 C between two points, the potential difference between them is

EAMCET | 1991

(a) 10.24 V (b) 24.10 V
(c) 14.50 V (d) 5.12 V

Answers

1.	(b)	**2.**	(b)	**3.**	(b)	**4.**	(d)	**5.**	(c)	**6.**	(a)	**7.**	(b)	**8.**	(d)	**9.**	(a)	**10.**	(c)
11.	(d)	**12.**	(a)	**13.**	(c)	**14.**	(a)	**15.**	(a)	**16.**	(b)	**17.**	(b)	**18.**	(b)	**19.**	(d)	**20.**	(a)
21.	(a)	**22.**	(b)	**23.**	(b)	**24.**	(c)	**25.**	(a)	**26.**	(c)	**27.**	(d)	**28.**	(c)	**29.**	(a)	**30.**	(d)
31.	(d)	**32.**	(a)	**33.**	(a)	**34.**	(d)	**35.**	(c)	**36.**	(a)	**37.**	(d)	**38.**	(b)	**39.**	(d)	**40.**	(d)
41.	(c)	**42.**	(a)	**43.**	(b)	**44.**	(c)	**45.**	(a)	**46.**	(b)	**47.**	(d)	**48.**	(b)	**49.**	(a)		

Hints & Solutions

1. Ratio of charges = 2 : 3

$\therefore \quad q_1 = \frac{2}{5} \times 1\mu C$ and $q_2 = \frac{3}{5} \times 1\mu C$

Electrostatic force between the two charges

$$F = \frac{1}{4\pi\varepsilon_0}\frac{q_1 q_2}{r^2}$$

$$= \frac{9\times10^9 \times 2\times10^{-6}\times3\times10^{-6}}{5\times5\times(1)^2}$$

$$= 2.16 \times 10^{-3} \text{ N}$$

2. At equatorial point

$$E_e = \frac{1}{4\pi\varepsilon_0}\frac{P}{r^3}$$

(directed from $+q$ to $-q$) and $V_e = 0$.

3. As $r >> a$, so $r > 2a$

So, potential at point P

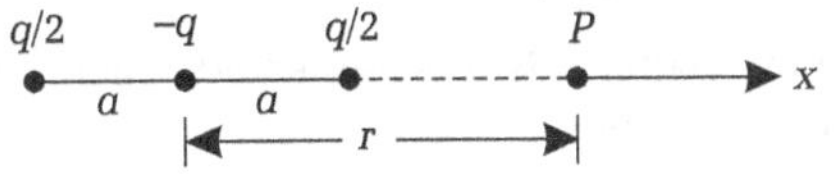

$$V = \frac{1}{4\pi\varepsilon_0}\left[\frac{q/2}{r+a} - \frac{q}{r} + \frac{q/2}{r-a}\right]$$

$$= \frac{1}{4\pi\varepsilon_0}\cdot\frac{q}{2}\left[\frac{1}{r+a} - \frac{2}{r} + \frac{1}{r-a}\right]$$

$$= \frac{q}{8\pi\varepsilon_0}\left[\frac{r(r-a) - 2(r^2 - a^2) + r(r+a)}{r(r^2 - a^2)}\right]$$

$$= \frac{q}{8\pi\varepsilon_0}\left[\frac{2a^2}{r(r^2 - a^2)}\right]$$

$$= \frac{qa^2}{4\pi\varepsilon_0 r^3} \qquad \text{(as } r >> a\text{)}$$

4. For equilibrium, we have

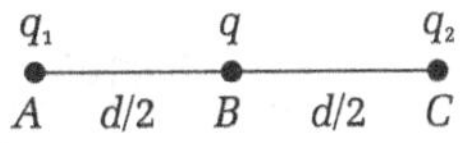

$$F_{AB} + F_{AC} = 0$$

or $\quad \frac{1}{4\pi\varepsilon_0}\frac{q_1 q}{(d/2)^2} + \frac{1}{4\pi\varepsilon_0} \times \frac{q_1 q_2}{d^2} = 0$

Given, $\quad q_1 = q_2 = -1\,\mu C$

So, $\quad -\frac{q}{(d/2)^2} + \frac{1}{d^2} = 0$

or $\quad q = \frac{1}{4} = 0.25$ C

5. There will be electrostatic repulsion between two charged bobs, but it does not affect the motion of pendulum. Thus, time period of pendulum remains same *i.e.*, $T = 2\pi\sqrt{\frac{l}{g}}$.

6. In the steady state, no current flows through capacitor branch.

Current in the circuit

$$i = \frac{\text{net emf}}{\text{net resistance}} = \frac{2E - E}{r + 2r} = \frac{E}{3r}$$

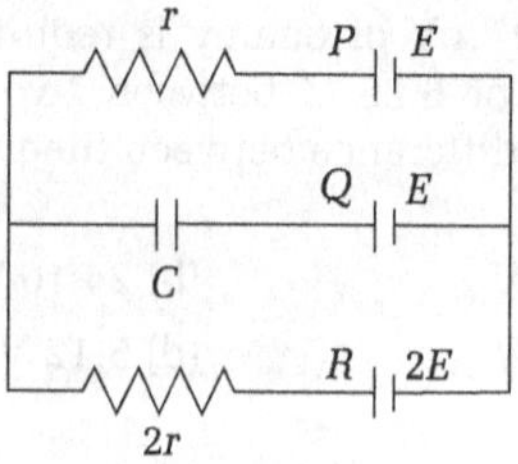

So, potential drop across capacitor

$$V = ir = \frac{E}{3r} \times r = \frac{E}{3}$$

7. Charge stored at the capacitor

$$q = C_1V_1 = 4 \times 200 = 800\ \mu C$$

When this capacitor is connected with a uncharged capacitor, then common potential on both capacitors.

$$V = \frac{C_1V_1 + C_2V_2}{C_1 + C_2}$$

$$= \frac{800+0}{4+2}$$

$$= \frac{800}{6}\ \text{volt}$$

Loss in energy = Initial energy – final energy

$$= \frac{1}{2}C_1V_1^2 - \frac{1}{2}(C_1 + C_2)V^2$$

$$= \frac{1}{2} \times 4 \times 10^{-6} \times (200)^2 - \frac{1}{2}(4+2) \times 10^{-6} \times \left(\frac{800}{6}\right)^2$$

$$= 2 \times 10^{-6} \times 4 \times 10^4 - \frac{3 \times 10^{-6} \times 64 \times 10^4}{36}$$

$$= 8 \times 10^{-2} - \frac{64}{12} \times 10^{-2}$$

$$= 8 \times 10^{-2} - 5.33 \times 10^{-2}$$

$$= 2.67 \times 10^{-2}\ \text{J}$$

8. Initial force, $F = k\,\frac{q_1q_2}{r^2}$

$$F_1 = k \cdot \frac{(2)(6)}{r^2}$$

New force, $F_2 = k\frac{(2-4)(6-4)}{r^2}$

$$= k\frac{(-2)(2)}{r^2}$$

$$\therefore \quad \frac{F_1}{F_2} = \frac{(2 \times 6)}{(-2 \times 2)}$$

$$\frac{12 \times 10^3}{F_2} = -3$$

$$F_2 = -4 \times 10^3\ \text{N}$$

Force is negative, so it will be of attraction.

9. Given, $m = 1 \times 10^{-26}$ kg, $q = 1.6 \times 10^{-19}$ C, $v = 1.28 \times 10^6\ \text{ms}^{-1}$

Electric field, $\vec{E} = -102.4 \times 10^3\ \hat{k}$ N/C

Magnetic field, $\vec{B} = 8 \times 10^{-2}\ \hat{j}$ Wbm^{-2}

$$\frac{|\vec{E}|}{|\vec{B}|} = \frac{102.4 \times 10^3}{8 \times 10^{-2}}$$

$$= \frac{10.24 \times 10^6}{8} = 1.28 \times 10^6$$

Hence, $|\vec{v}| = \frac{|\vec{E}|}{|\vec{B}|}$

So, particle will remain undeflected, hence direction of motion of particle is along the positive x-axis.

10. $$\frac{\varepsilon_0 A}{d} = \frac{\varepsilon_0 A}{d' - t + \frac{t}{K}}$$

$$\Rightarrow \quad d = d' - t + \frac{t}{K}$$

$$\Rightarrow \quad d' - d = t\left(1 - \frac{1}{K}\right)$$

Here, $d' - d = 3.2$ mm, $t = 4$ mm

$$\therefore \quad 3.2 = 4\left(1 - \frac{1}{K}\right) 1 - \frac{1}{K}$$

$$\Rightarrow \quad \frac{3.2}{4} = 1 - \frac{1}{K}$$

$$\Rightarrow \quad 1 - \frac{1}{K} = \frac{4}{5}$$

$$\therefore \quad K = 5$$

11. Work done by the external force must be zero.

12. Capacitance of parallel plate capacitor

$$C_0 = \frac{\varepsilon_0 A}{d}$$

where, A = area of the plates,

d = separation between the plates.

Charged stored in the capacitor

$$Q = C_0 V_0$$

When battery is disconnected, then charge remains same.

So, energy, $E_1 = \frac{1}{2}\frac{Q^2}{C}$

where, C = capacitance when plate separation is doubled

So, $$C_1 = \frac{C_0}{2}$$

$$E_1 = \frac{1}{2}\frac{Q^2}{C_0/2} = \frac{Q^2}{C_0}$$

$$= \frac{C_0^2V_0^2}{C_0} = C_0V_0^2$$

When battery is connected, then

Energy, $\quad E_2 = \frac{1}{2}CV_0^2$

where, $\quad E_2 = \frac{1}{2}\,\frac{C_0}{2}V_0^2$

$$= \frac{1}{4}(C_0V_0^2)$$

$$\therefore \quad \frac{E_1}{E_2} = \frac{C_0V_0^2}{\frac{1}{4}C_0V_0^2} = \frac{4}{1}$$

$E_1 : E_2 = 4 : 1$

13. Electric field intensity due to a point charge

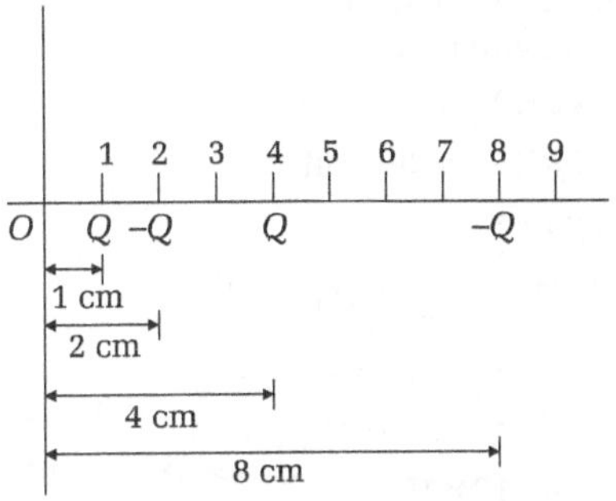

$$E = \frac{1}{4\pi\varepsilon_0}\frac{Q}{r^2}$$

The consecutive charges are of opposite signs.

$\therefore$ Net electric field at $x = 0$, is

$$E = \frac{1}{4\pi\varepsilon_0}\left[\frac{Q}{r_1^2} - \frac{Q}{r_2^2} + \frac{Q}{r_3^2} - \frac{Q}{r_4^2}\ldots\ldots\infty\right]$$

$$= \frac{Q}{4\pi\varepsilon_0}\left[\frac{1}{r_1^2} - \frac{1}{r_2^2} + \frac{1}{r_3^2} - \frac{1}{r_4^2}\ldots\ldots\infty\right]$$

$$= 9 \times 10^9 \times 5 \times 10^{-9}$$

$$\left[\frac{1}{(1\times10^{-2})^{-2}} - \frac{1}{(2\times10^{-2})^2} + \frac{1}{(4\times10^{-2})^2} + \ldots\ldots\infty\right]$$

$$= \frac{45}{10^{-4}}\left[\frac{1}{1^2} - \frac{1}{2^2} + \frac{1}{4^2} - \frac{1}{8^2} + \ldots\ldots\infty\right]$$

$$= 45 \times 10^4\left[\frac{1}{1^2} - \frac{1}{2^2} + \frac{1}{4^2} - \frac{1}{8^2} + \ldots\ldots\infty\right]$$

$$\left[\frac{1}{1^2} - \frac{1}{2^2} + \frac{1}{4^2} - \frac{1}{8^2} + \ldots\ldots\infty\right] = \frac{\frac{1}{1^2}}{1 - \left(\frac{-1}{2}\right)^2}$$

$$\left[\text{Sum of infinite GP} = \frac{a}{1-r}\right]$$

$$= \frac{1}{1 + \frac{1}{4}}$$

$$= \frac{4}{5}$$

$$\therefore E = 45 \times 10^4 \times \frac{4}{5} = 36 \times 10^4 \text{ N/C}$$

14. GIven, $\quad m = 1\text{ g} = 10^{-3}$ kg,

$v = 20 \text{ cms}^{-1} = 20 \times 10^{-2} \text{ ms}^{-1}$

$q = 10^{-8}$ C

$V_P = 600$ volt

$V_Q = 0$ volt

Work done in moving the charge from P to Q

$$W = q\,V_{PQ} = 10^{-8}(600 - 0)$$

$$= 600 \times 10^{-8} \text{ J}$$

From work energy theorem

Work done = change in KE

$$600 \times 10^{-8} = \frac{1}{2}m(20\times10^{-2})^2 - \frac{1}{2}mv^2$$

$$600 \times 10^{-8} = \frac{1}{2}\times10^{-3}\times4\times10^{-2} - \frac{1}{2}\times10^{-3}\times v^2$$

$$\frac{1}{2}\times10^{-3}\times v^2 = 2 \times 10^{-5} - 600 \times 10^{-8}$$

$$= 2 \times 10^{-5} - 0.6 \times 10^{-5}$$

$$v^2 = 1.4 \times 10^{-2} \times 2$$

$$= 2.8 \times 10^{-2}$$

$$v = \sqrt{2.8\times10^{-2}} = \sqrt{0.028} \text{ ms}^{-1}$$

15. Given, $\quad C = 100\,\mu$F, $V = 50$ volt

Capacitance of parallel plate capacitor

$$C = \frac{\varepsilon_0 A}{d}$$

d – separation between the plates.

Initial energy, $E_1 = \frac{1}{2}CV^2$

$$= \frac{1}{2}\times(100\times10^{-6})\times(50)^2$$

$$= 50 \times 10^{-6} \times 2500$$

$$= 125 \times 10^{-3} \text{ J}$$

When distance between the plates becomes double, then capacitance $C' = \frac{C}{2} = \frac{100}{2} = 50\,\mu$F

Final energy, $\quad E_2 = \frac{1}{2}C'V^2$

$$= \frac{1}{2}\times50\times10^{-6}\times(50)^2$$

$$= 25 \times 10^{-6} \times 2500$$

$= 625 \times 10^{-4}$

$= 62.5 \times 10^{-3}$ J

Additional energy $= E_1 - E_2$

$= 125 \times 10^{-3} - 62.5 \times 10^{-3}$

$= 62.5 \times 10^{-3}$

$= \frac{125}{2} \times 10^{-3}$ J

16. Total charge, $Q = CV$

$= 1000 \times 10^{-6} \times 20$

$= 20{,}000\ \mu$ C

Rate of charge $= 200\ \mu$C/s

$\therefore$ Time taken $= \frac{20{,}000}{200}$

$= 100$ s

17. Energy stored, $E \propto q^2$

$$\frac{E_1}{E_2} = \left(\frac{q_1}{q_2}\right)^2$$

$$\frac{100}{121} = \left(\frac{q}{q+2}\right)^2$$

$$\left(\frac{10}{11}\right)^2 = \left(\frac{q}{q+2}\right)^2$$

$$\frac{10}{11} = \frac{q}{q+2}$$

$\Rightarrow 10\,q + 20 = 11\,q$

$q = 20$ C

18. Given, $q_1 = 9\ \mu$C, $q_2 = -3\ \mu$C, $r = 0.16$ m

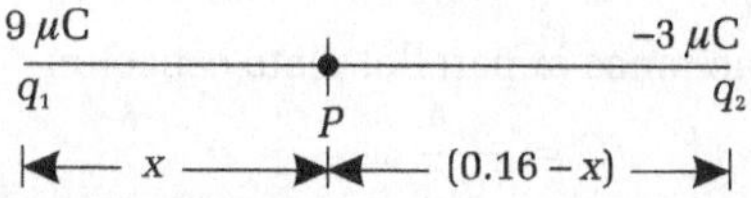

Potential at point P

$V_1 + V_2 = 0$

or $V_1 = -V_2$

$$\frac{1}{4\pi\varepsilon_0}\frac{q_1}{r_1} = \frac{-1}{4\pi\varepsilon_0}\frac{q_2}{r_2}$$

$$\frac{9}{x} = \frac{-(-3)}{(0.16-x)}$$

$\Rightarrow 3\,(0.16 - x) = x$

$0.48 - 3\,x = x$

$4x = 0.48$

$\Rightarrow x = 0.12$ m

19. Given, $C_1 = 20$ F, $V = 5$ volt

$C_2 = 30$ F

Decrease in energy

$$\Delta U = \frac{1}{2}\frac{C_1C_2}{C_1+C_2}(V_1 - V_2)^2$$

$$= \frac{1}{2}\times\frac{20\times30}{20+30}(5-0)^2$$

$$= \frac{300}{50}\times 25 = 150 \text{ J}$$

20. $E = 10^3$ V/m (along y-axis)

$m = 1$ g $= 1 \times 10^{-3}$ kg,

$q = 10^{-6}$ C, $v = 10$ m/s

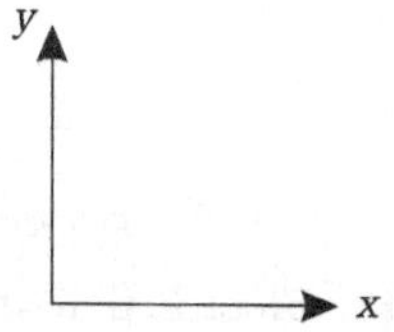

The charged body is moving perpendicularly to the direction of electric field, so no force acts on it, so the velocity of the body remains same.

21. $C_1 = 4\ \mu$F, $V_1 = 80$ volt,

$C_2 = 6\ \mu$F, $V_2 = 30$ volt

Energy loss

$$\Delta U = \frac{1}{2}\frac{C_1C_2}{C_1+C_2}(V_1 - V_2)^2$$

$$= \frac{1}{2}\times\frac{4\times10^{-6}\times6\times10^{-6}}{4\times10^{-6}+6\times10^{-6}}(80-30)^2$$

$$= \frac{12\times10^{-6}}{10}\times 2500$$

$= 1.2 \times 25 \times 10^{-4}$

$= 30 \times 10^{-4} = 3 \times 10^{-3}$ J

Initial energy of 4 μF capacitor

$$E_1 = \frac{1}{2}C_1V_1^2$$

$$= \frac{1}{2}\times 4\times10^{-6}\times(80)^2$$

$= 2 \times 10^{-6} \times 6400$

$= 12.8 \times 10^{-3}$ J

Energy lost by, $C_1 = 12.8 \times 10^{-3} - 3 \times 10^{-3}$

$= 9.8 \times 10^{-3}$ J

$= 9.8$ mJ

22. Given, $m = 3 \times 10^{-6}$ kg, $E = 10^6$ NC^{-1}

For particle to be stationary

Electric force = weight of the particle

$qE = -mg$

($\because$ Electric field is vertically downward)

$$\therefore \quad q = \frac{-mg}{E} = \frac{-3\times10^{-6}\times10}{10^6}$$

$= -3 \times 10^{-11}$ C

$= -3 \times 10^{-5}\ \mu$C

23. $AB = BC = AC = 10\text{ cm} = 10 \times 10^{-2}\text{ m}$

Force applied by the charge on A, on the charge at C.

$$F_1 = \frac{1}{4\pi\varepsilon_0}\frac{q_1 q_2}{AC^2}$$

$$= 9\times10^9 \times \frac{(1\times10^{-6})(2\times10^{-6})}{(10\times10^{-2})^2} = 1.8\text{ N}$$

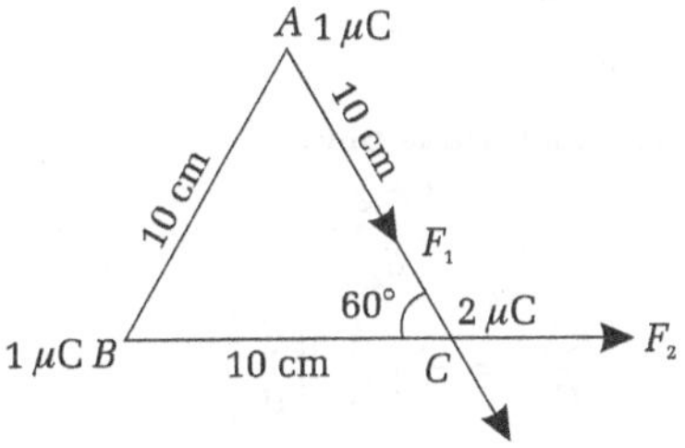

Similarly, force applied by the charge on B, on the charge at C

$$F_2 = \frac{1}{4\pi\varepsilon_0}\frac{q_1 q_2}{BC^2}$$

$$= 9\times10^9 \frac{(1\times10^{-6})(2\times10^{-6})}{(10\times10^{-2})^2}$$

$$= 1.8\text{ N}$$

Resultant of F_1 and F_2

$$F = \sqrt{F_1^2 + F_2^2 + 2F_1F_2\cos\theta}$$

$$= \sqrt{(1.8)^2 + (1.8)^2 + 2(1.8)(1.8)\cos 60^\circ}$$

$$= \sqrt{(1.8)^2 + (1.8)^2 + 2(1.8)^2 \times \frac{1}{2}}$$

$$= 1.8\sqrt{3}\text{ N}$$

24. Given, $q_1 = 12\,\mu\text{C}$, $q_2 = -6\,\mu\text{C}$, $r = 20\text{ cm}$

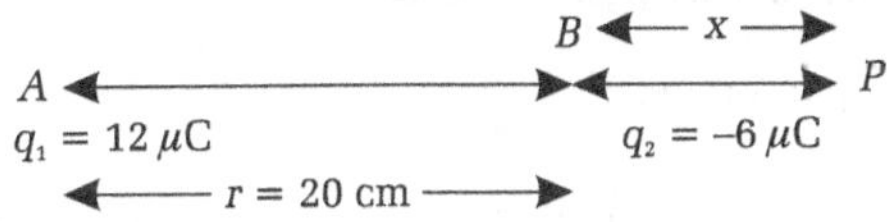

Total potential at point P is zero

$$\text{So, } \frac{1}{4\pi\varepsilon_0}\frac{q_1}{(r+x)} + \frac{1}{4\pi\varepsilon_0}\frac{q_2}{x} = 0$$

$$\frac{q_1}{r_1 + x} + \frac{q_2}{x} = 0$$

$$\frac{12\times10^{-6}}{(20+x)} + \frac{(-6\times10^{-6})}{x} = 0$$

$$\frac{12\times10^{-6}}{20+x} = \frac{6\times10^{-6}}{x}$$

$$2x = 20 + x$$

$$x = 20\text{ cm} = 0.2\text{ m}$$

25. Work done by electric field

$$W = \vec{F}\cdot\vec{r} = (Q\vec{E})\cdot\vec{r} = Q(\vec{E}\cdot\vec{r})$$

$$= Q[(c_1\hat{i} + c_2\hat{j} + c_3\hat{k})\cdot(a\hat{i} + b\hat{j})]$$

$$= Q(c_1 a + c_2 b)$$

26. $q_1 = 8\text{ C}$, $q_2 = -6\text{ C}$

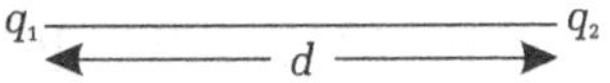

$$\text{Initial force, } F = k\frac{q_1q_2}{d^2} = k\frac{(8)(-6)}{d^2}$$

$$= k\frac{(-48)}{d^2}$$

New charges, $q_1 = 8 + 8 = 16\text{ C}$

$q_2 = -6 + 8 = 2\text{ C}$

Distance $= d/3$

$$\therefore \text{ New force } F' = k\frac{q_1q_2}{(d/3)}$$

$$= k\frac{(16)(2)}{d^2/9} = k\frac{288}{d^2}$$

$$\therefore \quad \frac{F'}{F} = \frac{k(288)/d^2}{k(-48)/d^2}$$

$$= \frac{288}{48} = 6$$

$$\therefore \quad F' = 6F$$

27. Given, $r = 20\text{ cm} = 20 \times 10^{-2}\text{ m}$,

$E = 4.5 \times 10^5\text{ N/C}$

$$\text{Electric field intensity, } E = \frac{1}{4\pi\varepsilon_0}\frac{Q}{r^2}$$

$$4.5 \times 10^5 = 9\times10^9 \times \frac{Q}{(20\times10^{-2})^2}$$

$$4.5 \times 10^5 = 9 \times 10^9 \times \frac{Q}{400\times10^{-4}}$$

$$Q = \frac{4.5\times10^5 \times 400\times10^{-4}}{9\times10^9}$$

$$= 200 \times 10^{-8}$$

$$= 2 \times 10^{-6}\text{ C} = 2\,\mu\text{C}$$

28. Energy of a capacitor, $E = \dfrac{q^2}{2C}$

$$\therefore \quad E \propto \frac{1}{C}$$

$$\frac{E_1}{E_2} = \frac{C_2}{C_1}$$

$$\frac{E}{E_2} = \frac{k_2 C}{k_1 C} = \frac{k_2}{k_1}$$

$$\frac{E}{E_2} = \frac{k_2}{k_1}$$

$$\frac{E}{E_2} = \frac{2}{5}$$

$$\Rightarrow \quad E_2 = \frac{5E}{2}$$

$$E_2 = 2.5\ E$$

29. Given, $q_1 = +5\ \mu C, = 5 \times 10^{-6}\ C$

$q_2 = +10\ \mu C, = 10 \times 10^{-6}\ C$

$r = 20\ cm = 20 \times 10^{-2}\ m$

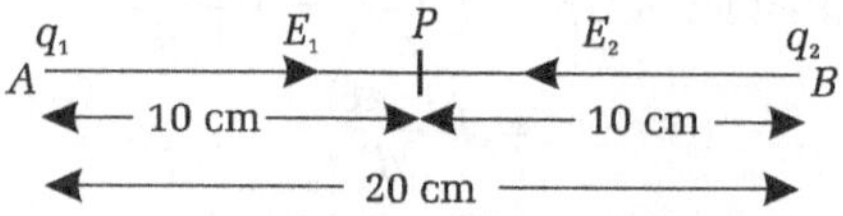

The electric field at the mid point due to q_1 and q_2 will be in opposite directions (for like charges)

$\therefore$ Net field at point P (mid point), $E = E_2 - E_1$

$$= \frac{1}{4\pi\varepsilon_0}\frac{q_2}{(r/2)^2} - \frac{1}{4\pi\varepsilon_0}\frac{q_1}{(r/2)^2}$$

$$= \frac{1}{4\pi\varepsilon_0 (r/2)^2}[q_2 - q_1]$$

$$= \frac{9\times10^9\times4}{(20\times10^{-2})^2}[10\times10^{-6} - 5\times10^{-6}]$$

$$= \frac{9\times10^9\times4}{(20\times10^{-2})^2}\times5\times10^{-6}$$

$$= \frac{180\times10^3}{400\times10^{-4}}$$

$$= \frac{180\times10^7}{400}$$

$= 4.5 \times 10^6$ N/C (towards + 5 μC)

30. $\frac{C_{air}}{C_{medium}} = \frac{1}{K}$ (dielectric constant)

$$\therefore \quad C_{air} = \frac{C_{medium}}{K} = \frac{C}{2}$$

31. For the system to be in equilibrium, there should no force at any charge.

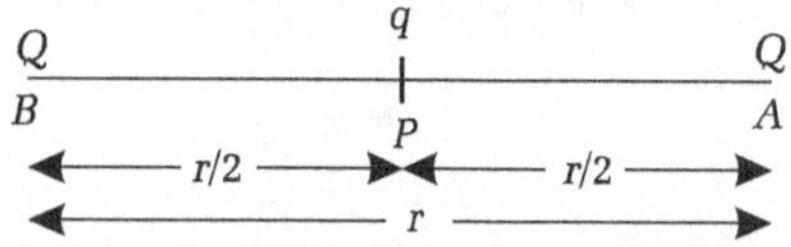

$\therefore$ Total force on $q = 0$

$$F_{qQ} + F_{QQ} = 0$$

$$k\frac{qQ}{(r/2)^2} + k\frac{QQ}{r^2} = 0$$

$$\frac{q}{r^2/4} + \frac{Q}{r^2} = 0$$

$$4q + Q = 0$$

$$q = -\frac{Q}{4}$$

32. Capacitance of parallel plate capacitor

Ist case

$$C_1 = \frac{A_1\varepsilon_0}{d_1} \quad \text{(For air)}$$

IInd case

(when dielectric is placed)

$$C_2 = \frac{KA_2\varepsilon_0}{d_2}$$

$$\therefore \quad \frac{C_1}{C_2} = \frac{1}{K}\left(\frac{A_1}{A_2}\right)\left(\frac{d_2}{d_1}\right)$$

In both the cases area is kept same.

So, $A_1 = A_2$

But distance is reduced to half in second case.

$\therefore \quad d_2 = d_1/2$

but, $d_1 = 0.4$ cm, $d_2 = 0.2$ cm

So, $$\frac{C_1}{C_2} = \frac{1}{K}\left(\frac{d_2}{d_1}\right)$$

$$\frac{2}{C_2} = \frac{1}{2.8}\times\left(\frac{0.2}{0.4}\right)$$

$$C_2 = \frac{2\times0.4\times2.8}{0.2}$$

$= 4 \times 2.8 = 11.2\ \mu$F

33. When a dielectric material is introduced between the plates of a charged condenser then its capacitance increases therefore electric field between its plates decreases.

34. Capacitance, $C = \frac{q}{V}$

$$\Rightarrow \quad V = \frac{q}{C} \quad \text{...(i)}$$

and capacitance of parallel plate capacitor

$$C = \frac{\varepsilon_0 A}{d}$$

$$\Rightarrow \quad C \propto \frac{1}{d} \quad \text{...(ii)}$$

On disconnection from the battery, the charge q on the condenser becomes constant.

When the plates are moved further apart, then d increases, so capacitance decreases (Eq. ii) therefore voltage between the plates increases (Eq. i).

35. Potential at point, $x = 0$

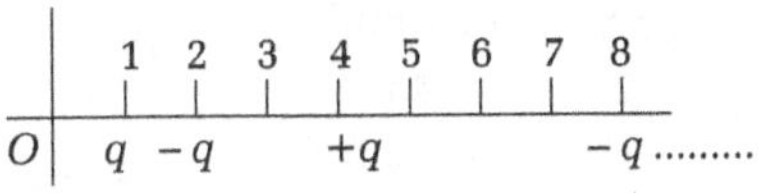

$$V = \frac{1}{4\pi\varepsilon_0}\sum\frac{q}{r}$$

$$= \frac{1}{4\pi\varepsilon_0}\left[\frac{q}{r_1}-\frac{q}{r_2}+\frac{q}{r_3}-\frac{q}{r_4}+.....\infty\right]$$

$$= \frac{q}{4\pi\varepsilon_0}\left[\frac{1}{r_1}-\frac{1}{r_2}+\frac{1}{r_3}-\frac{1}{r_4}+.....\infty\right]$$

$$= \frac{q}{4\pi\varepsilon_0}\left[\frac{1}{1}-\frac{1}{2}-\frac{1}{4}-\frac{1}{8}+.....\infty\right]$$

$$V = \frac{q}{4\pi\varepsilon_0}\left[\frac{1}{1-\left(\frac{-1}{2}\right)}\right]$$

$$\left[\text{Sum of infinite terms of GP} = \frac{a}{1-r}\right]$$

$$= \frac{q}{4\pi\varepsilon_0}\left[\frac{1}{1+\frac{1}{2}}\right]$$

$$= \frac{q}{4\pi\varepsilon_0}\frac{2}{3}$$

$$\therefore \quad V \propto \frac{2q}{3}$$

36. Equivalent capacitance of C_1 and C_2 (in series)

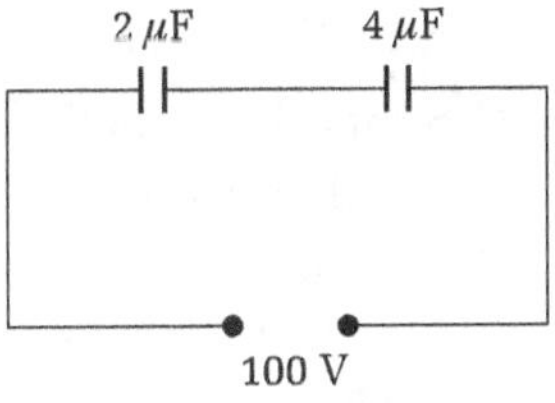

$$C = \frac{C_1C_2}{C_1+C_2} = \frac{2\times4}{2+4}$$

$$= \frac{8}{6} = \frac{4}{3}\mu\text{F}$$

$$= \frac{4}{3}\times10^{-6}\text{F}$$

$$\therefore \text{ Energy stored, } E = \frac{1}{2}CV^2$$

$$= \frac{1}{2}\times\frac{4}{3}\times10^{-6}\times(100)^2$$

$$= \frac{2}{3}\times10^{-6}\times10^4$$

$$= \frac{2}{3}\times10^{-2}$$

$$= 0.0067 \text{ J}$$

37. The electric potential at the centre of a charged conductor is equal to the electric potential at the surface of the conductor.

38. The energy stored in a capacitor

$$E = \frac{1}{2}qV$$

where, q = among of charge on the capacitor

V = potential difference between the plates of the capacitor

39. Capacitance without dielectric, $C_a = 10\ \mu$F

Dielectric constant, $K = 2$

Thickness of slab, $t = d/2$

where, d = distance between the plates of the capacitor

From formula, $C_a = \dfrac{A\varepsilon_0}{d}$

With dielectric, $C = \dfrac{A\varepsilon_0}{d-t+\frac{t}{K}}$

$$= \frac{A\varepsilon_0}{d-\frac{d}{2}+\frac{d}{2K}} = \frac{A\varepsilon_0}{\frac{d}{2}+\frac{d}{2K}}$$

$$= \frac{2A\varepsilon_0}{d\left(1+\frac{1}{K}\right)}$$

$$= \frac{2C_a}{1+\frac{1}{K}}$$

$$= \frac{2\times10}{1+\frac{1}{2}} = \frac{2\times10\times2}{3}$$

$$= 13.33\ \mu\text{F}$$

40. Original capacitance (without dielectric)

$$C_a = \frac{A\varepsilon_0}{d}$$

Capacitance with dielectric slab

$$C' = \frac{A\varepsilon_0}{d-t+\frac{t}{K}}$$

where, t = thickness of slab = $\dfrac{2d}{3}$

K = dielectric constant

$$\therefore \quad C' = \frac{A\varepsilon_0}{d-\frac{2d}{3}+\frac{2d/3}{K}} = \frac{A\varepsilon_0}{\frac{d}{3}+\frac{2d}{3K}}$$

$$= \frac{3A\varepsilon_0}{d\left(1+\frac{2}{K}\right)} = \frac{3C_a}{\left(1+\frac{2}{K}\right)}$$

But, $C' = 2.25\, C_a$

$$\therefore \quad 2.25\, C_a = \frac{3C_a}{\left(1+\frac{2}{K}\right)}$$

$$1+\frac{2}{K} = \frac{3}{2.25}$$

$$\Rightarrow \quad \frac{2}{K} = \frac{3}{2.25} - 1$$

$$\frac{2}{K} = \frac{0.75}{2.25}$$

$$K = \frac{2\times 2.25}{0.75} = 6$$

41. Capacitance of parallel plate capacitor

$$C = \frac{\varepsilon_0 A}{d} = 4\text{ F}$$

Capacitance of Ist half

$$C_1 = \frac{\varepsilon_0 A/2}{d} = \frac{\varepsilon_0 A}{2d}$$

$$= \frac{4\text{F}}{2} = 2\text{ F}$$

Capacitance of IInd half

$$C_2 = \frac{K\varepsilon_0 A/2}{d} = \frac{K}{2}\left(\frac{\varepsilon_0 A}{d}\right)$$

$$= \frac{3}{2}\times 4 = 6\text{ F}$$

C_1 and C_2 are connected in parallel.

So, net capacitance $C = C_1 + C_2 = 2 + 6 = 8$ F

42. $+Q$ is to be placed between two opposite charge, so it should be placed on the left of 2 μC.

Force applied by q_1 is

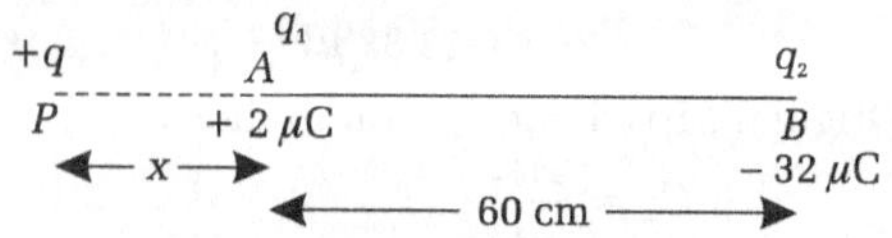

$$F_1 = k\frac{Qq_1}{x^2} \text{ (along } AP)$$

Force applied by q_2

$$F_2 = k\frac{Qq_2}{(x+60)^2} \text{ (along } PA)$$

F_1 and F_2 are opposite, so for zero force on Q

$$F_1 = F_2$$

$$k\frac{Qq_1}{x^2} = k\frac{Qq_2}{(x+60)^2}$$

$$\frac{q_1}{x^2} = \frac{q_2}{(x+60)^2}$$

$$\frac{2}{x^2} = \frac{32}{(x+60)^2}$$

$$(x+60)^2 = 16x^2$$

$$x + 60 = 4x$$

$$3x = 60$$

$$\Rightarrow \quad x = 20\text{ cm}$$

So, the distance of point is 20 cm left to $+2\mu$C.

43. Maximum capacitance will be obtained in parallel order.

So, $C_{max} = C_1 + C_2 + C_3$

$$= 1 + 2 + 3$$

$$= 6\,\mu\text{F}$$

Minimum capacitance will be obtained in series order, so

$$\frac{1}{C_{min}} = \frac{1}{C_1}+\frac{1}{C_2}+\frac{1}{C_3}$$

$$= \frac{1}{1}+\frac{1}{2}+\frac{1}{3}$$

$$= \frac{6+3+2}{6} = \frac{11}{6}$$

$$\therefore \quad C_{min} = \frac{6}{11}\mu\text{F}$$

44. Heat produced in the resistance

H = Energy of the condenser

$$= \frac{1}{2}CV^2$$

where, C = capacitance of the condenser

$= 2\,\mu\text{F} = 2 \times 10^{-6}$ F

V = potential difference between the plates of the condenser

$= 500$ V

$$\therefore \quad H = \frac{1}{2}\times 2\times 10^{-6}\times (500)^2$$

$$= 1 \times 10^{-6} \times 25 \times 10^4$$

$$= 0.25\text{ J}$$

46. For the system to be in equilibrium, the force on any charge out of three charges should be zero.

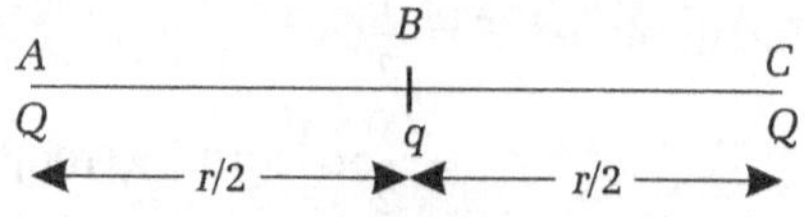

So, force on charge, $Q = 0$

$$\therefore \quad F_{Qq} + F_{qQ} = 0$$

$$k\frac{Qq}{(r/2)^2}+k\frac{Qq}{r^2} = 0$$

$$\frac{4q}{r^2}+\frac{Q}{r^2} = 0$$

$$4q = -Q$$

$\therefore$ $$q = -Q/4$$

47. Capacitance of parallel plate capacitor

$$C = \frac{\varepsilon_0 A}{d}$$

After disconnection of battery the charge becomes constant, on moving the plates of the capacitor further apart (d increases). So, capacitance (C) decreases.

So, from $V = \dfrac{q}{C}$

$\Rightarrow$ $$V \propto \frac{1}{C}$$

i.e., voltage across the plate increases.

48. Equivalent capacitance in series order

$$\frac{1}{C_s} = \frac{1}{C_1}+\frac{1}{C_2}+\frac{1}{C_3}+\frac{1}{C_4}+\frac{1}{C_5}$$

All the capacitors are of equal capacitance,

So, $$\frac{1}{C_s} = \frac{5}{C}$$

$\Rightarrow$ $$C = 5\,C_s = 5 \times 4 = 20\,\mu\text{F}$$

Equivalent capacitance in parallel

$$C_p = C_1 + C_2 + C_3 + C_4 + C_5$$
$$= 5\,C = 5 \times 20 = 100\,\mu\text{F}$$
$$= 100 \times 10^{-6}\text{ F}$$

$\therefore$ Energy stored, $U = \dfrac{1}{2}C_p V^2$

$$= \frac{1}{2}\times 100\times 10^{-6}(400)^2$$
$$= 50 \times 10^{-6} \times 16 \times 10^4$$
$$= 800 \times 10^{-2}$$
$$= 8\text{ J}$$

49. Energy, $U = 4 \times 10^{20}$ eV

$$= 4 \times 10^{20} \times 1.6 \times 10^{-19}\text{ J}$$
$$= 64\text{ J}$$

Charge, $Q = 6.25$ C

So, potential difference, $V = \dfrac{U}{q}$

$$= \frac{64}{6.25}$$
$$= 10.24\text{ V}$$

Chapter 12

Current Electricity

1. A current of 2 A flows in an electric circuit as shown in figure. The potential difference $(V_R - V_S)$, in volt (V_R and V_S are potentials at R and S respectively) is **EAMCET | 2008**

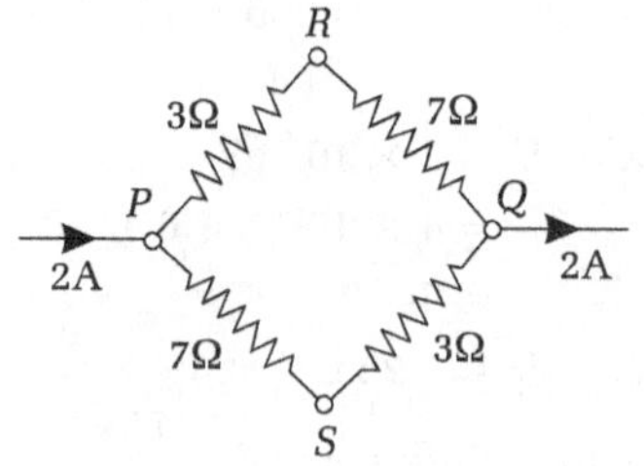

(a) –4 (b) +2 (c) +4 (d) – 2

2. When a battery connected across a resistor of 16 Ω, the voltage across the resistor is 12 V. When the same battery is connected across a resistor of 10 Ω, voltage across it is 11 V. The internal resistance of the battery in ohm is **EAMCET | 2008**

(a) $\frac{10}{7}$ (b) $\frac{20}{7}$ (c) $\frac{25}{7}$ (d) $\frac{30}{7}$

3. In a galvanometer 5% of the total current in the circuit passes through it. If the resistance of the galvanometer is G, the shunt resistance S connected to the galvanometer is **EAMCET | 2008**

(a) 19 G (b) $\frac{G}{19}$ (c) 20 G (d) $\frac{G}{20}$

4. In a meter bridge experiment, the ratio of the left gap resistance to right gap resistance is 2 : 3, the balance point from left is **EAMCET | 2007**

(a) 60 cm (b) 50 cm (c) 40 cm (d) 20 cm

5. An aluminium (resistivity $\rho = 2.2 \times 10^{-8}$ Ω-m) wire of a diameter 1.4 mm is used to make a 4Ω resistor. The length of the wire is **EAMCET | 2007**

(a) 220 m (b) 1000 m
(c) 280 m (d) 1 m

6. Twelve cells, each having emf E volt are connected in series and are kept in a closed box. Some of these cells are wrongly connected with positive and negative terminals reversed. This 12 cell battery is connected in series with an ammeter, an external resistance R ohms and a two-cell battery (two cells of the same type used earlier, connected perfectly in series). The current in the circuit when the 12-cell battery and 2-cell battery aid each other is 3A and is 2A when they oppose each other. Then, the number of cells in 12-cell battery that are connected wrongly is **EAMCET | 2006**

(a) 4 (b) 3 (c) 2 (d) 1

7. A 6 V cell with 0.5 Ω internal resistance, a 10 V cell with 1 Ω internal resistance and a 12 Ω external resistance are connected in parallel. The current (in ampere) through the 10 V cell is **EAMCET | 2005**

(a) 0.60 (b) 2.27 (c) 2.87 (d) 5.14

8. In a meter bridge a 30 Ω resistance is connected in the left gap and a pair of resistances P and Q in the right gap. Measured from the left, the balance point is 37.5 cm, when P and Q are in series and 71.4 cm when they the parallel. The values of P and Q (in Ω) are **EAMCET | 2005**

(a) 40, 10 (b) 35, 15
(c) 30, 20 (d) 25, 25

9. n conducting wires of same dimensions but having resistivities 1, 2, 3, ... n are connected in series. The equivalent resistivity of the combination is **EAMCET | 2004**

(a) $\frac{n(n+1)}{2}$ (b) $\frac{n+1}{2}$
(c) $\frac{n+2}{2n}$ (d) $\frac{2n}{n+1}$

10. Two cells A and B are connected in the secondary circuit of a potentiometer one at a time and the balancing length are respectively 400 cm and 440 cm. The emf of the cell A is 1.08 V. The emf of the second cell B in volt is **EAMCET | 2004**

(a) 1.08 (b) 1.188 (c) 11.88 (d) 12.8

11. Two resistances of 400 Ω and 800 Ω are connected in series with 6 V battery of negligible internal resistance. A voltmeter of resistance 10000 Ω is used to measure the

potential difference across 400 Ω. The error in the measurement of potential difference in volt approximately is **EAMCET | 2003**

(a) 0.01 (b) 0.02 (c) 0.03 (d) 0.05

12. Three unequal resistors in parallel are equivalent to a resistance 1 Ω. If two of them are in the ratio 1 : 2 and if no resistance value is fractional, the largest of the three resistances in ohm is **EAMCET | 2003**

(a) 4 (b) 6 (c) 8 (d) 12

13. A galvanometer, having a resistance of 50 Ω, gives a full scale deflection for a current of 0.05 A. The length in metre of a resistance wire of area of cross-section 2.97×10^{-2} cm^2 that can be used to convert the galvanometer into an ammeter which can read a maximum of 5 A current is (specific resistance of the wire $= 5 \times 10^{-7}$ Ω-m) **EAMCET | 2003**

(a) 9 (b) 6 (c) 3 (d) 1.5

14. The balancing length for a cell is 560 cm in a potentiometer experiment. When an external resistance of 10 Ω is connected in parallel to a cell, the balancing length changes by 60 cm. The internal resistance of the cell in ohm, is **EAMCET | 2002**

(a) 1.6 (b) 1.4 (c) 1.2 (d) 0.12

15. A conductor of resistance 3 Ω is stretched uniformly till its length is doubled. The wire is now bent in the form of an equivalent triangle. The effective resistance between the ends of any side of the triangle in ohm is **EAMCET | 2002**

(a) $\frac{9}{2}$ (b) $\frac{8}{3}$ (c) 2 (d) 1

16. A uniform conductor of resistance R is cut into 20 equal pieces. Half of them are joined in series and the remaining half of them are connected in parallel. If the two combinations are joined in series, the effective resistance of all the pieces is **EAMCET | 2002**

(a) R (b) $\frac{R}{2}$ (c) $\frac{101\,R}{200}$ (d) $\frac{201\,R}{200}$

17. A moving coil galvanometer of resistance 100 Ω shows full scale deflection when a current of 100 μA passes through it. If it is intended to show full scale deflection when a current of 1 mA passes through it, the value of shunt resistance in ohm to be connected to the galvanometer is **EAMCET | 2002**

(a) $\frac{9}{4}$ (b) $\frac{10}{3}$ (c) $\frac{100}{9}$ (d) $\frac{900}{7}$

18. A nichrome wire 50 cm long and 1 mm^2 cross-section carries a current of 4 A. When connected to 2 V battery. The resistivity of nichrome wire in Ω-m is **EAMCET | 2001**

(a) 1×10^{-6} (b) 4×10^{-7}
(c) 3×10^{-7} (d) 2×10^{-7}

19. When a resistor of 11 Ω is connected in series with an electric cell, the current flowing in it is 0.5 A. Instead, when a resistor of 5 Ω is connected to the same electric cell in series, the current increases by 0.4 A. The internal resistance of the cell is **EAMCET | 2001**

(a) 1.5 Ω (b) 2 Ω (c) 2.5 Ω (d) 3.5 Ω

20. An ammeter and a voltmeter of resistance R are connected in series to an electric cell of negligible internal resistance. Their readings are A and V respectively. If another resistance R is connected in parallel with voltmeter **EAMCET | 2000**

(a) both A and V will increase
(b) both A and V will decrease
(c) A will decrease and V will increase
(d) A will increase and V will decrease

21. Two wires of equal diameters of resistivities ρ_1 and ρ_2 and lengths x_1 and x_2 respectively are joined in series. The equivalent resistivity of the combination is **EAMCET | 2000**

(a) $\frac{\rho_1 x_1 + \rho_2 x_2}{x_1 + x_2}$ (b) $\frac{\rho_1 x_2 - \rho_2 x_1}{x_1 - x_2}$
(c) $\frac{\rho_1 x_2 + \rho_2 x_1}{x_1 + x_2}$ (d) $\frac{\rho_1 x_1 - \rho_2 x_2}{x_1 - x_2}$

22. In a meter bridge the gaps are closed by resistances 2 Ω and 3 Ω. The value of shunt to be added to 3 Ω resistor to shift the balancing point by 22.5 cm is **EAMCET | 1999**

(a) 1 Ω (b) 2 Ω (c) 2.5 Ω (d) 5 Ω

23. A wire of resistance 1 Ω is elongated by 10%, the resistance of the elongated wire **EAMCET | 1998**

(a) 11 Ω (b) 11.1 Ω
(c) 12.1 Ω (d) 13.1 Ω

24. In a meter bridge the balancing length from the left end (standard resistance of 1 Ω is in the right gap) is found to be 20 cm. The value of the unknown resistance is **EAMCET | 1998**

(a) 0.3 Ω (b) 0.25 Ω
(c) 0.4 Ω (d) 0.5 Ω

25. A galvanometer has a resistance of 50 Ω and a current of 0.01 A will cause full scale deflection. To convert this into an ammeter with full scale deflection for 5 A, we have to connect approximately. **EAMCET | 1998**

(a) 0.1 Ω in series
(b) 0.1 Ω in parallel
(c) 0.2 Ω in series
(d) 0.2 Ω in parallel

26. The emf of a daniel cell is 1.08 V. When the terminals of the cell are connected to resistance of 3 Ω, the potential difference across the terminals is found to be 0.6 V. Then, the internal resistance of the cell is **EAMCET | 1997**

(a) 1.8 Ω (b) 2.4 Ω
(c) 3.24 Ω (d) 0.2 Ω

27. A sensitive galvanometer like a moving coil galvanometer can be converted into an ammeter or into a voltmeter by connecting a proper resistance to it. Then, which of the following statements is not true? **EAMCET | 1997**

(a) An ammeter is connected in series in a circuit and the potential difference across it is small
(b) An ammeter is connected in series in a circuit and the current through it is negligible
(c) A voltmeter is connected in parallel in a circuit and the current through it is negligible
(d) A voltmeter is connected in parallel a circuit the potential difference across it is maximum

28. The potential difference across the terminals of a battery is 50 V when 11 A are drawn and 60 V when 1A is drawn. The emf and the internal resistance of the battery are **EAMCET | 1996**

(a) 62 V, 2 Ω (b) 63 V, 1 Ω
(c) 61 V, 1 Ω (d) 64 V, 2 Ω

29. If in a Wheatstone bridge the battery and galvanometer are interchanged the condition for balance **EAMCET | 1996**

(a) is disturbed
(b) is not disturbed
(c) depends on the internal resistance of the bridge
(d) depends on the values of the resistances in the bridge

30. An ammeter whose resistance is 180 Ω shows full scale deflection when the current is 2 mA. The shunt required to convert into an ammeter reading 20 mA is (in ohm) **EAMCET | 1995**

(a) 18 (b) 20 (c) 0.1 (d) 10

31. A current is passed through two coils connected in series. The potential difference across the first coil is 3 V and that of the second coil 4.5 V. If the first coil has resistance of 2 Ω, the resistance of the second coil is **EAMCET | 1994**

(a) 3 Ω (b) 5 Ω (c) 7 Ω (d) 9 Ω

32. To convert a 800 mV range millivoltmeter of resistance 40 Ω, into a milliammeter of 100 mA range, the resistance to be connected as shunt is **EAMCET | 1993**

(a) 5 Ω (b) 10 Ω (c) 15 Ω (d) 20 Ω

Answers

1. (c)	2. (b)	3. (b)	4. (c)	5. (c)	6. (d)	7. (c)	8. (c)	9. (a)	10. (b)
11. (d)	12. (b)	13. (c)	14. (c)	15. (b)	16. (c)	17. (c)	18. (a)	19. (c)	20. (d)
21. (a)	22. (b)	23. (c)	24. (b)	25. (b)	26. (b)	27. (b)	28. (c)	29. (b)	30. (b)
31. (a)	32. (b)								

Hints & Solutions

1. Current through each arm

PRQ and $PSQ = 1$ A

$$V_P - V_R = 3\text{ V} \quad \text{...(i)}$$

$$V_P - V_S = 7\text{ V} \quad \text{...(ii)}$$

From Eqs. (i) and (ii), we get

$$V_R - V_S = +4\text{ V}$$

2. Here; $V < E$

$\therefore$ $E = V + Ir$

For first case

$$E = 12 + \frac{12}{16}r \quad \text{...(i)}$$

For second case

$$E = 11 + \frac{11}{10}r \quad \text{...(ii)}$$

From Eqs. (i) and (ii),

$$12 + \frac{12}{16}r = 11 + \frac{11}{10}r$$

$$\Rightarrow \quad r = \frac{20}{7}\ \Omega$$

3. Shunt of an ammeter,

$$S = \frac{I_g \times G}{I - I_g}$$

$$= \frac{5 \times G}{100 - 5} = \frac{G}{19}$$

4. Here, $\frac{P}{Q} = \frac{2}{3}$

We know

$$\frac{P}{Q} = \frac{l}{100 - l}$$

$$\Rightarrow \quad \frac{2}{3} = \frac{l}{100 - l}$$

$$\Rightarrow \quad l = 40\text{ cm}$$

5. Length of the wire is

$$l = \frac{RA}{\rho}$$

$$\therefore \quad l = \frac{4 \times \pi \times (0.7 \times 10^{-3})^2}{2.2 \times 10^{-8}}$$

$$= 280\text{ m}$$

6. Let polarity of m cells in a 12 cells battery is reversed, then equivalent emf of the battery

$$= (12 - 2m)E$$

Now, the circuit can be drawn as:

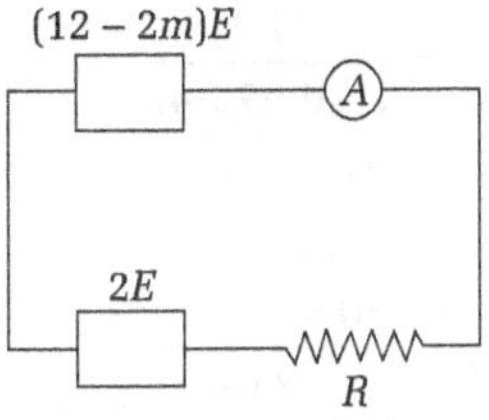

When 12 cell battery and 2 cell battery aid each other, then current through the circuit,

$$i_1 = \frac{(12 - 2m)E + 2E}{R}$$

or $$3 = \frac{(14 - 2m)E}{R} \quad \text{...(i)}$$

When they oppose each other, the current through the circuit.

$$i_2 = \frac{(12 - 2\,m)E - 2E}{R}$$

or $$2 = \frac{(10 - 2\,m)E}{R} \quad \text{...(ii)}$$

Dividing Eq. (i) by Eq. (ii), we have

$$\frac{3}{2} = \frac{14 - 2m}{10 - 2m}$$

or $30 - 6m = 28 - 4m$

or $2m = 2$

$\therefore$ $m = 1$

7. In closed loop $ABGFEHA$

$$10 - i_2 \times 1 + i_1 \times 0.5 - 6 = 0$$

$$0.5\, i_1 - i_2 = -4 \quad \text{...(i)}$$

In closed loop $BCDEB$

$$(i_1 + i_2) \times 12 + i_2 \times 1 - 10 = 0$$

$$12\, i_1 + 13\, i_2 = 10 \quad \text{...(ii)}$$

From Eqs. (i) and (ii)

$$i_2 = 2.87\text{ A}$$

8. **Ist case**

$$\frac{30}{P+Q} = \frac{l}{(100 - l)}$$

$$\frac{30}{P+Q} = \frac{37.5}{(100 - 37.5)}$$

$$\frac{30}{P+Q} = \frac{37.5}{62.5}$$

$$P + Q = \frac{30 \times 62.5}{37.5}$$

$$P + Q = 50 \quad \text{...(i)}$$

IInd case

$$\frac{30}{\frac{PQ}{P+Q}} = \frac{l}{(100-l)}$$

$$\frac{30(P+Q)}{PQ} = \frac{71.4}{(100-71.4)}$$

$$\frac{30\times 50}{PQ} = \frac{71.4}{28.6}$$

$$PQ = \frac{30\times 50\times 28.6}{71.4}$$

$$PQ \approx 600 \qquad \text{...(ii)}$$

So, from Eqs. (i) and (ii),

$$P = 30\ \Omega,\ Q = 20\ \Omega$$

9. Resistivity of the combination

$$= (1 + 2 + 3 + ... + n)$$

$$= \frac{n(n+1)}{2}$$

10.
$$\frac{E_1}{E_2} = \frac{l_1}{l_2}$$

$$\Rightarrow \frac{1.08}{E_2} = \frac{400}{440}$$

$$\Rightarrow E_2 = \frac{440\times 1.08}{400}$$

$$= 1.188\ \text{V}$$

11. $R_1 = 400\ \Omega$, $R_2 = 800\ \Omega$

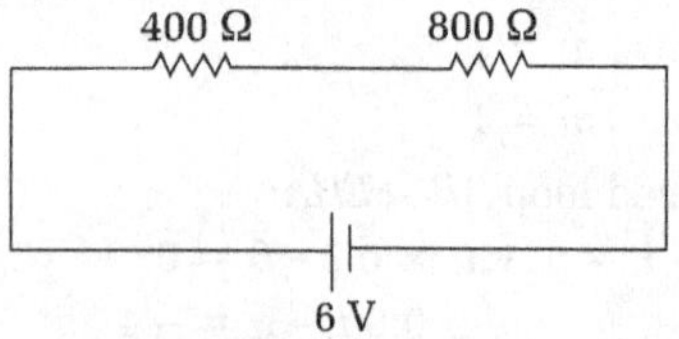

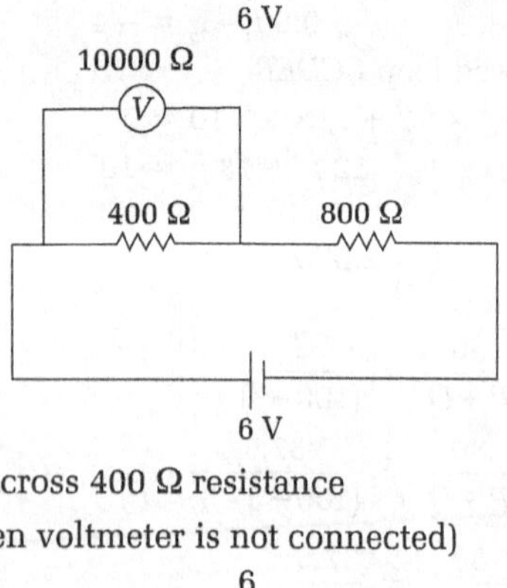

PD across 400 Ω resistance
(when voltmeter is not connected)

$$V_1 = \frac{6}{(400+800)}\times 400$$

$$= \frac{6\times 400}{1200} = 2\ \text{volt}$$

When voltmeter is connected, total resistance of the circuit

$$R = \left(\frac{10000\times 400}{10000+400}\right)+800$$

$$= \frac{10000\times 400}{10400}+800$$

$$= \frac{40000}{104}+800$$

$$= \frac{40000+83200}{104}$$

$$= \frac{123200}{104}$$

$$= \frac{30800}{26}$$

$$= \frac{15400}{13}$$

New PD across 400 Ω resistance

$$V_2 = 6-800\left(\frac{6}{15400/13}\right)$$

$$= 6-\frac{800\times 13\times 6}{15400}$$

$$= 6 - 4.052$$

$$= 1.95\ \text{volt}$$

$$\therefore \quad \text{Error} = V_1 - V_2$$

$$= 2 - 1.95$$

$$= 0.05$$

12. Let the resistances be R_1, R_2 and R_3

$$\therefore \quad \frac{R_1}{R_2} = \frac{1}{2}$$

$$\Rightarrow \quad R_1 = k,\ R_2 = 2\,k$$

In parallel
$$\frac{1}{R} = \frac{1}{R_1}+\frac{1}{R_2}+\frac{1}{R_3}$$

$$\frac{1}{1} = \frac{1}{k}+\frac{1}{2k}+\frac{1}{R_3}$$

$$\frac{1}{R_3} = 1-\frac{1}{k}-\frac{1}{2k}$$

$$= \frac{2k-2-1}{2k}$$

$$= \frac{2k-3}{2k}$$

$$R_3 = \frac{2k}{2k-3}$$

If $k = 1$, then R_3 is found to be negative, which is impossible.

If $k = 2$, then $R_1 = 2$, $R_2 = 4$, $R_3 = 4$

$R_2 = R_3$, not satisfying the condition of the question that all resistances are unequal.

If $k = 3$ then $R_1 = 3$, $R_2 = 6$, $R_3 = 2\ \Omega$

$\therefore$ Largest resistance $= 6\ \Omega$

13. Resistance of galvanometer

$$G = 50\ \Omega$$

Full scale current, $i_g = 0.05$

$$A = 2.97 \times 10^{-2}\ \text{cm}^2$$
$$= 2.97 \times 10^{-2} \times 10^{-4}\ \text{m}^2$$
$$= 2.97 \times 10^{-6}\ \text{m}^2$$
$$i = 5\ \text{A}$$
$$\rho = 5 \times 10^{-7}\ \Omega\text{-m}$$

Required resistance to convert the galvanometer into ammeter.

$$R = \frac{i_g G}{i - i_g} = \frac{0.05 \times 50}{5 - 0.05}$$
$$= \frac{2.5}{4.95}$$
$$\rho \frac{l}{A} = \frac{50}{99}$$
$$l = \frac{50}{99} \times \frac{A}{\rho}$$
$$= \frac{50}{99} \times \frac{2.97 \times 10^{-6}}{5 \times 10^{-7}}$$
$$= \frac{50}{99} \times \frac{29.7}{5}$$
$$= 10 \times 0.3 = 3\ \text{m}$$

14. Given, $l_1 = 560$ cm,

$l_2 = 500$ cm,

$R = 10\ \Omega$.

Internal resistance, $r = \left(\frac{l_1 - l_2}{l_2}\right) \times R$

$$= \frac{560 - 500}{500} \times 10$$
$$= \frac{60}{500} \times 10$$
$$= \frac{6}{5} - 1.2\ \Omega$$

15. Resistance, $R \propto l^2$

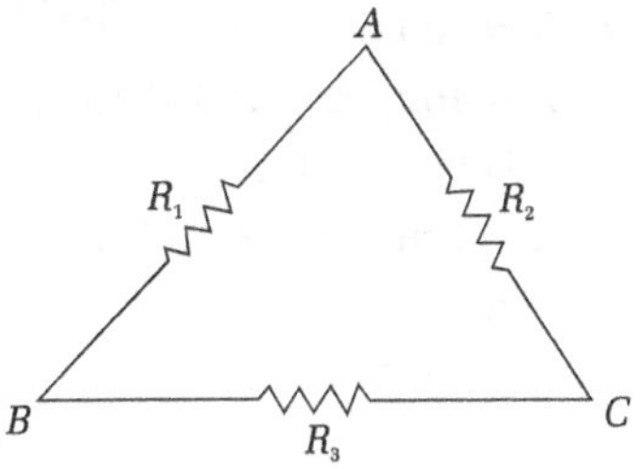

$$\frac{R_1}{R_2} = \left(\frac{l_1}{l_2}\right)^2$$
$$\frac{3}{R_2} = \left(\frac{l}{2l}\right)^2$$
$$\Rightarrow \quad R_2 = 12\ \Omega$$

Stretched wire is bent in the form of an equilateral triangle.

$\therefore$ Resistance of each side $= \frac{12}{3} = 4\ \Omega$

$$R_1 = R_2 = R_3 = 4\ \Omega$$

Equivalent resistance of R_1 and R_2 (in series)

$$R' = R_1 + R_2$$
$$= 4 + 4 = 8\ \Omega$$

Now, R' and R_3 are in parallel so that resistance,

$$R = \frac{R'R_3}{R' + R_3} = \frac{8 \times 4}{8 + 4} = \frac{32}{12} = \frac{8}{3}\Omega$$

16. Resistance of each piece $= \frac{R}{20}\Omega$

Equivalent resistance of 10 such pieces connectod in series

$$R_1 = 10 \times \frac{R}{20} = \frac{R}{2}$$

Similarly, equivalent resistance of 10 such pieces connected in parallel

$$\frac{1}{R_2} = \frac{1}{R/20} + \text{....... 10 times}$$
$$= \frac{10}{R/20} = \frac{200}{R}$$
$$R_2 = \frac{R}{200}$$

Now, R_1 and R_2 are connected in series so total resistance $= R_1 + R_2$

$$= \frac{R}{2} + \frac{R}{200}$$
$$= \frac{100\,R + R}{200} = \frac{101\,R}{200}$$

17. Resistance of galvanometer

$$G = 100\ \Omega$$

$$I_g = 100\ \mu A = 100 \times 10^{-6}\ A$$

$$= 0.1 \times 10^{-3}\ A$$

$$I = 1\ mA = 1 \times 10^{-3}\ A$$

Shunt resistance

$$S = \frac{I_g G}{I - I_g}$$

$$= \frac{0.1 \times 10^{-3} \times 100}{1 \times 10^{-3} - 0.1 \times 10^{-3}}$$

$$= \frac{1 \times 10^{-2}}{0.9 \times 10^{-3}}$$

$$= \frac{10^2}{9} = \frac{100}{9}\Omega$$

18. Given, $l = 50\ cm = 50 \times 10^{-2}\ m$

$$A = 1\ mm^2 = 1 \times 10^{-6}\ m^2$$

$$i = 4\ A, V = 2\ volt$$

$\therefore$ Resistance of wire, $R = \frac{V}{i} = \frac{2}{4}$

$$= 0.5\ \Omega$$

$\therefore$ Resistivity, $\rho = R\frac{A}{l} = 0.5 \times \frac{1 \times 10^{-6}}{50 \times 10^{-2}}$

$$= \frac{0.5 \times 1 \times 10^{-4}}{50}$$

$$= 1 \times 10^{-6}\ \Omega\text{-m}$$

19. Current taken from the cell $i = \frac{E}{R + r}$

where, R = external resistance and

r = internal resistance

Ist case $i_1 = \frac{E}{R_1 + r}$

$$0.5 = \frac{E}{11 + r} \quad ...(i)$$

IInd case $0.5 + 0.4 = \frac{E}{5 + r}$

$$\Rightarrow \quad 0.9 = \frac{E}{5 + r} \quad ...(ii)$$

Dividing Eq. (ii) by Eq. (i)

$$\frac{0.5}{0.9} = \frac{E/(11 + r)}{E/(5 + r)}$$

$$\frac{5}{9} = \frac{5 + r}{11 + r}$$

$$\Rightarrow 55 + 5r = 45 + 9r$$

$$10 = 4r$$

$$\Rightarrow \quad r = 2.5\ \Omega$$

20. On connecting the resistance R in parallel with the voltmeter, the total resistance of the circuit decreases, so reading of ammeter (A) will increase, but reading of voltmeter (V) will decrease, because effective resistance of voltmeter decreases.

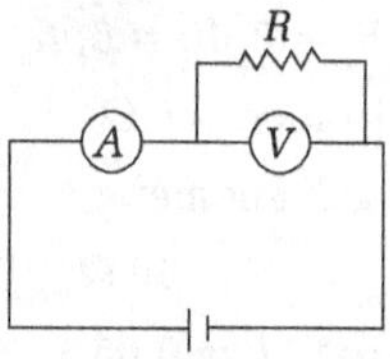

21. The diameters of both the wires is equal, so their cross-sectional areas will also be equal.

$\therefore$ Resistance of first wire, $R_1 = \rho_1 \frac{x_1}{A}$

Similarly, $R_2 = \rho_2 \frac{x_2}{A}$

Equivalent resistance in series order

$$R = R_1 + R_2$$

$$R = \frac{\rho(x_1 + x_2)}{A} = \frac{\rho_1 x_1}{A} + \frac{\rho_2 x_2}{A}$$

Equivalent resistivity, $\rho = \frac{\rho_1 x_1 + \rho_2 x_2}{x_1 + x_2}$

22. $R_1 = 2\ \Omega, R_2 = 3\ \Omega$

For meter bridge, $\frac{R_1}{R_2} = \frac{l}{100 - l}$

$$\frac{2}{3} = \frac{l}{100 - l}$$

$$\Rightarrow \quad 200 - 2l = 3l$$

$$l = 40\ cm$$

Balance point in shifted by 22.5 cm

$\therefore$ New balancing length $= 40 + 22.5$

$$= 62.5\ cm$$

Let on connecting the shunt the resistance R_2 becomes R'

$$\therefore \quad \frac{R_1}{R'} = \frac{62.5}{100 - 62.5}$$

$$\frac{R_1}{R'} = \frac{62.5}{37.5}$$

$$\Rightarrow \quad \frac{2}{R'} = \frac{5}{3}$$

$$R' = \frac{6}{5}$$

$$\therefore \quad \frac{1}{R_2} + \frac{1}{x} = \frac{1}{R'}$$

$$\Rightarrow \quad \frac{1}{3}+\frac{1}{x} = \frac{1}{6/5}$$

$$\frac{1}{3}+\frac{1}{x} = \frac{5}{6}$$

$$\Rightarrow \quad \frac{1}{x} = \frac{5}{6}-\frac{1}{3} = \frac{1}{2}$$

$$\therefore \quad x = 2\ \Omega$$

23. Let initial length, $l_1 = 100$

$\therefore$ Final length, $l_2 = 100 + 10 = 110$

Resistance, $R \propto l^2$

(In case of stretching of wire)

$$\therefore \quad \frac{R_1}{R_2} = \left(\frac{l_1}{l_2}\right)^2$$

$$\Rightarrow \quad \frac{10}{R_2} = \left(\frac{100}{110}\right)^2$$

$$R_2 = 10 \times \left(\frac{11}{10}\right)^2$$

$$= \frac{10\times121}{100} = 12.1\ \Omega$$

24. For meter bridge

$$\frac{R_1}{R_2} = \frac{l_1}{l_2}$$

$$\Rightarrow \quad \frac{1}{R_2} = \frac{80}{20}$$

$$\Rightarrow \quad R_2 = \frac{1}{4}\Omega$$

$$= 0.25\ \Omega$$

25. Given, $G = 50\ \Omega, i_g = 0.01\text{ A}, i = 5\text{ A}$

Required shunt resistance, $S = \dfrac{i_g G}{i-i_g}$

$$= \frac{0.01\times50}{5-0.01} = \frac{0.5}{4.99} = 0.1\ \Omega$$

To convert a galvanometer into ammeter, resistance is connected in parallel order.

26. Emf, $E = 1.08\text{ V}, R = 3\ \Omega,$

$V = 0.6$ volt

Internal resistance of the cell

$$r = R\left(\frac{E}{V}-1\right)$$

$$r = 3\left(\frac{1.08}{0.6}-1\right)$$

$$= 3\ (1.8 - 1) = 3 \times 0.8$$

$$= 2.4\ \Omega$$

27. Out of the given statements option (b) is not true because through ammeter is maximum.

28. Let the internal resistance of the battery is r.

Ist case $E = V_1 + I_1 r$

$E = 50 + 11\,r$ ...(i)

IInd case $E = 60 + 1r$

$E = 60 + r$ ...(ii)

$\therefore \quad 60 + r = 50 + 11\,r$

$10 = 10\,r$

$\Rightarrow \quad r = 1\ \Omega$

$\therefore \quad E = 60 + 1 = 61\text{ V}$

29. If in a Wheatstone bridge the battery and galvanometer are interchanged the condition for balance is not disturbed.

30. Resistance of ammeter, $G = 180\ \Omega$

$i_g = 2\text{ mA}$

$i = 20\text{ mA}$

Required shunt resistance

$$R_5 = \frac{i_g G}{i-i_g} = \frac{2\times180}{20-2}$$

$$= \frac{2\times180}{18} = 20\ \Omega$$

31. Potential difference across first coil

$V_1 = 3$ volt

Similarly, $V_2 = 4.5$ volt

In series order the current is same.

So, $\dfrac{V_1}{R_1} = \dfrac{V_2}{R_2}$

$$\frac{3}{2} = \frac{4.5}{R_2}$$

$$R_2 = \frac{4.5\times2}{3} = \frac{9}{3} = 3\ \Omega$$

32. Resistance of millivoltmeter

$G = 40\ \Omega$

Voltage range, $V_g = 800\text{ mV}$

Range of milliammeter, $i = 100\text{ mA}$

Current through millivoltmeter

$$i_g = \frac{V_g}{G} = \frac{800}{40}$$

$$= 20\text{ mA}$$

Required shunt resistance

$$S = \frac{i_g G}{i-i_g} = \frac{20\times40}{100-20}$$

$$= \frac{20\times40}{80} = \frac{800}{80}$$

$$= 10\ \Omega$$

Chapter 13

Thermal and Chemical Effects of Current

1. One junction of a certain thermoelectric couple is at a fixed temperature T_r and the other junction is at temperature T. the thermo-electromotive force for this is expressed by $E = k(T - T_r)\left[T_0 - \frac{1}{2}(T + T_r)\right]$. At temperature $T = \frac{1}{2}T_0$, the thermoelectric power is **EAMCET | 2008**

(a) $\frac{1}{2}kT_0$ (b) kT_0

(c) $\frac{1}{2}kT_0^2$ (d) $\frac{1}{2}k(T_0 - T_r)^2$

2. Temperature of cold junction in a thermocouple is 10°C and neutral temperature is 270°C, then the temperature of inversion is **EAMCET | 2007**

(a) 540°C (b) 530°C

(c) 280°C (d) 260°C

3. If the cold junction is held at 0°C, the same thermo emf V of a thermocouple varies as $V = 10\times10^{-6}t - \frac{1}{40}\times10^{-6}t^2$, where t is the temperature of the hot junction in °C. The neutral temperature and the maximum value of thermo emf are respectively **EAMCET | 2006**

(a) 200°C; 2 mV (b) 400°C; 2 mV

(c) 100°C; 1 mV (d) 200°C; 1 mV

4. Consider the following statements A and B and identify the correct answer given below **EAMCET | 2005**

A. Peltier coefficient is numerically equal to the potential difference across the junctions of the thermocouple through which current is flowing.

B. According to Thomson, energy is neither absorbed nor evolved at the junction of a thermocouple but is observed or evolved only along the lengths of both the conductors.

(a) Both A and B are true

(b) Both A and B are false

(c) A is true but B is false

(d) A is false but B is true

5. **Assertion (A)** Rapidly changing temperatures can be measured by thermocouples.
Reason (R) The thermal capacity of the junction of a thermocouple is very small. **EAMCET | 2004**

(a) Both (A) and (R) are true and (R) is not the correct explanation of (A)

(b) Both (A) and (R) are true but (R) is not the correct explanation of (A)

(c) (A) is true but (R) is false

(d) (A) is false but (R) is true

6. Consider the two following statements A and B, and identify the correct choice given in the answers

A. Duddell's thermo galvanometer is suitable to measure direct current only.

B. Thermopile can measure temperature difference of the order of 10^{-3} °C. **EAMCET | 2003**

(a) Both A and B are true

(b) Both A and B are false

(c) A is true but B is false

(d) A is false but B is true

7. The cold junction of a thermocouple is at 0°C. The thermo emf produced in the thermocouple is given by an equation $E = 16T - 0.04\ T^2$, where T is the temperature of the hot junction. The temperature of inversion and neutral temperature of the thermocouple are **EAMCET | 2002**

(a) 200°C; 400°C (b) 400°C; 200°C

(c) 200°C; 300°C (d) 300°C; 200°C

8. The neutral temperature of a thermocouple with cold junction at 20°C is 220°C. Its temperature of inversion is **EAMCET | 1999**

(a) 420°C (b) 120°C

(c) 110°C (d) 440°C

9. Four bulbs each marked 40 W, 250 V are connected in series with 250 V source. The total power output is **EAMCET | 1995**

(a) 10 W (b) 40 W

(c) 160 W (d) 320 W

10. The equation connecting thermo emf with the temperature difference between the junctions t of a thermocouple, whose cold junction is maintained at 0°C, is given by $e = 2040\,t - 6.2\,t^2$. The neutral and inversion temperatures of the thermocouple in °C are respectively and nearly equal to **EAMCET | 1994**
(a) 164.5 and 329 (b) 329 and 164.5
(c) 82.25 (d) 164.5 and 82.25

11. For a thermocouple, keeping the cold junction at constant temperature, if the hot junction temperature is increased, the thermo emf increases to a maximum at a temperature called **EAMCET | 1993**
(a) neutral temperature
(b) temperature of inversion
(c) transitional temperature
(d) null temperature

12. 3 lamps of 250 W, 500 W, 1000 W are connected in series across the mains. The one which will light the brightest is **EAMCET | 1993**
(a) 250 W
(b) 500 W
(c) 1000 W
(d) all three will light with equal brightness

13. Four 2 Ω resistors are connected together along the edges of a square. A 10 V battery of negligible internal resistance is connected across a pair of the diagonally opposite corners of the square. The power dissipated in the circuit is **EAMCET | 1992**
(a) 500 W (b) 50 W
(c) 5 W (d) 10 W

Answers

1.	(a)	2.	(b)	3.	(d)	4.	(c)	5.	(a)	6.	(d)	7.	(b)	8.	(a)	9.	(a)	10.	(b)
11.	(a)	12.	(a)	13.	(b)														

Hints & Solutions

1. We know that thermoelectric power

$$S = \frac{dE}{dT}$$

Given, $E = k(T - T_r)\left[T_0 - \frac{1}{2}(T + T_r)\right]$

By differentiating the above equation w.r.t. T and putting $T = \frac{1}{2}T_0$, we get $S = \frac{1}{2}kT_0$

2. Temperature of inversion is

$$T_i = 2T_n - T_0$$

$\therefore$ $T_i = 2 \times 270 - 10 = 530°C$

3. Given, $V = 10 \times 10^{-6}t - \frac{1}{40}\times 10^{-6}t^2$

At neutral temperature

$$\frac{dV}{dt} = 0$$

$\therefore$ $10\times 10^{-6} - \frac{1}{20}\times 10^{-6}t_n = 0$

or $t_n = 200°C$

Also at neutral temperature, thormo emf is maximum.

Thus,

$$V_{max} = 10 \times 10^{-6}(200) - \frac{1}{40}\times 10^{-6}(200)^2$$
$$= 2 \times 10^{-3} - 1 \times 10^{-3}$$
$$= 1\text{ mV}$$

4. If cold junction is at temperature T and hot junction at $T + dT$. If E is the thermo emf produced, then

$$\frac{\pi}{T} = \frac{dE}{dT}$$

The absorption or evolution of heat along the length of a wire, when current is passed through a wire whose one end is hot and other is kept cold is known as Thomson effect.

7. Thermo emf $E = 16\,T - 0.04\,T^2$

At inversion temperature (T_i), $E = 0$

$\therefore$ $0 = 16\,T_i - 0.04\,T_i^2$

$$16\,T_i = 0.04\,T_i^2$$

$$T_i = \frac{16}{0.04} = 400°C$$

Neutral temperature, $T_n = \frac{T_i + T}{2}$

T = Temperature of cold end

$$T_n = \frac{400+0}{2} = 200°C$$

8. Given, $T_n = 220°$ C, $T_c = 20°$ C

$\therefore$ Neutral temperature, $T_n = \frac{T_i + T_c}{2}$

T_i = Inversion temperature

$$220 = \frac{T_i + 20}{2}$$

$$T_i + 20 = 440$$

$$T_i = 440 - 20 = 420° \text{ C}$$

9. Rating of bulb = 40 W, 250 V

Power, $P = 40$ W, $V = 250$ volt

$\therefore$ Resistance of each bulb, $R = \frac{V^2}{P}$

$$= \frac{(250)^2}{40} = \frac{250 \times 250}{40}$$

$$= \frac{6250}{4} \Omega$$

Total resistance of four bulbs in series = 4 R

$$= \frac{6250}{4} \times 4$$

$$= 6250 \ \Omega$$

$\therefore$ Power consumption, $P = \frac{V^2}{R} = \frac{(250)^2}{6250}$

$$= \frac{250 \times 250}{6250}$$

$$= 10 \text{ W}$$

10. Thermo emf $e = 2040\, t - 6.2\, t^2$

Comparing with standard equation

$$e = At + Bt^2$$

$$A = 2040, B = -6.2$$

$\therefore$ Inversion temperature

$$T_i = -\frac{A}{B} = \frac{-2040}{-6.2} = 329°C$$

Neutral temperature, $T_n = \frac{T_i}{2} = \frac{329}{2}$

$$= 164.5° \text{ C}$$

11. The temperature of hot junction, at which the thermo emf produced in the thermocouple becomes maximum, is called neutral temperature.

12. Let the voltage rating of each bulb is V (equal).

$$P_1 = 250 \text{ W},$$

$$P_2 = 500 \text{ W},$$

$$P_3 = 1000 \text{ W}$$

Resistance of bulb, $R = \frac{V^2}{P}$

$\therefore$ $R \propto \frac{1}{P}$

As $P_1 < P_2 < P_3$

So, $R_1 > R_2 > R_3$

Hence, resistance of 250 W bulb will highest, so in series order maximum potential will drop across this bulb so it will glow brightest.

13. Equivalent resistance of R_1 and R_2

$$R' = R_1 + R_2 \quad \text{(In series)}$$

$$= 2 + 2 = 4 \ \Omega$$

Equivalent resistance of R_3 and R_4

$$R'' = R_3 + R_4 = 2 + 2 = 4 \ \Omega$$

R' and R'' are in parallel,

So, equivalent resistance

$$R = \frac{R' R''}{R' + R''}$$

$$= \frac{4 \times 4}{4+4} = 2 \ \Omega$$

Power consumed, $P = \frac{V^2}{R}$

$$= \frac{(10)^2}{2} = \frac{100}{2}$$

$$= 50 \text{ W}$$

Chapter

14

Magnetic Effects of Current

1. Two concentric coils of 10 turns each are placed in the same plane. Their radii are 20 cm and 40 cm and carry 0.2 A and 0.3 A current respectively in opposite directions. The magnetic induction (in T) at the centre is **EAMCET | 2008**

(a) $\frac{3}{4}\mu_0$ (b) $\frac{5}{4}\mu_0$ (c) $\frac{7}{4}\mu_0$ (d) $\frac{9}{4}\mu_0$

2. Two wires A and B are of lengths 40 cm and 30 cm. A is bent into a circle of radius r and B into an arc of radius r. A current i_1 is passed through A and i_2 through B. To have the same magnetic inductions at the centre, the ratio of $i_1 : i_2$ is **EAMCET | 2007**

(a) 3 : 4 (b) 3 : 5 (c) 2 : 3 (d) 4 : 3

3. An electron beam travels with a velocity of 1.6×10^7 ms^{-1} perpendicular to magnetic field of intensity 0.1 T. The radius of the path of the electron beam ($m_e = 9 \times 10^{-31}$ kg) **EAMCET | 2007**

(a) 9×10^{-5} m (b) 9×10^{-2} m
(c) 9×10^{-4} m (d) 9×10^{-3} m

4. When a positively charged particle enters a uniform magnetic field with uniform velocity, its trajectory can be **EAMCET | 2006**

(1) a straight line
(2) a circle
(3) a helix

(a) (1) only
(b) (1) or (2)
(c) (1) or (3)
(d) Any one of (1), (2) and (3)

5. Two parallel rails of a railway track insulated from each other and with the ground are connected to a millivoltmeter. The distance between the rails is 1 m. A train is travelling with a velocity of 72 kmh^{-1} along the track. The reading of the millivoltmeter (in mV) is (vertical component of the earth's magnetic induction is 2×10^{-5} T) **EAMCET | 2005**

(a) 1.44 (b) 0.72 (c) 0.4 (d) 0.2

6. Magnetic field induction at the centre of a circular coil of radius 5 cm and carrying a current 0.9 A is (in SI units)
(ε_0 = absolute permittivity of air in SI units; velocity of light = 3×10^8 ms^{-1}) **EAMCET | 2005**

(a) $\frac{1}{\varepsilon_0 10^{16}}$ (b) $\frac{10^{16}}{\varepsilon_0}$
(c) $\frac{\varepsilon_0}{10^{16}}$ (d) $10^{16}\varepsilon_0$

7. A wire of length l is bent into a circular coil of one turn of radius R_1. Another wire of the same material and same area of cross-section and same lengths is bent into a circular coil of two turns of radius R_2. When the same current flows, through the two coils, the ratio of magnetic induction at the centres of the two coils is **EAMCET | 2004**

(a) 1 : 2 (b) 1 : 1 (c) 1 : 4 (d) 3 : 1

8. A long straight wire carrying a current of 30 A is placed in an external uniform magnetic field of induction 4×10^{-4} T. The magnetic field is acting parallel to the direction of current. The magnitude of the resultant magnetic induction in tesla at a point 2.0 cm away from the wire is ($\mu_0 = 4\pi \times 10^{-7}$ Hm^{-1}) **EAMCET | 2003**

(a) 10^{-4} (b) 3×10^{-4}
(c) 5×10^{-4} (d) 6×10^{-4}

9. Two ions having masses in the ratio 1 : 1 and charges 1 : 2 are projected into uniform magnetic field perpendicular to the field with speeds in the ratio 2 : 3. The ratio of the radii of circular paths along which the two particles move is **EAMCET | 2003**

(a) 4 : 3 (b) 2 : 3 (c) 3 : 1 (d) 1 : 4

10. An electron revolves in a circle of radius 0.4 Å with a speed of 10^6 ms^{-1} in a hydrogen atom. The magnetic field produced at the centre of the orbit due to the motion of the electron (in tesla) is [$\mu_0 = 4\pi \times 10^{-7}$ Hm^{-1}, charge on the electron = 1.6×10^{-19} C] **EAMCET | 2002**

(a) 0.1 (b) 1.0 (c) 10 (d) 100

11. A proton of velocity $(3\hat{i}+2\hat{j})\ ms^{-1}$ enters a field of magnetic induction $(2\hat{j}+3\hat{k})$ T, the acceleration produced in the proton in ms^{-2} is (specific charge of proton = 0.96×10^8 C-kg^{-1}) **EAMCET | 2002**

(a) $2.8 \times 10^8\ (2\hat{i}-3\hat{j})$

(b) $2.88 \times 10^8\ (2\hat{i}-3\hat{j}+2\hat{k})$

(c) $2.8 \times 10^8\ (2\hat{i}+3\hat{k})$

(d) $2.88 \times 10^8\ (\hat{i}-3\hat{j}+2\hat{k})$

12. A wire in the form of a square of side a carries a current i. Then, the magnetic induction at the centre of the square is (magnetic permeability of free space = μ_0) **EAMCET | 2001**

(a) $\frac{\mu_0 i}{2\pi a}$ (b) $\frac{\mu_0 i\sqrt{2}}{\pi a}$

(c) $\frac{2\sqrt{2}\mu_0 i}{\pi a}$ (d) $\frac{\mu_0 i}{\sqrt{2}\pi a}$

13. A particle of mass 0.6 g and having charge of 25 nC is moving horizontally with a uniform velocity $1.2 \times 10^4\ ms^{-1}$ in a uniform magnetic field, then the value of the magnetic induction is ($g = 10\ ms^{-2}$) **EAMCET | 2001**

(a) zero (b) 10 T

(c) 20 T (d) 200 T

14. Two long parallel copper wires carrying currents in the opposite directions of 5 A each. If the wires are separated by a distance of 0.5 m, then the force per unit length between the two wires is **EAMCET | 2000**

(a) 10^{-5} N attractive force

(b) 10^{-5} N repulsive force

(c) 2×10^5 N attractive force

(d) 2×10^{-5} N repulsive force

15. When two infinitely long parallel wires separated by a distance of 1 m, each carry a current of 3 A, the force in Nm^{-1} length experienced by each will be given $\mu_0 = 4\pi \times 10^{-7}\ Hm^{-1}$ SI units **EAMCET | 1999**

(a) 2×10^{-7} (b) 3×10^{-7}

(c) 6×10^{-7} (d) 18×10^{-7}

16. If a long hollow copper pipe carries a current, the magnetic field produced will be **EAMCET | 1998**

(a) inside the pipe only

(b) outside the pipe only

(c) neither inside nor outside the pipe

(d) both inside and outside the pipe

17. A current carrying wire produces in the neighbourhood **EAMCET | 1998**

(a) electric and magnetic fields

(b) electric field only

(c) magnetic field only

(d) no field

18. Two parallel wires of length 9 m each, are separated by a distance of 0.15 m. If they carry equal current in the same direction and exert a total force of 30×10^{-7} N on each other, the value of the current must be **EAMCET | 1997**

(a) 1.5 A (b) 2.25 A

(c) 0.5 A (d) 0.25 A

19. An electric current passes through a long straight wire. At a distance 5 cm from the wire, the magnetic field is B. The field at 20 cm from the wire would be **EAMCET | 1996**

(a) $2B$ (b) $\frac{B}{4}$ (c) $\frac{B}{2}$ (d) B

20. Two circular coils are made of two identical wires of the same length. If the number of turns in the two coils are 4 and 2, then the ratio of magnetic inductions at the centre will be **EAMCET | 1996**

(a) 4 : 1 (b) 2 : 1

(c) 1 : 2 (d) 1 : 1

21. If the magnitude of the intensity of a magnetic field at a distance x on the axial line and at a distance y on the equatorial line of a given dipole have the same value the ratio $x : y$ is **EAMCET | 1994**

(a) $1 : \sqrt{2}$ (b) $\sqrt{2} : 1$

(c) 1 : 2 (d) $2^{1/3} : 1$

22. The magnetic induction at a point, distance x from the centre, on the axis of a circular current carrying coil is inversely proportional to (if $x >>$ radius of coil) **EAMCET | 1993**

(a) x (b) x^2 (c) x^{-3} (d) $x^{3/2}$

23. To a charged particle which is moving with a constant initial velocity $\vec{v}$, uniform magnetic field is applied in the direction of the velocity **EAMCET | 1992**

(a) the particle moves in a spiral path

(b) the particle moves in a circular path

(c) the particle moves in a parabolic path

(d) there is no change in the motion of the particle

24. A and B are sections of two long parallel wires placed perpendicular to the plane of the paper. They carry currents of 5 A and 10 A respectively in the directions indicated in the figure. If the separation between them is 3 m the zero of the magnetic field in the plane of the paper is at a point **EAMCET | 1992**

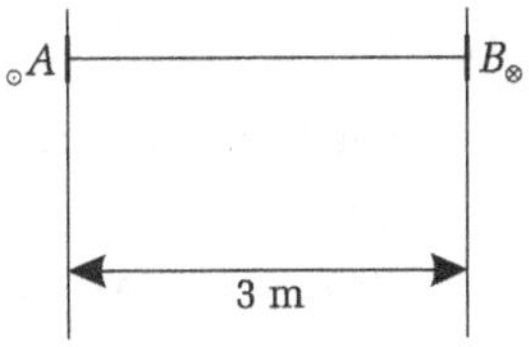

(a) 3 m to the left of A
(b) 3 m to the right of B
(c) 2 m to the right of A
(d) 2 m to the left of B

25. When the radius of a circular current carrying coil is doubled and current in it is halved, the magnetic dipole moment of coil originally 4 units become. **EAMCET | 1991**

(a) 18 unit (b) 16 unit
(c) 8 unit (d) 4 unit

Answers

1.	(b)	**2.**	(a)	**3.**	(c)	**4.**	(d)	**5.**	(c)	**6.**	(a)	**7.**	(c)	**8.**	(c)	**9.**	(a)	**10.**	(c)
11.	(b)	**12.**	(c)	**13.**	(c)	**14.**	(b)	**15.**	(d)	**16.**	(b)	**17.**	(c)	**18.**	(c)	**19.**	(b)	**20.**	(a)
21.	(d)	**22.**	(c)	**23.**	(d)	**24.**	(d)	**25.**	(c)										

Hints & Solutions

1. Two coils carry currents in opposite directions, hence net magnetic field at centre will be difference of the two fields.

i.e., $$B_{\text{net}} = \frac{\mu_0}{4\pi} \cdot 2\pi N \left[\frac{i_1}{r_1} - \frac{i_2}{r_2}\right]$$

$$= \frac{10\mu_0}{2}\left[\frac{0.2}{0.2} - \frac{0.3}{0.4}\right] = \frac{5}{4}\mu_0$$

2. For wire A, $$B_1 = \frac{\mu_0 i_1}{2r}$$

where, $$r = \frac{40}{2\pi}$$

For wire B, Circumference = length

$$n\pi r = 30$$

or $$n\pi = \frac{30}{r} = \frac{30}{40/2\pi} = \frac{3}{2}\pi$$

or $$\theta = n\pi = \frac{3}{2}\pi$$

$\therefore$ $$B_2 = \frac{\mu_0}{4\pi}\left(\frac{i_2}{r}\right)\theta$$

But, $$B_1 = B_2$$

or $$\frac{\mu_0 i_1}{2r} = \frac{\mu_0}{4\pi}\left(\frac{i_2}{r}\right)\theta$$

or $$\frac{i_1}{i_2} = \frac{3}{4}$$

3. In a perpendicular magnetic field, the radius of circular path travelled by electron beam is

$$r = \frac{mv}{eB}$$

$\therefore$ $$r = \frac{9\times10^{-31}\times1.6\times10^{7}}{1.6\times10^{-19}\times0.1}$$

$$= 9 \times 10^{-4} \text{ m}$$

5. Induced emf, $e = Bvl$

v = velocity of train

$$= 72 \times \frac{5}{18} = 20 \text{ ms}^{-1}$$

$$= 2 \times 10^{-5} \times 20 \times 1$$

$$= 2 \times 10^{-5} \times 20$$

$$= 40 \times 10^{-5} \text{ V}$$

$$= 40 \times 10^{-2} \text{ mV}$$

$$= 0.4 \text{ mV}$$

6. Magnetic field induction at the centre of circular coil

$$B = \frac{\mu_0 I}{2r} \quad \text{...(i)}$$

$$c^2 = \frac{1}{\mu_0 \varepsilon_0}$$

$\therefore$ $$\mu_0 = \frac{1}{\varepsilon_0 c^2}$$

So, from Eq. (i)

$$B = \frac{1}{\varepsilon_0 c^2}\frac{I}{2r}$$

$$= \frac{1}{\varepsilon_0 \times (3\times10^8)^2} \times \frac{0.9}{2\times5\times10^{-2}}$$

$$= \frac{1\times9}{\varepsilon_0\times9\times10^{16}} = \frac{1}{\varepsilon_0\times10^{16}}$$

7. Magnetic induction at the centre of a circular coil

$$B = \frac{\mu_0}{2}\cdot\frac{ni}{R}$$

$$\Rightarrow \quad B \propto \frac{n}{R}$$

Here, $n_1 = 1, n_2 = 2,$

$$l = 2\pi R_1 = 2\times 2\pi R_2$$

$$\Rightarrow \quad R_2 = \frac{R_1}{2}$$

$$\therefore \quad \frac{B_1}{B_2} = \frac{n_1}{n_2}\times\frac{R_2}{R_1}$$

$$= \frac{1}{2}\times\frac{R_1/2}{R_1} = \frac{1}{4}$$

$$\Rightarrow \quad B_1 : B_2 = 1:4$$

8. Given, $i = 30$ A, $B = 4\times10^{-4}$ T,

$r = 2$ cm $= 2\times10^{-2}$ m

Initial magnetic field (parallel to the wire)

$$B_1 = 4\times10^{-4}\text{ T}$$

Magnetic field produced by the straight wire

$$B_2 = \frac{\mu_0 i}{2\pi r}$$

$$= \frac{2\times10^{-7}\times30}{2\times10^{-2}}$$

$$= 3\times10^{-4}\text{ T}$$

B_2 will be in the plane perpendicular to the plane of wire, so B_1 and B_2 are perpendicular to each other.

∴ Resultant magnetic field

$$B = \sqrt{B_1^2 + B_2^2}$$

$$= \sqrt{(4\times10^{-4})^2 + (3\times10^{-4})^2}$$

$$= 5\times10^{-4}$$

9. Given, $m_1 : m_2 = 1:1$

$q_1 : q_2 = 1:2$

$v_1 : v_2 = 2:3$

Radius of path of charged particle moving in uniform magnetic field

$$r = \frac{mv}{Bq}$$

$$\therefore \quad \frac{r_1}{r_2} = \left(\frac{m_1}{m_2}\right)\left(\frac{v_1}{v_2}\right)\times\left(\frac{q_2}{q_1}\right)$$

$$= \frac{1}{1}\times\frac{2}{3}\times\frac{2}{1} = \frac{4}{3}$$

$$r_1 : r_2 = 4:3$$

10. Given, $r = 0.4$ Å, $= 0.4\times10^{-10}$ m,

$v = 10^6$ ms^{-1}

The moving electron will constitute an electric current.

Electric current, $i = \dfrac{q}{t}$

$$i = \frac{q}{\frac{2\pi r}{v}} = \frac{qv}{2\pi r}$$

$$i = \frac{1.6\times10^{-19}\times10^6}{2\pi\times0.4\times10^{-10}}$$

$$= \frac{1.6\times10^{-3}}{0.8\pi}$$

Magnetic produced at the centre

$$B = \frac{\mu_0 i}{2r}$$

$$B = \frac{4\pi\times10^{-7}}{2\times0.4\times10^{-10}}\times\frac{1.6\times10^{-3}}{0.8\pi}$$

$$= \frac{4\pi\times1.6}{0.8\times0.8\pi}$$

$$= \frac{6.4}{0.64} = 10\text{ T}$$

11. Given, $\vec{v} = (3\hat{i}+2\hat{j})$ ms^{-1}, $\vec{B} = (2\hat{j}+3\hat{k})$ T

Specific charge, $\dfrac{e}{m} = 0.96\times10^8$ Ckg^{-1}

Force acting on the proton $\vec{F} = q(\vec{v}\times\vec{B})$

$$\vec{v}\times\vec{B} = \begin{vmatrix}\hat{i} & \hat{j} & \hat{k}\\ 3 & 2 & 0\\ 0 & 2 & 3\end{vmatrix}$$

$$= 6\hat{i} - 9\hat{j} + 6\hat{k}$$

$$\therefore \quad F = q(6\hat{i} - 9\hat{j} + 6\hat{k})$$

From Newton's law $\vec{F} = m\vec{a}$

$$m\vec{a} = q(6\hat{i} - 9\hat{j} + 6\hat{k})$$

∴ Acceleration

$$\vec{a} = \frac{q}{m}(6\hat{i} - 9\hat{j} + 6\hat{k})$$

$$= \frac{e}{m}(6\hat{i} - 9\hat{j} + 6\hat{k})$$

$= 0.96 \times 10^8 \times 3(2\hat{i} - 3\hat{j} + 2\hat{k})$

$= 2.88 \times 10^8 (2\hat{i} - 3\hat{j} + 2\hat{k})$

12. Magnetic field produced by side AB at the centre.

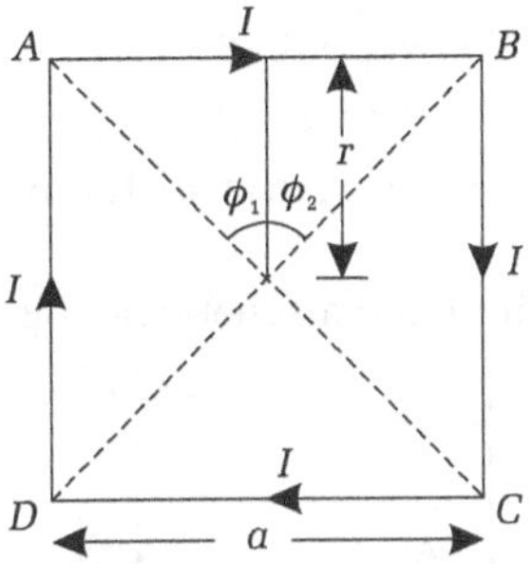

$$B_1 = \frac{\mu_0 i}{4\pi r}(\sin\phi_1 + \sin\phi_2)$$

$$= \frac{\mu_0 i}{4\pi\, a/2}(\sin 45° + \sin 45°)$$

$$= \frac{2\mu_0 i}{4\pi a}\left(\frac{1}{\sqrt{2}} + \frac{1}{\sqrt{2}}\right)$$

$$= \frac{2\sqrt{2}\mu_0 i}{4\pi a}$$

$\therefore$ Total magnetic field at the centre

$$B = 4B_1$$

$$= 4\left(\frac{2\sqrt{2}\mu_0 i}{4\pi a}\right)$$

$$= \frac{2\sqrt{2}\mu_0 i}{\pi a}$$

13. Given, $m = 0.6$ g

$= 0.6 \times 10^{-3}$ kg,

$q = 25$ nC $= 25 \times 10^{-9}$ C

$v = 1.2 \times 10^4$ ms^{-1}

The particle is moving with uniform velocity (acceleration is zero), so magnetic force will be balancing the weight of the particle.

$$mg = Bqv$$

$$0.6 \times 10^{-3} \times 10 = B \times 25 \times 10^{-9} \times 1.2 \times 10^4$$

$$B = \frac{0.6\times10^{-3}\times10}{25\times10^{-9}\times1.2\times10^4}$$

$$= \frac{6\times10^{-3}}{30\times10^{-5}} = \frac{6\times10^2}{30} = 20 \text{ T}$$

14. $i_1 = i_2 = 5$ A, $r = 0.5$ m

Force per unit length between the two wires

$$F = \frac{\mu_0}{2\pi}\frac{i_1 i_2}{r}$$

$$= 2 \times 10^{-7} \times \frac{5\times5}{0.5}$$

$$= 10^{-5} \text{ N}$$

The currents are in the opposite directions, so force will be repulsive.

15. Given, $i_1 = i_2 = 3$ A, $r = 1$ m

Force per unit length between the wires

$$f = \frac{\mu_0}{2\pi}\frac{i_1 i_2}{r}$$

$$= 2 \times 10^{-7} \times \frac{3\times3}{1}$$

$$= 18 \times 10^{-7} \text{ Nm}^{-1}$$

16. For a current carrying conductor, the magnetic field is outside only and inside the conductor it is zero.

17. A current carrying wire produces magnetic field around it.

18. Given, $l_1 = l_2 = l = 9$ m,

$r = 0.15$ m, $i_1 = i_2 = i$

$F = 30 \times 10^{-7}$ N

Force exerted between two parallel current carrying wires

$$F = \frac{\mu_0}{2\pi}\frac{i_1 i_2}{r} l$$

$$30 \times 10^{-7} = 2\times10^{-7}\frac{i \cdot i}{0.15}\times9$$

$$i^2 = \frac{30\times0.15}{2\times9} = \frac{4.5}{18} = \frac{1}{4}$$

$$i = \sqrt{\frac{1}{4}} = \frac{1}{2} = 0.5 \text{ A}$$

19. Magnetic field at a point due to a straight wire

$$B = \frac{\mu_0 i}{2\pi r}$$

$$B \propto \frac{1}{r}$$

$$\therefore \quad \frac{B_1}{B_2} = \frac{r_2}{r_1}$$

$$\frac{B}{B_2} = \frac{20}{5}$$

$$B_2 = \frac{B}{4}$$

20. Let the length of the wire be l. Ist case, for the coil of 4 turns

$$4(2\pi r_1) = l$$

$$r_1 = \frac{l}{8\pi}$$

IInd case, for the coil of 2 turns

$$2(2\pi r_2) = l$$

$$r_2 = \frac{l}{4\pi}$$

Magnetic field at the centre of a coil

$$B = \frac{\mu_0 n i}{2r}$$

$$\therefore \quad \frac{B_1}{B_2} = \frac{n_1}{n_2} \cdot \frac{r_2}{r_1}$$

$$= \frac{4}{2} \times \frac{l/4\pi}{l/8\pi}$$

$$= \frac{4}{2} \times 2 = \frac{4}{1}$$

$$B_1 : B_2 = 4 : 1$$

21. Magnetic intensity of magnetic field on axial line of a magnetic dipole

$$B_1 = \frac{\mu_0}{4\pi} \frac{2M}{x^3}$$

On equatorial line, $B_2 = \frac{\mu_0}{4\pi} \frac{M}{y^3}$

According to question

$$B_1 = B_2$$

$$\frac{\mu_0}{4\pi} \frac{2M}{x^3} = \frac{\mu_0}{4\pi} \frac{M}{y^3}$$

$$\Rightarrow \quad \frac{x^3}{y^3} = \frac{2}{1}$$

$$\frac{x}{y} = \frac{2^{1/3}}{1}$$

22. Magnetic induction at a point (x distance away from centre) on the axis of a current carrying circular coil

$$B = \frac{\mu_0 n i a^2}{(a^2 + x^2)^{3/2}}$$

where, a = radius of the coil

Since, $x >> a$, so a can be neglected

$$\therefore \quad B = \frac{\mu_0 n i a^2}{x^3}$$

$$\therefore \quad B \propto \frac{1}{x^3}$$

23. Force applied on the moving charged particle in uniform magnetic field.

$$F = q v B \sin\theta$$

where, q = charge of the particle

v = velocity of the particle

B = magnetic field

θ = angle between the direction of velocity and direction of magnetic field

Here, $\theta = 0°$

($\because$ Field is applied in the direction of velocity)

So, $F = q v \sin\theta$

$= q v B \times 0 \quad (\because \sin\theta = 0)$

So, there is no change in the motion of the particle.

24. Let at point P the magnetic field is zero.

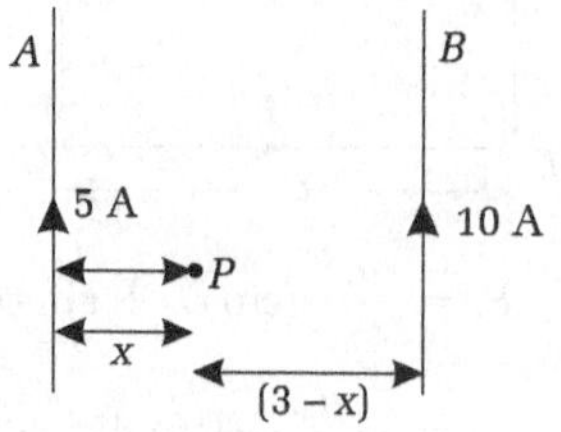

So, at point P the magnetic field introduced by both the wires should be equal and opposite.

So, $$\frac{\mu_0 i_1}{2\pi r_1} = \frac{\mu_0 i_2}{2\pi r_2}$$

$$\frac{i_1}{r_1} = \frac{i_2}{r_2}$$

$$\frac{5}{x} = \frac{10}{(3-x)}$$

$$15 - 5x = 10x$$

$$\Rightarrow \quad 15x = 15$$

$$x = 1 \text{ m}$$

The point P is $(3 - 1) = 2$ m left of B.

25. Magnetic moment $M = iA$

$$\therefore \quad \frac{M_1}{M_2} = \left(\frac{i_1}{i_2}\right)\left(\frac{A_1}{A_2}\right) = \left(\frac{i_1}{i_2}\right)\left(\frac{\pi r_1^2}{\pi r_2^2}\right)$$

Here, current is halved, so $i_1 = 2 i_2$ and radius is double so, $r_2 = 2 r_1$

$$\therefore \quad \frac{4}{M_2} = \left(\frac{2i_2}{i_2}\right)\left(\frac{r_1}{2r_1}\right)^2$$

$$= 2\left(\frac{1}{2}\right)^2 = 2 \times \frac{1}{4}$$

$$\frac{4}{M_2} = \frac{1}{2}$$

$$\therefore \quad M_2 = 4 \times 2 = 8 \text{ unit}$$

Chapter

15

Magnetism

1. With a standard rectangular bar magnet the time period of a vibration magnetometer is 4 s. The bar magnet is cut parallel to its length into four equal pieces. The time period of vibration magnetometer when one piece is used (in second) (bar magnet breadth is small) is **EAMCET | 2008**

(a) 16 (b) 8 (c) 4 (d) 2

2. The magnetised wire of moment M and length l is bent in the form of semicircle of radius r. Then, its magnetic moment is **EAMCET | 2008**

(a) $\frac{2M}{\pi}$ (b) $2M$ (c) $\frac{M}{\pi}$ (d) zero

3. A bar magnet of moment of inertia 49×10^{-2} kg-m^2 vibrates in a magnetic field of induction 0.5×10^{-4} T. The time period of vibration is 8. 8 s. The magnetic moment of the bar magnet is **EAMCET | 2007**

(a) 350 A-m^2 (b) 490 A-m^2
(c) 3300 A-m^2 (d) 5000 A-m^2

4. A bar magnet of magnetic moment M and moment of inertia I is freely suspended such that the magnetic axial line is in the direction of magnetic meridian. If the magnet is displaced by a very small angle (θ), the angular acceleration is (magnetic induction of earth's horizontal field $= B_H$) **EAMCET | 2007**

(a) $\frac{MB_H\theta}{I}$ (b) $\frac{IB_H\theta}{M}$
(c) $\frac{M\theta}{IB_H}$ (d) $\frac{I\theta}{MB_H}$

5. The effect due to uniform magnetic field on a freely suspended magnetic needle is as follows **EAMCET | 2006**

(a) both torque and net force are present
(b) torque is present but no net force
(c) both torque and net force are absent
(d) net force is present but not torque

6. Two short magnets AB and CD are in the xy-plane and are parallel to X-axis and coordinates of their centres respectively are (0, 2) and (2, 0). Line joining the north-south poles of CD is opposite to that of AB and lies along the positive X-axis. The resultant field induction due to AB and CD at a point P (2, 2) is 100×10^{-7} T. When the poles of the magnet CD are reversed, the resultant field induction is 50×10^{-7} T. The value of magnetic moments of AB and CD (in Am^2) are **EAMCET | 2006**

(a) 300; 200 (b) 600; 400
(c) 200; 100 (d) 300; 150

7. With a standard rectangular bar magnet of length (l), breadth (b; $b << l$) and magnetic moment M, the time period of the magnet in a vibration magnetometer is 4 s. If the magnet is cut normal to its length into four equal pieces, the time period (in second) with one of the piece is **EAMCET | 2005**

(a) 16 (b) 2 (c) 1 (d) 1/4

8. If two identical bar magnets, each of length l, pole strength m and magnetic moment M are placed perpendicular to each other with their unlike poles in contact, the magnetic moment of the combination is **EAMCET | 2005**

(a) $\frac{M}{\sqrt{2}}$ (b) $lm\ (\sqrt{2})$
(c) $2\ lm\ (\sqrt{2})$ (d) $2\ M$

9. The magnetic induction and the intensity of magnetic field inside an iron core of an electromagnet are 1 Wb-m^{-2} and 150 Am^{-1} respectively. The relative permeability of iron is ($\mu_0 = 4\pi \times 10^{-7}$ Hm^{-1}) **EAMCET | 2004**

(a) $\frac{10^6}{4\pi}$ (b) $\frac{10^6}{6\pi}$ (c) $\frac{10^5}{4\pi}$ (d) $\frac{10^5}{6\pi}$

10. The magnetic needle of a vibration magnetometer makes 12 oscillations per minute in the horizontal component of earth's magnetic field. When an external short bar magnet is placed at some distance along the axis of the needle in the same line, it makes 15 oscillations per minute. If the poles of the bar magnet are interchanged, the number of oscillations it makes per minute is **EAMCET | 2004**

(a) $\sqrt{61}$ (b) $\sqrt{63}$ (c) $\sqrt{65}$ (d) $\sqrt{67}$

11. Magnetic induction at the centre of a circular loop of area πm^2 is 0.1 T. The magnetic moment of the loop is (μ_0 = permeability of air)

EAMCET | 2004

(a) $\frac{0.1\pi}{\mu_0}$ (b) $\frac{0.2\pi}{\mu_0}$

(c) $\frac{0.3\pi}{\mu_0}$ (d) $\frac{0.4\pi}{\mu_0}$

12. A vibration magnetometer consists of two identical bar magnets placed one over the other such that they are perpendicular and bisect each other. The time period of oscillation in a horizontal magnetic field $2^{5/4}$ s. One of the magnets is removed and if the other magnet oscillates in the same field, then the time period in second is

EAMCET | 2003

(a) $2^{1/4}$ (b) $2^{1/2}$ (c) 2 (d) $2^{5/4}$

13. The magnetic susceptibility of the material of a rod is 499. Permeability of vacuum is $4\pi \times 10^{-7}$ Hm^{-1}. Absolute permeability of the material of the rod in H/m is

EAMCET | 2003

(a) $\pi \times 10^{-4}$ (b) $2\pi \times 10^{-4}$

(c) $3\pi \times 10^{-4}$ (d) $4\pi \times 10^{-4}$

14. A thin magnetic iron rod of length 30 cm is suspended in a uniform magnetic field. Its time period of oscillation is 4 s. It is broken into three equal parts. The time period in second of oscillation of one part when suspended in the same magnetic field is

EAMCET | 2002

(a) $\frac{1}{\sqrt{3}}$ (b) $\frac{2}{\sqrt{3}}$ (c) $\sqrt{3}$ (d) $\frac{4}{\sqrt{3}}$

15. Consider the following two statements A and B and identify the correct choice in the given answers

A. Paramagnetism is explained by domain theory.

B. Susceptibility of a diamagnetic substance is independent of temperature.

EAMCET | 2002

(a) Both A and B are correct

(b) Both A and B are wrong

(c) A is correct and B is wrong

(d) A is wrong and B is correct

16. A magnet freely suspended in a vibration magnetometer makes 40 oscillations per minute at place A and 20 oscillations per minute at a place B. If the horizontal component of earth's magnetic field at A is 36×10^{-6} T, then its value at B is

EAMCET | 2001

(a) 30×10^{-6} T (b) 9×10^{-6} T

(c) 144×10^{-6} T (d) 288×10^{-6} T

17. A magnet of length 10 cm and magnetic moment 1 Am^2 is placed along side AB of an equilateral triangle ABC. If the length of the side AB is 10 cm. The magnetic induction at the point C is ($\mu_0 = 4\pi \times 10^{-7}$ Hm^{-1})

EAMCET | 2001

(a) 10^{-9} T (b) 10^{-7} T

(c) 10^{-5} T (d) 10^{-4} T

18. The pole strength of a 12 cm long bar magnet is 2.0 A-m. The magnetic induction at a point 10 cm away from the centre of the magnet on the axial line is $\left(\frac{\mu_0}{4\pi} = 10^{-7}\text{Hm}^{-1}\right)$

EAMCET | 2000

(a) 1.1×10^{-4} T (b) 2.2×10^{3} T

(c) 1.1×10^{-2} T (d) 2.2×10^{-2} T

19. There is no couple acting when two bar magnets are placed coaxially separated by a distance because

EAMCET | 2000

(a) there are no forces on the poles

(b) the forces are parallel and their lines of action do not coincide

(c) the forces are perpendicular to each other

(d) the forces act along the same line

20. Two similar moments P and Q each of magnetic moment M are taken. If P is cut along its axial line and Q is cut along its equatorial line all the four pieces obtained have each of

EAMCET | 2000

(a) equal pole strength

(b) magnetic moment $\frac{M}{4}$

(c) magnetic moment $\frac{M}{2}$

(d) magnetic moment M

21. A short bar magnet with its north pole facing north forms a neutral point at P in the horizontal plane. If the magnet is rotated by 90° in the horizontal plane, the net magnetic induction at P is (horizontal component of earth's magnetic field = B_H)

EAMCET | 2000

(a) zero (b) $2B_H$ (c) $\frac{\sqrt{5}}{2}B_H$ (d) $\sqrt{5}B_H$

22. The temperature at which a ferromagnetic material becomes paramagnetic is called

EAMCET | 1999

(a) neutral temperature
(b) curie temperature
(c) inversion temperature
(d) None of the above

23. The magnetic field strength at a point at a distance d from the centre, on the axial line of a very short bar magnet of magnetic moment M, is B. The magnetic induction at a distance $2d$ from centre, on equatorial line of magnet of magnetic moment $8M$, will be **EAMCET | 1999**

(a) $4B$ (b) $\frac{B}{2}$ (c) $2B$ (d) $\frac{B}{4}$

24. A magnetic needle is placed with its north pole facing north in north south direction. In its map of magnetic field the null point will be **EAMCET | 1999**

(a) on its equatorial line
(b) on its axial line
(c) on line making 45° with its axial line
(d) at a distance equal to twice the length of magnet on both line

25. The null points are on the equatorial line of a bar magnet when the north pole of the magnet is pointing **EAMCET | 1998**

(a) north (b) south
(c) east (d) west

26. Diamagnetic substances are **EAMCET | 1998**

(a) feebly attracted by magnets
(b) strongly attracted by magnets
(c) feebly repelled by magnets
(d) strongly repelled by magnets

27. A bar magnet of pole strength 2 A-m is kept in a magnetic field of induction 4×10^{-5} Wbm^{-2} such that the axis of the magnet makes an angle 30° with the direction of the field. The couple acting on the magnet is found to be 80×10^{-7} N-m. Then, the distance between the poles of the magnet is **EAMCET | 1997**

(a) 20 cm (b) 2 m (c) 3 cm (d) 20 cm

28. In a deflection magnetometer experiment in tan A position, a short bar magnet placed at 18 cm from the centre of the compass needle produces a deflection of 30°. If another magnet of same length but 16 times pole strength as that of first magnet is placed in tan B position at 36 cm, the deflection will be

EAMCET | 1997

(a) 0° (b) 30° (c) 45° (d) 60°

29. A bar magnet of magnetic moment 2.0 Am^2 is free to rotate about a vertical axis passing through its centre. The magnet is released from rest from east-west position. Then, the kinetic energy of the magnet as it takes north-south position is (horizontal component of earth field is 25 μT) **EAMCET | 1996**

(a) 25 μJ (b) 50 μJ (c) 100 μJ (d) 12.5 μJ

30. In a deflection magnetometer experiment the deflections produced separately by two short bar magnets kept at the same distance are 45° and 30°. Then, the ratio of the magnetic moments of the two magnets is

EAMCET | 1996

(a) $\sqrt{3}:2$ (b) $\sqrt{3}:1$ (c) $\sqrt{2}:1$ (d) $1:\sqrt{3}$

31. The moment of a magnet is 1 μWb-m and the force acting on each pole in a uniform magnetic field of strength 0.38 oersted is 1.024×10^{-4} N. Distance between the poles of the magnet is **EAMCET | 1996**

(a) 1.56×10^{-4} cm (b) 0.37×10^{-4} cm
(c) 2.34×10^{-4} cm (d) 1.17×10^{-4} cm

32. A bar magnet of magnetic moment $\vec{M}$ is placed in a magnetic field of induction $\vec{B}$. The torque exerted on it is **EAMCET | 1995**

(a) $\vec{M}\vec{B}$ (b) $-\vec{M}\times\vec{B}$
(c) $\vec{M}\times\vec{B}$ (d) $\vec{B}\times\vec{M}$

33. When a diamagnetic substance is brought near north or south pole of a bar magnet it is

EAMCET | 1995

(a) attracted by the poles
(b) repelled by the poles
(c) attracted by the north pole and repelled by the south pole
(d) repelled by the north pole and attracted by the south pole

34. Substance which when placed in a magnetic field, acquire feeble magnetization in a direction opposite to that of the applied field are called **EAMCET | 1994**

(a) diamagnetic substances
(b) paramagnetic substances
(c) ferromagnetic substances
(d) ferrimagnetic substances

35. The couple acting on a magnet of length 10 cm placed in a uniform magnetic field of intensity 40 NA^{-1}m^{-1} such that the axis of the magnet makes 45° with the field direction is $\sqrt{2}/10$ Nm. The pole strength of the magnet (in Wb) is EAMCET | 1994

(a) 5×10^{-3} (b) 0.5 (c) 0.05 (d) 5.0

36. In the experiment to verify inverse square law, with deflection magnetometer the value of $\frac{\tan \theta_A}{\tan \theta_B}$ will come out as EAMCET | 1993

(a) 0.25 (b) 0.5 (c) 1 (d) 2

37. A material for which magnetic susceptibility is independent of temperature and applied magnetic field, is EAMCET | 1993

(a) diamagnetic
(b) paramagnetic
(c) ferromagnetic
(d) antiferromagnetic

38. Which one of the following statement is true? EAMCET | 1992

(a) Paramagnetism ceases to exist below a certain temperature
(b) Ferromagnetism ceases to exist below a certain temperature
(c) Onset of paramagnetism requires the presence of paramagnet magnetic dipoles
(d) Ferromagnetism ceases to exist above a certain temperature

39. If a bar magnet of moment μ is suspended in a uniform magnetic field B and it is given an angular deflection θ w.r.t. its equilibrium position, the restoring torque on magnet is EAMCET | 1992

(a) $\mu B \sin \theta$ (b) $\mu B \cos \theta$
(c) $\mu B \tan \theta$ (d) $\mu^2 B^2 \sin \theta \cos \theta$

40. When a material is placed in magnetic fields B magnetic moment proportional to B but opposite in direction is induced. The material is EAMCET | 1991

(a) diamagnetic (b) paramagnetic
(c) ferromagnetic (d) anti-ferromagnetic

41. The ratio of magnetic moments of two short magnets which give deflection in tan B position when placed at 12 cm and 18 cm from centre of a deflection magnetometer is EAMCET | 1991

(a) $\frac{2}{3}$ (b) $\frac{4}{9}$ (c) $\frac{8}{27}$ (d) $\frac{8}{9}$

42. Material getting magnetized by orientation of atomic magnetic moment in external magnetic fields are EAMCET | 1991

(a) diamagnetic (b) paramagnetic
(c) ferromagnetic (d) antiferromagnetic

Answers

1. (c)	2. (a)	3. (d)	4. (a)	5. (b)	6. (a)	7. (c)	8. (b)	9. (d)	10. (b)
11. (b)	12. (c)	13. (b)	14. (d)	15. (d)	16. (b)	17. (d)	18. (a)	19. (d)	20. (c)
21. (d)	22. (b)	23. (b)	24. (a)	25. (a)	26. (c)	27. (a)	28. (b)	29. (b)	30. (b)
31. (b)	32. (c)	33. (b)	34. (a)	35. (c)	36. (d)	37. (a)	38. (d)	39. (a)	40. (a)
41. (c)	42. (b)								

■ Hints & Solutions

1. Time period of magnet, $T = 2\pi\sqrt{\frac{I}{MB}}$

When magnet is cut parallel to its length into four equal pieces. Then, new magnetic moment,

$$M' = \frac{M}{4}$$

New moment of inertia, $I' = \frac{I}{4}$

∴ New time period, $T' = 2\pi\sqrt{\frac{I'}{M'B}}$

$$T = T' = 4\text{ s}$$

2. On bending a wire its pole strength remains unchanged whereas its magnetic moment changes.

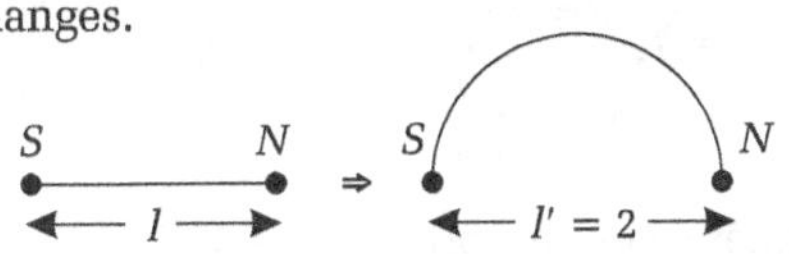

New magnetic moment,

$$M' = m(2r) = m\left(\frac{2l}{\pi}\right) = \frac{2M}{\pi}$$

3. Time period of magnet is

$$T = 2\pi\sqrt{\frac{I}{MH}}$$

or $M = \frac{4\pi^2 I}{T^2 H}$

or $M = \frac{4\times(3.14)^2\times49\times10^{-2}}{(8.8)^2\times0.5\times10^{-4}}$

or $M = 5000\text{ A-m}^2$

4. When magnet is displaced by a very small angle θ, then restoring couple acting on the magnet is

$$\tau = -MB_H\sin\theta$$

Negative sign shows the restoring nature of torque. Now since $\tau = I\alpha$ and $\sin\theta \approx \theta$ for small angular displacement

∴ $I\alpha = MB_H\theta$

or α = angular acceleration

$$= \frac{MB_H\theta}{I}$$

5. When a magnetic needle is placed in a uniform magnetic field, equal and opposite forces act on the poles of the needle which give rise to a torque, but not net force.

6. As shown in figure,

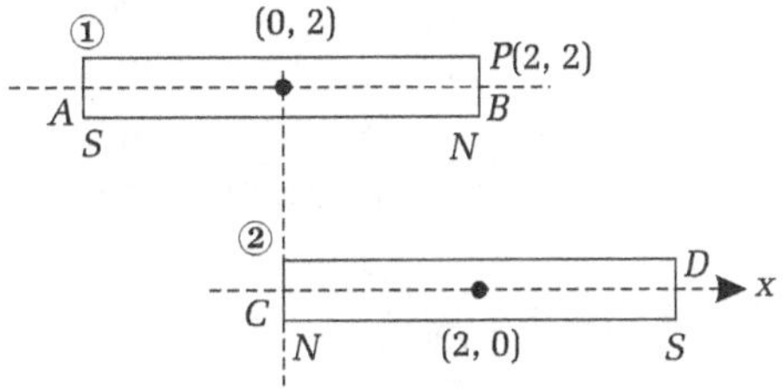

$$B = B_1 + B_2 = \frac{\mu_0}{4\pi}\left(\frac{2M_1}{r_1^3} + \frac{M_2}{r_2^3}\right)$$

$$100\times10^{-7} = 10^{-7}\left(\frac{2M_1}{8} + \frac{M_2}{8}\right)$$

⇒ $2M_1 + M_2 = 800$ ...(i)

If the poles of the magnet CD are reversed, then

$$50\times10^{-7} = 10^{-7}\left(\frac{2M_1}{8} - \frac{M_2}{8}\right)$$

⇒ $2M_1 - M_2 = 400$ ...(ii)

Solving Eqs. (i) and (ii), we obtain

$$M_1 = 300\text{ Am}^2, M_2 = 200\text{ Am}^2$$

7. Time period of magnet in vibration magnetometer

$$T = 2\pi\sqrt{\frac{I}{MH}}$$

where, I = moment of inertia of magnet

M = magnetic moment

H = horizontal component of earth's magnetic field

∴ $\frac{T_1}{T_2} = \sqrt{\frac{I_1}{I_2}\cdot\frac{M_2}{M_1}}$

$$\frac{4}{T_2} = \sqrt{\frac{ml^2/12}{m/4(1/4)^2/12}}$$

$$= \sqrt{\frac{4\times16\times12}{12\times4}} = \sqrt{16}$$

$$\frac{4}{T_2} = 4$$

⇒ $T_2 = 1\text{ s}$

8. When magnets are placed perpendicular to each other then,

Resultant magnetic moment

$$M' = \sqrt{M_1^2 + M_2^2}$$

Here, $M_1 = M_2 = M$

So, $M' = M\sqrt{2}$

$= ml\sqrt{2}$

9. We know $B = \mu H = \mu_r \mu_0 H$

where, μ_r is relative permeability $= \dfrac{\mu}{\mu_0}$

$$\therefore \quad \mu_r = \frac{B}{\mu_0 H}$$

$$= \frac{1}{(4\pi \times 10^{-7})(150)} = \frac{10^5}{6\pi}$$

10. Ist case $n = \dfrac{1}{2\pi}\sqrt{\dfrac{MH}{I}}$

$$\Rightarrow \quad n \propto \sqrt{H}$$

$$\Rightarrow \quad \frac{n_1}{n_2} = \sqrt{\frac{H}{H+H_1}}$$

$$\Rightarrow \quad \frac{12}{15} = \sqrt{\frac{H}{H+H_1}}$$

$$\Rightarrow \quad H_1 = \frac{9}{16}H$$

IInd case

$$\frac{n_2}{n_3} = \sqrt{\frac{H+H_1}{H-H_1}}$$

$$\Rightarrow \quad \frac{15}{n_3} = \sqrt{\frac{H+\frac{9}{16}H}{H-\frac{9}{16}H}}$$

$$\therefore \quad n_3 = \sqrt{63}$$

11. Magnetic induction at the centre of circular loop

$$B = \frac{\mu_0}{2} \cdot \frac{ni}{r}$$

Magnetic moment of the loop

$$M = niA = \frac{2BrA}{\mu_0}$$

$$= \frac{2 \times 0.1 \times 1 \times \pi \times (1)^2}{\mu_0}$$

$$= \frac{0.2\pi}{\mu_0} \qquad [\because r = 1]$$

12. Time period of magnet in vibration magnetometer

$$T = 2\pi\sqrt{\frac{I}{MH}}$$

First case, $T_1 = 2\pi\sqrt{\dfrac{I_1 + I_2}{M'H}}$

where, M = resultant magnetic moment of two magnets

Here, two identical magnets are placed perpendicular to each other.

$\therefore \quad I_1 = I_2 = I$ (Let)

and $M' = \sqrt{M^2 + M^2} = M\sqrt{2}$

$$\therefore \quad T_1 = 2\pi\sqrt{\frac{2I}{\sqrt{2}MH}}$$

$$2^{5/4} = 2\pi\sqrt{\frac{2I}{\sqrt{2}MH}} \qquad \text{...(i)}$$

When one magnet is removed, then time period

$$T_2 = 2\pi\sqrt{\frac{I}{MH}} \qquad \text{...(ii)}$$

Dividing Eq. (i) by Eq. (ii)

$$\frac{2^{5/4}}{T_2} = \sqrt{\frac{2}{\sqrt{2}}} = \sqrt{\sqrt{2}}$$

$$\frac{2^{5/4}}{T_2} = 2^{1/4}$$

$$T_2 = \frac{2^{5/4}}{2^{1/4}} = 2 \text{ s}$$

13. Magnetic susceptibility, $\chi = 499$

$\mu_0 = 4\pi \times 10^{-7}$ Hm^{-1}

Relative permeability of the rod

$\mu_r = 1 + \chi = 1 + 499 = 500$

Absolute permeability, $\mu = \mu_r \mu_0$

$= 500 \times 4\pi \times 10^{-7}$

$= 20\pi \times 10^{-5}$

$= 2\pi \times 10^{-4}$

14. Time period of magnet

$$T = 2\pi\sqrt{\frac{I}{MH}}$$

M = magnetic moment $= m \times l$

I = moment of inertia $= \dfrac{ml^2}{12}$

When magnet is broken into three equal parts

Then, $M' = m \times \dfrac{l}{3} = \dfrac{M}{3}$

$$I' = \frac{m(l/3)^2}{12} = \frac{ml^2}{9 \times 12} = \frac{I}{9}$$

$\therefore$ Now, time period, $T' = 2\pi\sqrt{\dfrac{I'}{M'H}}$

$$= 2\pi\sqrt{\frac{I/9}{\frac{M}{3}H}} = 2\pi\sqrt{\frac{I}{MH \times 3}}$$

$$= \frac{T}{\sqrt{3}} = \frac{4}{\sqrt{3}} \text{ s}$$

15. Only ferromagnetism is explained by domain theory, so statement (A) is wrong susceptibility of diamagnetic substance does not depend on temperature, so statement (B) is correct.

16. Time period of magnet, $T = 2\pi\sqrt{\frac{I}{MH}}$

In both the condition magnet is same.

So, $T \propto \frac{1}{\sqrt{H}}$

$$\frac{T_A}{T_B} = \sqrt{\frac{H_B}{H_A}}$$

$$\frac{60/40}{60/20} = \sqrt{\frac{H_B}{36\times10^{-6}}}$$

$$\frac{1}{2} = \sqrt{\frac{H_B}{36\times10^{-6}}}$$

Squaring both sides

$$\frac{1}{4} = \frac{H_B}{36\times10^{-6}}$$

$\Rightarrow$ $H_B = 9 \times 10^{-6}$ T

17. Given, $l = 10$ cm, $M = 1$ Am^2

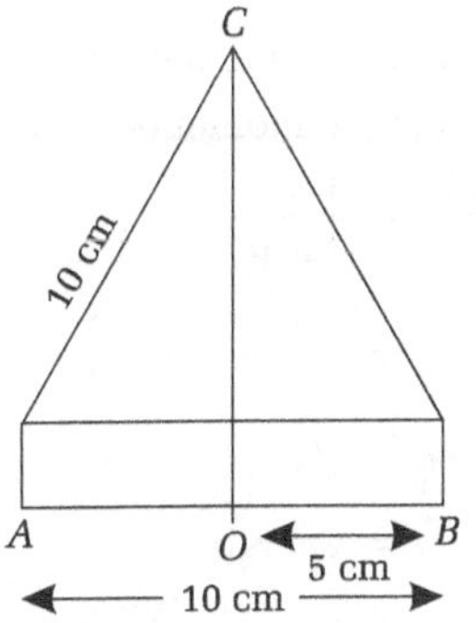

Magnetic induction at point C

(In equatorial position)

$$B = \frac{\mu_0}{4\pi}\frac{M}{(CO)^3}$$

$$= 10^{-7} \times \frac{1}{(\sqrt{10^2-5^2})^3}$$

$$= \frac{10^{-7}\times1}{(\sqrt{75})^3} = \frac{10^{-7}}{(5\sqrt{3}\times10^{-2})^3}$$

$$= \frac{10^{-7}}{125\times3\sqrt{3}\times10^{-6}}$$

$$= \frac{10^{-1}}{375\times1.732}$$

$= 0.000154 = 1.54 \times 10^{-4}$ T

$\approx 10^{-4}$ T

18. Length of magnet, $2l = 12$ cm

$= 12 \times 10^{-2}$ m

Pole strength, $m = 2$ A-m

$d = 10$ cm $= 10 \times 10^{-2}$ m

Magnetic field in the axial position

$$B = \frac{\mu_0}{4\pi}\frac{2md}{(d^2-l^2)^2}$$

$$= \frac{\mu_0}{4\pi}\frac{2(m\times2l)\times d}{(d^2-l^2)^2}$$

$$= \frac{10^{-7}\times2\times2\times12\times10^{-2}\times10\times10^{-2}}{\left[(10\times10^{-2})^2-\left(\frac{12\times10^{-2}}{2}\right)^2\right]^2}$$

$$= \frac{48\times10^{-10}}{(100\times10^{-4}-36\times10^{-4})^2}$$

$$= \frac{48\times10^{-10}}{64\times64\times10^{-8}}$$

$= 0.011 \times 10^{-2}$

$= 1.1 \times 10^{-4}$ T

19. Couple acting between the magnets

$C = MB \sin\theta$

When magnets are placed coaxially, then $\theta = 0$

$\therefore$ $\sin\theta = 0$ $(\because \sin 0° = 0)$

So, $C = 0$

20. Magnetic moment, $M = m \times 2l$

when magnet is cut along its axial line, then length $(2l)$ of magnet remains same but pole strength (m) becomes half.

So, new magnetic moment $= \frac{M}{2}$

when magnet is cut along its equatorial line then, length of the magnet becomes half but pole strength remains same, so

new magnetic moment $= \frac{M}{2}$

$\therefore$ Magnetic moment of each piece $= M/2$

21. Initially the point P lies on the equatorial line of the magnet.

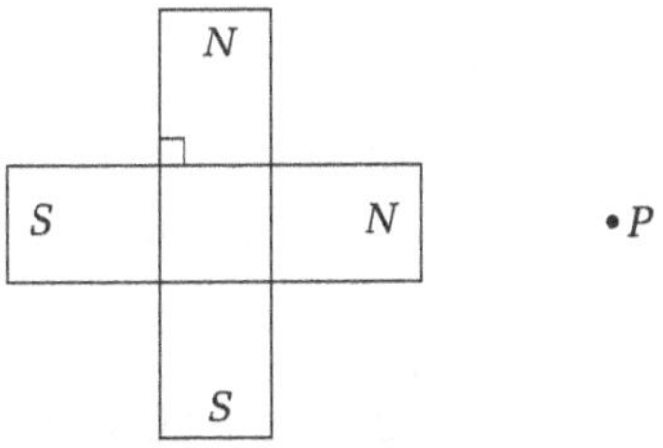

$\therefore \quad B_1 = \frac{\mu_0}{4\pi}\frac{m}{d^3}$

On rotating the magnet point P comes in the axial position of the magnet.

$\therefore \quad B_2 = \frac{\mu_0}{4\pi}\frac{2m}{d^3}$

Resultant magnetic induction at point P

$$B = \sqrt{B_1^2 + B_2^2}$$

$$= \sqrt{\left(\frac{\mu_0}{4\pi}\frac{m}{d^3}\right)^2 + \left(\frac{\mu_0}{4\pi}\frac{2m}{d^3}\right)^2}$$

$$= \frac{\mu_0}{4\pi}\frac{m}{d^3}\sqrt{5}$$

$$B = B_1\sqrt{5}$$

$$B = \sqrt{5}B_H \qquad (\because B_1 = B_H)$$

22. At Curie temperature the ferromagnetic substance becomes paramagnetic.

23. **I^st case** $\quad B = \frac{\mu_0}{4\pi}\frac{2M}{d^3}$ (In axial position)

IInd case $\quad B' = \frac{\mu_0}{4\pi}\frac{M'}{(2d)^3} = \frac{\mu_0}{4\pi}\frac{8M}{8d^3}$

$$= \frac{\mu_0}{4\pi}\frac{M}{d^3} = \frac{1}{2}\left(\frac{\mu_0}{4\pi}\frac{2M}{d^3}\right) = \frac{B}{2}$$

24. The null point of the magnet always lies on its equatorial line.

25. When the north pole of the magnet is towards north then null points are on the equatorial line of the magnet.

26. The substance which are feebly repelled by magnets are called diamagnetic substances.

27. Pole strength $m = 2$ Am

$B = 4 \times 10^{-5}$ Wbm^{-2}

$\theta = 30°, \tau = 80 \times 10^{-7}$ N-m

Torque acting on the magnet, $\tau = MB \sin\theta$

where M = magnetic moment of the magnet

$= ml$

l = distance between the poles of the magnet

$\therefore \quad \tau = m\,l\,B\sin\theta$

$\therefore \quad l = \frac{\tau}{mB\sin\theta}$

$$= \frac{80\times10^{-7}}{2\times4\times10^{-5}\times\sin30°}$$

$$= \frac{80\times10^{-7}}{8\times10^{-5}\times0.5}$$

$= 10 \times 10^{-2} \times 2 = 20 \times 10^{-2}$ m

$= 20$ cm

28. For tan A position

$$B\tan\theta_1 = \frac{\mu_0}{4\pi}\frac{2(m_1\times2l)}{d_1^3} \qquad \text{...(i)}$$

For tan B position

$$B\tan\theta_2 = \frac{\mu_0}{4\pi}\frac{(m_2\times2l)}{d_2^3} \qquad \text{...(ii)}$$

$$\therefore \quad \frac{\tan\theta_1}{\tan\theta_2} = 2\left(\frac{m_1}{m_2}\right)\left(\frac{d_2}{d_1}\right)^3$$

$$\frac{\tan30°}{\tan\theta_2} = 2\left(\frac{m}{16m}\right)\left(\frac{36}{18}\right)^3$$

$$= 2\times\frac{1}{16}\times8 = 1$$

$$\tan\theta_2 = \tan30°$$

$$\therefore \quad \theta_2 = 30°$$

29. Given, $\quad M = 2$ Am^2, $B = 25\,\mu$T $= 25 \times 10^{-6}$ T

KE of the magnet = Work done on it in rotating

$= MB(1 - \cos\theta)$

$= 2 \times 25 \times 10^{-6}(1 - \cos 90°)$

$= 50 \times 10^{-6}(1 - 0)$

$= 50\,\mu$ J

30. In case of deflection magnetometer.

Ratio of magnetic moments

$$\frac{M_1}{M_2} = \frac{\tan\theta_1}{\tan\theta_2}$$

$$= \frac{\tan45°}{\tan30°} = \frac{1}{\frac{1}{\sqrt{3}}}$$

$$M_1 : M_2 = \sqrt{3} : 1$$

31. Moment, $M = 1\,\mu$ Wb-m

$= 1 \times 10^{-6}$ Wb-m

$B = 0.38$ oersted,

$= 0.38 \times 10^{-4}$ T

$F = 1.024 \times 10^{-4}$ N

Force acting on each pole, $F = mB$

when, $\quad m$ = pole strength of the magnet

$= \frac{M}{l}$ (l = length of the magnet)

$\therefore \quad F = \frac{M}{l}B$

$$\Rightarrow \quad l = \frac{MB}{F} = \frac{1\times10^{-6}\times0.38\times10^{-4}}{1.024\times10^{-4}}$$

$= 0.37 \times 10^{-6}$ m

$= 0.37 \times 10^{-4}$ cm

32. Torque exerted on a bar magnet on placing it in magnetic field.

$$\tau = MB \sin\theta$$

θ = angle between the direction of magnetic field and axis of the magnet

In vector form, $\vec{\tau} = \vec{M} \times \vec{B}$

33. Diamagnetic substances are those substances which are feebly repelled by magnets.

35. Couple, $\tau = \frac{\sqrt{2}}{10}$ Nm

$\theta = 45°, B = 40$ NA^{-1}m^{-1}

$2l = 10$ cm

$= 10 \times 10^{-2}$ m

Couple, $\tau = MB \sin\theta$

where, M = dipole moment of the magnet

$$\therefore \quad \frac{\sqrt{2}}{10} = M \times 40 \times \sin 45°$$

$$\frac{\sqrt{2}}{10} = M \times 40 \times \frac{1}{\sqrt{2}}$$

$$M = \frac{\sqrt{2} \times \sqrt{2}}{40 \times 10} = \frac{2}{400}$$

$$= \frac{1}{200}$$

But, $M = m \times 2l$

where, m = pole intensity of the magnet

$$\therefore \quad \frac{1}{200} = m \times 10 \times 10^{-2}$$

$$m = \frac{1}{200 \times 10 \times 10^{-2}}$$

$$= \frac{1}{20} = 0.05$$

36. From tangent law

$$B = H \tan\theta$$

For a position (axial position)

$$\frac{\mu_0}{4\pi} \frac{2M}{d^3} = H \tan\theta_A \quad \text{...(i)}$$

For B position (equatorial position)

$$\frac{\mu_0}{4\pi} \frac{M}{d^3} = H \tan\theta_B \quad \text{...(ii)}$$

From Eqs. (i) and (ii)

$$\frac{\tan\theta_A}{\tan\theta_B} = \frac{2}{1}$$

38. Above Curie temperature the ferromagnetism converts into paramagnetism, so statement (d) is correct.

39. Torque acting on the bar magnet

$$\tau = MB \sin\theta$$

Here dipole moment $(M) = \mu$

So, $\tau = \mu B \sin\theta$

40. In case of diamagnetic substances, the magnetic moment is in opposite direction to external magnetic field.

41. $d_1 = 12$ cm, $d_2 = 18$ cm

Ratio of magnetic moments

$$\frac{M_1}{M_2} = \left(\frac{d_1}{d_2}\right)^3 = \left(\frac{12}{18}\right)^3$$

$$= \left(\frac{2}{3}\right)^3 = \frac{8}{27}$$

42. Material getting magnetized by orientation of atomic magnetic moment is external magnetic fields are paramagnetic substances.

Chapter

16

Electromagnetic Induction

1. The number of turns in primary and secondary coils of a transformer is 50 and 200 respectively. If the current in the primary coil is 4 A, then the current in the secondary coil is

EAMCET | 2008

(a) 1 A (b) 2 A (c) 4 A (d) 5 A

2. A rectangular loop of length l and breadth b is placed at distance of x from infinitely long wire carrying current i such that the direction of current is parallel to breadth. If the loop moves away from the current wire in a direction perpendicular to it with a velocity v, the magnitude of the emf in the loop is (μ_0 = permeability of free space)

EAMCET | 2006

(a) $\frac{\mu_0 iv}{2\pi x}\left(\frac{l+b}{b}\right)$ (b) $\frac{\mu_0 i^2 v}{4\pi^2 x}\log\left(\frac{b}{l}\right)$

(c) $\frac{\mu_0 ilbv}{2\pi x(l+x)}$ (d) $\frac{\mu_0 ilbv}{2\pi}\log\left(\frac{x+l}{x}\right)$

3. A small square loop of wire of side l is placed inside a large square loop of side $L (L >> l)$. If the loops are coplanar and their centres coincide, the mutual induction of the system is directly proportional to EAMCET | 2006

(a) $\frac{L}{l}$ (b) $\frac{l}{L}$ (c) $\frac{L^2}{l}$ (d) $\frac{l^2}{L}$

4. An inductance 1 H is connected in series with an AC source of 220 V and 50 Hz. The inductive reactance (in ohm) is

EAMCET | 2005

(a) 2π (b) $50\,\pi$

(c) $100\,\pi$ (d) $1000\,\pi$

5. A coil has 1,000 turns and 500 cm^2 as its area. The plane of the coil is placed at right angles to a magnetic induction field of 2×10^{-5} Wbm^{-2}. The coil is rotated through 180° in 0.2 s. The average emf induced in the coil, in mV, is

EAMCET | 2003

(a) 5 (b) 10 (c) 15 (d) 20

6. A conducting rod of length L rotates with angular speed ω in a uniform magnetic field of induction B which is perpendicular to its motion. The induced emf developed between the two ends of the rod is EAMCET | 2002

(a) $\frac{BL^2\omega}{4}$ (b) $\frac{BL^2\omega}{2}$

(c) $BL^2\omega$ (d) $2BL^2\omega$

7. If a change in current of 0.01 A in one coil produces a change in magnetic flux of 2×10^{-2} Wb in the other coil, then the mutual inductance of the two coils in henry is

EAMCET | 2001

(a) zero (b) 0.5 (c) 2 (d) 3

8. A varying current in a coil changes from 10 A to zero in 0.5 s. If the average emf induced in the coil is 2 V, the self inductance of the coil is

EAMCET | 1999

(a) 5.0 H (b) 0.1 H (c) 11.0 H (d) 12.0 H

9. A varying current in a coil changes from 10 A to zero in 0.5 s. If the average emf induced in the coil is 220 V, the self-inductance of the coil is

EAMCET | 1994

(a) 5.0 H (b) 10.0 H

(c) 11.0 H (d) 12.0 H

Answers

1.	(a)	2.	(c)	3.	(d)	4.	(c)	5.	(b)	6.	(b)	7.	(c)	8.	(b)	9.	(c)

■ Hints & Solutions

1. In a transformer

$\therefore \quad \dfrac{N_P}{N_S} = \dfrac{I_S}{I_P}$

$\dfrac{50}{200} = \dfrac{I_S}{4}$

$\Rightarrow \quad I_S = 1\text{ A}$

2. We can show the situation as:

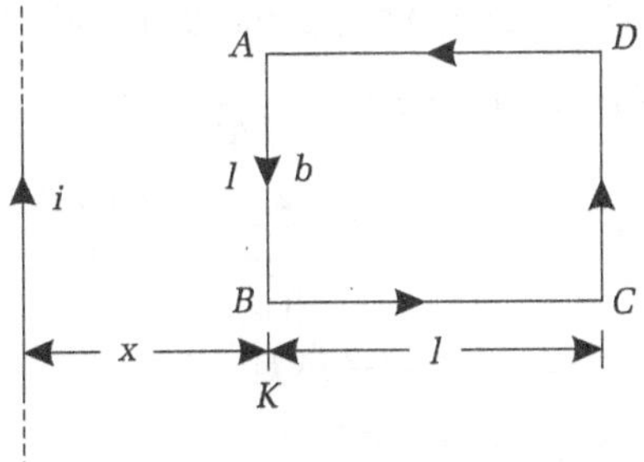

Since, loop is moving away from the wire, so the direction of current in the loop will be as shown in the figure.

Net magnetic field on the loop due to wire

$$B = \frac{\mu_0 i}{2\pi}\left(\frac{1}{x} - \frac{1}{l+x}\right)$$

$$= \frac{\mu_0 il}{2\pi x(l+x)}$$

So, the magnitude of the emf in the loop

$$e = vBb = \frac{\mu_0 ilvb}{2\pi x(l+x)}$$

3. Consider the larger loop to the made up of four rods each of length L, the field at the centre, *i.e.*, at a distance $\left(\dfrac{L}{2}\right)$ from each rod, will be

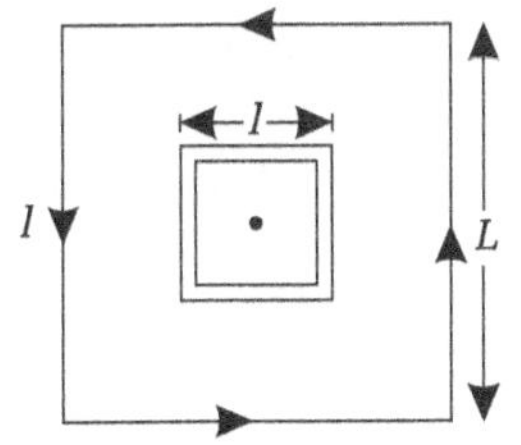

$$B = 4\times\frac{\mu_0}{4\pi}\frac{I}{d}[\sin\alpha + \sin\beta]$$

i.e., $$B = 4\times\frac{\mu_0}{4\pi}\frac{I}{\left(\frac{L}{2}\right)}\times 2\sin 45°$$

i.e., $$B_1 = \frac{\mu_0}{4\pi}\frac{8\sqrt{2}}{L}I$$

So, the flux with smaller loop

$$\phi_2 = B_1 S_2 = \frac{\mu_0}{4\pi}\frac{8\sqrt{2}}{L}l^2 I$$

and hence, $M = \dfrac{\phi_2}{I} = 2\sqrt{2}\dfrac{\mu_0}{\pi}\dfrac{l^2}{L}$

or $\quad M \propto \dfrac{l^2}{L}$

4. Inductive reactance, $X_L = \omega L$

$= 2\pi\nu L$

$= 2\pi \times 50 \times 1$

$= 100\,\pi$

5. Given, $N = 1000$,

$A = 500\text{ cm}^2 = 500 \times 10^{-4}$

$= 5 \times 10^{-2}\text{ m}^2$

$B = 2 \times 10^{-5}\text{ Wbm}^{-2}$, $\theta_1 = 0°$,

$\theta_2 = 180°$, $\Delta t = 0.2$ s

Initial flux linked with coil

$\phi_1 = NBA\cos\theta_1$

$= NBA\cos 0°$

$= NBA$

Final flux, $\phi_2 = NBA\cos 180°$

$= NBA(-1) = -NBA$

Change in flux, $\phi = \phi_2 - \phi_1$

$= -NBA - (NBA)$

$= -2\,NBA$

$\therefore$ Induced emf

$$e = -\frac{\Delta\phi}{\Delta t}$$

$$= -\frac{(-2\,NBA)}{\Delta t}$$

$$= \frac{2\,NBA}{\Delta t}$$

$$= \frac{2\times1000\times2\times10^{-5}\times5\times10^{-2}}{0.2}$$

$= 10 \times 10^{-3}$ V

$= 10$ mV

6. Linear velocity of the rod, $v = r\omega = \dfrac{L\omega}{2}$

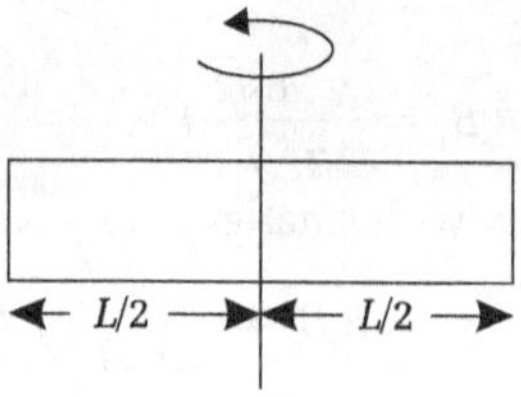

$\therefore$ Induced emf

$$e = BvL = B \times \frac{L\omega}{2} \cdot L = \frac{1}{2} B\omega L^2$$

7. Given, $\Delta i = 0.01$ A, $\Delta\phi = 2 \times 10^{-2}$ Wb

Mutual inductance, $M = \dfrac{\Delta\phi}{\Delta i}$

$$= \frac{2\times10^{-2}}{0.01}$$

$$= \frac{2\times10^{-2}}{10^{-2}} = 2\text{ H}$$

8. Given, $\Delta i = (0 - 10) = -10$ A, $\Delta t = 0.5$ s

$e = 2$ V

Induced emf, $e = \dfrac{-L\,\Delta i}{\Delta t}$

$$L = \frac{e}{\frac{-\Delta i}{\Delta t}} = \frac{2}{\frac{-(-10)}{(0.5)}}$$

$$= \frac{2\times0.5}{10} = 0.1\text{ H}$$

9. Given, $\Delta i = 0 - 10 = -10$ A

$\Delta t = 0.5$ s, Induced emf, $e = 220$ V

Self-inductance, $L = \dfrac{-e}{\Delta i / \Delta t}$

$$= \frac{-220}{\frac{-10}{0.5}} = \frac{220\times0.5}{10}$$

$$= 11\text{ H}$$

Chapter

17

Ray Optics

1. The refractive index of a material of a plano-concave lens is 5/3, the radius of curvature is 0.3 m. The focal length of the lens in air is
EAMCET | 2008
(a) – 0.45 m (b) – 0.6 m
(c) – 0.75 m (d) – 1.0 m

2. An achromatic combination of lenses produces
EAMCET | 2008
(a) images in black and white
(b) coloured images
(c) images unaffected by variation of refractive index with wavelength
(d) highly enlarged images are formed

3. Match the following columns.

	Column I		Column II
(1)	Burning candle	(i)	Line spectrum
(2)	Sodium vapour	(ii)	Continuous spectrum
(3)	Bunsen flame	(iii)	Band spectrum
(4)	Dark lines in solar spectrum	(iv)	Absroption spectrum

EAMCET | 2007
(a) 1–(iii) 2–(i) 3–(ii) 4–(iv)
(b) 1–(iii) 2–(ii) 3–(i) 4–(iv)
(c) 1–(ii) 2–(iii) 3–(i) 4–(iv)
(d) 1–(ii) 2–(i) 3–(iii) 4–(iv)

4. The refractive index of the material of a double convex lens is 1.5 and its focal length is 5 cm. If the radii of curvature are equal, the value of the radius of curvature (in cm) is
EAMCET | 2007
(a) 5.0 (b) 6.5 (c) 8.0 (d) 9.5

5. In Ramsden eyepiece, the two planoconvex lenses each of focal length *f* are separated by a distance 12 cm. The equivalent focal length (in cm) of the eyepiece is EAMCET | 2007
(a) 10.5 (b) 12.0 (c) 13.5 (d) 15.5

6. The two surfaces of a biconvex lens has same radii of curvatures. This lens is made of glass of refractive index 1.5 and has a focal length 10 cm in air. The lens is cut into two equal halves along a plane perpendicular to its principal axis to yield two plano-convex lenses. The two pieces are glued such that the convex surfaces touch each other. If this combination lens is immersed in water (refractive index = 4/3), its focal length (in cm) is EAMCET | 2006
(a) 5 (b) 10 (c) 20 (d) 40

7. Dispersive power depends on the following
EAMCET | 2006
(a) material of the prism
(b) shape of the prism
(c) size of the prism
(d) size, shape and material of the prism

8. Match the appropriate pairs from columns I and II.

	Column I		Column II
1.	Nitrogen molecules	(A)	Continuous spectrum
2.	Incandescent solids	(B)	Absorption spectrum
3.	Fraunhofer lines	(C)	Band spectrum
4.	Electric arc between iron rods	(D)	Emission spectrum

EAMCET | 2006
(a) 1–C, 2–A, 3–B, 4–D
(b) 1–B, 2–A, 3–D, 4–C
(c) 1–D, 2–A, 3–B, 4–C
(d) 1–A, 2–C, 3–D, 4–B

9. **Assertion (A)** Propagation of light through an optical fibre is due to total internal reflection taking place at the core-clad interface.
Reason (R) Refractive index of the material of the core of the optical fibre is greater than that of air. EAMCET | 2005
(a) Both (A) and (R) are true and (R) is the correct explanation of (A)

(b) Both (A) and (R) are true but (R) is not the correct explanation of (A)
(c) (A) is true but (R) is false
(d) (A) is false but (R) is true

10. The focal length of an equi-convex lens is greater than the radius of curvature of any of the surfaces. Then, the refractive index of the material of the lens is **EAMCET | 2005**

(a) greater than zero but less than 1.5
(b) greater than 1.5 but less than 2.0
(c) greater than 2.0 but less than 2.5
(d) greater than 2.5 but less than 2.0

11. **Assertion (A)** Optical fibres are widely used in communication network.
Reason (R) Optical fibres are small in size, light weight, flexible and there is no scope for interference in them. **EAMCET | 2004**

(a) Both (A) and (R) are true and (R) is the correct explanation of (A)
(b) Both (A) and (R) are true but (R) is not the correct explanation of (A)
(c) (A) is true but (R) is false
(d) (A) is false but (R) is true

12. The refracting angle of a prism is A and the refractive index of the material of the prism is cot $(A/2)$. The angle of minimum deviation of the prism is **EAMCET | 2004**

(a) $\pi + 2A$ (b) $\pi - 2A$
(c) $\frac{\pi}{2}+A$ (d) $\frac{\pi}{2}-A$

13. The principal section of a glass prism is an isosceles triangle ABC with $AB = AC$. The face AC is silvered. A ray of light is incident normally on the face AB and after two reflections, it emerges from the base BC perpendicular to the base. Angle BAC of the prism is **EAMCET | 2004**

(a) 30° (b) 36° (c) 60° (d) 72°

14. A ray of light is incident on the hypotenuse of a right-angled prism after travelling parallel to the base inside the prism. If μ is the refractive index of the material of the prism, the maximum value of the base angle for which light is totally reflected from the hypotenuse is **EAMCET | 2003**

(a) $\sin^{-1}\left(\frac{1}{\mu}\right)$ (b) $\tan^{-1}\left(\frac{1}{\mu}\right)$
(c) $\sin^{-1}\left(\frac{\mu-1}{\mu}\right)$ (d) $\cos^{-1}\left(\frac{1}{\mu}\right)$

15. A prism of refractive index μ and angle A is placed in the minimum deviation position. If the angle of minimum deviation is A, then the value of A in terms of μ is **EAMCET | 2003**

(a) $\sin^{-1}\left(\frac{\mu}{2}\right)$ (b) $\sin^{-1}\sqrt{\frac{\mu-1}{2}}$
(c) $2\cos^{-1}\left(\frac{\mu}{2}\right)$ (d) $\cos^{-1}\left(\frac{\mu}{2}\right)$

16. Consider the following statements A and B. Identify the correct choice in the given answers.
A. The refractive index of the extra-ordinary ray depends on the angle of incidence in double refraction.
B. The vibrations of light waves acquire one sidedness for both ordinary and extraordinary rays in double refraction. **EAMCET | 2002**

(a) A and B are wrong
(b) A and B are correct
(c) A is correct and B is wrong
(d) A is wrong and B is correct

17. A convex lens of focal length 0.15 m is made of a material of refractive index $\frac{3}{2}$. When it is placed in a liquid, its focal length is increased by 0.225 m. The refractive index of the liquid is **EAMCET | 2002**

(a) $\frac{7}{4}$ (b) $\frac{5}{4}$ (c) $\frac{9}{4}$ (d) $\frac{3}{2}$

18. A prism is made up of material of refractive index $\sqrt{3}$. The angle of the prism is Å. If the angle of minimum deviation is equal to the angle of the prism, then the value of A is **EAMCET | 2002**

(a) 30° (b) 45° (c) 60° (d) 75°

19. The difference in the number of wavelengths, when yellow light propagates through air and vacuum columns of the same thickness, is one. The thickness of the air column is
Refractive index of air μ_c = 1.0003, wavelength of yellow light in vacuum = 6000 Å **EAMCET | 2001**

(a) 1.8 mm (b) 2 mm (c) 2 cm (d) 2.2 cm

20. When a glass prism of refracting angle 60° is immersed in a liquid its angle of minimum deviation is 30°. The critical angle of glass with respect to the liquid medium is **EAMCET | 2001**

(a) 42° (b) 45° (c) 50° (d) 52°

21. One face of the glass prism is silver polished. A light ray falls at an angle of 45° on the other face. After reflection it is subsequently reflected from the silvered face and then retraces its path. The refracting angle of prism is 30°. The refractive index of the prism is **EAMCET | 2001**

(a) $\frac{3}{2}$ (b) $\sqrt{2}$ (c) $\frac{\sqrt{3}}{2}$ (d) $\sqrt{3}$

22. In the visible region the dispersive powers and the mean angular deviations for crown and flint glass prisms are ω, ω' and d, d' respectively. The condition of getting dispersion with zero deviation, when the two prisms are combined is **EAMCET | 2001**

(a) $\sqrt{\omega d} + \sqrt{\omega' d'} = 0$

(b) $\omega' d + \omega d' = 0$

(c) $\omega d + \omega' d' = 0$

(d) $(\omega d)^2 + (\omega' d')^2 = 0$

23. Under minimum deviation condition in a prism, if a ray is incident at an angle of 30°. The angle between the emergent ray and the second refracting surface of the prism is **EAMCET | 2000**

(a) 0° (b) 30° (c) 45° (d) 60°

24. Consider the following statements A and B and identify the correct choice in the given answers
A. Line spectra is due to atoms in gaseous state.
B. Band spectra is due to molecules. **EAMCET | 2000**

(a) Both A and B are false

(b) A is true and B is false

(c) A is false and B is true

(d) Both A and B are true

25. In a compound microscope cross wires are fixed at the point **EAMCET | 2000**

(a) where the image is formed by the objective

(b) where the image is formed by the eye-piece

(c) where the focal point of objective lies

(d) where the focal point of eye-piece lies

26. The focal length of the lenses of an astronomical telescope are 50 cm and 5 cm. The length of the telescope when the image is formed at the least distance of distinct vision is **EAMCET | 2000**

(a) 45 cm (b) 55 cm

(c) $\frac{275}{6}$ cm (d) $\frac{325}{6}$ cm

27. The final image in an astronomical telescope is **EAMCET | 1999**

(a) real, erect (b) virtual, inverted

(c) real, inverted (d) None of these

28. The least distance of distinct vision is 25 cm. If the focal length of convex lens is 10 cm, it acts as a simple microscope of maximum magnification **EAMCET | 1999**

(a) 2.5 (b) 3 (c) 3.5 (d) 5

29. In a Huygen's eye-piece, with an eye-piece of focal length F, the distance between the eye-piece and field lens should be **EAMCET | 1999**

(a) $\frac{2}{3}F$ (b) F (c) $2F$ (d) $3F$

30. In a spectrometer experiment three prisms A, B and C with same angle of prism but of different materials of refractive indices $\mu_A = 1.33$, $\mu_B = 1.55$, $\mu_C = 1.44$ are used. The corresponding angles of minimum deviation D_A, D_B, D_C measured will be such that **EAMCET | 1999**

(a) $D_A > D_B > D_C$ (b) $D_A < D_B < D_C$

(c) $D_A < D_C < D_B$ (d) None of these

31. An object is placed 40 cm in front of a convex mirror of radius of curvature 20 cm. The image **EAMCET | 1998**

(a) is real and 8 cm behind the mirror

(b) is real and 8 cm in front of the mirror

(c) is virtual and 8 cm in front of the mirror

(d) is virtual and 8 cm behind the mirror

32. A compound microscope has an objective of focal length 4 mm and an eye-piece of focal length 25 mm. The objective produces a real image at a distance of 180 mm. If the eye-piece is in normal adjustment the magnification is **EAMCET | 1998**

(a) 45 (b) 90 (c) 225 (d) 440

33. In the achromatic prism, we have **EAMCET | 1998**

(a) deviation without dispersion

(b) deviation without division

(c) refraction without deviation

(d) deviation and dispersion

34. Fraunhofer lines are due to **EAMCET | 1998, 2005**

(a) absorption by chromosphere of the light emitted by photosphere

(b) absorption by photosphere of the light emitted by chromosphere

(c) light emitted by photosphere

(d) light emitted by chromosphere

35. Which of the following statements is not true in the case of Huygen's eye-piece? **EAMCET | 1997**

(a) It is achromatic

(b) It satisfies condition for minimum spherical aberration

(c) It has cross wires

(d) It cannot be used for measurement

36. The dark lines in the solar spectrum are due to **EAMCET | 1997**

(a) absorption of certain wavelengths by elements present in the outer layer

(b) absence of certain elements in the sun

(c) black body radiation from the sun

(d) scattering of light

37. An incandescent filament emits a spectrum which is a **EAMCET | 1996**

(a) line spectrum

(b) band spectrum

(c) continuous spectrum

(d) characteristic spectrum

38. Reflection of a light wave at a fixed point results in a phase difference between the incident and reflected wave of **EAMCET | 1996**

(a) $\frac{3\pi}{2}$ rad (b) 2π rad

(c) π rad (d) $\frac{\pi}{2}$ rad

39. In a Huygen's eye-piece the eye lens has a focal length of f. The equivalent focal length of eye-piece is **EAMCET | 1996**

(a) $\frac{4}{3}f$ (b) $4f$ (c) $2f$ (d) $\frac{3f}{2}$

40. An astronomical telescope has a length of 310 cm and a magnifying power of 30. The focal length of its objective is **EAMCET | 1996**

(a) 310 cm (b) 300 cm

(c) 155 cm (d) 150 cm

41. If $\hat{i}$ denotes a unit vector along incident light ray, $\hat{r}$ a unit vector along refracted ray into medium of refractive index μ and $\hat{n}$ a vector normal to boundary of media directed towards incident medium, then the law of refraction can be written as **EAMCET | 1995**

(a) $\hat{i}\cdot\hat{n} = \mu(\hat{r}\cdot\hat{n})$ (b) $\hat{i}\times\hat{n} = \mu(\hat{n}\times\hat{r})$

(c) $\hat{i}\times\hat{n} = \mu(\hat{r}\times\hat{n})$ (d) $\mu(\hat{i}\times\hat{n}) = \hat{r}\times\hat{n}$

42. In an equilateral triangular prism, the angle of minimum deviation for a certain wavelength is 40°. The corresponding angle of incidence is **EAMCET | 1995**

(a) 30° (b) 60° (c) 45° (d) 50°

43. The least distance of distinct vision is 25 cm. The magnifying power of a simple microscope of focal length 5 cm is **EAMCET | 1995**

(a) $\frac{1}{5}$ (b) 5 (c) $\frac{1}{6}$ (d) 6

44. Which of the following wavelength is in the infrared region? **EAMCET | 1994**

(a) 5460 Å (b) 5893 Å

(c) 4320 Å (d) 7000 Å

45. If Foucoult's method for determining the velocity of light in air, the distance between the concave mirror and the rotating mirror was 5 km. The speed of rotation of the rotating mirror was 300 rev/s. If the reflected ray is displaced through $\pi/60$ radian, the velocity of light in air is **EAMCET | 1994**

(a) 3×10^3 km/s (b) 2.98×10^3 m/s

(c) 3×10^3 m/s (d) None of these

46. A hollow prism made of transparent glass is filled with a transparent liquid. The angle between the two refracting faces of the prism is 90°. If light incident on one of the faces at grazing angle comes out of the other also at a grazing angle, the refractive index of the liquid is **EAMCET | 1994**

(a) 1.414 (b) 1.333 (c) 1.35 (d) 1.4

47. In a Ramsden eyepiece of effective focal length 3 cm the focal length of eye lens, in cm, is **EAMCET | 1993**

(a) 1.5 (b) 8/3 (c) 3 (d) 4

48. The angle of a prism is 60° and the angle of minimum deviation of light passing through it is observed to be 40°. The angle of incidence of light is **EAMCET | 1993**

(a) 30° (b) 40° (c) 50° (d) 60°

49. An astronomical telescope of magnifying power 12, has an objective of focal length 1.08 m. The focal length of its eyepiece will be **EAMCET | 1993**

(a) 0.08 m (b) 0.09 m

(c) 0.07 m (d) 0.06 m

50. Two lenses of focal lengths 75 cm and 25 cm, will form a combination satisfying the conditions for no chromatic aberration and minimum spherical aberration, when they are placed with a distance of separation **EAMCET | 1993**

(a) 100 cm (b) 50 cm (c) 25 cm (d) 12 cm

51. If μ for water is $\frac{4}{3}$ and the velocity of light in vacuum is 3×10^8 m/s, the time taken for light to travel a distance of 450 m in water will be **EAMCET | 1993**

(a) 2×10^{-6} s (b) 1×10^{-6} s
(c) 0.5×10^{-6} s (d) 2×10^{-4} s

52. In Foucoult's method of determining the velocity of light, the distance between the rotating mirror and the concave mirror is made to pass along a tube of water ($\mu = 1.33$) instead of air, the displacement is **EAMCET | 1992**

(a) $\frac{t}{1.33}$ (b) $1.33\,t$
(c) $(1.33)^2\,t$ (d) $1.33\,t^2$

53. In an astronomical telescope the distance between the eye-piece and the objective is **EAMCET | 1992**

(a) f_o (b) f_e
(c) $f_o - f_e$ (d) $f_o + f_e$

54. If c is velocity of light in free space, the time taken by the light to travel a distance x in a medium of refractive index μ is given by **EAMCET | 1991**

(a) $\mu x c$ (b) $\frac{\mu x}{c}$ (c) $\frac{\mu c}{x}$ (d) $\frac{x}{\mu}$

55. A double convex lens of $f = 6$ cm is made of glass of refractive index 1.5. The radius of curvature of the surface which is doubled that of other surface will be **EAMCET | 1991**

(a) 1.5 cm (b) 2.5 cm
(c) 3.5 cm (d) 4.5 cm

56. To minimize spherical aberration two lenses of focal lengths f_1 and f_2 are placed with a distance of separation equal to **EAMCET | 1991**

(a) f_2 (b) f_1
(c) $f_2 - f_1$ (d) $f_2 + f_1$

57. The distance between the eye lens and cross wire in a Ramsden eye-piece, which has a field lens of focal length 1.2 cm is **EAMCET | 1991**

(a) 0.3 cm (b) 0.6 cm
(c) 0.7 cm (d) 0.9 cm

Answers

1.	(a)	**2.**	(c)	**3.**	(d)	**4.**	(a)	**5.**	(c)	**6.**	(d)	**7.**	(a)	**8.**	(a)	**9.**	(b)	**10.**	(a)
11.	(b)	**12.**	(b)	**13.**	(b)	**14.**	(d)	**15.**	(c)	**16.**	(b)	**17.**	(b)	**18.**	(c)	**19.**	(b)	**20.**	(b)
21.	(b)	**22.**	(c)	**23.**	(d)	**24.**	(d)	**25.**	(a)	**26.**	(d)	**27.**	(b)	**28.**	(c)	**29.**	(c)	**30.**	(c)
31.	(d)	**32.**	(d)	**33.**	(a)	**34.**	(a)	**35.**	(d)	**36.**	(a)	**37.**	(c)	**38.**	(c)	**39.**	(d)	**40.**	(b)
41.	(c)	**42.**	(d)	**43.**	(d)	**44.**	(d)	**45.**	(d)	**46.**	(a)	**47.**	(d)	**48.**	(c)	**49.**	(b)	**50.**	(b)
51.	(a)	**52.**	(b)	**53.**	(d)	**54.**	(b)	**55.**	(d)	**56.**	(c)	**57.**	(a)						

Hints & Solutions

1. Lens Maker's formula

$$\frac{1}{f} = (\mu - 1)\left[\frac{1}{R_1} - \frac{1}{R_2}\right]$$

where, $R_2 = \infty$, $R_1 = 0.3$ m

$$\therefore \quad \frac{1}{f} = \left(\frac{5}{3} - 1\right)\left(\frac{1}{0.3} - \frac{1}{\infty}\right)$$

$$\Rightarrow \quad \frac{1}{f} = \frac{2}{3} \times \frac{1}{0.3}$$

or $f = 0.45$ m

2. The image of an object in white light formed by a lens is usually coloured and blurred. This defect of image is called chromatic aberration and arises due to the fact that focal length of a lens is different for different colours. In case of two thin lenses in contact, the combination will be free from chromatic aberration. The lens combination which satisfies this condition are called achromatic lenses.

3. Burning candle gives continuous spectrum, sodium vapour gives line spectrum, Bunsen flame gives band spectrum and dark lines in solar spectrum are due to absorption spectrum.

4. $$\frac{1}{f} = (\mu-1)\left(\frac{1}{R_1}-\frac{1}{R_2}\right)$$

For double convex lens, $R_1 = R$, $R_2 = -R$

$$\therefore \quad \frac{1}{5} = (1.5-1)\left(\frac{1}{R}+\frac{1}{R}\right)$$

or $$\frac{1}{5} = 0.5 \times \frac{2}{R}$$

or $$R = 5 \text{ cm}$$

5. $$d = \frac{2f}{3}$$

or $$f = \frac{3d}{2} = \frac{3\times12}{2} = 18 \text{ cm}$$

Equivalent focal length is

$$f' = \frac{f_1 f_2}{f_1+f_2} + \frac{f}{4} = \frac{18\times18}{18+8}+\frac{18}{4}$$

$$= 9 + 4.5 = 13.5 \text{ cm}$$

6. If a lens of focal length f is divided into two equal parts as shown in figure (1) and each has a focal length f' then

$$\frac{1}{f} = \frac{1}{f'}+\frac{1}{f'}$$

i.e., $$f' = 2f$$

i.e., each part will have focal length $2f$.

Now, if these parts are put in contact as in figure (2), then resultant focal length of the combination will be

$$\frac{1}{F} = \frac{1}{2f}+\frac{1}{2f}$$

i.e., $F = f$ (initial value)

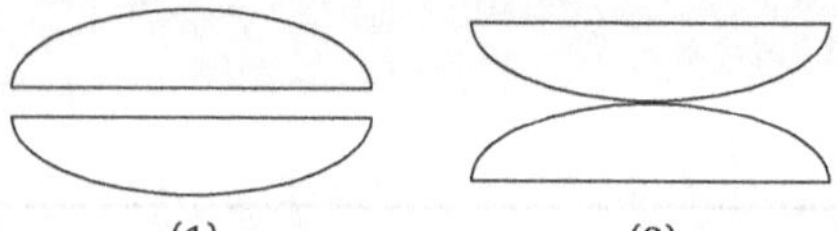

(1) (2)

For this combination,

$$\frac{1}{F} = ({}_a\mu_g-1)\left(\frac{1}{R_1}-\frac{1}{R_2}\right) \quad \text{...(i)}$$

Now, if this combination is immersed in liquid, then

$$\frac{1}{F'} = ({}_l\mu_g-1)\left(\frac{1}{R_1}-\frac{1}{R_2}\right) \quad \text{...(ii)}$$

$$\therefore \quad \frac{F'}{f} = \frac{({}_a\mu_g-1)}{({}_l\mu_g-1)} = \frac{(1.5-1)}{\left(\frac{\frac{3}{2}}{\frac{4}{3}}-1\right)}$$

or $$\frac{F'}{f} = \frac{0.5}{\left(\frac{9}{8}-1\right)}$$

$$\frac{F'}{f} = 0.5 \times 8$$

$$F' = 0.5 \times 8 \times 10$$

$$= 40 \text{ cm}$$

7. Dispersive power does not depend on the shape and size of the prism. It depends only on the material of the prism.

9. Optical fibres are based on the principle of total internal reflection.
Statement 2 is also correct as refractive index of the material of the core of the optical fibre is greater than that of air.

10. Focal length of lens

$$\frac{1}{f} = (\mu-1)\left(\frac{1}{R_1}-\frac{1}{R_2}\right)$$

For equi-convex lens,

$$R_1 = +R, R_2 = -R$$

$$\therefore \quad \frac{1}{f} = (\mu-1)\left(\frac{1}{R}-\frac{1}{R}\right)$$

$$\frac{1}{f} = (\mu-1)\left(\frac{2}{R}\right)$$

$$f = \frac{R}{2(\mu-1)}$$

$$f < R, \text{ so, } 2(\mu-1) < 1$$

i.e., $$(\mu-1) < \frac{1}{2}$$

or $$(\mu-1) < 0.5$$

or $$\mu < 1.5$$

Focal length of convex lens is positive. So, μ cannot be negative, hence μ should be greater than zero but less than 1.5.

11. In optical communication, light is transmitted in form of light pulses along an optical fibre as transmission medium. Since wavelength of light is very small as compared to the radio waves, it provides a very large band width and can carry a huge amount of information.
In optical fibres there occurs a total internal reflection of light so interference phenomenon must not occur.

12. $$\mu = \cot\frac{A}{2} = \frac{\sin\left(\frac{A+\delta_m}{2}\right)}{\sin A/2}$$

or $$\frac{\cos\frac{A}{2}}{\sin\frac{A}{2}} = \frac{\sin\left(\frac{A+\delta_m}{2}\right)}{\sin\frac{A}{2}}$$

or $$\sin\left(90^\circ - \frac{A}{2}\right) = \sin\left(\frac{A+\delta_m}{2}\right)$$

or $$90^\circ - \frac{A}{2} = \frac{A+\delta_m}{2}$$

or $$180^\circ - A = A + \delta_m$$

$$\therefore \quad \delta_m = 180^\circ - 2A = \pi - 2A.$$

13. From the figure

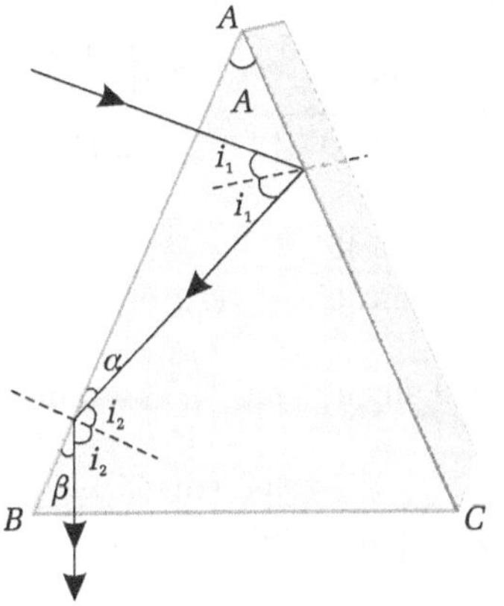

$$i_1 = 90^\circ - (90^\circ - A) = A$$

and $$\alpha = 90^\circ - 2i_1 = 90^\circ - 2A$$

$$\therefore \quad i_2 = 90^\circ - \alpha = 90^\circ - (90^\circ - 2A) = 2A$$

$$\therefore \quad \beta = 90^\circ - i_2 = 90^\circ - 2A$$

From the geometry of the figure

$$A + 2A + 2A = 180^\circ$$

$$\therefore \quad A = 36^\circ$$

14. For total internal reflection

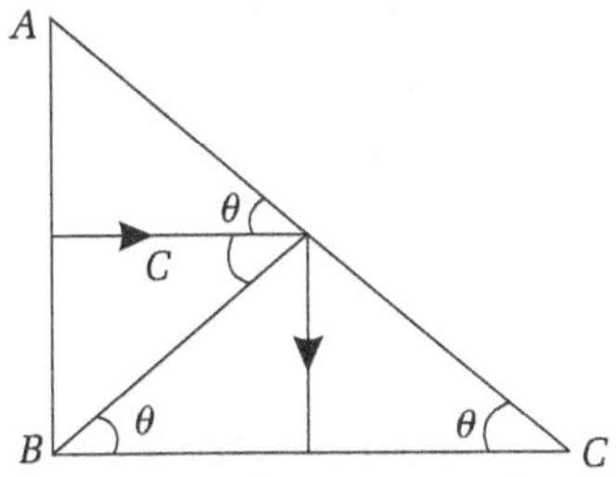

$$\mu = \frac{1}{\sin C}$$

$$\mu = \frac{1}{\sin(90^\circ - \theta)}$$

$$\mu = \frac{1}{\cos\theta}$$

$$\Rightarrow \quad \cos\theta = \frac{1}{\mu}$$

$$\theta = \cos^{-1}\left(\frac{1}{\mu}\right)$$

15. Refractive index of material of prism

$$\mu = \frac{\sin\left(\frac{A+\delta_m}{2}\right)}{\sin\frac{A}{2}}$$

but, $\delta_m = A$

$$\mu = \frac{\sin\left(\frac{A+A}{2}\right)}{\sin\frac{A}{2}}$$

$$\mu = \frac{\sin A}{\sin A/2}$$

$$\mu = \frac{2\sin A/2 \cos A/2}{\sin A/2}$$

$$\cos\frac{A}{2} = \frac{\mu}{2}$$

$$\frac{A}{2} = \cos^{-1}\left(\frac{\mu}{2}\right)$$

$$A = 2\cos^{-1}\left(\frac{\mu}{2}\right)$$

16. In certain crystals like calcite, quartz and tourmaline, etc, incident unpolarized light splits up into two light beams of equal intensities with perpendicular polarization. One of the ray is ordinary ray (O-ray) it obey's Snell's law. Another ray's extra ordinary ray (E-ray) it doesn't obey the Snell's law.

17. Given, $f_a = 0.15$ m, $\mu_g = 3/2$, $f_e = 0.225 + 0.15$
$= 0.375$ m

From lens formula

For air, $$\frac{1}{f_a} = \left(\frac{\mu_g}{\mu_a} - 1\right)\left(\frac{1}{R_1} - \frac{1}{R_2}\right)$$

For liquid, $$\frac{1}{f_l} = \left(\frac{\mu_g}{\mu_l} - 1\right)\left(\frac{1}{R_1} - \frac{1}{R_2}\right)$$

$$\therefore \quad \frac{1/f_a}{1/f_l} = \frac{(\mu_g/\mu_a - 1)}{\left(\frac{\mu_g}{\mu_l} - 1\right)}$$

$$\frac{f_l}{f_a} = \frac{\left(\frac{3/2}{1}-1\right)}{\left(\frac{3/2}{\mu_l}-1\right)}$$

$$\frac{0.375}{0.15} = \frac{1/2}{\left(\frac{3}{2\mu_l}-1\right)}$$

$$\left(\frac{3}{2\mu_l}-1\right) = \frac{1/2}{5/2}$$

$$\frac{3}{2\mu_l}-1 = \frac{1}{5}$$

$$\frac{3}{2\mu_l} = \frac{1}{5}+1$$

$$\Rightarrow \frac{3}{2\mu_l} = \frac{6}{5}$$

$$\mu_l = \frac{5}{4}$$

18. Given, $\mu = \sqrt{3}, \delta_m = A$

For prism, $\mu = \frac{\sin\frac{A+\delta_m}{2}}{\sin A/2}$

$$\sqrt{3} = \frac{\sin\frac{A+A}{2}}{\sin A/2}$$

$$\sqrt{3} = \frac{\sin A}{\sin A/2}$$

$$\Rightarrow \sqrt{3} = \frac{2\sin A/2\cos A/2}{\sin A/2}$$

$$\cos\frac{A}{2} = \frac{\sqrt{3}}{2}$$

$$\Rightarrow \cos\frac{A}{2} = 30°$$

$$\therefore \frac{A}{2} = 30°$$

$$\Rightarrow A = 60°$$

19. Difference in the number of wavelength = 1
If L is the thickness of air and vacuum columns.

$$\therefore \frac{L}{\lambda_{air}} - \frac{L}{\lambda_{vacuum}} = 1$$

$$L\left(\frac{1}{\lambda_{air}} - \frac{1}{\lambda_{vacuum}}\right) = 1$$

$$L\left(\frac{1}{\frac{\lambda_{vacuum}}{\mu_{air}}} - \frac{1}{\lambda_{vacuum}}\right) = 1$$

$$L\left(\frac{\mu_{air}}{\lambda_{vacuum}} - \frac{1}{\lambda_{vacuum}}\right) = 1$$

$$\frac{L}{\lambda_{vacuum}}(\mu_{air}-1) = 1$$

$$\frac{L}{6000\times10^{-10}}(1.0003-1) = 1$$

$$L = \frac{6000\times10^{-10}}{0.0003}$$

$$= \frac{6\times10^{-7}}{3\times10^{-4}}$$

$$= 2\times10^{-3}\text{ m}$$

$$= 2\text{ mm}$$

20. Given, $A = 60°$, $\delta = 30°$,
Refractive index of prism with respect to liquid

$$\mu = \frac{\sin\frac{A+\delta_m}{2}}{\sin A/2} = \frac{\sin\left(\frac{60°+30°}{2}\right)}{\sin\left(\frac{60°}{2}\right)}$$

$$= \frac{\sin 45°}{\sin 30°} = \frac{1/\sqrt{2}}{1/2} = \sqrt{2}$$

$$\therefore \text{Critical angle} = \sin^{-1}\left(\frac{1}{\mu}\right) = \sin^{-1}\left(\frac{1}{\sqrt{2}}\right)$$

$$= \sin^{-1}(\sin 45°) = 45°$$

21. $\angle r = 90° - [180° - (90° + 30°)]$

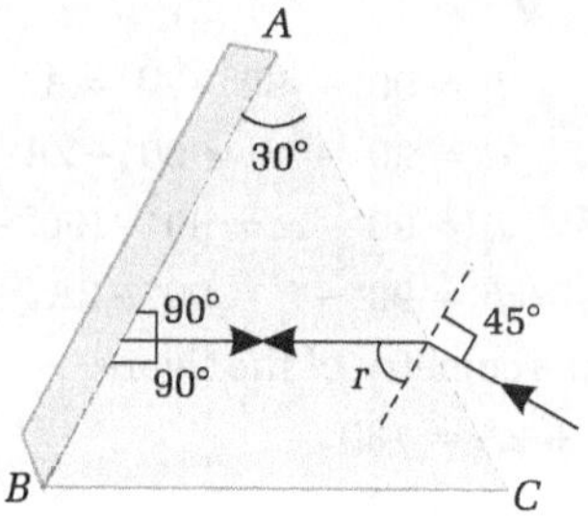

$$= 90° - [180° - 120°]$$

$$= 90° - 60° = 30°$$

$$\angle i = 45°$$

$$\mu = \frac{\sin i}{\sin r}$$

$$\Rightarrow \mu = \frac{\sin 45°}{\sin 30°}$$

$$\mu = \frac{\frac{1}{\sqrt{2}}}{\frac{1}{2}} = \sqrt{2}$$

22. The condition of getting dispersion with zero deviation, when two prisms are combined is

$$\omega d + \omega' d' = 0$$

23. $\angle i = 30°$

under minimum deviation condition in a prism the angle between emergent ray and second refracting surface $= 90° - i$

$$= 90° - 30° = 60°$$

24. Line spectrum is produced by an excited source in atomic state whereas band spectrum is produced by an excited source in molecular state.

25. In a compound microscope, cross wires are fixed at the point where the image is formed by the objective.

26. Given, $f_o = 50$ cm, $f_e = 5$ cm

length of telescope in the given condition

$$= v_o + u_e$$

For object $\frac{1}{v_o} - \frac{1}{u_o} = \frac{1}{f_o}$

$$\frac{1}{v_o} - \frac{1}{\infty} = \frac{1}{50}$$

$$\Rightarrow \quad v_o = 50 \text{ cm}$$

For eye lens

$$\frac{1}{v_e} - \frac{1}{u_e} = \frac{1}{f_e}$$

$$\frac{1}{-D} - \frac{1}{-u_e} = \frac{1}{5}$$

$$\frac{1}{u_e} = \frac{1}{D} + \frac{1}{5} = \frac{1}{25} + \frac{1}{5} = \frac{6}{25}$$

$$u_e = \frac{25}{6}$$

$\therefore$ Length of telescope $= v_o + u_e$

$$= 50 + \frac{25}{6} = \frac{325}{6} \text{ cm}$$

27. Final image of astronomical telescope is virtual and inverted with respect to object.

28. $D = 25$ cm, $f = 10$ cm

Magnification of simple microscope

$$M = 1 + \frac{D}{f} = 1 + \frac{25}{10} = 1 + 2.5$$

$$= 3.5$$

29. In a Huygen's eye-piece the distance between the eye-piece and field lens should be 2 *F*.

30. Angle of minimum deviation

$$D_m = (\mu - 1)A$$

$$D_m \propto \mu$$

Since, $\mu_A < \mu_C < \mu_B$

$\therefore \quad D_A < D_C < D_B$

31. Given, $u = -40$ cm, $R = 20$ cm,

$$\therefore \quad f = \frac{R}{2} = \frac{20}{2} = 10 \text{ cm}$$

From mirror formula

$$\frac{1}{f} = \frac{1}{u} + \frac{1}{v}$$

$$\frac{1}{10} = -\frac{1}{40} + \frac{1}{v}$$

$$\frac{1}{v} = \frac{1}{10} + \frac{1}{40}$$

$$= \frac{4+1}{40}$$

$$v = \frac{40}{5} = 8 \text{ cm}$$

Convex mirror always forms virtual image and behind the mirror.

32. Given, $f_o = 4$ mm, $f_e = 25$ mm,

$v_o = 180$ mm.

For objective lens

$$\frac{1}{f_o} = \frac{1}{v_o} - \frac{1}{u_o}$$

$$\frac{1}{4} = \frac{1}{180} - \frac{1}{u_o}$$

$$\frac{1}{u_o} = \frac{1}{180} - \frac{1}{4}$$

$$= \frac{1-45}{180} = -\frac{44}{180}$$

$$u_o = -\frac{180}{44}$$

In normal adjustment of compound microscope, its magnification power

$$m = \frac{v_o}{u_o} \frac{D}{f_e}$$

D = least distance of distinct vision

$= 250$ mm

$$\therefore \quad m = \frac{180}{180/44} \times \frac{250}{25}$$

$$= 44 \times 10 = 440$$

33. In achromatic prism we have deviation without dispersion

$$\delta_{\text{net}} = \delta\left(1 - \frac{\omega}{\omega'}\right)$$

34. The central part (photosphere) of the sun is very hot end emits all possible wavelengths of the visible light. However, the outer part (chromosphere) consists of vapours of different elements. When the light emitted from the photosphere passes through the chromosphere, certain wavelengths are absorbed. Hence, in the spectrum of sunlight a large number of dark lines are seen called Fraunhofer lines.

36. The dark lines *i.e.*, Fraunhofer lines in solar spectrum are due to the absorption of certain wavelengths by element present in photosphere *i.e.*, in outer layer.

37. An incandescent filament emits a continuous spectrum.

38. In case of reflection at a fixed point, the light ray goes back, so the phase difference is 180° or π.

39. For Huygen's eye-piece, equivalent focal length

$$= \frac{3}{2}f$$

40. Length of telescope L = 310 cm

$$\therefore \quad f_o + f_e = 310 \text{ cm} \qquad \text{...(i)}$$

Magnifying power, M = 30

$$\frac{f_o}{f_e} = 3$$

$$\Rightarrow \quad f_o = 30 f_e$$

From Eq. (i)

$$30 f_e + f_e = 310$$

$$31 f_e = 310$$

$$\Rightarrow \quad f_e = 10 \text{ cm}$$

$$\therefore \quad f_o = 30 \times 10 = 300 \text{ cm}$$

41. In this case

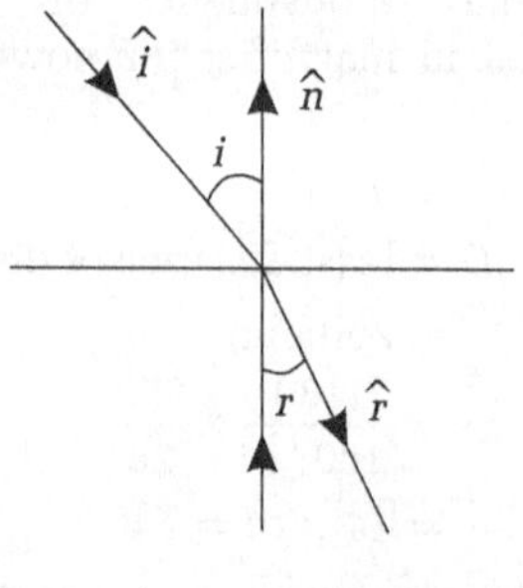

$$\hat{i} \times \hat{n} = |\hat{i}||\hat{n}| \sin i$$

$$= 1 \times 1 \times \sin i = \sin i$$

Similarly, $\hat{r} \times \hat{n} = |\hat{r}||\hat{n}| \sin r$

$$= 1 \times 1 \times \sin r = \sin r$$

Law of refraction, $\mu = \dfrac{\sin i}{\sin r}$

$$\mu = \frac{\hat{i} \times \hat{n}}{\hat{r} \times \hat{n}}$$

$$\hat{i} \times \hat{n} = \mu(\hat{r} \times \hat{n})$$

42. Angle of minimum deviation, $\delta_m = 40°$

Angle of incidence, $i = \dfrac{A + \delta_m}{2}$

For equilateral prism, $A = 60°$

$$\therefore \quad i = \frac{60° + 40°}{2} = 50°$$

43. Least distance of distinct vision

$$D = 25 \text{ cm}$$

Focal length, f = 5 cm

$\therefore$ Magnifying power, $M = 1 + \dfrac{D}{f} = 1 + \dfrac{25}{5}$

$$= 1 + 5 = 6$$

44. Infrared rays have wavelength range ($7 \times 10^{-7} - 3 \times 10^{-5}$) m.

45. From Foucoult's method, velocity of light in air

$$c = \frac{4\pi nr}{\theta}$$

where n = number of revolutions per second

= 300

r = distance between concave mirror and rotating mirror

= 5 km = 5×10^3 m

$$\theta = \frac{\pi}{60} \text{ radian}$$

$$\therefore \quad c = \frac{4\pi \times 300}{\pi / 60} \times 5 \times 10^3$$

$$= 4 \times 300 \times 60 \times 5 \times 10^3$$

$$= 360 \times 10^6$$

$$= 36 \times 10^7 \text{ m/s}$$

46. Angle of prism $A = 90°$

The light incident on one of the faces at grazing angle,

So, critical angle, $c = \dfrac{A}{2} = \dfrac{90°}{2} = 45°$

$\therefore$ Refractive index of prism

$$\mu = \frac{1}{\sin C} = \frac{1}{\sin 45°} = \frac{1}{1/\sqrt{2}}$$

$$= \sqrt{2} = 1.414$$

47. In Ramsden's eyepiece, the focal length of eyepiece $f_e = \dfrac{4}{3}f$

where, f = effective focal length = 3 cm

$\therefore \quad f_e = \frac{4}{3} \times 3 = 4$ cm

48. Angle of prism, $A = 60°$

Angle of minimum deviation, $\delta_m = 40°$

Angle of incidence, $i = \frac{A + \delta_m}{2} = \frac{60° + 40°}{2}$

$= 50°$

49. Focal length of objective lens

$f_o = 1.08$ m

Magnifying power, $M = 12$

For astronomical telescope, $M = \frac{f_o}{f_e}$

Focal length of eyepiece, $f_e = \frac{f_o}{M} = \frac{1.08}{12}$

$= 0.09$ m

50. Focal length of first lens $f_1 = 75$ cm

Focal length of second lens $f_2 = 25$ cm

For no chromatic aberration and minimum spherical aberration, the separation between the lens $= f_1 - f_2 = 75 - 25 = 50$ cm.

51. Time taken by light to travel s distance in water

$t = \frac{\mu_w s}{c}$

μ_w = refractive index of water $= \frac{4}{3}$

$s = 450$ m,

c = speed of light in vacuum

$= 3 \times 10^8$ ms^{-1} (given)

$\therefore \quad t = \frac{4/3 \times 450}{3 \times 10^8}$

$= \frac{600}{3 \times 10^8} = 200 \times 10^{-8}$

$= 2 \times 10^{-6}$ s

52. Let initial displacement is t then, displacement with water $= \mu t$

where, μ = Refractive index of water

$= 1.33$

$\therefore$ Displacement with water $= 1.33\, t$

53. In an astronomical telescope the distance between eye-piece and objective $= f_o + f_e$

= sum of focal lengths of the objective and eye-piece.

54. Velocity of light in the medium $v = \frac{c}{\mu}$

$\therefore$ Time taken, $t = \frac{x}{v} = \frac{x}{c/\mu}$

$= \frac{\mu x}{c}$

55. From lens Maker formula

$$\frac{1}{f} = (\mu - 1)\left(\frac{1}{R_1} - \frac{1}{R_2}\right)$$

f = Focal length of lens = 6 cm

μ = Refractive index of material of lens = 1.5

and R_1, R_2 = Radii of curvature of spherical surfaces of the lenses.

Here, $\quad R_1 = R$ and $R_2 = -2R$

$$\therefore \quad \frac{1}{f} = (\mu - 1)\left(\frac{1}{R} - \frac{1}{-2R}\right)$$

$$\frac{1}{f} = (\mu - 1)\left(\frac{3}{2R}\right)$$

$$R = 0.5 \times 6 \times \frac{3}{2}$$

$$= \frac{9}{2} = 4.5 \text{ cm}$$

56. A simple method to reduce spherical aberration is to use a stop before and infront of the lens. Also by using plano-convex lens, using two lenses separated by $d = f_2 - f_1$, using crossed lens.

57. The distance between the eye lens and crosswire in

$= \frac{\text{focal length of field lens}}{4}$

$= \frac{1.2}{4}$ cm

$= 0.3$ cm

Chapter

18

Wave Optics

1. **Assertion (A)** Using Huygen's eye-piece measurements can be taken but are not correct.
Reason (R) The cross wires, scale and final image are not magnified proportionately because the image of the object is magnified by two lenses, whereas the cross wire scale is magnified by one lens only.
Identify the correct one of the following.
EAMCET | 2008
(a) Both (A) and (R) are true, (R) explains (A).
(b) Both (A) and (R) are true, but (R) cannot explain (A).
(c) Only (A) is correct, but (R) is wrong.
(d) Both (A) and (R) are wrong.

2. In Fraunhofer diffraction experiment, L is the distance between screen and the obstacle, b is the size of obstacle and λ is wavelength of incident light. The general condition for the applicability of Fraunhofer diffraction is
EAMCET | 2008
(a) $\frac{b^2}{L\lambda} >> 1$ (b) $\frac{b^2}{L\lambda} = 1$
(c) $\frac{b^2}{L\lambda} << 1$ (d) $\frac{b^2}{L\lambda} \neq 1$

3. In Huygen's eyepiece **EAMCET | 2007**
(a) the cross wires are outside the eyepiece
(b) condition for achromatism is satisfied
(c) condition for minimum spherical aberration is not satisfied
(d) the image formed by the objective is a virtual image

4. In Young's double slit experiment, first slit has width four times the width of the second slit. The ratio of the maximum intensity to the minimum intensity in the interference fringe system is **EAMCET | 2006**
(a) 2 : 1 (b) 4 : 1 (c) 9 : 1 (d) 8 : 1

5. A light ray of wavelength λ is passing through a pin hole of diameter D and the effect is observed on a screen placed at a distance L from the pin hole. The approximations of geometrical optics are applicable if **EAMCET | 2005**
(a) $D \leq \lambda$ (b) $\frac{L\lambda}{D^2} = 1$
(c) $\frac{L\lambda}{D^2} << 1$ (d) $\frac{L\lambda}{D^2} >> 1$

6. Consider the following statements A and B and identify the correct answer.
A. Fresnel's diffraction pattern occurs when the source of light or the screen on which the diffraction pattern is seen or when both are at finite distance from the aperture.
B. Diffracted light can be used to estimate the helical structure of nucleic acids.
EAMCET | 2004
(a) A and B are true
(b) A and B are false
(c) A is true but B is false
(d) A is false but B is true

7. In Young's double slit experiment, an interference pattern is obtained on a screen by a light of wavelength 6000 Å coming from the coherent sources S_1 and S_2. At certain point P on the screen third dark fringe is formed. Then, the path difference $S_1P - S_2P$ in micron is **EAMCET | 2003**
(a) 0.75 (b) 1.5 (c) 3.0 (d) 4.5

8. In Young's double slit interference experiment the wavelength of light used is 6000 Å. If the path difference between waves reaching a point P on the screen is 1.5 μ, then at that point P **EAMCET | 2002**
(a) second bright band occurs
(b) second dark band occurs
(c) third dark band occurs
(d) third bright band occurs

9. Light waves producing interference have their amplitudes in the ratio 3 : 2. The intensity ratio of maximum and minimum of interference fringes is **EAMCET | 2001**
(a) 36 : 1 (b) 9 : 4 (c) 25 : 1 (d) 6 : 4

Answers

1.	(a)	**2.**	(c)	**3.**	(b)	**4.**	(c)	**5.**	(c)	**6.**	(c)	**7.**	(b)	**8.**	(c)	**9.**	(c)

Hints & Solutions

1. Using Huygen's eye-piece measurements can be taken but not accurately due to the reason given.

2. The general condition for Fraunhofer diffraction is $\frac{b^2}{L\lambda} << 1$.

3. Huygen's eyepiece satisfies the conditions for elimination of the chromatic aberration as well as spherical aberration.

4. Let intensity of light coming from each slit of a coherent source is I.

As first slit has width 4 times the width of the second slit, so

$$I_1 = 4I \text{ and } I_2 = I$$

$$\therefore \quad \frac{I_{max}}{I_{min}} = \frac{(\sqrt{I_1}+\sqrt{I_2})^2}{(\sqrt{I_1}-\sqrt{I_2})^2}$$

$$= \frac{(\sqrt{4I}+\sqrt{I})^2}{(\sqrt{4I}-\sqrt{I})^2} = \frac{9}{1}$$

5. The approximations of geometrical optics are applicable if $\frac{L\lambda}{D^2} << 1$.

7. $\lambda = 6000$ Å $= 6 \times 10^{-7}$ m

Path difference for dark fringe

$$\Delta x = (2n+1)\lambda/2$$

For third dark fringe, $n = 2$

$$\therefore \quad \Delta x = (2\times2+1)\times\frac{6\times10^{-7}}{2}$$

$$= \frac{5\times6\times10^{-7}}{2}$$

$$= 15 \times 10^{-7}$$

$$= 1.5 \times 10^{-6} \text{ m}$$

$$= 1.5\,\mu$$

8.

$$\lambda = 6000 \text{ Å}, \Delta x = 1.5\,\mu$$

$$= 6 \times 10^{-7} \text{ m}, = 1.5 \times 10^{-6} \text{ m}$$

Path difference for maxima

$$\Delta x = n\lambda$$

$$1.5 \times 10^{-6} = n \times 6 \times 10^{-7}$$

$$n = \frac{1.5\times10^{-6}}{6\times10^{-7}} = \frac{15}{6}$$

$$= 2.5 = \frac{5}{2}$$

Value of n is always an integer for maxima, so point P is not a maxima.

$\therefore$ For maxima

$$\Delta x = (2n+1)\lambda/2$$

$$1.5 \times 10^{-6} = (2n+1) \times \frac{6\times10^{-7}}{2}$$

$$(2n+1) = \frac{1.5\times10^{-6}\times2}{6\times10^{-7}}$$

$$2n = 5 - 1$$

$$2n = 4$$

$$\Rightarrow \quad n = 2$$

So, at P third dark band occurs.

9. Ratio of amplitudes $\frac{a_1}{a_2} = \frac{3}{2}$

$$\therefore \quad a_1 = 3k, a_2 = 2k$$

$$\frac{I_{max}}{I_{min}} = \frac{(a_1+a_2)^2}{(a_1-a_2)^2}$$

$$= \frac{(3k+2k)^2}{(3k-2k)^2} = \frac{25}{1}$$

$$I_{max} : I_{min} = 25 : 1$$

Chapter

19

Electrons and Protons

1. X-rays of wavelength 0.140 nm are scattered from a block of carbon. What will be the wavelength of X-rays scattered at 90°? **EAMCET | 2008**

(a) 0.140 nm (b) 0.142 nm
(c) 0.144 nm (d) 0.146 nm

2. An X-ray tube produces a continuous spectrum of radiation with its shortest wavelength of 45×10^{-2} Å. The maximum energy of a photon in the radiation in eV is
($h = 6.62 \times 10^{-34}$ J-s, $c = 3 \times 10^8$ ms^{-1}) **EAMCET | 2008**

(a) 27,500 (b) 22,500
(c) 17,500 (d) 12,500

3. The work function of the nickel is 5 eV. When a light of wavelength 2000 Å falls on it, it emits photoelectrons in the circuit. Then, the potential difference necessary to stop the fastest electrons emitted is (Given, $h = 6.67 \times 10^{-34}$ J-s) **EAMCET | 2007**

(a) 1.0 V (b) 1.75 V
(c) 1.25 V (d) 0.75 V

4. In an experiment on photoelectric emission from a metallic surface, wavelength of incident light is 2×10^{-7} m and stopping potential is 2.5 V. The threshold frequency of the metal (in Hz) approximately
(charge of electron, $e = 1.6 \times 10^{-19}$ C, Planck's constant, $h = 6.6 \times 10^{-34}$ J-s) **EAMCET | 2007**

(a) 12×10^{15} (b) 9×10^{15}
(c) 9×10^{14} (d) 12×10^{13}

5. A oil drop having a mass 4.8×10^{-18} g and charge 2.4×10^{-18} C stands still between two charged horizontal plates separated by a distance of 1 cm. If now the polarity of the plates is changed, instantaneous acceleration of the drop is ($g = 10$ ms^{-2}) **EAMCET | 2006**

(a) 5 ms^{-2} (b) 10 ms^{-2}
(c) 15 ms^{-2} (d) 20 ms^{-2}

6. According to Moseley's law, the frequency (ν) of the K_α line and the atomic number Z of the element have the relation (A and B are constants) **EAMCET | 2005**

(a) $\frac{\nu}{(Z-A)} = B$ (b) $\frac{\sqrt{\nu}}{(Z-A)} = B$
(c) $\nu\,(Z-A) = B$ (d) $\nu\,(Z-A)^2 = B$

7. $\Delta\lambda$ is the difference between the wavelengths of K_α line and the minimum wavelength of the continuous X-ray spectrum when the X-ray tube is operated at a voltage V. If the operating voltage is changed to $V/3$, the above difference is $\Delta\lambda'$. Then **EAMCET | 2004**

(a) $\Delta\lambda' = 5\Delta\lambda$ (b) $\Delta\lambda' = 4\Delta\lambda$
(c) $\Delta\lambda' = 3\Delta\lambda$ (d) $\Delta\lambda' < 3\Delta\lambda$

8. Electrons ejected from the surface of a metal, when light of certain frequency is incident on it, are stopped fully by a retarding potential of 3 V. Photoelectric effect in this metallic surface begins at a frequency 6×10^{14} s^{-1}. The frequency of the incident light in s^{-1} is [Planck's constant = 6.4×10^{-34} Js, charge on the electron = 1.6×10^{-19} C] **EAMCET | 2004**

(a) 7.5×10^{13} (b) 13.5×10^{13}
(c) 13.5×10^{14} (d) 7.5×10^{15}

9. Match the pairs in two columns given below.

	Column I		Column II
(1)	Spectra produced by light from incandescent solid	(i)	Photon
		(ii)	Continuous spectra
(2)	Elementary particles with zero mass and with a spin of unity	(iii)	Photo emissive cell
(3)	Photocell in which current changes with change in intensity of light after time gap.	(iv)	Photo-conducting cell
		(v)	Neutrino
		(vi)	Band spectra

EAMCET | 2004

(a) 1-ii, 2-v, 3-iv (b) 1-vi, 2-v, 3-iii
(c) 1-ii, 2-v, 3-iii (d) 1-vi, 2-i, 3-iv

10. Consider the two following statements A and B, and identify the correct choice given in the answers.
A. In photovoltaic cells the photoelectric current produced is not proportional to the intensity of incident light.
B. In gas filled photoemissive cells, the velocity of photoelectrons depends on the wavelength of the incident radiation.
EAMCET | 2003

(a) Both A and B are true
(b) Both A and B are false
(c) A is true but B is false
(d) A is false but B is true

11. When radiation of the wavelength λ is incident on a metallic surface, the stopping potential is 4.8 V. If the same surface is illuminated with radiation of double the wavelength, then the stopping potential becomes 1.6 V. Then, the threshold wavelength for the surface is
EAMCET | 2003

(a) 2λ (b) 4λ (c) 6λ (d) 8λ

12. Two photons of energies twice and thrice the work function of a metal are incident on the metal surface. Then, the ratio of maximum velocities of the photoelectrons emitted in the two cases respectively, is **EAMCET | 2002**

(a) $\sqrt{2}:1$ (b) $\sqrt{3}:3$
(c) $\sqrt{3}:\sqrt{2}$ (d) $1:\sqrt{2}$

13. In compton scattering process, the incident X-radiation is scattered at an angle 60°. The wavelength of the scattered radiation is 0.22 Å. The wavelength of the incident X-radiation in Å units is **EAMCET | 2002**

(a) 0.508 (b) 0.408 (c) 0.232 (d) 0.208

14. If λ_0 is the de-Broglie wavelength for a proton accelerated through a potential difference of 100 V, the de-Broglie wavelength for α-particle accelerated through the same potential difference is **EAMCET | 2002**

(a) $2\sqrt{2\lambda_0}$ (b) $\frac{\lambda_0}{2}$ (c) $\frac{\lambda_0}{2\sqrt{2}}$ (d) $\frac{\lambda_0}{\sqrt{2}}$

15. Photoelectric emission is observed from a metallic surface for frequencies ν_1 and ν_2 of the incident light rays ($\nu_1 > \nu_2$). If the maximum values of kinetic energy of the photoelectrons emitted in the two cases are in the ratio of $1:k$, then the threshold frequency of the metallic surface is **EAMCET | 2001**

(a) $\frac{\nu_2-\nu_1}{k-1}$ (b) $\frac{k\nu_1-\nu_2}{k-1}$
(c) $\frac{k\nu_2-\nu_1}{k-1}$ (d) $\frac{\nu_2-\nu_1}{k}$

16. The de-Broglie wavelength of an electron having 80 eV energy is nearly
($1\text{ eV} = 1.6 \times 10^{-19}$ J)
Mass of the electron $= 9 \times 10^{-31}$ kg
Planck's constant $= 6.6 \times 10^{-34}$ J-s
EAMCET | 2001

(a) 140 Å (b) 0.14 Å
(c) 14 Å (d) 1.4 Å

17. Consider the following statements A and B and identify the correct choice in the given answers.
A. Tightly bound electrons of target material scatter X-ray photon, resulting in the Compton effect.
B. Photoelectric effect takes place with free electrons. **EAMCET | 2001**

(a) Both A and B are true
(b) A is true but B is false
(c) A is false but B is true
(d) Both A and B are false

18. The *X*-ray wavelength of L_α line of platinum ($Z = 78$) is 1.30 Å. The *X*-ray wavelength of L_α line of molybdenum ($Z = 42$) is
EAMCET | 2000

(a) 5.41 Å (b) 4.59 Å
(c) 2.70 Å (d) 1.35 Å

19. When a metal surface is illuminated by a light of wavelength 400 nm and 250 nm. The maximum velocities of the photo electrons ejected are v and $2v$ respectively. The work function of the metal is (h = Planck's constant, c = velocity of light in air) **EAMCET | 2000**

(a) $2\,hc \times 10^6$ J (b) $1.5\,hc \times 10^6$ J
(c) $hc \times 10^6$ J (d) $0.5\,hc \times 10^6$ J

20. The energy of an X-ray photon of wavelength 1.65 Å is
($h = 6.6 \times 10^{-34}$ Js, $c = 3 \times 10^8$ ms^{-1};
$1\text{ eV} = 1.6 \times 10^{-19}$ J) **EAMCET | 2000**

(a) 3.5 keV (b) 5.5 keV
(c) 7.5 keV (d) 9.5 keV

21. In a photoelectric experiment, the maximum velocity of photoelectrons emitted
EAMCET | 1999

(a) depends on intensity of incident radiation
(b) does not depend on the cathode material
(c) depends on frequency of incident radiation
(d) does not depend on wavelength of the incident radiation

22. The photoelectric work function of a metal surface is 2 eV. When light of frequency 1.5×10^{15} Hz is incident on it, the maximum kinetic energy of the photo electrons, approximately is **EAMCET | 1998**

(a) 8 eV (b) 6 eV (c) 2 eV (d) 4 eV

23. An electron remains undeflected when passing perpendicular to mutually perpendicular electric and magnetic fields. If the magnetic field is 8 Gauss and the electric field is 400 Vm^{-1}, the velocity of the electron is **EAMCET | 1998**

(a) 2×10^6 ms^{-1} (b) 5×10^5 ms^{-1}
(c) 6×10^6 ms^{-1} (d) 7.5×10^6 ms^{-1}

24. An electron beam is allowed to pass normally through magnetic and electric fields which are mutually perpendicular. When the magnetic field induction and electric field strength are 0.0004 Wbm^{-2} and 3000 Vm^{-1} respectively, the beam suffers no deflection. Then, the velocity of electron is **EAMCET | 1997**

(a) 7.5×10^6 ms^{-1} (b) 7.5×10^4 ms^{-1}
(c) 7.5×10^2 ms^{-1} (d) 1.2×10^6 ms^{-1}

25. In a photoelectric phenomenon, the number of photoelectrons emitted depends on **EAMCET | 1996**

(a) the intensity of incident radiation
(b) the frequency of incident radiation
(c) the velocity of incident radiation
(d) the work function of the photo cathode

26. According to the Moseley's law, the frequency of a spectral line in *X*-ray spectrum varies as **EAMCET | 1996**

(a) atomic number of the element
(b) square of atomic number of the element
(c) square root of atomic number of element
(d) fourth power of atomic number of the element

27. The photoelectric work function for a metal surface is 4.125 eV. The cut-off wavelength for this surface is **EAMCET | 1996**

(a) 4125 Å (b) 2062.5 Å
(c) 3000 Å (d) 6000 Å

28. The threshold wavelength for a certain metal is 2000 Å. The work function of the metal is **EAMCET | 1995**

(a) 6.2 J (b) 6.2 eV
(c) 6.2 MeV (d) 6.2 keV

29. *X*-rays are a stream of **EAMCET | 1995**

(a) electrons (b) phonons
(c) photons (d) protons

30. A beam of charged particles of charge q and mass m are accelerated from rest through a potential difference of 100 V. They pass through crossed electric and magnetic fields which together produce null deflection. If these electronic and magnetic fields are respectively 15×10^3 Vm^{-1} and 5 Wbm^{-2}, then q/m has a value, in C kg^{-1}, equal to **EAMCET | 1994**

(a) 9×10^4 (b) 15
(c) 4.5×10^4 (d) 4.5×10^2

31. Photons of energy 2.0 eV and wavelength λ fall on a metal plate and release photoelectrons with a maximum velocity v. By decreasing λ by 25% the maximum velocity of photoelectrons is doubled. The work function of the material of the metal plate in eV is **EAMCET | 1994**

(a) 2.22 (b) 1.985 (c) 2/35 (d) 1.80

32. Photoelectric current can be increased by using **EAMCET | 1993**

(a) higher frequency radiation
(b) higher intensity radiation
(c) higher work function of metal plates
(d) None of the above

33. The speed of electrons in a cathode ray beam, which remains undeflected, in Thomson experiment, under the simultaneously action of a magnetic field 2×10^{-3} Wbm^{-2} and that of an electric field 3.4×10^4 Vm^{-1} is **EAMCET | 1993**

(a) 1.7×10^7 ms^{-1} (b) 2.8×10^7 ms^{-1}
(c) 1.2×10^6 ms^{-1} (d) 5.4×10^6 ms^{-1}

34. If Planck's constant is given as 6.4×10^{-34} J-s and electron charge is 1.6×10^{-19} C, the maximum wavelength of *X*-rays emitted, when a 10 keV electron is completely stopped by a target, is **EAMCET | 1993**

(a) 6.2 Å (b) 3.4 Å (c) 1.8 Å (d) 1.2 Å

35. Emission of electrons in photoelectric effect is possible if **EAMCET | 1992**

(a) metal surface is lightly polished

(b) the incident light is of sufficiently high intensity

(c) the light is incident at right angles to surface of the metal

(d) the incident light is of sufficiently low wavelength

36. A force is experienced by cathode rays when they pass through uniform electric field **EAMCET | 1992**

(a) in the direction of electric field

(b) in the direction opposite to that of electric field

(c) perpendicular to electric field

(d) zero, because the cathode rays do not have the charge

37. Photoelectrons are emitted from a metal surface when photons of energy 3.1 eV or more impinge on it. In an experiment with this metal using a monochromatic radiation the stopping potential was found to be 2.5 V. The energy of the photons used in the experiment is **EAMCET | 1992**

(a) 7.8 eV (b) 6.2 eV (c) 5.6 eV (d) 4.2 eV

38. Light of frequency 1.5 times the threshold frequency, incident on a photo sensitive material. If the frequency of incident light is halved and the intensity is doubled the photo current becomes **EAMCET | 1991**

(a) one-fourth (b) doubled

(c) halved (d) zero

39. In photoelectric effect the slope of the straight line graph between stopping potential and frequency of incident radiation gives the ratio of Planck constant to **EAMCET | 1991**

(a) velocity of light

(b) mass of electron

(c) charge of electron

(d) intensity of photon

Answers

1.	(b)	**2.**	(a)	**3.**	(c)	**4.**	(c)	**5.**	(b)	**6.**	(b)	**7.**	(c)	**8.**	(c)	**9.**	(a)	**10.**	(d)
11.	(b)	**12.**	(d)	**13.**	(d)	**14.**	(c)	**15.**	(b)	**16.**	(d)	**17.**	(d)	**18.**	(b)	**19.**	(a)	**20.**	(c)
21.	(c)	**22.**	(d)	**23.**	(b)	**24.**	(a)	**25.**	(a)	**26.**	(b)	**27.**	(c)	**28.**	(b)	**29.**	(c)	**30.**	(c)
31.	(d)	**32.**	(b)	**33.**	(a)	**34.**	(d)	**35.**	(d)	**36.**	(b)	**37.**	(c)	**38.**	(d)	**39.**	(c)		

Hints & Solutions

1. For $\phi = 90°$, $\cos\phi = 0°$

So, $\lambda' = \lambda + \dfrac{h}{m_e c}$

$= 0.140 \times 10^{-19} + \dfrac{6.63\times10^{-34}}{(9.1\times10^{-31})(3\times10^{8})}$

$= (0.140 \times 10^{-9} + 2.4 \times 10^{-12})$ m

$= 0.142$ nm

2. $E = \dfrac{hc}{\lambda}$

$= \dfrac{6.62\times10^{-34}\times3\times10^{8}}{45\times10^{-12}}$

$= \dfrac{0.44\times10^{-14}}{1.6\times10^{-19}} = 0.275 \times 10^{5}$ eV

3. Stopping potential is given by

$eV_0 = \dfrac{hc}{\lambda} - \phi$

$\therefore eV_0 = \dfrac{6.67\times10^{-34}\times3\times10^{8}}{2\times10^{-7}} - 5 \times 1.6 \times 10^{-19}$

$= 10.005 \times 10^{-19} - 8 \times 10^{-19}$

$= 2.005 \times 10^{-19}$

or $V_0 = \dfrac{2.005\times10^{-19}}{1.6\times10^{-19}}$ volt

$= 1.25$ V

4. $eV_0 = h\nu - h\nu_0$

$\therefore$ Threshold frequency,

$\nu_0 = \nu - \dfrac{eV_0}{h}$

$= \dfrac{c}{\lambda} - \dfrac{eV_0}{h}$

$\therefore \quad \nu_0 = \dfrac{3\times10^{8}}{2\times10^{-7}} - \dfrac{1.6\times10^{-19}\times2.5}{6.6\times10^{-34}}$

$= 9.0 \times 10^{14}$ Hz

5. $a = \frac{F}{m} = \frac{qE}{m} = \frac{mg}{m}$

$g = 10\ ms^{-2}$

6. According to Moseley's law

$$\sqrt{\nu} = B(Z - A)$$

7. We know $eV = \frac{hc}{\lambda}$

$$\Rightarrow \quad \frac{V}{V'} = \frac{\Delta\lambda'}{\Delta\lambda}$$

$$\Rightarrow \quad \frac{V}{V/3} = \frac{\Delta\lambda'}{\Delta\lambda}$$

$$\Rightarrow \quad \Delta\lambda' = 3(\Delta\lambda)$$

8. Einstein's photoelectric equation is given by

$$h\nu = h\nu_0 + \phi = h\nu_0 + eV$$

$$\Rightarrow \quad \nu = \nu_0 + \frac{eV_0}{h}$$

$$= (6 \times 10^{14}) + \frac{(1.6\times10^{-19})(3)}{(6.4\times10^{-34})}$$

$$= 13.5 \times 10^{14}\ s^{-1}$$

10. In photovoltaic cells the photoelectric current produced is proportional to the intensity of incident light, so statement A is false.

The velocity of photoelectrons depends on the maximum kinetic energy of photoelectrons, which depends on the frequency and hence on the wavelength of incident radiation, so statement B is true.

11. Stopping potential

$$V_0 = \frac{hc}{e}\left(\frac{1}{\lambda} - \frac{1}{\lambda_0}\right)$$

where λ_0 = threshold potential

Ist case, $4.8 = \frac{hc}{e}\left(\frac{1}{\lambda} - \frac{1}{\lambda_0}\right)$ ...(i)

IInd case, $1.6 = \frac{hc}{e}\left(\frac{1}{2\lambda} - \frac{1}{\lambda_0}\right)$ ...(ii)

Dividing Eq. (i) by Eq. (ii)

$$3 = \frac{\left(\frac{1}{\lambda} - \frac{1}{\lambda_0}\right)}{\left(\frac{1}{2\lambda} - \frac{1}{\lambda_0}\right)}$$

$$\frac{3}{2\lambda} - \frac{3}{\lambda_0} = \frac{1}{\lambda} - \frac{1}{\lambda_0}$$

$$\frac{1}{\lambda_0} - \frac{3}{\lambda_0} = \frac{1}{\lambda} - \frac{3}{2\lambda}$$

$$\frac{-2}{\lambda_0} = \frac{2-3}{2\lambda}$$

$$\frac{2}{\lambda_0} = \frac{1}{2\lambda}$$

$$\lambda_0 = 4\lambda$$

12. Let the work function of the metal be W

Then, energy of Ist photon, $E_1 = 2W$

Energy of IInd photon, $E_2 = 3W$

Maximum KE of photoelectron

$(KE)_{max} = E - W$ (Einstein's equation)

For first photon, $(KE_1)_{max} = 2W - W = W$

For second photon, $(KE_2)_{max} = 3W - W = 2W$

$$\frac{(KE_1)_{max}}{(KE_2)_{max}} = \frac{1}{2}$$

$$\frac{\frac{1}{2}mv_1^2}{\frac{1}{2}mv_2^2} = \frac{1}{2}$$

$$\Rightarrow \quad \frac{v_1}{v_2} = \sqrt{\frac{1}{2}}$$

$$v_1 : v_2 = 1 : \sqrt{2}$$

13. For Compton effect we have the relation

$$\lambda_2 - \lambda_1 = \frac{h}{m_0 c}(1 - \cos\theta)$$

where, λ_1 = wavelength of incident radiation

λ_2 = wavelength of scattered radiation

$$\therefore\ 0.22 - \lambda_1 = 0.024\,(1 - \cos 60°)$$

$$0.22 - \lambda_1 = 0.024\left(1 - \frac{1}{2}\right)$$

$$0.22 - \lambda_1 = 0.024 \times \frac{1}{2}$$

$$\lambda_1 = 0.22 - 0.012 = 0.208\ Å$$

14. $$\lambda_0 = \frac{h}{\sqrt{2m_p q_p V}}$$

de-Broglie wavelength of α-particle

$$\lambda = \frac{h}{\sqrt{2m_\alpha q_\alpha V}}$$

$$m_\alpha = 4\,m_p$$

(Mass of α-particle is four times of proton $q_\alpha = 2\,q_p$)

(Charge of α-particle is twice of proton)

$$\therefore \quad \lambda = \frac{h}{\sqrt{2(4m_p)(2q_p)V}}$$

$$= \frac{1}{\sqrt{8}} \frac{h}{\sqrt{2m_p q_p V}} = \frac{\lambda_0}{\sqrt{8}}$$

$$= \frac{\lambda_0}{2\sqrt{2}}$$

15. Maximum kinetic energy of photoelectrons

$$(KE)_{max} = h\nu - h\nu_0$$

ν = frequency of incident radiation

ν_0 = threshold frequency

Ist case $(KE_{max})_1 = h\nu_1 - h\nu_0$

IInd case $(KE_{max})_2 = h\nu_2 - h\nu_0$

$$\frac{(KE_{max})_1}{(KE_{max})_2} = \frac{h(\nu_1 - \nu_0)}{h(\nu_2 - \nu_0)}$$

$$\frac{1}{k} = \frac{\nu_1 - \nu_0}{\nu_2 - \nu_0}$$

$$\nu_2 - \nu_0 = k\nu_1 - k\nu_0$$

$$k\nu_0 - \nu_0 = k\nu_1 - \nu_2$$

$$\Rightarrow \quad \nu_0 = \frac{k\nu_1 - \nu_2}{k-1}$$

16. Kinetic energy, KE = 80 eV

$$= 80 \times 1.6 \times 10^{-19} \text{ J}$$

$$= 128 \times 10^{-19} \text{ J}$$

de-Broglie wavelength

$$\lambda = \frac{h}{\sqrt{2m(KE)}} = \frac{6.6\times10^{-34}}{\sqrt{2\times9\times10^{-31}\times128\times10^{-19}}}$$

$$= \frac{6.6\times10^{-34}}{\sqrt{256\times9\times10^{-50}}}$$

$$= \frac{6.6\times10^{-34}}{16\times3\times10^{-25}} = \frac{6.6}{48}\times10^{-9}$$

$$= \frac{66}{48}\times10^{-10} = 1.4 \times 10^{-10} \text{ m} = 1.4 \text{ Å}$$

18. Wavelength, $\frac{1}{\lambda} = R(Z-1)^2\left(\frac{1}{n_1^2} - \frac{1}{n_2^2}\right)$

$$\therefore \quad \frac{\lambda_1}{\lambda_2} = \frac{(Z_2-1)^2}{(Z_1-1)^2}$$

$$\frac{1.30}{\lambda_2} = \frac{(42-1)^2}{(78-1)^2}$$

$$\lambda_2 = \frac{1.30\times77\times77}{41\times41}$$

$$= 4.585 \text{ Å}$$

$$= 4.59 \text{ Å}$$

19. Given, $\lambda_1 = 400$ nm, $(v_1)_{max} = v$

$\lambda_2 = 250$ nm, $(v_2)_{max} = 2v$

From Einstein's photoelectric equation

$$\frac{1}{2}mv_{max}^2 = \frac{hc}{\lambda} - W$$

where, W = work function

Ist case $\frac{1}{2}m(v_1)_{max}^2 = \frac{hc}{\lambda_1} - W$ ...(i)

IInd case $\frac{1}{2}m(v_2)_{max}^2 = \frac{hc}{\lambda_2} - W$ ...(ii)

Equation (i) ÷ (ii)

$$\frac{(v_1^2)_{max}}{(v_2^2)_{max}} = \frac{\frac{hc}{\lambda_1} - W}{\frac{hc}{\lambda_2} - W}$$

$$\frac{v^2}{(2v)^2} = \frac{\frac{hc}{\lambda_1} - W}{\frac{hc}{\lambda_2} - W}$$

$$\frac{hc}{\lambda_2} - W = 4\left(\frac{hc}{\lambda_1} - W\right)$$

$$\frac{hc}{\lambda_2} - W = 4\frac{hc}{\lambda_1} - 4W$$

$$\Rightarrow \quad 3W = 4\frac{hc}{\lambda_1} - \frac{hc}{\lambda_2}$$

$$W = \frac{hc}{3}\left(\frac{4}{\lambda_1} - \frac{1}{\lambda_2}\right)$$

$$= \frac{hc}{3}\left(\frac{4}{400\times10^{-9}} - \frac{1}{250\times10^{-9}}\right)$$

$$= \frac{hc}{3}\left(10^7 - \frac{100\times10^7}{250}\right)$$

$$= \frac{hc}{3}\times10^7(1-0.4) = 2hc \times 10^6 \text{ J}$$

20. Energy of X-ray photon, $E = \frac{hc}{\lambda}$

h = Planck's constant = 6.6×10^{-34} Js^{-1}

c = speed of light = 3×10^8 ms^{-1}

λ = wavelength

= 1.65 Å = 1.65×10^{-10} m

$$\therefore \quad E = \frac{6.6\times10^{-34}\times3\times10^8}{1.65\times10^{-10}} = 12 \times 10^{-16} \text{ J}$$

$$= \frac{12\times10^{-16}}{1.6\times10^{-19}} \text{ eV}$$

$$= 7.5 \times 10^3 \text{ eV}$$

$$= 7.5 \text{ keV}$$

21. From Einstein's photoelectric equation

$$\frac{1}{2}mv^2_{max} = hv - hv_0$$

From this formula it is clear that, maximum velocity of photo electrons depends on frequency of incident radiation.

22. Work function, $W = 2$ eV,

$$= 2 \times 1.6 \times 10^{19} \text{ J}$$
$$= 3.2 \times 10^{-19} \text{ J}$$
$$v = 1.5 \times 10^{15} \text{ Hz}$$

∴ Maximum KE of photoelectrons

$$(KE)_{max} = hv - W$$

where, h = Planck's constant

$$= 6.6 \times 10^{-34} \text{ J}$$
$$(KE)_{max} = 6.6 \times 10^{-34} \times 1.5 \times 10^{15} - 3.2 \times 10^{-19}$$
$$= 9.9 \times 10^{-19} - 3.2 \times 10^{-19}$$
$$= 6.7 \times 10^{-19} \text{ J}$$
$$= \frac{6.7 \times 10^{-19}}{1.6 \times 10^{-19}} \text{ eV}$$
$$= 4.2 \text{ eV}$$
$$= 4 \text{ eV}$$

23. Given, $B = 8$ G $= 8 \times 10^{-4}$ T, $E = 400$ Vm^{-1}

If electron remains undeflected, then

Velocity of electron, $v = \frac{E}{B}$

$$\Rightarrow \quad v = \frac{400}{8 \times 10^{-4}}$$
$$= 50 \times 10^4 = 5 \times 10^5 \text{ ms}^{-1}$$

24. Electric field intensity, $E = 3000$ Vm^{-1}

Magnetic field, $B = 0.0004$ Wbm^{-2}

$$= 4 \times 10^{-4} \text{ Wbm}^{-2}$$

When electron beam suffers no deflection.

Then, velocity

$$v = \frac{E}{B} = \frac{3000}{4 \times 10^{-4}}$$
$$= 750 \times 10^4$$
$$= 7.5 \times 10^6 \text{ ms}^{-1}$$

25. The number of photoelectrons emitted depends on the number of photon incident per sec *i.e.*, on the intensity of incident radiation.

26. According to Moseley's law, frequency of *X*-ray spectrum

$$v = a(Z - b)^2$$
$$\therefore \quad v \propto Z^2$$

27. Work function, $W = 4.125$ eV

$$= 4.125 \times 1.6 \times 10^{-19} \text{ J}$$

∴ Cut-off wavelength, $\lambda_0 = \frac{hc}{W}$

where, $h = 6.6 \times 10^{-34}$ J-s,

$c = 3 \times 10^8$ ms^{-1}

$$\therefore \quad \lambda_0 = \frac{6.6 \times 10^{-34} \times 3 \times 10^8}{4.125 \times 1.6 \times 10^{-19}}$$
$$= \frac{6.6 \times 3 \times 10^{-7}}{4.125 \times 1.6}$$
$$= 3 \times 10^{-7} \text{ m}$$
$$= 3000 \text{ Å}$$

28. Threshold wavelength, $\lambda_0 = 2000$ Å

$$= 2 \times 10^{-7} \text{ m}$$

Work function, $W = \frac{hc}{\lambda_0}$

Here, $h = 6.6 \times 10^{-34}$ J-s

$c = 3 \times 10^8$ ms^{-1}

$$\therefore \quad W = \frac{6.6 \times 10^{-34} \times 3 \times 10^8}{2 \times 10^{-7}}$$
$$= 3.3 \times 3 \times 10^{-19} = 9.9 \times 10^{-19} \text{ J}$$
$$= \frac{9.9 \times 10^{-19}}{1.6 \times 10^{-19}} \text{ eV}$$
$$= 6.2 \text{ eV}$$

29. *X*-rays are electromagnetic waves, so these are stream of photons.

30. Velocity of charged particle (if they pass undeflected)

$$v = \frac{E}{B} = \frac{15 \times 10^3}{5}$$
$$= 3 \times 10^3 \text{ ms}^{-1}$$

Kinetic energy of particles $= \frac{1}{2}mv^2$

but kinetic energy $= qV$

where, V = accelerating potential

$$\therefore \quad qV = \frac{1}{2}mv^2$$
$$\therefore \quad \frac{q}{m} = \frac{1}{2}\frac{v^2}{V} = \frac{1}{2} \times \frac{(3 \times 10^3)^2}{100}$$
$$= \frac{1}{2} \times \frac{9 \times 10^6}{100}$$
$$= 4.5 \times 10^4 \text{ C kg}^{-1}$$

31. From Einstein's photoelectric equation

$$(KE)_{max} = \frac{1}{2}mv^2_{max} = \frac{hc}{\lambda} - W$$

where, h = Planck's constant

c = speed of light in vacuum

λ = wavelength of incident light

W = work function for the metal surface.

1st case

$$(KE)_{max} = \frac{1}{2}mv^2 = \frac{hc}{\lambda} - W \quad ...(i)$$

IInd case

$$\frac{1}{2}m(2v)^2 = \frac{hc}{\lambda - \lambda \times \frac{25}{100}} - W = \frac{4\,hc}{3\lambda} - W$$

$$4\left[\frac{1}{2}mv^2\right] = \frac{4}{3}\frac{hc}{\lambda} - W \quad ...(ii)$$

From Eq. (i)

$$4\left[\frac{hc}{\lambda} - W\right] = \frac{4}{3}\frac{hc}{\lambda} - W$$

$$4\frac{hc}{\lambda} - 4W = \frac{4}{3}\frac{hc}{\lambda} - W$$

$$3\,W = 4\frac{hc}{\lambda} - \frac{4}{3}\frac{hc}{\lambda} = \frac{8}{3}\frac{hc}{\lambda}$$

$$W = \frac{8}{9}\frac{hc}{\lambda}$$

Energy of photon = 2 eV

$\therefore \quad \frac{hc}{\lambda} = 2$ eV

So, $\quad W = \frac{8}{9} \times 2 = \frac{16}{9} = 1.8$ eV

32. In the phenomenon of photoelectric emission the photoelectric current is directly proportional to the intensity of incident radiation.

33. Given, magnetic field, $B = 2 \times 10^{-3}$ Wbm^{-2}

Electric field, $E = 3.4 \times 10^4$ Vm^{-1}

The beam of electrons remain undeflected,

So, speed of electrons $= \frac{E}{B} = \frac{3.4 \times 10^4}{2 \times 10^{-3}}$

$= 1.7 \times 10^7$ ms^{-1}

34. Maximum wavelength of X-rays emitted

$$\lambda_{max} = \frac{hc}{E}$$

where, E = energy of electrons

$= 10$ k eV $= 10 \times 1.6 \times 10^{-16}$

$= 1.6 \times 10^{-15}$ J

$$\therefore \quad \lambda_{max} = \frac{6.4 \times 10^{-34} \times 3 \times 10^8}{1.6 \times 10^{-15}}$$

$$= \frac{19.2 \times 10^{-11}}{1.6}$$

$= 12 \times 10^{-11} - 1.2 \times 10^{-10}$

$= 1.2$ Å

35. Emission of photoelectrons is possible if frequency of incident radiation is high *i.e.*, wavelength of incident light is sufficiently low.

36. Cathode rays consists of negatively charged particles, so the force experienced by cathode rays is in the direction opposite to that of electric field.

37. From Einstein's photoelectric equation

$$\frac{1}{2}(KE)_{max} = E - W$$

where, E = Energy of incident photon.

W = Work function for metal surface.

Ist case, $0 = E - W$

$W = E$

$\therefore \quad W = 3.1$ eV

IInd case, stopping potential

$V_0 = 2.5$ volt

$\therefore \quad (KE)_{max} = eV_0$

$= 2.5$ eV

Again using Einstein's equation

$(KE)_{max} = E - W$

$E = (KE)_{max} + W$

$= 2.5 + 3.1$

$= 5.6$ eV

38. Frequency of incident radiation $= 1.5\,\nu_0$

When frequency is halved, then new frequency

$\nu' = 0.75\,\nu_0$

i.e., $\quad \nu' < \nu_0$

So, there will be no emission of photoelectrons, hence photoelectric current will be zero.

39. From Einstein equation

$$eV_0 = h\nu - h\nu_0$$

or $\quad V_0 = \frac{h\nu}{e} - \frac{h\nu_0}{e}$

It is an equation of straight line having slope $\frac{h}{e}$ and makes an intercept $\frac{-h\nu_0}{e}$ on the stopping potential axis.

Chapter

20

Atomic Physics

1. The ratio of the maximum and minimum wavelengths in Bracket series of hydrogen spectra is EAMCET | 2000
(a) $\frac{25}{9}$ (b) $\frac{17}{6}$ (c) $\frac{9}{5}$ (d) $\frac{4}{3}$

2. In Bohr model of hydrogen atom, the ratio of period of revolution of an electron in $n = 2$ and $n = 1$ orbit is EAMCET | 2000
(a) 2 : 1 (b) 4 : 1
(c) 8 : 1 (d) 16 : 1

3. In hydrogen spectrum the shortest wavelength in Balmer series is λ. The shortest wavelength in Bracket series will be EAMCET | 1999
(a) 2λ (b) 4λ (c) 9λ (d) 16λ

4. The radius of the Bohr orbit depends on n as EAMCET | 1998
(a) $\frac{1}{n}$ (b) $\frac{1}{n^2}$ (c) n (d) n^2

5. When the electron in hydrogen atom is excited from the 4th stationary orbit to the 5th stationary orbit, the change in the angular momentum of the electron in J-s is (Planck's constant $h = 6.64 \times 10^{-34}$ J-s) EAMCET | 1997
(a) 4.16×10^{-34} (b) 3.32×10^{-34}
(c) 1.05×10^{-34} (d) 2.08×10^{-34}

6. The age of pottery is determined by archeologists using a radio isotope of EAMCET | 1995
(a) carbon (b) cobalt
(c) iodine (d) phosphorus

7. The first line in the Lyman series has wavelength λ. The first line in Balmer series has wavelength EAMCET | 1995
(a) $\frac{27}{5}\lambda$ (b) $\frac{5}{27}\lambda$ (c) $\frac{9}{2}\lambda$ (d) $\frac{2}{9}\lambda$

8. Neutron was discovered by EAMCET | 1994
(a) Madam Curie (b) Moseley
(c) Rutherford (d) Chadwick

9. The radius of the hydrogen atom in the ground state is the order of EAMCET | 1994
(a) 10^{-4} cm (b) 10^{-5} cm
(c) 10^{-7} cm (d) 10^{-8} cm

10. The Balmer's general formula for hydrogen is obtained by putting, n_1 equal to EAMCET | 1994
(a) 2 (b) 1 (c) 3 (d) ∞

11. If a is the radius of first Bohr orbit in hydrogen atom, the radius of 3rd orbit is EAMCET | 1993
(a) $3a$ (b) $9a$ (c) $27a$ (d) $81a$

12. In neutron discovery experiment, berillium element is bombarded by EAMCET | 1993
(a) α-particle (b) β-particle
(c) neutrons (d) protons

13. For an electron in H-atom the frequency of photon for transition between levels 1 and 2 is ν. The photon frequency for transition between levels 2 and 3 is closest to EAMCET | 1992
(a) $0.2\,\nu$ (b) $0.1\,\nu$ (c) ν (d) $0.5\,\nu$

14. The closest distance of approach of an α-particle travelling with a velocity v to a certain nucleus is x. The distance of closest approach of α-particles travelling with a velocity $3v$ to the same nucleus is EAMCET | 1992
(a) $x/5$ (b) $x/6$ (c) $x/9$ (d) $x/10$

15. If two elements have their atomic numbers as Z_1 and Z_2. The ratio of the wavelengths λ_1 and λ_2 corresponding to their K_α lines is EAMCET | 1992
(a) $\frac{(Z_2-1)}{(Z_1-1)}$ (b) Z_1/Z_2
(c) $\frac{Z_2}{Z_1}$ (d) $\frac{(Z_2-1)^2}{(Z_1-1)^2}$

16. From Bohr's theory when electrons jump from higher energy orbits to second orbit spectral lines that occur belongs to EAMCET | 1991
(a) Lyman series (b) Balmer series
(c) Paschen series (d) Pfund series

Answers

1.	(a)	**2.**	(c)	**3.**	(b)	**4.**	(d)	**5.**	(c)	**6.**	(a)	**7.**	(a)	**8.**	(d)	**9.**	(d)	**10.**	(a)
11.	(b)	**12.**	(a)	**13.**	(a)	**14.**	(c)	**15.**	(d)	**16.**	(b)								

Hints & Solutions

1. For Bracket series

$$\frac{1}{\lambda} = R\left(\frac{1}{4^2}-\frac{1}{n^2}\right)$$

where, $n = 5, 6, 7, \ldots..$

For maximum wavelength, $n = 5$

$$\frac{1}{\lambda_{max}} = R\left(\frac{1}{4^2}-\frac{1}{5^2}\right) = R\left(\frac{1}{16}-\frac{1}{25}\right)$$

$$= \frac{9R}{400}$$

$$\Rightarrow \quad \lambda_{max} = \frac{400}{9R}$$

For minimum wavelength, $n = \infty$

$$\therefore \quad \frac{1}{\lambda_{min}} = R\left(\frac{1}{4^2}-\frac{1}{\infty}\right) = \frac{R}{16}$$

$$\lambda_{min} = \frac{16}{R}$$

$$\frac{\lambda_{max}}{\lambda_{min}} = \frac{400/9R}{16/R}$$

$$= \frac{400}{9R}\times\frac{R}{16} = \frac{25}{9}$$

2. From Bohr's model

$$T^2 \propto r^3$$

$$\frac{T_1}{T_2} = \left(\frac{r_1}{r_2}\right)^{3/2}$$

But radius of orbit, $r \propto \frac{1}{n^2}$

$$\therefore \quad \frac{r_1}{r_2} = \left(\frac{n_2}{n_1}\right)^2 = \left(\frac{1}{2}\right)^2$$

$$= \frac{1}{4}$$

$$\therefore \quad \frac{T_1}{T_2} = \left(\frac{1}{4}\right)^{\frac{3}{2}}$$

$$= 1:8$$

$$\Rightarrow \quad T_2 : T_1 = 8:1$$

3. Wavelength, $\frac{1}{\lambda} = R\left[\frac{1}{n_1^2}-\frac{1}{n_2^2}\right]$

For shortest wavelength in Balmer series

$$n_1 = 2, n_2 = \infty$$

$$\frac{1}{\lambda} = R\left[\frac{1}{2^2}-\frac{1}{\infty^2}\right]$$

$$\frac{1}{\lambda} = \frac{R}{4}$$

$$\Rightarrow \quad R = \frac{4}{\lambda}$$

For shortest wavelength in Bracket series

$$n_1 = 4, n = \infty$$

$$\frac{1}{\lambda'} = R\left[\frac{1}{4^2}-\frac{1}{\infty}\right]$$

$$= \frac{R}{16} = \frac{4/\lambda}{16} = \frac{1}{4\lambda}$$

$$\therefore \quad \lambda' = 4\lambda$$

4. The radius of Bohr orbit

$$r = \frac{n^2h^2\varepsilon_0}{\pi mze^2}$$

$$\therefore \quad r \propto n^2$$

5. From Bohr's theory

Angular momentum of electron

$$= n\frac{h}{2\pi}$$

Change in angular momentum

$$\Delta L = \frac{h}{2\pi}(n_2-n_1)$$

where, h = Planck's constant

$$= 6.6 \times 10^{-34} \text{ J-s}$$

$$\Delta L = \frac{6.6\times10^{-34}}{2\times3.14}(5-4)$$

$$= 1.05 \times 10^{-34} \text{ J-s}$$

6. Age of pottery is determined by the radio isotope of carbon.

7. For Lyman series, $\frac{1}{\lambda_L} = R\left[\frac{1}{n_1^2} - \frac{1}{n_2^2}\right]$

For first line $n_1 = 1, n_2 = 2$

$$\therefore \quad \frac{1}{\lambda_L} = R\left[\frac{1}{1^2} - \frac{1}{2^2}\right] = R\left[1 - \frac{1}{4}\right]$$

$$\Rightarrow \quad \frac{1}{\lambda_L} = \frac{3}{4}R$$

$$\Rightarrow \quad R = \frac{4}{3\lambda_L}$$

For Balmer series

$$\frac{1}{\lambda_B} = R\left[\frac{1}{n_1^2} - \frac{1}{n_2^2}\right]$$

For first line, $n_1 = 2, n_2 = 3$

$$\therefore \quad \frac{1}{\lambda_B} = \frac{4}{3\lambda}\left[\frac{1}{2^2} - \frac{1}{3^2}\right]$$

$$= \frac{4}{3\lambda}\left[\frac{1}{4} - \frac{1}{9}\right] = \frac{4}{3\lambda}\left[\frac{5}{36}\right]$$

$$\lambda_B = \frac{3\lambda}{4} \times \frac{36}{5} = \frac{27}{5}\lambda$$

9. From Bohr's theory

Radius of hydrogen atom, $r = \frac{h^2\varepsilon_0}{\pi m e^2}$

Here, $h = 6.6 \times 10^{-34}$ J-s,

$\varepsilon_0 = 8.85 \times 10^{-12}$ C^2Nm^{-2}, $\pi = 3.14$

$m = 9.1 \times 10^{-31}$ kg, $e = 1.6 \times 10^{-19}$ C

Substituting the values, we get $r = 10^{-8}$ cm

10. General formula

$$\frac{1}{\lambda} = R\left[\frac{1}{n_1^2} - \frac{1}{n_2^2}\right]$$

For Balmer series

$$n_1 = 2, n_2 = 3, 4, 5, ...$$

11. Radius of Bohr's orbit $r \propto n^2$

$$\therefore \quad \frac{r_1}{r_2} = \left(\frac{n_1}{n_2}\right)^2$$

$$\Rightarrow \quad \frac{a}{r_2} = \left(\frac{1}{3}\right)^2$$

$$\Rightarrow \quad r_2 = 9\,a$$

12. When berilium element is bombarded by α-particle then

$${}_4Be^9 + {}_2He^4\,(\alpha) \rightarrow {}_6C^{12} + X$$

Atomic number of $X = (4 + 2) - 6 = 0$

Mass number of $X = (9 + 4) - 12 = 1$

$\therefore X$ is ${}_0n^1$.

13. $$\frac{1}{\lambda} = R\left(\frac{1}{n_1^2} - \frac{1}{n_2^2}\right)$$

$\therefore$ Frequency, $\nu = cR\left(\frac{1}{n_1^2} - \frac{1}{n_2^2}\right)$

where, c = speed of light in vacuum.

For transition between levels 1 and 2.

$$\nu = cR\left(\frac{1}{1^2} - \frac{1}{2^2}\right)$$

$$\nu = cR\left(1 - \frac{1}{4}\right)$$

$$\nu = \frac{3}{4}cR$$

$$\Rightarrow \quad cR = \frac{4}{3}\nu$$

For transition between levels 2 and 3.

$$\nu_1 = cR\left(\frac{1}{2^2} - \frac{1}{3^2}\right) = cR\left(\frac{1}{4} - \frac{1}{9}\right)$$

$$= 5\,\frac{cR}{36} = \frac{5}{36}\left(\frac{4}{3}\nu\right) = \frac{5}{27}\nu$$

$$= 0.18\,\nu \approx 0.2\,\nu$$

14. Distance of closest approach of α-particle

$$r_0 = \frac{1}{4\pi\varepsilon_0}\frac{2ze^2}{\frac{1}{2}mv^2}$$

$$\therefore \quad r_0 \propto \frac{1}{v^2}$$

$$\Rightarrow \quad \frac{r_1}{r_2} = \left(\frac{v_2}{v_1}\right)^2$$

$$\frac{x}{r_2} = \left(\frac{3v}{v}\right)^2$$

$$\Rightarrow \quad r_2 = \frac{x}{9}$$

15. From Moseley's law

Frequency of X-rays $\nu \propto (Z-1)^2$

$\therefore$ Wavelength, $\lambda \propto \frac{1}{(Z-1)^2}$

So, $$\frac{\lambda_1}{\lambda_2} = \frac{(Z_2 - 1)^2}{(Z_1 - 1)^2}$$

16. According to Bohr's theory when electrons jump from higher energy orbits to second orbit spectral lines that occur belongs to Balmer series.

Chapter

21

Nuclear Physics

1. F_{pp}, F_{nn} and F_{np} are the nuclear forces between proton-proton, neutron-neutron and neutron-proton respectively. Then, relation between them is EAMCET | 2008

(a) $F_{pp} = F_{nn} \neq F_{np}$ (b) $F_{pp} \neq F_{nn} = F_{np}$
(c) $F_{pp} = F_{nn} = F_{np}$ (d) $F_{pp} \neq F_{nn} \neq F_{np}$

2. In sun, the important source of energy is EAMCET | 2007

(a) proton-proton cycle
(b) carbon-nitrogen cycle
(c) carbon-carbon cycle
(d) nitrogen-nitrogen cycle

3. A free neutron decays spontaneously into EAMCET | 2006

(a) a proton, an electron and anti-neutrino
(b) a proton, an electron and a-neutrino
(c) a proton and an electron
(d) a proton, and an electron, a neutrino and an anti-neutrino.

4. Particles and their anti-particles have EAMCET | 2005

(a) the same masses but opposite spins
(b) the same masses but opposite magnetic moments
(c) the same masses and same magnetic moments
(d) opposite spins and some magnetic moments

5. Consider the following two statements A and B and identify the correct answer given below.
A. Nuclear density is same for all nuclei.
B. Radius of the nucleus R and its mass number A are related as $\sqrt{A} \propto R^{1/6}$. EAMCET | 2004

(a) Both A and B are true
(b) Both A and B are false
(c) A is true but B is false
(d) A is false but B is true

6. The mass defect in a particular nuclear reaction is 0.3 g. The amount of energy liberated, in kWh is (velocity of light = 3×10^8 ms^{-1}) EAMCET | 2003

(a) 1.5×10^6 (b) 2.5×10^6
(c) 3×10^6 (d) 7.5×10^6

7. The masses of neutron, proton and deuteron in amu are 1.00893, 1.00813 and 2.01473 respectively. The packing fraction of the deuteron in amu is EAMCET | 2002

(a) 11.65×10^{-4} (b) 23.5×10^{-4}
(c) 33.5×10^{-4} (d) 47.15×10^{-4}

8. To generate power of 3.2 MW, the number of fissions of U^{235} per minute is (Energy released per fission = 200 MeV; 1 eV = 1.6×10^{-19} J) EAMCET | 2000

(a) 6×10^{18} (b) 6×10^{17}
(c) 10^{17} (d) 6×10^{16}

9. In a nuclear reactor, material used for control rods is EAMCET | 1999

(a) uranium (b) graphite
(c) liquid sodium (d) cadmium

10. When $_{15}P^{30}$ decays to become $_{14}Si^{30}$ the particle released is EAMCET | 1998

(a) electron (b) α-particle
(c) neutron (d) positron

11. The number of α and β particles, respectively, emitted in the radioactive decay $_{90}X^{200} \rightarrow {}_{80}Y^{168}$ are EAMCET | 1998

(a) 8 α and 8 β (b) 6 α and 8 β
(c) 8 α and 6 β (d) 6 α and 6 β

12. In the carbon cycle of fusion EAMCET | 1998

(a) four $_1H^1$ fuse to form $_2He^4$ and two positrons
(b) four $_1H^1$ fuse to form $_2He^4$ and two electrons
(c) two $_1H^2$ fuse to form $_2He^4$
(d) two $_1H^2$ fuse to form $_2He^4$ and two neutrons

13. When a slow neutron is captured by U^{235} nucleus nuclear fission takes place, each fission releases an energy of 200 MeV. The number of fissions required to occur (per sec) to produce a power of 1 MW is EAMCET | 1997

(a) 6.2×10^{16} (b) 6.2×10^{15}
(c) 1.56×10^{16} (d) 3.125×10^{16}

14. In the following reaction, the energy released is

$$4\,{}_1H^1 \rightarrow 2\,He^4 + 2e^+ + \text{energy}$$

(Given: Mass of ${}_1H^2$ = 4.031300 amu, mass of ${}_2He^4$ = 4.0026603 amu, mass of $2\,{}_1e^0$ = 0.001098 amu.) **EAMCET | 1997**

(a) 12.33 MeV (b) 24.67 MeV
(c) 25.6 MeV (d) 49.34 MeV

15. A nuclear reactor has power of 16 kW. If the energy per fission is 200 MeV, the number of fissions per second are **EAMCET | 1996**

(a) 5×10^{16} (b) 5×10^{17}
(c) 5×10^{14} (d) 5×10^{15}

16. The mass number of a nucleus is **EAMCET | 1996**

(a) always less than atomic number
(b) always more than atomic number
(c) equal to atomic number
(d) sometimes more than and sometimes equal to atomic number

17. In which of the following decays, the element does not change? **EAMCET | 1996**

(a) α-decay (b) β^+-decay
(c) β-decay (d) γ-decay

18. The element which was first observed in the solar spectrum is **EAMCET | 1996**

(a) helium (b) xenon
(c) neon (d) argon

19. The energy produced in the sun is by **EAMCET | 1995**

(a) burning of fossil fuel
(b) radioactivity
(c) fission
(d) fusion

20. In a nuclear reactor the function of the moderator is **EAMCET | 1995**

(a) to slow down neutrons
(b) to absorb neutrons
(c) to speed up neutrons
(d) to catalyse the reaction

21. Energy obtained when 1 mg mass is completely converted to energy is (in joule) **EAMCET | 1995**

(a) 3×10^2 (b) 3×10^{10}
(c) 9×10^{10} (d) 9×10^2

22. Nuclear forces are **EAMCET | 1995**

(a) short range and charge dependent
(b) short range and charge independent
(c) long range and charge dependent
(d) long range and charge independent

23. When two deuterium nuclei fuse together to form tritium, we get a **EAMCET | 1994**

(a) neutron (b) proton
(c) α-particle (d) deuteron

24. After 2 h, 1/16 of the initial amount of a certain radioactive isotope remains undecayed. The half-life of the isotope is **EAMCET | 1994**

(a) 15 min (b) 30 min
(c) 45 min (d) 60 min

25. Which of the following is more effective in inducing nuclear fission? **EAMCET | 1994**

(a) Fast neutron (b) Fast proton
(c) Slow proton (d) Slow neutron

26. A radioactive sample has half-life of 5 days. To decay from 8 μCu to 1 μCu, the number of days taken will be **EAMCET | 1993**

(a) 40 (b) 25 (c) 15 (d) 10

27. How many neutrons the nucleus of ${}_{56}Ba^{141}$ contains **EAMCET | 1993**

(a) 75 (b) 85 (c) 95 (d) 100

28. The overall process of carbon-nitrogen fussion cycle results in fusion of four protons to yield the helium nucleus and two **EAMCET | 1993**

(a) positron (b) electron
(c) neutron (d) proton

29. In two isotopes of an element, the number of protons in their nuclei will be and number of neutrons in their nuclei will **EAMCET | 1992**

(a) same, same (b) same, different
(c) different, same (d) different, different

30. It is assumed that nuclear mass is of the order of 10^{-27} kg and nuclear radius is of the order of 10^{-15} m. The nuclear density is of the order of **EAMCET | 1992**

(a) 10^{15} (b) 10^{10} (c) 10^{18} (d) 10^{23}

31. A radio station operates at a frequency of 10 MHz with a power output of 265.2 kW. Given that the Planck's constant $h = 6.63 \times 10^{-34}$ J-s. The rate of emission of photon from the station is **EAMCET | 1992**

(a) 4×10^{20} (b) 4×10^{31}
(c) 5×10^{18} (d) 5×10^{12}

32. A radio active nucleus with mass number A splits into the nuclei whose mass numbers are in the ratio 3 : 2, the ratio of their radii is
EAMCET | 1992

(a) $\left(\frac{3}{2}\right)$ (b) $\left(\frac{3}{2}\right)^{1/3}$

(c) $\left(\frac{3}{2}\right)^{1/2}$ (d) 1

33. A radioactive source has a half-like of 3 h. A freshly prepared sample of the same exhibits radioactivity 16 times the permissible safe value. The minimum time after which it would be possible to work safely with the source is
EAMCET | 1991

(a) 8 h (b) 10 h (c) 12 h (d) 14 h

34. An element X decays first by positron emission and then two α-particles are emitted in succesive radioactive decay. If the product nucleus has mass number 227 and atomic number 89 the mass number and atomic number of element X are
EAMCET | 1991

(a) (273, 93) (b) (235, 94)

(c) (238, 93) (d) (237, 92)

Answers

1.	(c)	**2.**	(a)	**3.**	(a)	**4.**	(b)	**5.**	(c)	**6.**	(d)	**7.**	(a)	**8.**	(a)	**9.**	(d)	**10.**	(d)
11.	(c)	**12.**	(a)	**13.**	(d)	**14.**	(c)	**15.**	(c)	**16.**	(d)	**17.**	(d)	**18.**	(a)	**19.**	(d)	**20.**	(a)
21.	(c)	**22.**	(b)	**23.**	(b)	**24.**	(b)	**25.**	(d)	**26.**	(c)	**27.**	(b)	**28.**	(a)	**29.**	(b)	**30.**	(c)
31.	(b)	**32.**	(b)	**33.**	(c)	**34.**	(b)												

Hints & Solutions

1. Nuclear force between two particles is independent of charges of particle.

$\Rightarrow \quad F_{pp} = F_{nn} = F_{np}$

2. In sun, the important source of energy is proton-proton cycle. According to this cycle nuclei of hydrogen through many reactions fuse to form nucleus of helium and in this process huge amount of energy is released.

3. $n \rightarrow p + e^- + \bar{\nu}$ (anti-neutrino)

4. Particles and their antiparticles have the same masses but opposite magnetic moments.

5. Nuclear density for all nuclei is same and equal to 10^{17} kgm^{-3}.

Radius of nucleus and mass number are related as

$$R = R_0(A)^{1/3}$$

or $\quad R \propto (A)^{1/3}$

Thus, (A) is true and (B) is false.

6. Given, $\Delta m = 0.3$ g

$= 0.3 \times 10^{-3}$ kg $= 3 \times 10^{-4}$ kg

Energy liberated, $E = \Delta mc^2$

$= 3 \times 10^{-4} \times (3 \times 10^8)^2$

$= 3 \times 10^{-4} \times 9 \times 10^{16}$

$= 27 \times 10^{12}$ J

$= \frac{27 \times 10^{12}}{3.6 \times 10^6}$ kWh

$= 7.5 \times 10^6$ kWh

7. Given, $m_n = 1.00893$, $m_p = 1.00813$, $m_d = 2.01473$

Deuteron ($_1H^2$) nucleus consist of one proton and one neutron.

$\therefore$ Mass defect, $\Delta m = (m_n + m_p) - m_d$

$= (1.00893 + 1.00813) - 2.01473$

$= 0.00233$

Packing fraction $= \frac{\Delta m}{A}$

$= \frac{0.00233}{2} = 11.65 \times 10^{-4}$

8. $P = 3.2$ MW $= 3.2 \times 10^6$ Js^{-1}

$= 3.2 \times 10^6 \times 60$ Jmin^{-1}

Energy produced per fission $= 200$ MeV

$= 200 \times 1.6 \times 10^{-13}$ J

$= 3.2 \times 10^{-11}$ J

$\therefore$ Number of fissions required per min

$= \frac{3.2 \times 10^6 \times 60}{3.2 \times 10^{-11}} = 6 \times 10^{18}$

9. In a nuclear reactor control rods are made of cadmium.

10. ${}_{15}P^{30} \rightarrow X + {}_{14}Si^{30}$

Atomic number of $X = 15 - 14 = 1$

Mass number of $X = 30 - 30 = 0$

$\therefore X$ is ${}_{+1}e^0$ *i.e.* positron.

11. Difference in mass number = 200 – 168 = 32

$\therefore$ Number of α-particles emitted $= \frac{32}{8} = 8$

Difference in atomic number = 90 – 80 = 10

Difference due to 8 α-particles $= 8 \times 2 = 16$

$\therefore$ Number of β-particles emitted

$= 16 - 10 = 6$

12. Reaction for carbon cycle is

$4\,{}_1H^1 \rightarrow {}_2He^4 + 2\,{}_{+1}\beta^0 + 2\nu$ + energy

(*i.e.* Four ${}_1H^1$ fuse to form ${}_2He^4$ and two positrons.)

13. Energy required per second = 1 MW

$= 1 \times 10^6\ Js^{-1} = 10^6\ Js^{-1}$

Energy released during one fission

= 200 MeV

$= 200 \times 1.6 \times 10^{-13}$ J

$= 3.2 \times 10^{-11}$ J

$\therefore$ Number of fissions per second

$$= \frac{10^6}{3.2 \times 10^{-11}} = \frac{10^{17}}{3.2}$$

$= 3.125 \times 10^{16}$

14. $4\,{}_1H^1 \rightarrow {}_2He^4 + 2\,{}_1e^0$ + energy

Mass of $4\,{}_1H^1$ = 4.031300 amu

Mass of ${}_2He^4$ = 4.0026603 amu

Mass of $2\,{}_1e^0$ = 0.001098 amu

Mass defect

$\Delta m = 4.031300 - (4.0026603 + 0.001098)$

= 0.02754 amu

$\therefore$ Energy released $= \Delta m \times 931$ MeV

$= 0.02754 \times 931 = 25.6$ MeV

15. Power = 16 kW $= 16 \times 10^3\ Js^{-1}$

Energy produced per fission = 200 MeV

$= 200 \times 1.6 \times 10^{-13}$ J

$= 3.2 \times 10^{-11}$ J

$\therefore$ Number of fissions required per second

$$= \frac{16 \times 10^3}{3.2 \times 10^{-11}} = 5 \times 10^{14}$$

16. Mass number of nucleus

= Total number of protons and neutrons

Atomic number = Number of protons

In case of hydrogen atomic number and mass number are equal ($\because$ It has no neutrons) but except this, mass number is greater than the atomic number.

17. During γ-decay the element does not change, because it is an electromagnetic radiation and has no mass and charge.

18. Helium was first observed in the solar spectrum.

19. The energy produced in sun is by fusion process. In fusion reaction on sun, hydrogen nuclei combine with each other to form helium nuclei, due to which a large amount of energy is released.

20. In nuclear reactor, the function of moderator is to slow down the fast moving thermal neutrons which are produced in the reaction.

21. From Einstein's mass-energy equivalence relation, energy released

$E = mc^2$

where, c = speed of light in vacuum

$= 3 \times 10^8$ m/s

$\therefore \quad E = 1 \times 10^{-6} \times (3 \times 10^8)^2$

$= 1 \times 10^{-6} \times 9 \times 10^{16}$

$= 9 \times 10^{10}$ J

23. The fusion reaction of two deuterium nuclei is

${}_1H^2 + {}_1H^2 \rightarrow {}_1H^3 + X$

deuterium tritium

Mass number of $X = (2 + 2) - 3 = 1$

Atomic number of $X = (1 + 1) - 1 = 1$

$\therefore X$ is ${}_1H^1$, *i.e.*, X is proton.

24. Total time T = 2 h, Half-life $T_{1/2}$ = ?

Undecayed amount, $N = \frac{N_0}{16}$

From the relation, $N = N_0\left(\frac{1}{2}\right)^n$

where, n = number of half-lives

$$\therefore \quad \frac{N_0}{16} = N_0\left(\frac{1}{2}\right)^n$$

$$\Rightarrow \quad \left(\frac{1}{2}\right)^4 = \left(\frac{1}{2}\right)^n$$

$n = 4$

Half-life $T_{1/2} = \frac{T}{4} = \frac{2}{4} = 0.5$ h $= 0.5 \times 60$

= 30 min

25. Slow neutrons are more effective in inducing nuclear fission than fast moving neutrons.

26. Half-life, $T_{1/2} = 5$ days

Initial activity, $R_0 = 8\,\mu$Cu

Final activity, $R = 1\,\mu$Cu

From the relation

$$R = R_0\left(\frac{1}{2}\right)^n$$

where, n = Number of half lives

$$1 = 8\left(\frac{1}{2}\right)^n$$

$$\Rightarrow \quad \frac{1}{8} = \left(\frac{1}{2}\right)^n$$

$$\left(\frac{1}{2}\right)^3 = \left(\frac{1}{2}\right)^n$$

$$\Rightarrow \quad n = 3$$

$\therefore$ Number of days taken $= n\,T_{1/2} = 3 \times 5$
$= 15$ days

27. In $_{56}\text{Ba}^{141}$

Atomic number = 56

Mass number = 141

Number of neutrons

= mass number – atomic number

= 141 – 56 = 85

28. The overall equation of carbon cycle is

$$4\,{}_1\text{H}^1 \rightarrow \underset{\text{(Helium nucleus)}}{{}_2\text{H}^4} + 2\,\underset{\text{(Positron)}}{{}_{+1}\beta^0} + 2\nu + \text{(energy)}$$

30. Order of nuclear density

$$= \frac{\text{order of mass}}{\text{order of volume}}$$

$$= \frac{10^{-27}}{(10^{-15})^3} = \frac{10^{-27}}{10^{-45}} = 10^{18}$$

31. Frequency, $\nu = 10$ MHz

$= 10 \times 10^6$ Hz

Power, $P = 265.2$ kW

$= 265.2 \times 10^3$ W

Let rate of emission of photon is n *i.e.*, n photons are emitted per sec.

$$\therefore \quad P = nh\nu$$

$$\therefore \quad n = \frac{P}{h\nu}$$

$$= \frac{265.2\times10^3}{6.63\times10^{-34}\times10\times10^6}$$

$$= 4 \times 10^{31}$$

32. Nucleus radius $R \propto (A)^{1/3}$

where, A = mass number

$$\therefore \quad \frac{R_1}{R_2} = \left(\frac{A_1}{A_2}\right)^{1/3} = \left(\frac{3}{2}\right)^{1/3}$$

33. Half-life, $T_{1/2} = 3$ h

Initial activity, $R_0 = 16\,R$

where, R = final activity

So, $$R = R_0\left(\frac{1}{2}\right)^n$$

$$R = 16\,R\left(\frac{1}{2}\right)^n$$

$$\Rightarrow \quad \frac{1}{16} = \left(\frac{1}{2}\right)^n$$

$$\left(\frac{1}{2}\right)^4 = \left(\frac{1}{2}\right)^n$$

$$\Rightarrow \quad n = 4$$

Number of half-lives = 4

$\therefore$ Required time $= nT_{1/2} = 4 \times 3 = 12$ h

34. Let mass number and atomic number of X are A and B respectively, so

$${}_BX^A \xrightarrow{{}_{+1}e^0} {}_{B-1}Y^A \xrightarrow{-\alpha} {}_{B-1-2}Z^{A-4} \xrightarrow{-\alpha} {}_{B-1-2-2}U^{A-8}$$

According to question

$B - 1 - 2 - 2 = 89$

$B = 89 + 5 = 94$

$A - 8 = 227$

$\Rightarrow \quad A = 235$

Chapter

22

Solids and Semiconductor Devices

1. Which of the following statements is not correct when a junction diode is in forward bias? **EAMCET | 2008**
   (a) The width of depletion region decreases.
   (b) Free electrons on *n*-side will move towards the junction.
   (c) Holes on *p*-side move towards the junction.
   (d) Electron on *n*-side and holes on *p*-side will move away from junction.

2. In an *n*-type semiconductor, the fermi energy level lies **EAMCET | 2007**
   (a) in the forbidden energy gap nearer to the conduction band
   (b) in the forbidden energy gap nearer to the valence band
   (c) in the middle of forbidden energy gap
   (d) outside the forbidden energy gap

3. Consider a *p-n* junction as a capacitor, formed with *p* and *n*-materials acting as thin metal electrodes and depletion layer width acting as separation between them. Biasing on this, assume that a *n-p-n* transistor is working as an amplifier in *CE* configuration. If C_1 and C_2 are the base-emitter and collector-emitter junction capacitances, then **EAMCET | 2006**
   (a) $C_1 > C_2$ (b) $C_1 < C_2$
   (c) $C_1 = C_2$ (d) $C_1 = C_2 = 0$

4. An *n-p-n* transistor power amplifier in *C-E* configuration gives **EAMCET | 2005**
   (a) voltage amplification only
   (b) current amplification only
   (c) both current and voltage amplifications
   (d) only power gain of unity

5. In *n-p-n* transistor, in *CE* configuration
   (1) The emitter is heavily doped than the collector.
   (2) Emitter and collector can be interchanged.
   (3) The base region is very thin but is heavily doped.
   (4) The conventional current flows from base to emitter. **EAMCET | 2004**
   (a) (1) and (2) are correct
   (b) (1) and (3) are correct
   (c) (1) and (4) are correct
   (d) (2) and (3) are correct

6. When *n-p-n* transistor is used as an amplifier **EAMCET | 2003**
   (a) electrons move from base to collector
   (b) holes move from emitter to base
   (c) holes move from collector to base
   (d) holes move from base to emitter

7. While a collector to emitter voltage is constant in a transistor, the collector current changes by 8.2 mA when the emitter current changes by 8.3 mA. The value of forward current ratio is **EAMCET | 2003**
   (a) 82 (b) 83 (c) 8.2 (d) 8.3

8. In a transistor circuit, when the base current is increased by 50 μA keeping the collector voltage fixed at 2 V, the collector current increases by 1 mA. The current gain of the transistor is **EAMCET | 2002**
   (a) 20 (b) 40 (c) 60 (d) 80

9. A common emitter transistor amplifier has a current gain of 50. If the load resistance is 4 kΩ and input resistance is 500 Ω, the voltage gain of the amplifier is **EAMCET | 2002**
   (a) 100 (b) 200 (c) 300 (d) 400

10. Consider the following statements A and B and identify the correct choice of the given answers.
    A. The width of the depletion layer in a *p-n* junction diode increases in forward bias.
    B. In a intrinsic semiconductor the fermi energy level is exactly in the middle of the forbidden energy gap. **EAMCET | 2000**
    (a) A is true and B is false
    (b) Both A and B are false
    (c) A is false and B is true
    (d) Both A and B are true

11. In intrinsic semiconductor **EAMCET | 1999**

(a) the conduction band and valence band overlap

(b) the gap between conduction band and valence band is more than 16 eV

(c) the gap between conduction and valence band is near about 1 eV

(d) None of the above

12. The element that can be used as acceptor impurity to dope silicon is **EAMCET | 1999**

(a) antimony (b) arsenic

(c) boron (d) phosphorus

13. A hole is **EAMCET | 1998**

(a) a positively charged electron

(b) an electron in the valence band

(c) an unfulfilled covalent bond

(d) an excess electron in covalent bond

14. The potential in the depletion layer is due to **EAMCET | 1998**

(a) electrons (b) holes

(c) Both (a) and (b) (d) forbidden band

15. The value indicated by fermi energy level in an intrinsic semiconductor is **EAMCET | 1997**

(a) the average energy of electrons and holes

(b) the energy of electrons in conduction band

(c) the energy of holes in valence band

(d) the energy of forbidden region

16. The two diodes A and B are biased as shown, then

− 5 V	A	− 9 V
− 3 V	B	− 6 V

EAMCET | 1997

(a) the diodes A and B are reverse biased

(b) the diode A is forward biased and B is reverse biased

(c) the diode B is forward biased and diode A is reverse biased

(d) the diodes A and B are forward biased

17. Two pieces, one of germanium and the other of aluminium are cooled from T_1 K to T_2 K. The resistance of **EAMCET | 1996**

(a) aluminium increases and that of germanium decreases

(b) each of them decreases

(c) aluminium decreases and that of germanium increases

(d) each of them increases

18. When a p-n junction diode is reverse biased, the thickness of the depletion layer **EAMCET | 1996**

(a) increases (b) decreases

(c) become zero (d) remains constant

19. Energy band gap E_g in an insulator is of the order of **EAMCET | 1995**

(a) 6 eV (b) 0.6 eV

(c) − 6 eV (d) zero

20. Indium impurity in germanium makes it into a **EAMCET | 1995**

(a) n-type semiconductor

(b) p-type semiconductor

(c) insulator

(d) intrinsic semiconductor

21. In an intrinsic semiconductor at room temperature number of electrons and holes are **EAMCET | 1995**

(a) equal (b) zero

(c) unequal (d) infinity

22. In forward bias in a p-n junction, the potential barrier **EAMCET | 1995**

(a) decreases (b) increases

(c) remains unchanged (d) becomes zero

23. In a reverse biased condition of a p-n junction **EAMCET | 1994**

(a) the potential barrier increases

(b) the potential barrier decreases

(c) the current flow increases

(d) the potential barrier remains the same

24. Which one of the following is an incorrect statement? **EAMCET | 1994**

(a) In an intrinsic semiconductor, the number of holes in the valence band is equal to the number of electrons in the conduction band

(b) When heated the conductivity of an intrinsic semiconductor, increases

(c) The fermi level lies near the valence band in an intrinsic semiconductor

(d) The majority carries in a p-type semiconductor are holes

25. Covalent bond exists in **EAMCET | 1994**

(a) sodium chloride crystal

(b) germanium

(c) copper

(d) helium

26. In a p-type semiconductor, the electrical conduction is due to **EAMCET | 1994**
(a) only holes
(b) only electrons
(c) a large number of holes and small number of electrons
(d) a large number of electrons and a small number of holes

27. To obtain p-type extrinsic semiconductor, the impurity element to be added to germanium should be of valency **EAMCET | 1993**
(a) 2 (b) 3 (c) 4 (d) 5

28. If a battery is connected across a p-n junction with p-type connected to the negative terminal, the junction is said to be **EAMCET | 1993**
(a) reverse biased (b) forward biased
(c) unbiased (d) None of these

29. The majority carriers in a p-type semiconductor are **EAMCET | 1993**
(a) protons (b) neutrons
(c) electrons (d) holes

30. If an intrinsic semiconductor a pentavalent element is added as impurity, one gets **EAMCET | 1993**
(a) p-type semiconductor
(b) n-type semiconductor
(c) insulator
(d) None of the above

31. In an intrinsic semiconductor the charge carriers responsible for electrical conduction are **EAMCET | 1992**
(a) electrons
(b) holes
(c) Both electrons and holes
(d) neither electrons nor holes

32. A semiconductor device which is used for detecting light intensity is called a **EAMCET | 1992**
(a) solar cells (b) zener diode
(c) LED (d) photodiode

33. A piece of aluminium and germanium each are cooled from T_1 K to T_2 K. The resistance of **EAMCET | 1991**
(a) each of them decreases
(b) each of them increases
(c) aluminium increases and that of germanium decreases
(d) aluminium decreases and that of germanium increases

34. The energy level stationed at the centre of forbidden energy gap of an intrinsic semiconductor is **EAMCET | 1991**
(a) fermi level (b) transition level
(c) neutral level (d) None of these

35. The method of connecting the negative pole of battery to p-material and positive pole to n-material of a p-n junction is called **EAMCET | 1991**
(a) forward bias connection
(b) reverse bias connection
(c) Both (a) and (b)
(d) Neither (a) nor (b)

36. When boron is added as impurity to silicon, the resulting material is **EAMCET | 1991**
(a) p-type semiconductor
(b) n-type semiconductor
(c) insulator
(d) intrinsic semiconductor

Answers

1.	(d)	2.	(a)	3.	(a)	4.	(c)	5.	(c)	6.	(a)	7.	(a)	8.	(a)	9.	(d)	10.	(c)
11.	(c)	12.	(c)	13.	(c)	14.	(c)	15.	(a)	16.	(d)	17.	(c)	18.	(a)	19.	(a)	20.	(b)
21.	(a)	22.	(a)	23.	(a)	24.	(c)	25.	(b)	26.	(c)	27.	(b)	28.	(a)	29.	(d)	30.	(b)
31.	(c)	32.	(d)	33.	(d)	34.	(a)	35.	(b)	36.	(a)								

Hints & Solutions

1. In forward biasing both electrons and protons move towards the junction and hence the width of depletion region decreases.
2. In an n-type semiconductor, the fermi energy level lies near the conduction band in the forbidden energy gap.
3. In the given case $C_1 > C_2$.
4. An amplifier in *CE* configuration gives both current and voltage amplification.
5. In n-p-n transistor, in *CE* configuration, the emitter is heavily doped than the collector and the conventional current flows from base to emitter.
6. When n-p-n transistor is used as an amplifier then collector is kept positive, so electrons move from base to collector.
7. $$\Delta I_c = 8.2 \text{ mA}$$
$$\Delta I_e = 8.3 \text{ mA}$$
Base current, $\Delta I_b = \Delta I_e - \Delta I_c = 8.3 - 8.2$
$= 0.1$ mA
$\therefore$ Forward current ratio $= \dfrac{\Delta I_c}{\Delta I_b} = \dfrac{8.2}{0.1} = 82$
8. Increase in base current, $\Delta I_b = 50\,\mu\text{A}$
Increase in collector current, $\Delta I_c = 1$ mA
Current gain, $\beta = \dfrac{\Delta I_c}{\Delta I_b} = \dfrac{1\times10^{-3}}{50\times10^{-6}}$
$= \dfrac{10^3}{50} = 20$
9. Given, $\beta = 50,\ R_L = 4\text{ k}\Omega = 4000\ \Omega,$
$R_i = 500\ \Omega$
$\beta = \dfrac{I_c}{I_b}$
Voltage gain of amplifier
$$= \frac{\text{output voltage}}{\text{input voltate}} = \frac{I_c \times R_L}{I_b \times R_i}$$
$$= \beta\left(\frac{R_L}{R_i}\right) = \frac{50\times4000}{500} = 400$$
10. The width of the depletion layer in a p-n junction diode decreases in forward bias. In an intrinsic semiconductor the fermi energy level is exactly in the middle of the forbidden energy gap.
11. In intrinsic semiconductors the gap between conduction and valence band is nearly about 1 eV.
12. Elements of 3rd group are used as accepter impurity to dope silicon, therefore boron can be used.
13. A hole is vacancy of electron in a covalent bond *i.e.*, an unfulfilled covalent bond.
14. The potential in the depletion layer is due to presence of electrons and holes in it.
15. The fermi energy level in an intrinsic semiconductor is the average energy of electrons and holes.
16. For diode A
Potential on p-type, $V_1 = -5$ V
Potential on n-type, $V_2 = -9$ V
$\therefore \quad V_1 > V_2$
So, diode A is in forward bias.
In the same way diode B is also in forward bias.
17. Aluminium is a conductor, so on decreasing, its temperature, its resistance will decrease, but germanium is a semiconductor, so on decreasing its temperature, its resistance will increase.
18. In reverse biasing of p-n junction diode the potential barrier of depletion layer is supported, so it becomes thick.
19. In an insulator the energy band gap is of the order of 6 eV to 7 eV.
20. When germanium is doped with indium impurity, then it becomes p-type semiconductor, because indium in trivalent impurity, so out of four covalent bonds, one bond has a vacancy of electron *i.e.*, one hole is produced.
21. In an intrinsic semiconductor (pure semiconductor) at room temperature the number of electrons and holes are equal.
22. When a junction diode is in forward bias, then the electric field inside the depletion layer is opposed, so potential barrier decreases.
23. In reverse biasing of a p-n junction the potential barrier increases because in this condition the internal electric field of depletion layer is supported by the external applied electric field.

24. In an intrinsic semiconductor there is no impurity, so the number of holes in the valence band is equal to the number of electrons in conduction band. So, statement (a) is correct.

On heating, *i.e.*, on increasing the temperature, the conductivity of intrinsic semiconductor increases. So, it is also correct statement. In intrinsic semiconductor the fermi level lies in the middle of forbidden energy gap. So, statement (c) is incorrect.

25. Covalent bond exists in germanium because it is a semiconductor and cannot loose the electrons, so it shares the electrons.

26. In a *p*-type semiconductor the majority charge carriers are holes and minority charge carriers are electrons.

27. To obtain *p*-type extrinsic semiconductor, a trivalent impurity should be added, because by doing so one covalent bond out of four covalent bonds of germanium will have the defficiency of one electron *i.e.*, will have a hole.

28. In reverse biasing positive terminal of the battery is connected to *n*-crystal and negative terminal of the battery connected to *p*-crystal.

29. The majority carriers in a *p*-type semiconductor are holes.

30. When a pentavalent impurity is added to an intrinsic semiconductor, then four electrons of the impurity, takes place in four covalent bonds of semiconductor hence one electron is left free, which works as charge carrier *i.e.*, charge carrier is negatively charged, so *n*-type semiconductor is obtained.

31. In intrinsic semiconductors there are both electrons and holes.

32. Photo diode is a special type of photo detector used for detecting light intensity.

33. Aluminium is a conductor, so on decreasing its temperature, the resistance will decrease but germanium is semiconductor, so on decreasing the temperature its resistance will increase.

35. The method of connecting the negative pole of battery to *p*-material and positive pole to *n*-material of *p*-*n* junction is called reverse bias connection.

36. Boron is trivalent element, so when it is added to silicon, one covalent bond of silicon out of four covalent bonds has a vacancy of one electron, *i.e.*, one hole is produced, so *p*-type semiconductor is obtained.